JAMES TREFIL • ROBERT M. HAZEN

INTEGRATED SCIENCES

Eighth Edition

FLORIDA TECH

EDS 1021: General Physical Science

EDS 1022: General Biological Science

Wiley Custom Learning Solutions

ISBN 978-1-119-27459-9
Printed and bound by LSC Communications

10 9 8 7 6 5 4 3

EDS 1021: General Physical Science

Week 1

Chapter 1 **Science: A Way of Knowing**

Chapter 2 **The Ordered Universe**

Week 2

Chapter 3 **Energy**

Chapter 4 **Heat and the Second Law of Thermodynamics**

Week 3

Chapter 5 **Electricity and Magnetism**

Week 4

Chapter 6 **Waves and Electromagnetic Radiation**

Week 5

Chapter 8 **The Atom**

Chapter 10 **Atoms in Combination: The Chemical Bond**

Week 6

Chapter 12 **The Nucleus of the Atom**

Week 7

Chapters 14 **The Stars**

Chapter 15 **Cosmology**

Week 8

EDS 1022: General Biological Science

Week 1

Week 2

Week 3

Week 4

Week 5

Week 6

Week 7

Week 8

8th Edition

The Sciences
An Integrated Approach

James Trefil

Robert M. Hazen

WILEY

VICE PRESIDENT AND DIRECTOR	Petra Recter
SENIOR ACQUISITION EDITOR	Nick Ferrari
SENIOR MARKET SOLUTIONS ASSISTANT	Mallory Fryc
SENIOR CONTENT MANAGER	Kevin Holm
EXECUTIVE MARKETING MANAGER	Kristine Ruff
INTERIOR DESIGNER	Tom Nery
SENIOR PRODUCTION EDITOR	Trish McFadden
SENIOR PHOTO EDITOR	Billy Ray
MEDIA SPECIALIST	Svetlana Barskaya
PHOTO COVER CREDITS	Conall McCaughey / Getty Images, Inc.

This book was set in 10/12 pt KeplerStd-Light by Thomson Digital and printed and bound by Quad Graphics. The cover was printed by Quad Graphics

This book is printed on acid free paper. ∞

Founded in 1807, John Wiley & Sons, Inc. has been a valued source of knowledge and understanding for more than 200 years, helping people around the world meet their needs and fulfill their aspirations. Our company is built on a foundation of principles that include responsibility to the communities we serve and where we live and work. In 2008, we launched a Corporate Citizenship Initiative, a global effort to address the environmental, social, economic, and ethical challenges we face in our business. Among the issues we are addressing are carbon impact, paper specifications and procurement, ethical conduct within our business and among our vendors, and community and charitable support. For more information, please visit our website: www.wiley.com/go/citizenship.

Evaluation copies are provided to qualified academics and professionals for review purposes only, for use in their courses during the next academic year. These copies are licensed and may not be sold or transferred to a third party. Upon completion of the review period, please return the evaluation copy to Wiley. Return instructions and a free of charge return shipping label are available at www.wiley.com/go/returnlabel. If you have chosen to adopt this textbook for use in your course, please accept this book as your complimentary desk copy. Outside of the United States, please contact your local sales representative.

ISBN: 9781119049685
Printed in the United States of America

10 9 8 7 6 5 4 3 2 1

The inside back cover will contain printing identification and country of origin if omitted from this page. In addition, if the ISBN on the back cover differs from the ISBN on this page, the one on the back cover is correct.

Preface

Scientific advances touch our lives every day. We benefit from new materials in the form of cosmetics, appliances, clothing, and sports equipment. We rely on new sources of energy and more efficient ways to use that energy for transportation, communication, heating, and lighting. We call upon science to find new ways to treat disease and to allow people to lead longer, healthier lives. Science represents our best hope in solving the many pressing problems faced by modern societies.

In spite of the central role that science plays in modern life, most Americans are poorly equipped to deal with basic scientific principles and methods. Surveys routinely show that large numbers of Americans are unaware that Earth orbits Sun or that human beings and dinosaurs didn't live at the same time. At a time when molecular biology is making breakthrough discoveries almost daily, only a little over a quarter of Americans understand the term *DNA*, and only about 10% understand the term *molecule*. There can be little doubt that we are faced with a generation of citizens who lack the critical knowledge to make informed personal and professional decisions regarding health, safety, resources, and the environment.

Science Education Today

Science education has been a persistent problem in the United States. Over the last 30 years many reports—the most prominent being *A Nation at Risk* (1983) and *The Gathering Storm* (2006)—warned that our system of science education was failing to produce enough scientists and engineers to drive our economy forward.

In fact, we can define two problems with science education. The first is the aspect on which national reports tend to spend most of their time—the need to produce a technologically skilled workforce. For the relatively small number of students pursuing these sorts of careers, specialized courses are vital, as they must learn an appropriate vocabulary and develop skills in experimental method and mathematical manipulations to solve problems.

The second important task of university education, however, is to deal with the fact that most students are not on track to become scientists or engineers. For these students, the kind of specialized courses taken by those who major in the sciences tends to divorce science from its familiar day-to-day context. All too often, students in these courses leave the university with a view that science is difficult, uninteresting, and irrelevant. It is clear that to equip students to deal with these sorts of issues, those students need to acquire a broad base in all branches of the sciences. The problem with most introductory science courses at the college level, even among those science courses specifically designed for nonscientists, is that they rarely integrate physics, astronomy, chemistry, Earth science, and biology. In short, the traditional science curricula of most colleges and universities fail to provide the basic science education that is necessary to understand the many scientific and technological issues facing our society.

This situation is slowly changing. Since the preliminary edition of *The Sciences: An Integrated Approach* appeared in 1993, hundreds of colleges and universities have begun the process of instituting new integrated science courses as an option for undergraduates. In the process, we have had the opportunity to interact with hundreds of our colleagues across the country, as well as more than 9,000 of our own students at George Mason University, and have received invaluable guidance in preparing this extensively revised edition.

The Need for a New Science Education

In the coming decades, the 1996 publication of the *National Science Education Standards* by the National Research Council may be seen as a pivotal event in American science education. The *Standards*, which represented the collective effort and consensus of more than 20,000 scientists, educators, administrators, and parents, offered a dramatically new vision of science education for all of America. The authors of this book were part of a small team that put together the final version of the *Standards*, and thus have had a ring-side seat as the standards have been modified and adopted in states throughout the country.

A central emphasis throughout the *Standards* is the development of a student's understanding of the scientific process, as opposed to just the accumulation of scientific facts. Emphasis is placed on the role of experiments in probing nature and the importance of mathematics in describing its behavior. Rather than developing esoteric vocabulary and specialized knowledge, the *Standards* strives to empower students to read and appreciate popular accounts of major discoveries in physics, astronomy, chemistry, geology, and biology, as well as advances in medicine, information technology, and new materials. Students should develop an understanding that a few universal laws describe the behavior of our physical surroundings—laws that operate every day, in every action of our lives.

Achieving this kind of scientific proficiency requires a curriculum quite different from the traditional, departmentally based requirements for majors. As we pointed out above, most societal issues concerning science and technology draw on a broad range of knowledge. The scientific principles involved must be integrated with other factors such as economics, energy demand, perceptions of risk, and demographics.

The Goals of This Book

This text, based on our course "Great Ideas in Science," which has been developed at George Mason University, is an attempt to respond to the future needs of today's students. Our approach recognizes that science forms a seamless web of knowledge about the universe. Our integrated course encompasses physics, chemistry, astronomy, Earth sciences, and biology, and emphasizes general principles and their application to real-world situations rather than esoteric detail.

Having set as our goal providing education for people who will not be scientists but who need some knowledge of science to function as citizens, we have to address another issue. There is no question that anyone who actually does science will be required to use high levels of mathematics to carry out his or her work. We would argue, however, that this same level of mathematics is not required by the average person confronting political issues.

There are two central features of *The Sciences: An Integrated Approach* that allow us to offer a text with the expressed goal of helping students achieve scientific literacy. These features are (1) organization around Great Ideas, and (2) an explicit integration of the sciences, starting with the first chapter.

GREAT IDEAS

One of the best-kept secrets in the world is this: the core ideas of the sciences are really quite simple. Furthermore, these core ideas form a framework for our understanding of the universe—they give our ideas structure and form. As we argue in the text, these Great Ideas represent a hierarchy in the sciences that transcend the boundaries of specific disciplines. The conservation of energy, for example, is part of the intellectual framework of sciences from astronomy to zoology.

By organizing our presentation around the central Great Ideas rather than around specific disciplines, students can deal with the universe as it presents itself to them, rather than with disciplinary divisions that have little meaning for them, no matter how important they are to working scientists.

No one can predict what the major subjects of public concern will be in 30 years' time—certainly no one 30 years ago would have guessed that we would be arguing about stem cells today.

What we can guarantee, however, is that whatever those future issues are, they will present themselves in relation to the Great Ideas.

INTEGRATION

Every chapter in this book opens with a list of how the concepts to be discussed relate to every area of science. In the chapters themselves, we use the Special Features described below to bring in aspects of science from other areas. For us, integration is more than a cosmetic feature—it goes to the very heart of science. The universe presents itself to us as a seamless web of interacting phenomena, and our understanding of science should do the same.

The Organization of *The Sciences*

We were, in fact, the first to adopt a distinctive and innovative approach to science education based on the principle that general science courses are a key to a balanced and effective college-level science education for nonmajors and future elementary and high school teachers, and a broadening experience for science majors. We organize the text around a series of 25 scientific concepts. The most basic principle, the starting point of all science, is the idea that the universe can be studied by observation and experiment (Chapter 1). A surprising number of students, even science majors, have no clear idea of how this central concept sets science apart from religion, philosophy, and the arts as a way to understand our place in the cosmos.

Once students understand the nature of science and its practice, they can appreciate some of the basic principles shared by all the sciences: Newton's laws governing force and motion (Chapter 2); the laws of thermodynamics that govern energy and entropy (Chapters 3 and 4); the equivalence of electricity and magnetism (Chapters 5 and 6); and the atomic structure of all matter (Chapters 8–11). In one form or another, all of these ideas appear in virtually every elementary science textbook, but often in abstract form. As educators, we must strive to make them part of every student's day-to-day experience. An optional chapter on the theory of relativity (Chapter 7) examines the consequences of a universe in which all observers discern the same laws of nature.

Having established these general principles, we go on to examine specific natural systems such as atoms, Earth, or living things. The realm of the nucleus (Chapter 12) and subatomic particles (Chapter 13), for example, must follow the basic rules governing all matter and energy.

In sections on astronomy and cosmology (Chapters 14–16), students learn that stars and planets form and move as predicted by Newton's laws, that stars eventually burn up according to the laws of thermodynamics, that nuclear reactions fuel stars by the conversion of mass into energy, and that stars produce light as a consequence of electromagnetic processes.

Plate tectonics (Chapter 17) and the cycles of rocks, water, and the atmosphere (Chapter 18) unify the Earth sciences. The laws of thermodynamics, which decree that no feature on Earth's surface is permanent, can be used to explain geological time, gradualism, and the causes of earthquakes and volcanoes.

Living things (Chapters 19–25) are arguably the most complex systems that scientists attempt to understand. We identify seven basic principles that apply to all living systems: interdependent collections of living things (ecosystems) recycle matter while energy flows through them; living things use many strategies to maintain and reproduce life; all living things obey the laws of chemistry and physics; all living things incorporate a few simple molecular building blocks; all living things are made of cells; all living things use the same genetic code; and all living things evolved by natural selection.

The sections covering living things has been extensively revised. Chapter 19 includes new information on ecosystems and their importance to the environment. One chapter (20) covers the organization and characteristics of living things. A revised chapter on biotechnology (24) explores several recent advances in our molecular understanding of life that helps to cure diseases and to better the human condition. We end the book with a discussion of evolution (25) that emphasizes observational evidence first.

The text has been designed so that four chapters—relativity (7), quantum mechanics (9), particle physics (13), and cosmology (15)—may be skipped without loss of continuity.

Major Changes in the Eighth Edition

We are always amazed at how much of the scientific content of this book has to be updated when we undertake a new edition, and the eighth edition is no exception. It has been updated to provide the most current scientific coverage and the most useful pedagogical elements to students taking integrated science courses. Additionally, each chapter has new end-of-chapter questions to address new material and to provide students with better study tools.

Some of the most significant changes to this edition include the following:

Chapter 1 This chapter now features an expanded discussion of citizen science, a new way for people to become involved.

Chapter 2 The discussion of deterministic chaos in the "Thinking More About" section has been expanded.

Chapter 3 The section of energy use in the United States and the section on renewable energy sources have been extensively updated to reflect the rapidly changing energy landscape.

Chapter 4 Heat and the Second Law of Thermodynamics contains an expanded discussion of temperature scales and a new "Thinking More About" on the use of fossil fuels.

Chapter 5 A new discussion of the electrification of America underscores the importance of electricity and magnetism in everyday life.

Chapter 6 We feature a new "Technology" section on cell phones.

Chapter 7 We have expanded discussion of the experimental tests of special relativity as well as a new section on gravitational waves.

Chapter 8 The presentation of the periodic table has been modified to stress its role as an organizing principle in chemistry.

Chapter 9 We have updated the section on quantum computing and expanded the "Thinking More About" section on the subject of consciousness.

Chapter 10 We have added a new "Science in the Making" section on "Polymers and the Origins of Life."

Chapter 11 We have updated the section on computers and added a new "Technology" feature on light-emitting diodes.

Chapter 12 The Nucleus of the Atom has an updated section on fusion, emphasizing forefront experiments at NIF and ITER.

Chapter 13 The Ultimate Structure of Matter includes updated material on accelerators, the Higgs Boson, and CERN, as well as a new discussion of quantum loop gravity.

Chapter 14 The Stars contains the updated list of both terrestrial and orbiting observatories, discussion of IceCube and black hole search results, and a new section on space weather.

Chapter 15 Cosmology has been updated to include new results from dark matter searches and a description of the LUX experiments.

Chapter 16 Earth and Other Planets has been expanded to update discussions of space probes and the Mars rovers, present a fuller discussion of the oceans of Europa and planned drilling missions, and greatly expand the discussion of exoplanets and the Kepler spacecraft.

Chapter 17 Plate Tectonics contains an updated discussion of the Fukushima earthquake in 2011 and the personal account of one of the authors (RMH) who was in Japan when it struck.

Chapter 19 Ecology, Ecosystems, and the Environment has been updated with new data on climate change.

Chapter 20 The section on taxonomy now contains a discussion of cladistics as well as an "Ongoing Process of Science" on the taxonomic problems associated with the classification of fungi.

Chapter 22   The Molecules of Life now has a completely revised and simplified "Return to the Integrated Question."

Chapter 23   This chapter now contains an expanded discussion of Mendelian genetics and DNA transcription as well as updated material on the human genome.

Chapter 24   The New Science of Life starts with a new integrated question. It has updated discussions of DNA fingerprinting, genetic engineering, and genetically modified crops, as well as new sections on epigenetics and synthetic biology.

Chapter 25   Evolution includes significantly updated and enhanced coverage on the origin of life (especially chemical evolution), as well as a completely rewritten section on the Neanderthals based on their DNA.

Special Features

In an effort to aid student learning and underscore the integration of the sciences, we have attempted to relate scientific principles to each student's everyday life. To this end, we have incorporated several distinctive features throughout the book.

GREAT IDEAS

Each chapter begins with a statement of a great unifying idea or theme in science, so that students immediately grasp the chief concept of that chapter. These statements are not intended to be recited or memorized, but rather to provide a framework for placing everyday experiences into a broad context.

GREAT IDEAS ACROSS THE SCIENCES

Our theme of integration is reinforced with a radiating diagram that appears at the beginning of every chapter. The diagram ties together some of the examples discussed in the text and shows how the Great Idea has been applied to different branches of science and to everyday life.

SCIENCE THROUGH THE DAY

Each chapter begins with a "Science Through the Day" section in which we tie the chapter's main theme to common experiences such as eating, driving a car, or suntanning.

THE SCIENCE OF LIFE

To help show the interdisciplinary nature of the many concepts we introduce, we have included sections on living things in most chapters. Thus, while chapters emphasizing principles specifically related to life are at the end of the book, biological examples appear throughout.

SCIENCE IN THE MAKING

These historical episodes trace the progress of scientific discovery and portray the lives of some of the central figures in science. In these episodes, we have tried to illustrate the process of science, examine the interplay of science and society, and reveal the role of serendipity in scientific discovery.

THE ONGOING PROCESS OF SCIENCE

Science is a never-ending process of asking questions and seeking answers. In these features, we examine some of the most exciting questions currently being addressed by scientists.

STOP & THINK

At various points in each chapter, we ask students to pause and think about the implications of a scientific discovery or principle.

TECHNOLOGY

The application of scientific ideas to commerce, industry, and other modern technological concerns is perhaps the most immediate way in which students encounter science.

MATHEMATICAL EQUATIONS AND WORKED EXAMPLES

Unlike the content of many science texts, formulas and mathematical derivations play a subsidiary role in our treatment of the subject matter. We rely much more on real-world experiences and on everyday vocabulary. We believe that every student should understand the role of mathematics in science. Therefore, in many chapters, we have included a few key equations and the appropriate worked examples. Whenever an equation is introduced, it is presented in three steps: first as an English sentence, second as a word equation, and finally in its traditional symbolic form. In this way, students can focus on the meaning rather than the abstraction of the mathematics. We also include an appendix on English and SI units.

SCIENCE BY THE NUMBERS

We also think that students should understand the importance of simple mathematical calculations in areas of magnitude. Thus, we have incorporated many nontraditional calculations.

THINKING MORE ABOUT

Each chapter ends with a section that addresses a social or philosophical issue tied to science such as federal funding of the sciences, nuclear waste disposal, cloning, and priorities in medical research.

DISCOVERY LABS

The eighth edition features updated "kitchen sink" labs contributed by Larry McClellan and Meena Jagasia who provide students with additional real-world science applications. These labs may be conducted in a class or lab, or they may be assigned for students to complete at home.

RETURN TO THE INTEGRATED SCIENCE QUESTION

Each chapter of *The Sciences* opens with an Integrated Science Question that draws from the many branches of science discussed in the chapter. New to the eighth edition, we now return to this question at the end of the chapter to illustrate for students how the material draws together to answer this question and creates a problem-solving framework for students to apply to future questions.

OTHER FEATURES

Key Words. Most science texts suffer from too complex a vocabulary. We have tried to avoid unnecessary jargon. Because the scientifically literate student must be familiar with many words and concepts that appear regularly in newspaper articles or other material for general readers, each chapter contains key words that appear in boldface type. These words are also listed at the end of each chapter.

There are many other scientific terms that are more specialized but also important. We have highlighted these terms in italics. We strongly recommend that students learn the meaning and context of all the key words but not be expected to memorize the words that appear in italics. We encourage all adopters of this text to provide their own lists of key words and other terms, both those we might have omitted and those they feel should be eliminated from our list.

Questions. We feature four levels of end-of-chapter questions, and we revise at least 30% of them in each new edition. "Review Questions" test important factual information covered in the text and are provided to emphasize key points. Many of the Review Questions have been substantially rewritten for this edition. "Discussion Questions" are also based on material in the text, but they also examine student comprehension and explore the application and analysis of the scientific concepts. "Problems" are quantitative questions that require students to use mathematical operations, typically those introduced in worked examples or "Science by the Numbers." Finally, "Investigations" require additional research outside the classroom. Each instructor should decide which level of questions is most appropriate for his or her students. We welcome suggestions for additional questions, which we will add to the next edition of this text.

Illustrations. This book has been extensively illustrated with color images in an effort to help amplify the key ideas and principles. All the diagrams and graphs have been designed for maximum clarity and impact.

Great Ideas in Science: A Reader in the Classic Literature of Science. In conjunction with University Readers of San Diego, California, Robert Hazen and James Trefil have edited a collection of 50 excerpts from original sources to illustrate transformational discoveries in science history. The readings are grouped into 25 chapters that parallel this volume. Taken together, these readings reveal dramatic changes in the process and progress of science.

ANCILLARIES FOR THE SCIENCES, EIGHTH EDITION
WILEYPLUS LEARNING SPACE

The factors that contribute to success–both in college and in life–aren't comprised of intellectual capabilities alone. In fact, there are other traits, strategies, and even daily habits that contribute to the overall picture of success. Studies show that people who can delay instant gratification, work through tasks even if they are not immediately rewarding, and follow through with a plan have the skills that are not only valuable in the classroom, but also in the workplace and their personal lives.

A place where students can define their strengths and nurture these skills, WileyPLUS Learning Space transforms course content into an online learning community. WileyPLUS Learning Space invites students to experience learning activities, work through self-assessment, ask questions and share insights. As they interact with the course content, peers and their instructor, WileyPLUS Learning Space creates a personalized study guide for each student.

As research shows, when students collaborate with each other, they make deeper connections to the content. When students work together, they also feel part of a community so that they can grow in areas beyond topics in the course. With WileyPLUS Learning Space, students are invested in their learning experience and can use their time efficiently as they develop skills like critical thinking and teamwork.

Through a flexible course design, you can quickly organize learning activities, manage student collaboration, and customize your course–having full control over content as well as the amount of interactivity between students.

WileyPLUS Learning Space lets you:

- Assign activities and add your own materials
- Guide your students through what›s important in the interactive e-textbook by easily assigning specific content
- Set up and monitor group learning
- Assess student engagement
- Gain immediate insights to help inform teaching

Defining a clear path to action, the visual reports in WileyPLUS Learning Space help both you and your students gauge problem areas and act on what›s most important.

With the visual reports, you can:

- See exactly where your students are struggling for early intervention
- Help students see exactly what they don't know to better prepare for exams
- Give students insight into their strengths and weaknesses so that they can succeed in your course

For Students
Personalize the learning experience.

Different learning styles, different levels of proficiency, different levels of preparation—each of your students is unique. WileyPLUS Learning Space empowers them to take advantage of their individual strengths:

- Students receive timely access to resources that address their demonstrated needs, and they get immediate feedback and remediation when needed.
- Integrated, multimedia resources include:

  Virtual Discovery Labs bring select core concepts to life in an online lab setting.
  Animations illustrate select text concepts.
  Science in the News Video Clips are linked right into the eBook in WileyPLUS for easy in-context access and give students a look into how science works in the real world.

- WileyPLUS Learning Space includes many opportunities for self-assessment linked to the relevant portions of the text. Students can take control of their own learning and practice until they master the material.

For Instructors
Personalize the teaching experience.

WileyPLUS Learning Space empowers you with the tools and resources you need to make your teaching even more effective:

- You can customize your classroom presentation with a wealth of resources and functionality from PowerPoint slides to a database of rich visuals. You can even add your own materials to your WileyPLUS Learning Space course.
- With WileyPLUS Learning Space you can identify those students who are falling behind and intervene accordingly, without having to wait for them to come to office hours.
- WileyPLUS Learning Space simplifies and automates such tasks as student performance assessment, making assignments, scoring student work, keeping grades, and more.

Virtual Discovery Labs authored by Brian Shmaefsky of Lone Star College bring select core concepts to life in an online lab setting. Virtual Discovery Labs offer students an excellent alternative to hands-on lab work with assignable lab reports and question assignments.

Test Bank by David King of Auburn University is available on both the instructor companion site and within WileyPLUS Learning Space. Containing approximately 50 multiple-choice and essay test items per chapter, this test bank offers assessment of both basic understanding and conceptual applications. *The Sciences*, Eighth Edition Test Bank is offered in two formats: MS Word files and a Computerized Test Bank. The easy-to-use test-generation program fully supports graphics, print tests, student answer sheets, and answer keys. The software's advanced features allow you to create an exam to your exact specifications.

Instructor's Manual prepared by Jack Giannattasio, Monmouth University, contains teaching suggestions, lecture notes, answers to problems from the textbook, additional problems, and over 70 creative ideas for in-class activities. Available in WileyPLUS Learning Space and on the instructor companion site.

Science in the News Video Clips and Lecture Launcher Presentations provide instructors with a presentation tool to give students a look into how science works in the real world. Videos can be presented in class or assigned with questions in WileyPLUS Learning Space.

Animations. Select text concepts are illustrated using flash animation, designed for use in classroom presentations.

All line illustrations and photos from *The Sciences*, Eighth Edition in jpeg files and PowerPoint format are available both on the instructor companion site and within WileyPLUS Learning Space.

Biology Visual Library containing all of the line illustrations in the textbook in jpeg format, as well as access to numerous other life science illustrations from other Wiley texts, is available in WileyPLUS and on the instructor companion site.

PowerPoint presentations by John Gudenas of Aurora University are tailored to *The Sciences*, Eighth Edition's topical coverage and learning objectives. These presentations are designed to convey key text concepts, illustrated by embedded text art. An effort has been made to reduce the amount of words on each slide and increase the use of visuals to illustrate concepts. Personal Response System questions are specifically designed to foster student discussion and debate in class.

Book Companion Site (www.wiley.com/college/trefil)

For the Student:

- Quizzes for student self-testing
- Biology NewsFinder; Flash Cards; and Animations

For the Instructor:

- Biology Visual Library; all images in jpg and PowerPoint formats.
- Instructor's Manual; Test Bank; Lecture PowerPoint presentations, and Personal Response System questions, and Instructor Resources are password protected.

Acknowledgments

The development of this text has benefited immensely from the help and advice of numerous people. Students in our "Great Ideas in Science" course at George Mason University have played a central role in designing this text. Approximately 9,000 students, the majority of whom were non-science majors, have enrolled in the course over the past 24 years. They represent a diverse cross section of American students: more than half were women, and many minority, foreign-born, and adult learners were enrolled. Their candid assessments of course content and objectives, as well as their constructive suggestions for improvements, have helped shape our text.

FACULTY INPUT

We thank the many teachers across the country who are developing integrated science courses. Their letters and suggestions to us and responses to our publisher's survey inspired us as we wrote this edition. We especially thank the professors who have used and class-tested the earlier editions, sharing with us the responses of their students and their own analyses. Their classroom experience continues to help us shape the book.

PUBLISHER SUPPORT

Finally, as in the previous editions, we gratefully acknowledge the dedicated people at John Wiley and Sons who originally proposed this textbook and have helped us in developing every aspect of its planning and production for all eight editions. We thank our Senior Editor, Nick Ferrari for his support and innovative ideas. Senior Market Solutions Assistant, Mallory Fryc served with skill and professionalism. Executive Marketing Manager Kristine Ruff championed the book in her marketing and sales efforts.

We also thank the production team of the eighth edition. The project was ably managed by Patricia McFadden and meticulously produced by Jeanine Furino who dealt with the countless technical details associated with an integrated science book. Tom Nery designed the handsome text and the cover. Billy Ray researched the numerous new photos for the eighth edition. Anna Melhorn coordinated the development of our new illustrations. To all the staff at John Wiley, we owe a great debt for their enthusiastic support, constant encouragement, and sincere dedication to science education reform.

Reviewers for The Eighth Edition

Darlene Dickens
East Georgia State College

Jack Giannattasio
Monmouth University

Oliver Graudejus
Arizona State University

John Gudenas
Aurora University

Kristy McBride
Belmont University

Martin Saltzman
Providence College

Kevin Vogel
Saint Bonaventure University

Wendi Wolfram
Hardin-Simmons University

Contents

James Trefil (right) has authored or coauthored numerous books on science for the general audience. His interest in science literacy began with a contributed essay to E. D. Hirsch's Cultural Literacy and continued with his work on the Content Review Board for the National Science Education Standards. He is a frequent lecturer on science and the law at state and federal judicial conferences. He received undergraduate degrees from the University of Illinois and Oxford University. After receiving a doctorate in theoretical physics from Stanford University, he held post-doctorate and faculty appointments in Europe and the United States. He is the Clarence Robinson Professor of Physics at George Mason University. He has made contributions to researching elementary particle physics, fluid mechanics, medical physics (including cancer research), and the earth sciences. Trefil was awarded the Gemant Prize of the American Institute of Physics for his efforts to present science to the public. His most recent book is *Science in World History*.

Robert M. Hazen (left) is the Clarence Robinson Professor of Earth Science at George Mason University and Staff Scientist at the Carnegie Institution of Washington's Geophysical Laboratory. Hazen developed a fascination for rocks and minerals as a child growing up in mineral-rich Northern New Jersey, and he pursued that interest as an undergraduate at the Massachusetts Institute of Technology. After receiving a doctorate in earth sciences from Harvard University, he spent a year at Cambridge University as a NATO Postdoctoral Fellow. In addition to teaching courses on scientific literacy, scientific ethics, symmetry in art and science, and visual thinking, he performs research on the roles that minerals may have played in the origin of life. His current studies explore the hypothesis that life arose in a deep, high-pressure environment. Hazen is active in presenting science to the public. He developed a 60-lecture video version of the textbook *The Joy of Science*, which is available nationally through The Teaching Company. He has appeared on numerous radio and television shows, including NOVA and Today. His most recent popular book is *The Story of Earth*.

WileyPLUS Learning Space

An easy way to help your students learn, collaborate, and grow.

Diagnose Early

Educators assess the real-time proficiency of each student to inform teaching decisions. Students always know what they need to work on.

Facilitate Engagement

Educators can quickly organize learning activities, manage student collaboration, and customize their course. Students can collaborate and have meaningful discussions on concepts they are learning.

Measure Outcomes

With visual reports, it's easy for both educators and students to gauge problem areas and act on what's most important.

Instructor Benefits

- Assign activities and add your own materials
- Guide students through what's important in the interactive e-textbook by easily assigning specific content
- Set up and monitor collaborative learning groups
- Assess learner engagement
- Gain immediate insights to help inform teaching

Student Benefits

- Instantly know what you need to work on
- Create a personal study plan
- Assess progress along the way
- Participate in class discussions
- Remember what you have learned because you have made deeper connections to the content

Science: A Way of Knowing

How do you know what you know?

PHYSICS

What forces exist in the universe? (Ch. 8)

BIOLOGY

How do complex organisms develop from a single cell? (Ch. 25)

CHEMISTRY

How can we combine atoms to form new materials? (Ch. 11)

TECHNOLOGY

How can we design more efficient power plants? (Ch. 4)

GREAT IDEA

Science is a way of asking and answering questions about the natural universe.

ENVIRONMENT

Do human activities affect Earth's global climate? (Ch. 19)

ASTRONOMY

What will be the ultimate fate of the universe? (Ch. 15)

HEALTH & SAFETY

What causes cancer? (Ch. 24)

GEOLOGY

What dynamic processes occur in Earth's deep interior? (Ch. 17)

 = applications of the great idea discussed in this chapter

 = other applications, some of which are discussed in other chapters

Sunlight streams through your east window. As you wake up, you remember it's Saturday. No classes! And you're headed to the beach with friends. It looks like it's going to be a beautiful day, just like the weather forecast promised.

We take so much about the natural world for granted. Every day the Sun rises at a precisely predictable time in the east. Every day the Sun sets in the west. So, too, the phases of the Moon and the seasons of the year follow their familiar repetitive cycles.

Ancient humans took note of these and many other predictable aspects of nature, and they patterned their lives and cultures accordingly. Today, we formalize this search for regularities in nature, and we call the process science.

◉ 1.1 The Role of Science

Our lives are filled with choices. What should I eat? Is it safe to cross the street? Should I bother to recycle an aluminum can, or should I just throw it in the trash? Every day we have to make dozens of decisions; each choice is based, in part, on the knowledge that actions in a physical world have predictable consequences. By what process do you make those decisions?

Making Choices

When you pull into a gas station, you have to ask yourself what sort of gasoline to buy for your car (Figure 1-1). Over a period of time you may try many different types—different brands, regular or premium, different levels of ethanol—observing how your car responds to each. In the end, you may conclude that a particular brand and grade suits your car best, and you decide to buy that one in the future. You engage in a similar process of inquiry and experimentation when you buy shampoo, pain relievers, athletic shoes, and scores of other products.

These simple examples illustrate one way we learn about the universe. First, we look at the world to see what is there and to learn how it works. Then we generalize, making rules that seem to fit what we see. Finally, we apply those general rules to new situations we've never encountered before, and we fully expect the rules to work.

There doesn't seem to be anything Earth-shattering about choosing a brand of gasoline or shampoo. But the same basic procedure of asking questions, making observations, and arriving at a conclusion can be applied in a more formal and quantitative way when we want to understand the workings of a distant star or a living cell. In these cases, the enterprise is called science, and the people who study these questions for a living are called scientists.

Why Study Science?

Science gives us our most powerful tool to understand how our world works and how we interact with our physical surroundings. Science not only incorporates basic ideas and theories about how our universe behaves, but it also provides a framework for learning more and tackling new questions and concerns that come our way. Science represents our best hope for predicting and coping with natural disasters, curing diseases, and discovering new materials and new technologies with which to shape our world. Science also provides an unparalleled view of the magnificent order and symmetry of the universe and its workings—from the unseen world of the atomic nucleus to the inconceivable vastness of space.

FIGURE 1-1 Even something simple like choosing a brand of gasoline can involve observation and experiment.

Pick up your local newspaper any morning of the week and glance at the headlines. On a typical day you'll see articles about the weather, environmental concerns, and long-range planning by one of your local utility companies. There might be news about a new treatment for cancer, an earthquake in California, or new advances in biotechnology. The editorial pages might feature comments on cloning humans, arguments for a NASA planetary mission, debates about teaching evolution, or perhaps a trial involving DNA fingerprinting. What do all of these stories have in common? They may affect your life in one way or another, and they all depend, to a significant degree, on science.

We live in a world of matter and energy, forces and motions. The process of science is based on the idea that everything we experience in our lives takes place in an ordered universe with regular and predictable phenomena. You have learned to survive in this universe, so many of these scientific ideas are second nature to you. When you drive a car, cook a meal, or play a pickup game of basketball, you instinctively take advantage of a few simple physical laws. As you eat, sleep, work, or play, you experience the world as a living biological system and must come to terms with the natural laws governing all living things.

So why should you study science? Chances are you aren't going to be a professional scientist. Even so, your job may well depend on advances in science and technology. New technologies are a driving force in economics, business, and even many aspects of law: new semiconductor technology, agricultural methods, and information processing have altered our world. Biological research and drug development play crucial roles in the medical professions: stories about genetic diseases, flu vaccines, viral epidemics, and nutritional information appear in the news every day. Even professional athletes must constantly evaluate and use new and improved gear, rely on improved medical treatments and therapies, and weigh the potential medical risks of legal performance-enhancing drugs. By studying science, you will not only be better able to incorporate these advances into your professional life, but you will also better understand the process by which such advances were made.

Science is no less central to your everyday life away from school or work. As a consumer, you are besieged by new products and processes, not to mention a bewildering variety of warnings about health and safety. As a taxpayer, you must vote on issues that directly affect your community—energy taxes, recycling proposals, government spending on research, and more. As a living being, you must make informed decisions about diet and lifestyle. And as a parent, you will have to nurture and guide your children through an ever-more-complex world. A firm grasp of the principles and methods of science will help you make life's important decisions in a more informed way. As an extra bonus, you will be poised to share in the excitement of the scientific discoveries that, week-by-week, transform our understanding of the universe and our place in it. Science opens up astonishing, unimagined worlds—bizarre life forms in deep oceans, exploding stars in deep space, and aspects of the history of life and our world more wondrous than any fiction.

◉ 1.2 The Scientific Method

Science is a way of asking and answering questions about the physical universe. It's not simply a set of facts or a catalog of answers, but rather a process for conducting an ongoing dialogue with our physical surroundings. Like any human activity, science is enormously varied and rich in subtleties. Nevertheless, a few basic steps taken together can be said to comprise the **scientific method**.

Observation

If our goal is to learn about the world, then the first thing we have to do is look around us and see what's there. This statement may seem obvious to us in our modern technological age, yet throughout much of history, learned men and women rejected the idea that you can understand the world simply by observing it.

Some Greek philosophers living during the Golden Age of Athens argued that one cannot deduce the true nature of the universe by trusting the senses. The senses lie, they would have said. Only the use of reason and the insights of the human mind can lead us to true understanding. In his famous book *The Republic*, Plato compared human beings to people living in a cave, watching shadows on a wall but unable to see the objects causing the shadows (Figure 1-2). In just the same way, he argued, observing the physical world will never put us in contact with reality, but will doom us to a lifetime of wrestling with shadows. Only with the "eye of the mind" can we break free from illusion and arrive at the truth, Plato argued.

In the Middle Ages in Europe, a similar frame of mind was to be found, but with a trust in received wisdom replacing the use of human reason as the ultimate tool in the search for truth. A story (probably apocryphal) about an Oxford College debate on the question "How many teeth does a horse have?" underscores this point. One learned scholar got up and quoted the Greek scientist Aristotle on the subject, and another quoted the theologian St. Augustine to put forward a different answer. Finally, a young man at the back of the hall got up and noted that since there was a horse outside, they could settle the question by looking in its mouth. At this point, the manuscript states, the assembled scholars "fell upon him, smote him hip and thigh, and cast him from the company of educated men."

As these examples illustrate, many distinguished thinkers have attacked the problem of learning about the physical world without actually making observations and measurements. These approaches are perfectly self-consistent and were pursued by people every bit as intelligent as we are. They are not, however, the methods of science, nor did they produce the kinds of advanced technologies and knowledge that we associate with modern societies.

In the remainder of this book, we differentiate between **observations**, in which we observe nature without manipulating it, and **experiments**, in which we manipulate some aspect of nature and observe the outcome. An astronomer, for example, observes distant stars without changing them, while a chemist may experiment by mixing materials together and seeing what happens.

School of Athens, detail of the centre showing Plato and Aristotle with students including Michelangelo and Diogenes, 1510-11 by Raphael (Raffaello Sanzio of Urbino) (1483-1520) ©Vatican Museums and Galleries, Vatican City, Italy/ The Bridgeman Art Library

FIGURE 1-2 Plato argued that humans observing nature were like men watching shadows on the wall of a cave.

Identifying Patterns and Regularities

When we observe a particular phenomenon over and over again, we begin to get a sense of how nature behaves. We start to recognize patterns in nature. Eventually, we generalize our experience into a synthesis that summarizes what we have learned about the way the world works. We may, for example, notice that whenever we drop something, it falls. This statement represents a summary of the results of many observations.

It often happens that at this stage scientists summarize the results of their observations in mathematical form, particularly if they have been making quantitative **measurements**. Every measurement involves a number that is recorded in some standard *unit of measurement*. In the case of a falling object, for example, you might measure the time (measured in the familiar time unit of seconds) that it takes an object to fall a certain distance (measured in the distance unit of meters, for example). More examples of units of measurement are given in Appendix B.

Quantitative measurements thus provide a more exact description than just noticing that the object falls. The standard scientific procedure is to collect careful measurements in the form of a table of data (see Table 1-1). These data could also be presented in the form of a graph, in which distance of the fall (in meters) is plotted against time of the fall (in seconds; Figure 1-3). As we explore the many different branches of science, from physics to biology, we'll see that most scientific measurements require both a number and a unit of measurement, and we'll encounter many different units in the coming chapters.

After preparing tables and graphs of their data, scientists would notice that the longer something falls, the farther it travels. Furthermore, the distance isn't simply proportional to the time of fall. If one object falls twice as long as another, it will travel four times as far; if it falls three times longer, it will travel nine times as far; and so on. This statement can be summarized in three ways (a format used throughout this book):

In words: The distance traveled is proportional to the square of the time of travel.

In equation form:

$$\text{distance} = \text{constant} \times (\text{time})^2$$

In symbols:

$$d = k \times t^2$$

The constant, k, has to be determined from the measurements. We'll return to the subject of constants in the next chapter.

Identifying a regularity in nature may take a long time, since it requires an accumulation of experience in a particular area. Furthermore, scientists may go through several phases in their thinking. At first, they may make a *hypothesis*, an educated guess as to what the regularity they are studying will turn out to be—"I think that if I drop things they will fall." Given enough confirmation, the hypothesis can be upgraded to a regularity.

Mathematics: The Language of Science

To many people science brings to mind obscure equations written in strange, undecipherable symbols. The next time you're in the science area of your college or university, look into an advanced classroom. Chances are you'll see a confusing jumble of formulas on the blackboard. Have you ever wondered why scientists need all those complex mathematical equations? Science is supposed to help us understand the physical world around us, so why can't scientists just use plain English?

Take a stroll outside and look carefully at a favorite tree. Think about how you might describe the tree in as much detail as possible so that a distant friend could envision exactly what you see and distinguish that tree from all others.

A cursory description would note the rough brown bark, branching limbs, and canopy of green leaves, but that description would do little to distinguish your tree from most others. You might use adjectives such as *lofty*, *graceful*, or *stately* to convey an overall impression of the tree (Figure 1-4). Better yet, you could identify the exact kind of tree and specify its stage of growth—a sugar maple at the peak of autumn color, for example—but even then your friend has relatively little to go on.

TABLE 1-1 Measurements of Falling Objects

Time of Fall (seconds)	Distance of Fall (meters)
1	5
2	20
3	45
4	80
5	125

FIGURE 1-3 Measurements of a falling object can be presented visually in the form of a graph. Time of fall in seconds (on the horizontal axis) is plotted versus distance of fall in meters (on the vertical axis).

FIGURE 1-4 There are many ways of describing a tree.

Your description would be far more accurate if you gave exact dimensions of the tree—measurements expressed in units, such as its height, the distance spanned by its branches, or the diameter of the trunk. You could document the shape and size of leaves, the thickness and texture of the bark, the angles and spacing of the branching limbs, and the tree's approximate age. You could approach measuring the tree from other perspectives as well—by calculating the number of board feet of lumber the tree could yield (Figure 1-5), or how much life-supporting oxygen the tree produces every day. Finally, you could talk about the basic molecular processes that allow the tree to extract energy from sunlight and carry out the other chemical tasks we associate with life.

As we move through these descriptions of the tree, our language becomes more and more quantitative. In some cases, such as supplying a detailed description of the tree's shape or its chemistry, that description could become quite long and cumbersome. That's why scientists employ **mathematics**, which is a concise language that allows them to communicate their results in compact form and often, as an added benefit, allows them to make very precise predictions about expected outcomes of experiments or observations. But anything that can be said in an equation can also be said (albeit in a less concise way) in a plain English sentence. When you encounter equations in your science courses, you should always ask, "What English sentence does this equation represent?" Learning to "read" equations will keep the mathematics from obscuring the simple ideas that lie behind most equations.

DEVELOPMENT OF A THEORY

Once scientists have established a regularity in nature, they can go on to ask an important question: What must the world be like in order for this regularity to exist? They will, in other words, construct a theory—a mental (and usually mathematical) picture of how the world operates. In the next chapter, for example, we will see how the English scientist Isaac Newton formulated a theory about why things fall—a far reaching theory embodied in what we now call the law of universal gravitation. As we shall see below, a theory must be tested against nature, but once it has met this test it represents our best guess as to what the world is like.

We are already encountering terms that we often use when talking about the scientific process, and the way these terms are used are often different from the way they are used in everyday speech. For the sake of clarity, we define some of these terms below:

FIGURE 1-5 One way of looking at a tree is to think about the lumber it might produce.

Fact: A statement of something that happens in nature—"I dropped my keys and they fell."

Hypothesis: A conjecture, based on past observations or theoretical considerations, about something that will happen—"If I drop my keys again, they will fall."

Law and **Theory**: Scientists, who are normally extremely careful about data and calculations, don't pay a lot of attention to the way they use these terms. In general, whatever label is applied to a set of ideas when it is first proposed usually sticks to it, regardless of how well it fares in making predictions. Thus, "theory" can refer to a fully fleshed out (but as yet untested) hypothesis like the so-called string theories we'll discuss in Chapter 13. It can also, however, refer to a set of ideas that have met many experimental tests and are widely accepted by scientists, such as the theory of general relativity (Chapter 7) and the theory of evolution (Chapter 25). The term "law" is generally used to refer to statements that have met many tests, such as the law of universal gravitation, which we will discuss in Chapter 2. It is important to realize, however, that there is no real distinction in scientific usage between a generally accepted theory and a generally accepted law, nor is there any implied ranking between them. For example, the *law* of universal gravitation is actually part of the much broader and more complete *theory* of general relativity.

Prediction and Testing

In science, every idea must be tested by using it to make **predictions** about how a particular system will behave, then observing nature to see if the system behaves as predicted. The theory of evolution, for example, makes countless specific testable predictions about the similarities and differences of modern living organisms, as well as the nature and distribution of extinct fossil organisms.

Think about the hypothesis that all objects fall when they are dropped. That idea can be tested by dropping all sorts of objects (Figure 1-6). Each drop constitutes a test of our prediction, and the more successful tests we perform, the more confidence we have that the hypothesis is correct. As long as we restrict our tests to solids or liquids on Earth's surface, then the hypothesis is consistently confirmed. Test a helium-filled balloon, however, and we discover a clear exception to the rule. The balloon "falls" up. The original hypothesis, which worked so well for most objects, fails for certain gases. And more tests would show there are other limitations. If you were an astronaut in a space shuttle, every time you held something out and let it go, it would just float in space. Evidently, our hypothesis is invalid in the orbiting space shuttle as well.

This example illustrates an important aspect about testing ideas in science. Tests do not necessarily prove or disprove an idea; instead, they often serve to define the range of situations under which the idea is valid. We may, for example, observe that nature behaves in a certain way only at high temperatures or only at low velocities. In these sorts of situations, it usually happens that the original hypothesis is seen to be a special case of a deeper, more general theory. In the case of the balloon, for example, the simple "things fall down" will be replaced by a much more general theory of gravitation, based on statements called Newton's laws of motion and the law of universal gravitation—laws we'll study in the next chapter. These laws of nature describe and predict the motion of dropped objects both on Earth and in space and, therefore, are a more successful set of statements than the original hypothesis. We will discuss them in more detail in the next chapter.

Photri/Age Fotostock America, Inc.

We will encounter many such laws and theories in this book, all backed by millions of observations and measurements. Remember, however, where these laws and theories come from. They are not written on tablets of stone, nor are they simply good ideas that someone once had. They arise from repeated and rigorous observation and testing. They represent our best understanding of how nature works.

We never stop questioning the validity of our hypotheses, theories, or laws of nature. Scientists constantly think up new, more rigorous experiments to test the limits of our theories. In fact, one of the central tenets of science is this:

● **Every law and theory of nature is subject to change, based on new observations.**

FIGURE 1-6 Equations allow us to describe with precision the behavior of objects in our physical world. One such equation predicts the behavior of falling objects.

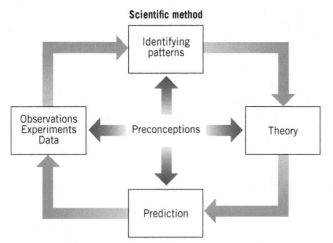

Scientific method

Identifying patterns

Observations Experiments Data

Preconceptions

Theory

Prediction

FIGURE 1-7 The scientific method can be illustrated as an endless cycle of collecting observations (data), identifying patterns and regularities in the data, creating theories, making predictions, and collecting more observations.

This is an extremely important statement about science, and one that is often ignored in public debates. It means that it must be possible, in principle, that every statement in a scientific model *could* be false. You should, in other words, be able to imagine an experimental outcome that would prove the statement false, even if that outcome never happens in the real world.

Consider the theory of evolution (see Chapter 25), which makes countless predictions about the historical sequence of organisms that have lived on Earth. According to the current model of life's evolution, for example, dinosaurs became extinct millions of years before human beings appeared. Consequently, if a paleontologist found a human leg bone in the same geological formation with a *Tyrannosaurus rex*, then that discovery would call into question the theory of evolution.

The Scientific Method in Operation

These elements—observation, regularity, theory, prediction, and testing—together comprise the scientific method. In practice, you can think of the method as working as shown in Figure 1-7. It's a never-ending cycle in which observations lead to theories, which lead to more observations.

If observations support a theory, then more tests may be devised. If the theory fails, then the new observations are used to revise it, after which the revised theory is tested again. Scientists continue this process until the limits of existing equipment are reached, in which case researchers often try to develop better instruments to do even more tests. If and when it appears that there's just no point to going further, the hypothesis may be elevated to a law of nature.

It's important to realize, however, that while the orderly cycle shown in Figure 1-7 provides a useful framework to help us think about science, it shouldn't be thought of as a rigid cookbook-style set of steps to follow. Science can be every bit as creative an endeavor as art or music. Because human beings do science, it involves occasional bursts of intuition, sudden leaps, a joyful breaking of the rules, and all the other characteristics we associate with other human activities.

Several other important points should be made about the scientific method:

1. Scientists are not required to observe nature with an "open mind," with no preconceptions about what they are going to find. Most experiments and observations are designed and undertaken with a specific hypothesis in mind, and most researchers have preconceptions about whether that hypothesis is right or wrong. Nevertheless, scientists have to believe the results of their experiments and observations, whether or not they fit preconceived notions. Science demands that whatever our preconceptions, we must be ready to change those ideas if the evidence forces us to do so.

2. There is no "right" place to enter the cycle. Scientists can (and have) started their work by making extensive observations, but they can also start with a theory and test it. It makes no difference where you enter the cycle—eventually the scientific process takes you all the way around.

3. Observations and experiments must be reported in such a way that anyone with the proper equipment can verify the results. Scientific results, in other words, must be **reproducible**, and they must be reproducible by anyone with appropriate equipment and training, not just the original experimenters.

4. The cycle is continuous; it has no end. Science does not provide final answers, nor is it a search for ultimate truth. Instead, it is a way of producing successively more detailed and exact descriptions of wider and wider areas of the physical world—descriptions that allow us to predict more of the behavior of that world with higher and higher levels of confidence.

THE ONGOING PROCESS OF SCIENCE
The Duke Forest Experiments

One of the most important experimental techniques in all the sciences consists of comparing two situations that differ from each other in only one aspect. For example, in experiments on plant growth, you might compare one group of plants that received a particular soil supplement to another group that did not receive that supplement. In the language of science, we call the latter plants the 'control group,' and including such controls is an important part of the design of experiments.

In Chapter 19 we will see that one of the important facts about the current state of our planet is that human activities are increasing the levels of carbon dioxide in the atmosphere. Since plants need atmospheric carbon dioxide to grow, it's important to understand how plant behavior is affected by higher concentrations of the gas. One method of answering this question is to add carbon dioxide to the air in an enclosed space, such as a greenhouse, but it would obviously be more useful to see how increased carbon dioxide affects plants in their normal environment. The so-called 'Free Air CO_2 Enrichment' (FACE) experiments have been designed to study this question, and one of the oldest of these efforts is in a forest managed by Duke University in North Carolina (Figure 1-8).

In the nineteenth century the 7000-acre plot now occupied by Duke Forest was farmed for cotton, but since 1931 it has reverted to forest. In 1982 some areas were clear cut and planted in loblolly pines (a native southern tree). Starting in 1994 seven experimental areas were set up. Each area was surrounded by a hollow pipe 30 m (about 90 feet) in diameter. In four of the areas, carbon dioxide was pumped in through the pipes to raise the gas concentration in the air to what scientists expect it will be in 2050. In the other three areas, to establish the control group, ambient air was pumped in instead. The scientists then monitored the growth of the forests in each area over time.

FIGURE 1-8 The Duke Forest experiments measure the effects of atmospheric carbon dioxide on the growth rates of trees.

The results of the experiment were clear. The rate of photosynthesis in the enriched plots increased by 50% and the rate of biomass production increased by 27%. Other aspects of growth, such as root production and the amount of forest litter, increased as well. Over the years, FACE experiments have been conducted in many environments, from the Nevada desert to Tasmanian grasslands to Australian wheat fields. The results vary somewhat depending on the type of plant being studied, water availability, and ozone concentrations, but the general results are similar to those in the Duke forest.

Having said this, it should be stressed that these experiments also indicate that only a relatively small percentage of the carbon dioxide put into the atmosphere by human activity in the future can be offset by enhanced plant growth. If carbon dioxide levels in the atmosphere have to be reduced, some other methods will have to be developed.

SCIENCE IN THE MAKING
Dimitri Mendeleev and the Periodic Table

Discoveries of previously unrecognized patterns in nature, a key step in the scientific method, provide scientists with some of their most exhilarating moments. Dimitri Mendeleev (1834–1907), a popular chemistry professor at the Technological Institute of St. Petersburg in Russia, experienced such a breakthrough in 1869 as he was tabulating data for a new chemistry textbook (Figure 1-9).

FIGURE 1-9 Dimitri Mendeleev recognized regular patterns in the properties of known chemical elements and thereby devised the first periodic table of elements.

The mid-nineteenth century was a time of great excitement in chemistry. Almost every year saw the discovery of one or two new chemical elements, and new apparatuses and processes were greatly expanding the repertoire of laboratory and industrial chemists. In such a stimulating field, it was no easy job to keep up to date with all the developments and summarize them in a textbook. In an effort to consolidate the current state of knowledge about the most basic chemical building blocks, Mendeleev listed various properties of the 63 known chemical elements (substances that could not be divided by chemical means). He arranged his list in order of increasing atomic weight and then noted the distinctive chemical behavior of each element.

Examining his list, Mendeleev detected an extraordinary pattern: elements with similar chemical properties appeared at regular, or *periodic,* intervals. In one group of elements, including lithium, sodium, potassium, and rubidium (he called them group-one elements), all were soft, silvery metals that formed compounds with chlorine in a one-to-one ratio. Immediately following the group-one elements in the list were beryllium, magnesium, calcium, and barium—group-two elements that form compounds with chlorine in a one-to-two ratio, and so on.

As other similar patterns emerged from his list, Mendeleev realized that the elements could be arranged in the form of a table (Figure 1-10). Not only did this so-called periodic table highlight previously unrecognized relationships among the elements, it also revealed obvious gaps where as-yet undiscovered elements must lie. The power of Mendeleev's periodic table of the elements was underscored when several new elements, with atomic weights and chemical properties just as he had predicted, were discovered in the following years.

The discovery of the periodic table ranks as one of the great achievements of science. It was so important, in fact, that Mendeleev's students carried a large poster of it behind his coffin in his funeral procession.

FIGURE 1-10 The periodic table systematizes all known chemical elements.

THE SCIENCE OF LIFE
William Harvey and the Blood's Circulation

It's common knowledge that blood circulates in your body, but stop and think for a moment. How do we know? One of the great puzzles faced by scientists who studied the human body was deducing the role played by the blood. English physician William Harvey (1578–1657) gave us our current picture of the pattern of circulation, in which blood is pumped from the heart to all parts of the body through arteries, and returned to the heart through veins. His experiments reveal the scientific method at work.

Prior to Harvey's work, several competing hypotheses had been proposed. Some scientists had taught that blood didn't move at all, but simply pulsed in response to pumping of the heart. Others taught that the arteries and veins constituted different systems, with blood in the veins flowing from the liver to the various parts of the body, where it was absorbed and its nutrients were taken in. Harvey, on the other hand, adopted the hypothesis that blood circulates through a connected system of arteries and veins. When confronted with such conflicting hypotheses, a scientist must devise experiments that test the distinctive predictions of each competing idea.

To establish the circulation of the blood, Harvey first performed careful dissections of animals to trace out the veins and arteries. Second, he undertook studies of live animals, often killing them so that he could observe the veins and arteries as the heart stopped beating. Then, as now, animals were sometimes sacrificed to advance medical science (see Investigation 7). Finally, Harvey performed a series of experiments to establish that blood in the veins did indeed flow back to the heart, rather than simply being absorbed in tissue like a stream of water in the desert. One of those experiments is shown in Figure 1-11. A tourniquet was applied to a subject's arm, and he was asked to squeeze something so that the veins filled with blood and "popped." (You have probably done the same thing when having blood drawn in a doctor's office.) Harvey would then press down on the vein and note that it would subside (indicating that the blood was leaving it) on the side toward the heart. This result is just the opposite of what would occur if blood were flowing from the liver to the extremities. Based on this experiment, and many others like it, Harvey eventually concluded that blood circulates continuously.

Before

(a)

After

(b)

FIGURE 1-11 One of William Harvey's famous experiments on the circulation of the blood tested the hypothesis that blood flows from veins to the heart. Harvey first applied a tourniquet to a subject's arm and had the subject squeeze something to raise the veins *(a)*. Pressing down on the vein caused it to gradually subside *(b)*, indicating that the blood was indeed flowing back to the heart.

SCIENCE BY THE NUMBERS
The Circulation of the Blood

William Harvey was partially motivated in his studies of the circulation of the blood by some simple mathematical calculations. At the time, the accepted dogma, promulgated by the great Roman physician Galen centuries before, was that blood was made in the liver and flowed outward to the cells, where it was largely consumed. Harvey took hearts from cadavers he was dissecting and measured the amount of water they could hold. It turned out that a normal heart can hold about 2 ounces of fluid. Harvey knew that the heart in a normal adult beats about 72 times a minute (you can check your own pulse to verify this number). Thus, in 1 minute, the amount of blood pumped by the heart must be

$$72 \text{ beats} \times 2 \text{ ounces/beat} = 144 \text{ ounces/minute}$$

There are 16 ounces in a pound, so

$$144 \text{ ounces/minute} \times 1/16 \text{ pound/ounce} = 9 \text{ pounds/minute}$$

There are 60 minutes in an hour and 24 hours in a day, so in one day the heart must pump

$$9 \text{ pounds/minute} \times 60 \text{ minutes/hour} \times 24 \text{ hours/day} = 12,960 \text{ pounds per day}$$

Harvey knew that no one can take in this much food in a day, so the sort of "one-way" circulation and consumption of blood Galen had posited simply couldn't be right. It made much more sense to have the heart pump the same supply of blood around continuously. (For historical accuracy, we should note that there was an ill defined way in Galen's physiology for some blood to return to the liver—think of something like the ebb and flow of the tide—but the idea that the blood was consumed in the body remained central.)

◉ 1.3 Other Ways of Knowing

Scientists discover laws that describe how nature works by performing reproducible observations and measurements. Every idea in science must be subject to this kind of testing. If an idea cannot be tested in a manner that yields reproducible results, even if that idea is correct, then it simply isn't a part of science.

Different Kinds of Questions

The first step in any scientific investigation is to ask a question about the physical world. A scientist can ask, for example, whether a particular painting was completed in the seventeenth century. Various physical and chemical tests can be used to find the age of the paint, study the canvas, X-ray the painting, and so on. The question of whether the painting is old or a modern forgery can indeed be investigated by the scientific method.

But the methods of science cannot answer other equally valid questions. No physical or chemical test will tell us whether the painting is beautiful or how we are to respond to it. These questions are simply outside the realm of science.

The scientific method is not the only way to answer questions that matter in our lives. Science provides us with a powerful way of tackling questions about the physical world—how it works and how we can shape it to our needs. But many questions lie beyond the scope of science and scientific methods. Some of these questions are deeply philosophical: What is the meaning of life? Why does the world hold so much suffering? Is there a God? Other important personal questions also lie outside of science: What career should I choose? Whom should I marry? Should I have children? Scientific information might influence some of our personal choices, but we cannot answer these questions fully by the cycle of observation, hypothesis, and testing. For answers, we turn instead to religion, philosophy, and the arts.

Symphonies, poems, and paintings are created to be enjoyed and are not, in the end, experiences that need to be analyzed scientifically. This is not a criticism. These art forms address different human needs than science, and they use different methods. The same can be said about religious faith. Strictly speaking, there should be no conflict between the questions asked by science and religion, because they deal with different aspects of life. Conflicts arise only when people attempt to apply their methods to questions where those methods aren't applicable.

FIGURE 1-12 Fortune telling, astrology, and other activities at this psychic's shop in Hollywood are examples of pseudoscience.

iStockphoto

Pseudoscience

Many claims of natural phenomena, including extrasensory perception (ESP), unidentified flying objects (UFOs), astrology, crystal power, reincarnation, or many other notions you see in the tabloids at supermarket checkout counters, fail the elementary test that defines the sciences. None of these subjects, collectively labeled **pseudoscience**, can be tested in the sense that we are using the term (Figure 1-12). There is no reproducible test you can imagine that will convince people who believe in these notions that their ideas are incorrect. Yet, as we have seen, the central property of scientific ideas is that they are testable and could be wrong, at least in principle. Pseudoscience lies outside the domain of science and falls instead in the realm of belief or dogma.

In the following "Science by the Numbers" feature we examine the nature of one pseudoscience, astrology. When confronted with other kinds of pseudoscience, you can ask a number of questions to come to your own conclusions:

1. Are the "facts" true as stated?

The first step is to be sure that the facts stated in support of a pseudoscientific claim are actually true. For example, the Great Pyramids of Egypt are frequently the subject of these sorts of arguments. In one version, it is argued that the pyramids must have been built by extraterrestrials because, among other things, their bases are perfect squares and laying out a perfect square was beyond the capability of Egyptian engineers. In fact, according to modern surveys of the pyramids, the longest side of the Pyramid of Cheops is 8 inches longer than the shortest side—it is not a perfect square at all. Digging out the true facts can sometimes be tedious, but it is a necessary first step.

2. Is there an alternative explanation?

In dealing with UFO sightings, it often happens that you can't prove that the object seen wasn't a UFO, but there exists a "normal" explanation for the same event. For example, a light in the sky could be an extraterrestrial spaceship, but it could also be the planet Venus (the most commonly reported UFO). In this case, it is necessary to invoke a doctrine called the "burden of proof." If someone makes a claim, it is up to that person to establish the claim: it is not up to you to disprove it. Furthermore, the more far-reaching the claim, the higher the standard of proof becomes. In the words of the noted planetary astronomer and public television science educator Carl Sagan (1934–1996), "Extraordinary claims require extraordinary proofs."

3. Is the claim falsifiable?

As we stated above, a central aspect of the scientific method is that every scientific statement is subject to experimental or observational tests, so that it is possible to imagine an experimental result that would prove the statement wrong (although whether that result will ever actually be seen is a separate question). Such statements are said to be *falsifiable*. Statements that are not falsifiable are simply not part of science. For example, some creationists talk about the doctrine of "created antiquity," by which they mean that the universe was created to look *exactly* as if it were billions of years old, even though it was really created by God a few thousand years ago. This statement is not falsifiable, and therefore this doctrine is not part of science.

STOP & THINK! Can any experiment or observation (in principle) show created antiquity to be false?

4. Have the claims been rigorously tested?

Many pseudoscientific claims are based on anecdotes and stories. An example is provided by the practice known as "dowsing" or "water witching," in which someone walking on the surface (usually holding a forked stick) can detect the presence of underground water. Stories about this practice can be found in almost any rural area of the United States. Yet when the Committee for the Scientific Investigation of Claims of the Paranormal (CSICOP; now Committee for Skeptical Inquiry) conducted controlled tests in which water pipes were buried beneath a plowed surface, dowsers did no better than chance at locating the water. Tests like these are difficult to arrange, and often do not get much publicity, but they are worth looking for (see, for example, http://www.csicop.org)

5. Do the claims require unreasonable changes in accepted ideas?

Often a pseudoscientific claim will seem to explain a small set of facts but at the same time will require that a much wider assortment of facts be ignored. The psychiatrist Immanuel Velikovsky, for example, looked at stories in ancient texts and tried to alter astronomy (violating most of the laws of physics in the process) in order to preserve the texts as literal statements of fact, rather than as allegory or metaphor. From a scientific perspective, it is much more reasonable to accept the well-verified laws of physics and give up the literal reading of the text.

SCIENCE BY THE NUMBERS
Astrology

Astrology is a very old system of beliefs that most modern scientists would call a pseudoscience. The central belief of astrology is that the positions of objects in the sky at a given time (a person's birth, for example) influence a person's future (Figure 1-13). Astrology as it has been practiced in the Western world developed as part of a complex set of omen systems used by the Babylonians, and it was practiced by many famous astronomers well into modern times.

Gianni Dagli Orti/The Art Archive at Art Resource, NY

FIGURE 1-13 Astrology is a pseudo-science that is based on the belief that the positions of astronomical objects influence our personal lives.

As Earth travels around the Sun, the stars in the night sky change. The band of background stars through which the Sun, the Moon, and the planets appear to move is called the zodiac. The stars of the zodiac are customarily divided into 12 constellations, which are called "signs" or "houses." If you could block out the light of the Sun, these stars would appear (as they do during a total solar eclipse). You would then notice the Sun's position to lie within a certain zodiac constellation, just as the Moon and planets do at night. Furthermore, if you watched the Moon and planets from night to night, you would see them appear to move through these constellations.

At any time, the Sun, the Moon, and the planets all appear in one of these constellations, and a diagram showing these positions is called a horoscope. Astrologers have a complex (and far from unified) system in which each combination of heavenly bodies and signs is believed to signify particular things. The Sun, for example, is thought to indicate the outgoing, expressive aspects of one's character, the Moon the inner-directed ones, and so on. When this system was first introduced, the constellation in which the Sun appeared at the time of your birth was said to be your "Sun sign," or, simply, your "sign." Today, the position of the Sun in the sky has shifted due to the motion of Earth's axis, but the original dates for the "signs" are still used.

Scientists reject astrology for two reasons. First, there is no known way that planets and stars could exert a significant influence on a child at birth. It is true, as we shall learn in Chapter 2, that they exert a miniscule gravitational force on the infant, but the gravitational force applied by the delivering physician (who is smaller but much closer) is much greater than that exerted by any celestial object.

Second, and more importantly, scientists reject astrology because it just doesn't work. Over the millennia, there has been no evidence at all that the stars can predict the future.

You can test the ideas of astrology for yourself, if you like. Try this: Have a member of the class take the horoscopes from yesterday's newspaper and type them on a sheet of paper without indicating which horoscope goes with which sign. Then ask members of your class to indicate the horoscope that best matches the day they actually had. Have them write their birthday (or sign) on the paper as well.

If people just picked horoscopes at random, you would expect about 1 person in 12 to pick the horoscope corresponding to his or her sign. Are the results of your survey any better than that? What does this tell you about the predictive power of astrology?

◎ 1.4 The Organization of Science

Scientists investigate all sorts of natural objects and phenomena: the tiniest elementary particles, microscopic living cells, rocks and minerals, the human body, forests, Earth, stars, and the entire cosmos. Throughout this vast sweep, the same scientific method can be applied. Men and women have been carrying out this task for hundreds of years, and by now we have a pretty good idea about how the many parts of our universe work. In the process, scientists have also developed a social structure that provides unity to the pursuit of scientific knowledge, as well as recognition of important disciplinary differences within the larger scientific framework.

The Divisions of Science

Science is a human endeavor, and humans invariably form themselves into groups with shared interests. When modern science first started in the seventeenth century, it was possible for one person to know almost all there was to know about the physical world and the "three kingdoms" of animals, vegetables, and minerals. In the seventeenth century, Isaac Newton could do forefront research in astronomy, in the physics of moving objects, in the behavior of light, and in mathematics. Thus, for a time prior to the mid-nineteenth century, scholars who studied the workings of the physical universe formed a more or less cohesive group, calling themselves "natural philosophers." But as human understanding expanded and knowledge of nature became more detailed and technical, science began to fragment into increasingly specialized disciplines and subdisciplines.

Today, our knowledge and understanding of the world is so much more sophisticated and complex that no one person could possibly be at the frontier in such a wide variety of fields. Today most scientists choose a major field—biology, chemistry, physics, and so on—and study one small part of the subject at great length (Figure 1-14). Each of these broad disciplines boasts hundreds of different subspecialties. In physics, for example, a student may elect to study the behavior of light, the properties of materials, the nucleus of the atom, elementary particles, or the origin of the universe. The amount of information and expertise required to get to the frontier in any of these fields is so large that most students have to ignore almost everything else to learn their specialty. Even so, many of the most interesting problems in science, from the origin of life to the properties of matter to curing cancer, are interdisciplinary, and require the collective efforts of many scientists with different specialties.

Science is further divided because scientists within each subspecialty approach problems in different ways. Some scientists are *field researchers*, who go into natural settings to observe nature at work. Other scientists are *experimentalists*, who manipulate nature with controlled experiments. Still other scientists, called *theorists*, spend their time imagining universes that might exist. These different kinds of scientists need to work together to make progress.

The fragmentation of science into disciplines was formalized by a peculiar aspect of the European university system. In Europe, each academic department traditionally had only one "professor." All other teachers, no matter how famous and distinguished, had to settle for less prestigious titles. And so, as the number of outstanding scientists grew in the nineteenth century, universities were forced to create new departments to attract new professors. A number of German universities, for example, supported separate departments of theoretical and experimental physics. And Cambridge University in England at one point had seven different specialized departments of chemistry!

In North America, each academic department generally has many professors. Nevertheless, American science faculties are often divided into several departments, including physics, chemistry, astronomy, earth sciences, and biology—the so-called branches of science.

FIGURE 1-14 Scientists work at many different tasks.

The Branches of Science

Several branches of science are distinguished by the scope and content of the questions they address:

Physics is the search for laws that describe the most fundamental aspects of nature: matter, energy, forces, motion, heat, light, and other phenomena. All natural systems, including planets, stars, cells, and people, display these basic phenomena, so physics is the starting point for almost any study of how nature works.

Chemistry is the study of atoms in combination. Chemicals form every material object of our world, while chemical reactions initiate vital changes in our environment and our bodies. Chemistry is thus an immensely practical (and profitable) science.

Astronomy is the study of stars, planets, and other objects in space. We are living in an era of unprecedented astronomical discovery thanks to the development of powerful new telescopes and robotic space exploration.

Earth Sciences is the study of the origin, evolution, and present state of our home, planet Earth. Many earth science departments also emphasize the study of other planets as a way to understand the unique character of our own world. The earth sciences include fields like geology, oceanography, and meteorology that used to be thought of as separate disciplines.

FIGURE 1-15 The interconnected web of scientific knowledge.

Biology is the study of living systems. Biologists document life at many scales, from individual microscopic molecules and cells to expansive ecosystems.

In spite of this practical division of science into separate disciplines, all branches of science are interconnected in a single web of knowledge. Most natural processes can only be studied by resorting to an integrated approach. Understanding such diverse topics as changes in the global climate, the availability of natural resources, the safe storage of nuclear waste, and the discovery of alternative sources of energy requires expertise in physics, chemistry, geology, and biology. All of the sciences are integrated in the natural world.

The Web of Knowledge

The organization of science can be compared to an intricate spider web (Figure 1-15). Around the periphery of the web are all the objects and phenomena examined by scientists, from atoms to trees to comets. Moving toward the web's center, we find the cross-linking hypotheses that scientists have developed to explain how these phenomena work. The farther in we move, the more general these hypotheses become and the more they explain. Radiating out from the center of the web, connecting all the parts and holding the entire structure together, we find a small number of very general principles that have attained the rank of laws of nature.

No matter where you start on the web, no matter what part of nature you investigate, you will eventually come to one of the fundamental overarching ideas that intersect at the central core. Everything that happens in the universe happens because one or more of these physical laws is operating.

The hierarchical organization of scientific knowledge provides an ideal way to approach the study of science. At the center of any scientific question are a few laws of nature. We begin by looking at those laws that describe everyday forces and motions in the universe. These overarching principles of science are accepted and shared by all scientists, no matter what their field of research. These ideas recur over and over again as we study different parts of the world. You will find that many of these ideas and their consequences seem quite simple—perhaps even obvious—because you are intimately familiar with the physical world in which these laws of nature constantly operate.

After introducing these general principles, we look at how the scientific method is applied to specific physical systems in nature. We examine the nature of materials and the atoms that make them, for example, and we look at the chemical reactions that form them. We explore the planet on which we live and discover how mountains and oceans, rivers and plains are formed and evolve over time. And we examine living organisms at the scale of molecules, cells, organisms, and ecosystems.

By the time you have finished this journey, you will have touched on many of the great discoveries about the physical universe that scientists have deduced over the centuries. You will explore how the different parts of our universe operate and how all the parts fit together, and you will know that there are still profound and fascinating unanswered questions that drive scientists today. You will understand some of the great scientific and technological challenges that face our society, and more importantly, you will know enough about how the world works to deal with many of the new problems that will arise in the future.

Basic Research, Applied Research, and Technology

The physical universe can be studied in many ways, and many reasons exist for doing so. Many scientists are simply interested in finding out how the world works—in knowledge for its own sake. They are engaged in **basic research** and may be found studying the behavior of distant stars, obscure life forms, rare minerals, or subatomic particles. Although discoveries made by basic researchers may have profound effects on society (see the discussion of the discovery of

TABLE 1-2 **Major Research Laboratories**

Facility	Type	Location
Argonne National Laboratory	Government/University	Near Chicago, IL
AT&T Bell Laboratories	Industrial	Murray Hill, NJ
Brookhaven National Laboratory	Government	Long Island, NY
Carnegie Institution	Private	California, Maryland, and Washington, DC
Dupont R&D Center	Industrial	Wilmington, DE
Fermi National Accelerator Lab	Government/University	Near Chicago, IL
IBM Watson Research Laboratory	Industrial	Yorktown Heights, NY
Keck Telescope	University	Mauna Kea, HI
Los Alamos National Laboratory	Government	Los Alamos, NM
National Institutes of Health	Government	Bethesda, MD
National Institutes of Standards and Technology	Government	Gaithersburg, MD
Oak Ridge National Laboratory	Government	Oak Ridge, TN
Stanford Linear Accelerator	Government/University	Stanford, CA
Texas Center for Superconductivity	University	Houston, TX
United States Geological Survey	Government	Reston, VA
Woods Hole Oceanographic Institution	University	Woods Hole, MA

the electric generator in Chapter 5, for example), practical applications are not the primary personal goal of most of these scientists.

Many other scientists approach their work with specific practical goals in mind. They wish to develop **technology,** in which they apply the results of science to specific commercial or industrial goals. These scientists are said to be doing **applied research**, and their ideas are often translated into practical systems by large-scale **research and development (R&D)** projects.

Government laboratories, colleges and universities, and private industries all support both basic and applied research; however, most large-scale R&D (as well as most applied research) is done in government laboratories and private industry (Table 1-2).

TECHNOLOGY
SETI@HOME

The Search for Extraterrestrial Intelligence (SETI) has had a long and somewhat varied history. Scientists in the early 1960s realized that radio telescopes then in operation could detect signals from other civilizations (provided, of course, that the signals were being sent). Since that time, astronomers have looked for these signals without success. Nevertheless, the importance of finding even one extraterrestrial civilization is so great that the search goes on.

Hunting for a signal is a little like looking for a radio station in an unfamiliar city. You dial across the frequencies, listening for a moment to each station, until you find what you are looking for. In the same way, SETI astronomers point their telescope at a small region of the sky, dial through the frequencies, and then move on to the next region. Because there is a lot of sky and many frequencies, the sheer volume of data that has to be analyzed has been the primary roadblock in the search.

Scientists at the University of California at Berkeley harnessed the Internet to attack this problem. Radio data is sorted into small chunks. These data chunks are then sent out to participants in the *SETI@home* project—millions of participants in hundreds of countries worldwide

FIGURE 1-16 The radio telescope at Arecibo, in Puerto Rico, is one instrument used in SETI.

(Figure 1-16). Typically, these participants use downloaded software to let their personal computers analyze the data when the machine isn't doing anything else (a typical setup uses the SETI program as a screen saver). When the chunk of data is analyzed, it is sent back to Berkeley and new data are returned. The success of this project has led other scientists to tap this computational resource, and today citizens can participate in projects as wide ranging as sociological studies, ecosystem population counts, and even the operation of old NASA space probes.

Several mission computers connected in this way form perhaps the largest computing project on Earth. More importantly, they are a taste of things to come, for distributed computers, working part-time, already help scientists analyze massive data sets in all sorts of fields. If you want to join the SETI search, the address is http://setiathome.ssl.berkeley.edu.

The success of this kind of cooperative venture has produced many similar operations. Today home computers can be harnessed to analyze anything from climate data to the results of experiments at major laboratories.

Funding for Science

An overwhelming proportion of funding for American scientific research comes from various agencies of the federal government—your tax dollars at work (see Table 1-3). In 2013, the U.S. government's total research and development budget was about $130 billion. The *National Science Foundation,* with an annual budget of about 5.3 billion dollars, supports research and education in all areas of science. Other agencies, including the National Institutes of Health, the Department of Energy, the Department of Defense, the Environmental Protection Agency, and

TABLE 1-3 Your Tax Dollars: 2013 Federal Science Funding

Total Federal Research and Development Funding by Agency for 2013	
Agency	**Amount in Millions of Dollars**
Department of Defense	65,540
Department of Health and Human Services	29,802
National Aeronautics and Space Administration	10,999
Department of Energy	10,705
National Science Foundation	5,329
Department of Agriculture	1,818
Department of Commerce	1,297
Department of Homeland Security	684
Department of Transportation	818
Department of the Interior	785
Department of Veterans Affairs	1,164
Smithsonian Institution	168
Environmental Protection Agency	530

the National Aeronautics and Space Administration, fund research and science education in their own particular areas of interest, while Congress may appropriate additional money for special projects.

An individual scientist seeking funding for research will usually submit a grant proposal to the appropriate federal agency. Such a proposal will include an outline of the planned research together with a statement about why the work is important. The agency evaluating the proposals asks panels of independent scientists to rank them in order of importance, and funds as many as it can. Depending on the field, a proposal has a 5 to 20% chance of being successful. This money from federal grants buys experimental equipment and computer time, pays the salaries of researchers, and supports advanced graduate students. Without this support, much of the scientific research in the United States would come to a halt. The funding of science by the federal government is one place where the opinions and ideas of the citizen, through his or her elected representatives, have a direct effect on the development of science.

As you might expect, scientists and politicians engage in many debates about how this research money should be spent. One constant point of contention, for example, concerns the question of basic versus applied research. How much money should we put into applied research, which can be expected to show a quick payoff, as opposed to basic research, which may not have a payoff for years (if at all)?

Communication Among Scientists

Sometimes it's easier to do your homework with other students than by yourself, and the same is true of the work that scientists do. Working in isolation can be very hard, and scientists often seek out other people with whom to converse and collaborate. The popular stereotype of the lonely genius changing the course of history seldom describes the world of the working scientist. The next time you walk down the hall of a science department at your university, you will probably see faculty and students deep in conversation, talking and scribbling on blackboards. This direct contact between colleagues is the simplest type of scientific communication.

Scientific meetings provide a more formal and structured forum for communication. Every week of the year, at conference retreats and convention centers across the country, groups of scientists gather to trade ideas. You may notice that science stories in your newspapers often originate in the largest of these meetings, where thousands of scientists converge at one time, and a cadre of science reporters with their own special briefing room is poised to publicize exciting results. Scientists often hold off announcing important discoveries until they can make a splash at such a well-attended meeting and press conference.

Finally, scientists communicate with each other in writing. In addition to rapid communications such as e-mail, telephone, and social media, almost all scientific fields have specialized journals to publish the results of research. The system works like this: When a group of scientists finishes a piece of research and wants to communicate their results, they write a concise paper describing exactly what they've done, giving the technical details of their method so that others can reproduce the data and stating their results and conclusions. The journal editor sends the submitted manuscript to one or more knowledgeable scientists who act as referees. These reviewers, whose identities are not usually revealed to the authors, read the paper carefully, checking for mistakes, misstatements, or questionable procedures. Each reviewer then sends the editor a list of necessary modifications and corrections. If they tell the editor that the work passes muster, it will probably be published. In many fields papers are published online almost immediately, with archival paper copies following some weeks later. This system, called **peer review**, is one of the cornerstones of modern science.

Peer review provides a clear protocol for entering new results into the scientific literature. Little wonder then that scientists get so upset when one of their colleagues tries to bypass the system and announces results at a press conference. Such work has not been subject to the thorough review process, and no one can be sure that it meets established standards. When the results turn out to be irreproducible, overstated, or just plain wrong, it damages the credibility of the entire scientific community. So, if you read about a new discovery in the newspaper or on the Internet and you can't track the story back to a published, peer-reviewed journal article, then you should question the veracity of that finding.

THINKING MORE ABOUT **BASIC RESEARCH**

Modern science can be very expensive. The kind of orbiting astronomical observatories described in Chapter 14 and the Large Hadron Collider discussed in Chapter 13 can cost many billions of dollars. These sorts of machines are devoted to basic research, to discovering the fundamental laws that govern the operation of the universe. We simply don't know whether those discoveries will ever have a practical benefit for humanity at some time in the future. This is a feature of basic research.

It's not hard to justify spending money on research when an obvious benefit is in the offing—a new drug or a faster computer, for example. But how do you justify spending that money when there is no obvious and immediate benefit?

Those who oppose large expenditures on basic research argue that the world faces many serious problems that have to be solved right now, and maintain that the benefits of basic research are too tenuous and too far in the future to justify spending money now. Those who support these expenditures argue that basic research has always provided the foundation from which practical benefits flow, and that not funding it now will impoverish future generations.

What proportion of the money spent on scientific research do you think ought to be directed toward work that will have no obvious immediate benefits? How do you balance the immediate benefit of working on current problems against the long-term benefits that have always flowed from basic research? Who do you think ought to make such decisions?

RETURN TO THE INTEGRATED QUESTION

How do you know what you know?

- We obtain knowledge of our world in many ways: through experience, received wisdom, scientific observations and experiments, or as Plato suggested a reliance on reason and intuition. All of these methods have limitations.
  - The scientific method was developed to overcome the inherent limitations in our attempts to gain knowledge of the world.
  - Science uses mathematics to quantify observations so that patterns and regularities may be systematically identified.
  - Prediction and testing develop and refine scientific knowledge.
  - Competition between rival theories and hypotheses fuel scientific progress, while communication between researchers leads to a greater knowledge and understanding of our world.
  - All scientific laws and theories are subject to change with improved observations and measurements, which advance our scientific understanding of our world.

- Researchers communicate their results via peer-reviewed publications. The process of publication codifies our knowledge while disseminating valuable information to the world at large.
- Science attempts to answer questions using observable facts, reproducible experiments, logical hypotheses, and testable predictions. Nevertheless, there are many questions that science cannot answer (e.g., is there a God?).
  - Other "ways of knowing," including art, philosophy, ethics, and religion, address different kinds of questions and thus complement science.
  - Science is not the only method for gaining an understanding of the world in which we live. Nevertheless, it is an invaluable tool that provides an unparalleled framework for acquiring knowledge of our physical world.

SUMMARY

Science is a way of learning about our physical universe. The *scientific method* relies on making *reproducible observations* and *experiments* based on careful *measurements* of the natural world. Once scientists have collected a number of *facts*, which are confirmed observations about the natural world, then they can form a *hypothesis*—a tentative educated guess about how the world works. Hypotheses, in turn, lead to *predictions* that can be tested

with more observations and experiments. A scientific *law* arises when numerous measurements point to a regular, predictable pattern of behavior in nature, whereas a scientific *theory* is a well-substantiated explanation of the natural world based on a large number of independently verified observational and experimental tests. Laws and theories, no matter how successful, are always subject to further testing. The language of *mathematics* often guides experimental analyses and the development of theories. Science and the scientific method differ from other ways of knowing, including religion, philosophy, and the arts, and differ from *pseudosciences*.

Science is organized around a hierarchy of fundamental principles. Overarching concepts about forces, motion, matter, and energy apply to all scientific disciplines, including *physics, chemistry, astronomy, geology,* and *biology*. Additional great ideas relate to specific systems —molecules, cells, planets, or stars. This body of scientific knowledge forms a seamless web, in which every detail fits into a larger, integrated picture of our universe.

Scientists engage in *basic research* to acquire fundamental knowledge, as well as *applied research* and *research and development (R&D)*, which are aimed at specific problems. *Technology* is developed by this process. Scientific results are communicated in *peer-reviewed* publications. The federal government plays the important role of funding most scientific research and advanced science education in the United States.

KEY TERMS

scientific method	**theory**	**biology**
observations	**prediction**	**basic research**
experiment	**reproducible**	**technology**
measurement	**pseudoscience**	**applied research**
mathematics	**physics**	**research and development (R&D)**
fact	**chemistry**	**peer review**
hypothesis	**astronomy**	
law	**earth sciences**	

DISCOVERY LAB

Does the material of a ball affect its bounce? Perform an experiment to see if your hypothesis holds true. For this experiment you will need a tennis ball, golf ball, ping pong ball, bouncy ball, soft ball, meter stick, and masking tape. Tape the meter stick to a table leg so that the 100 centimeter end is facing up. Hold the tennis ball so that its bottom is level with the 100 centimeter mark. Drop the ball and read the height of the bounce to the nearest centimeter. Record the bounce height. Repeat the process of dropping the ball 3 to 5 more times. In order to obtain accurate results, get to the level of the ball to read the height. After repeating the experiment 3 to 5 times for 100 centimeters, repeat the same investigation by changing one of the independent variables. In this experiment, your independent variable will be the ball type. Determine which ball has the greatest bounce. Now try dropping the ball from decreasing heights of 80 centimeters, 60 centimeters, and 40 centimeters and measure the bounce of the ball each time. Why is repetition important? What was kept constant? To visually demonstrate your quantitative data, make a graph of the average bounce versus height from which the ball was dropped. What if you changed other variables such as the type of surface on which the ball is bounced, the size of the ball, the mass of the ball, or the temperature of the ball? Did your data agree with your hypothesis or was it disproved? Think of all the steps taken in this experiment that make up the scientific process.

Drop the ball from 100-cm mark

Drop the ball from decreasing heights

Record the height of bounce

REVIEW QUESTIONS

1. How have human beings benefitted from science in the past?

2. In what ways does your everyday life involve science?

3. How might the ancient Greek philosopher Plato, a medieval scholar at Oxford, and the Italian scientist Galileo have differed in the importance each placed on the role of rational processes, observations, and received wisdom in the study of nature?

4. How is observation different from imagination?

5. How might a scientist find patterns in nature? By what means might he or she determine regularities?

6. Why is mathematics considered the "language of science"?

7. Write an equation in words and then in symbols for the following sentence: The price of coffee beans is equal to the weight of the beans times the price of the beans per pound.

8. What are the steps in the development of a theory?

9. What are the branches of science? In terms of the "Web of Knowledge," how are they organized?

10. Describe the steps of the scientific method.

11. Describe the roles of hypotheses, theories, and predictions in the scientific method.

12. Describe the difference between an observation and an experiment.

13. Why can we think of the *scientific method* as a cycle?

14. What does it mean to say that not all questions can be answered using the scientific method?

15. What does it mean for a statement to be falsifiable? Give an example of a statement that is not falsifiable.

16. Describe the difference between basic and applied research. Give examples of basic and applied research that might be undertaken in the fields of transportation and health.

17. In what ways do scientists communicate with their colleagues? Why is peer review and communication amongst researchers an essential ingredient in scientific progress?

18. Describe the steps a scientist would take to obtain funding for a research project. What sources of funds might be available? What role would peer review play in the process?

DISCUSSION QUESTIONS

1. Advocates of Creation Science, widely regarded in the scientific community as a pseudoscience, in turn describe Evolution as tantamount to a religious belief that requires faith to be considered true. What evidence can you think of that supports Evolution as a theory and what do you think could potentially falsify it? Likewise, what do you think could falsify Creation Science?

2. Which of the following statements could be tested scientifically to determine whether it is true or false?

   a. Women are on average shorter than men.

   b. Most of the Sun's energy is in the form of heat energy.

   c. Unicorns are now extinct.

   d. Beethoven wrote beautiful music.

   e. Earth was created over 4 billion years ago.

   f. Earth was created in a miraculous event.

   g. Diamond is harder than steel.

   h. Football is a better sport than baseball.

   i. God exists.

3. What role did observation play in the creation of the periodic table by Dimitri Mendeleev?

4. In 1935, Yukawa Hideki predicted the existence of a subatomic particle known as a "meson" and described some of its expected characteristics. Following the discovery of such particles bearing those properties, Yukawa was awarded the 1949 Nobel Prize in Physics. Subsequently, Yukawa's rationale for the existence of the meson was shown to be wrong. Would it be reasonable to say Yukawa's meson theory failed to advance our understanding of sub-atomic physics?

5. How did William Harvey use experimentation to find how blood circulates in the human body?

6. Categorize the following examples as basic research or applied research.

   a. the discovery of a new species of bird

   b. the development of a more fuel-efficient vehicle

   c. the breeding of a new variety of disease-resistant wheat

   d. a study of the ecological role of grizzly bears in Yellowstone National Park

   e. the identification of a new chemical compound

   f. the development of a new drug for cancer or AIDS patients

   g. the improvement of wind turbines for energy production

7. Issues involving climate science play a significant role in American political discussions and the development of economic policy. In your opinion, how significant is the scientific consensus on this issue in determining public policy?

8. Many products claim to "lower cholesterol" and to promote a "healthy heart." How might you test these statements in a laboratory? Would this be a form of basic or applied research?

9. Research into human genetics is starting to allow scientists to manipulate the human genome. While this ability has the potential to minimize or even eradicate congenital diseases, it may also be used to manipulate non-medical conditions such as eye color or height. To what extent should religious, moral, and ethical beliefs play a role in determining limitations on genetic manipulation?

10. Isaac Newton once said, "If I have seen further, it is by standing on the shoulders of giants"? What does this statement tell us about the way that science progresses over time?

11. Which branch of science do you think has had the most impact on your day-to-day existence? Describe instances in your daily life where you use the results of physics, chemistry, biology, geology, and astronomy.

12. Are both basic and applied research necessary? Which should get more funding from the federal government?

13. Why is "peer review" so important to the scientific community? Is the peer review system overly stifling or onerous? If so, how could it be improved without impairing its current utility?

14. Several individuals such as Aristotle and Leonardo da Vinci have been described as "the last person to know everything worth knowing." One of the most recent persons to be realistically ascribed this title is Thomas Young, an English polymath who died in 1829. What do you think is the minimum number of people nowadays you would need whose combined body of knowledge encompasses "everything worth knowing"?

15. An American football star from the 1970's and 1980's, Lyle Alzado, had begun using steroids in the late 1960's. He blamed the use of steroids for the brain tumor that led to his death at age 43. However, current scientific research doesn't show a statistical correlation between steroid use and the development of brain tumors. Does this negate Alzado's contention about the cause of his death?

16. The German-American rocket scientist Wernher von Braun was once quoted as saying, "Basic research is what I am doing when I don't know what I am doing." What do you think he meant?

17. After getting approval to perform tests on humans, a pharmaceutical company devises an experiment to test the level of impairment of mental acuity people experience after consuming a certain drug by having them take a test with differing amount of the drug in their systems. Which of the following best describes the control group for this experiment?
    a) People who take the highest dose
    b) People who take the lowest dose
    c) People who take no dose
    d) People who don't take the test

18. Prior to the discovery of oxygen as a chemical element, the theory of why materials burned was known as the "Phlogiston Theory." This theory said that a substance that could be burned contained phlogiston, which was consumed in the process of combustion, leaving behind the non-phlogiston residue. How could the Phlogiston Theory be falsified?

19. Consider an experiment in which you drop an ordinary sheet of paper and then drop the same sheet of paper but after it has been crumpled up. Devise a hypothesis for this phenomenon and then make predictions of possible experiments based on it.

PROBLEMS

1. Amanda is a college student who keeps a diary of her daily caloric intake over the course of a month. In the first week of one particular February, she averaged 1500 calories per day. The next week, faced with a stressful period of exams, she averaged 1800 calories per day. She tried to make up for it the following week by averaging 1400 calories per day. In the final week of the month, she returned to what she felt was her usual average of 1500 calories per day. What is an efficient way for Amanda to display her data? What other measurements should she consider recording to give her a fuller description of caloric consumption and usage?

2. Compare data from your science classes *versus* your non-science classes. For instance, examine the male-to-female ratios in each type of class. Try to get other students to help out with their classes so as to increase your sample size. What expectations do you have? How do the actual data compare to your expectations?

3. Pick one of your favorite kinds of music and describe it using adjectives that you feel aren't scientifically measurable. Next, describe the music in ways that you feel could be scientifically measured. Try to make measurements of some of these characteristics. For the ones you can't measure, what equipment do you think you would need to carry out these measurements?

4. In February 2011, a number of residents near the city of Vancouver in British Columbia, Canada, reported seeing a UFO moving around the sky. They all gave consistent descriptions and there were videos made of the sighting that showed flashing lights and rapid accelerations. What other measurements should have been made to distinguish whether or not this object was extraterrestrial in origin?

5. Isaac Newton's 2nd Law of Motion says that the acceleration a an object experiences is proportional to the total force F acting on the object and inversely proportional to the mass m of the object. Identify the mathematical expression that embodies this idea.
    a) $a = Fm$
    b) $a = F/m$
    c) $a = (1/F) * (1/m)$
    d) $aFm = 1$

INVESTIGATIONS

1. What is the closest major government research laboratory to your school? What is the closest industrial laboratory? Describe one research project that is now underway at one of these laboratories.

2. What are the major science departments at your school? How many professors are performing research in each department? Are these professors doing basic or applied research? Describe a program of scientific research carried out by a member of

your school's faculty. How is the scientific method employed in this research?

3. Identify a current piece of legislation relating to science or technology (perhaps an environmental or energy bill). How did your representatives in Congress vote on this issue?

4. Look at a recent newspaper article about a scientific subject. What federal agency funded the research? Is the research basic or applied?

5. Find a science story in a newspaper or popular magazine. Who were the scientists who conducted the research? Where did they do the work?

6. Consider the way that scientists are portrayed in any recent film. Were you convinced by these portrayals? Why? How do these portrayals compare with the faculty doing research at your school?

7. Was Harvey justified in his use of animals in studies of the circulatory system? What limits should scientists accept in research using animals?

8. What organizations (e.g., institutional animal control and review boards) at your school protect research animals from unnecessary harm? What specific drugs, medicines, and procedures were developed using animal research?

9. Design an experiment to test the relative strengths of three different kinds of aluminum can. What data would you need to collect? What laboratory equipment would you need? How might you present these data in tables and graphically?

10. Malaria, the deadliest infectious disease in the world, kills more than 2 million people (mostly children in poor countries) every year. The annual malaria research budget in the United States is less than a million dollars, a minuscule fraction of spending on cancer, heart disease, and AIDS. Should the United States devote more research funds to this disease, which does not occur in North America? Why or why not? Can we use the scientific method to answer this question?

11. Does your school recycle? If so, why? What are the benefits of recycling paper, metal, or plastic? Is there a benefit to recycling paper since we can always grow more trees?

12. Think of an idea or a topic in which you are interested. Go to Google Scholar: http://scholar.google.com/ and search peer-reviewed journals to read about how research scientists with your interests have studied the idea.

The Ordered Universe

Why do planets appear to wander slowly across the sky?

PHYSICS
A launch of the space shuttle illustrates the laws of motion.

CHEMISTRY
A force different from gravity must be responsible for the chemical bonding of atoms to each other. (Ch. 10)

BIOLOGY
Land plants and animals must develop strong supportive structures to counteract the force of gravity. (Ch. 20)

GREAT IDEA
Newton's laws of motion and gravity predict the behavior of objects on Earth and in space.

ENVIRONMENT
Gravity may cause land to collapse in regions where too much groundwater is pumped out of the ground. (Ch.18)

TECHNOLOGY
The laws of motion allow us to design cars that will protect drivers during accidents.

ASTRONOMY
The universal law of gravitation can tell you why the Moon orbits Earth and Earth orbits the Sun.

GEOLOGY
Gravity controls the flow of water through vast systems of streams and rivers. (Ch. 18)

HEALTH & SAFETY
Air bags reduce injuries from high-speed automobile collisions.

 = applications of the great idea discussed in this chapter

 = other applications, some of which are discussed in other chapters

Cause and Effect

You jump out of bed, eager to start the day. The air smells fresh and cool, but the Sun's rays already feel warm. It should be perfect beach weather.

When the Sun comes up in the morning, you expect temperatures to become warmer; in the evening, as the Sun goes down, you expect temperatures to fall. When you turn the key in the ignition in your car, you expect it to start. When you flip a light switch, you expect a light to go on.

Our world is filled with ordinary events like these—events we take so much for granted that we scarcely notice them. Yet they set the background for the way we think about the world. We believe in cause and effect because it's so much a part of our lives.

The regular passage of seasons, with the shortening and lengthening of days and gradual changes in temperature, provides a template for our lives. We plant and harvest crops, purchase wardrobes, and even schedule vacations around this predictable cycle, with the knowledge that we must adapt and prepare for nature's cycles. Indeed, the predictability of our physical world has become the central principle of science—an idea so important that science could never have developed had it not been true.

Ryan Nelson/Alamy

◎ 2.1 The Night Sky

Among the most predictable objects in the universe are the lights we see in the sky at night—the stars and planets. Modern men and women, living in large metropolitan areas, are no longer very conscious of the richness of the night sky's shifting patterns. But think about the last time you were out in the country on a clear moonless night, far from the lights of town. There, the stars seem very close, very real. Before the nineteenth-century development of artificial lighting, human beings often experienced jet-black skies filled with brilliant pinpoint stars.

The sky changes; it's never quite the same from one night to the next. Living with this display all the time, our ancestors noticed regularities in the arrangement and movements of stars and planets, and they wove these almost lifelike patterns into their religion and mythology. They learned that when the Sun rose in a certain place, it was time to plant crops because spring was on its way. They learned to predict the times of the month when a full Moon would illuminate the ground, allowing them to continue harvesting and hunting after sunset. To these people, knowing the behavior of the sky was not an intellectual game or an educational frill, it was an essential part of their lives. It is no wonder, then, that astronomy, the study of objects in the heavens, was one of the first sciences to develop.

By relying on their observations and records of the regular motions of the stars and planets, ancient observers of the sky were perhaps the first humans to accept the most basic tenet of science:

● **Physical events are quantifiable and therefore predictable.**

Without the predictability of physical events, the scientific method could not proceed.

Stonehenge

No symbol of humankind's early preoccupation with astronomy is more dramatic than Stonehenge, the great prehistoric stone monument on Salisbury Plain in southern England. The structure consists of a large circular bank of earth surrounding a ring of single upright stones, which in turn encircle a horseshoe-shaped structure of five giant stone archways. Each arch is constructed from three massive blocks—two vertical supports several meters tall capped by a great stone lintel. The open end of the horseshoe aligns with an avenue that leads northeast to another large stone, called the "heel stone" (see Figure 2-1).

Stonehenge was built in spurts over a long period of time, starting in about 2800 BC. Despite various legends assigning it to the Druids, Julius Caesar, the magician Merlin (who was supposed to have levitated the stones from Ireland), or other mysterious unknown races, archaeologists have shown that Stonehenge was built by several groups of people, none of whom had a written language and some of whom even lacked metal tools. Why would these people expend such a great effort to erect one of the world's great monuments?

Stonehenge, like many similar structures scattered around the world, was built to mark the passage of time. It served as a giant calendar based on the movement of objects in the sky. The most famous astronomical function of Stonehenge was to mark the passage of the seasons. In an agricultural society, after all, one has to know when it's time to plant the crops, and one can't always tell by looking at the weather. At Stonehenge, this job was done by sighting through the stones. On midsummer's morning, for example, someone standing in the center of the monument will see the Sun rising directly over the heel stone.

Building a structure like Stonehenge required accumulation of a great deal of knowledge about the sky—knowledge that could have been gained only through many years of observation. Without a written language, people would have had to pass complex information about the movements of the Sun, the Moon, and the planets from one generation to the next. How else could they have aligned their stones so perfectly that modern-day Druids in England can still greet the midsummer sunrise over the heel stone?

If the universe was not regular and predictable, if repeated observation could not show us patterns that occur over and over again, the very concept of a monument like Stonehenge would be impossible. And yet, there it stands after almost 5,000 years, a testament to human ingenuity and to the possibility of predicting the behavior of the universe we live in.

Having made the point that Stonehenge functioned as a calendar, we must also point out that this doesn't mean it was only a calendar. The area around Stonehenge is littered with graves, and in 2009, archaeologists discovered holes that once held another stone circle—stones that were later incorporated into Stonehenge itself. The smaller circle may have functioned as a location for cremations, leading one archaeologist to suggest that Stonehenge served as the center of the "Land of the Dead" in ancient times.

FIGURE 2-1 (a) The ancient monument at Stonehenge in southern England is thought to have served as a calendar. (b) The layout of the structures at Stonehenge.

Jeremy Walker/Getty Images

(a)

(b)

SCIENCE IN THE MAKING
The Discovery of the Spread of Disease

Observing nature is a crucial part of the scientific method. During the nineteenth century, for example, Europe experienced an epidemic of cholera, a severe and often fatal intestinal disease. No one knew the cause of the disease—the discovery of the germ theory of disease was still decades in the future. The very name of the disease is derived from the early days of medicine, when "choler" was seen as one of the "humors" that governed human health. But even without knowing the cause of the disease, physicians and scientists could observe the places and times when it occurred.

John Snow (1823–1858) was a distinguished London physician who is remembered in medicine as one of the pioneers in the new field of anesthesiology. He even attended the birth of Queen Victoria's last children, administering chloroform during labor. For many years, he had been convinced that the incidence of cholera was connected in some way to London's water supply. At that time, many people got their water from public pumps, and even water delivered to private homes came through a chaotic maze of pipes, so that water delivered to neighboring buildings could come from very different sources. Over the years, Snow patiently cataloged data on water sources and the frequent cholera outbreaks in the city.

In 1854, Snow made a dramatic discovery. He noticed that the incidence of cholera that year seemed to be concentrated around a place called Golden Square, a poor neighborhood where people drew their water from a place called the Broad Street pump. Upon investigation, Snow found that the square was surrounded by a large number of homes where human waste was dumped into backyard pits. He argued that these findings suggested the disease was somehow related to contamination of the water supply (Figure 2-2).

Driven by the accumulation of data like this, the city of London (and soon all major population centers) eventually began to require that human waste be carried away from dwellings into sewers and not just dumped into a river upstream of the intakes for the drinking water supply. Thus, Snow's discovery of a regularity in nature (in this case between disease and polluted water) was the foundation on which modern sanitation and public health systems are based.

Just as the builders of Stonehenge had no idea of the structure of the solar system or why the heavens behave as they do, Snow had no idea why keeping human waste out of the drinking water supply should eliminate a disease such as cholera. It wasn't until the early 1890s, in fact, that the German scientist Robert Koch first suggested that the disease was caused by a particular bacterium, *Vibrio cholerae*, that is carried in human waste. •

FIGURE 2-2 John Snow plotted the number of cases of cholera versus the date for residents in the vicinity of the Broad Street pump. The number of cases declined in early September because most residents fled the area, but few new cases occurred after the pump handle was removed on September 8.

SCIENCE BY THE NUMBERS
Ancient Astronauts

Confronted by a monument such as Stonehenge, with its precise orientation and epic proportions, some people refuse to accept the notion that it could have been built by the ingenuity and hard work of ancient peoples. Instead, they assume that there must have been some outside intervention, frequently in the form of visitors from other planets whose handiwork survives in the monument today. Many ancient monuments, including the pyramids of Egypt, the Mayan temples of Central America, and the giant statues of Easter Island, have been ascribed to these mysterious aliens.

Such conjecture is unconvincing unless you first show that building the monument was beyond the capabilities of the indigenous people. Suppose, for example, that Columbus had found a glass-and-steel skyscraper when he landed in America. Both the ability to produce the materials (steel, glass, and plastic, for example) and the ability to construct a building dozens of stories tall were beyond the abilities of Native Americans at that time. A reasonable case could have been made for the intervention of ancient astronauts or some other advanced intelligence.

Is Stonehenge a similar case? The material, local stone, was certainly available to anyone who wanted to use it. Working and shaping stone was also a skill, albeit a laborious one, that was available to early civilizations. The key question, then, is whether people without steel tools or wheeled vehicles could have moved the stones from the quarry to the construction site (Figure 2-3).

The largest stone, about 10 meters (more than 30 feet) in length, weighs about 50 metric tons (50,000 kilograms, or about 100,000 pounds) and had to be moved over land some 30 kilometers (20 miles) from quarries to the north. Could this massive block have been moved by primitive people, equipped only with wood and ropes?

While Stonehenge was being built, it snowed frequently in southern England, so the stones could have been hauled on sleds. A single person can easily haul 100 kilograms on a sled (think of pulling a couple of your friends). How many people would it take to haul a 50,000-kilogram stone?

$$\frac{50,000}{100 \text{ kilograms pulled by each person}} = 500 \text{ people}$$

FIGURE 2-3 One puzzling aspect of the construction of Stonehenge is the raising of the giant lintel stones. Three steps in the process were probably: *(a)* to dig a pit for each of the upright stones and then to tip the stone into the pit as shown; *(b)* to pile dirt into a long, sloping ramp up to the level of the two uprights so that the lintel stones could be rolled into place; and *(c)* to cart away the dirt, thus leaving the stone archway.

(a)

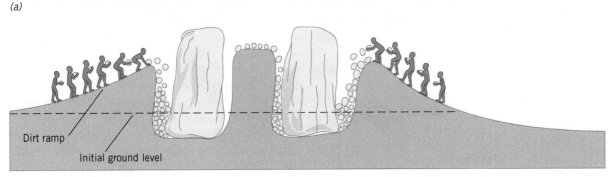

Dirt ramp

Initial ground level

(b)

Lintel stone

(c)

ScienceNews

The Building of Stonehenge
Go to your WileyPLUS course to
view video on this topic.

Organizing 500 people for the job would have been a major social achievement, of course, but there's nothing physically impossible about it. So, although scientists cannot absolutely disprove the possibility that Stonehenge was constructed by some strange, forgotten technology, why should we invoke such alien intervention when the concerted actions of a dedicated, hard-working human society would have sufficed?

When confronted with phenomena in a physical world, we should accept the most straightforward and reasonable explanation as the most likely. This procedure is called *Ockham's razor,* after William of Ockham, a fourteenth-century English philosopher who argued that "postulates must not be multiplied without necessity"—that is, given a choice, the simplest solution to a problem is most likely to be right. Scientists thus reject the notion of ancient astronauts building Stonehenge, and they relegate such speculation to the realm of pseudoscience. •

The Birth of Modern Astronomy

Far from the city, when you look up at the night sky you see a dazzling array of objects. Thousands of visible stars fill the heavens and appear to move each night in stately circular arcs centered on the North Star. The relative positions of these stars never seem to change, and closely spaced groups of stars called *constellations* have been given names such as the Big Dipper and Leo the Lion. Moving across this fixed starry background are Earth's Moon, with its regular succession of phases, and a half-dozen planets that wander through the path in the sky known as the zodiac. You might also see swift streaking meteors or long-tailed comets—transient objects that grace the night sky from time to time.

What causes these objects to move, and what do those motions tell us about the universe in which we live?

The Historical Background: Ptolemy and Copernicus

Since before recorded history, people have observed the distinctive motions of objects in the sky and have tried to explain them. Most societies created legends and myths tied to these movements, and some (the Babylonians, for example) had long records of sophisticated astronomical observations. It was the Greeks, however, who devised the first astronomical explanations that incorporated elements of modern science.

Claudius Ptolemy, an Egyptian-born Greek astronomer and geographer who lived in Alexandria in the second century AD, proposed the first widely accepted explanation for complex celestial motions. Working with the accumulated observations of earlier Babylonian and Greek astronomers, he put together a singularly successful model—a theory, to use the modern term—about how the heavens had to be arranged to produce the display we see every night. In the Ptolemaic description of the universe, Earth sat unmoved at the center. Around it, on a concentric series of rotating spheres, moved the stars and planets. The model was carefully crafted to take account of observations. The planets, for example, were attached to small spheres rolling inside the larger spheres so that their uneven motion across the sky could be understood.

This system remained the best explanation of the universe for almost 1,500 years. It successfully predicted planetary motions, eclipses, and a host of other heavenly phenomena, and was one of the longest-lived scientific theories ever devised.

During the first decades of the sixteenth century, however, a Polish cleric by the name of Nicolaus Copernicus (1473–1543) considered a competing hypothesis that was to herald the end of Ptolemy's crystal spheres. His ideas were published in 1543 under the title *On the Revolutions of the Heavenly Spheres.* Copernicus retained the notions of a spherical universe with circular orbits, and even kept the ideas of spheres rolling within a sphere, but he asked a simple and extraordinary question: "Is it possible to construct a model of the heavens whose predictions are as accurate as Ptolemy's, but in which the Sun, rather than Earth, is at the center?" We do not know how Copernicus, a busy man of affairs in medieval Poland, conceived this question, nor do we know why he devoted his spare time for most of his adult life to answering it.

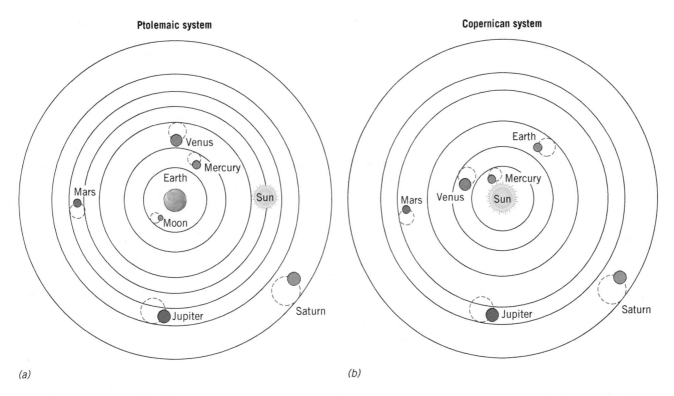

Ptolemaic system

Copernican system

(a)

(b)

We do know, however, that in 1543, for the first time in over a millennium, the Ptolemaic system was faced by a serious challenger (see Figure 2-4).

Observations: Tycho Brahe and Johannes Kepler

With the publication of the Copernican theory, astronomers were confronted by two competing models of the universe. The Ptolemaic and Copernican systems differed in a fundamental way that had far-reaching implications about the place of humanity in the cosmos. They both described possible universes, but in one, Earth (and by implication humankind) was no longer at the center. The astronomers' task was to decide which model best describes the universe we actually live in.

To resolve the question, astronomers had to compare the predictions of the two competing hypotheses to the observations of what was actually seen in the sky. When they performed these observations, a fundamental problem became apparent. Although the two models made different predictions about the position of a planet at midnight, for example, or the time of moonrise, the differences were too small to be measured with equipment available at the time. The telescope had not yet been invented, but astronomers were skilled in recording planetary positions by depending entirely on naked-eye measurements with awkward instruments. Until the accuracy of measurement was improved, the question of whether Earth was at the center of the universe couldn't be decided.

The Danish nobleman Tycho Brahe (1546–1601) showed the way out of this impasse. Tycho, as he was known, is one of those people who, in addition to making important contributions to knowledge, led a truly bizarre life. As a young man, for example, he lost the bridge of his nose in a duel with a fellow student over who was the better mathematician; for the rest of his life he had to wear a metal prosthesis.

Tycho's scientific reputation was firmly established at the age of 25, when he observed and described a new star in the sky (in fact, a supernova—see Chapter 14). This dramatic discovery challenged the prevailing wisdom that the heavens are unchanging. Within the next 5 years, the Danish king had given him the island of Hveen off the coast of Denmark and funds to construct a royal observatory there.

Tycho built his career on the design and use of vastly improved observational instruments. He determined the position of each star or planet with a "quadrant," a large, sloping

FIGURE 2-4 The Ptolemaic (a) and Copernican (b) systems both assumed that all orbits are circular. The fundamental difference is that Copernicus placed the Sun at the center.

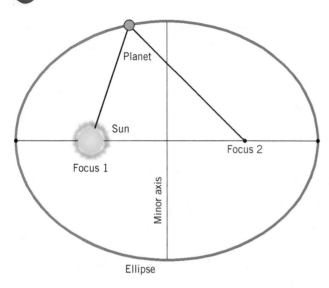

Ellipse

FIGURE 2-5 Kepler's first law, shown schematically, states that the orbit of every planet is an ellipse, a geometrical figure in which the sum of the distances to two fixed points (each of which is called a focus) is always the same. For planetary orbits in the solar system, the Sun is at one focus of the ellipse (greatly exaggerated in this figure).

device something like a gunsight, recording each position as two angles. If you were to do this today, you might, for example, measure one angle up from the horizon and a second angle around from due north. Tycho constructed his sighting device of carefully selected materials, and he learned to correct his measurements for thermal contraction—the slight shrinkage of brass and iron components that occurred during the cold Danish nights. Over a period of 25 years, he used these instruments to accumulate extremely accurate data on the positions of the planets.

When Tycho died in 1601, his data passed into the hands of his assistant, Johannes Kepler (1571–1630), a skilled German mathematician who had joined Tycho 2 years before. Kepler analyzed Tycho Brahe's decades of planetary data in new ways, and he found that the data could be summarized in three mathematical statements about the solar system. Kepler's first and most important law (shown in Figure 2-5) states that all planets, including Earth, orbit the Sun in elliptical, not circular, paths. In this picture, the spheres-within-spheres are gone because ellipses fully account for the observed planetary motions. Not only do Kepler's laws give a better description of what is observed in the sky, but they present a simpler picture of the solar system as well.

Previous astronomers had assumed that planetary orbits must be perfect circles, and many believed on theological or philosophical grounds that Earth had to be the center of a spherical universe. In science, such assumptions of ideality may guide thinking, but they must be replaced when observations prove them wrong.

The work of Tycho Brahe and Johannes Kepler firmly established that Earth is not at the center of the universe, that planetary orbits are not circular, and that the answer to the contest between the Ptolemaic and Copernican universes is "neither of the above." This research also illustrates a recurrent point about scientific progress. The ability to answer scientific questions, even questions dealing with the most fundamental aspects of human existence, often depends on the kinds of instruments scientists have at their disposal and on the ability of scientists to apply advanced mathematical reasoning to their data.

At the end of this historical episode, astronomers had Kepler's laws that describe how the planets in the solar system move, but they had no idea *why* planets behave the way they do. The answer to that question was to come from an unexpected source.

◉ 2.2 The Birth of Mechanics

Mechanics is an old word for the branch of science that deals with the motions of material objects. A rock rolling down a hill, a ball thrown into the air, and a sailboat skimming over the waves are all fit subjects for this science. Since ancient times, philosophers had speculated on why things move the way they do, but it wasn't until the seventeenth century that our modern understanding of the subject began to emerge.

Galileo Galilei

FIGURE 2-6 Galileo Galilei (1564–1642).

Uffizi, Florence, Italy/Scala/Art Resource

The Italian physicist and philosopher Galileo Galilei (1564–1642) was, in many ways, a forerunner of the modern scientist (Figure 2-6). A professor of mathematics at the University of Padua, he quickly became an advisor to the powerful court of the Medici at Florence as well as a consultant at the Arsenal of Venice, the most advanced naval construction center in the world. He invented many practical devices, such as the first thermometer, the pendulum clock, and the proportional compass that craftsmen still use today. Galileo is also famous as the first person to record observations of the heavens with a telescope, which he built after hearing of the instrument from others (Figure 2-7). His astronomical writings, which supported the Sun-centered Copernican model of the universe, led to his trial by the Inquisition.

SCIENCE IN THE MAKING
The Heresy Trial of Galileo

In spite of his great scientific advances, Galileo is remembered primarily because of his heresy trial in 1633. In 1610, Galileo had published a summary of his telescopic observations in *The Starry Messenger*. Some readers complained that these ideas violated Catholic Church doctrine, and in 1616, Galileo was called before the College of Cardinals. The Catholic Church supposedly warned Galileo not to discuss Copernican ideas unless he treated them as an unproven hypothesis.

In spite of these instructions, in 1632, Galileo published *A Dialogue Concerning Two World Systems,* which was a long defense of the Copernican system. This action led to the famous trial, at which Galileo purged himself of suspicion of heresy by denying that he held the views in his book. He was already an old man by this time, and he spent his last few years under house arrest in his villa near Florence.

The legend of Galileo's trial, in which an earnest seeker of truth is crushed by a rigid hierarchy, bears little resemblance to the historical events. The Catholic Church had not banned Copernican ideas. Copernicus, after all, was a savvy Church politician who knew how to get his ideas across without ruffling feathers. But Galileo's confrontational tactics—notably putting the Pope's favorite arguments into the mouth of a foolish character in the book—brought the predictable reaction.

A footnote: In 1992, the Catholic Church reopened the case of Galileo and, in effect, issued a retroactive "not guilty." The grounds for the reversal were that the original judges had not separated questions of faith from questions of scientific fact. •

FIGURE 2-7 Telescopes used by Galileo Galilei in his astronomical studies.

Speed, Velocity, and Acceleration

To lay the groundwork for understanding Galileo's study of moving objects (and ultimately to understand the workings of the solar system), we have to begin with precise definitions of three familiar terms: *speed, velocity,* and *acceleration*.

Speed and Velocity

Speed and velocity are everyday words that have precise scientific meanings. **Speed** is the distance an object travels divided by the time it takes to travel that distance. **Velocity** has the same numerical value as speed, but it is a quantity that also includes information on the direction of travel. The speed of a car might be 40 miles per hour, for example, while the velocity is 40 miles per hour due west. Quantities such as velocity that involve both a speed and a direction are called *vectors*. Velocity and speed are both measured in units of distance per time, such as meters per second, feet per second, or miles per hour.

In equation form:

$$\text{velocity or speed (m/s)} = \frac{\text{distance traveled (m)}}{\text{time of travel (s)}}$$

In symbols:

$$V = \frac{d}{t}$$

Thus, if you know the distance traveled and the time elapsed during the travel, you can calculate the speed.

EXAMPLE 2-1

DRIVING

If your car travels 30 miles per hour, how many miles will you go in 15 minutes?

Reasoning and Solution: This question involves changing units, as well as applying the equation that relates time, speed, and distance. First, we must know the travel time in hours:

$$\frac{15 \text{ minutes}}{(60 \text{ minutes/hour})} = 1/4 \text{ hour}$$

Then, rearranging the relationship between speed, distance, and time given above, we find:

$$\text{Distance} = \text{speed} \times \text{time}$$
$$\text{Distance} = 30 \text{ miles/hour} \times 1/4 \text{ hour}$$
$$= 7.5 \text{ miles}$$

It would take the average person about 2 hours to walk this far.

A word about units: You may have noticed that in the example we put ¼ hour into the equation for the time instead of 15 minutes. We did this because we needed to be consistent with the units in which an automobile speedometer measures speed. Since the automobile dial reads in miles per hour, we also put the time in hours to make the equation balance. A useful way to deal with such situations is to imagine that the units are quantities that can be canceled in fractions, just like numbers. In this case, we would have:

$$\text{distance} = (\text{miles/hour}) \times \text{hour}$$
$$= \text{miles}$$

If, however, we put the time in minutes, we'd have:

$$\text{distance} = (\text{miles/hour}) \times \text{minutes}$$

and there would be no cancellation.

Whenever you do a problem like this one, it's a good idea to check to make sure the units come out correctly. This important process is known as *dimensional analysis*.

Acceleration

Acceleration is a measure of the rate of change of velocity. Whenever an object changes speed or direction, it accelerates. When you step on the gas pedal in your car, for example, the car accelerates forward. When you slam on the brakes, the car accelerates backward (what is sometimes called *deceleration*). When you go around a curve in your car, even if the car's speed stays exactly the same, the car is still accelerating because the direction of motion is changing. The most thrilling amusement park rides combine these different kinds of acceleration—speeding up, slowing down, and changing direction in bumps, tight turns, and rapid spins.

In words: Acceleration is the amount of change in velocity divided by the time it takes that change to occur.

In equation form:

$$\text{Acceleration (m/s}^2) = \frac{(\text{final velocity} - \text{initial velocity})}{\text{time}}$$

In symbols:

$$a = \frac{(v_f - v_i)}{t}$$

Like velocity, acceleration requires information about the direction, and it is therefore a vector.

When velocity changes, it may be by a certain number of feet per second or meters per second in each second. Consequently, the units of acceleration are meters per second squared, usually described as "meters per second per second" (and abbreviated m/s^2), where the first "meters per second" refers to the velocity and the last "per second" refers to the time it takes for the velocity to change.

To understand the difference between acceleration and velocity, think about the last time you were behind the wheel of a car driving down a long, straight road. You glance at your speedometer. If the needle is unmoving (at 30 miles per hour, for example), you are moving at a constant speed. Suppose, however, that the needle isn't stationary on the speedometer scale (perhaps because you have your foot on the gas or on the brake). Your speed is changing and, by the preceding definition, you are accelerating. The higher the acceleration, the faster the needle moves. If the needle doesn't move, however, *this doesn't mean you and the car aren't moving.* As we know, an unmoving needle simply means that you are traveling at a constant speed. Motion at a constant speed in a single direction is called *uniform motion.*

The Founder of Experimental Science

Galileo devised an ingenious experiment to determine the relationships among distance, time, velocity, and acceleration. Many scientists now view Galileo's greatest achievement as this experimental work on the behavior of objects thrown or dropped on the surface of Earth. Greek philosophers, using pure reason, had taught that heavier objects must fall faster than light ones. In a series of classic experiments, Galileo showed that this was not the case—that at Earth's surface all objects accelerate at the same rate as they fall downward. Ironically, Galileo probably never performed the one experiment for which he is most famous—dropping two different weights from the Leaning Tower of Pisa to see which would land first.

To describe falling objects, it's necessary to make precise measurements of two variables: distance and time. Galileo and his contemporaries easily measured distance using rulers, but their timepieces were not precise enough to measure the brief times it took objects to fall straight down. Previous workers had simply observed the behavior of falling objects, but Galileo constructed a special apparatus designed purely to measure acceleration (see Figure 2-8). He slowed down the time of fall by rolling large balls down an inclined plane crafted of brass and hard wood, and measured the time of descent by listening to the "ping" as the ball rolled over wires stretched along its path. (The human ear is quite good at hearing equal time intervals.) The balls accelerated as they moved down the plane, and by increasing the angle of elevation of the plane, Galileo could increase that acceleration. At an elevation of 90 degrees, of course, the ball would fall freely.

Galileo's experiments convinced him that any object accelerating toward Earth's surface, no matter how heavy or light, falls with exactly the same constant acceleration. For balls on his plane, his results can be summarized in a simple equation:

In words: The velocity of an accelerating object that starts from rest is proportional to the length of time that it has been falling.

In equation form:

$$\text{velocity (m/s)} = \text{constant } a \text{ (m/s}^2\text{)} \times \text{time (s)}$$

In symbols:

$$v = a \times t$$

FIGURE 2-8 Galileo's falling-ball apparatus with a table of measurements and a graph of distance versus time.

Galileo's apparatus inclined plane

Time	Distance
0	0
1	1
2	4
3	9
4	16
5	25
6	36

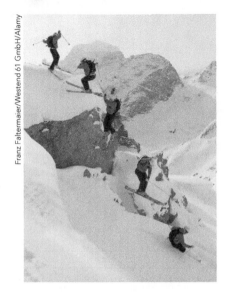

FIGURE 2-9 The accelerated motion of a falling skier is captured by a multiple-exposure photograph. In each successive time interval, the skier falls farther.

TABLE 2-1 **Equations Relating *d*, *v*, *a*, and *t***

$v = \dfrac{d}{t}$	$d = v \times t$
$t = \dfrac{d}{v}$	$a = \dfrac{v_f - v_i}{t}$
$v = a \times t$	$d = \frac{1}{2} \times a \times t^2$

The velocity of Galileo's objects, of course, was always directed downward.

This equation tells us that an object that falls for 2 seconds achieves a velocity twice that of an object that falls for only 1 second, whereas one that falls for 3 seconds will be moving three times as fast as one that falls for only 1 second, and so on. The exact value of the velocity depends on the acceleration, which, in Galileo's experiment, depended on the angle of elevation of the plane.

In the special case where the ball is falling freely (i.e., when the plane is at 90 degrees), the acceleration is such an important number that it is given a specific letter of the alphabet, *g*. This value is the acceleration that all objects experience at Earth's surface. (Note that the Moon and other planets have their own very different surface accelerations; *g* applies *only* to Earth's surface.) The value of *g* can be determined by measuring the fall rate of objects in a laboratory (Figure 2-9), and it turns out to be

$$g = 9.8 \text{ m/s}^2 = 32 \text{ feet/s}^2$$

This equation tells us that in the first second a falling object accelerates from a stationary position to a velocity of 9.8 meters per second (about 22 miles per hour), straight down. After 2 seconds the velocity doubles to 19.6 meters per second; after 3 seconds it triples to 29.4 meters per second; and so on.

Galileo's work also demonstrated that the distance covered by an accelerating object depends on the square of the travel time.

In equation form:

$$\text{distance traveled (m)} = 1/2 \times \text{acceleration (m/s}^2) \times \text{time}^2 \text{ (s}^2)$$

In symbols:

$$d = \frac{1}{2} \times a \times t^2$$

Armed with the several equations that relate distance, velocity, acceleration, and time (Table 2-1), scientists were poised to study motions throughout the cosmos.

EXAMPLE 2-2

OUT OF THE BLOCKS

A sprinter accelerates from the starting blocks to a speed of 3 meters per second in 1 second. Answer the following questions about the sprinter's speed, acceleration, time, and distance run. In each case, answer the question by substituting into the appropriate motion equation.

1. What is his acceleration?

$$\text{acceleration} = \frac{(\text{final velocity} - \text{initial velocity})}{\text{time}}$$

In this case, the sprinter starts at rest at the beginning of the race, so his initial velocity is 0.

$$\text{acceleration} = \frac{(3 \text{ m/s})}{1 \text{s}}$$
$$= 3 \text{ m/s}^2$$

2. How far does the sprinter travel during this 1 second of acceleration?

$$\text{distance} = 1/2 \times \text{acceleration} \times \text{time}^2$$
$$= 1/2 \times (3 \text{ m/s}^2) \times (1 \text{ s})^2$$
$$= 1.5 \text{ meters}$$

EXAMPLE 2-3

DROPPING A PENNY FROM THE WILLIS TOWER

The tallest building in the United States is the Willis Tower (formerly the Sears Tower) in Chicago, with a height of 1,454 feet. Ignoring wind resistance, how fast would a penny dropped from the top be moving when it hit the ground?

Reasoning: The penny is dropped with zero initial velocity. We first need to calculate the time it takes to fall 1,454 feet. From this time we can calculate the velocity at impact.

Step 1—Time of Fall: The distance traveled by an accelerating object is:

$$\text{distance} = 1/2 \times \text{acceleration} \times \text{time}^2$$
$$= 1/2 \times 32 \text{ ft/s}^2 \times t^2 = 16 \text{ ft/s}^2 \times t^2$$

Recall that distance equals 1,454 feet, so rearranging gives:

$$t^2 = \frac{1454 \text{ ft}}{16 \text{ ft/s}^2}$$
$$= 90.88 \text{ s}^2$$

Taking the square root of both sides gives time:

$$t = 9.5 \text{ s}$$

Step 2—Speed at Impact: The speed of an acceleration object is:

$$\text{Velocity} = \text{acceleration} \times \text{time}$$
$$= 32 \text{ ft/s}^2 \times 9.5 \text{ s} = 304 \text{ ft/s}$$

This high speed, about 200 miles per hour, could easily kill a person, so *don't* try this experiment! In fact, most objects dropped in air will not accelerate indefinitely. Because of air resistance, an object will accelerate until it reaches its *terminal velocity;* after that point it will continue falling at a constant speed. The terminal velocity of a falling penny would be considerably less than 200 miles an hour. In addition, it would depend on whether the penny was falling face down or on edge because the air resistance would be different in those two cases.

THE SCIENCE OF LIFE
Experiencing Extreme Acceleration

You experience accelerations every day of your life. Just lying in bed you feel acceleration equal to *g,* due to Earth's gravitational pull. When you travel in a car or plane, ride an elevator, and especially when you enjoy amusement park rides, your body is subjected to additional accelerations, though rarely exceeding 2 *g.* But jet pilots and astronauts experience accelerations many times that caused by Earth's gravitational pull during takeoffs, sharp turns, and emergency ejections. What happens to the human body under extreme acceleration, and how can equipment be designed to reduce the risk of injury? In the early days of rocket flights and high-speed jet design, government scientists had to know.

Controlled laboratory accelerations were produced by rocket sleds (Figure 2-10) or centrifuges, which may reach accelerations exceeding 10 *g.* Researchers quickly discovered that muscles and bones behave as an effectively rigid framework. Sudden extreme acceleration, such as that experienced in a car crash, may cause damage, but these parts can withstand the more gradual changes in acceleration associated with flight.

The body's fluids, on the other hand, shift and flow under sustained acceleration. A pilot in a sharp curve will be pushed down into the seat and experience something like the feeling you get when an elevator starts upward. The blood in the arteries leading up to the brain

Acceleration

Science Source

FIGURE 2-10 Colonel John Stapp experienced extreme acceleration in rocket sled experiments. The severe contortion of soft facial tissues was recorded by a movie camera.

will also be pushed down, and, if the acceleration is big enough, the net effect will be to drain blood temporarily from the brain. The heart simply can't push the blood upward hard enough to overcome the downward pull. As a result, a pilot may experience a blackout, followed by unconsciousness. Greater accelerations could be tolerated in the prone position adopted by the first astronauts, who had to endure sustained 8 *g* conditions during takeoffs.

One of the authors (J. T.) once rode in a centrifuge and experienced an 8 *g* acceleration. The machine itself was a gray, egg-shaped capsule located at the end of a long steel arm. When in operation, the arm moved in a horizontal circle. Funny things happen at 8 *g*. For example, the skin of your face is pulled down, so that it's hard to keep your mouth open to breathe. The added weight feels like a very heavy person sitting on your chest.

There is, however, one advantage to having had this particular experience. Now, whenever he encounters the question, "What is the most you have ever weighed?" on a medical form, the author can write "1,600 pounds." •

FIGURE 2-11 Isaac Newton (1642–1727).

magno/Getty Images, Inc.

◉ 2.3 Isaac Newton and the Universal Laws of Motion

With Galileo's work, scientists began to isolate and observe the motion of material objects in nature and to summarize their results into mathematical relationships. As to why bodies should behave this way, however, they had no suggestions. And there was certainly little reason to believe that the measurements of falling objects at Earth's surface had anything at all to do with motions of planets and stars in the heavens.

The English scientist Isaac Newton (1642–1727), arguably the most brilliant scientist who ever lived (Figure 2-11), synthesized the work of Galileo and others into a statement of the basic principles that govern the motion of everything in the universe, from stars and planets to clouds, cannonballs, and the muscles in your body. These results, called **Newton's laws of motion,** sound so simple and obvious that it's hard to realize they represent the results of centuries of experiment and observation, and even harder to appreciate what an extraordinary effect they had on the development of science.

The young Newton was interested in mechanical devices and eventually enrolled as a student at Cambridge University. For most of the 1665–1666 school year, the university was closed due to a recurrence in England of the Great Plague that had devastated much of Europe in the past. Isaac Newton spent the time at a family farm in Lincolnshire, reading and thinking about the physical world. There he began thinking through his extraordinary discoveries in the nature of motion, as well as pivotal advances in optics and mathematics.

Three laws summarize Newton's description of motions.

The First Law

A moving object will continue moving in a straight line at a constant speed, and a stationary object will remain at rest, unless acted on by an unbalanced force.

Newton's first law seems to state the obvious: If you leave an object alone, it won't change its state of motion. In order to change it, you have to push it or pull it, thus applying a force. Yet virtually all scientists from the Greeks to Copernicus would have argued that the first law is wrong. They believed that because the circle is the most perfect geometrical shape, objects will move in circles unless something interferes. They also believed that heavenly objects would keep turning without any outside force acting (indeed, they had to believe this or face the question of why the heavens didn't slow down and stop).

Newton, basing his arguments on observations and the work of his predecessors, turned this notion around. An object left to itself will move in a straight line, and if you want to get it to move in a circle, you have to apply a force (Figure 2-12). You know this is true—if you swing something around your head, it will move in a circle only as long as you hold on to it. Let go, and off it goes in a straight line.

This simple observation led Newton to recognize two different kinds of motion. An object is in **uniform motion** if it travels in a straight line at constant speed. *All other motions are called acceleration.* Accelerations can involve changes of speed, changes of direction, or both.

Newton's first law tells us that when we see acceleration, something must have acted to produce that change. We define a **force** as something that produces a change in the state of motion of an object. In fact, we will use the first law of motion extensively in this book to tell us how to recognize when a force, particularly a new kind of force, is acting.

The tendency of an object to remain in uniform motion is called *inertia*. A body at rest tends to stay at rest because of its inertia, while a moving body tends to keep moving because of its inertia. We often use this idea in everyday speech; for example, we may talk about the inertia in a company or government organization that is resistant to change.

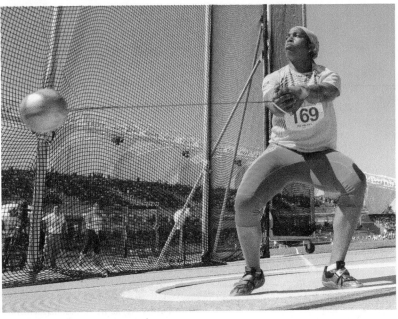

FIGURE 2-12 This hammer thrower is applying a force to keep the weight moving in a circle.

Martin Bernetti/AFP/Getty Images, Inc.

The Second Law

The acceleration produced on a body by a force is proportional to the magnitude of the force and inversely proportional to the mass of the object.

If Newton's first law of motion tells you when a force is acting, then the second law of motion tells you what the force does when it acts. This law conforms to our everyday experience: It's easier to lift a child than an adult, and easier to move a ballerina than a defensive tackle.

Newton's second law is often expressed as an equation.

In words: The greater the force, the greater the acceleration; but the more massive the object being acted on by a given force, the smaller the acceleration.

In equation form:

$$\text{force} = \text{mass (kg)} \times \text{acceleration (m/s}^2)$$

In symbols:

$$F = m \times a$$

This equation, well known to generations of physics majors, tells us that if we know the forces acting on a system of known mass, we can predict its future motion. The equation conforms to our experience that an object's acceleration is a balance between two factors: force and **mass,** which is related to the amount of matter in an object.

A force causes the acceleration. The greater the force, the greater the acceleration. The harder you throw a ball, the faster it goes. Mass measures the amount of matter in any object. The greater the object's mass, the more "stuff" you have to accelerate, the less effect a given force is going to have. A given force will accelerate a golf ball more than a bowling ball, for example. Newton's second law of motion thus defines the balance between force and mass in producing an acceleration.

Newton's first law defines the concept of force as something that causes a mass to accelerate, but the second law goes much further. It tells us the exact magnitude of the force necessary to cause a given mass to achieve a given acceleration. Because force equals mass times acceleration, the units of force must be the same as mass times acceleration. Mass is measured in kilograms (kg) and acceleration in meters per second per second (m/s^2), so the unit of force is the "kilogram-meter-per-second-squared" (kg-m/s^2). One kg-m/s^2 is called the "newton." The symbol for the newton is N.

EXAMPLE 2-4

FROM ZERO TO TEN IN LESS THAN A SECOND

What is the force needed to accelerate a 75-kilogram sprinter from rest to a speed of 10 meters per second (a very fast run) in a half second?

Reasoning and Solution: We must first find the acceleration and then use Newton's second law to find the force.

$$\text{acceleration (m/s}^2) = \frac{[\text{final velocity} - \text{initial velocity (m/s)}]}{\text{time (s)}}$$

$$= \frac{(10 \text{ m/s} - 0 \text{ m/s})}{0.5 \text{ s}}$$

$$= 20 \text{ m/s}^2$$

What force is needed to produce this acceleration? From Newton's second law,

$$\text{force (N)} = \text{mass (kg)} \times \text{acceleration (m/s}^2)$$

$$= 75 \text{ kg} \times 20 \text{ m/s}^2$$

$$= 1,500 \text{ newtons}$$

The second law of motion does not imply that every time a force acts, motion must result. A book placed on a table still feels the force of gravity, and you can push against a wall without moving it. In these situations, the atoms in the table or the wall shift around and exert their own force that balances the one that acts on them. It is only the net, or unbalanced, force that actually gives rise to acceleration.

The Third Law

For every action there is an equal and opposite reaction.

Newton's third law of motion tells us that whenever a force is applied to an object, that object simultaneously exerts an equal and opposite force. When you push on a wall, for example, it instantaneously pushes back on you; you can feel the force on the palm of your hand. In fact, the force the wall exerts on you is equal in magnitude (but opposite in direction) to the force you exert on it.

The third law of motion is perhaps the least intuitive of the three. We tend to think of our world in terms of causes and effects, in which big or fast objects exert forces on smaller, slower ones: a car slams into a tree, a batter drives the ball into deep left field, a boxer hits a punching bag (Figure 2-13). But in terms of Newton's third law, it is equally valid to think of these events the "other way around." The tree stops the car's motion, the baseball alters the swing of the bat, and the punching bag blocks the thrust of the boxer's glove, thus exerting a force and changing the direction and speed of the punch.

Forces always act simultaneously in pairs. You can convince yourself of this fact by thinking about any of your day's myriad activities. As you recline on a sofa reading this book, your weight exerts a force on the sofa, but the sofa exerts an equal and opposite force (called a contact force) on you, preventing you from falling to the floor (Figure 2-14). The book feels heavy in your hands as it presses down, but your hands hold the book up, exerting an equal and opposite force. You may feel a slight draft from an open window or fan, but as the air exerts that gentle force on you, your skin just as surely exerts an equal and opposite force on the air, causing it to change its path.

It is important to realize that although forces of the same magnitude act on both objects—your hand and the wall, for example—the results of the action of those forces can be different, depending on the objects involved. When a bug hits the windshield of a car, for example, it exerts a force on the car at the same time the car exerts an equal and opposite force on it. The consequences of the action of those forces are quite different, however. The tiny deceleration of the car is imperceptible, but the bug is squashed.

It is also important to note that although the forces are equal and opposite, they do not cancel each other since they act on different objects.

Newton's Laws at Work

Every motion in your life—indeed, every motion in the universe—involves the constant interplay of all three of Newton's laws. The laws of motion never occur in isolation but rather are interlocking aspects of every object's behavior. The interdependence of Newton's three laws of motion can be envisioned by a simple example. Imagine a boy standing on roller skates holding a stack of baseballs. He throws the balls, one by one. Each time he throws a baseball, the first law tells us that he has to exert a force so that the ball accelerates. The third law tells us that the baseball will exert an equal and opposite force on the boy. This force acting on the boy will, according to the second law, cause him to recoil backward.

Although the example of the boy and the baseballs may seem a bit contrived, it exactly illustrates the principle by which fish swim and rockets fly. As a fish moves its tail, it applies a force against the water. The water, in turn, pushes back on the fish and propels it forward. In a rocket motor, forces are exerted on hot gases, accelerating them out the tail end (Figure 2-15).

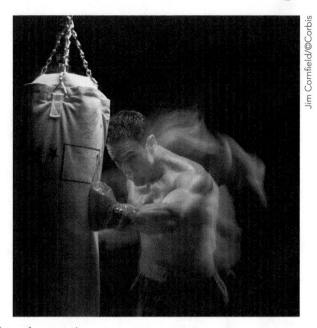

FIGURE 2-13 This boxer demonstrates Newton's laws of motion.

FIGURE 2-14 Newton's laws of motion can be seen in operation in many places, including while reading this book.

Forces act simultaneously in pairs

Skin exerts a force on the air

Gravity exerts a downward force

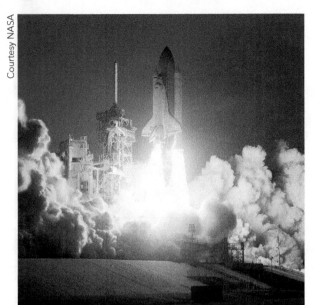

FIGURE 2-15 The space shuttle *Discovery* rises from its launch pad at Cape Canaveral, Florida. As hot gases accelerate violently out the rocket's engine, the shuttle experiences an equal and opposite acceleration that lifts it into orbit.

The argument just presented shows that the gases must exert an equal and opposite force on the rocket, propelling it forward. Every rocket, from simple fireworks to a space shuttle, works this way.

STOP & THINK It is sometimes argued that rockets propel themselves by pushing on the air around them. Can this be right? (*Hint:* Think about how rockets can move in the vacuum of space).

Isaac Newton's three laws of motion form a comprehensive description of all possible motions, as well as the forces that lead to them. In and of themselves, however, Newton's laws do not say anything about the nature of those forces. In fact, much of the progress of science since Newton's time has been associated with the discovery and elucidation of the forces of nature.

◉ 2.4 Momentum

Newton's laws tell us that the only way to change the motion of an object is to apply a force. We all have an intuitive understanding of this tendency. We sense, for example, that a massive object such as a large train, even if it is moving slowly, is very hard to stop. This knowledge is often used by people who make science fiction movies. It's almost a cliché now that when a spaceship is huge and bulky, the filmmakers supply a deep, rumbling soundtrack that mimics a slowly moving train. (In this case, artistic effect conflicts with the laws of nature because in the vacuum of space there can be no sound waves.)

At the same time, a small object moving very fast—a rifle bullet, for example—is very hard to stop as well. Thus, our everyday experience tells us that the tendency of a moving object to remain in motion depends both on the mass of the object and on its speed. The higher the mass and the higher the speed, the more difficult it is to stop the object or change its direction of motion.

Physicists encapsulate these notions in a quantity called *linear momentum,* which equals the product of an object's mass times its velocity.

In equation form:

$$\text{momentum (kg-m/s)} = \text{mass (kg)} \times \text{velocity (m/s)}$$

In symbols:

$$p = m \times v$$

EXAMPLE 2-5

PLAY BALL

A baseball with a mass of 0.15 kilogram moves to the right with a velocity of 30 meters/second (about the speed of a good fastball). What is its momentum?

Solution: The momentum is defined to be

$$p = m \times v$$

If we substitute the numbers for mass and velocity, we find that

$$p = 0.15 \text{ kg} \times 30 \text{ m/s} = 4.5 \text{ kg-m/s}$$

Conservation of Linear Momentum

We can derive a very important consequence from Newton's laws. If no external forces act on a system, then Newton's second law says that the change in the total momentum of a system is zero. When physicists find a quantity that does not change, they say that the quantity is *conserved*. The conclusion we have just reached, therefore, is called the *law of conservation of linear momentum*.

It's important to keep in mind that the law of conservation of momentum doesn't say that momentum can never change. It just says that it won't change unless an outside force is applied. If a soccer ball is rolling across a field and a player kicks it, a force is applied to the ball as soon as the player's foot touches it. At that moment, the momentum of the ball changes, and that change is reflected in its change of direction and speed.

You saw the consequences of the conservation of momentum the last time you watched a fireworks display (Figure 2-16). The rocket arches up and explodes just at the moment that the rocket is stationary at the top of its path, at the instant when its total momentum is zero. After the explosion, brightly colored burning bits of material fly out in all directions. Each of these pieces has a mass and a velocity, so each has some momentum. Conservation of momentum, however, tells us that when we add up all the momenta of the pieces, they should cancel each other out and give a total momentum of zero. Thus, for example, if there is a 1-gram piece moving to the right at 10 meters per second, there has to be the equivalent of a 1-gram piece moving to the left at the same velocity. Thus, conservation of momentum gives fireworks their characteristic symmetric starburst pattern.

FIGURE 2-16 This symmetrical fireworks display illustrates the law of conservation of linear momentum.

Angular Momentum

Just as an object moving in a straight line will keep moving unless a force acts, an object that is rotating will keep rotating unless a twisting force called a *torque* acts to make it stop. A spinning top will keep spinning until the friction between its point of contact and the floor slows it down. A wheel will keep turning until friction in its bearing stops it. This tendency to keep rotating is called *angular momentum.*

Think about some common experiences with spinning objects. Two factors increase an object's angular momentum and thus make it more difficult to slow down and stop the rotating object. The first factor is simply the rate of spin; the faster an object spins, the harder it is to stop. The second, more subtle factor relates to the distribution of mass. Spinning objects with more mass, or with mass located farther away from the central axis of rotation, have greater angular momentum. Thus, a solid metal wheel has more angular momentum than an air-filled tire of the same diameter and rate of spin.

The consequences of the conservation of angular momentum you're most likely to experience occur when something happens to change a spinning object's distribution of mass. A striking illustration of this point can be seen in figure skating competitions. As a skater goes into a spin with her arms spread, she spins slowly. As she pulls her arms in tight to her body, her angular momentum must remain constant, since no outside force acts to affect the spin (Figure 2-17). Her rate of spin must increase.

FIGURE 2-17 When the skater spins faster as she pulls in her arms, she is demonstrating the conservation of angular momentum.

TECHNOLOGY
Inertial Guidance System

The conservation of angular momentum plays an important role in so-called inertial guidance systems for navigation in airplanes and satellites. The idea behind such systems is very simple. A massive object like a sphere or a flat circular disk is set into rotation inside a device in which very little resistance (that is, almost no torque) is exerted by the bearings. When such an object is set into rotation, its angular momentum continues to point in the same direction, regardless of how the spaceship moves around it. By sensing the constant rotation and seeing how it is related to the orientation of the satellite, engineers can tell which way the satellite is pointed. •

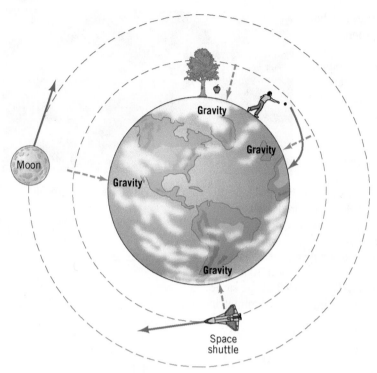

FIGURE 2-18 An apple falling, a ball being thrown, a space shuttle orbiting Earth, and the orbiting Moon, all display the influence of the force of gravity.

● 2.5 The Universal Force of Gravity

Gravity is the most obvious force in our daily lives. It holds you down in your chair and it keeps you from floating off into space. It guarantees that when you drop things they fall. The effects of what we call gravity were known to the ancients, and its quantitative properties were studied by Galileo and many of his contemporaries, but Isaac Newton revealed its universality.

By Newton's account, he experienced his great insight in an apple orchard. He saw an apple fall and, at the same time, saw the Moon in the sky behind it. He knew that in order for the Moon to keep moving in a circular path, a force had to be acting on it. He wondered whether the gravity that caused the apple to move downward could extend far outward to the Moon, supplying the force that kept it from flying off.

Look at the problem this way: If the Moon goes around Earth, then it isn't moving in a straight line. From the first law of motion it follows that a force must be acting on it. Newton hypothesized that this was the same force that made the apple fall—the familiar force of gravity (see Figure 2-18).

Eventually, Newton realized that the orbits of all the planets could be understood if gravity was not restricted to the surface of Earth but was a force found throughout the universe. He formulated this insight (an insight that has been overwhelmingly confirmed by observations) in what is called **Newton's law of universal gravitation.** •

In words: Between any two objects in the universe there is an attractive force (gravity) that is proportional to the masses of the objects and inversely proportional to the square of the distance between them.

In equation form:

$$\text{force of gravity (newtons)} = \frac{[G \times \text{mass}_1\,(\text{kg}) \times \text{mass}_2\,(\text{kg})]}{[\text{distance (m)}]^2}$$

In symbols:

$$F = \frac{(G \times m_1 \times m_2)}{d^2}$$

where G is a number known as the *gravitational constant* (see below).

In everyday words, this law tells us that the more massive two objects are, the greater the force between them will be; the farther apart they are, the less the force will be.

The Gravitational Constant, G

When we say that A is *directly proportional* to B, we mean that if A increases, B must increase by the same proportion. If A doubles, then B must double as well. We can state this idea in mathematical form by writing

$$A = k \times B$$

where k is a number known as the constant of proportionality between A and B. This equation tells us that if we know the constant k and either A or B, then we can calculate the exact value of the other. Thus, the constant of proportionality in a relationship is a useful thing to know.

The gravitational constant, G, is a constant of direct proportionality; it expresses the exact numerical relation between the masses of two objects and their separation, on the one hand, and the force between them on the other.

$$F = \frac{(G \times m_1 \times m_2)}{d^2}$$

Unlike g, however, which applies only to Earth's surface, G is a universal constant that applies to any two masses anywhere in the universe.

Henry Cavendish (1731–1810), a student at Cambridge University in England, first measured G in 1798 by using the experimental apparatus shown in Figure 2-19. Cavendish suspended a dumbbell made of two small lead balls by a stiff wire and fixed two larger lead spheres near the suspended balls. The gravitational attraction between the hanging lead balls and the fixed spheres caused the wire to twist slightly. By measuring the amount of twisting force, or torque, on the wire, Cavendish could calculate the gravitational force on the dumbbells. This force, together with knowledge of the masses of the dumbbells (m_1 in the equation) and the heavy spheres (m_2), as well as their final separation (d), gave him the numerical value of everything in Newton's law of universal gravitation except G, which he then calculated using simple arithmetic. In metric units, the value of G is 6.67×10^{-11} m^3/s^2-kg, or 6.67×10^{-11} N-m^2/kg^2 (recall that N is the symbol for a newton, the unit of force). This constant appears to be universal, holding true everywhere in our universe.

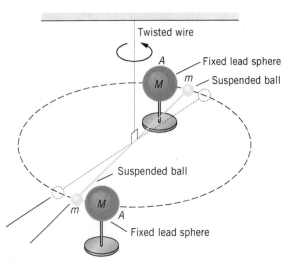

FIGURE 2-19 The Cavendish balance measures the universal gravitational constant G. This experimental device balances the gravitational attractive force between the suspended balls and fixed spheres, against the force exerted by a twisted wire.

Weight and Gravity

The law of universal gravitation says that there is a force between any two objects in the universe: two dancers, two stars, this book and you—all exert forces on each other. The gravitational attraction between you and Earth would pull you down if you weren't standing on the ground. As it is, the ground exerts a force equal and opposite to that of gravity, a force you can feel in the soles of your feet. If you were standing on a scale, the gravitational pull of Earth would pull you down until a spring or other mechanism in the scale exerted the opposing force. In this case, the size of that counterbalancing force registers on a display and you call it your **weight.**

Weight, in fact, is just the force of gravity on an object located at a particular point. Weight depends on where you are; on the surface of Earth you weigh one thing, on the surface of the Moon another, and in the depths of interstellar space you would weigh next to nothing. You even weigh a little less on a high mountaintop than you do at sea level because you are farther from Earth's center. Weight contrasts with your mass (the amount of matter), which stays the same no matter where you go.

Big G and Little g

The law of universal gravitation, coupled with the experimental results on bodies falling near Earth, can be used to reveal a close relationship between the universal constant G and Earth's gravitational acceleration g. According to the law of universal gravitation, the gravitational force on an object of any mass at Earth's surface is

$$\text{force} = \frac{(G \times mass \times M_E)}{R_E^2}$$

where M_E and R_E are Earth's mass and radius, respectively. On the other hand, Newton's second law says that

$$\text{force} = mass \times g$$

Equating the right sides of these two equations,

$$mass \times g = \frac{(G \times mass \times M_E)}{R_E^2}$$

Dividing both sides by mass,

$$g = \frac{(G \times M_E)}{R_E^2}$$

But the values of G, M_E, and R_E have been measured:

$$g = \frac{(6.67 \times 10^{-11} \text{ N-m}^2/\text{kg}^2) \times (6.02 \times 10^{24} \text{ kg})]}{(6.40 \times 10^6 \text{ m})^2}$$

$$= \frac{(4.015 \times 10^{14} \text{ N-m}^2/\text{kg})}{(4.10 \times 10^{13} \text{ m}^2)}$$

$$= 9.8 \text{ N-kg} = 9.8 \text{ m}/\text{s}^2$$

Thus, the value of Earth's gravitational acceleration, g, can be calculated from Newton's universal equation for gravity.

This result is extremely important. For Galileo, g was a number to be measured, but whose value he could not predict. For Newtonians, on the other hand, g was a number that could be calculated purely from Earth's size and mass. Because we understand where g comes from, we can now predict the appropriate value of gravitational acceleration not only for Earth but also for any body in the universe, provided we know its mass and radius.

STOP & THINK Can the gravitational force between two objects in the universe ever be equal to zero? Why or why not?

EXAMPLE 2-6

WEIGHT ON THE MOON

The mass of the Moon is $M_M = 7.18 \times 10^{22}$ kilograms, and its radius R_M is 1,738 kilometers. If your mass is 100 kilograms, what would you weigh on the Moon?

Reasoning: We have to calculate the force exerted on an object at the surface of an astronomical body. This time, both the mass and the radius of the body are different from that of Earth, although G is the same.

Solution: From the equation that defines weight, we have

$$\text{weight} = \frac{(G \times \text{mass}_1 \times \text{mass}_2)}{\text{distance}^2}$$

$$= \frac{(G \times 100 \text{ kg} \times M_M)}{R_M^2}$$

$$= \frac{[(6.67 \times 10^{11} \text{ N-m}^2/\text{kg}^2)100 \text{ kg} \times (7.18 \times 10^{22} \text{ kg})}{(1.738 \times 10^6 \text{ m})^2}$$

$$= \frac{[(6.67 \times 10^{-11} \text{ N-m}^2/\text{kg}^2) \times (7.18 \times 10^{24} \text{ kg}^2)]}{(3.02 \times 10^{12} \text{ m}^2)}$$

$$= \frac{(4.79 \times 10^{14} \text{ N-m}^2)}{(3.02 \times 10^{12} \text{ m}^2)}$$

$$= 159 \text{ newtons}$$

This weight is about one-sixth of the weight that the same object would have on Earth, *even though its mass is the same in both places.*

Newton bequeathed a picture of the universe that is beautiful and ordered. The planets orbit the Sun in stately paths, forever trying to move off in straight lines, forever prevented from doing so by the inward tug of gravity. The same laws that operate in the cosmos operate on Earth, and these laws were discovered by the application of the scientific method. To a Newtonian observer, the universe was like a clock. It had been wound up and was ticking along according to God's laws. Newton and his followers were persuaded that in carrying out their work, they were discovering what was in the mind of God when the universe was created.

Of all celestial phenomena, none seemed more portentous and magical than comets, yet even these chance wanderers were subject to Newton's laws. In 1682, British astronomer Edmond Halley (1656–1742) used Newtonian logic to compute the orbit of the comet that bears his name, and he predicted its return in 1758 (Figure 2-20). The "recovery" of Halley's Comet on Christmas Eve of that year was celebrated around the world as a triumph for the Newtonian system.

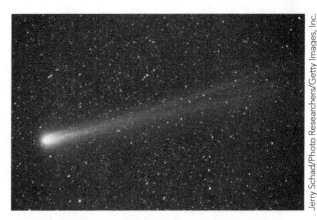

Jerry Schad/Photo Researchers, Inc.

FIGURE 2-20 Halley's comet as it appeared on its last visit to Earth, in 1985.

THINKING MORE ABOUT **THE ORDERED UNIVERSE**

Predictability

The Newtonian universe seemed regular and predictable in the extreme. Indeed, from the point of view of the Newtonians, if you knew the present state of a system and the forces acting on it, the laws of motion would allow you to predict its entire future. This notion was taken to the extreme by the French mathematician Pierre Simon Laplace (1749–1827), who proposed the notion of the *Divine Calculator*. His argument (in modern language) was this: If we knew the position and velocity of every atom in the universe and we had infinite computational power, then we could predict the position and velocity of every atom in the universe for all future times. There is no distinction in this argument between an atom in a rock and an atom in your hand. Therefore, Laplace would say that all of your movements are completely determined by the laws of physics to the end of time. You cannot choose your future. What is to be was determined from the very beginning.

This idea has been negated by two modern developments in science. One of these, the Heisenberg uncertainty principle (see Chapter 9), tells us that at the level of the atom it is impossible to know simultaneously and exactly both the position and velocity of any particle with perfect precision. Thus, you can never get the information the Divine Calculator needs to begin working.

Furthermore, scientists working with computer models have recently discovered that many systems in nature can be described in simple Newtonian terms, but have futures that are, for all intents and purposes, unpredictable. These situations are called *chaotic systems*, and their field of study is called *chaos*.

Whitewater in a mountain stream is a familiar chaotic system. If you put two chips of wood down on the upstream side of the rapids, those chips (and the water on which they ride) will be widely separated by the time they get to the end. This is true no matter how small you make the chips or how close together they are at the beginning. If you know the exact initial position of a chip and every aspect of the waterway in such a system with complete mathematical precision, you can, in principle, predict where it will come out downstream. But if there is the slightest error in your initial description, no matter how small, the actual position of the chip and your prediction may differ significantly. Every measurement in the real world has some error associated with it, so it is never possible to determine the exact position of the chip at the start of its trip. Therefore, you cannot predict exactly where it will come out *even if you know all the forces acting on it*.

The existence of chaos, then, tells us that the philosophical conclusions drawn from the Newtonian vision of the universe don't apply to some systems in nature. The flow of Earth's atmosphere and the long-term development of weather, for example, appear to be chaotic, and it may turn out that some ecosystems (see Chapter 19) behave this way as well. If this is true, what implications might there be when governments have to deal with issues such as global warming (see Chapter 19) and the preservation of endangered species? How confident do you have to be that something bad is going to happen before you start taking steps to avoid it?

⬅ RETURN TO THE INTEGRATED QUESTION

Why do planets appear to wander slowly across the sky?

- Since before recorded history, people have observed the movement of the lights in the evening and night sky (i.e., the planets and stars).
- Some of the most predictable objects in the universe are the stars and planets that we see each night.
- From an Earthly vantage point, the planets appear to wander across the nighttime sky as Earth rotates around its axis and revolves around the Sun.
- Based on its apparent centrality to the movement of the planets, early astronomers such as Ptolemy constructed theories placing Earth at the center of the universe.
- Copernicus improved Ptolemy's earlier work by placing the Sun, rather than Earth, at the center of the solar system.

- The Italian physicist Galileo Galilei's greatest accomplishment may have been his experimental work on the behavior of objects thrown or dropped near the surface of Earth. This work led to the development of the science of mechanics.
- Sir Isaac Newton synthesized the work of the early astronomers and Galileo into a simple and elegant statement of the basic principles of mechanics that govern the motion of everything in the universe, from stars and planets to cannonballs and clouds.

Newton realized that if gravity was not restricted to the surface of Earth, then his laws of motion could explain the movements of the planets in their orbits as they appear to wander across the nighttime sky.

SUMMARY

Since before recorded history, people have observed regularities in the heavens and have built monuments such as Stonehenge to help order their lives. Models such as the Earth-centered system of Ptolemy and the Sun-centered system of Copernicus attempted to explain these regular motions of stars and planets. New, more precise astronomical data by Tycho Brahe led mathematician Johannes Kepler to propose his laws of planetary motion, which state that planets orbit the Sun in elliptical orbits, not circular orbits as had been previously assumed.

Meanwhile, Galileo Galilei and other scientists investigated the science of *mechanics*—the way things move near Earth's surface. These investigators recognized two fundamentally different kinds of motion: *uniform motion*, which involves a constant *speed* and direction (*velocity*), and *acceleration*, which entails a change in either speed or direction of travel. Galileo's experiments revealed that all objects fall the same way, at the constant acceleration of 9.8 meters/second^2. Isaac Newton combined the work of Kepler, Galileo, and others in his sweeping *laws of motion* and the *law of universal gravitation*. Newton realized that nothing accelerates without a *force* acting on it, and that the amount of acceleration is proportional to the force applied, but inversely proportional to the *mass*. He also pointed out that forces always act in pairs.

This understanding of forces and motions led Newton to describe *gravity*, the most obvious force in our daily lives. An object's *weight* is the force it exerts due to gravity. He demonstrated that the same force that pulls a falling apple to Earth causes the Moon to curve around Earth in its elliptical orbit. Indeed, the force of gravity operates everywhere, with pairs of forces between every pair of masses in the universe.

KEY TERMS

mechanics	Newton's laws of motion	gravity
speed	uniform motion	Newton's law of universal gravitation
velocity	force	weight
acceleration	mass	

DISCOVERY LAB

Film canister
Seltzer tablet
Water
Canister lid

Isaac Newton's third law of motion tells us that "for every action there is an equal and opposite reaction." Whether we walk forward by pushing backward, or a bird's wings push back and down to fly forward, Newton's third law of motion is all around us. Even when you push against a wall, the wall exerts an equal force back on you, with an equal and opposite magnitude to the force you have exerted on the wall. In this experiment gather these items: two seltzer tablets, goggles, a teaspoon, water in a short cup, and a 35 mm film canister from your local photo shop. Next, find a safe cement area outside to perform the experiment. After placing your goggles on, put one-half teaspoon of water inside the film canister. Ask a friend to drop a tablet of seltzer in the canister, as you quickly place the lid on. Rapidly shake the canister 10 times and then quickly place it vertically (lid down) on the cement. Stand back and watch it for at least 30 seconds. What do you predict will happen? What law(s) of Newton are operative here, and can you explain why? What are the variables in this experiment, and how can you change the results? How can any of these variables change the reaction time or propel the canister to a higher altitude? Is this experiment measurable, and can you graph the results?

REVIEW QUESTIONS

1. With what ancient science is Stonehenge associated?

2. Why do some archaeologists refer to Stonehenge as the "Land of the Dead"?

3. Would Stonehenge have been of value if the universe was unpredictable?

4. Why was the Ptolemaic system accepted as an explanation of celestial motion for over a thousand years? What did it explain? What system challenged the idea that Earth was the center of the universe?

5. What were Tycho Brahe's principal contributions to science? How did he try to resolve the question of the structure of the universe?

6. What was Kepler's role in interpreting Tycho Brahe's data?

7. How did Galileo apply the scientific method to his study of falling objects?

8. A soccer player kicks a ball across the field, which stops in the net after scoring a goal. Explain how each of Newton's laws of motion applies to this situation.

9. What is uniform motion? How did Newton's description of uniform motion differ from that of previous scholars?

10. Why is gravity called a universal force?

11. What is the difference between the constants g and G?

12. What similarities did Newton see between the Moon and an apple?

13. What is the difference between weight and mass?

14. How does velocity differ from speed? What does it mean to say that velocity is a vector? Name some other vectors.

DISCUSSION QUESTIONS

1. What role did observation and the regularity of nature play in the development of modern sanitation? (*Hint:* John Snow, 1823–1858.)

2. What does it mean that Stonehenge was not just a calendar? What other uses might it have had?

3. Why was Earth at the center of the universe in Ptolemy's system?

4. Can you give an everyday example that illustrates the difference between acceleration and velocity?

5. Which of the following is in uniform motion, and which is in accelerated motion?

   a. A car heading west at 55 mph on a level road

   b. A car heading west at 55 mph on a hill

   c. A car going around a curve at 55 mph

   d. A dolphin leaping out of the water

6. Which, if any, of the following objects does not exert a gravitational force on you?

   a. This book

   b. The Sun

   c. The nearest star

   d. A distant galaxy

7. What pairs of forces act in the following situations?

   a. A pitcher throws a baseball

   b. A batter hits a baseball out of the park

   c. The Moon orbits Earth

   d. You sit in a chair

8. What are the observational effects on Earth of the gravitational pull of the Moon? (*Hint:* Think of the ocean.)

9. Why are the results of the science of mechanics written in equations rather than words?

10. In what sense is the Newtonian universe simpler than Ptolemy's? Suppose observations had shown that the two did equally well at explaining the data. Construct an argument to say that Newton's universe should still be preferred.

11. Why don't the planets just fly off into space? What keeps them in their orbits?

12. How did Henry Cavendish's experiment fit into the scientific method?

13. Why do historians refer to the recovery of Halley's comet as a confirmation of the Newtonian worldview?

14. Why are observatories built as far away from major cities as possible?

15. Why is it possible for a rocket to travel in space? Which of Newton's laws of motion explain an accelerating rocket?

16. What forces keep a pendulum swinging back and forth?

17. Why does the existence of chaotic systems limit our predictions of some natural phenomena (e.g., long-term weather development)?

PROBLEMS

1. If a person weighs 150 pounds at Earth's surface, what does he weigh in newtons?

2. If your car goes from 0 to 60 miles per hour in 6 seconds, what is your acceleration? If you step on the brake and your car goes from 60 miles per hour to 0 in 3 seconds, what is your acceleration?

3. How much force are you exerting when you lift a 50-pound dumbbell at a constant rate of speed? What units will you use to describe this force?

4. The mass of the planet Mercury is 3.3×10^{23} kilograms, and its radius is 2.5×10^6 kilometers. What would you weigh on Mercury?

5. Calculate the gravitational attraction between the Sun and Earth. If you wanted to replace the force of gravity by using a steel cable, what would the diameter of the cable have to be? (*Hint:* Look up the tensile strength of steel.)

INVESTIGATIONS

1. Galileo was arrested and imprisoned for his studies and publications. Discuss the dilemma faced by scientists whose discoveries offend conventional ideas. What scientific research does today's society find offensive or immoral? Why?

2. Do you think that LaPlace was right when he argued against the existence of free will? Why or why not?

3. The study of monuments such as Stonehenge is part of a field called *archeoastronomy*. What other monuments around the world are thought to have had astronomical significance? (*Hint:* Look up the observatory at Chichen Itza and the Medicine Wheel in Wyoming.)

4. Investigate the scientific contributions of Galileo. What other experiments did he design? What instrumentation did he use? How was this research funded? Was he engaging in basic or applied research?

5. The gravitational constant is now known to one part in 10,000, yet physicists are still trying to measure this constant. Why?

6. People have claimed that the Great Pyramids of Egypt had to have been built by ancient astronauts because the Egyptians were too primitive to have built them. Look up the weight of the largest stones in the pyramids and estimate the number of people it would take to move them. Then comment on the ancient astronaut argument.

7. Throw a frisbee to a friend. Describe the path the frisbee takes as it travels from one person to another. What forces cause the frisbee to travel the way it does? How might you describe that path using mathematics as well as words?

8. Galileo was one of the first people to look at the planets through a telescope. He discovered the four largest moons of Jupiter, which are still called the *Galilean moons*. Why did this discovery cast doubt on the Ptolemaic system? What else did Galileo see through his telescope?

9. How does gravity affect the flow of blood in your body? The flow of sap in trees? How have organisms evolved to counteract the force of gravity?

10. Galileo built his own telescope after learning about it from others. Search the Web for links that would help you build your own telescope. What materials would you need? Where did Galileo get his materials?

11. How does a sundial work? How would you build a sundial differently in Canada from one in Mexico?

12. What role does momentum play in bowling? In billiards or pool?

13. Look up how a gyroscope works. How does this utilize the conservation of angular momentum?

14. Newton made a number of contributions to the field of mathematics. What were they, and why are they important?

15. Take a bathroom scale into an elevator. Record your weight when you are moving up and then when you are moving down. Explain your results using Newton's laws.

3 Energy

Why must animals eat to stay alive?

PHYSICS

When a bowler bowls a strike, some of the bowling ball's kinetic energy is transferred to scatter the pins.

BIOLOGY

Plants convert the radiant energy of sunlight into the chemical energy necessary to sustain life for organisms at every trophic level.

CHEMISTRY

Stored chemical energy in fossil fuels (coal, gas, and oil) is converted to heat energy during the process of burning.

TECHNOLOGY

A new generation of powerful and lightweight batteries that convert chemical potential energy into electricity is needed to power electric cars. (Ch. 15)

GREAT IDEA

The many different forms of energy are interchangeable, and the total amount of energy in an isolated system is conserved.

ENVIRONMENT

Wind and rain obtain their energy through the conservation of the Sun's radiant energy. (Ch. 18)

ASTRONOMY

Stars convert the element hydrogen into helium and radiate energy through the process of nuclear fusion. (Ch. 14)

HEALTH & SAFETY

Vigorous exercise converts the body's stored chemical energy into kinetic energy and heat.

GEOLOGY

During an earthquake, elastic potential energy stored in rock is suddenly converted to kinetic energy as the rock breaks. (Ch. 17)

 = applications of the great idea discussed in this chapter

 = other applications, some of which are discussed in other chapters

Morning Routine

The daily routine begins. You turn on the overhead light, squinting as your eyes adjust to the brightness. Then you take your morning shower; it feels great to just stand there and let the hot water wash over you. Soon you'll boil water for coffee, eat a hearty breakfast, and then drive to the beach.

During every one of these ordinary actions—indeed, every moment of every day—you use energy in its many varied and interchangeable forms.

Marcus Mok/Asia Images/Getty Images, Inc.

◎ 3.1 The Great Chain of Energy

Hundreds of millions of years ago, a bit of energy was generated in the core of the Sun. For thousands of years, that energy percolated outward to the Sun's surface; then, in a mere 8 minutes, it made the trip through empty space to Earth in the form of sunlight. Unlike other bits of energy that were reflected back into space by clouds or simply served to warm Earth's soil, this particular energy was absorbed by organisms known as algae floating on the warm ocean surface.

Through the process of photosynthesis (see Chapter 22), these algae transformed the Sun's energy into the chemical energy needed to hold together its complex molecules. Eventually these algae died and sank to the bottom of the ocean, where, over long eons, they were buried deeper and deeper. Under the influence of pressure and heat, the dead algae were eventually transformed into fossil fuel—petroleum.

FIGURE 3-1 This oil pump in Colorado is bringing up solar energy stored millions of years ago.

Lowell Georgia/Photo Researchers

Then, a short while ago, engineers pumped that petroleum with its stored energy up out of the ground (Figure 3-1). At a refinery, the large molecules were broken down into gasoline, and the gasoline was shipped to your town. A few days ago you put it into the tank of your car. The last time you drove you burned that gasoline, converting the stored energy into the engine's mechanical energy that moved your car. When you parked the car, the hot engine slowly cooled, and that bit of heat, after having been delayed for a few hundred million years, was radiated out into space to continue its voyage away from the solar system. As you read these words, the energy you freed yesterday has long since left the vicinity of Earth and is moving out toward the depths of interstellar space.

Scientifically Speaking

At this moment, trillions of cells in your body are hard at work turning the chemical energy of the food you ate yesterday into the chemical energy that will keep you alive today. Energy in the atmosphere generates sweeping winds and powerful storms, whereas the ocean's energy drives mighty currents and incessant tides. Meanwhile, deep within Earth, energy in the form of heat is moving the continent on which you are standing.

All situations where energy is expended have one thing in common. If you look at the event closely enough, you will find that, in accord with Newton's laws of motion (Chapter 2), a force is being exerted on an object to make it move. When your car burns gasoline, the fuel's energy ultimately turns the wheels of your car, which then exert a force on the road; the road exerts an equal and opposite force on the car, pushing it forward. When you climb the stairs, your muscles exert a force that lifts you upward against gravity. Even in your body's cells, a force is exerted on molecules in chemical reactions. Energy thus is intimately connected with the application of a force.

In everyday conversation we speak of someone having lots of energy, but in science the term *energy* has a precise definition that is somewhat different from the ordinary meaning. To see what scientists mean when they talk about energy, we must first introduce the familiar concept of work.

Work

Scientists say that **work** is done whenever a force is exerted over a distance. Pick up this book and raise it a foot. Your muscles applied a force equal to the weight of the book over a distance of a foot. You did work.

This definition of work differs considerably from everyday usage. From a physicist's point of view, if you accidentally drive into a tree and smash your fender, work has been done because a force deformed the car's metal a measurable distance. On the other hand, a physicist would say that you haven't done any work if you spend an hour in a futile effort to move a large boulder, no matter how tired you get. Even though you have exerted a considerable force, the distance over which you exerted it is negligible.

Physicists provide an exact mathematical definition of their notion of work.

In words: Work is equal to the force that is exerted times the distance over which it is exerted.

In equation form:

$$\text{work (joules)} = \text{force (newtons)} \times \text{distance (meters)}$$

where a joule is the unit of work, as defined in the following paragraph.

In symbols:

$$W = F \times d$$

In practical terms, even a small force can do a lot of work if it is exerted over a long distance.

As you might expect from this equation, units of work are equal to a force unit times a distance unit (Figure 3-2). In the metric system of units, where force is measured in *newtons* (abbreviated N), work is measured in newton-meters (N-m). For reference, a newton is roughly equal to the force exerted on your hand by a baseball (or by seven Fig Newtons!).

This unit is given the special name "joule," after the English scientist James Prescott

FIGURE 3-2 A weightlifter applies a force (in newtons) over a distance (in meters).

Matthias Tunger/Stone/Getty Images

Joule (1818–1889), one of the first people to understand the properties of energy. One *joule* is defined as the amount of work done when a force of one newton is exerted over a distance of one meter.

$$1 \text{ joule of work} = 1 \text{ N of force} \times 1 \text{ m of distance}$$

In the English system of units (see Appendix B), where force is measured in pounds, work is measured in a unit called the foot-pound (usually abbreviated ft-lb).

EXAMPLE 3-1

WORKING AGAINST GRAVITY

How much work do you do when you carry a 20-kilogram television set up a flight of stairs (about 4 meters)?

Reasoning: We must first calculate the force exerted by a 20-kilogram mass before we can determine work. From the previous chapter, we know that to lift a 20-kilogram mass against the acceleration of gravity (9.8 m/s^2) requires a force given by

$$
\begin{aligned}
\text{force} &= \text{mass} \times g \\
&= 20 \text{ kg} \times 9.8 \text{ m/s}^2 \\
&= 196 \text{ newtons}
\end{aligned}
$$

Solution: Then, from the equation for work,

$$
\begin{aligned}
\text{work} &= \text{force} \times \text{distance} \\
&= 196 \text{ N} \times 4 \text{ m} \\
&= 784 \text{ joules}
\end{aligned}
$$

Energy

Energy is defined as the ability to do work. If a system is capable of exerting a force over a distance, then that system possesses energy. The amount of a system's energy, which can be recorded in joules or foot-pounds (the same units used for work), is a measure of how much work the system might do. When a system runs out of energy, it simply can't do any more work.

Power

Power provides a measure of both the amount of work done (or, equivalently, the amount of energy expended) and the time it takes to do that work. In order to complete a physical task quickly, you must generate more power than if you do the same task slowly. If you run up a flight of stairs, your muscles need to generate more power than they would if you walked up the same flight, even though you expend the same amount of energy in either case. A power hitter in baseball swings the bat faster, converting the chemical energy in his muscles to kinetic energy more quickly than most other players (Figure 3-3).

Scientists define power as the rate at which work is done, or the rate at which energy is expended.

In words: Power is the amount of work done divided by the time it takes to do that work.

where the watt is the unit of power, as defined in the following paragraph.

In equation form:

$$\text{power (watts)} = \frac{\text{work (joules)}}{\text{time (seconds)}}$$

FIGURE 3-3 Athletes strive to generate maximum power—that is, to release their energy as quickly as possible—to succeed in sports such as professional baseball.

Christopher Pasatieri/Getty Images, Inc.

In symbols:

$$P = \frac{W}{t}$$

If you do more work in a given span of time, or do a task in a shorter time, you use more power.

In the metric system, power is measured in *watts* after James Watt (1736–1819), the Scottish inventor who developed the modern steam engine that powered the Industrial Revolution (Figure 3-4). The watt, a unit of measurement that you probably encounter every day, is defined as the expenditure of 1 joule of energy in 1 second:

$$1 \text{ watt of power} = \frac{(1 \text{ joule of energy})}{(1 \text{ second of time})}$$

The unit of 1000 watts (corresponding to an expenditure of 1000 joules per second) is called a *kilowatt* and is a commonly used measurement of electrical power. The English system, on the other hand, uses the more colorful unit *horsepower*, which is defined as 550 foot-pounds per second.

The familiar rating of a lightbulb (50 watts, for example) is a measure of the rate of energy that the lightbulb consumes when it is operating. As another familiar example, most electric hand tools or appliances in your home will be labeled with a power rating in watts.

The equation we have introduced defining power as energy divided by time may be rewritten as follows:

$$\text{energy (joules)} = \text{power (watts)} \times \text{time (seconds)}$$

This important equation allows you (and the electric company) to calculate how much energy you consume (and how much you have to pay for). Note from this equation that, while the joule is the standard scientific unit for energy, energy can also be measured in units of power × time, such as the familiar kilowatt-hour (often abbreviated kWh) that appears on your electric bill. Table 3-1 summarizes the important terms we've used for force, work, energy, and power.

 ## SCIENCE IN THE MAKING
James Watt and the Horsepower

The horsepower, a unit of power with a colorful history, was devised by James Watt so that he could sell his steam engines. Watt knew that the main use of his engines would be in mines, where owners traditionally used horses to drive pumps that removed water. The easiest way to promote his new engines was to tell the mining engineers how many horses each engine would replace. Consequently, he conducted a series of experiments to determine how much energy a horse could generate over a given amount of time. Watt found that an average, healthy horse can do 550 foot-pounds of work every second over an average working day—a unit he defined to be the horsepower, and so he rated his engines accordingly. We still use this unit (the engines of virtually all cars and trucks are rated in horsepower), although we seldom build engines to replace horses these days.

FIGURE 3-4 James Watt's first "Sun and Planet" steam engine, now in the Science Museum in London, England, transformed heat energy into kinetic energy.

TABLE 3-1 Important Terms

Quantity	Definition	Units
Force	mass × acceleration	newtons
Work	force × distance	joules
Energy	ability to do work	joules
Energy	power × time	joules
Power	work/time = energy/time	watts

EXAMPLE 3-2

PAYING THE PIPER

A typical CD system uses 250 watts of electrical power. If you play your system for three hours in an evening, how much energy do you use? If energy costs 12 cents per kilowatt-hour, how much do you owe the electrical company?

Reasoning and Solution: The total amount of energy you use will be given by

$$\text{energy} = \text{power} \times \text{time}$$
$$= 250 \text{ W} \times 3 \text{ h}$$
$$= 750 \text{ Wh}$$

Because 750 watts equals 0.75 kilowatt,

$$\text{energy} = 0.75 \, \text{kWh}$$

The cost will be as follows:

$$\text{cost} = 12 \text{ cents per kWh} \times 0.75 \, \text{kWh}$$
$$= 9 \text{ cents}$$

◉ 3.2 Forms of Energy

Energy, the ability to do work, appears in all natural systems, and it comes in many forms. The identification of these forms posed a great challenge to scientists in the nineteenth century. Ultimately, they recognized two very broad categories. **kinetic energy** is energy associated with moving objects—and stored or **potential energy**—is energy waiting to be released.

Kinetic Energy

Think about a cannonball flying through the air. When it hits a wooden target, the ball exerts a force on the fibers in the wood, splintering and pushing them apart and creating a hole. Work has to be done to make that hole; fibers have to be moved aside, which means that a force must be exerted over the distance they move. When the cannonball hits the wood, it does work, and so a cannonball in flight clearly has the *ability* to do work—that is, it has energy—because of its motion. This energy of motion is what we call kinetic energy.

You can find countless examples of kinetic energy in nature. A whale moving through water (Figure 3-5), a bird flying, and a predator catching its prey all have kinetic energy. So do a speeding car, a flying Frisbee, a falling leaf, and anything else that is moving.

Our intuition tells us that two factors govern the amount of kinetic energy contained in any moving object. First, heavier objects that are moving have more kinetic energy than lighter ones: a bowling ball traveling at 10 meters per second (a very fast sprint) carries a lot more kinetic energy than a golf ball traveling at the same speed. In fact, kinetic energy is directly proportional to mass: if you double the mass, then you double the kinetic energy.

Second, the faster something is moving, the greater force it is capable of exerting and the greater energy it possesses. A high-speed collision causes much more damage than a fender bender in a parking lot. It turns out that an object's kinetic energy increases as the square of its speed. A car moving 40 miles per hour has four times as much kinetic energy as one moving 20 miles per hour, while at 60 miles per hour a car carries nine times as much kinetic energy as at 20 miles per hour. Thus a modest increase in speed can cause a large increase in kinetic energy.

These ideas are combined in the equation for kinetic energy.

In words: Kinetic energy equals the mass of the moving object times the square of that object's speed, times the constant $\frac{1}{2}$.

In equation form:

$$\text{kinetic energy (joules)} = \tfrac{1}{2} \times \text{mass (kg)} \times [\text{speed (m/s)}]^2$$

In symbols:

$$KE = \tfrac{1}{2} \times m \times v^2$$

FIGURE 3-5 This breaching humpback whale has kinetic energy because he is moving.

Francois Gohier/Photo Researchers

EXAMPLE 3-3

BOWLING BALLS AND BASEBALLS

What is the kinetic energy of a 4-kilogram (about 8-pound) bowling ball rolling down a bowling lane at 10 meters per second (about 22 mph)? Compare this energy with that of a 250-gram (about half a pound) baseball traveling 50 meters per second (almost

110 mph). Which object would hurt more if it hit you (i.e., which object has the greater kinetic energy)?

Reasoning: We have to substitute numbers into the equation for kinetic energy.

Solution: For the 4-kilogram bowling ball traveling at 10 meters/second:

$$\text{kinetic energy (joules)} = \tfrac{1}{2} \times \text{mass (kg)} \times [\text{speed (m/s)}]^2$$
$$= \tfrac{1}{2} \times 4 \text{ kg} \times (10 \text{ m/s})^2$$
$$= \tfrac{1}{2} \times 4 \text{ kg} \times 100 \text{ m}^2/\text{s}^2$$
$$= 200 \text{ kg-m}^2/\text{s}^2$$

Note that

$$200 \text{ kg-m}^2/\text{s}^2 = 200 \, (\text{kg-m/s}^2) \times \text{m}$$
$$= 200 \text{ N} \times \text{m}$$
$$= 200 \text{ joules}$$

For the 250-gram baseball traveling at 50 meters/second:

$$\text{kinetic energy (joules)} = \tfrac{1}{2} \times \text{mass (kg)} \times [\text{speed (m/s)}]^2$$

A gram is a thousandth of a kilogram, so 250 g = 0.25 kg:

$$\text{kinetic energy (joules)} = \tfrac{1}{2} \times 0.25 \text{ kg} \times 2500 \text{ m}^2/\text{s}^2$$
$$= 312.5 \text{ kg-m}^2/\text{s}^2$$
$$= 312.5 \text{ joules}$$

Even though the bowling ball is much more massive than the baseball, a hard-hit baseball carries more kinetic energy than a typical bowling ball because of its high speed.

Potential Energy

Almost every mountain range in the country has a "balancing rock"—a boulder precariously perched on top of a hill so that it looks as if a little push would send it tumbling down the slope (Figure 3-6a). If the balancing rock were to fall, it would clearly acquire kinetic energy, and it would do "work" on anything it smashed. The balancing rock has the ability to do work even though it's not doing work right now, and even though it's not necessarily going to be doing work any time in the near future. The boulder possesses energy just by virtue of its position.

This kind of energy, which could result in the exertion of a force over distance but is not doing so now, is called potential energy. In the case of the balancing rock, it is called *gravitational potential energy* because the force of gravity gives the rock the capability of exerting its own force. An object that has been lifted above Earth's surface possesses an amount of gravitational potential energy exactly equal to the total amount of work you would have to do to lift it from the ground to its present position.

In words: The gravitational potential energy of any object equals its weight (the gravitational force exerted downward by the object) times its height above the ground.

In equation form:

$$\text{gravitational potential energy (joules)} = \text{mass (kg)} \times g \, (\text{m/s}^2) \times \text{height (m)}$$

here g is the acceleration due to gravity at Earth's surface (see Chapter 2).

In symbols:

$$PE = m \times g \times h$$

In Example 3-1 we saw that it requires 784 joules of energy to carry a 20-kilogram television set 4 meters distance up the stairs. Thus 784 joules is the amount of work that would be done

(a) (b) (c)

FIGURE 3-6 Potential energy comes in many forms: a precariously perched boulder (a) has gravitational potential energy, sticks of dynamite (b) store chemical potential energy, and a tautly drawn bow (c) holds elastic potential energy.

if the television set were allowed to fall, and it is the amount of gravitational potential energy stored in the elevated television set.

We encounter many other kinds of potential energy besides the gravitational kind in our daily lives. *Chemical potential energy* is stored in the gasoline that moves your car, the batteries that power your radio, a stick of dynamite (Figure 3-6b), and the food you eat. All animals depend on the chemical potential energy of food, and all living things rely on molecules that store chemical energy for future use. In each of these situations, potential energy is stored in the chemical bonds between atoms (see Chapter 9).

Wall outlets in your home and at work provide a means to tap into *electrical potential energy*, waiting to turn a fan or drive a vacuum cleaner. A tightly coiled spring, a flexed muscle (Figure 3-6c), and a stretched rubber band contain *elastic potential energy*, while a refrigerator magnet carries *magnetic potential energy*. In every case, energy is stored, ready to do work.

Heat, or Thermal Energy

Two centuries ago, scientists understood the basic behavior of kinetic and potential energy, but the nature of heat was far more mysterious. It's easy to feel and measure the effects of heat, but what are the physical causes underlying the behavior of hot and cold objects?

We now know that all matter is made of minute objects called *atoms*, which often clump together into discrete collections of two or more atoms called *molecules*. We'll examine details of the structure and behavior of atoms and molecules, which are much too small to be seen with an ordinary light microscope, in Chapters 8 through 10. A key discovery regarding these minute particles is that the properties of all the materials in our environment depend on their constituent atoms and how they're linked together. The contrast between solid ice, liquid water, and gaseous steam, all of which are made from molecules of three atoms (two hydrogen atoms linked to one oxygen atom, or H_2O), for example, is a consequence of how strongly adjacent atoms or molecules interact with each other (Chapter 10).

The key to understanding the nature of heat is that all atoms and molecules are in constant random motion. These particles that make up all matter move around and vibrate, and therefore these particles possess kinetic energy. The tiny forces that they exert only affect other atoms and molecules, but the small scale doesn't make the forces any less real. If molecules in a material begin to move more rapidly, then they have more kinetic energy and are capable of exerting greater forces on each other in collisions. If you touch an object whose molecules are moving fast, then the collisions of those molecules with molecules in your hand will exert greater force, and you will perceive the object to be hot. By contrast, if the molecules in your hand are moving faster than those of the object you touch, then you will perceive the object to be cold. What we normally call **heat**, therefore, is simply **thermal energy**—the random kinetic energy of atoms and molecules.

SCIENCE IN THE MAKING
Discovering the Nature of Heat

What is heat? How would you apply the scientific method to determine its origins? That was the problem facing scientists 200 years ago.

In many respects, they realized, heat behaves like a fluid. It flows from place to place, and it seems to spread out evenly like water that has been spilled on the floor. Some objects soak up heat faster than others, and many materials seem to swell up when heated, just like water-logged wood. Thus, in 1800, after years of observations and experiments, many physicists mistakenly accepted the theory that heat is an invisible fluid—they called it "caloric." According to the caloric theory of heat, the best fuels, such as coal, are saturated with caloric, while ice is virtually devoid of the substance.

One of the most influential investigators of heat was the Massachusetts-born Benjamin Thompson (1752–1814), who led a remarkably adventurous life. At the age of 19 he married an extremely wealthy widow, 14 years his senior. He sided with the British during the Revolutionary War, first working as a spy, then as an officer in the British Army of Occupation in New York. After the Americans won the war, Thompson abandoned his wife and infant daughter and fled to Europe, where he was knighted by King George III. Later in his turbulent life he was forced to flee England on suspicion of spying for the French, and he eventually wound up in the employ of the Elector of Bavaria, where his duties included the manufacture and machining of cannons.

If heat is a fluid, then each object must contain a fixed quantity of that substance. But Thompson noted that the increase in temperature that accompanies boring a cannon had nothing at all to do with the quantity of brass to be drilled (Figure 3-7). Sharp tools, he found, cut brass quickly with minimum heat generation, while dull tools made slow progress and produced prodigious amounts of heat.

Thompson proposed an alternative hypothesis. He suggested that the increase in temperature in the brass was a consequence of the mechanical energy of friction, not some theoretical, invisible fluid. He proved his point by immersing an entire cannon boring machine in water, turning it on, and watching the heat that was generated turn the water to steam. British chemist and popular science lecturer Sir Humphry Davy (1778–1829) further dramatized Thompson's point when he generated heat by rubbing pieces of ice together on a cold London day.

The work of Thompson, Davy, and others inspired English researcher James Prescott Joule to devise a special experiment to test the predictions of the rival theories. As shown in Figure 3-8, Joule's apparatus employed a weight that was lifted up and attached to a rope. The rope turned a paddle wheel immersed in a tub of water. The weight had gravitational potential energy, and, as it fell, that energy was converted into kinetic energy of the rotating paddle. The paddle wheel's kinetic energy, in turn, was transferred to kinetic energy of water molecules. As Joule suspected, the water heated up by an amount equal to the gravitational potential energy released by the weights. Heat, he declared, is just another form of energy.

FIGURE 3-7 Benjamin Thompson, Count Rumford, in a Bavarian cannon foundry in 1798, calling attention to the transformation of mechanical energy into heat.

FIGURE 3-8 Joule's experiment demonstrated that heat is another form of energy by showing that the kinetic energy of a paddle wheel is transferred to thermal energy of the agitated water.

Wave Energy

Anyone who has watched surf battering the seashore has firsthand knowledge of **wave energy**. In the case of water waves, the type of energy involved is obvious. Large amounts of water are in rapid motion and therefore possess kinetic energy. It is this energy that we see released when waves hit the shore.

Other kinds of waves possess energy, as well. For example, when a *sound wave* is generated, molecules in the air are set in motion and the energy of the sound wave is associated with the kinetic energy of those molecules. Similar sound waves traveling through the solid Earth, called *seismic waves,* can carry the potentially destructive energy that is unleashed in earthquakes (see Chapter 17). In Chapter 6 we will meet another important kind of wave, the kind associated with electromagnetic radiation, such as the radiant energy (light) that streams from the Sun. This kind of wave stores its energy in changing electrical and magnetic fields. Thus, each type of wave possesses one of the forms of energy that we have been discussing. Because different types of waves have many similarities, as we shall discuss in Chapter 6, we group them together here.

Mass as Energy

The discovery that certain atoms, such as uranium, spontaneously release energy as they disintegrate—the phenomenon of radioactivity—led to the realization in the early twentieth century that mass is a form of energy. This principle is the focus of Chapter 7, but the main idea is summarized in Albert Einstein's most famous equation.

In words: Every object at rest contains potential energy equivalent to the product of its mass times a constant, which is the speed of light squared.

In equation form:

$$\text{energy (joules)} = \text{mass (kg)} \times [\text{speed of light (m/s)}]^2$$

In symbols:

$$E = mc^2$$

where c is the symbol for the speed of light, a constant equal to 300,000,000 meters per second (3×10^8 m/s).

This equation, which has achieved the rank of a cultural icon, tells us that it is possible to transform mass into energy and to use energy to create mass. (Note: This equation does not mean the mass has to be traveling at the speed of light; the mass is assumed to be at rest.) Furthermore, because the speed of light is so great, the energy stored in even a tiny amount of mass is enormous.

EXAMPLE 3-4

LOTS OF POTENTIAL

According to Einstein's equation, how much potential energy is contained in the mass of a grain of sand with a mass of 0.001 gram?

Reasoning and Solution: Substitute the mass, 0.001 gram, into Einstein's famous equation. Remember that 1 gram is a thousandth of a kilogram, so a thousandth of a gram equals a millionth of a kilogram (10^{-6} kg). Also, the speed of light is a constant, 3×10^8 m/s.

$$\begin{aligned}
\text{energy (joules)} &= \text{mass (kg)} \times [\text{speed of light (m/s)}]^2 \\
&= 10^{-6} \text{ kg} \times (3 \times 10^8 \text{ m/s})^2 \\
&= 10^{-6} \times (9 \times 10^{16} \text{ kg-m}^2/\text{s}^2) \\
&= 9 \times 10^{10} \text{ joules}
\end{aligned}$$

The energy contained in the mass of a single grain of sand is prodigious: almost 100 billion joules, which is 25,000 kilowatt-hours. The average American family uses about 1000 kilowatt-hours of electricity per month, so a sand grain—if we had the means to convert its mass entirely to electrical energy (which we don't)—could satisfy your home's energy needs for the next 2 years!

In practical terms, Einstein's equation showed that mass could be used to generate electricity in nuclear power plants, in which a few pounds of nuclear fuel is enough to power an entire city.

● 3.3 The Interchangeability of Energy

You know from everyday experience that energy can be changed from one form to another (Table 3-2 and Figure 3-9). Plants absorb light streaming from the Sun and convert that radiant energy into the stored chemical energy of cells and plant tissues. You eat plants and convert the

TABLE 3-2 **Some Forms of Energy**

Potential Energy	Kinetic Energy	Other
Gravitational	Moving objects	Mass
Chemical	Heat	
Elastic	Sound and other waves	
Electromagnetic		

chemical energy into the kinetic energy of your muscles—energy of motion that in turn can be converted into gravitational potential energy when you climb a flight of stairs, elastic potential energy when you stretch a rubber band, or heat when you rub your hands together. The lesson from these examples is clear.

Andy Washnik

FIGURE 3-9 A Slinky provides a dramatic example of energy changing from one form to another. Can you identify some of the kinds of energy changes involved?

● **The many different forms of energy are interchangeable.**

Energy in one form can be converted into others.

Bungee jumping provides a dramatic illustration of this rule (Figure 3-10). Bungee jumpers climb to a high bridge or platform, where elastic cords are attached to their ankles. Then they launch themselves into space and fall toward the ground until the cords stretch, slow them down, and stop their fall.

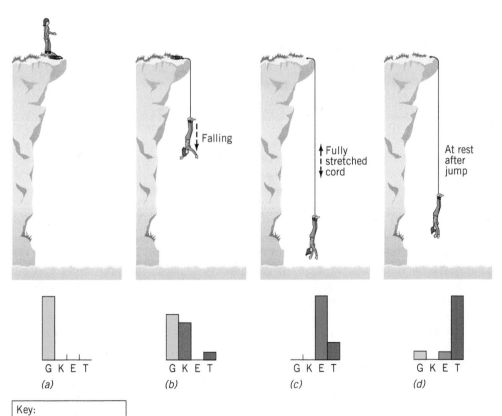

FIGURE 3-10 Energy changes form during a bungee jump, though the total energy is constant. Histograms display the distribution of energy among gravitational potential (G), kinetic (K), elastic potential (E), and thermal (T). Initially (a), all of the energy to be used in the jump is stored as gravitational potential energy. During the descent (b), the gravitational potential energy is converted to kinetic energy. At the bottom of the jump, the bungee cord stretches (c), so that most energy is in the form of elastic potential. At the end of the jump (d) most of the energy winds up as heat.

Key:
G = gravitational
K = kinetic
E = elastic potential
T = thermal

From an energy point of view, a bungee jumper uses the chemical potential energy generated from food to walk up to the launching platform. The work that had been done against gravity provides the jumper with gravitational potential energy. During the long descent, the gravitational potential energy diminishes, while the jumper's kinetic energy simultaneously increases. As the cords begin to stretch, the jumper slows down and kinetic energy gradually is converted to stored elastic potential energy in the cords. Eventually, the gravitational potential energy that the jumper had at the beginning is completely transferred to the stretched elastic cords, which then rebound, converting some of the stored elastic energy back into kinetic energy and gravitational potential energy. All the time, some of the energy is also converted to thermal energy: increased temperature in the stressed cord, on the jumper's ankles, and the air as it is pushed aside.

One of the most fundamental properties of the universe in which we live is that every form of energy on our list can be converted to every other form of energy.

THE SCIENCE OF LIFE
Energy for Life and Trophic Levels

All of Earth's systems, both living and nonliving, transform the Sun's radiant energy into other forms. Just how much energy is available, and how is it used by living organisms?

At the top of Earth's atmosphere, the Sun's incoming energy is 1400 watts per square meter. To calculate the total energy of this solar power, we first need to calculate Earth's cross-sectional area in square meters. Earth's radius is 6375 kilometers (6,375,000 meters), and so the cross-sectional area is

$$
\begin{aligned}
\text{area of a circle} &= \text{pi} \times (\text{radius})^2 \\
&= 3.14 \times (6{,}375{,}000 \text{ m})^2 \\
&= 1.28 \times 10^{14} \text{ m}^2
\end{aligned}
$$

Thus the total power received at the top of Earth's atmosphere is

$$
\begin{aligned}
\text{power} &= \text{solar energy per m}^2 \times \text{Earth's cross-sectional area} \\
&= 1400 \text{ watts/m}^2 \times 1.28 \times 10^{14} \text{ m}^2 \\
&= 1.79 \times 10^{17} \text{ watts}
\end{aligned}
$$

Each second, the top of Earth's atmosphere receives 1.79×10^{17} joules of energy, but that is more than twice the amount that reaches the ground. When solar radiation encounters the top of the atmosphere, about 25% of it is immediately reflected back into space. Another 25% is absorbed by gases in the atmosphere, and Earth's surface reflects an additional 5% back into space. These processes leave about 45% of the initial amount to be absorbed at Earth's surface.

All living systems take their energy from this 45% but absorb only a small portion of this amount—only about 4% to run photosynthesis and supply the entire food chain. A much larger portion heats the ground or air, or evaporates water from lakes, rivers, and oceans.

The concept of the food chain and its trophic levels is particularly useful when tracking the many changes of energy as it flows through living systems of Earth. A **trophic level** consists of all organisms that get their energy from the same source (Figure 3-11). In this ranking scheme, all plants that produce energy from photosynthesis are in the *first trophic level*. These plants all absorb energy from sunlight and use it to drive chemical reactions that make plant tissues and other complex molecules subsequently used as energy sources by organisms in higher trophic levels.

The *second trophic level* includes all *herbivores*—animals that get their energy by eating plants of the first trophic level. Cows, rabbits, and many insects occupy this level. The *third trophic level*, as you might expect, consists of *carnivores*—animals that get their energy by eating organisms in the second trophic level. This third level includes such familiar animals as wolves, eagles, and lions, as well as insect-eating birds, blood-sucking ticks and mosquitoes, and many other organisms.

A few more groups of organisms fill out the scheme of trophic levels on Earth. Carnivores that eat other carnivores, such as killer whales, occupy the fourth trophic level. Termites,

Fourth trophic level

Third trophic level

Second trophic level

First trophic level

FIGURE 3-11 The food chain. Living organisms are arranged in trophic levels according to how they obtain energy. The first trophic level consists of plants that produce energy from photosynthesis. In the higher trophic levels, animals get their energy by feeding on organisms from the next lowest level.

vultures, and a host of bacteria and fungi get their energy from feeding on dead organisms and are generally placed in a trophic level separate from the four we have just described. (The usual convention is that this trophic level is not given a number because the dead organisms can come from any of the other trophic levels.)

A number of animals and plants span the trophic levels. Human beings, raccoons, and bears, for example, are *omnivores* that gain energy from plants and from organisms in other trophic levels, while the Venus flytrap is a green plant that supplements its diet with trapped insects.

STOP & THINK From which trophic levels did you obtain energy during the past 24 hours?

Although you might expect it to be otherwise, the efficiency with which solar energy is used by Earth's organisms is very low, despite the struggle by all these organisms to use energy efficiently. When sunlight falls, for example, on a cornfield in the middle of Iowa in August—arguably one of the best situations in the world for plant growth—only a small percentage of the solar energy striking the field is actually transformed as chemical energy in the plants. All the rest of the energy is reflected, heats up the soil, evaporates water, or performs some other function. It is a general rule that no plants anywhere transform as much as 10% of solar energy available to them.

The same situation applies to trophic levels above the first. Typically, less than 10% of a plant's chemical potential energy winds up as tissue in the animal of the second trophic level that eats the plants. That is, less than about 1% (10% of 10%) of the original energy in sunlight is transformed into chemical energy of the second trophic level. Continuing with the same pattern, animals in the third trophic level also use less than 10% of the energy available from the second level.

You can do a rough verification of this statement in your supermarket. Whole grains (those that have not been processed heavily) typically cost about one-tenth as much per pound as fresh meat. Examined from an energy point of view, this cost differential is not surprising. It takes 10 times as much energy to make a pound of beef as it does to make a pound of wheat or rice, and this fact is reflected in the price.

One of the most interesting examples of energy flow through trophic levels can be seen in the fossils of dinosaurs. In many museum exhibits, the most dramatic and memorable specimen is a giant carnivore—a *Tyrannosaurus* or *Allosaurus* with 6-inch dagger teeth and powerful claws. So often are these impressive skeletons illustrated that you might get the impression that these finds are common. In fact, fossil carnivores are extremely rare and represent only a small fraction of known dinosaur specimens. Our knowledge of the fearsome *Tyrannosaurus,* for example, is based on only about a dozen skeletons, and most of those are quite fragmentary. By contrast, paleontologists have found hundreds of skeletons of plant-eating dinosaurs. This distribution is hardly chance. Carnivorous dinosaurs, like modern lions and tigers, were relatively scarce compared to their herbivorous victims. In fact, statistical studies of all dinosaur skeletons reveal a roughly ten-to-one herbivore-to-carnivore ratio, a value approaching what we find today for the ratio of warm-blooded herbivores to warm-blooded carnivores, and much higher than the herbivore-to-carnivore ratio observed in modern cold-blooded reptiles. Many paleontologists cite this pattern as evidence that dinosaurs were warm-blooded.

◎ 3.4 The First Law of Thermodynamics: Energy Is Conserved

Scientists are always on the lookout for attributes of the ever-changing universe that are constant and unchanging. If the total number of atoms, electrons, or electrical charges is constant, then that attribute is said to be conserved. Any statement that an attribute is *conserved* is called a **conservation law**. (Note that these meanings of "conserved" and "conservation" are different from the more common uses of the words associated with modest consumption and recycling.)

Before describing the conservation law that relates to energy, we must first introduce the idea of a system. You can think of a **system** as an imaginary box into which you put some matter and some energy that you would like to study. Scientists might want to study a system containing only a pan of water, or one consisting of a forest, or even the entire planet Earth. Doctors examine your nervous system, astronomers explore the solar system, and biologists observe a variety of ecosystems. In each case, the investigation of nature is simplified by focusing on one small part of the universe.

If the system under study can exchange matter and energy with its surroundings—a pan full of water that is heated on a stove and gradually evaporates, for example—then it is an *open system* (Figure 3-12a). An open system is like an open box where you can take things out and put things back in. Alternatively, if matter and energy in a system do not freely exchange with their surroundings, as in a tightly shut box, then the system is said to be *closed* or isolated. Earth and its primary source of energy, the Sun, together make a system that may be thought of for most purposes as closed, because no significant amounts of matter or energy being are added from outside sources (Figure 3-12b).

The most important conservation law in the sciences is the law of *conservation of energy*. This law is also called the **first law of thermodynamics**. (*Thermodynamics*—literally the study

FIGURE 3-12 An open system is like an open box *(a)* where heat energy and matter can be added or removed. Alternatively, if matter and energy in a system do not freely exchange with their surroundings, as in a tightly shut box *(b)*, then the system is said to be closed or isolated.

Open system

Closed system

(a)

(b)

of the movement of heat—is a term used for the science of heat, energy, and work.) The law can be stated as follows:

● **In an isolated system the total amount of energy, including heat, is conserved.**

This law tells us that, although the kind of energy in a given system can change, the total amount cannot. For example, when a bungee jumper hurls herself into space, the gravitational potential energy she had at the beginning of the fall is converted to an equal amount of other kinds of energy. When she's moving, some of the gravitational potential energy changes into kinetic energy, some into elastic potential energy, and some into the increased temperature of the surroundings. At each point during the fall, however, the sum of kinetic, elastic potential, gravitational potential, and heat energies has to be the same as the gravitational energy at the beginning.

Energy is something like an economy with an absolutely fixed amount of money. You can earn it, store it in a bank or under your pillow, and spend it here and there when you want to. But the total amount of money doesn't change just because it passes through your hands. Likewise, in any physical situation you can shuffle energy from one place to another. You could take it out of the account labeled "kinetic" and put it into the account labeled "potential;" you could spread it around into accounts labeled "chemical potential," "elastic potential," "heat," and so on; but the first law of thermodynamics tells us that, in a closed system, you can never have more or less energy than you started with.

SCIENCE BY THE NUMBERS
Diet and Calories

The first law of thermodynamics has a great deal to say about the American obsession with weight and diet. Human beings take in energy with their food, energy we usually measure in *calories*. (Note that the calorie we talk about in foods is defined as the amount of energy needed to raise the temperature of a kilogram of water by 1° Celsius, a unit we will later call a kilocalorie.) When a certain amount of energy is taken in, the first law says that only one of two things can happen to it: it can be converted into work and a corresponding increase in the temperature of the surroundings, or it can be stored. If we take in more energy than we expend, the excess is stored in fat. If, on the other hand, we take in less than we expend, energy must be removed from storage to meet the deficit, and the amount of body fat decreases.

Here are a couple of rough rules you can use to calculate calories in your diet:

1. Under most circumstances, normal body maintenance uses up about 15 calories per day for each pound of body weight.

2. You must consume about 3500 calories to gain a pound of fat.

Suppose you weigh 150 pounds. To keep your weight constant, you have to take in

$$150 \text{ pounds} \times 15 \text{ calories/pound} = 2250 \text{ calories per day}$$

If you wanted to lose one pound (3500 calories) a week (7 days), you would have to reduce your daily calorie intake by

$$\frac{3500 \text{ calories}}{7 \text{ days}} = 500 \text{ calories per day}$$

Another way of saying this is that you would have to reduce your calorie intake to 1750 calories—the equivalent of skipping dessert every day.

Alternatively, the first law says you can increase your energy use through exercise. Roughly speaking, to burn off 500 calories you would have to run 5 miles, bike 15 miles, or swim for an hour.

It's a whole lot easier to refrain from eating than to burn off the weight by exercise. In fact, most researchers now say that the main benefit of exercise in weight control has to do with its ability to help people control their appetites.

SCIENCE IN THE MAKING
Lord Kelvin and Earth's Age

The first law of thermodynamics provided physicists with a powerful tool for describing and analyzing their universe. Every isolated system, the law tells us, has a fixed amount of energy. Naturally, one of the first systems that scientists considered was the Sun and Earth.

British physicist William Thomson (1824–1907), ennobled as Lord Kelvin (Figure 3-13), asked a simple question: How much energy could be stored inside Earth? And, given the present rate at which energy radiates out into space, how old might Earth be? Though simple, these questions had profound implications for philosophers and theologians who had their own ideas about Earth's relative antiquity. Some biblical scholars believed that Earth could be no more than a few thousand years old. Most geologists, on the other hand, saw evidence in layered rocks to suggest an Earth at least hundreds of millions of years old. Biologists also required vast amounts of time to account for the gradual evolution of life on Earth. Who was correct?

Kelvin assumed, as did most of his contemporaries, that Earth had formed from a contracting cloud of interstellar dust (see Chapter 16). He thought that Earth began as a hot body because impacts of large objects on it early in its history must have converted huge amounts of gravitational potential energy into thermal energy. He used new developments in mathematics to calculate how long it took for a hot Earth to cool to its present temperature. He assumed that there were no sources of energy inside Earth, and he found that Earth's age had to be less than about 100 million years. He soundly rejected the geologists' and biologists' claims of an older Earth because these claims seemed to violate the first law of thermodynamics.

Seldom have scientists come to such a bitter impasse. Two competing theories about Earth's age, each supported by seemingly sound observations, were at odds. The calculations of the physicist seemed unassailable, yet the observations of biologists and geologists in the field were equally meticulous. What could possibly resolve the dilemma? Had the scientific method failed? The solution came from a totally unexpected source when scientists discovered in the 1890s that rocks hold a previously unknown source of energy, radioactivity (see Chapter 11), in which thermal energy is generated by the conversion of mass. Lord Kelvin's rigorous age calculations were in error only because he and his contemporaries were unaware of this critical component of Earth's energy budget. Earth's deep interior, we now know, gains approximately half of its thermal energy from radioactive decay. Revised calculations suggest an Earth several billions of years old, in conformity with geological and biological observations.

FIGURE 3-13 William Thomson, Lord Kelvin (1824–1907).

● 3.5 The United States and Its Energy Future

The growth of modern technological societies since the Industrial Revolution has been driven by the availability of cheap, high-grade sources of energy. When fuel wood became expensive and scarce at the end of the eighteenth century, men like James Watt figured out how to tap into the solar energy stored in coal. In the early twentieth century, the development of the internal combustion engine and other new technologies made petroleum the fuel of choice. Both of these transitions took about 30 years.

Fuels like *oil (petroleum)*, *coal*, and *natural* gas are called *fossil fuels* because they are the result of processes that happened long ago. As you can see from Figure 3-14, the economy of the United States today depends almost completely on the burning of fossil fuels. This state of affairs leads to two difficult problems. One characteristic of fossil fuels is that they are not replaceable—once you burn a ton of coal or a barrel of oil, it is gone as far as any timescale meaningful to human beings is concerned. Another characteristic, as we shall discuss in Chapter 19, is that inevitably adds burning fossil fuels is the addition of carbon dioxide to the atmosphere. This change in the atmosphere's composition, in turn, may lead to significant global warming. Thus, the search for alternate energy sources to drive our economy is well under way.

Renewable Energy Sources

Renewable energy sources, as the name implies, are not "used up" when they are consumed because they are constantly being replaced. The two most important alternate energy sources being considered these days are solar energy and wind. Neither contributes to global warming, and both are considered to be part of the process of weaning ourselves from fossil fuels. The energy in the wind comes, ultimately, from the Sun and the rotation of Earth, while solar energy comes directly from the Sun. In addition, because of the large part of our energy resource devoted to transportation, we should consider ethanol, whose energy derives from plants, as another type of renewable energy. Like any other energy sources, each of these options has both positive and negative aspects.

The question of when these energy sources will be available in commercially useful quantities is a complicated mix of technology and economics. As an example, think about generating electricity from these sources. Commercial electrical generation in the United States can be divided into two types—*base-load* and *peak-load*. Base-load is electricity that has to be delivered day in and day out to run essential services such as lighting and manufacturing. Peak-load refers to the extra electricity that has to be delivered on, for example, a hot day when everyone turns on his or her air conditioner. Typically, base-load power is delivered by large coal or nuclear plants. These plants are expensive to build, but since the construction cost is spread out over a long time period, the net cost per kilowatt-hour is low. Peak-load, on the other hand, is typically delivered by systems such as gas turbines. These plants are cheap to build but expensive to operate because they typically use more expensive fuels. Thus, peak-load electricity is usually more expensive than base-load power. (You probably don't see this difference in your electricity bill because the costs are folded together). Thus, the best place for alternate energy sources to enter the economy is in the peak-load market.

U.S Energy Consumption by Energy Source, 2011

Total: 97.5 quadrillion Btu

Total: 9 quadrillion Btu

Petroleum 36%
Coal 20%
Renewable Energy 9%
Nuclear Electric Power 8%
Natural Gas 25%

Solar 1%
Geothermal 2%
Wind 13%
Biomass waste 5%
Biofuels 21%
Wood 22%
Hydropower 35%
Biomass 48%

Source: U.S. Energy Information Administration, *Monthly Energy Review*, Table 10.1 (March 2012), preliminary 2011 data.

FIGURE 3-14 Sources of energy for the United States and other industrial nations. Note that most of our energy comes from fossil fuels.

Wind Energy

The United States has a huge wind resource. The "wind belt" stretching from the Dakotas south to New Mexico is one place where strong, steady winds blow, but there are others as well. Mountain passes and offshore location like Cape Cod and the eastern shore of Lakes Michigan and Erie have all been proposed as sites for wind farms. As we shall see in Chapter 18, the energy sources for winds on Earth's surface are incoming sunlight and the rotation of the planet, so the energy in the wind is, for all practical purposes, inexhaustible.

When modern windmills began being erected in the 1970s and 1980s, the electricity they generated was quite expensive—as much as 10 to 20 times as expensive as electricity generated by coal. Over the years, however, improvements in design and engineering have brought this cost down to the point that today the cost of wind-generated electricity is comparable to peak load costs for electricity generated by conventional means. This improvement in engineering, as well as government support for renewable energy, is why you are seeing wind farms going up all over the place (Figure 3-15).

Calculations indicate that it would be theoretically possible to produce all of America's electrical energy from wind. It would, however, require that a windmill be built every quarter mile across the entire states of North and South Dakota. Most analysts argue that a much more likely scenario is that wind farms will be built in many places, but that other forms of energy generation will continue to play a role in the future.

Solar Energy

Just as the United States has a huge wind resource, it also has a huge solar resource—just think of the deserts of the American Southwest. Enormous amounts of energy in the form of sunlight fall on these places, and the problem is to find ways to tap that energy at a reasonable cost.

FIGURE 3-15 Electricity generated from this sort of wind turbine is starting to become economically competitive in the United States.

ML. Sinibaldi/© Corbis

(a) (b) (c)

FIGURE 3-16 Solar photovoltaic panels can be used in many ways. Relatively small panels can be used to power traffic signs (a), while larger arrays of panels can be put on a roof to provide energy for an individual house (b). Finally, extensive arrays of solar panels can be used to generate electricity at the commercial level (c).

Two different methods are being developed for converting the energy of sunlight into electricity. One of these methods, termed *solar photovoltaic*, involves the use of semiconductors to convert sunlight directly into electric current. (The details of how this technique works will be discussed in Chapter 11.) This process produces the familiar racks of black circles we see on solar installations. Photovoltaic cells can be used for small installations, such as traffic signs, on rooftops, or in large arrays (Figure 3-16).

The other technique being developed is called *thermal solar energy* (Figure 3-17). In these systems, sunlight is collected and focused by mirrors, then used to heat a fluid. This heated fluid is used to run a large electrical generator of the type we will describe in Chapter 5, typically by producing steam. An electrical generating plant of this type has been run in the California desert for many years.

The cost of solar energy depends, to a certain extent, on the location of the solar collector, since the farther north you go the less sunlight is available. Roughly speaking, today solar electricity costs at least five times more than that generated by coal, and analysts do not expect either form of solar energy to become competitive with large-scale conventional generating plants before 2030. What scientists call "end-use" solar energy (on individual rooftops, for example) may expand before that time, however. As was the case with wind, solar energy will most likely enter the market to supply peak load power on days when the Sun is hot and all those air conditioners are on.

It is estimated that we could generate all of America's electricity needs by covering an area roughly the size of Massachusetts with solar panels. As is the case with wind, though, most analysts think that the Sun will be one of many different energy sources in our country's future.

FIGURE 3-17 In this solar thermal facility in Barstow, California, mirrors reflect sunlight to a tall tower, where the concentrated energy is used to create steam to run an electrical generator.

STOP & THINK You often see highway signs and traffic counters being powered by solar cells. Given the high cost of solar energy, why do you suppose these devices are used even in areas where it would be easy to hook up to the ordinary electrical power grid?

Ethanol

When you go to a gas station, you may notice a sign on the pump informing you that the fuel contains 10% ethanol. Ethanol is a form of alcohol. It is the same substance found in wine and other alcoholic drinks, and can be used as a fuel in internal combustion engines. In the United States, Congress has mandated that a certain percentage of ethanol be mixed with all motor fuels, mainly because ethanol is made from crops like corn rather than foreign oil.

The ethanol you buy at the gas station is usually made from corn grown in America's massive corn belt. The fact that it is made from the corn kernels leads to one of the most frequent criticisms of the use of ethanol as a fuel—the fact that this use competes with the use of corn as food for humans and feed for animals. At the moment there is no way around this dilemma. Agricultural land can be used only for one use or the other. Scientists at places like National Renewable Energy Laboratory in Colorado, however, are trying to find ways to convert the non-edible parts of plants into what is called *cellulosic ethanol*. This type of fuel is identical to the stuff that is mixed with gasoline at your service station, but does not compete with the use of the plant for food. These research efforts, which may include genetically engineered bacteria (see Chapter 24), could remove the major objection to the use of ethanol as a fuel.

Problems with Renewable Energy Systems

Solar energy (and, to a lesser extent, wind energy) is by its nature intermittent—that is, the Sun doesn't always shine and the wind doesn't always blow. In particular, solar energy is not available at night, and it is often the case that peak wind speeds at a given site do not coincide with peak load electricity use. This situation means that any system that derives a large part of its electricity from capturing these types of energy will have to include some sort of storage mechanism, so that energy collected during a sunny day (for example) can be used the next night or during cloudy days. At the moment, the most economical and efficient storage systems involve a process by which water is pumped uphill when the Sun is shining or the wind is blowing and then run downhill to generate electricity. Other scientists are trying to develop massive batteries to do the same job. There is even a pilot solar plant in Spain in which solar electricity is used to pump compressed air into an underground cavern, and the air is then released to run turbines during the night. The need for storage will obviously increase the cost of both solar and wind energy. This is a problem that is just starting to be addressed by engineers.

Transportation and Energy Use

A major area of energy use in the United States is in transportation, which consumes about a third of the country's energy budget. Much of this energy is used to run gasoline-powered internal combustion engines (ICEs) in cars and trucks. Two of the leading contenders to replace the ICE are hybrids and electric cars.

Hybrids A hybrid vehicle is one in which a small gasoline motor operates a generator that charges a bank of batteries that, in turn, powers an electric motor that drives the car. Because the car runs on batteries until they are discharged, at which point the ICE comes on and recharges the batteries, the car can operate with fewer batteries than are required in a fully electric vehicle. In addition, because the drive system can use the car's energy of motion during deceleration to generate electricity, a hybrid vehicle consumes much less gasoline than a conventional ICE. The first hybrid to enter the American market was the Toyota Prius, which has sold more than 5 million cars. Many other types of hybrids are now available, as well.

One of the authors (RMH) drove a hybrid for several years. The car's detailed changing display of gasoline consumption, battery charging, and the distance one can travel before the next fill-up (the "range") made driving something like a video game, in which the driver optimizes gas useage in real time by accelerating a little more slowly, coasting down hills, and other simple tricks. With a little practice it was possible to maximize the use of the battery and minimize the use of gas to achieve more than 50 miles per gallon—all using the first law of thermodynamics.

The next step in the development of this type of vehicle was the *plug-in hybrid*, a car whose batteries can be recharged each night through a cable plugged into an ordinary electrical outlet. Such a car is typically capable of traveling about 40 miles before having to switch over to using gasoline, and hence would be operated primarily in the electric mode for most commuters.

Electric cars Electric cars, which do not have an ICE, are gradually appearing on the market. Batteries power electric cars, so that their energy comes directly from the electrical power grid; however, the best current batteries don't store a lot of energy per pound of weight. It takes about 800 pounds of ordinary car batteries to store the energy found in a gallon of gasoline. Because of

Hadrian / Shutterstock

FIGURE 3-18 Electric vehicles like the Tesla employ advanced battery technology for energy storage.

this problem, the range of electric cars is typically less than 100 miles—a relatively short distance that leads to what is called "range anxiety" by engineers. This problem can be overcome, but it costs a lot. The Tesla Model S, (Figure 3-18) for example, has a range of over 200 miles but retails at $80,000.

The Joint Center for Energy Storage Research, headquartered at Argonne National Laboratories outside of Chicago is focused on developing new, high-efficiency, lightweight batteries, so we can expect to see electric cars play a bigger role in the country's transportation system in the future.

STOP & THINK Where does the energy used to recharge an electric car or a plug-in hybrid come from? What are the environmental consequences of using that energy?

THINKING MORE ABOUT **ENERGY**

Coal and Oil

All life is rich in the element carbon, which plays a key role in virtually all the chemicals that make up our cells. Life uses the Sun's energy, directly through photosynthesis or indirectly through food, to form these carbon-based substances that store chemical potential energy. When living things die, they may collect in layers at the bottoms of ponds, lakes, or oceans. Over time, as the layers become buried, Earth's temperature and pressure may alter the chemicals of life into deposits of coal and petroleum.

Geologists estimate that it takes tens of millions of years of gradual burial under layers of sediments, combined with the transforming effects of temperature and pressure, to form a coal seam or petroleum deposit. Coal forms from layer upon layer of plants that thrived in vast ancient swamps, while petroleum represents primarily the organic matter once contained in plankton, microscopic organisms that float near the ocean's surface. Although these natural processes continue today, the rate of coal and pe-

troleum formation in Earth's crust is much slower than the rate at which fossil fuels are being consumed. For this reason, fossil fuels are classified as *nonrenewable resources*.

One consequence of this situation is clear. Humans cannot continue to rely on these fossil fuels forever. Reserves of high-grade crude oil and the cleanest-burning varieties of coal may last less than 100 more years. Less efficient forms of fossil fuels, including lower grades of coal and oil shales in which petroleum is dispersed through solid rock, could be depleted within a few centuries. All the energy now locked up in those valuable energy reserves will still exist, but in the form of unusable heat radiating far into space. Given the irreversibility of burning up our fossil fuel reserves, what steps should we take to promote energy conservation? Should energy be taxed at a higher rate? Should we assume that natural gas and other energy sources will become available as they are needed?

 RETURN TO THE INTEGRATED QUESTION

Why must animals eat to stay alive?

- All living organisms need an energy source to fuel their metabolic processes, and build and maintain tissues.
  - Plants and animals acquire the necessary energy from different sources.
- All living systems on Earth ultimately derive their energy from the Sun.

- The first trophic level is comprised of photosynthetic plants that use sunlight to drive the metabolic processes necessary for survival. Therefore, since plant obtains their energy from the Sun, they do not need to eat.
  - All the energy that supports life in the other trophic levels is provided by the first trophic level (i.e., photosynthetic plants).

- The second trophic level includes animals known as herbivores. These animals cannot use sunlight as an energy source. Herbivores obtain their energy by eating the plants of the first trophic level.
- Less than 10% of the chemical potential energy in the first trophic level is transformed into the chemical energy of the second trophic level; thus, it takes ten times as much energy to produce a pound of beef as it does to produce a pound of wheat or rice.

- The third trophic level consists of carnivores. Organisms in this level eat other animals to obtain the energy necessary for survival.
- Because animals cannot use sunlight to synthesize energy, they must eat in order to obtain the chemical energy necessary to drive the metabolic processes that support life.

SUMMARY

Work, measured in *joules* (or foot-pounds), is defined as a force applied over a distance. You do work every time you move an object. Every action of our lives requires *energy* (also measured in joules), which is the ability to do work. *Power*, measured in *watts* or *kilowatts*, indicates the rate at which energy is expended.

Energy comes in several forms. *Kinetic energy* is the energy associated with moving objects such as cars or cannonballs. *Potential energy*, on the other hand, is stored, ready-to-use energy, such as the chemical energy of coal, the elastic energy of a coiled spring, the gravitational energy of dammed-up water, or the electrical energy in your wall socket. *Thermal energy* or *heat* is the form of kinetic energy associated with vibrating atoms and molecules. Energy can also take the form of *wave energy,* such as sound waves or light waves. And early in the twentieth century it was discovered that mass is also a form of energy. All around us energy constantly

shifts from one form to another, and all of these kinds of energy are interchangeable.

Energy from the Sun is used by photosynthetic plants in the first *trophic level*; these plants provide the energy for animals in higher trophic levels. Roughly speaking, only about 10% of the energy available at one trophic level finds its way to the next.

The most fundamental idea about energy, expressed in the *first law of thermodynamics*, is that it is *conserved:* the total amount of energy in an isolated *system* never changes. Energy can shift back and forth between the different kinds, but the sum of all energy is constant.

At present, most industrialized countries use fossil fuels to run their economies. Alternative sources for the future include solar and wind energy and, for transportation, hybrid and electric cars.

KEY TERMS

work (measured in joules)
energy (measured in joules)
power (measured in watts or kilowatts)
kinetic energy

potential energy
thermal energy (heat)
wave energy
trophic level

conservation law
system
first law of thermodynamics

KEY EQUATIONS

work (joules) = force (newtons) × distance (meters)
energy (joules) = power (watts) × time (seconds)
kinetic energy (joules) = $\frac{1}{2}$ mass (kg) × [speed (m/s)]^2
gravitational potential energy (joules) = g × mass (kg) × height (m)

energy associated with mass at rest (joules) × mass (kg) × [speed of light (m/s)]^2

Constant
$c = 3 \times 10^8$ m/s = speed of light

DISCOVERY LAB

Have you ever wondered how potential energy and kinetic energy affect a falling body? To see how energy is transformed, you will need bungee cords (numerous rubber bands), a stop watch, and a plastic doll, approximately 11½ inches in height. Find the mass of the doll in grams and convert it into kilograms. Convert the mass into weight by multiplying the kilograms by the gravitational constant (6.67300×10^{-11} m^3 kg^{-1} s^{-2}). Make a double-loop with the rubber band to wrap around the doll's feet. A double-loop is made by tying one rubber band to another with a slip knot. Wrap one end of the loop around the doll's feet. Hold the end of the rub-

ber bands at the jump line with one hand, and drop the doll from the line with the other hand. Through trial and error determine the number of rubber bands necessary to drop the doll from the designated height of 0.5 meters, 1.0 meters, 1.5 meters, and 2.0 meters. Only the doll's hair should touch the ground in this bungee jump. Once the correct number of rubber bands for the selected heights is determined, record the time it takes the doll to bungee to the floor. Now repeat the steps for different heights. Determine the potential energy of the doll at each height by using the equation PE = weight × height.

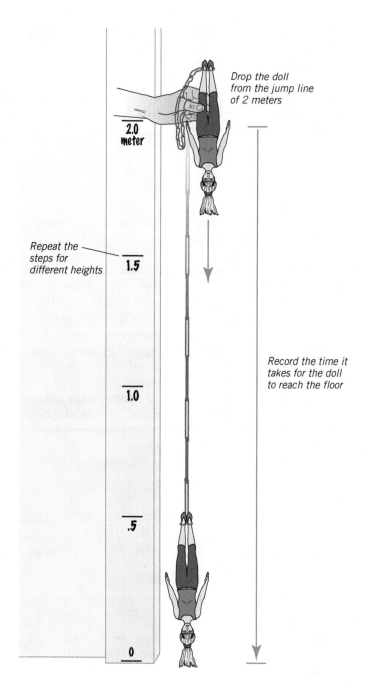

Drop the doll from the jump line of 2 meters

2.0 meter

Repeat the steps for different heights

1.5

Record the time it takes for the doll to reach the floor

1.0

.5

0

Determine the bungee jumping doll's velocity during the jumps using the following equation: V = d/t. Determine the kinetic energy of the doll using the following equation: $KE = \frac{1}{2} \times m \times v^2$. Make a graph of the number of rubber bands and jump distance.

From the data gathered, determine the number of rubber bands needed for the doll to jump from a height of 5 meters, 10 meters, 15 meters, or any other desired height. To make this more interesting, have different groups compete by dropping the doll from a height of 5 meters and check if the number of rubber bands was exact for the doll's hair to touch a large tub of water placed below the jump line.

REVIEW QUESTIONS

1. How do scientists define "work"?

2. What is a joule? What is the equivalent unit in the English system?

3. What is the difference between energy and power? What is a unit of power?

4. How do mass and speed relate to kinetic energy?

5. What is the relationship between heat, energy, and the motion of atoms?

6. Explain how sound is actually a form of energy. In what medium do sound waves travel?

7. What does it mean to say that different forms of energy are interchangeable?

8. Give examples of changes of energy from potential to kinetic and from kinetic to potential.

9. What is a trophic level? Give some examples. How much energy is lost in moving from one trophic level to the next higher level?

10. Does the total amount of energy in an isolated system change over time? Why or why not?

11. How did the discovery that mass is a form of energy resolve the debate over Earth's age?

12. Trace the flow of energy from sunlight to the electricity you use in your home.

DISCUSSION QUESTIONS

1. Imagine an everyday situation in which you could use the word "power." For instance, consider a basketball player about whom a commentator might say, "She showed a lot of power on that drive to the hoop!" How is this use of the word "power" the same or different from the scientifically accepted definition?

2. What forms of energy are used in the following activities?
  a. Bowling
  b. American football
  c. Studying for a test
  d. Weight training
  e. Eating
  f. Scuba diving

3. Why are people more likely to use solar water heaters in Israel than in Alaska?

4. Pick foods from three different food groups that you like. From what trophic level is each food? What is the energy chain that leads to each one?

5. Identify the trophic levels from which each of the following organisms takes in energy. In each case, where does the energy go?
  a. Cow
  b. Lion
  c. Fungus
  d. Chimpanzee
  e. Robin

6. What form (or forms) of energy is used in the manufacturing and use of the following common objects? In each case, where does the energy go?
  a. Computer
  b. Car
  c. Paper
  d. Shoe

7. Look up estimates for energy that could be derived from alternate sources in the United States. How does this total energy compare to current energy consumption?

8. What are fossil fuels? How are coal and oil forms of solar energy?

9. Why do you think fossil fuels are called "*fossil*" fuels? Is the origin of the energy in fossil fuels ultimately from living organisms?

10. Ancient human societies are described as labor intensive, while modern society is said to be energy intensive. What is meant by these terms?

11. Research in the field of paleoclimatology suggests that the average temperature before the extinction of the dinosaurs 65 million years ago was about 6°C higher than it is now. How do you think that may influence the debate on whether dinosaurs were warm-blooded or cold-blooded?

12. Do you think that the government should offer more incentives for people to buy hybrid and other fuel-efficient vehicles?

13. A person who prefers a meat-based diet tends to extract energy from higher levels of the trophic system. What consequences, if any, does this have on energy consumption at the national level?

14. The fastest land animal is the cheetah, which can attain a top speed in excess of 60 miles per hour. However, the cheetah can't maintain this speed for more than about 10 seconds. Why do you think that the sprint can be maintained for only a few seconds? Where does the energy go?

15. When you train with weights, you repeatedly lift a dumbbell or barbell and then return the weight to where it began. A physicist would say the total work done was zero since the weight is back to where it started. How do you reconcile that statement with the fact that your arms are now tired?

PROBLEMS

1. How much work against gravity do you perform when you walk up a flight of stairs 5 meters high (assuming that your body mass is 75 kilograms)? Compare this work to that done by a 100-watt lightbulb in an hour. How many times would you have to walk up those stairs to equal the work of the light bulb in one hour? What if the light bulb was an energy-efficient 15-watt compact fluorescent bulb?

2. Which has more gravitational potential energy: a 100-kilogram boulder 2 meters off the ground or a 1-kilogram rock 200 meters off the ground? When each is released from rest, which one will strike the ground with a higher kinetic energy?

3. Compared to a car moving at 10 miles per hour, how much more kinetic energy does that same car have when it moves at 20 miles per hour? 50? 75? Graph your results. Considering that the work necessary to stop a car goes as (Force × Distance) and the stopping force from the brakes is the same whether the car is moving at 10 miles per hour or 75 miles per hour, how much farther does a car travel coming to a halt from 75 miles per hour *versus* coming to a halt from 10 miles per hour?

4. Albert Einstein's famous equation from his Theory of Relativity, $E = mc^2$, says that mass is a form of energy. How much energy does a 70-kg adult contain? How many kilowatt·hours is this? Note that there are 3,600,000 J in 1 kilowatt·hour.

5. 1 horsepower is equivalent to 550 foot-pounds per second. How many joules is 550 foot-pounds? What does that make the power output in watts of an engine with a rating of 150 hp?

6. If you eat 600 calories per day (roughly one dessert) below your energy needs, how long would it take to lose 10 pounds? How long would you have to walk (assuming 80 calories burned per mile walked) to lose 10 pounds?

7. If the price of beef is $2.50 per pound, estimate what the price of lion meat might be, and give reasons for your prediction. Why are both forms of meat more expensive, pound for pound, than carrots?

8. What is the kinetic energy of a cheetah moving at top speed? A typical adult cheetah has a mass of 70 kg and can sprint as fast as 27 m/s.
   a. 52,000 J
   b. 945 J
   c. 25,500 J
   d. 1890 J

9. You are training with weights. You perform a biceps exercise by curling a 20-pound dumbbell with your arm. You raise the dumbbell 1.2 feet in the process. How much work in J did you do on the weight?
   a. 24 J
   b. 32.6 J
   c. 320 J
   d. 235 J

10. The Sun irradiates Earth with about 1400 Watts per square meter. Over the course of one day, how many joules of energy does each square meter receive? Assume during that particular day the Sun shines for 10 hours.
   a. 50.4 million J
   b. 840,000 J
   c. 14,000 J
   d. 5.04 million J

11. An athlete wishes to gain muscle mass. Along with weight training, she eats 3500 calories per day and finds her weight going up—largely due to muscle gain—1 pound a week. If it takes 3500 calories to build a pound of muscle, how many calories per day must this athlete eat just to maintain her weight?
   a. 2000 calories per day
   b. 2500 calories per day
   c. 3000 calories per day
   d. 3500 calories per day

INVESTIGATIONS

1. Look at your most recent electric bill and find the cost of 1 kilowatt-hour in your area. Then,
   a. Look at the back of your CD player or an appliance and find the power rating in watts. How much does it cost for you to operate the device for 1 hour?
   b. If you leave a 100-watt lightbulb on all the time, how much will you pay in a year of electric bills?
   c. If you had to pay $10 for a high-efficiency bulb that provided the same light as the 100-watt bulb with only 10 watts of power, how much would you save per year of electric bills, assuming you used the light 5 hours per day? Would it be worth your while to buy the energy-efficient bulb if the ordinary bulb cost $1 and each bulb lasts 3 years?

2. In this chapter we introduced several energy units: the joule, the foot-pound, the kilowatt-hour, and the calorie. There are other energy units as well, including the BTU, the erg, the electron-volt, and many more. Look in a science reference book for conversion factors between different pairs of energy units; you may find more than a dozen different units. Who uses each of these different units? Why are there so many different units for the same phenomenon—energy?

3. What kind of fuel is used at your local power plant? What are the implications of the first law of thermodynamics regarding our use of fossil fuels? our use of solar energy?

4. Keep a record of the calorie content of the food you eat and the amount of exercise you do for a few days. If you wanted to lose a pound per month for the next year, how might you change your current habits?

5. Look up the average energy consumption of the American household.
   a. How many times does a weight-lifter have to lift a 50-kilogram mass one meter to expend the equivalent amount of energy?
   b. How much mass would have to be converted into energy to produce this amount ($E = mc^2$)?

6. Investigate the history of the controversy between Lord Kelvin and his contemporaries regarding Earth's age. When did the debate begin? How long did it last? What kinds of evidence did biologists, geologists, and physicists use to support their differing calculations of Earth's age? Is there still a debate as to the age of the Earth?

7. Investigate and find out how your household's hot water is heated. Do you use oil, natural gas, solar, or electricity? Why do you suppose this form of energy is used in your home?

8. Rub your hands together. What conversion of energy is occurring?

9. The geyser "Old Faithful" in Yellowstone National Park sprays water and steam hundreds of feet into the air. What form of energy is being used? Will "Old Faithful" ever run out of energy?

10. Why do electric and hybrid cars cost more than other compact cars? What is the environmental impact of disposing of large numbers of batteries?

11. If you work out on a stationary bike at a power output of 100 watts for 30 minutes, does this energy output compensate for eating a 250-calorie jelly-filled doughnut? (Assume that the body converts 20% of the energy input to work and the other 80% is lost as heat and extraneous movements.) 1 food "calorie" = 1 kilocalorie; and 1 calorie = 4.2 kilojoules.

12. The next time you are in an appliance store, check out the efficiency ratings of major appliances such as dryers and dishwashers. Suppose an energy-efficient dishwasher operates at a rate 50 watts lower than a conventional dishwasher but costs $100 more. If you use the dishwasher for 1 hour each day and the electricity costs $.08 per kilowatt-hour, how long will it take to recoup the $100 difference in price? Is the dishwasher likely to last that long?

13. Both kinetic energy (this chapter) and momentum (see Chapter 2) depend on mass and velocity. Why do you think these different concepts depend on the same quantities?

14. Different parts of the United States receive varying amounts of sunshine. How much solar energy reaches the ground in your part of the country on an average summer day and an average winter day? Is solar power a possibility in your area during the summer? During the winter?

Heat and the Second Law of Thermodynamics

Why is it easier to make an omelet from an egg than to make an egg from an omelet?

PHYSICS
A pot of boiling water gradually cools as heat energy dissipates into the surroundings.

BIOLOGY
All living things grow old and die, as molecular defects in cells increase. (Ch. 22)

CHEMISTRY
The chemical energy of gasoline, once released by burning, cannot be reused.

TECHNOLOGY
Modern high-efficiency appliances are designed to minimize the production of waste heat.

GREAT IDEA
Heat is a form of energy that flows from warmer to cooler objects.

ENVIRONMENT
Violent weather, including thunderstorms and tornadoes, occurs when warmer and cooler air masses collide. (Ch. 18)

ASTRONOMY
Heat energy from the Sun flows outward from its core, first by conduction, then convection, then radiation. (Ch. 14)

HEALTH & SAFETY
Living organisms have different strategies for controlling the flow of heat in their bodies.

GEOLOGY
Volcanoes transfer heat energy from Earth's interior. (Ch. 17)

 = applications of the great idea discussed in this chapter

 = other applications, some of which are discussed in other chapters

A Hot Breakfast

Woody Stock/Alamy

Time for a hearty breakfast. You scramble eggs, squeeze some fresh juice, toast a muffin, and brew a pot of coffee. As you prepare the meal, you notice an obvious but extraordinary fact: nature seems to have a direction. Many events in daily life progress only one way in time. It's easy to scramble eggs but impossible to unscramble them. You can squeeze juice from a piece of fruit, but never unsqueeze it. Toast can't be untoasted and coffee can't be unbrewed.

But why should this be? Nothing in Newton's laws of motion or the law of gravity suggests that events work only in one way. Nothing that we have learned about energy explains the directionality of nature.

As you drink your cold juice and hot coffee, you realize that food and drinks that are very hot or very cold display a similar kind of direction. A glass of ice-cold juice gradually gets warmer, while a cup of steaming hot coffee soon cools. Heat spreads out uniformly.

These everyday events are so familiar that we take them for granted, yet underlying the scrambling of an egg and the cooling of a hot drink is one of nature's most subtle and fascinating laws: the second law of thermodynamics.

◉ 4.1 Nature's Direction

Think about the dozens of directional events that happen every day. A drop of perfume quickly pervades an entire room with scent, but you'd be hard pressed to collect all those perfume molecules into a single drop again. Your dorm room seems to get messy in the course of the week all by itself, but it takes time and effort to clean it up. And you constantly experience the inevitable, irreversible process of aging.

The first law of thermodynamics—conservation of energy—in no way prohibits events from progressing in the "wrong" direction. For example, when you cook a hard-boiled egg, heat energy from your stove is converted into the chemical potential energy of the cooked egg. According to the first law of thermodynamics, the energy that was added to cook the egg is exactly the same as the energy that would be released if you could uncook the egg. The energy of a room with perfume molecules dispersed throughout is the same as the energy of the room with those molecules tightly bottled. And the energy that went into strewing things about your room is exactly the same energy it takes to reverse the process and put everything back again. Yet there seems to be some natural tendency for things to become less orderly with time.

This directionality in nature can be traced, ultimately, to the behavior of the minute particles called atoms and molecules that form all materials. If you hold an object in your hand, for example, its atoms are moving at more or less the same average speed. If you introduce one more atom into this collection, an atom that is moving much faster than any of its neighbors, you will have a situation in which many atoms move slowly and one atom moves rapidly.

Over the course of time, the fast atom will collide again and again with the others. In each collision it will probably lose some of its energy, much as a fast-moving billiard ball slows down

FIGURE 4-1 The second law of thermodynamics tells us that it is easier to tear something down than to build it. This law is shown dramatically in this sequence of photos showing the demolition of an apartment building.

after it collides with a couple of other billiard balls. If you wait long enough, the fast-moving atom will share its energy with all the other atoms. Consequently, every atom in the collection will be moving slightly faster than those in the original collection, and there will be no single fast atom.

If you watch this collection of atoms for a long period of time, it's extremely unlikely that the collisions will ever arrange themselves in such a way that one atom moves very fast in a collection of very slow ones. In the language of the physicists, the original state with only one fast atom is highly improbable. Over the course of time, any unlikely initial state will evolve into a more probable state—a situation like the one in which all the atoms have approximately the same energy.

The tendency of all systems to evolve from improbable to more probable states accounts for the directionality that we see in the universe around us (Figure 4-1). There's no reason from the point of view of energy alone that improbable situations can't occur. Fifteen slow-moving billiard balls have enough energy to produce one fast-moving ball. The fact that this situation doesn't occur in nature is an important clue as to how things work at the atomic level.

Nineteenth-century scientists discovered the underlying reasons for nature's directionality by studying heat, which is a consequence of the motion of atoms and molecules. Before dealing with the details of these discoveries, as summarized in the second law of thermodynamics, let's consider some properties of heat.

◉ 4.2 Coming to Terms with Heat

Atoms never sit still. They are always moving, and in the process they distribute their kinetic energy—what we call *thermal energy,* or *internal energy.* If you have ever tried to warm a house during a cold winter day, you have practical experience of this fact. If you turn off the furnace, the energy in the house gradually leaks away to the outside, and the house begins to get cold. The only way you can keep the house warm is to keep adding more thermal energy. Similarly, our bodies constantly produce energy to maintain our core body temperature close to 98.6 degrees Fahrenheit (37°C). Both your furnace and your body produce energy on the inside—energy that will inevitably flow to the outside as heat. You use that heat on the fly, as it were.

In order to understand the nature of heat and its movement, we need to define three closely related terms: heat, temperature, and specific heat capacity.

Heat and Temperature

In everyday conversation we often use the words "temperature" and "heat" interchangeably, but to scientists the words have different meanings. Heat is a form of energy that moves from a warmer object to a cooler object; heat is thus energy in motion. Any object that is hot can transfer its internal energy to the surroundings as heat. A gallon of boiling water contains more internal energy than a pint of boiling water and it can thus transfer more heat to its surroundings.

Heat is often measured in calories, a common unit of energy defined as the amount of heat required to raise 1 gram of room-temperature water by 1° Celsius in temperature. (Don't confuse this calorie, abbreviated cal, with the calorie unit commonly used in nutrition discussions. The dietary calorie, abbreviated Cal, equals 1000 calories; see Appendix B.)

Temperature is a term that compares how vigorously atoms in a substance are moving and colliding in different substances. Two objects are defined to be at the same temperature if no net heat flows spontaneously from one to the other. A gallon of boiling water, therefore, is at the same temperature as a pint of boiling water. The difference in temperature between two objects is one of the factors that determine how quickly heat is transferred between those two objects: the larger the temperature difference, the more rapidly heat is transferred. You may have seen this phenomenon at work in the summertime when violent winds, often accompanied by a line of thunderstorms, precede a cold front. The strong winds are the result of convection (see below), which helps to transfer heat between two air masses at very different temperatures.

Temperature scales provide a convenient way to compare the temperatures of two objects. Many different temperature scales have been proposed, and all scales and temperature units are arbitrary in the sense that there is no one correct temperature scale. We construct temperature scales by choosing two easily reproducible temperatures (the freezing and boiling points of water are common choices) and then finding some measurable quantity, such as the expansion of mercury in a tube or the resistance of a piece of wire, that varies with temperature. We then divide the change in that quantity between the two reference points to define the degree of temperature in that scale.

THE ONGOING PROCESS OF SCIENCE
The Fahrenheit Temperature Scale

Daniel Fahrenheit (1686-1736) was an instrument maker and glass blower in Amsterdam. He was interested in developing and selling an instrument for measuring temperature so that people in different places could compare the results of their experiments. Consequently, he had to develop a temperature scale that could be used with his instruments (which eventually used the expansion of mercury as an indicator). He wanted all of his temperatures to be positive numbers, so he defined zero degrees in his scale as the coldest mixture he could produce in his laboratory (a mixture of water, ice, and a salt), and the temperature of the human body as 96 degrees. In this scale, water freezes at 32° and boils at 212. Fahrenheit published these numbers, and the scale that bears his name was established with these two reference points. In the modern Fahrenheit scale human body temperature is 98.6°, not Fahrenheit's original 96.

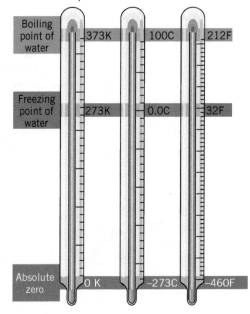

FIGURE 4-2 The Kelvin, Celsius, and Fahrenheit temperature scales compared.

In the *Fahrenheit scale*, 32 and 212° mark the freezing and boiling points of water, respectively. In the *Celsius scale*, these temperatures are 0 and 100°, respectively. The *Kelvin temperature scale* uses the same degree as the Celsius scale, with 100 increments between the freezing and boiling points of water. This scale defines 0 Kelvin (abbreviated K) as **absolute zero**, which is the coldest attainable temperature—the temperature at which it is impossible to extract any heat at all from atoms or molecules. The temperature of absolute zero is approximately –273°C, or –460°F. It turns out, therefore, that freezing and boiling occur at about 273 and 373 Kelvins, respectively (Figure 4-2).

Although all temperatures today are given in one of these three scales, it should be obvious that there is no "correct" temperature scale. There were, for example, some 35 different temperature scales in existence when Fahrenheit began his work. Isaac Newton developed a precursor of the Celsius scale based on the expansion of linseed oil, and the Rankine scale, which starts at absolute zero but uses Fahrenheit degrees, was used by engineers well into the twentieth century. Some old European breweries even used a scale based on the freezing and boiling points of alcohol, rather than water, until after World War II.

Temperature Conversions

It's often necessary to convert from one temperature scale to another. American travelers, for example, commonly want to convert from degrees Celsius (used in most of the rest of the world) to degrees Fahrenheit. We note that in the Fahrenheit scale there are 180 degrees between the freezing and boiling points of water, while in the Celsius scale there are 100. This difference means that a Celsius degree is $(180/100 = 1.8)$ as big as a Fahrenheit degree. The conversion between the two, then, requires the following formula:

$$°F = (1.8 \times °C) + 32$$

Where the 32 reflects the fact that water freezes at 32°F but 0°C. To convert the opposite way, from Fahrenheit to Celsius, the formula is:

$$°C = (°F - 32) / 1.8$$

Remember, all temperature scales measure the exact same phenomenon; they just use different number scales to do so.

EXAMPLE 4-1

WHAT TO WEAR?

You awake in Paris to a forecast high temperature of 32°C. Should you wear gloves and an overcoat?

Reasoning and Solution: Apply the equation to convert temperature from Celsius to Fahrenheit:

$$°F = (1.8 \times °C) + 32$$
$$= (1.8 \times 32) + 32$$
$$= 89.6°F$$

Looks like you won't be needing your overcoat today!

TECHNOLOGY
Thermometers

A *thermometer* is a device used to measure temperature. Most thermometers display temperature either digitally or on a numbered scale. Thermometers work by incorporating material whose properties change significantly with temperature. Many materials expand when heated and contract when cooled, and this behavior can be used to gauge temperature (Figure 4-3). In the old-style mercury thermometer, for example, a bead of mercury expands into a thin glass column with increasing temperature; you read the height of the mercury against a scale marked in degrees. Many other (much safer) thermometers rely on changes in the electrical properties of a temperature sensor. The thermometer your doctor uses when you visit his or her office, for example, uses these electrical properties to get your body temperature.

Richard Higgins/Alamy

FIGURE 4-3 One of the most visually intriguing types of thermometers, invented by Galileo Galilei in the early 1600s, employs changes in liquid density as a function of temperature. The "Galilean thermometer" consists of a large sealed flask with a liquid that changes density as it is heated. Suspended in this liquid are dozens of small numbered weights, each of a slightly different density. At low temperature, most of the weights rise to the top of the flask. As temperature increases, the denser weights sink one-by-one to the bottom. The temperature is read simply as the lowest number on the weights that remain floating at the top of the thermometer.

Specific Heat Capacity

Specific heat capacity is a measure of the ability of a material to absorb heat and is defined as the quantity of heat required to raise the temperature of one gram of that material by 1°C. Water displays the largest heat capacity of any common substance; by definition, one calorie is required to raise the temperature of a gram of water by 1°C. By contrast, you know that metals heat up quickly in a fire, so a small amount of absorbed heat can cause a significant increase in the metal's temperature.

Think about the last time you boiled water in a copper-bottomed pot. It doesn't take long to raise the temperature of a copper pot to above the boiling point of water because copper, like most other metals, heats up rapidly as it absorbs heat. In fact, one calorie will raise the temperature of a gram of copper by about 10°C. But water is a different matter; it must absorb 10 times more heat per gram than copper to raise its temperature. Thus, even at the highest stove setting, it can take several minutes to boil a pot of water. This ability of water to store thermal energy plays a critical role in Earth's climate, which is moderated by the relatively steady temperatures of the oceans.

STOP & THINK Why are the freezing and boiling points of pure water commonly used as standards for temperature scales? Can you think of other standards that would be useful for everyday measurements?

◉ 4.3 Heat Transfer

You can't prevent heat from moving from an object at high temperature to its cooler surroundings; you can only slow the rate of movement. In fact, scientists and engineers have spent centuries studying the phenomenon known as **heat transfer**—the process by which heat moves from one place to another. Heat transfers by three basic mechanisms—conduction, convection, and radiation—each of which is important to different aspects of everyday experience.

FIGURE 4-4 Heat energy moves by conduction through the action of atoms or molecules that jostle their neighbors.

Conduction

Have you ever reached for a pan on a hot stove, only to have your fingers burned when you grasped the metal handle? If so, you have had firsthand experience of conduction, the movement of heat by atomic-scale collisions.

As shown in Figure 4-4, **conduction** works through the action of individual atoms or molecules that are linked together by chemical bonds. If a piece of metal is heated at one end, the atoms and their electrons at that end begin to move faster. When they vibrate and collide with atoms farther away from the heat source, they are likely to transfer energy to those atoms, so that the molecules farther away will begin to move faster as well. A chain of collisions occurs, with atoms progressively farther and farther away from the heat source moving faster and faster as time goes by.

Conduction of heat is responsible for a large part of the heating bills in homes and office buildings. The process works like this:

Atoms at cool end vibrate slower

Atoms at hot end vibrate faster

Atoms collide in the middle

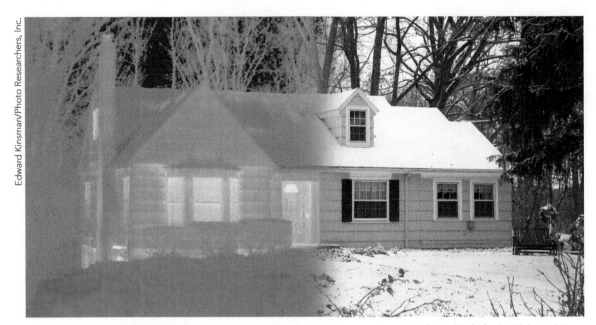

Edward Kinsman/Photo Researchers, Inc.

FIGURE 4-5 A house appears differently in photographs with infrared (left) and visible (right) light. The brighter areas on the infrared image, including the door and windows, reveal surfaces where internal heat is being lost most rapidly to the cold exterior.

The air inside a house in winter is kept warmer than the air outside, so that the molecules of the air inside are moving faster than the molecules in the air outside. When the molecules inside collide with materials in the wall (a windowpane, for example), they impart some of their heat to the molecules in those materials. At that point conduction takes over and heat is transferred to the outside of the wall. There the heat is transferred to the outdoors by convection and radiation, processes that we will describe in a moment. The key point, however, is that you can think about every part of your house as being a kind of conduit carrying heat from the interior to the outside on cold days, and from the outside to the interior on hot days.

One way of slowing down the flow of heat into or out of a house is to add insulation to the walls or to use special kinds of glass for the windows. These processes work because materials differ in their **thermal conductivity**—their ability to transfer heat from one molecule to the next by conduction. Have you ever noticed that a piece of wood at room temperature feels "normal," while a piece of metal at the same temperature feels cold to the touch? The wood and metal are at exactly the same temperature, but the metal feels cold because it is a good *heat conductor*—it moves heat rapidly away from your skin, which is generally warmer than air temperature. The wood, on the other hand, is a good *heat insulator*—it impedes the flow of heat, and so it feels comparatively warm. The insulation in your home is designed to have especially low thermal conductivity, so that heat transfer is slowed down (but never completely stopped). Thus, when you use special insulated windowpanes or put certain kinds of insulation in your walls, you make it more difficult for heat to flow outside, and thereby allow yourself to use the heat longer before it ultimately leaks away (Figure 4-5).

Convection

Let's look carefully at a pot of boiling water on a stove. On the surface of the water you will see a rolling, churning motion as the water moves and mixes. If you put your hand above the water, you feel heat. Heat has been transferred from the water at the bottom of the pot to the top by **convection**, the transfer of heat by the bulk motion of the water itself, as shown in Figure 4-6.

Water near the bottom of the pan expands as the flames heat it. The heated water weighs less per unit volume than the colder water immediately above it, creating an unstable situation with colder, denser water above and warmer, less dense water below.

FIGURE 4-6 Convection. Heat is transferred by the bulk motion of a fluid, such as air or water. In the case of a boiling pot, hot water rises as cooler water sinks.

Water cools

Cooler water sinks   Hot water rises   Cooler water sinks

The denser fluid tends to descend and displace the less dense fluid, which in turn begins to rise. Consequently, the warm water from the bottom rises to the top, while the cool water from the top sinks to the bottom. In convection, masses of water move in bulk and carry the fast-moving molecules with them.

Convection is a continuous, cyclic process as long as heat is added to the water. As cool water from the top of a pot arrives at the bottom, it begins to be heated by the burner. As hot water gets to the top, its heat is sent off into the air. The water on the top cools and contracts, while the water on the bottom heats and expands. The original situation is repeated continuously, with the less dense fluid on the bottom always rising and the more dense fluid on the top always sinking. This transfer of fluids results in a kind of a rolling motion, which you see when you look at the surface of boiling water.

Each of these regions of rising and sinking water is called a **convection cell**. The areas of clear water, which seem to be bubbling up, are the places where warm water is rising. The places where bubbles and scum tend to collect—the places that look rather stagnant—are where the cool water is sinking, leaving behind whatever passengers (such as minerals) it happened to be carrying at the surface. Heat is carried from the burner through the convection of the water and is eventually transferred to the atmosphere. Convection is thus a very efficient way of transferring heat.

You experience many examples of the convection process, from the small-scale circulation of cold water in a glass of iced tea, to air rising above a radiator or toaster, to large-scale motions of Earth's atmosphere (Figure 4-7). You may even have seen convection cells in operation in large urban areas. When you're in the parking lot of a large shopping mall on a hot summer day you have probably noticed the air shimmer. What you are seeing is air, heated by the hot asphalt, rising upward. Some place farther away, perhaps out in the countryside, cooler air is falling. The shopping center is called a "heat island" and is the hot part of a convection cell.

You may also have noticed that the temperature in big cities is usually a few degrees warmer than in outlying suburbs. Cities help create their own weather because they are heat islands where convection cells develop. Rainfall is typically higher in cities than in the surrounding atmosphere because cities set up convection cells that draw in cool moist air from surrounding areas.

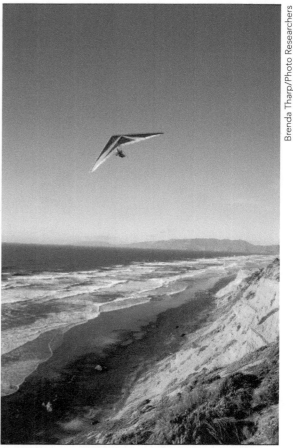

FIGURE 4-7 Convection cells in the air keep this hang glider in California aloft.

TECHNOLOGY
Home Insulation

Today's homebuilders take heat convection and conduction very seriously. An energy-efficient dwelling has to hold onto its heat in the winter and remain cool in the summer. A variety of materials provide effective solutions to this insulation problem.

Fiberglass, the most widely used insulation, is made of loosely intertwined strands of glass. It works by minimizing the opportunities for conduction and convection of heat out of your home. Solid glass is a rather poor heat insulator, but it takes a long time for heat to move along a thin, twisted glass fiber, and even longer for heat to transfer across the occasional contact points between pairs of crossed fibers. Furthermore, a cloth-like mat of fiberglass disrupts airflow and prevents heat transfer by convection. A thick, continuous layer of fiberglass in your walls and ceiling thus acts as an ideal barrier to the flow of heat (Figure 4-8).

Windows pose a special insulation problem. Old-style single-pane windows conduct heat rapidly, so how do we let light in without letting heat out? One solution is double-pane windows with sealed, airtight spaces between the panes that greatly restrict heat

FIGURE 4-8 A thick layer of fiberglass insulation will reduce the transfer of heat between your home and the surroundings, and thus will reduce your heating bills in the winter and cooling bills in the summer.

conduction. In addition, builders employ a variety of caulking and foam insulation to seal any possible leaks around windows and doors.

Recent high-tech materials are providing new types of insulation. Like fiberglass, most of these new materials depend on the insulating properties of trapped air for their effectiveness. Older homes are now routinely insulated by injecting liquid foams between exterior and interior walls, for example. When the foam hardens, tiny bubbles of trapped air slow down the transfer of heat. In new construction, sheets of solid Styrofoam, which contain the same kind of trapped air bubbles, are often used instead of fiberglass, and foams are sprayed onto the inner surface of concrete to increase its insulating power.

THE SCIENCE OF LIFE
Animal Insulation: Fur and Feathers

Houses aren't the only place where insulation can be seen in our world. Two kinds of animals—birds and mammals—maintain a constant body temperature despite the temperature of their surroundings, and both have evolved methods to control the flow of heat into and out of their bodies. Part of these strategies involves the use of insulating materials—furs, feathers, and fat—that serve to slow down the heat flow (Figure 4-9). Because most of the time an animal's body is warmer than the environment, the most common situation is one in which the insulation works to keep heat in.

Whales, walruses, and seals are examples of animals that have thick layers of fat to insulate them from the cold arctic waters in which they swim. Fat is a poor conductor of heat and plays much the same role in their bodies as the fiberglass insulation in your attic. Feathers are another kind of insulation; in fact, many biologists suspect that feathers evolved first as a kind of insulation to help birds maintain their body temperature, and only later were they adapted for flight. Feathers are made of light, hollow tubes connected to each other by an array of small interlocking spikes. They have some insulating properties themselves, but their main effect comes from the fact that they trap air next to the body, and, as we have pointed out, stationary air is a rather good insulator. Birds often react to extreme cold by contracting muscles in their

FIGURE 4-9 Feathers, fur, and fat help animals by providing insulation to keep body heat in.

skin so that the feathers fluff out. This has the effect of increasing the thickness (and hence the insulating power) of the layer of trapped air. (Incidentally, birds need insulation more than we do because their normal body temperature is 41°C or 106°F.)

Hair (or fur) is actually made up of dead cells similar to those in the outer layer of the skin. Like feathers, hair serves as an insulator in its own right and traps a layer of air near the body. In some animals (for example, polar bears), the insulating power of the hair is increased because each hair contains tiny bubbles of trapped air. The reflection of light from these bubbles makes polar bear fur appear white—the strands of hair are actually translucent.

Hair grows from follicles in the skin, and small muscles allow animals to make their hair stand up to increase its insulating power. Human beings, who evolved in a warm climate, have lost much of their body hair as well as the ability to make most of it stand up. We have a reminder of our mammalian nature, however, in the phenomenon of "goosebumps," which is the attempt by muscles in the skin to make the hair stand up.

Radiation

Everyone has had the experience of coming inside on a cold day and finding a fire in the fireplace or an electric heater glowing red hot. The normal reaction is to walk up to the source of heat, hold out your hands, and feel the warmth moving into your skin.

How did the heat get from the fire to your hands? It couldn't have done so by conduction; it's too hard to carry heat through the air that way. It couldn't have been convection either because you don't feel a hot breeze.

What you experience is the third kind of heat transfer—**radiation**, or the transfer of heat by electromagnetic radiation, which is a form of wave energy that we will discuss in Chapter 6. A fire or an electric heater radiates energy in the form of *infrared radiation*. This radiation travels from the source of heat to your hand, where it is absorbed and converted into the thermal energy of molecules. You perceive heat because of the energy that the infrared radiation carries to your hand.

Objects throughout the universe radiate energy in this way. Under normal circumstances, as an object gives off radiation to its surroundings, it also receives radiation from those surroundings. Thus a kind of equilibrium is set up, and there is no net loss of energy because the object is at the same temperature as its surroundings. If, however, the object is at a higher temperature than its surroundings, it will radiate more energy than it receives. Your body, for example, constantly radiates energy into its cooler surroundings. You will continue to radiate this energy as long as your body processes the food that keeps you alive (see Chapter 20).

Radiation is the only kind of energy that can travel through the emptiness of space. Conduction requires atoms or molecules that can vibrate and collide with each other. Convection requires atoms or molecules of liquid or gas in bulk, so that they can move. Remarkably, however, radiation doesn't require any medium to move heat; radiation can even travel through a vacuum. The energy that falls on Earth in the form of sunlight, which is almost all of the energy that sustains life on Earth, travels through 93 million miles (150 million kilometers) of intervening empty space in the form of radiation.

In the real world, all three types of heat transfer—conduction, convection, and radiation—occur all the time. Any one can occur by itself or in combination with another, or all three can occur simultaneously. At this moment, heat is being generated in your body. It travels by conduction through tissues, by convection through blood circulation, and by radiation from the surface of your skin. In fact, everywhere in the natural world heat is constantly being transferred by these three mechanisms.

THE SCIENCE OF LIFE
Temperature Regulation

Animals get the energy they need to run their metabolism by "burning" fuels they take in as food, and the laws of thermodynamics tell us that this process must generate waste heat. For small animals, this heat can be dumped into the environment by simple conduction, but the larger an animal is, the more complex the system for disposing waste heat has to be.

FIGURE 4-10 Sweating while exercising helps the athlete maintain her body temperature.

By the same token, animals must be able to absorb heat from their environment to maintain their internal temperature. Some animals (reptiles, for example) absorb energy directly from radiation. This is why you often see snakes and lizards "sunning" themselves on warm days and why they are so sluggish on cold mornings. Other animals, such as mammals (a group that includes human beings) and birds, have intricate mechanisms for maintaining a constant body temperature.

Human beings have complex ways of raising and lowering the body's temperature in response to changes in the temperature of the environment. If your body temperature starts to rise, blood vessels near the surface of your skin dilate so that the blood can carry more heat to the surface by convection. There, the excess heat can be radiated away. This response is why you often appear flushed after being in the Sun for a while. In addition, you start to sweat. The purpose of sweating is to put water on your skin, which then evaporates through your body heat (Figure 4-10).

When the temperature falls, the blood vessels near the surface contract, lowering the blood's ability to carry heat to the surface. In extreme cases, this situation can lead to frostbite, a condition by which cells die because they are denied oxygen and other substances normally carried to them by the blood. Consequently, your body's metabolism increases and generates more heat in response to cold weather. Shivering, for example, is a response in which the heat generated by involuntary contractions of the muscles is used to counterbalance the falling temperature.

Incidentally, you may recall that you often start shivering at the onset of a fever. This seemingly paradoxical response occurs because, in response to the disease, the body's internal "thermostat" is adjusted to a higher than normal setting. You shiver and feel cold because, when this happens, normal body temperature is below the new setting of the "thermostat" and more heat is needed to raise the body's temperature.

STOP & THINK The ears of an elephant are believed to function partly to keep the animal from overheating. What properties of the ears would make them well suited to this function? What types of heat transfer would be involved?

◎ 4.4 The Second Law of Thermodynamics

Throughout the universe the behavior of energy is regular and predictable. According to the first law of thermodynamics, the total amount of energy is constant, though energy may change from one form to another over and over again. Energy in the form of heat can flow from one place to another by conduction, convection, and radiation. But everyday experience tells us that there is more to the behavior of energy—that there is a direction to energy's flow. Hot things tend to cool off, cold things tend to warm up, and an egg, once broken, can never be reassembled. These commonsense ideas are the domain of the **second law of thermodynamics**, which is one of the most fascinating and powerful ideas in science.

The second law of thermodynamics places restrictions on the way heat and other forms of energy can be transferred and used to do work. In this section we explore three different statements of this law:

1. Heat will not flow spontaneously from a cold to a hot body.
2. You cannot construct an engine that does nothing but convert heat to useful work.
3. Every isolated system becomes more disordered with time.

Although these three statements appear very different, they are actually logically equivalent—given any one statement, you can derive the other two as a consequence. Given the statement that heat flows from hot to cold objects, for example, a physicist could produce a set of mathematical steps that would show that no engine can convert heat to work with 100% efficiency. In this sense, the three statements of the law all say the same thing.

1. Heat Will Not Flow Spontaneously from a Cold to a Hot Body

The first statement of the second law of thermodynamics describes the behavior of two objects at different temperatures. If you take an ice cream cone outside on a hot summer afternoon, it will melt. In the language of energy, heat will flow from the warm atmosphere to the cold ice cream cone and cause its temperature to rise above the melting point. By the same token, if you take a cup of hot chocolate outside on a cold day, it will cool as heat flows from the cup into the surroundings.

From the point of view of energy alone, there is no reason things should work this way. Energy would be conserved if heat stayed put, or even if heat flowed from an ice cream cone into the warm atmosphere, making the ice cream cone grow colder. Our everyday experience (and many experiments) convinces us that our universe does not work this way. In our universe heat flows in only one direction, from hot to cold. This everyday observation may seem trivial, but in this statement is hidden all the mystery of those changes that make the future different from the past.

This version of the second law is easy to explain at the molecular level. If two objects collide and one of them is moving faster than the other, chances are that the slower object will be speeded up and the faster object slowed down by the collision. It's unlikely that events will go the other way. Thus, as we saw in the discussion of heat conduction, faster-moving molecules tend to share their energy with slower-moving ones.

On the macroscopic scale, this process is seen as heat flowing from warm regions to cold ones by conduction. For the second law to be violated, the molecules in a substance would have to conspire so that collisions would cause slower-moving molecules to slow down even more, giving up their energy to faster molecules so they could go even faster. Experience tells us that this doesn't happen.

The second law does not state that it's impossible for heat to flow from a cold to a hot body. When a refrigerator is operating, heat is removed from the colder interior to the warmer exterior, a fact that you can verify by putting your hand under the refrigerator and feeling the warm air coming off it. The second law merely says that this action cannot take place spontaneously, of its own accord. If you wish to cool something in this way, you must supply energy. In fact, an alternative statement of the second law of thermodynamics could be: A refrigerator won't work unless it's plugged in.

The second law doesn't tell you that you can't make ice cubes, only that you can't make ice cubes without expending energy. Paying the electric bill, of course, is another part of our everyday experience.

2. You Cannot Construct an Engine That Does Nothing but Convert Heat to Useful Work

The second statement of the second law of thermodynamics places a severe restriction on the way we can use energy. At first glance, this statement about heat and work seems to have very little to do with the idea that heat never flows spontaneously from a cold object to a hot object. Yet the two statements are logically equivalent—given the one, the other must follow.

Energy can be defined as the ability to do work. This second statement of the second law tells us that whenever energy is transformed from heat to another type—from heat to an electrical current, for example—some of that heat must be dumped into the environment and is unavailable to do work. This energy is neither lost nor destroyed, but it can't be used to make electricity to play your radio or gasoline to drive your car. Scientists and engineers have defined a specific term, *efficiency*, to quantify the loss of useful energy. **Efficiency** is the amount of work you get from an engine, divided by the amount of energy you put into it.

In Chapter 3 we discovered that heat and other forms of energy are interchangeable, and the total amount of energy is conserved. From the point of view of the first law of thermodynamics, there is no reason why energy in the form of heat could not be converted to electrical energy with 100% efficiency. But the second law of thermodynamics predicts that such a process is not

Beginning of intake stroke	Middle of intake stroke	Beginning of compression stroke	Beginning of power stroke	Beginning of exhaust stroke
	Gasoline–air mixture enters cylinder through open intake port	Cylinder sealed as both intake valve and exhaust valve are closed	Spark plug fires, igniting the compressed mixture of gasoline and air and begins the power stroke	Combustion products are swept out of the cylinder through the open exhaust port
(a)	(b)	(c)	(d)	(e)

FIGURE 4-11 The cycle of an engine's piston. (a) The beginning of the intake stroke. (b) The middle of the intake stroke as a gasoline-air mixture enters the cylinder. (c) The beginning of the compression stroke. (d) At the beginning of the power stroke the spark plug fires, igniting the compressed mixture of gasoline and air. (e) At the beginning of the exhaust stroke, combustion products are swept out. Note that each cycle involves two complete rotations of the crankshaft.

possible. The flow of energy, like time, has a direction. Another way of stating this law is to say that energy always goes from a more useful to a less useful form.

Your car engine provides a familiar example of this everyday rule of nature. When you turn on the ignition, an exploding mixture of gasoline and air creates a high-temperature, high-pressure gas that pushes down on a piston. The piston's motion is converted into rotational motion of a series of machine parts that eventually turn the car's wheels. Some of the energy is lost because of friction, but the second law of thermodynamics predicts that our use of the energy is restricted even if friction did not exist, and even if every machine in the world was perfectly designed.

Look at the various stages of an engine's operation (Figure 4-11). There seems to be no obvious reason why energy in the form of heat in the exploding air-gas mixture could not be converted with 100% efficiency into energy of motion of the engine's piston, which is translated into the motion of the car. But you can't just think about the downward motion of a piston, what engineers call the *power stroke*, in the operation of your car's engine. If that was all the engine did, then the engine in every car could turn over only once. The problem is that once you have the piston pushed all the way down—once you have extracted useful work from the air-gas mixture—you have to return the piston to the top of the cylinder so that the cycle can be repeated. In other words, in order to reset the engine to its original position so that more useful work can be done, some energy has to be expended to lift the piston back up.

Ignore for a moment the fact that a real engine is more complicated than the one we are discussing. Suppose that all you had to do was to lift the piston up after you had gotten the work from it. The cylinder is full of air; consequently when you lift the piston up the air will be compressed and heated. In order to return the engine to the precise state it was in before the explosion, the heat from this compressed air has to be taken away. In practice, it is dumped into the atmosphere.

In the language of physics, the exploding hot gas-air mixture is called a *high temperature reservoir*, and the atmosphere into which the heat of compression is dumped is called a *low-temperature reservoir*. The second law of thermodynamics says that any engine operating between two temperatures must dump some energy in the form of heat into the low-temperature reservoir. In your car's engine, for example, heat produced by moving the piston back up has to be dumped. A similar argument can be made for any conceivable engine you could build.

Some of the chemical potential energy stored in gasoline can be used to run your car, but most of the energy must be dumped into the low-temperature reservoir of the atmosphere. Once that heat has gone into the atmosphere, it can no longer be used to run the engine. Thus this version of the second law tells us that any real engine operating in the world, even an engine in which there is no friction, must waste some of the energy that goes into it.

This version of the second law explains why petroleum reserves and coal deposits play such an important role in the world economy. These fossil fuels are high-grade and nonrenewable sources of energy that can be used to produce high-temperature reservoirs. They are also sources of energy that can be used only once. When fossil fuels are burned to produce a high-temperature reservoir and generate electricity, for example, a large portion of energy must simply be thrown away.

Although the second law predicts rather stringent limits on engines that work in cycles, it does not apply to many other uses of energy. No engine is involved if you burn natural gas to heat your home or use solar energy to heat water, for example. Consequently, these limits needn't apply. Thus burning fossil fuels or employing solar energy to supply heat directly can be considerably more efficient than using it to generate electricity.

SCIENCE BY THE NUMBERS
Efficiency

The second law of thermodynamics can be used to calculate the maximum possible efficiency of an engine. Let's say that the high-temperature reservoir is at a temperature T_{hot} and the low-temperature reservoir is at a temperature T_{cold} (temperatures are measured in the Kelvin scale). The maximum theoretical efficiency—the percentage of energy available to do useful work—of any engine in the real world can be calculated as follows.

In words: Efficiency is obtained by comparing the temperature difference between the high-temperature and low-temperature reservoirs with the temperature of the high-temperature reservoir.

In equation form:

$$\text{efficiency (percent)} = \frac{(\text{temperature}_{hot} - \text{temperature}_{cold})}{\text{temperature}_{hot}} \times 100$$

In symbols:

$$\text{efficiency (percent)} = \frac{(T_{hot} - T_{cold})}{T_{hot}} \times 100$$

Any loss of energy due to friction in pulleys or gears or wheels in a real machine will make the actual efficiency less than this theoretical maximum. This maximum is actually a very stringent constraint on real engines.

Consider the efficiency of a normal coal-fired electrical generating plant. The temperature of the high-energy steam (the hot reservoir) is about 500 K, while the temperature of the air into which waste heat must be dumped (the "cold" reservoir) is around room temperature, or 300 K. The maximum possible efficiency of such a plant is given by the second law to be:

$$\text{efficiency (percent)} = \frac{(T_{hot} - T_{cold})}{T_{hot}} \times 100$$

$$= \frac{(500 - 300)}{500} \times 100$$

$$= 40.0\%$$

Highly ordered

Disordered

This change tends to be

spontaneous

Highly ordered
solid – low probability
(a)

Disordered liquid –
higher probability

An improbable way
for bricks to fall
(b)

A more probable way
for bricks to fall

FIGURE 4-12 Highly ordered, regular patterns of objects are less likely to occur than disordered, irregular patterns. Colored marbles that are layered in a jar (a) will spontaneously become randomly mixed if you jostle the jar. Bricks that are tossed into a pile (b) are unlikely to form a neat stack. These and many other examples illustrate the second law of thermodynamics.

Most of the energy in this coal will be wasted when it is converted to electricity.

© Don Smetzer / Alamy Inc

In other words, more than half of the energy produced in a typical coal-burning power plant must be dumped into the atmosphere as waste heat. This fundamental limit is independent of the engineers' ability to make the plant operate efficiently. In fact, engineers do very well in this regard—most generating plants operate within a few percentage points of the maximum efficiency allowed by the second law of thermodynamics. This result has important implications for energy policy. It tells us that there are fundamental limits to the efficiency with which we can convert heat generated by coal or nuclear reactors to electricity. The only way around this restriction is to produce higher temperatures. There are, for example, theoretical proposals for nuclear reactors that would operate at temperatures of 700 K. What would the efficiency of such a reactor be?

3. Every Isolated System Becomes More Disordered with Time

The third statement of the second law of thermodynamics, in many ways the most profound, describes the familiar tendency of systems all around us to become increasingly disordered. Your carefully cleaned room gets messy, your brand new car becomes dirty and scratched, and we all age as our bodies gradually wear out. For physicists, however, this statement of the second law has a very precise and special meaning.

To understand this statement of the second law, you need to know what a physicist means by "order" and "disorder." An ordered system is one in which a number of objects, be they atoms or automobiles, are positioned in a completely regular and predictable pattern. A jar filled with colored marbles in two layers is more ordered than one in which the marbles are jumbled up, while a neat stack of bricks is more ordered than an irregular pile (Figure 4-12). Similarly, atoms in a perfect crystal or automobiles in a perfect line, represent highly ordered systems. A disordered system, on the other hand, contains objects that are randomly situated, without any obvious pattern. Atoms in a gas or in automobiles after a multicar pileup on a freeway are examples of disordered systems.

A mathematical definition of order and disorder requires considering the number of different ways a system can be arranged. To get a feel for this idea, consider three orange balls numbered 1, 2, and 3, and three green balls numbered 4, 5 and 6. Ask yourself, how many different ways are there to arrange these six balls in a row? (See Figure 4-13.) There are six different possibilities for the first ball, five possibilities for the second, four for the third, and soon. So if you multiply that out:

$$6 \times 5 \times 4 \times 3 \times 2 \times 1 = 720$$

It turns out that there are 720 ways to arrange these six numbered balls in a row—720 different possible configurations.

But how many of those arrangements have the ordered state with three orange balls followed by three green balls assuming that there is no way of distinguishing the same colored balls from each other? There are exactly six different ways to arrange three orange balls $(3 \times 2 \times 1)$, and then six different ways to arrange the three green balls. Altogether, that's 6×6, or 36 different configurations with three orange balls followed by three green balls out of 720 total configurations. Only 5% of all possible arrangements (36/720) are ordered in this way. All of the remaining 684 configurations are different. So, by a 19-to-1 margin, these other arrangements are much more probable because there are many more ways to achieve a disordered state than an ordered one.

You can repeat this exercise for other numbers of balls (see Problems 4 and 5). For a sequence of 10 balls (five orange and five green), it turns out that there are more than 3.6 million different configurations, but only 120 of those sequences have five orange followed by five green balls. That's only 0.003% of all possible arrangements!

As the number of objects increases from 6 to 10 to many trillions (as we find in even a very small collection of atoms), the fraction of arrangements that is highly ordered becomes infinitesimally small. In other words, highly ordered configurations are improbable because almost every possible configuration is disordered. This concept of a system's state of disorder is described by the term **entropy**. The second law of thermodynamics can be restated as:

FIGURE 4-13 There are 720 different ways to arrange six numbered balls. If three balls are orange and three are green, then only a small fraction of these arrangements are ordered by color.

● **The entropy of an isolated system remains constant or increases.**

The word *entropy* was proposed by the German engineer Rudolf Clausius (1822–1888), who played a central role in formulating the second law of thermodynamics. In his own words: "I propose to name the [quantity] entropy . . . from the Greek word for a transformation. I have intentionally formed the word entropy so as to be as similar as possible to the word energy, since both these quantities . . . are so nearly related to each other."

The definition of entropy, as a measure of disorder, may seem a bit fuzzy, but it was placed on a firm quantitative footing in the late nineteenth century by the German physicist Ludwig Boltzmann (1844–1906). Boltzmann used probability theory to demonstrate that the entropy of any arrangement of atoms is related to the number of possible ways that you can achieve that arrangement. The numerical value of entropy is thus related to the number of ways a system like the numbered balls in a row can be rearranged. If you have a collection of sodium and chlorine atoms, for example, there are many more ways to mix those atoms randomly in a liquid than there are to have them strictly alternating, as they do in a salt crystal. That's why the entropy of sodium and chlorine atoms dissolved in water is much greater than the entropy of those atoms in a salt crystal.

According to the second law of thermodynamics, any system left to itself will evolve toward the most disordered state, the state with the maximum uncertainty in the arrangement of its parts. Without careful chemical and physical controls, atoms and molecules will tend to become more intermixed; without careful driving, collections of automobiles will also tend to become more disordered.

The example we gave at the beginning of the chapter, with the one fast atom in a collection of slow atoms, shows very clearly how such a process works. In the most likely situation, when all of the atoms are in the same low-energy state, the entropy is maximized. A much less probable situation occurs when one of the atoms is in a high-velocity state. Another way of saying this is that systems tend to avoid states of high improbability.

Although systems tend to become more disordered, the second law does not require every system to approach a state of lower order. Think about water, a substance of high disorder because water molecules are arranged at random. If you put water into a freezer you get an ice cube, a much more ordered state in which water molecules have formed a regular crystal structure. You have caused a system to evolve to a state of higher order. How can this be reconciled with our statement of the second law?

The answer to this seeming paradox lies in the simple word "isolated." The freezer in which you make the ice cubes is not an isolated system because it has a power cord plugged into the wall and is ultimately connected to the generating plant. The isolated system in this case is the freezer plus the generating plant. The second law of thermodynamics says that the system's total entropy must increase. It does not say that the entropy has to increase in all the different parts of the system.

In this example, one part of the system (the ice cube) becomes more ordered, while another part of the system (the generating plant, its burning fuel, and the surrounding air) becomes more disordered. All that the second law requires is that the increase of disorder at the generating plant be greater than the increase of order at the ice cube. As long as this requirement is met, the second law is not violated. In fact, in this particular example, the disorder at the generating plant greatly exceeds any possible order that could take place inside your refrigerator.

SCIENCE IN THE MAKING
The Heat Death of the Universe

The nineteenth-century discovery of the second law of thermodynamics was a gloomy event. The prevailing philosophy of the time was that life, society, and the universe in general were on a never-ending upward spiral of progress. In this optimistic climate, the discovery that the energy in the universe was being steadily and irrevocably degraded was very hard for nineteenth-century scientists and philosophers to accept. The second law seemed to imply that all the energy in the universe would eventually be degraded into waste heat and that everything in the universe would eventually come to the same temperature. This outcome was called the "heat death" of the universe, and some scholars saw it as the ultimate consequence of the laws of thermodynamics.

This notion even affected the literature and music of the time. For example, here is an excerpt from Algernon Swinburne's "The Garden of Proserpine":

> From too much love of living
> From hope and death set free
> We thank with weak thanksgiving
> Whatever gods there be
> That no man lives forever
> That dead men rise up never
> That even the weariest river
> Flows somewhere safe to sea.

Today, we have a more nuanced view of how the universe will end—a view that will be discussed in Chapter 15. Suffice to say, however, that Swinburne and his colleagues may have been premature in their gloom (although one could argue that poets of that period seemed to grab at any excuse for being gloomy).

4.5 Consequences of the Second Law

The Arrow of Time

We live in a world of four dimensions. Three of these—the dimensions of space—have no obvious directionality. You can go east or west, north or south, and up or down in our universe, but there is nothing forcing you to go in any particular direction. But time, the fourth dimension, has a direction in which you are constrained to move.

Take one of your favorite home movies or just about any video and play it in reverse. Chances are that before too long you'll see something silly—something that couldn't possibly happen, that will make you laugh. Springboard divers fly out of the water and land completely dry on the diving board. From a complete stop golf balls fly off toward the tee. Ocean spray coalesces into smooth waves that recede from shore. Most physical laws, such as Newton's laws of motion or the first law of thermodynamics, say nothing about time. The motions predicted by Newton and the conservation of energy are independent of time. They work just as well if you play a video forward or backward.

The second law of thermodynamics is different. By defining a sequence of events—heat flows from hot to cold; concentrated fuels burn to produce waste heat; the disorder of isolated systems never spontaneously decreases; you get older—we have established a direction to time. We experience the passage of events as dictated by the second law. Scientists cannot answer the deeper philosophical question of why we perceive the arrow of time in only one direction, but through the second law they can describe the effects of that directionality.

Built-in Limitations of the Universe

The second law of thermodynamics has both practical and philosophical consequences. It poses severe limits on the way that human beings can manipulate nature and on the way that nature itself operates. It tells us that some things cannot happen in our universe.

At the practical level, the second law tells us that if we continue to generate electricity by burning fossil fuels or by nuclear fission, we are using up energy that is locked in those concentrated nonrenewable resources. These limitations are not a question of sloppy engineering or poor design; they're simply built into the laws of nature. If you could design an engine or other device that would extract energy from coal and oil with higher efficiency than the second law limits, then you could also design a refrigerator that would work when it wasn't plugged in.

At the philosophical level, the second law tells us that nature has a built-in hierarchy of more useful and less useful forms of energy. The lowest or least useful state of energy is the low-temperature reservoir into which all energy eventually gets dumped. Once the energy is in that lowest-energy reservoir, it can no longer be used to do work. For Earth, energy passes through the region that supports life, the biosphere, but is eventually lost as it is radiated into the black void of space.

THE SCIENCE OF LIFE
Does Evolution Violate the Second Law?

Creationists, who argue that life on Earth was created in a single miraculous event, often use the second law of thermodynamics to argue against theories of life's gradual evolution. These arguments reflect a common misunderstanding of the second law.

Creationists point out that because life is a highly ordered system, in which trillions of atoms and molecules must occur in exactly the right sequence, it could not possibly have arisen spontaneously without violating the second law. What they neglect to consider, however, is that the energy that drives living systems is sunlight, so that the "isolated system" that the second law speaks of is Earth's biosphere plus the Sun. All that you need to make the evolution of life consistent with the second law is that the order observed in living things must be offset by a greater amount of disorder in the Sun. Once again, as with the earlier example of the ice cube, this requirement is easily met by the Sun and the biosphere taken together. Science cannot yet give a complete, detailed description of how life arose on our planet, but it can show that this development is in no way inconsistent with the universal laws of thermodynamics.

THINKING MORE ABOUT ENERGY GENERATION
Energy and the Second Law

We saw in our discussion of the second law that nature imposes a limit on the efficiency with which heat can be converted into useful work via the generation of electricity. In addition, we saw in Chapter 3 that the great majority of American energy, including energy used to generate electricity, comes from fossil fuels. Taking the result from the *Science by the Numbers* on page 89, we can say that when fossil fuels are used to generate electricity, roughly two-thirds of the energy stored in the fuel will be dumped into the atmosphere as waste heat.

A common sight in the western United States are mile-long trains carrying coal from mines to generating plants. Our result tells us that only the coal in every third car is destined to be used. The rest of the coal will just be wasted. A similar statement can be made about the gasoline in the tank of your car.

This is a disturbing fact because fossil fuels have other uses than as sources of energy. They also contain huge stores of long carbon chain molecules. As we shall see in Chapter 10, these types of molecules are the basic building blocks of many materials that form the essential structural core of modern technological society. Look around you. How much of what you see is made from some sort of plastic?

An important question we will have to debate in the future is whether it is better to use our stocks of coal and petroleum to generate electricity, thereby converting most of them to waste heat, or retain them for use in the production of synthetic materials such as plastic. How would you propose to resolve this problem?

← RETURN TO THE INTEGRATED QUESTION

Why is it easier to make an omelet from an egg than to make an egg from an omelet?

- Nature's direction
  - When you make an omelet by cooking an egg, heat energy from your stove is converted into the chemical potential energy of your cooked egg.
  - The process of heating dramatically alters the structure of the protein molecules of the egg, creating a change in viscosity (i.e., resistance to flow) of the egg white. The translucent and viscous egg white becomes opaque and firm as the cooking progresses.

- According to the first law of thermodynamics, the heat energy that was used to cook the egg is the same as the energy that would be released if you could uncook the egg. Nevertheless, the uncooking of an egg is a highly unlikely event due to the natural tendency of all systems to evolve from improbable states to states that are more probable.

- The relative irreversibility of your omelet making process is therefore due to the inherent directionality of nature as expressed in the second law of thermodynamics.

SUMMARY

All objects in the universe are at a *temperature* above *absolute zero,* and thus they hold some internal energy—the kinetic energy of moving atoms. *Heat* is energy that moves spontaneously from a warmer to a cooler object. *Specific heat capacity* defines how much energy is required to raise 1 gram of a substance by 1°C.

Heat transfer between two objects that are at different temperatures may occur in three ways. *Conduction* involves the transfer of heat through collisions at the scale of atoms and electrons. *Thermal conductivity* is a measure of how easily this energy transfer occurs. *Convection* involves the motion of a mass of fluid in a *convection cell,* in which warmer atoms are physically transported from one place to another. Heat can also be transferred by *radiation*—infrared energy and other forms of light that travel across a room or across the vastness of space until they are absorbed.

The first law of thermodynamics promises that the amount of energy never changes, no matter how it shifts from one form to another, but the *second law of thermodynamics* restricts how you

can shift energy. Three different but equivalent statements of the second law underscore these restrictions.

1. Heat will not flow spontaneously from a colder to a hotter body. This first statement places a restriction on the transfer of heat; for example, you have to supply an external source of energy to a refrigerator before it will work.

2. It is impossible to construct a machine that does nothing but convert heat into useful work. This different but equivalent statement of the second law precludes the construction of an engine that operates with 100% *efficiency.* All engines operate on a cycle, and every engine must expend some of its energy returning to its initial state.

3. The *entropy* of an isolated system always increases. The third statement of the second law of thermodynamics introduces the concept of entropy—the tendency of isolated systems to become more disordered with time. This directionality of energy flow in the universe defines our sense of the direction of time.

KEY TERMS

temperature	**conduction**	**radiation**
absolute zero	**thermal conductivity**	**second law of thermodynamics**
specific heat capacity	**convection**	**efficiency**
heat transfer	**convection cell**	**entropy**

KEY EQUATION

$$\text{efficiency (percent)} = \frac{(\text{temperature}_{hot} - \text{temperature}_{cold})}{\text{temperature}_{hot}} \times 100$$

DISCOVERY **LAB**

 Insulators are substances that prevent heat from entering or leaving a medium. Certain materials are better insulators than others. The better the insulator, the slower the temperature change. To test different insulators, you will need five medicine vials with lids (these can be substituted with bottles containing caps or test tubes with rubber stoppers); five containers for insulating

Fill medicine vials with hot water

Nest vials in coffee cans filled with insulating material

Sand

Sawdust

Styrofoam

Straw

Thermometer

Record the water temperature of each vial

Empty can (control)

(coffee cans, beakers, or any other type of containers larger than vial); and insulating material (including sand, sawdust, Styrofoam, and straw). You will also need a thermometer and a timer.

Fill up all five vials with hot water and record the temperature. Nest one of the vials in the insulating container and surround it with sand. Repeat the process with three of the other vials, using different insulating material every time. Place the fifth vial in the insulating container without any insulating material. This vial serves as a control. Record the temperature of the water every 5 minutes and continue recording for the next 30 minutes. Which insulator worked the best? Make a graph of time versus temperature.

Can the same insulators keep things cold? Find out by repeating the same experiment just described. Replace hot water with crushed ice or snow. Test with different insulating materials such as cotton, wool, popcorn kernels, popped corn, beans, aluminum foil, paper, and so on.

Which insulator works the best? Do plants and animals use insulators? One example of insulator in nature is birds' nests. Think of other examples of insulators in nature and in your own home.

REVIEW QUESTIONS

1. Does the First Law of Thermodynamics imply a directionality in nature?

2. What is specific heat capacity? Which heats more quickly, a kilogram of water or a kilogram of copper? Why?

3. What are the three different ways by which heat is transferred? Give an example of how each of them works in your house.

4. What is the difference between temperature and heat?

5. How did Daniel Fahrenheit produce the temperature scale that bears his name?

6. What makes a good conductor of heat? What makes a good insulator?

7. Explain why heat only flows spontaneously from hot to cold objects.

8. What form of energy can travel through a vacuum?

9. Describe three common temperature scales. What fixed points are used to calibrate them?

10. State the second law of thermodynamics in three different ways. In what ways are these three statements equivalent?

11. What is the high-temperature reservoir in your car's engine? What is the low-temperature reservoir?

12. What is entropy? Give an example of a situation in which entropy increases. Can the entropy of an isolated system decrease? If so, how?

13. In what way is aging an example of the second law of thermodynamics?

14. What is meant by the "heat death" of the universe?

DISCUSSION QUESTIONS

1. Why do you suppose that walking on a carpeted floor on a cold winter morning is more comfortable than walking on a tile floor?

2. After driving a car for a long time, you can feel how warm the engine is when you place your hand on the hood or even just close to the hood. What form (or forms) of heat transfer are taking place?

3. Many power plants use heat to boil water into steam and then channel the steam to turn turbines to create electric power. If heat is used like this, why do power plants have huge, tall cooling stacks?

4. Give three examples of the directionality of nature that you have experienced since you woke up this morning. How do these examples relate to the second law of thermodynamics?

5. Why is it easier to demolish a building than it was to build it?

6. Imagine lying on a hot beach on a sunny summer day. In what different ways is heat transferred to your body? In each case what was the original source of the energy? What happens to some of that thermal energy if you jump into the ocean?

7. Does the Second Law limit the efficiency of a furnace that burns natural gas? Why or why not?

8. Cogeneration is a term used to describe systems in which waste heat from electrical generating plants is used to heat nearby homes and businesses with efficiencies much greater than 50%. Does cogeneration violate the second law? Why or why not?

9. The United States Patent Office maintains a web page listing what applications for patents that it calls "Perpetual Motion Gimmicks." Why does the USPTO refer to them as "gimmicks"?

10. Which do you think has more thermal energy, a giant iceberg or a campfire? What is your reasoning?

11. Describe at least three examples of heat transfer that occur when you go for a long walk on a cold day. In each instance, state whether the heat transfer is by conduction, convection, or radiation. Where does the energy come from? Where does it end up?

12. What methods have animals evolved to control the flow of heat into and out of their bodies? Why can penguins, whales, and seals survive in near-freezing water? What role does fat play in the maintenance of body heat?

13. Why does a cool breeze feel so refreshing on a hot day? Why does the same breeze feel colder when it is raining and you are soaking wet?

14. After sunset on a hot summer day, the bricks in the wall of a building feel warm, but the glass windows do not. Why?

15. You sip from a hot mug of coffee carefully to not burn yourself but you hold the mug with no concerns. Why?

16. Consider the example of the three numbered orange balls and the three numbered green balls discussed in the text. The odds of the balls being arranged in the order (Orange 1, Orange 2, Orange 3, Green 1, Green 2, Green 3) are the same of having them in the order (Green 3, Orange 2, Green 1, Green 2, Orange 1, Orange 3). If they have the same odds of happening, why is the first situation considered to have lower entropy?

17. Imagine filming an activity and then watching it backwards. If you have trouble determining whether or not the video is actually running backwards, then that activity is called "reversible." A reversible process doesn't increase entropy. Tossing a ball up and catching it would appear to be reversible. Do you think this activity increases entropy? Why or why not?

18. You come across an animal with an extremely thick layer of body fat. If you find this animal in its natural habitat, where are you most likely to be?

    a. The Amazon Rainforest in Brazil
    b. The Siberian tundra in Russia
    c. Off the coast of Hawai'i in the United States
    d. The Atacama Desert in Chile

19. Which of the following forms of heat transfer is most likely enhanced by placing a heat source along a wall and on the floor of a room?

    a. Conduction
    b. Convection
    c. Radiation
    d. All of the above are equally enhanced.

20. A two-toed tree sloth can have a body temperature as low as 75°F while still being healthy. What is this temperature in Celcius?

    a. 77.4°C
    b. 59.4°C
    c. 41.7°C
    d. 19.1°C

21. The specific heat capacity of aluminum is 0.215 cal/(g*°C). An aluminum pot has a mass of 500 g. How many calories of heat are needed to raise its temperature by just 1°C?

    a. 107.5 cal
    b. 59.7 cal
    c. 193.5 cal
    d. 75.5 cal

PROBLEMS

1. A power plant combusts natural gas at a temperature of 700 K and vents the exhaust into the atmosphere, which is at a temperature of 300 K. What is the maximum possible efficiency? What would the maximum possible efficiency be for a power plant in the Russian city of Yakutsk, where the atmospheric temperature can be as low as 230 K?

2. In January 1913, Death Valley recorded its lowest-ever temperature of 15°F and its highest-ever temperature of 134°F the following July. What were the temperature extremes of Death Valley in 1913 in degrees Celsius?

3. While traveling in Europe over the winter holidays you stay in a hotel room. The management has asked you to not adjust the thermostat higher than 20°C. How many degrees Fahrenheit is this?

4. You have four colored balls: two green ones numbered "1" and "2" and two orange ones also numbered "1" and "2." What percentage of possible arrangements has two green balls followed by two orange balls?

5. A Diesel engine on a large ocean liner can have an efficiency in excess of 50%. If the efficiency is 50% and the waste heat is exhausted into a 290-K environment, what is the operating temperature of the engine?

6. The specific heat capacity of stainless steel is about 0.120 cal/(g*°C) and the specific heat capacity of gold is 0.0310 cal/(g*°C). For 1 gram of each substance, by how much will the temperature change if we add 20 calories of heat to it?

7. The Ocean Thermal Electric Conversion system (OTEC) is a kind of a high-tech electric generator. It takes advantage of the fact that in the tropics, deep ocean water is at a temperature of 4°C, while the water at the surface is at a temperature around 25°C. The idea is to find a material that boils between these temperatures. The material in fluid form is brought up through a large pipe from the depths, and the expansion associated with its boiling is used to drive an electric turbine. The gas is then pumped back to the depths, where it condenses back to a liquid and the whole process repeats itself.

   a. What is the maximum efficiency with which OTEC can produce electricity? (*Hint:* Remember to convert all temperatures to the Kelvin scale.)

   b. Why do you suppose engineers are willing to pursue the scheme, given your answer in part (a)?

   c. What is the ultimate source of the energy generated by OTEC?

8. Repeat Problem 4 for a collection of 12 numbered balls (6 blue and 6 green). What happens to the probability of an ordered configuration as the total number of balls doubles?

9. What is your body temperature in degrees Celsius? If you had a fever of 102.5° in Fahrenheit, what would it be in Kelvin and Celsius?

INVESTIGATIONS

1. Investigate the daily high and low temperatures for the past week in a coastal city like New York or San Diego, a city in the U.S. Midwest such as Kansas City or St. Louis, and a city in the desert such as Las Vegas or Tucson. On average, what is the difference in temperature? What causes this difference? What part does the ocean play in the regulation of temperature?

2. How are your home's walls, windows, and doors insulated? What could you do to improve your home's insulation? What form of energy transfer is most important with regard to energy loss in home heating? conduction? convection? or radiation?

3. Fill a glass, an aluminum cup, a coffee mug, and a plastic drinking cup with hot water. Which transfers the heat to your hand the most quickly? Which holds the heat longest? What does this mean in terms of heat capacities and conductivity?

4. Propose an experiment that you could perform at home to measure the relative heat capacities of different substances such as soap, wood, and glass.

5. Are any buildings at your university considered "green"? What does it mean for a building to be "green"?

6. What does a LEED rating for a building mean? What factors are considered in giving these ratings?

7. Play a videotape of a favorite movie backward. How many violations of the second law of thermodynamics can you spot?

8. Boil a pan of water on your stove. Can you identify the convection cells in the pan? How hot does the water have to be before convection starts? (*Hint:* A small amount of food coloring can reveal the formation of convection cells.)

9. Research how night vision equipment, including video cameras, works. What forms of energy are used in the production of these images?

10. Cosmologists speculate that there might be other universes where the laws of nature are different from ours. Suppose that such a universe had no Second Law of Thermodynamics. How would it differ from ours?

5 Electricity and Magnetism

What is lightning?

PHYSICS

Electricity can be generated by rotating coils of wire in the vicinity of a magnet.

BIOLOGY

Nerve impulses are electrical signals that travel along fibers (nerves) to and from the brain.

CHEMISTRY

Chemical energy stored in batteries can be used to supply electrical energy.

TECHNOLOGY

Photocopiers rely on static electricity to transfer black particles to white paper.

GREAT IDEA

Electricity and magnetism are two different aspects of one force—the electromagnetic force.

ENVIRONMENT

Emissions from electrical generating plants may be a major source of air pollution.

ASTRONOMY

Earth and other planets behave like giant magnets.

HEALTH & SAFETY

Doctors use magnetic resonance imaging (MRI) machines, which employ strong magnetic fields, to probe the body's internal structures without potentially dangerous radiation.

GEOLOGY

Lightning conducts electricity between negative charges in a cloud and positive charges on the ground.

 = applications of the great idea discussed in this chapter

 = other applications, some of which are discussed in other chapters

The Hidden Force

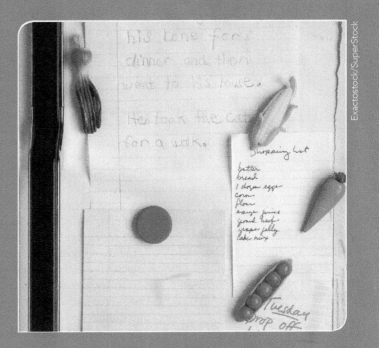

Time to clean up from breakfast. You rinse off your dishes and turn on the garbage disposal; the powerful motor whirs into action. As you open the refrigerator to put away the milk and butter, the light comes on and the refrigerator's compressor hums. On the refrigerator door you see the magnet that holds the note reminding you to renew your driver's license. Then your digital watch beeps the hour; 8 a.m.—better get moving.

All of these familiar objects—lights, motors, magnets, beepers, and dozens of other essential technologies—owe their existence to the pervasive, invisible force called electromagnetism.

5.1 Nature's Other Forces

According to Newton's laws of motion, nothing happens without a force, but the law of gravity that Newton discussed cannot explain many everyday events. How does a refrigerator magnet cling to metal, defying gravity? How does a compass needle swing around to the north? How can static cling wrinkle your shirt, or lightning shatter an old tree? These phenomena point to the existence of some underlying force that is different from gravity.

Newton may not have known about these forces, but he did give us a method for studying them. First observe natural phenomena and learn how they behave, then organize those observations into a series of natural laws, and finally use those laws to predict future behavior of the physical world. This is the process we have called the scientific method.

In particular, we will find Newton's first law of motion (see Chapter 2) to be very useful in our investigation of nature's other forces. According to this law, whenever we see a change in the state of motion of any material object, we know that a force has acted to produce that change. Thus, whenever we see such a change and can rule out the action of known forces such as gravity, we can conclude that the change must have been caused by a hitherto unknown force. We shall use this line of reasoning to show that electrical and magnetic forces exist in the natural world.

Our understanding of the phenomena associated with static electricity and magnetism began in the eighteenth century with a group of scientists in Europe and North America who called themselves "electricians." These researchers were fascinated by the many curious phenomena associated with nature's unseen forces. Their thoughts were not focused on practical applications, nor could they have imagined how their work would transform the world.

◎ 5.2 Static Electricity

Have you ever noticed how your hair tends to stand on end and your clothes stick together on dry winter days? Such phenomena related to static electricity have been known since ancient times. The Greeks knew that if you rub a piece of amber with cat's fur and then touch other objects with the amber, those other objects are repelled from each other. The same thing would happen, they found, if you rub a piece of glass with silk: objects touched with the glass are repelled from each other. On the other hand, if you bring objects that have been touched with the amber near objects touched with the glass, they are attracted toward each other. Objects that behave in this way are said to possess **electrical charge**, or to be "charged."

The force that moves objects toward and away from each other in these simple demonstrations was named **electricity** (from *electro,* the Greek word for amber). In these simple experiments, the electrical charge doesn't move once it has been placed on an object, so the force is also called **static electricity**.

The electrical force is clearly different from gravity. Unlike the electrical force, gravity can never be repulsive: when a gravitational force acts between two objects, it always pulls them together. The electrical force, on the other hand, can attract some objects toward each other and push other objects apart (Figure 5-1). Furthermore, the electrical force is vastly more powerful than gravity. A pocket comb charged with static electricity easily lifts a piece of paper against the entire gravitational pull of Earth.

Today, we understand that the properties of the electrical force arise from the existence of two kinds of electrical charges (Figure 5-2). We say that objects touched with the same source, be it amber or glass, have the same electrical charge and are repelled from each other. On the other hand, one object touched with amber will have a different electrical charge than a second object touched with glass. This difference is reflected in their behavior—they attract each other.

FIGURE 5-1 When the girl touched the electrically charged sphere, her hair became electrically charged as well. Individual hairs repel each other and thus "stand on end."

SCIENCE IN THE MAKING
Benjamin Franklin and Electrical Charge

The most famous North American "electrician" was Benjamin Franklin (1706–1790), one of the pioneers of electrical science as well as a central figure in the founding of the United States of America. Franklin, who had retired from a successful career as a printer and publisher, began his electrical experiments in 1746 with a study of electricity generated by friction. Most scientists of the time thought that electrical effects resulted from the interaction of two different "electrical fluids." Franklin, however, became convinced that all electrical phenomena could be explained by the transfer of a single electrical fluid from one object to another. He realized that objects could have an excess or a deficiency of this fluid, and he applied the names "negative" and "positive" to these two situations.

Following this work, Franklin is said to have demonstrated the electrical nature of lightning in June 1752 with his famous (and extremely dangerous) kite experiment (Figure 5-3). A mild lightning strike hit his kite and passed along the wet string to produce sparks and an electrical shock. Not content with acquiring experimental knowledge, Franklin followed his discovery of the electrical nature of lightning with the invention of the lightning rod, a metal rod with one end in the ground and the other end sticking up above the roof of a building. It carries the electrical charge of lightning into Earth's surface, diverting it away from the building. Lightning rods caught on quickly in the wooden cities of North America and Europe, preventing countless deadly fires. They are still widely used.

FIGURE 5-2 The two kinds of electrical charges. (a) Opposite charges attract, while (b) like charges repel.

Metal spheres with
opposite charges
are attracted to
each other.

(a)

Metal spheres with
the same charge are
repelled from
each other.

(b)

The Movement of Electrons

We now understand that there are two kinds of electrical charge, so observations of both attractive and repulsive behavior of charged objects are easy to understand. In modern language, we say that all objects are made up of minute building blocks called atoms and that all atoms consist of still smaller particles that have electrical charge. As we shall see in Chapter 8, negatively charged electrons move around a heavy, positively charged nucleus at the center of every atom. Electrons and the nucleus have opposite electrical charges, so an attractive force exists between them. This force in atoms plays a role similar to that played by gravity in keeping the solar system together. Most atoms are electrically neutral, because the positive charge of the nucleus cancels the negative charge of the electrons.

Electrons, particularly those in outer orbits far from the nucleus, tend to be rather loosely bound to their atoms. These electrons can be removed from the atom (for example, by friction) and, once removed, can move freely in metals or can react with other elements.

When negative electrons are stripped off of a material, they no longer cancel the positive charges in the nucleus. The result is a net excess of positive charge in the object, and we say that the object as a whole has acquired a **positive electrical charge**. Similarly, an object acquires a **negative electrical charge** when extra electrons are added to it. This addition of electrons happens when you run a comb through your hair on a dry day; electrons are stripped from your hair and added to the comb, so the comb acquires a negative charge (Figure 5-4). Simultaneously, your hair loses electrons, so individual strands become positively charged.

During a thunderstorm, the same phenomenon occurs on a much larger scale, as wind and rain disrupt the normal distribution of electrons in clouds. When a charged cloud passes over a tall tree or tower, the violent electrical discharge called lightning may result from the attraction of the positive charges on the ground and negative charges in the cloud (although in the case of lightning, both the positive and negative charges move).

Although historical investigations of electrical charge tended to concentrate on somewhat artificial experiments, we have come to know that electrically charged particles play important roles in many natural systems. Virtually all of the atoms in the Sun, for example, have lost electrons; the Sun is thus made of a turbulent mixture of positive atoms and negative electrons. In all advanced life forms (including human beings), charged atoms constantly move into and out of cells to maintain the processes of life. As you read these words, for example, positively charged potassium and sodium atoms are moving across the membranes of cells in your optic nerve to carry signals to your brain.

Coulomb's Law

The phenomenon of electricity remained something of a mild curiosity until the mid-eighteenth century, when scientists began applying the scientific method to investigate it. One of the first tasks was to develop a precise statement about the nature of the electrical force. The French scientist Charles Augustin de Coulomb (1736–1806) was most responsible for this work. During the 1780s, at the same time Benjamin Franklin and others were writing the U.S. Constitution, Coulomb devised a series of experiments

Museum of the City of New York/©Corbis

FIGURE 5-3 Benjamin Franklin engaged in his famous (and potentially lethal) kite experiment.

FIGURE 5-4 When a plastic comb is drawn through your hair, electrons move from your hair to the comb, leaving both with an electrical charge.

Electrons removed from the hair

Electrons added to the comb

Sabrina Vani/Radius Images/Getty Images, Inc.

in which he passed different amounts of electrical charge onto objects and then measured the force between them.

After repeated measurements Coulomb discovered that the electrical force was in some ways very similar to the gravitational force that Isaac Newton had discovered a century earlier. He observed that if two electrically charged objects are moved farther away from each other, the force between them gets smaller, just like gravity. In fact, if the distance between two objects is doubled, the force decreases by a factor of four— the familiar 1/distance^2, or inverse-square relationship, that we saw in the law of universal gravitation in Chapter 2. Coulomb also discovered that the size of the force depends on the product of the charges of the two objects—double the charge on either object and the force doubles; double the charge on both objects and the force increases by a factor of four.

Coulomb summarized his discoveries in a simple relationship known as **Coulomb's law**:

In words: The force between any two electrically charged objects is proportional to the product of their charges divided by the square of the distance between them.

In equation form:

$$\text{force (newtons)} = k \times \frac{\text{1st charge} \times \text{2nd charge}}{\text{distance}^2}$$

In symbols:

$$F = k \times \frac{q_1 \times q_2}{d^2}$$

where distance d is measured in meters, charge q is measured in a unit called the coulomb (see the following explanation), and k is the coulomb constant, a number that plays the same role in electricity that the gravitational constant G plays in gravity. Like G, k is a number (8.99×10^9 newton-meter^2/coulomb^2 in one common system of units) that can be determined experimentally and that turns out to be the same for all charges and all separations of those charges anywhere in the universe.

Coulomb's law is a summary of a large number of experiments done on stationary electrical charges, or static electricity. In order to come to such a result, scientists had to define a unit of electrical charge, called the *coulomb* (abbreviated C) after the scientist who did so much of this important work. Today, we define the coulomb as the charge on 6.3×10^{18} electrons—a very large number. When this many electrons have been added to or subtracted from an object, that object will have 1 coulomb of electrical charge.

SCIENCE BY THE NUMBERS
Two Forces Compared

In Chapter 8 we will examine compelling evidence that the atoms that compose all the materials in our physical surroundings have a definite internal structure. Tiny negatively charged particles called electrons circle in orbits around a positively charged nucleus. Thus, inside an atom, two forces act between the nucleus and an electron: the force of gravity and the electrical force. We can use this fact to get a sense of the relative strength of the two forces.

The simplest atom is hydrogen, in which a single electron moves around a single positively charged particle known as a proton (see Chapter 8). The masses of the electron and proton are 9×10^{-31} kg and 1.7×10^{-27} kg, respectively. The charge on the proton is 1.6×10^{-19} C, and the charge on the electron has the same magnitude but is negative. A typical separation of these two particles in an atom is 10^{-10} m.

Given these numbers, what are the values of the electrical and gravitational attractions between these two particles?

Gravity: The force of gravity between the two particles is given by Newton's law of gravity:

force of gravity (in newtons)

$$= G \times \frac{\text{mass}_1(\text{kg}) \times \text{mass}_2(\text{kg})}{\text{distance (m)}^2}$$

$$= \left(6.7 \times 10^{-11} \times \frac{\text{m}^3}{\text{kg} - \text{s}^2} \times \frac{(1.7 \times 10^{-27} \text{ kg}) \times (9 \times 10^{-31} \text{ kg})}{(10^{-10} \text{ m})^2} \right)$$

$$= 1.0 \times 10^{-47} \text{ N}$$

Electricity: The electrical force, on the other hand, is given by Coulomb's law:

force of static electricity (in newtons)

$$= k \times \frac{\text{charge}_1(\text{C}) \times \text{charge}_2(\text{C})}{\text{distance(m)}^2}$$

$$= \left(9 \times 10^9 \times \frac{\text{Nm}^2}{\text{C}^2} \right) \times (1.6 \times 10^{-19} \text{ C}) \times \frac{(1.6 \times 10^{-19} \text{ C})}{(10^{-10} \text{ m})^2}$$

$$= 2.3 \times 10^{-18} \text{ N}$$

From this simple calculation we can see that, in the atom, the electrical force (2.3×10^{-18} N) is almost 30 orders of magnitude (factors of 10) larger than the gravitational force (1.0×10^{-47} N)—a huge difference. This result explains why our discussion of the atom in subsequent chapters ignores the effects of gravity completely.

The Electrical Field

Imagine that you have an electrical charge sitting at a point (Figure 5-5). The charged object could be a piece of lint, an electron, or one of your hairs. If you brought a second charged object to a spot near the first, the second object would feel a force. If you then moved the second object to another spot near the lint, it would still feel a force, but the force would, in general, be a different magnitude and point in a different direction than at the first spot. In fact, the second charged object would feel a force at every point in space around the first.

Every charged object exerts forces on its surroundings to create an **electric field**. The electric field at a point is defined to be the force that would be felt by a positive 1-coulomb charge if it were brought to that point. The field is usually drawn so that the directions of the arrows correspond to the direction of the force, and the lengths of the arrows correspond to its magnitude. In this way you can make a picture that represents the electric field around the charged object, as shown in Figure 5-5. Notice that the electrical field is defined as the force that would be felt by another charge if that charge were located at a particular point, so that the field is present even if no other charge is in the region.

◉ 5.3 Magnetism

Just as electrical phenomena were known to the ancient philosophers, so too were the phenomena we place under the title of magnetism. The first known **magnets** were naturally occurring iron minerals. If you bring one of these minerals (a common one is magnetite or "lodestone") near a piece of iron, the iron will be attracted to it. You have undoubtedly seen experiments in which magnets were placed near nails, which jumped up and hung from them.

The fact that the nails behave in this way tells you that there must be yet another force in nature, a force seemingly different from both electricity and gravity. Electrical attraction doesn't make the nails move, nor is it gravity that causes the nails to jump up. The simple experiment of picking up a nail with a magnet illustrates beyond a shadow of a doubt that there is a **magnetic force** in the universe—a force that can be identified and described by the same methods we used to investigate gravity and electricity. Whereas electricity remained a curiosity until well into modern times, magnetism was put to practical use very early. The compass, invented in

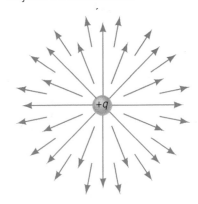

FIGURE 5-5 An electrical field surrounding a positive charge, +q, may be represented by lines of force radiating outward. Any charged object that approaches +q experiences a greater and greater electrical force the closer it gets. Positively charged objects will be repelled, while negatively charged objects will be attracted.

China and used by Europeans to navigate the oceans during the age of exploration, is the first magnetic device on record. A sliver of lodestone, left free to rotate, will align itself in a north–south direction. We use compasses so often these days that it's easy to forget how important it was for early travelers to know directions, particularly travelers who ventured out of sight of land in sailing ships.

In the late sixteenth century, the English scientist William Gilbert (1544–1603) conducted the first serious study of magnets. Though revered in his day as a doctor (he was physician to both Queen Elizabeth I and King James I), Gilbert achieved his most lasting fame through his discovery that every magnet can be characterized by what he called **poles**. If you take a piece of naturally occurring magnet and let it rotate, one end of the magnet points north and the other end points south. These two ends of the magnet are called poles. The two poles of a magnet are given the labels "north" and "south," and the resulting magnet is called a *dipole magnet*.

In the course of his research, Gilbert discovered many important properties of magnets. He learned to magnetize iron and steel rods by stroking them with a lodestone. He discovered that hammered iron becomes magnetic and that iron's magnetism can be destroyed by heating. He realized that planet Earth itself is a giant dipole magnet, a fact that, as we shall see, explains the operation of the compass. Gilbert found that if two magnets are brought near each other so that the north poles are close together, a repulsive force develops between the magnets and they are forced apart. The same thing happens if two south poles are brought together. If, however, the north pole of one magnet is brought near the south pole of another magnet, the resulting force is attractive. In this respect, magnetism seems to mimic the eighteenth century studies of static electricity. William Gilbert's results can be summarized in two simple statements.

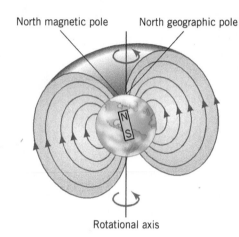

North magnetic pole   North geographic pole

Rotational axis

FIGURE 5-6 A compass needle and Earth. Any magnet will twist because of the forces between its poles and those of Earth. Note that Earth's north and south magnetic poles don't quite line up with Earth's axis of rotation.

1. Every magnet has two poles.
2. Like magnetic poles repel each other, while unlike poles attract.

Once you know that a magnet has two poles, you can understand how a compass behaves. Earth itself is a giant dipole magnet, with one pole in Canada and the other pole in Antarctica. If a piece of magnetized iron (for example, a compass needle) is allowed to rotate freely, one of its poles will be attracted to and twist around toward Canada in the north, and the other end will point to Antarctica in the south (see Figure 5-6).

Recall that an electrical force can be represented by an electric field, with arrows that represent the direction and strength of the field at every point (Figure 5-5). So, too, can the magnetic force be represented in terms of a **magnetic field**. Magnets display a curving field pattern, with arrows that indicate the direction and strength of magnetic forces at any point around the magnet. If many small compass needles are brought near the magnet, as shown in Figure 5-7, the forces exerted by the magnet will twist the needles around parallel to the magnetic field at each point. Taken together, these compass needles will follow curving lines that start and end at the north and south poles of the dipole magnet.

FIGURE 5-7 The curving lines of a magnetic field are revealed by an array of small compass needles that surround a bar magnet.

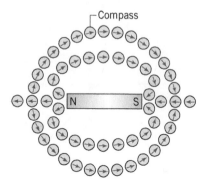

Just as we can imagine any collection of electrical charges as being surrounded by the imaginary lines of force of an electric field, we can envision every magnet as being surrounded by an imaginary set of lines of the magnetic field (Figure 5-8). These lines are drawn so that if a compass were brought to a point in space, the needle would turn and point along the line. The number of lines in a given area is a measure of the strength of the forces exerted on the compass. You can see one consequence of this effect in the northern lights, or aurora borealis (Figure 5-9). Charged particles streaming from the Sun can emit light when they interact with a magnetic field. The convergence of magnetic field lines near Earth's North and South Poles enhances this effect and produces the colorful display.

Magnetic
field lines

N S

(a)

(b)

Andy Washnik

FIGURE 5-8 *(a)* A bar magnet and its magnetic dipole field. *(b)* Iron filings placed near a bar magnet align themselves along the field.

Carson Ganci/Age Fotostock America, Inc.

FIGURE 5-9 A spectacular example of the aurora borealis, caused by particles from the Sun interacting with Earth's magnetic field.

THE SCIENCE OF LIFE
Magnetic Navigation

Many living things in addition to humans use Earth's magnetic field for navigation. Scientists at the Massachusetts Institute of Technology demonstrated this ability in 1975, when they were studying a single-celled bacterium that lived in the ooze at the bottom of nearby swamps. They found that the bacteria incorporate about 20 microscopic crystals of the mineral magnetite into their bodies (Figure 5-10). These minute crystals are strung out in a line, in effect forming a microscopic compass needle.

Because Earth's magnetic field dips into the surface in the Northern Hemisphere and rises up out of it in the Southern, the Massachusetts bacteria have a built-in "up" and "down" indicator. This internal magnet allows the bacteria to navigate down into the nutrient-rich ooze at the bottom of the pond. Interestingly enough, related bacteria in the Southern Hemisphere follow the field lines in the opposite direction to get to the bottom of their ponds.

Since 1975, similar internal magnets have been discovered in many animals. Some migratory birds, for example, use internal magnets as one of several cues to guide them on flights thousands of miles in length. In the case of the Australian silvereye, evidence suggests that the bird can "see" Earth's magnetic field, through a process involving modification of molecules normally involved in color vision.

FIGURE 5-10 Grains of iron minerals in this bacterium allow it to tell up from down.

Courtesy Brian Lower and Zachery Oestreicher

FIGURE 5-11 Cut magnets. If you break a dipole magnet in two, you get two smaller dipole magnets, not an isolated north or south pole.

Pairs of Poles

The dipole magnetic field shown in Figure 5-8 plays a very important role in nature. All magnets found in nature have both north and south poles—you never find one without the other. Even if you take an ordinary bar magnet and cut it in two, you don't get a north pole and a south pole in isolation, but rather two small magnets each with both a north and a south pole (Figure 5-11). If you took each of those halves and cut them in half, you would continue to get smaller and smaller dipole magnets. In fact, it seems to be a general rule of nature that:

● **There are no isolated magnetic poles in nature.**

In the language of physicists, a single isolated north or south magnetic pole would be called a *magnetic monopole*. Although physicists have conducted extensive searches for monopoles, no experiment has yet found clear evidence for their existence.

◉ 5.4 Batteries and Electric Circuits

Discovery of the surprising connection between electricity and magnetism had to await the invention of two familiar devices—the battery and the electric circuit. Remarkably, these commonplace technologies were inspired by the study of frogs.

THE SCIENCE OF LIFE
Luigi Galvani and Life's Electrical Force

Scientists of the eighteenth century discovered unexpected links between life and electricity. Of all the phenomena in nature, none fascinated these scientists more than the mysterious "life force," which seemed to allow animals to move and grow. An old doctrine called vitalism held that this force was found only in living organisms, and not in the rest of nature. Luigi Galvani (1737–1798), an Italian physician and anatomist, added fuel to the debate about the nature of life with a series of classic experiments demonstrating the effects of electricity on living things.

Galvani's most famous investigations employed an electric spark to induce convulsive twitching in amputated frogs' legs—a phenomenon not unlike a person's involuntary reaction to a jolt of electricity. Later he was able to produce a similar effect simply by poking a frog's leg simultaneously with one fork of copper and one of iron. In modern language, we would say that the electrical charge and the presence of the two metals in the salty fluid in the frog's leg led to a flow of electrical charge in the frog's nerves, a process that caused contractions of the muscles (Figure 5-12). Galvani, however, argued that his experiments showed that living systems possess a vital force, something he called "animal electricity," which made them different from inanimate matter. This idea gained some acceptance among the scientific community but provoked a long debate between Galvani and the Italian physicist Alessandro Volta (1745–1827). Volta argued that Galvani's effects were caused by chemical reactions between the metals and the salty fluids of the frogs' legs. In retrospect, both of these scientists had part of the truth. Muscle contractions are indeed initiated by electrical signals, even if there is no such thing as animal electricity, and electrical charges can be induced to flow by chemical reactions.

The controversy that surrounded Galvani's experiments had many surprising effects. On the practical side, as we discuss in the text, Volta's work on chemical reactions led to the development of the battery and, indirectly, to our modern understanding of electricity. The notion of animal electricity proved a great boon to medical quacks and con men, and for centuries various kinds of electrical devices were palmed off on the public as cures for almost every known disease. Some of these devices can be seen on sale today, in the form of magnets that, when strapped to the body, are supposed to cure various illnesses.

FIGURE 5-12 Luigi Galvani showed that the frog's legs would twitch when stimulated by electrical current, a phenomenon that eventually led to the invention of the battery (as well as the novel *Frankenstein*).

Mary Evans Picture Library/Alamy

Fig. 405.

FIGURE 5-13 The idea behind the legend of Frankenstein may have been suggested by early experiments on animal electricity.

Finally, in a bizarre epilogue to Galvani's research, other researchers used batteries to study the effects of electrical currents on human cadavers. In one famous public demonstration, a corpse was made to sit up and kick its legs by electrical stimulation. Such unorthodox experiments helped to inspire Mary Shelley's famous novel, *Frankenstein* (Figure 5-13).

Batteries and Electrical Current

Although we encounter static electricity in our everyday lives, most of our contact with electricity comes from moving charges. In your home, for example, negatively charged electrons move through wires to run all of your electric appliances. A flow of charged particles is called an **electrical current**.

Until the work of Alessandro Volta, scientists could not produce persistent electrical currents in their laboratories and therefore knew little about them. As a result of his investigations into Galvani's work, Volta developed the first **battery**, a device that converts stored chemical energy in the battery materials into kinetic energy of electrons running through an outside wire.

The first battery was a crude affair, but we now use its descendants to start our cars and run all sorts of portable electrical equipment. Your car battery, a reliable and beautifully engineered device, routinely performs for years before it needs replacing. It is made of alternating plates of two kinds of material, commonly lead and lead oxide, immersed in a bath of dilute sulfuric acid. When the battery is being discharged, the lead plates interact with the acid, producing lead sulphate (the white crud that collects around the posts of old batteries) and some free electrons. These electrons run through an external wire to the other plates, where they interact with the lead oxide and sulfuric acid to form more lead sulphate. The electrons running through the outside wire are the electric current that starts your car.

When the battery is completely discharged, it consists of plates of lead sulphate immersed in water, a configuration from which no energy can be obtained. Running a current backward through the battery, however, runs all the chemical reactions in reverse and restores the original configuration. We say that the battery has been recharged. Once recharged, the whole cycle can proceed again. In your car, the generator constantly recharges the battery whenever the engine is running, so that it's always ready to use.

FIGURE 5-14 Every electrical circuit incorporates a source of energy (1), a loop of wire (2), and a device such as a lightbulb (3).

Electric Circuits

Most people come into contact with electrical phenomena through electric circuits in their homes and cars. An **electric circuit** is an unbroken path of material that carries electricity. Such materials are called *electrical conductors*. Copper wire is an example of a conductor. The fluorescent light that you use to read this book, for example, is part of an electric circuit that begins at a power plant that generates electricity many miles away. That electricity continues through power lines into your town and is distributed on overhead or underground wires until it finally gets to where you live. There the circuit, of which the light is a part, is made up of wires that run through the walls of your home. One set of these wires goes first to a circuit breaker (to break the circuit in case of a dangerous overload of too much current), then to a switch, and finally to the bulb. When you turn on the switch, you complete an unbroken path that runs all the way from the generating plant to the bulb. When electricity flows through the gas in the fluorescent bulb, it excites the atoms and causes them to give off light. When you put the switch in the "off" position, it's like raising a drawbridge: the current is blocked from flowing into this part of the circuit, and none reaches the light. The room becomes dark.

Every circuit consists of three parts: a source of energy like a battery, a closed path usually made of metal wire through which the current can flow, and a device such as a motor or a lightbulb that uses the electrical energy (Figure 5-14).

Ohm's Law

One way to think about electric circuits is to draw an analogy between electrons flowing through a wire and water flowing through a pipe. In the case of water, we use two quantities to characterize the flow: the amount of water that passes a point each second, and the pressure behind that water. The numbers we use to describe the flow of electrons in an electric circuit are exactly the same.

The amount of current (the number of electrons) that actually flows in a wire is measured in a unit called the ampere or amp, named after French physicist André-Marie Ampère (1775–1836). One amp corresponds to a flow of 1 coulomb (the unit of electrical charge) per second past a point in the wire:

$$1 \text{ amp of current} = 1 \text{ coulomb of charge per second}$$

Electrical current, therefore, is analogous to the current of a river or stream. Typical household appliances use anywhere from about 1 amp (a 100-watt bulb) to 40 amps (an electric range with all burners and the oven blazing away).

We call the pressure produced by the energy source in a circuit the **voltage**, measured in *volts* (abbreviated V) and named after Alessandro Volta, the Italian scientist who invented the chemical battery. You can think of voltage in circuits much the same way you think of water pressure in your plumbing system. More volts in a circuit mean more "oomph" to the current, just as more water pressure makes the water flow faster. Typically, a new flashlight battery produces 1.5 volts, a fully charged car battery produces about 15 volts (even though they are called 12-volt batteries), and ordinary household circuits operate on either 115 or 230 volts.

Wires through which the current (electrons) flows are analogous to pipes carrying water: the smaller the pipe, the harder it is to push water through it. Similarly, it is harder to push electrons through some wires than others. The quantity that measures how hard it is to push electrons through wires is called **electrical resistance**, and it is measured in a unit called the *ohm* (Figure 5-15). As the resistance increases (i.e., the lower the efficiency), the more electron kinetic energy is converted into heat. Ordinary copper wire, for example, has a low resistance, which explains why we use it to carry electricity around our homes. Toasters and space heaters, on the other hand, employ high-resistance wires so that they will produce large amounts of heat when current flows through them. In transmission lines, it's important that as much energy as possible gets from one end of the line to the other; thus we use very thick low-resistance (high-efficiency) wires.

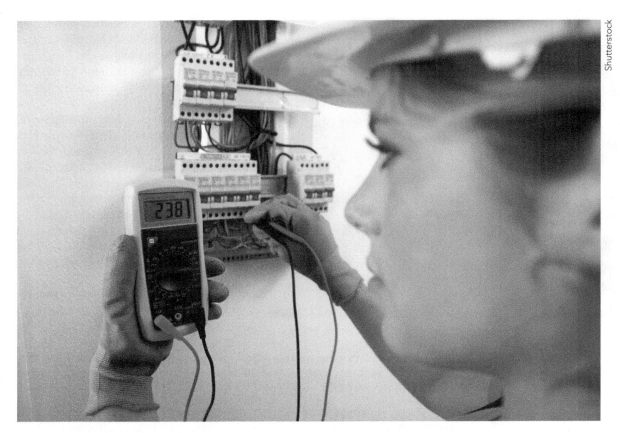

FIGURE 5-15 A multimeter is an instrument that measures the current flowing in a circuit, the voltage in the circuit, and the resistance. Here it is being used to measure the resistance of a small commercial resistor.

The relationship between the resistance in a circuit, the current that flows, and the voltage is called *Ohm's law*, after German scientist Georg Ohm (1787–1854). It states:

In words: The current in circuits is directly proportional to the voltage and inversely proportional to the resistance. The higher the electrical "pressure," the higher the flow of charge. The higher the resistance to flow, the smaller the flow.

In equation form:

$$\text{voltage (volts)} = \text{current (amps)} \times \text{resistance (ohms)}$$

In symbols:

$$V = I \times R$$

SCIENCE IN THE MAKING
The Lightning Rod

Every electric circuit can be characterized by its voltage, current, and resistance, so Ohm's law comes into play whenever electricity flows through a circuit. You can understand the behavior of lightning, for example, in terms of Ohm's law. In a thunderstorm, collisions between particles in the clouds produce a buildup of negative charge at the bottom of the cloud and a corresponding buildup of positive charge in objects on the ground underneath the cloud. The negative charges on the bottom of the cloud repel electrons in the ground, leaving the area under the cloud with a net positive charge. This buildup creates a voltage between cloud and ground, and the lightning stroke is the electrical current that runs between the two when the voltage is high enough.

FIGURE 5-16 These lightning strikes over Seattle are examples of electrical currents in nature.

Lightning, like any other electrical current, will flow along the path of least resistance. Lightning normally strikes tall objects like buildings and trees because the resistance of the building is lower than the resistance of the air (Figure 5-16).

As we mentioned earlier, the lightning rod, invented by Benjamin Franklin, uses this principle by allowing the lightning to flow through a low-resistance bar of metal instead of the building. This invention was quickly adopted in England and America, with the main debate centering on the best design for the tip of the rod. In France, however, some religious leaders argued that the use of the lightning rod thwarted God's plan, and that the device constituted "playing God," a common criticisms of new technologies. Eventually, however, the lightning rod came to be used universally.

STOP & THINK! In Franklin's time, people who opposed the lightning rod believed that one way to prevent lightning damage was to climb into church steeples and ring the bells. Was this a good idea? Why or why not?

The *load* in any electric circuit is the "business end"—the place where useful work gets done. The fluorescent bulb, the heating element in your hair dryer, or electromagnetic coils of wire in an electric motor are typical loads in household circuits. The power used by the load depends both on how much current flows through it and on the size of the voltage. The greater the current or voltage, the more power is used. A simple equation allows us to calculate the amount of electrical power used.

In words: The power consumed by an electric appliance is equal to the product of the current and the voltage.

In equation form:

$$\text{power (watts)} = \text{current (amps)} \times \text{voltage (volts)}$$

In symbols:

$$P = I \times V$$

This equation tells us that both the current and the voltage have to be high for a device to consume high levels of electrical power. Table 5-1 summarizes some key terms about electric circuits.

TABLE 5-1 Terms Related to Electric Circuits

Term	Definition	Unit	Plumbing Analog
Voltage	Electrical pressure	volt	Water pressure
Resistance	Resistance to electron flow	ohm	Pipe diameter
Current	Flow rate of electrons	amp	Flow rate
Power	Current × voltage	watt	Rate of work done by moving water

EXAMPLE 5-1

STARTING YOUR CAR

When you turn on the ignition of your automobile, your 15-volt car battery must turn a 400-amp starter motor. What is the resistance of this circuit, and how much power is required to start your car?

Reasoning and Solution: In order to calculate resistance, we need to rearrange Ohm's law:

$$\text{Resistance (ohms)} = \frac{\text{voltage (volts)}}{\text{current (amps)}}$$
$$= \frac{15 \text{ volts}}{400 \text{ amps}}$$
$$= 0.0375 \text{ ohms}$$

That's a very low resistance, less than a thousandth of the resistance of a typical lightbulb. In order to calculate electrical power, we need to multiply current times voltage:

$$\text{power (watts)} = \text{current (amps)} \times \text{voltage (volts)}$$
$$= 400 \text{ amps} \times 15 \text{ volts}$$
$$= 6000 \text{ watts} = 6 \text{ kilowatts}$$

Most early automobiles were started by a hand crank, which might have required 100 watts of power, a reasonable amount for an adult. Modern, high-compression automobile engines require much more starting power than could be generated by one person.

EXAMPLE 5-2

THE POWER OF SOUND

A typical compact disc system has a resistance of 50 ohms. Assuming that this system is plugged into a normal household outlet rated at 115 volts, how much current will flow through the stereo, and what is the power consumption?

Reasoning and Solution: The current can be calculated by rearranging Ohm's law:

$$\text{current (amps)} = \frac{\text{voltage (volts)}}{\text{resistance (ohms)}}$$
$$= \frac{115 \text{ volts}}{50 \text{ ohms}}$$
$$= 2.3 \text{ amps}$$

The power consumption can then be calculated:

$$\text{power (watts)} = \text{current (amps)} \times \text{voltage (volts)}$$
$$= 2.3 \text{ amps} \times 115 \text{ volts}$$
$$= 264.5 \text{ watts}$$

That's similar to the power consumption of three ordinary 100 watt lightbulbs.

THE SCIENCE OF LIFE
The Propagation of Nerve Signals

All of your body's movements, from the beating of your heart to the blinking of your eyes, are controlled by nerve impulses. Although nerve signals in the human body are electrical in nature, they bear little resemblance to the movement of electrons through a wire. Nerve cells

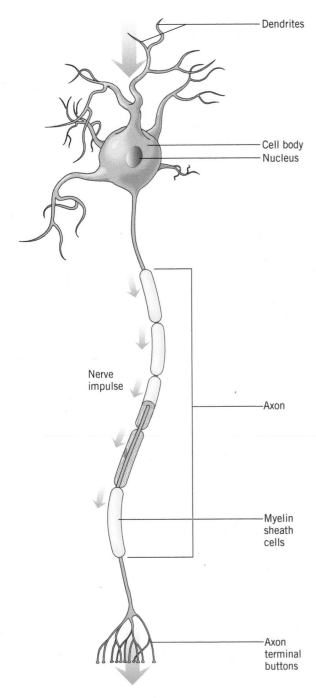

FIGURE 5-17 A nerve cell consists of a central body and a number of filaments. The dendrites receive incoming signals, and the axon conducts outgoing signals away from the cell body. The myelin sheath helps insulate the axon from neighboring electrical interference.

of the type illustrated in Figure 5-17 form the fundamental element of the nervous system. A nerve cell consists of a central body with a large number of filaments going out from it. These filaments connect one nerve cell to others. The branched filament that carries signals away from the central nerve body and delivers those signals to other cells is called the *axon*.

The membrane surrounding the axon is a complex structure, full of channels through which atoms and molecules can move. When the nerve cell is resting, positively charged objects tend to be outside the membrane, negatively charged ones inside. When an electrical signal triggers the axon, however, the membrane is distorted, and, for a short time, positive charges (mainly sodium atoms) pour into the cell. When the inside becomes more positively charged, the membrane changes again and positive charges (this time mainly potassium) move back outside to restore the original charge. This charge disturbance moves down the filament as a nerve signal. When the signal reaches the axon terminal buttons at the end of one of the filaments, it is transferred to the next cell by a group of molecules called *neurotransmitters* that are sprayed out from the end of the "upstream" cell, and received by special structures on the "downstream" cell. The reception of neurotransmitters initiates a complex and poorly understood process by which the nerve cell decides whether to send a signal down its axon to other cells. Thus, although the human nervous system is not an ordinary electric circuit, it does operate by electrical signals.

Two Kinds of Electric Circuits

Common household circuits come in two different types, depending on the arrangement of wires and loads. In *series circuits* (Figure 5-18a), two or more loads are linked along a single loop of wire. In *parallel circuits* (Figure 5-18b), by contrast, different loads are situated on different wire loops.

FIGURE 5-18 Two kinds of electric circuits. (a) In a series circuit more than one device lies on the same loop of wire. (b) In a parallel circuit devices lie on separate loops.

The differences between these two types of circuits can become obvious around Christmas-time. Many older strands of Christmas lights were linked by a single series circuit. If any one light burned out, the entire strand went dark because the electric circuit was broken (and it could be a frustrating experience trying to find the one bad bulb). Most modern light strands, on the other hand, feature several parallel loops, each with just a few lights. So today, if one light burns out, only a few bulbs along the strand will go dark.

● 5.5 Connections Between Electricity and Magnetism

In our everyday experience, static electricity and magnetism seem to be two unrelated phenomena. Yet scientists in the nineteenth century, probing deeper into the electrical and magnetic forces, discovered remarkable connections between the two—discoveries that transformed every aspect of technology.

Magnetic Effects from Electricity

In the spring of 1820, a strange thing happened during a physics lecture in Denmark. The lecturer, Professor Hans Christian Oersted (1777–1851), was using a battery to demonstrate some properties of electricity. By chance he noticed that whenever he connected the battery (so that an electrical current began to flow through a circuit), a compass needle on a nearby table began to twitch and move. When he disconnected the battery, the needle went back to pointing north. This accidental discovery led the way to one of the most profound insights in the history of science. Oersted had discovered that electricity and magnetism—two forces that seem as different from each other as night and day—are in fact intimately related to each other. They are two sides of the same coin. In subsequent studies, Oersted and his colleagues established that whenever electrical charge flows through a wire, a magnetic field will appear around that wire. A compass brought near the wire will twist around until it points along the direction of that field. This observation led to an important experimental finding in electricity and magnetism.

● **Magnetic fields can be created by motions of electrical charges.**

Like all fundamental advances, the discovery of this law of nature has important practical consequences. Perhaps most importantly, it led to the development of the **electromagnet**, a device composed of a coil of wire that produces a magnetic field whenever an electrical charge runs through the wire. Almost every electric appliance in modern technology uses this device.

The Electromagnet

Electromagnets work on a simple principle, as illustrated in Figure 5-19. If an electrical current flows in a loop of wire, then a magnetic field will be created around the wire, just as Oersted discovered in 1820. That magnetic field will have the shape sketched in the figure, a shape familiar to you as the dipole magnetic field shown in Figure 5-8.

In other words, we can create the equivalent of a magnetized piece of iron simply by running electrical current around a loop of wire. The stronger the current (i.e., the more electrical charge we push through the wire), the stronger the magnetic field will be. But unlike a bar magnet, an electromagnet can be turned on and off. To differentiate between these two sorts of magnets, we often refer to magnets made from materials such as iron as permanent magnets.

The electromagnet can be used in all sorts of practical ways, including buzzers, switches, and electric motors. In each of these devices a piece of iron is placed near the magnet. When a current flows in the loops of wire, the iron is pulled toward the magnet. In some cases, the electromagnet can be used to close a switch in an electrical circuit. As soon as the current is turned off in the electromagnet, a spring pushes the iron back, and the current in the larger circuit also shuts off.

FIGURE 5-19 A schematic drawing of an electromagnet reveals the principal components—a loop of wire and a source of electrical current. When a current flows through the wire loop, a magnetic field is created around it.

STEVE GSCHMEISSNER/Photo Researchers, Inc.

SM 11X

You use electromagnetic switches in many household appliances. For example, your home is probably heated by a furnace that is linked to a thermostat on the wall in your living room or hallway. You set the thermostat to a specific temperature. If the temperature in the room falls below the desired temperature, the thermostat responds by using an electromagnet to close a switch, allowing a small current to flow. While the current flows, the switch is closed and the furnace operates, heating the rooms in your house. When the temperature reaches the level you have set, the thermostat stops the current that flows to the electromagnet, the switch opens, and the furnace shuts off. In this way, you can adjust the temperature of your house without having to run to the basement every time you need to turn on the furnace.

TECHNOLOGY
The Electric Motor

FIGURE 5-20 A magnified view of electromagnets inside the disk drive of a computer. The six coils of wire are electromagnets that interact with permanent magnets on a turntable (not shown), causing the turntable to spin.

Look around your room and try to count the number of electric motors that you use every day. They're in fans, clocks, disk drives (Figure 5-20), CD players, hair dryers, electric razors, and dozens of other familiar objects. Electromagnets are crucial components in every one of those electric motors.

The simplest **electric motors**, as shown in Figure 5-21, employ a pair of permanent magnets and a rotating loop of wire inside the poles of the magnets. The current in the rotating loop adjusts so that when it is oriented as shown in Figure 5-21a, the south pole of the electromagnet lies near the north pole of the permanent magnet, and the north pole of the electromagnet lies near the south pole of the permanent magnet. The attractive forces between north and south poles cause the wire loop to spin. As soon as the loop gets to the position shown in Figure 5-21b, the current reverses so that the south pole of the electromagnet lies just past the south pole of the permanent magnet, and the north pole of the electromagnet lies just past the north pole of the permanent magnet. The repulsive forces between like magnetic poles act to continue the rotation. By alternating the current in the loop, a continuous rotational force is kept on the wire, and thus the wire keeps turning.

This simple diagram contains all the essential features of an electric motor, but most electric motors are much more complex. Typically, they have three or more different electromagnets

FIGURE 5-21 An electric motor. The simplest motors work by placing an electromagnet that can rotate between two permanent magnets. (a) When the current is turned on, the north and south poles of the electromagnet are attracted to the south and north poles of the permanent magnets. (b)–(d) As the electromagnet rotates, the current direction is switched, causing the electromagnet to continue rotating.

and at least three permanent magnets, and the alternation of the current direction is somewhat more complicated than we have indicated. By artfully juxtaposing electromagnets and permanent magnets, inventors have produced an astonishing variety of electric motors: fixed-speed for your CD player, variable-speed motors for your food processor, reversible motors for power screwdrivers and drills, and specialized motors for many industrial uses.

Why Magnetic Monopoles Don't Exist

Earlier we stated that isolated north or south magnetic poles don't exist in nature. Electromagnets provide a basis for understanding where this law comes from. At the atomic scale, an electron in motion around an atom constitutes a "current," analogous to the circle of wire in an electromagnet. As we shall see in Chapter 10, the magnetism in permanent magnets can be traced ultimately to the summation of the behavior of countless electrons, each in motion about an atom's nucleus. This fact explains why ordinary magnets can never be broken down into magnetic monopoles. If you break a magnet down to one last individual atom, you still have a dipole field because of the atomic-scale current loop. If you try to break the atom down further, the dipole field will disappear and there will be no magnetism except that associated with the particles themselves. Thus, magnetism in nature is ultimately related to the arrangement of electrical charges rather than to anything intrinsic to matter itself.

FIGURE 5-22 Magnetic resonance image (MRI) of the human head and shoulders, showing the ability of this technique to produce visualizations of soft tissue.

 THE SCIENCE OF LIFE
Magnetic Resonance

Just as the motion of electrons in atoms creates a current that produces a magnetic field, so too does the rotation of the nucleus of the atom. In fact, the nucleus of most atoms can be pictured as a microscopic dipole magnet. This fact gives rise to one of the most useful tools in modern medicine—magnetic resonance imaging (MRI).

In this technique, the patient is placed between the poles of a strong magnet. The magnetic field that permeates the patient's tissue causes the tiny nucleus-scale magnets in those tissues to rotate at frequencies characteristic of each kind of atom. Because of this effect, the nuclei absorb radio waves whose frequency is timed to coincide with the rotation. By sending radio waves into the patient's tissues and seeing which frequencies are absorbed by rotating nuclei, doctors can determine what sorts of atoms are present at each place in the body, and hence form detailed images of the body's tissues (Figure 5-22). Unlike X-rays, which have difficulty distinguishing between different kinds of soft tissue, MRI can provide detailed cross-sectional images of any part of the body.

● 5.6 Electrical Effects from Magnetism

Once Oersted and others demonstrated that magnetic effects arise from electricity, it did not take long for scientists to realize that electrical effects arise from magnetism. Several scientists contributed to this insight, but British physicist Michael Faraday (1791–1867) is most directly associated with this discovery.

Faraday's key experiment took place on August 29, 1831, when he placed two coils of wire—in effect, two electromagnets—side by side in his laboratory. He used a battery to pass an electrical current through one of the coils of wire, and he watched what happened to the other coil. Astonishingly, even though the second coil of wire was not connected to a battery, a strong electrical current developed in it. We now know what happened in Faraday's experiment: the loop of wire through which current was running produced a magnetic field in the neighborhood of

FIGURE 5-23 Electromagnetic induction. *(a)* When a current flows in the circuit on the left, a current is observed to flow in the circuit on the right, *even though there is no battery or power source in that circuit.* *(b)* Moving a magnet into the region of a coil of wire causes a current to flow in the circuit, even in the absence of a battery or other source of power.

Ammeter
Current flow detected
Coil
(a)

Bar magnet
S N
(b)

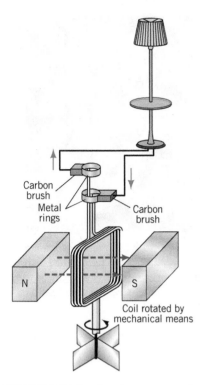

FIGURE 5-24 An electric generator. As long as the loop of wire rotates, there is a changing magnetic field near the loop and a current flows in the wire.

FIGURE 5-25 The first large-scale commercial plant to produce electricity was built on Pearl Street in New York in 1882 by Thomas Edison.

the second loop. This changing magnetic field, in turn, produced a current in the second loop by means of a process called *electromagnetic induction* (see Figure 5-23). An identical effect was observed when Faraday waved a permanent magnet in the vicinity of his wire coil. He produced an electrical current without a battery.

Michael Faraday's research can be summarized by a simple law:

● **Electrical fields and electrical currents can be produced by changing magnetic fields.**

Figure 5-24 illustrates the **electric generator**, or *dynamo,* a vital tool of modern technology that demonstrates this effect. Place a loop of electrical wire with no batteries or other power source between the north and south poles of a strong magnet. As long as the loop of wire stands still, no current flows in the wire, but as soon as we begin to rotate the loop, a current flows in the wire. This current flows in spite of the fact that there is no battery or other power source in the wire.

From the point of view of the electrons in the wire, any rotation changes the orientation of the magnetic field. The electrons sense a changing magnetic field and hence, by Faraday's findings, a current flows in the loop. If we spin the loop continuously, then a continuous current flows in it. The current flows in one direction for half of the rotation and then flows in the opposite direction for the other half of the rotation. This vitally important device, the electric generator, followed immediately from Faraday's discovery of electromagnetic induction. Current that reverses direction is this way is called **alternating current (AC)** as opposed to the current from a battery, which flows in one direction only and is called **direct current (DC).**

In an electric generator, some source of energy, such as water passing over a dam, steam produced by a nuclear reactor or coal-burning furnace, or wind-driven propeller blades, turns a shaft. In your car, the energy to turn the coils in a magnetic field comes from the gasoline that is burned in the engine. In every generator the rotating shaft links to coils of wire that spin in a magnetic field. Because of the rotation, electrical current flows in the wire, and that electricity can be tapped off onto external lines. Almost all the electricity used in the United States and elsewhere in the world is generated in this way.

You may have noticed a curious fact about electric motors and generators. In an electric motor, electrical energy is converted into the kinetic energy of the spinning shaft, while in a generator, the kinetic energy of the spinning shaft is converted into electrical energy. Thus motors and generators are, in a sense, exact opposites in the world of electromagnetism.

PLATE XIII.—EDISON'S STEAM DYNAMO.

TECHNOLOGY
The Electrification of America

As opposed to the steam engine, which delivers energy that must be utilized near the location of the engine itself, the electrical generator allows us to build systems in which energy is generated at one place and used at another, often distant, location. In the last few decades of the nineteenth century, the construction of our modern electrified infrastructure started to be built, and like all new types of technologies, it encountered some growing pains.

In the beginning, electricity had to compete with well-developed existing technologies. For examples, gas lamps were commonly used as a source for street lighting in American cities. The first attempt to install electric street light in Chicago in 1878 was far from successful—the system, which produced light by passing an arc between two carbon electrodes, blew up after one night of use.

In addition, there was a major debate about whether the American electrical supply should be AC or DC. The redoubtable Thomas Edison favored the latter, while AC was championed by the inventor Nikola Tesla and a young entrepreneur named George Westinghouse. AC eventually won because it is easier to transmit alternating current over long distances.

In the beginning, organizations that wanted to use electricity, such as the Palmer House Hotel in Chicago and Wannamaker's Department Store in Philadelphia, had to build their own generators. The first large scale commercial plant was built on Pearl Street in New York in 1882 by Thomas Edison (Figure 5-25). At first the high cost of copper wire limited the distance that could be economically served by such a plant to about half a mile (eight city blocks), but a long succession of nickel-and-dime engineering advances eventually eliminated this barrier to electrification. The final step in the electrification of America began in the 1930s, with the beginning of the Rural Electrification Administration. Roughly half of American farms were electrified by 1942 and virtually all by the 1950s.

SCIENCE IN THE MAKING
Michael Faraday

FIGURE 5-26 Michael Faraday (1791–1867).

Michael Faraday, one of the most honored scientists of the nineteenth century, did not come easily to his profession (Figure 5-26). The son of a blacksmith, he received only a rudimentary education as a member of a small Christian sect. Faraday was apprenticed at the age of 14 to a London book merchant, and he became a voracious reader as well as a skilled bookbinder. Chancing upon the *Encyclopedia Britannica*, he became fascinated by scientific articles and he determined then and there to make science his life.

The young Faraday pursued his scientific career in style. He attended a series of public lectures at the Royal Institution by London's most famous scientist, Sir Humphry Davy, a world leader in physical and chemical research. Then, in a bold and flamboyant move, Faraday transcribed his lecture notes into beautiful script, bound the manuscript in the finest tooled leather, and presented the volume to Davy as his calling card. Michael Faraday soon found himself working as Davy's laboratory assistant.

After a decade of work with Davy, Faraday had developed into a creative scientist in his own right. He discovered many new chemical compounds, including liquid benzene, and enjoyed great success with his own lectures for the general London public at the Royal Institution. But his most lasting claim to fame was a series of classic experiments through which he discovered a central idea that helped link electricity and magnetism.

Maxwell's Equations

Electricity and magnetism are not distinct phenomena at all, but are simply different manifestations of one underlying fundamental entity—the **electromagnetic force**. In the 1860s, Scottish physicist James Clerk Maxwell (1831–1879) realized that the four very different statements about electricity and magnetism that we have talked about constitute a single coherent description of electricity and magnetism. He was also able to add a technical detail to the third law listed below, a detail that completed the mathematical picture.

The four mathematical statements that he wrote down have come to be known as *Maxwell's equations*, because he was the first to realize their true import. Maxwell manipulated the mathematics to make important predictions, which we will discuss in detail in the next chapter. For reference, the four fundamental laws of electricity and magnetism known as Maxwell's equations (even though we present them here in statement form) are:

1. Coulomb's law: like charges repel, unlike attract.
2. There are no magnetic monopoles in nature.
3. Magnetic phenomena can be produced by electrical effects.
4. Electrical phenomena can be produced by magnetic effects.

THINKING MORE ABOUT **ELECTROMAGNETISM**

Basic Research

It's hard to imagine modern American society without electricity. We use it for transportation, communication, heat, light, and many other necessities and amenities of life. Yet the men who gave us this marvelous gift were not primarily concerned with developing better lamps or modes of transportation. In terms of the categories we introduced in Chapter 1, they were doing basic research. Galvani and Volta, for example, were drawn to the study of electricity by their research on frog muscles that contracted by jolts of electrical charge. Volta's first battery was built to duplicate the organs found in electric fish. Scientific discoveries, even those that bring enormous practical benefit to humanity, can come from unexpected sources.

What does this tell you about the problem of allocating government funds for research? Can you imagine trying to justify funding Galvani's experiments on frogs' legs to a government panel on the grounds that it would lead to something useful? Would a federal research grant designed to produce better lighting systems have produced the battery (and, eventually, the electric light), or would it more likely have led to an improvement in the oil lamp? How much funding do you think should go to offbeat areas (on the chance that they may produce a large payoff) as compared to projects that have a good chance of producing small but immediate improvements in the quality of life?

While you're thinking about these issues, you might want to keep in mind Michael Faraday's response to a question. When asked by a political leader what good his electric motor was, he is supposed to have answered, "What good is it? Why, Mr. Prime Minister, someday you will be able to tax it!"

RETURN TO THE INTEGRATED QUESTION

What is lightning?

- Lightning is an atmospheric release of an electrical charge. A lightning bolt (i.e., a discharge or release of an electrical force) can travel at speeds well in excess of 200,000 km/h and reach temperatures of 30,000°C.

  - The high energy associated with the discharge of the electrical force violently heats the surrounding air and causes a pressure wave that we hear as thunder.

- The electrical charge that results in lightning and thunder is caused by the same process that causes your hair to "stand on end" when you comb it on a dry day.

  - Electrons in orbits that are far from the nucleus are very loosely bound to their atoms. These electrons can be removed from the atom by a number of processes, including mechanical processes such as friction.

  - When electrons, which carry a negative charge, are stripped from a material, they no longer cancel the positive charges in the nucleus. The result is the acquisition of a positive electrical charge in the object.

- Similarly, an object acquires a negative electrical charge when extra electrons are added to it. This addition of electrons happens when you run a comb through your hair on a dry day; electrons are stripped from your hair and added to the comb, so the comb acquires a negative charge. Simultaneously, your hair loses electrons, so individual strands become positively charged.

- During a thunderstorm, the same phenomenon occurs on a much larger scale. Wind and rain disrupt the normal distribution of electrons in clouds and create positive and negative charges within the cloud. Lightning results from the attraction of charges on the ground and the opposing charges in the cloud.

- When a charged cloud passes over a tall tree or tower, the violent electrical discharge we call lightning may result.

- Despite the dramatic danger associated with lightning, your chances of being struck and killed by a lightning bolt is less than 1 in 2 million.

SUMMARY

The forces of *electricity* and *magnetism* are quite different from the universal gravitational force that Newton described in the seventeenth century. Nevertheless, Newton's laws of motion provided eighteenth- and nineteenth-century scientists with a model for going about describing and quantifying a range of intriguing electromagnetic behavior.

The phenomena of *static electricity*, including lightning and static cling, are caused by *electrical charges*, which arise from the transfer of electrons between objects. An excess of electrons imparts a *negative charge*, while a deficiency causes an object to have a *positive charge*. Objects with like charges experience a repulsive force, while oppositely charged objects attract each other. These observations were quantified in *Coulomb's law*, which states that the magnitude of electrostatic force between any two objects is proportional to the charges of the two objects and inversely proportional to the square of the distance between them.

Scientists investigating the very different phenomenon of magnetism observed that every *magnet* has a *north pole* and *south pole* and that magnets exert forces on each other. No matter how many times a magnet is divided, each of its pieces will have two poles—there are no isolated magnetic poles. Like magnetic poles repel each other, while opposite poles attract. A compass is a needle-shaped magnet that is designed to point at the poles of Earth's dipole magnetic field. Both *electrical* and *magnetic forces* can be described in terms of force *fields*—imaginary lines that reveal directions of forces that would be experienced in the vicinity of electrically charged or magnetic objects.

Batteries provide a continuous source of electricity. All electrical currents (measured in *amperes* or *amps*) are characterized by an electric "push" or *voltage* (measured in *volts*) and *electrical resistance* (measured in *ohms*). An *electric circuit* is a closed loop of material that carries electricity.

Nineteenth-century scientists discovered that the seemingly unrelated phenomena of electricity and magnetism are actually two aspects of one *electromagnetic force*. Hans Oersted found that an electrical current passing through a coil of wire produces a magnetic field. The *electromagnet* and *electric motor* were direct results of his work. Michael Faraday discovered the opposite effect when he induced an electrical current by placing a wire coil near a magnetic field, thus designing the first *electric generator,* which produced an *alternating current (AC)*. Batteries, on the other hand, develop a *direct current (DC)*.

James Clerk Maxwell realized that the many independent observations about electricity and magnetism constitute a complete description of electromagnetism.

KEY TERMS

electrical charge
electricity
static electricity
positive electrical charge
negative electrical charge
Coulomb's law
electric field
magnet

magnetic force
poles
magnetic field
electrical current
battery
electric circuit
voltage
electrical resistance

electromagnet
electric motor
electric generator
alternating current (AC)
direct current (DC)
electromagnetic force

KEY EQUATIONS

force (newtons) = $k \times$ 1st charge $\times$ 2nd charge/distance^2
voltage (volts) = current (amps) $\times$ resistance (ohms)
power (watts) = current (amps) $\times$ voltage (volts)

Constants
Electromagnetic constant: $k = 9 \times 10^9$ N-m^2/C^2

DISCOVERY LAB

Obtain two 6-volt dry cells, two large 10-penny steel nails, a 3-meter and a 6-meter length of insulated bell wire, wire strippers, some colored electrical tape, a box of small steel paper clips, and a pair of scissors. Four alligator clips would be helpful for ease of connections, as well as a single-blade knife switch. Nearly all of these items can be obtained from your local electronics store.

Strip both ends of the wire, leaving 1 inch of bare wire. Take the 3-meter bell wire and wrap a loop around the head of the nail, closing the loop with about 40 centimeters of wire hanging to one side. With one hand holding the nail carefully, and the other hand holding the longer side of the bell wire, begin to tightly wrap the bell wire—slowly moving toward the tip of the nail. Leave about 1.5 inches of nail showing and then tie that loop off near the tip. Connect both bare ends for the wires to a different dry cell terminal. Wrap some electrical tape completely around the wire layer. Next, stick the nail into the box of paper clips and dig down to the bottom, counting to three. Count how many paper clips can be lifted out of the box.

Now do precisely the same thing with the second nail, but do it with the 6-meter length of bell wire; wrap a full layer of wire around the nail and then a second layer over the first layer. When done, count the paper clips that are picked up like you did the first time. Do everything the same in both cases EXCEPT the second nail will have two layers of wire. How many more paper clips were picked up with a second layer of wire? What if you tried three layers?

For even more fun, try two dry cells hooked up together (+ to – terminal connection alternation) both with one layer of wire, and then try two dry cells with two layers of wire. Note the differences in the force of magnetism with the paper clip attraction. Write your observations and make a broken line graph to visually demonstrate your quantitative data. (Later attach the alligator clips to the wire ends and hook up the knife switch to open and close the circuit, making the attraction and release of paper clips a little more dramatic.) Where are these electromagnetic principles used in our world?

REVIEW QUESTIONS

1. How might you demonstrate the existence of an electrical force?

2. How did Benjamin Franklin explain electrical charge?

3. What observations led Coulomb to the conclusion that electrical forces were in some ways similar to the gravitational force discovered by Newton? Compare and contrast the behavior of an electrical force and gravity.

4. How is it possible that the movement of negative charges like electrons can produce both positively and negatively charged materials?

5. What roles did frog's legs and "animal electricity" play in the development of the battery?

6. How might you demonstrate the existence of a magnetic force?

7. What is a magnetic monopole?

8. What observation led Hans Christian Oersted to conclude that a fundamental relationship exists between magnetism and electricity?

9. Under what circumstances can electrical charges produce a magnetic field?

10. How does an electromagnet work?

11. How does an electromagnet differ from a permanent magnet?

12. Explain how electromagnets can be used in the design of an electric motor.

13. How does the movement of an electron in an atomic orbit produce an electric field?

14. Under what circumstances can a magnetic field produce an electrical current?

15. How does an electric generator work? In what sense is it the opposite of an electric motor?

16. Which of Maxwell's four equations was derived from observations of each the following:

   a. bar magnets

   b. wire loops carrying electrical current

   c. two different materials being rubbed together

   d. the effects of a current-carrying wire coil on a nearby coil

17. What properties of electrical currents are measured by amperes, volts, and ohms?

18. Explain how medical magnetic resonance imaging (MRI) exploits the magnetic properties of the nucleus.

19. What is the relation between the power an appliance consumes, the voltage across it, and the current through it?

DISCUSSION QUESTIONS

1. In Figure 5-15 of the text, the person measuring the resistance of the device is holding two probes with one probe on each side of the device being measured. Why do you think two probes are needed?

2. Consider the numerical values of k and G, 8.99×10^9 and 6.67×10^{-11}. What do these relative values suggest about the relative strength of the electrical force compared to the gravitational force?

3. The size of a battery doesn't indicate the amount of voltage supplied by a battery. For instance, consider a typical 9-volt battery *versus* a 6-volt lantern battery. Why do you think they make a battery so large despite such a small voltage?

4. An old-fashioned circuit fuse was constructed of a thin strip of metal with a low melting point. The fuse would act to stop the current if it exceeded a particular value. Once the fuse was tripped, it needed to be replaced. How do you think it worked?

5. Why can you start your car and drive around town many times without draining the battery, but if you leave the lights on when the engine is off, the battery is drained?

6. How many times a day do you think you use an electric motor?

7. Consider laundry pulled out of a dryer. Often, a sock will be sticking to another article of clothing through static cling. Why does this sock stick to something else? Is it true for all kinds of clothing? If you're unlucky, you'll not notice it and walk around in a shirt with a sock stuck to it. What does this say about the relative strength of the force of static cling *versus* the gravitational force?

8. When you run a comb through your hair on a dry day, why does your hair stand on end? Why do you think this phenomenon is much less likely to occur on a very humid day?

9. When the lightning rod was introduced, many people denounced it as going against the plans of God. Yet the lightning rod soon became widespread. What does this tell us about the way new technologies enter society?

10. The Northern Lights are caused by the interaction of electrically charged particles emitted by the Sun interacting with Earth's magnetic field. Why do you think you don't see this phenomenon at Earth's equator? If you lived on the Moon, do you think you would see the equivalent of the Northern Lights?

11. Identify five things in the room where you are sitting that would not have been possible without the discoveries in electromagnetism discussed in this chapter.

12. How do the First and Second Laws of Thermodynamics apply to electric circuits?

13. Explain how the Law of the Conservation of Energy affects the operation of an electrical generator. Where does the energy that is eventually carried in an electrical circuit come from and where does the energy go?

14. There is an old saying that lightning never strikes the same place twice. Given what you know about electrical charge, is this statement likely to be true? Why or why not?

15. How does a lightning rod work? Why does the electrical energy travel through the rod and not the building? Why should you never seek the shelter of a tree if you get caught out in a thunderstorm?

16. Why should you never operate an electrical appliance (e.g., a hair dryer) while you are in a bathtub filled with water?

17. Why does a spark sometimes jump from your hand to a doorknob when you've walked across a carpet? Where does that electrical charge come from?

18. The novel *Frankenstein* may have been inspired by nineteenth-century experiments examining "animal electricity." Can you give examples of twenty-first-century science inspiring the popular media?

PROBLEMS

1. Many bonds between atoms result from the attraction of positively and negatively charged atoms. Based on electrical charges and separations, which of the following atomic bonds is strongest? (*Hint:* You are interested only in the relative strengths, which depend only on the relative charges and distances.)

    a. a +1 sodium atom separated by 4.0 distance units from a −1 chlorine atom in table salt

    b. a +1 hydrogen atom separated by 2.0 distance units from a −2 oxygen atom in water

    c. a +4 silicon atom separated by 3 distance units from a −2 oxygen atom in glass

2. A circuit is connected to a 150-volt power source. If a current of 2.5 amps flows through the circuit, what is its resistance?

3. A flashlight uses the combined voltage of two 1.5-volt batteries to light a 5-watt bulb. What is the current running through the circuit when the flashlight is on? What must be the resistance of the circuit? Now replace the bulb with an energy-efficient 2.5-watt bulb. What are the current and the resistance with the same batteries?

4. When a video camera's nickel cadmium (Ni-Cad) or nickel metal hydride (Ni-MH) battery runs down, it is recharged by running current through it backward. Typically, you might run 4mAh (Milliampere-hour) at 6 volts for an hour. How much energy does it take to recharge this battery?

5. A typical household circuit has a breaker that trips when the current exceeds 15 amps. If the source provides 120 volts, how many 60-watt lightbulbs can be hooked up without the circuit getting tripped?

6. A heavy-duty household appliance like a clothes dryer typically has its own dedicated outlet from which it can draw up to 30 amps at 240 volts. What is the power drawn by this dryer while operating?

7. An energy-efficient water heater draws 4 amps in a 220-volt circuit. It costs $175 more than a standard water heater that draws 18 amps in a standard 115-volt circuit. If electricity costs 10 cents per kilowatt-hour, how long would you have to run the efficient water heater to recoup the difference in price?

8. A typical bolt of lightning can result from a voltage of 40 million volts and have a peak current of 30,000 amps through the air. What is the resistance of the air during this time?

    a. 1.2 trillion Ohms

    b. 1300 Ohms

    c. 0.044 Ohms

    d. 39.97 million Ohms

9. A single citizen of the United States uses, on average, 13,300 kilowatt-hours of electrical energy each year. If a kilowatt-hour costs 12 cents, how much does it cost per day for the average person to use electricity?

   a. 36.4 cents

   b. $4.37

   c. 3.03 cents

   d. $11.08

10. An energy-efficient compact fluorescent light (CFL) allows for a 20-watt bulb to effectively replace a 75-watt bulb. If the bulb is lit for 2 hours, how many joules of energy are saved by using the CFL in place of the regular bulb?

    a. 688,000 J

    b. 144,000 J

    c. 540,000 J

    d. 396,000 J

11. Two identical objects experience a mutual repulsion of 0.118 N from each other when the separation between them is 1.50 mm. Which of the following could be the charges on each of the objects?

    a. 5.4×10^{-9} C

    b. 3.0×10^{-17} C

    c. 0.79 C

    d. 2.7×10^{-7} C

INVESTIGATIONS

1. Look at the Underwriter's Lab tag on the back of the electrical appliances at your home. Make a list of the power consumption of each appliance.

2. Most household circuits have fuses or circuit breakers that open a switch when the current in the circuit exceeds 15 amps. How many of the appliances in the previous question could you run on the same circuit without overloading it?

3. Michael Faraday presented a hand-tooled, leather-bound manuscript to Sir Humphry Davy to obtain a position in his lab. How are such positions awarded today at your university?

4. Make a shopping list of all the materials you would need to make an electric motor.

5. Carefully examine your most recent electric bill. How much power did you use? How much did it cost? Is there a discount for electricity used at off-peak hours? Examine your use of electricity and plan a strategy for reducing your electric bill by 10% next month. You can reduce consumption by turning off lights and appliances when not in use, installing lower-wattage bulbs, or using electricity during low-rate times.

6. Find out where your electrical power is generated. Does your local utility buy additional power from some other place? What kind of fuel or energy is used to drive the turbines? Are there pollution controls that restrict the use of certain kinds of fuels at your local power plant? See if you can arrange a tour of the power plant.

7. How many kilowatts of electrical power does a typical commercial power plant generate? How much electricity does the United States use each year? Is this amount going up or down?

8. Explain the difference between the typical modern electric motor and the simple example of the electric motor described in the text.

9. How many electric motors are there in your car? Does your car have a generator?

10. Investigate how electric eels generate electrical shocks. Do any other living things create electrical currents?

11. How does an electroencephalogram (EEG) work? How does it differ from an electrocardiogram (EKG)?

12. Many kinds of living things, from bacteria to vertebrates, incorporate small magnetic particles. Investigate the ways in which living things use magnetism.

13. The novel *Frankenstein* was influenced by experiments on animal electricity. In what way does the novel reflect scientific knowledge of the time? How has scientific knowledge changed since then?

14. What is the current best range of electric cars? How does that compare to the average commute in your area?

15. How could you use one magnet to make another magnet levitate?

16. Are there any lightning rods on the buildings on your campus? Why does a building need more than one?

17. Look at a camera, watch, or calculator battery. Where are the negative and positive poles?

18. Use the Internet to find out how to make a battery with a potato or a lemon.

Waves and Electromagnetic Radiation

What is color?

PHYSICS

Radio and television signals are transmitted by electromagnetic waves.

BIOLOGY

Through a series of processes, the eye converts electromagnetic radiation into images and colors.

CHEMISTRY

X-rays are used to determine the atomic structure of minerals and other crystals.

GREAT IDEA

Whenever an electrically charged object is accelerated, it produces electromagnetic radiation—waves of energy that travel at the speed of light.

TECHNOLOGY

Microwave ovens rely on the fact that foods absorb microwave energy, while the walls of the oven reflect it.

ENVIRONMENT

A trace amount of the gas ozone in Earth's upper atmosphere protects life by absorbing much of the Sun's harmful ultraviolet radiation. (Ch. 19)

ASTRONOMY

Stars give off all wavelengths of electromagnetic radiation, from radio waves to gamma rays, which can be detected by orbiting telescopes. (Ch. 14)

HEALTH & SAFETY

Prolonged exposure to ultraviolet radiation can cause sunburn and increase the risk of skin cancer.

GEOLOGY

Doppler radar units track the movement of dangerous storms by measuring the frequency of electromagnetic waves. (Ch. 18)

 = applications of the great idea discussed in this chapter

 = other applications, some of which are discussed in other chapters

The Radio

The car is packed and ready to go. As you begin the 90-minute drive to the beach, you tune the radio to a favorite FM music station and turn up the volume to feel the beat. From time to time, though, you check an AM station that features traffic and weather reports, just to avoid any problems. The radio is so familiar and essential, yet it's still somewhat magical. How can music and news travel invisibly through air from the radio station? How can so many different stations broadcast at the same time without interfering with each other? The answers, surprisingly, are intimately tied to the behavior of waves and the electromagnetic force.

Lucenet Patrice/Phototeque Oredia/Age Fotostock America, Inc.

◉ 6.1 The Nature of Waves

Waves are all around us. Waves of water travel across the surface of the ocean and crash against the land. Waves of sound travel through the air when we listen to music. Some parts of the United States suffer from mighty waves of rock and soil called earthquakes. All of these waves must move through matter.

But the most remarkable waves of all can travel through an absolute vacuum at the speed of light. The sunlight that warms you at the beach and provides virtually all of the energy necessary for life on Earth is transmitted through space by just such a wave. The radio waves that carry your favorite music, the microwaves that heat your dinner, and the X-rays your dentist uses to check for cavities are also types of electromagnetic waves—invisible waves that carry energy and travel at the speed of light. In this chapter, we will look at waves in general and then focus on electromagnetic waves, which play an enormous role in our everyday life.

Waves are fascinating, at once familiar and yet somewhat odd. Waves, unlike flying cannonballs or speeding automobiles, have the ability to transfer energy without transferring mass.

Energy Transfer by Waves

Energy can be transferred in two forms in our everyday world: the particle and the wave. Suppose you have a domino sitting on a table and you want to knock it over—a process that requires transferring energy from you to the domino. One way to proceed would be to take another domino and throw it. From the standpoint of energy, you would say that the muscles in your arms impart kinetic energy to the moving domino, which, in turn, would impart enough of that energy to the standing domino to knock it over (Figure 6-1a). We say that the energy transfers by the motion of a solid piece of matter.

Alternatively, you could line up a row of standing dominoes, knock over the first, which would then knock over the second, which in turn would knock over the third, and so on (Figure 6-1b). Eventually the falling chain of dominoes would hit the last one, and you would have achieved the same goal. In the case of the lined-up dominoes, however, no single object traveled from you to the most distant domino. In the language of physics, we say that you started a wave of falling dominoes and the wave is what knocked over the final, domino. A **wave**, then, is a traveling disturbance; it carries energy from place to place without requiring matter to travel across the intervening distance. Remember in Chapter 4 when we examined the flow of heat from a campfire to your hand by the process of radiation? Radiation now reenters our story as the way that light waves transfer energy from one object to another.

FIGURE 6-1 You can use a domino to knock over other dominoes in two different ways: *(a)* you can throw a domino, or *(b)* you can trigger a wave of dominoes.

The Properties of Waves

Think about a familiar example of waves. You are standing on the banks of a quiet pond on a crisp autumn afternoon. There's no breeze and the pond in front of you is still and smooth. You pick up a pebble and toss it into the middle of the pond. As soon as the pebble hits the water, a series of ripples moves outward from the point of impact. In cross section, the ripples have the familiar wave shape shown in Figure 6-2. You can use five measurements to characterize the ripples.

1. **Wavelength** is the distance between crests, or the highest points of adjacent waves. On a pond the wavelength might be only a centimeter or two, while ocean waves may be tens or hundreds of meters between crests.

2. **Frequency** is the number of wave crests that go by a given point every second. A wave that sends one crest by every second (completing one cycle) is said to have a frequency of one cycle per second or one **hertz** (abbreviated 1 Hz). Small ripples on a pond might have a frequency of several hertz, while large ocean waves might arrive only once every few seconds.

3. *Period*, the time between adjacent waves, is the inverse of frequency (calculated as 1 divided by the frequency). So period is measured in "seconds per wave," while frequency is measured in "waves per second."

4. *Velocity* is the speed and direction of the wave crest itself. Water waves typically travel a few meters per second, about the speed of walking or jogging, whereas sound waves in air travel about 340 meters (1100 feet) per second.

5. *Amplitude* is the height of the wave crest above the undisturbed position, for example, the undisturbed water level.

FIGURE 6-2 A cross section of a wave reveals the characteristics of wavelength, velocity, and amplitude. Successive wave crests are numbered 1, 2, 3, and 4. An observer at the position of the clock records the number of crests that pass by in a second. This is the frequency, which is measured in cycles per second, or hertz.

The Relationship among Wavelength, Frequency, and Velocity

A simple relationship exists among wavelength, frequency, and velocity. In fact, if we know any two of the three, we can calculate the third from a simple equation.

To understand why this is so, think about waves on water. Suppose you are sitting on a sailboat, watching a series of wave crests passing by. You can count the number of

John Lund/©Corbis

FIGURE 6-3 Waves passing a sailboat reveal how wavelength, velocity, and frequency are related. If you know the distance between wave crests (the wavelength) and the number of crests that pass each second (the frequency), then you can calculate the wave's velocity.

wave crests going by every second (the frequency) and measure the distance between the crests (the wavelength). From these two numbers, the speed of the wave can be calculated.

If, for example, one wave arrives every 2 seconds and the wave crests are 6 meters apart, then the waves must be traveling 6 meters every 2 seconds—a velocity of 3 meters per second. You might look out across the water and see a particularly large wave crest that will arrive at the boat after four intervening smaller waves. You would predict that the big wave is 30 meters away (five times the wavelength) and that it will arrive in 10 seconds. That kind of information can be very helpful if you are plotting the best course for an America's Cup yacht race or estimating the path of potentially destructive ocean waves.

This relationship among wavelength, velocity, and frequency can be written in equation form:

In words: The velocity of a wave is equal to the length of each wave times the number of waves that pass by each second.

In equation form:

$$\text{wave velocity (m/s)} = \text{wavelength (m)} \times \text{frequency (Hz)}$$

In symbols:

$$v = \lambda \times f$$

where λ (the Greek letter lambda) and f are common symbols for wavelength and wave frequency, respectively. This simple equation holds for all kinds of waves (Figure 6-3).

EXAMPLE 6-1

AT THE BEACH

On a relatively calm day at the beach, ocean waves traveling 2 meters per second hit the shore once every 5 seconds. What is the wavelength of these ocean waves?

Reasoning: We can solve for wavelength, given the wave's velocity (2 meters per second) and frequency (1 wave per 5 seconds, or 1/5 Hz = 0.2 Hz):

$$\text{wave velocity (m/s)} = \text{wavelength (m)} \times \text{frequency (Hz)}$$

Solution: We can rearrange the equation to solve for wavelength.

$$\text{wavelength (m)} = \frac{\text{velocity (m/s)}}{\text{frequency (Hz)}}$$

$$= \frac{(2\ \text{m/s})}{0.2\ \text{Hz}}$$

$$= 10\ \text{m}$$

The Two Kinds of Waves: Transverse and Longitudinal

Imagine that a chip of bark or a piece of grass is lying on the surface of a pond when you throw a rock into the water. When the ripples go by, the floating object and the water around it move up and down; they do not move to a different spot. At the same time, however, the wave crest moves in a direction parallel to the surface of the water. This means that *the motion of the wave is different from the motion of the medium on which the wave moves.* This kind of wave, where the motion is perpendicular to the direction of the wave, is called a *transverse wave* (Figure 6-4a).

Transverse

(a)

Longitudinal

(b)

FIGURE 6-4 Transverse (a) and longitudinal (b) waves differ in the motion of the wave relative to the motion of individual particles.

You can observe (and participate in) this phenomenon if you ever go to a sporting event in a crowded stadium where fans "do the wave." Each individual simply stands up and sits down, but the visual effect is of a giant sweeping motion around the entire stadium. In this way, transverse waves can move great distances, even though individual pieces of the transmitting medium hardly move at all.

Not all waves are transverse waves like those on the surface of water—we used the example of a pond simply because it is so familiar and can be visualized. Sound is a form of wave that moves through the air. When you talk, for example, your vocal cords move air molecules back and forth. The vibrations of these air molecules set the adjacent molecules in motion, which sets the next set of molecules in motion and so forth. A wave moves out from your mouth, and that wave looks similar to ripples on a pond. Sound waves differ, however, because in the air the wave crest that is moving out is not a raised portion of a water surface, but a denser region of air molecules. In the language of physics, sound is a *longitudinal wave*. As a wave of sound moves through the air, gas molecules vibrate forward and back *in the same direction as the wave*. This motion is very different from the *transverse wave* of a ripple in water, where the water molecules move *perpendicular to the direction of the waves* (see Figure 6-4b). Note that in both longitudinal and transverse waves, the energy always moves in the direction of the wave.

STOP & THINK! How would you do a longitudinal wave in a stadium?

 ## SCIENCE BY THE NUMBERS
The Sound of Music

The speed of sound in air is more or less constant for all kinds of sound. The way we perceive a sound wave, therefore, depends on its other properties: wavelength, frequency, and amplitude. For example, what we sense as loudness depends on both the amplitude of a sound and its frequency—the greater the amplitude, for example, the louder the sound. Similarly, we hear higher-frequency sound waves (sound with shorter wavelengths) as higher pitches, while we perceive lower-frequency sound waves (with longer wavelengths) as lower-pitched sounds.

You can experience one consequence of this contrast when you listen to a symphony orchestra. The highest notes are played by small instruments, such as the piccolo and violins, while the lowest notes are the domain of the massive tuba and double basses (Figure 6-5). Similarly, the size of each of a big pipe organ's thousands of pipes determines which single note it will produce. An organ pipe

FIGURE 6-5 Different-sized instruments in a band play in different ranges. The larger string bass in the back plays lower notes, while the saxophones play in a higher range.

FIGURE 6-6 An organ pipe produces a single note. Air in the pipe vibrates and produces a sound wave with a wavelength related to the length of the pipe.

encloses a column of air in which a sound wave can travel back and forth, down the length of the pipe over and over again. The number of waves completing this circuit every second—the frequency—defines the pitch that you hear (see Figure 6-6).

We can calculate the necessary length of an organ pipe from the desired frequency and the known speed of sound. The note that we hear as "middle A," the pitch to which most orchestras tune, has a frequency of 440 Hz. Sound travels through air at about 340 meters per second. An organ pipe that is open at both ends produces a note with a wavelength twice as long as the pipe. Therefore, the length of an organ pipe air column that plays middle A is given by half the wavelength in the equation:

$$\text{wavelength (m)} = \frac{\text{velocity (m/s)}}{\text{frequency (Hz)}}$$

$$= \frac{(340 \text{ m/s})}{(440 \text{ Hz})}$$

$$= 0.773 \text{ m (about 2 ft)}$$

The length of the organ pipe is half the wavelength:

$$\text{organ pipe length (m)} = \frac{\text{wavelength (m)}}{2}$$

$$= \frac{0.773 \text{ m}}{2}$$

$$= 0.387 \text{ m (about 15 in)}$$

Notes in the middle range on the pipe organ are thus produced by pipes that are about one-half-meter long.

STOP & THINK! A clarinet has a series of open holes that are covered by metal keys. At which end of a clarinet would you expect to find the keys for playing low notes? Why?

EXAMPLE 6-2

THE LIMITS OF HUMAN HEARING

The human ear can hear sounds at frequencies from about 20 to 20,000 Hz. What are the longest and shortest wavelengths you can hear? What are the longest or shortest organ pipes you are likely to see?

Reasoning: Each organ pipe has a fixed length and produces just one note. We have to calculate the wavelength needed for both the lowest and highest frequency.

Solution: The lowest audible note, at 20 Hz, would require a wavelength as follows:

$$\text{wavelength (m)} = \frac{\text{velocity (m/s)}}{\text{frequency (Hz)}}$$

$$= \frac{(340 \text{ m/s})}{(20 \text{ Hz})}$$

$$= 17 \text{ m (about 50 ft)}$$

Similarly, the highest audible note, at 20,000 Hz, is produced by

$$\text{wavelength (m)} = \frac{\text{velocity (m/s)}}{\text{frequency (Hz)}}$$

$$= \frac{(340 \text{ m/s})}{(20,000 \text{ Hz})}$$

$$= 0.017 \text{ m (about two-thirds of an inch)}$$

Organ pipes producing these notes would be about half the wavelengths or approximately 8.5 and 0.009 meters, respectively. Most large pipe organs have pipes ranging from about 8 meters to less than 0.05 meter in length. Next time you have the chance, visit a church or auditorium with a large pipe organ and look at the variety of pipes. Not only are there many different lengths, but there are also many distinctive shapes, each sounding like a different musical instrument.

THE SCIENCE OF LIFE
Use of Sound by Animals

Humans use sound to communicate, of course, as do many other animals. But some animals have refined the use of sound in specialized ways. In 1793, Italian physiologist Lazzaro Spallanzani (1729–1799) did some experiments with bats and established that they use sound to locate their prey (Figure 6-7). He took bats that lived in the cathedral tower in Pavia, blinded them, and then turned them loose. Weeks later, those bats had fresh insects in their stomachs, proving that they didn't locate food by sight. Similar experiments with bats that were made deaf, however, showed that they could neither fly nor locate insects.

Today, we understand that bats navigate by emitting high-pitched sound waves and then listening with both ears for the reflection of those waves off of other objects. By measuring the time it takes for a pulse of sound waves to go out, be reflected, and come back to each ear, the bat can determine the distance and direction to surrounding objects, particularly the flying insects that make up its diet. Typically, a bat can detect the presence of an insect up to 10 meters away.

In an interesting application of the principle of natural selection (see Chapter 25), some species of moths have developed sophisticated sense organs to hear the sound emitted by bats. Using ears on their thorax or abdomen, these moths can hear the high-pitched sounds emitted by bats and thus can tell when they are being "seen." When they hear the sound, the moths take immediate evasive action. In a few cases, moths have developed an even more sophisticated defense. When a bat approaches, they emit a series of high-pitched clicks that "jam" the bat's detection system.

At the opposite end of the sound spectrum, when confronted by very low-frequency sounds, we often don't so much hear sound waves as feel them. We sense the vibrations in our bodies. You may have experienced this sensation when hearing very low notes on an organ. Some animals (elephants, for example) routinely use sound in the 20–40 Hz range to communicate with each other over long distances. The mating call of the female elephant, for example, is experienced as a vibration by humans but attracts bull elephants from many miles away.

Whales, dolphins, and porpoises use low-frequency sound echoes as a navigation tool in the ocean, much as bats do in air. Sometimes, however, the sounds that they emit are in the audible range for humans. Perhaps the most famous examples of sophisticated use of sound by animals are the songs of humpback whales, which have appeared on a number of commercial recordings. The functions of these songs are not clear. It appears, however, that all of the whales in a wide area of ocean (the South Atlantic, for example) sing the same song, although some individuals may leave out parts. The songs change every year, but the whales in a given area change their songs together.

FIGURE 6-7 A bat navigates by emitting high-pitched sounds and listening for their echoes.

Superstock/Age Fotostock America, Inc.

FIGURE 6-8 Two waves originating from different points create an interference pattern. Bright regions correspond to constructive interference, while dark regions correspond to destructive interference.

STOP & THINK! Today's scientists are much more concerned about the ethical treatment of animals than were naturalists of the eighteenth century. How might you conduct an experiment on the hearing of bats without injuring the animals?

Interference

Waves from different sources may overlap and affect each other in the phenomenon called interference. **Interference** describes what happens when waves from two different sources come together at a single point—each wave interferes with the other, and the observed height of the wave—the amplitude—is simply the sum of the amplitudes of the two interfering waves. Consider the common situation shown in Figure 6-8. Suppose you and a friend each throw rocks into a pond at two separate points as in the figure. The waves from each of these two points travel outward and eventually will meet. What will happen when the two waves come together?

One easy way to think about what happens is to imagine that each part of each wave carries with it a set of instructions for the water surface—"move down 2 inches," or "move up 1 inch." When two waves arrive simultaneously at a point, the surface responds to both sets of instructions. If one wave says to move down 2 inches and the other to move up 1 inch, the result will be that the water surface will move down a total of 1 inch. Thus each point on the surface of the water moves a different distance up or down depending on the instructions that are brought to it by the two waves.

One possible situation is shown in Figure 6-9a. Two waves, each carrying the command "go up 1 inch," arrive at a point together. The two waves act together to lift the water surface to the highest possible height it can have. By the same token, if two waves troughs, each 1-inch deep, meet then the net change will be a trough 2 inches deep. This effect is called *constructive interference,* or reinforcement. On the other hand, you could have a situation like the one shown in Figure 6-9b, where the two waves arrive at a point such that one is giving an instruction to go up 1 inch and the other to go down 1 inch. In this case, the two waves cancel each other out and the

FIGURE 6-9 Cross sections of interfering waves illustrate the phenomena of (a) constructive and (b) destructive interference.

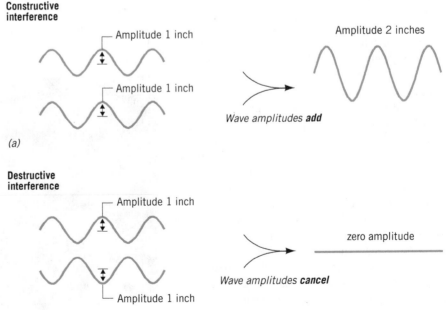

Constructive interference

Amplitude 1 inch

Amplitude 1 inch

Amplitude 2 inches

Wave amplitudes ***add***

(a)

Destructive interference

Amplitude 1 inch

zero amplitude

Amplitude 1 inch

Wave amplitudes ***cancel***

(b)

water surface will not move up or down at all. This situation is called *destructive interference,* or cancellation. And, of course, waves can interfere anywhere between these two extremes.

The most familiar example of destructive interference does not take place with water waves but with sound waves. Occasionally an auditorium may be designed in such a way that almost no sound can be heard in certain seats. This unfortunate situation results when two waves—for example, one directly from the stage and one bouncing off the ceiling—arrive at those seats in such a way as to cause partial or total destructive interference. One of the main goals of acoustical design of auditoriums, a field that relies on complex computer modeling of sound interference patterns, is to avoid such problems.

◎ 6.2 The Electromagnetic Wave

The last time you had your teeth X-rayed, or cooked a meal in a microwave oven, or listened to the radio you had firsthand experience with the phenomenon of electromagnetic waves.

Physicists characterize waves with a *wave equation,* which describes the movement of the wave's medium for every wave, whether it's a water wave moving through a liquid, a sound wave in air, or a seismic wave (a sound wave traveling through rocks) causing an earthquake. Physicists have learned that whenever an equation that describes motion has the distinctive form of a wave equation, then a corresponding wave should be seen in nature.

Soon after Maxwell wrote down the four equations that describe electricity and magnetism (see Chapter 5), he realized that some rather straightforward mathematical manipulation led to yet another equation, one that describes waves. The waves that Maxwell predicted from his wave equation are rather strange sorts of things, and we'll describe their anatomy in more detail later. The important point, however, is that these are waves in which energy is transferred not through matter, but through electrical and magnetic fields. It appears from the equations that whenever an electrical charge is accelerated, for example, one of these waves is emitted. Maxwell called this phenomenon **electromagnetic waves** or **electromagnetic radiation**. An electromagnetic wave is a wave that is made up of electrical and magnetic fields that fluctuate together; once that fluctuation starts, the wave keeps itself going, even in a vacuum.

Maxwell's equations also predicted exactly how fast the waves could move—the wave velocity depends only on known constants such as the universal electrostatic constant in Coulomb's equation (see Chapter 5). These numbers are known from experiment, and when Maxwell put the numbers into his expression for the velocity of his new waves, he found a very surprising answer. The predicted velocity of the mystery waves turned out to be 300,000 kilometers per second (186,000 miles per second).

If you just had an "aha!" moment, you can imagine how Maxwell felt. The number that he calculated is the speed of light, which means that the waves described by his equation are actually the familiar (but mysterious) waves we call "light."

This result was astonishing. For centuries scientists had puzzled over the origin and nature of light. Newton and others had discovered natural laws that describe the connections between forces and motion, as well as the behavior of matter and energy. But light remained an enigma. How did radiation from the Sun travel to Earth? What caused the light produced by a candle?

There is no obvious reason why static cling, refrigerator magnets, or the workings of an electric generator should be connected in any way to the behavior of visible light. Yet Maxwell discovered that **light** and other kinds of radiation are a type of wave that is generated whenever electrical charges are accelerated.

⬡ SCIENCE IN THE MAKING
The Ether

When Maxwell first proposed his idea of electromagnetic radiation, he was not prepared to deal with a wave that could travel in a vacuum—that required no medium whatsoever. Previous scientists who had studied light, including such luminaries as Isaac Newton, assumed that light must travel through a hypothetical substance called "ether" that permeates all space.

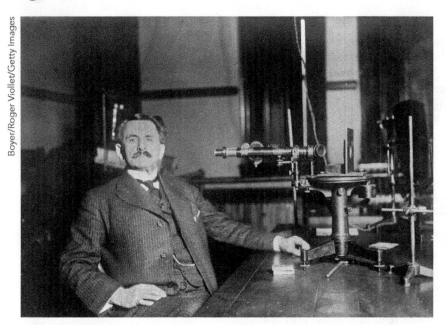

FIGURE 6-10 U. S. physicist Albert A. Michelson used precise optical measurements to prove that light waves can travel without a medium.

Ether, they thought, served as the medium for light, and so Maxwell assumed that ether provided the medium for his electromagnetic waves. In Maxwell's picture, the ether was a tenuous transparent substance, perhaps like invisible Jell-O, that filled all of space. An accelerating charge shook the Jell-O at one point, and after that the electromagnetic waves moved outward at the speed of light.

The idea of an ether goes back to the ancient Greeks, and for most of recorded history scholars logically assumed that the vacuum of space was filled with this imaginary substance. It wasn't until 1887 that two U.S. physicists, Albert A. Michelson (1852–1931) and Edward W. Morley (1838–1923), working at what is now Case Western Reserve University in Cleveland, performed experiments that demonstrated that the ether could not be detected. This failure was interpreted to mean that the ether did not exist.

The concept of the experiments was very simple. Michelson and Morley reasoned that if an ether really existed, then the motion of Earth around the Sun and the motion of the Sun around the center of our Milky Way galaxy would produce an apparent ether "wind" at Earth's surface, much as someone riding in a car on a still day feels a wind. They used very sensitive instruments to search for tiny differences in the speed of light as Earth moved through the ether in different directions. When their experiment turned up no such differences, they concluded that ether does not exist.

In 1907, Albert Michelson (Figure 6-10) became the first U.S. scientist to win a Nobel Prize, an honor that recognized his pioneering experimental studies of light.

The Anatomy of the Electromagnetic Wave

How does an electromagnetic wave move in the absence of any transmitting medium? A typical electromagnetic wave, shown in Figure 6-11, consists of electrical and magnetic fields arranged at right angles to each other and perpendicular to the direction in which the wave is moving. To understand how the waves form, go back to Maxwell's equations that describe how a changing magnetic field produces an electrical field, and vice versa (Chapter 5). At the point labeled A in Figure 6-11, the electrical and magnetic fields associated with the wave are at maximum strength, but these fields are changing slowly, so they both decrease in strength. At point B, the fields are at minimum strength, but they are changing rapidly and so begin to increase. Thus at point A, the magnetic and electrical fields begin to die out, whereas at point B just the reverse happens. In this way the electromagnetic wave leapfrogs through space, bouncing its energy back and forth between electrical and magnetic fields as it goes.

All of the other kinds of waves we've talked about—those on water or in air, for example—are easy to visualize because the wave moves through a medium. Electromagnetic waves are different, and therefore somewhat mysterious (indeed, many scientists found their behavior difficult to understand). However, once you understand that the electromagnetic wave has this kind of ping-pong arrangement between electricity and magnetism, you can get a sense of how it can travel through a vacuum. The key is that the motion of a wave is not the same as the motion of the medium. The electromagnetic wave is, in a sense, an extension of this idea. It's a wave that has no medium whatsoever, but simply keeps itself going through its own internal mechanisms. Electromagnetic waves, then, transfer energy—what we have called *radiation* (see Chapter 4). These waves are created when electrical charges accelerate, but once they start moving they no longer depend on the source that emitted them.

FIGURE 6-11 A diagram of an electromagnetic wave shows the relationship of the electrical field, the magnetic field, and the direction that the wave is moving. A and B indicate points of maximum and minimum field strength. A changing magnetic field produces an electrical field, and vice versa, so the wave keeps renewing itself.

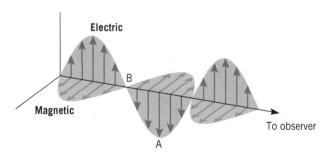

Light

Once Maxwell understood the connection between electromagnetism and light, his equations allowed him to draw several important conclusions. For one thing, because the velocity of the electromagnetic waves depends entirely on the nature of interactions between electrical charges and magnets, it cannot depend on the properties of the wave itself. Thus, every electromagnetic wave, regardless of its wavelength or frequency, has to move at exactly the same velocity (Figure 6-12). This velocity—the **speed of light**—turns out to be so important in science that we give it a special letter, c. The speed of electromagnetic waves in a vacuum is one of the fundamental constants of nature. (Note that light moving through solids, liquids, or gases appears to travel at a somewhat slower speed because the waves have to make slight "detours" around atoms—the denser the atoms, the slower the apparent speed of light.)

For electromagnetic waves traveling in the vacuum of space, the relation among velocity, wavelength, and frequency takes on a particularly simple form:

$$\text{wavelength} \times \text{frequency} = c$$
$$= 300{,}000 \text{ km/s} \; (= 186{,}000 \text{ mi/s})$$

In other words, if you know the wavelength of an electromagnetic wave, you can calculate its frequency and vice versa.

FIGURE 6-12 The speed of light is a universal constant.

The Energy of Electromagnetic Waves

Think about how you might produce an electromagnetic wave with a simple comb. Electromagnetic waves are generated any time a charged object is accelerated, so imagine combing your hair on a dry winter day when the comb picks up a static charge. Each time you move the comb back and forth, an electromagnetic wave traveling 300,000 kilometers per second is sent out from the comb.

If you wave the electrically charged comb up and down slowly, once every second, you create electromagnetic radiation, but you're not putting much energy into it. You produce a low-frequency, low-energy wave with a wavelength of about 300,000 kilometers. (Remember, each wave moves outward 300,000 kilometers in a second, which is the separation between wave crests.)

If, on the other hand, you could vibrate the comb vigorously—say at 300,000 times per second—you would produce a higher-energy, high-frequency wave with a 1-kilometer wavelength. By putting more energy into accelerating the electrical charge, you have more energy in the electromagnetic wave.

Visible light, the first example of an electromagnetic wave known to humans, bears out this kind of reasoning. A glowing ember has a dull red color, corresponding to a relatively low range of energies. Hotter, more energetic fires show a progression of more energetic colors, from the yellow of a candle flame to the blue-white flame of a blowtorch. These colors are merely different ranges of frequencies, and therefore different energies, of light; higher frequencies of light correspond to a blue color, lower frequencies to red.

Red light has wavelengths corresponding to a range of distances between about 600 and 700 nanometers (a nanometer is 10^{-9} meter, about 40 billionths of an inch). This wavelength corresponds to about 6000 atoms across. Red light includes the longest wavelengths that the human eye can see and is the least energetic of the visible electromagnetic waves. Violet light, on the other hand, has a range of shorter wavelengths corresponding to about 400 to 440 nanometers, (about 4000 atoms across) and includes the most energetic of the visible electromagnetic waves. All of the other colors have ranges of wavelengths and energies between those of red and violet.

EXAMPLE 6-3

FIGURING FREQUENCY

The average wavelength of yellow light is about 580 nanometers, or 5.8×10^{-7} m. What is the frequency of an average yellow light wave?

Reasoning: We know that for all electromagnetic waves,

$$\text{wavelength} \times \text{frequency} = 300{,}000 \text{ km/s}$$
$$= 3 \times 10^8 \text{ m/s}$$

We want to determine frequency, so we rearrange this equation:

$$\text{frequency} = \frac{(3 \times 10^8 \text{ m/s})}{\text{wavelength}}$$

Solution: This means that for yellow light with a wavelength of 5.8×10^{-7} m,

$$\text{frequency} = \frac{(3 \times 10^8 \text{ m/s})}{5.8 \times 10^{-7} \text{m}}$$
$$= 0.52 \times 10^{15} \text{ Hz}$$
$$= 5.2 \times 10^{14} \text{ Hz}$$

Remember, a hertz (Hz) equals one cycle per second. In order to generate yellow light by vibrating a charged comb you would have to wiggle it more than 500 trillion (520,000,000,000,000) times per second.

The Doppler Effect

Once waves have been generated, their motion is independent of the source. It doesn't matter what kind of charged object accelerates to produce an electromagnetic wave; once produced, all such waves behave exactly the same way. This statement has an important consequence that was discovered in 1842 by Austrian physicist Christian Johann Doppler (1803–1853). This consequence is called the **Doppler effect** in his honor. The Doppler effect describes the way the frequency of a wave appears to change if there is relative motion between the wave source and the observer.

Sound waves provide a familiar example. Figure 6-13a shows the way a sound wave looks when the source is stationary relative to a listener—when you listen to your radio, for example. In this case everything sounds "normal." If the source of sound—a racing ambulance with siren blaring, for example—is moving relative to the listener, however, a different situation occurs (Figure 6-13b). Periodically the crest of a sound wave moves away from the ambulance and travels out in a sphere *centered on the spot where the source was located when that particular crest was emitted.* By the time the ambulance is ready to emit another sound waves, it will have moved, and the second sound-wave sphere emitted will be centered at the new location. As the source continues to move, it will emit sound waves centered farther and farther to the right in the figure, producing a characteristic pattern as shown.

To a listener standing in front of the ambulance, these sound waves are bunched up so that the pitch of the siren sounds higher than it would be if the ambulance were standing still. On the other hand, if the observer is standing in back of the ambulance, the distance between sound waves will be stretched out, and the frequency and pitch of the siren will sound lower.

You probably have heard the Doppler effect. Think of standing on a highway while cars go by at high speeds. The engine noise appears to be very high-pitched as a car approaches you and then suddenly drops in pitch as the car passes you. This effect is particularly striking at automobile races where cars are moving at very high velocity.

This sort of change in pitch provided the first example of the Doppler effect to be studied. Scientists hired a band of trumpeters to sit on an open railroad car and blast a single long, loud note as the train whizzed by at a carefully controlled speed. Musicians on the ground determined the pitches they heard as the train approached and as it receded, and they compared those pitches to the actual note the musicians were playing.

The same sort of bunching up and stretching out of crests can happen for any wave, including light. If, on one hand, you are standing in the path of a source of light that is moving toward you, the light you see will be of higher frequency and hence will look bluer than it would ordinarily. (Remember, blue light has a higher frequency than red light.) We say the light is *blueshifted* (Figure 6-13c).

If, on the other hand, you are standing in back of the moving light source, the distance between crests will be stretched out and it will look to you as if the light had a lower frequency. We say that it is *redshifted*. In Chapter 15 we will see that the redshifting of light from distant moving sources is one of the main clues that we have about the structure of the universe.

The Doppler effect also has practical applications much closer to your home. Police radar units send out a pulse of electromagnetic waves that is absorbed by the metal in your car, then reemitted. The waves that come back will be Doppler shifted, and by comparing the frequency of the wave that went out and the wave that comes back, the speed of your car can be deduced. Similar techniques are used by bats, who rely on the Doppler shift to detect the motion of their insect prey, and by meteorologists, who employ Doppler radar to measure wind speed and direction during the approach of potentially damaging storms (see Chapter 18).

Transmission, Refraction, Absorption, Reflection, and Scattering

The only way we can know about electromagnetic radiation is to observe its interaction with matter. Our eyes, for example, interact with visible light and send nerve impulses to our brain—impulses that are interpreted as what we "see." When an electromagnetic wave hits matter, one of five processes takes place:

1. *Transmission.* The wave will often pass right through matter, as does the light that passes through your window or Earth's atmosphere. This process is called **transmission**. Transparent materials do not affect the wave other than slowing it down a bit while it is in transit.

2. *Refraction.* This slowing down of light as it passes through a transparent material can cause the light to change its direction slightly as in a lens or a glass of water—an important process called **refraction**. Lenses that bend and focus light are an important application of refraction. And when the different colors that make up white light bend differently, those colors of the spectrum are spread out in a beautiful display. The rainbow you see in the sky is formed by the interaction of light with falling raindrops (Figure 6-14).

(a)

(b)

(c)

FIGURE 6-13 The Doppler effect occurs whenever a source of waves is moving relative to the observer of the waves. *(a)* When sound waves spread out from a fixed source in all directions, stationary listeners will hear the same pitch. *(b)* Sound waves from a moving source seem to increase or decrease in pitch, depending on whether the sound is approaching or receding away from the listener. *(c)* The Doppler shift for light waves causes a blueshift for approaching light sources and a redshift for receding light sources.

FIGURE 6-14 A pencil in a glass of water appears bent, illustrating the phenomenon of refraction. Light passing through a prism is spread out.

FIGURE 6-15 The asphalt on this highway absorbs sunlight and heats up on warm days.

FIGURE 6-16 Clouds appear white because of diffuse scattering of sunlight.

FIGURE 6-17 Mirrors scatter light through the process of reflection.

3. *Absorption.* Other matter, like an asphalt driveway on a summer day, may soak up the wave and its energy—the process of **absorption**. The energy of absorbed electromagnetic radiation is converted into some other form of energy, usually heat. Black and dark colors, for example, absorb visible light: you've probably noticed how hot black pavement can become on a sunny day (Figure 6-15).

4. *Scattering.* Alternatively, electromagnetic waves may be absorbed and rapidly reemitted in the process of **diffuse scattering** (Figure 6-16). Most white materials, such as a wall or piece of paper, scatter all wavelengths of visible light in all directions. White objects such as clouds and snow, which scatter light from the Sun back into space, play a major role in controlling Earth's climate (see Chapter 18). Colored objects, by contrast, scatter only certain ranges of wavelengths. A red sweater, for example, will typically scatter light primarily in the red wavelengths, while absorbing light in the green wavelengths.

5. *Reflection.* Mirrors, on the other hand, scatter visible light at the same angle as the original wave in the process called **reflection** (Figure 6-17). This process produces a "mirror image" of the object being viewed.

All electromagnetic waves are detectable in some way. For each of them to be useful, researchers must find appropriate materials to transmit, absorb, and scatter the waves. For each wavelength there must be instruments that produce the waves and others that detect their presence. While the human eye can detect only a very narrow range of electromagnetic waves, scientists have devised an extraordinary range of transmitters and detectors to produce and measure electromagnetic radiation that we can't see.

TECHNOLOGY
Fiber Optics

If a light wave moving through a dense material like glass comes to an interface with a less dense material like air, the process of refraction will cause the beam in air to bend away from the vertical. If the light wave in glass approaches the interface at a small enough angle, though, the wave will not enter the air at all but will be reflected back into the glass. This process, called *total internal reflection,* is the basis for an important technological advance called *fiber optics.*

The point is that if a beam of light enters a long glass tube at the proper angle, it will undergo total internal reflection each time it comes to the edge of the glass. Light entering the tube will, in essence, bounce its way along until it comes to the end. This phenomenon means that information coded into the light waves can be transmitted by the glass. Furthermore, if you imagine a small bundle of such tubes, it's easy to see that an image could be transmitted as well because light entering each tube will be transmitted to the other end of the same tube.

Today, glass fibers with the cross-sectional area of a human hair are routinely packed into bundles and used to transmit telephone and television signals over long distances. The first telephone signal transmitted over a fiber optic cable was sent in 1977 in Long Beach, California, and the first trans-Atlantic optical cable was laid in 1988. Communication remains the major use of fiber optics today.

There are, however, many other applications of the technology. For example, surgeons routinely use narrow fiber optic cables to image internal organs in the human body. This technology allows them to perform operations without making large incisions to gain access to the region that needs repair—a process that leads to what has come to be called "band-aid surgery." The next time you hear of an athlete undergoing arthroscopic surgery on a knee, you can be sure that fiber optics played a role in the procedure.

◉ 6.3 The Electromagnetic Spectrum

A profound puzzle accompanied Maxwell's original discovery that light is an electromagnetic wave. Waves can be of almost any length. Water waves on the ocean, for example, range from tiny ripples to globe-spanning tides. Yet visible light spans an extremely narrow range of wavelengths, only about 390 to 710 nanometers (about 15 to 28 millionths of an inch). According to Maxwell's equations, electromagnetic waves could exist at any wavelength (and, consequently, any frequency) whatsoever. The only constraint is that the wavelength times the frequency must be equal to the speed of light. Yet when Maxwell looked into the universe, he saw visible light as the only obvious example of electromagnetic waves. It was as if a splendid symphony, ranging from the deep bass of the tuba to the sharp shrill of the piccolo, was playing, but you could hear only a couple of notes in the clarinets.

In such a situation, it would be natural to wonder what had happened to the rest of the waves. Scientists looked at Maxwell's equations, then at nature, and realized that something was missing. The equations predicted that there ought to be more kinds of electromagnetic waves than light—waves performing the waltz between electricity and magnetism, but with frequencies and wavelengths different from those of visible light. These as-yet unseen waves would have exactly the same structure as the one shown in Figure 6-11, but they could have either longer or shorter wavelengths than visible light depending on the acceleration of the electrical charge that created them. These waves would move at the speed of light, and would be exactly the same as visible light except for the differences in the wavelength and frequency.

Between 1885 and 1889, German physicist Heinrich Rudolf Hertz (1857–1894), after whom the unit of frequency is named, performed the first experiments that confirmed these predictions. He discovered the waves that we now know as radio. Since that time, all manner of electromagnetic waves have been discovered, from those with wavelengths longer than Earth's diameter to those with wavelengths shorter than the size of the nucleus of the atom. They include radio waves, microwaves, infrared, visible light, ultraviolet, X-rays, and gamma rays. This entire symphony of waves is called the **electromagnetic spectrum** (see Figure 6-18). Remember that every one of these waves, no matter what its wavelength or frequency, is the result of an accelerating electrical charge.

Radio Waves

The **radio wave** part of the electromagnetic spectrum ranges from the longest waves, those whose wavelength is longer than the size of Earth, to waves a few meters long. The resulting frequencies, from roughly a kilohertz (1,000 cycles per second, or kHz) to several hundred

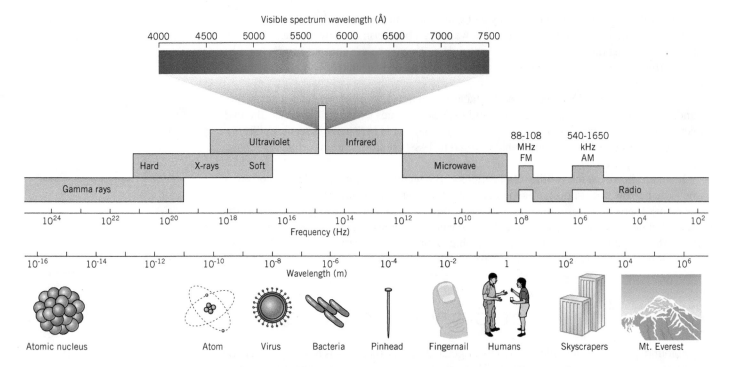

FIGURE 6-18 The electromagnetic spectrum includes all kinds of waves that travel at the speed of light in a vacuum, including radio, microwave, infrared, visible light, ultraviolet, X-rays, and gamma rays. Note that sound waves, water waves, seismic waves, and other kinds of waves that require matter in order to move travel *much* slower than light speed.

megahertz (1 million cycles per second, or MHz), correspond to the familiar numbers on your radio dial. Radio waves are subdivided in various ways, according to their use in military, commerce, or emergency response networks, but the most important fact about them is that, like light, they can penetrate long distances through the atmosphere. This feature makes radio waves very useful in communication systems.

Have you ever been driving at night and picked up a radio signal from a station a thousand miles away? If so, you have had firsthand experience of the ability of radio waves to travel long distances through the atmosphere. In Chapter 14 we will see how important this fact is for astronomy, where scientists speak of the "radio window" in the atmosphere, which allows Earth-based telescopes to monitor radio waves emitted by objects in the sky.

A typical radio wave used for communication can be produced by pushing electrons back and forth rapidly in a tall metal antenna. This acceleration of electrons produces outgoing radio waves, just as throwing a pebble in a pond produces outgoing ripples. When these waves encounter another piece of metal (for example, the antenna in your radio or TV set), the electrical fields in the waves accelerate electrons in that metal, so that its electrons move back and forth. This electron motion constitutes an electrical current that electronics in your receiver turn into a sound or a picture.

Most construction materials are at least partially transparent to radio waves. Thus you can listen to the radio even in the basement of most buildings. In long tunnels or deep valleys, however, absorption of radio waves by many feet of rock and soil may limit reception.

In the United States, the Federal Communications Commission (FCC) assigns frequencies in the electromagnetic spectrum for various uses. Each commercial radio station is assigned a frequency (which it uses in association with its call letters). All manner of private communication—ship-to-shore radio, civilian band (CB) radio, emergency police and fire channels, and so on—need their share of the spectrum as well. In fact, the right to use a part of the electromagnetic spectrum for communications is very highly prized because only a limited number of frequency slices or "bands" exist, and many more people want to use those frequencies than can do so.

TECHNOLOGY

AM and FM Radio Transmission

Radio waves carry signals in two ways: amplitude modulation (AM) and frequency modulation (FM). Broadcasters can send out their programs at only one narrow range of frequencies, a situation very different from music or speech, which use a wide range of frequencies. Thus radio stations cannot simply transform a range of sound-wave frequencies into a similar range of radio-wave frequencies. Instead, the information to be transmitted must be impressed in some way on the narrow frequency range of your station's radio waves.

This problem is similar to one you might experience if you had to send a message across a lake with a flashlight at night. You could adopt two strategies. You could send a coded message by turning the flashlight on and off, thus varying the brightness (the amplitude) of the light. Alternatively, you could change the color (the frequency) of the light by alternately passing blue and red filters in front of the beam.

Radio stations also adopt these two strategies (see Figure 6-19). All stations begin with a carrier wave of fixed frequency. AM radio stations typically broadcast at frequencies between about 530 and 1600 kHz, whereas the carrier frequencies of FM radio stations range from about 88 to 110 MHz.

The process called *amplitude modulation*, or *AM*, depends on varying the strength (or amplitude) of the radio's carrier wave according to the sound signal to be transmitted (Figure 6-19a). Thus the shape of the sound wave is impressed on the radio's carrier wave signal. When this signal is taken into your radio, the electronics are designed so that the original sound signal is recovered and used to run the speakers. The original sound signal is what you hear when you turn on your radio. Because AM frequencies easily scatter off the layers of the atmosphere, they can be heard over great distances.

Alternatively, you can slightly vary the frequency of the radio's wave according to the signal you want to transmit, a process called *frequency modulation*, or *FM*, as shown in Figure 6-19b. A radio that receives this particular signal will unscramble the changes in frequency and convert them into electrical signals that run the speakers so that you can hear the original signal.

Amplitude modulation (AM) | **Frequency modulation (FM)**

A. Original sound wave | A. Original sound wave

B. Carrier wave | B. Carrier wave

C. Modulated signal | C. Modulated signal

(a) | *(b)*

FIGURE 6-19 *(a)* AM (amplitude modulation) and *(b)* FM (frequency modulation) transmission differ in the way that a sound wave (A) is superimposed on a carrier wave of constant amplitude and frequency (B). The carrier wave can be varied, or modulated, to carry information (C) by altering its amplitude or its frequency.

Microwaves

Microwaves include electromagnetic waves whose wavelengths range from about 1 meter (a few feet) to 1 millimeter (0.001 meter, or about 0.04 inch). The longer wavelengths of microwaves travel easily through the atmosphere, like their cousins in the radio part of the spectrum, though rock and building materials absorb most microwaves. Therefore, microwaves are used extensively for line-of-sight communications. Most satellites broadcast signals to Earth in microwave channels, and these waves also commonly carry long-distance telephone calls and TV broadcasts. The satellite antennas that you see on private homes and businesses are designed primarily to receive microwave transmissions, as are the large cone-shaped receivers attached to the microwave relay towers found on many hills or tall buildings.

The distinctive transmission and absorption properties of microwaves make them ideal for use in aircraft radar. Solid objects, especially those made of metal, reflect most of the microwaves that hit them. By sending out timed pulses of microwaves and listening for the echo, you can judge the direction, distance (from the time it takes the wave to travel out and back), and speed (from the Doppler effect) of a flying object. Modern military radar is so sensitive that it can detect a single fly at a distance of a mile. To counteract this sensitivity, aircraft designers have developed planes with "stealth" technology—combinations of microwave-absorbing materials, angled shapes that reduce the apparent cross section of the plane, and electronic jamming to avoid detection (Figure 6-20).

FIGURE 6-20 The Stealth fighter has been engineered to reflect and absorb microwave radiation and thus avoid detection by radar.

U.S. Air Force Photo by Staff Sgt. Andy Dunaway, Department of Defense

TECHNOLOGY
Microwave Ovens

The same kind of waves used for phone calls and radar can be used to cook your dinner in an ordinary microwave oven. In this type of oven (Figure 6-21) a special electronic device accelerates electrons rapidly and produces the microwave radiation, which carries energy. These microwaves are guided into the main cavity of the oven, which is composed of material that scatters microwaves. Thus the wave energy remains inside the box until it is absorbed by something.

It turns out that water molecules rapidly absorb microwaves. This phenomenon means that the energy used to create microwaves is carried by those waves to food inside the oven, where it is absorbed by water and converted into heat. This absorption of microwave energy results in a very rapid rise in temperature, and rapid cooking. By contrast, microwaves don't heat paper and glass, which don't contain water molecules. Despite the different applications, from the point of view of the electromagnetic spectrum there is no fundamental difference between the microwaves used for cooking and those used for communication.

We should note in passing that we are not cooked by the microwave signals that are all around us because those waves have much less energy than the waves employed in a microwave oven.

Fan   Microwaves   Microwave generator

FIGURE 6-21 Every microwave oven contains a device that generates microwaves by accelerating electrons, and walls that scatter the microwaves until they are absorbed, usually by water molecules that get hot from the absorbed energy.

TECHNOLOGY
Cell Phones

The idea of a mobile phone has a long history, going back at least to 1908 when the Oakland Aerial Telephone and Power Company failed to deliver on a promise to produce such a device. In World War II, the "walkie-talkie"—essentially a small radio transmitter and receiver—was widely used for short-range communication by the military, and in the late 1940s Bell Labs introduced a bulky mobile phone system for use in automobiles. It wasn't until 1973, however, that engineers at Motorola produced something we would recognize as the ancestor of the modern cell phone. This phone weighed in at a little over 2½ pounds and was almost 10 inches long.

Cell phones employ the long-wavelength portion of the microwave spectrum for their signals, typically using frequencies between 800 and 2500 MHz, a range known as the UHF (ultra-high frequency) band. When you make a call, your phone sends out a microwave signal to a receiver located on a tower near you. As long as you remain near that tower, your call proceeds normally. If you move, however, your call is transferred to another tower near your new location. Each tower, in other words, controls a specific area, or "cell"—that's where the name "cell phone" comes from. If for some reason the transfer between towers fails to proceed properly, your call is lost, or "dropped."

Old cell pones are scarcely recognizable today.

STOP & THINK! Given that your phone uses line-of-sight communication with nearby towers, why do you suppose that moving around can sometimes improve the reception of your phone?

Infrared Radiation

Infrared radiation includes wavelengths of electromagnetic radiation that extend from a millimeter down to about a micron (10^{-6} meter, or less than a ten-thousandth of an inch). Our skin, which absorbs infrared radiation, provides a crude kind of detector. You feel infrared radiation when you reach your hands out to a warm fire or the cooking element of an electric stove. Infrared waves are what we feel as heat radiation (see Chapter 4).

All warm objects emit infrared radiation, and this fact has been used extensively in both civilian and military technology. Infrared detectors are used to guide air-to-air missiles to the exhaust of jet engines in enemy aircraft, and infrared detectors are often used to "see" human beings (Figure 6-22) and warm engines at night. Similarly, many insects (such as mosquitoes and moths) and other nocturnal animals (including opossums and some snakes) have developed sensitivity to infrared radiation; thus they can "see" in the dark.

Infrared detection is also used to find heat leaks in homes and buildings. If you take a picture of a house on a cold night using film that is sensitive to infrared radiation, places where heat is leaking out will show up as bright spots on the film. This information can be used to correct the heat loss and thus conserve energy. In a similar way, Earth scientists often monitor volcanoes with infrared detectors. The appearance of a new "hot spot" may signal an impending eruption.

STOP & THINK! We often say that we get heat from the Sun. What actually travels between the Sun and Earth?

FIGURE 6-22 A photograph using infrared film reveals heat escaping from an elephant. This "false-color" image is coded so that white is hottest, followed by red, pink, blue, and black.

Visible Light

What we perceive as the colors of the rainbow are contained in **visible light**, whose wavelengths range from red light at about 700 nanometers down to violet light at about 400 nanometers (Figure 6-23). From the point of view of the larger universe, the visible electromagnetic world in which we live is a very small part of the total picture (see Figure 6-18).

Our eyes distinguish several different *colors*, but these portions of the electromagnetic spectrum have no special significance except in our perceptions. In fact, the distinct colors that we see—red, orange, yellow, green, blue, and violet—represent very different-sized slices of the electromagnetic spectrum. The red and green portions of the spectrum are rather broad, spanning more than 50 nanometers of frequencies; we thus perceive many different wavelengths as red or blue. In contrast, the yellow part of the spectrum is quite narrow, encompassing wavelengths from only about 570 to 590 nanometers.

(a)

(b)

Why should our eyes be so sensitive to such a restricted range of the spectrum? The Sun's light is especially intense in this part of the spectrum, so some biologists suggest that our eyes evolved to be especially sensitive to these wavelengths, in order to take maximum advantage of the Sun's light. Our eyes are ideally adapted for the light produced by our Sun during daylight hours. Our eyes are also able to see visible light produced by a wide variety of common chemical reactions (see Chapter 10), most notably burning (Figure 6-24). By contrast, animals that hunt at night, such as owls and cats, have eyes that are more sensitive to infrared wavelengths—radiation that makes warm living things stand out against the cooler background.

FIGURE 6-23 *(a)* A glass prism separates light into the visible spectrum of colors, because different wavelengths of light bend different amounts. *(b)* Humans perceive the visible light spectrum as a sequence of color bands. The relative sensitivity of the human eye differs for different wavelengths. Our perception peaks near wavelengths that we perceive as yellow, though the colors we see have no special physical significance.

THE SCIENCE OF LIFE
The Eye

The light detector most familiar to us is one we carry around with us all the time—the human eye. Eyes are marvelously complex light-collecting organs that send nerve signals to the brain. Your brain converts these signals into images through a combination of physical and chemical processes (Figure 6-25).

(a)   *(b)*   *(c)*

FIGURE 6-24 *(a)* A variety of chemical reactions, including fire, produce light energy. *(b)* One way of producing light is to convert stored chemical energy, as is done in this emergency flare. *(c)* Chemical reactions also produce the light given off by a firefly.

Light waves enter the eye through a clear lens whose thickness can be changed by a sheath of muscles around it. The direction of the waves is changed by refraction in the lens so that they are focused at receptor cells located in the retina at the back of the eye. There the light is absorbed by two different kinds of cells, called rods and cones (the names come from their shape, not their function). The rods are sensitive to light and dark, including low levels of light; they give us night vision. Three kinds of cones, sensitive to red, blue, and green light, allow us to see colors.

The energy of incoming light triggers complex changes in molecules in the rods and cones, initiating a series of reactions that eventually leads to a nerve signal that travels along the optic nerve to the brain (see Chapter 5).

Ultraviolet Radiation

At wavelengths shorter than visible light, we begin to find waves of high frequency and therefore high energy and potential danger. The wavelengths of **ultraviolet radiation** range from 400 nanometers down to about 100 nanometers in length. The energy contained in

FIGURE 6-25 A cross section of the human eye reveals the path of light, which enters through the protective cornea and travels through the colored iris. The pupil changes the size of the aperture through which light passes, thus controlling the amount of light entering the eye. Muscles move the eye and change the shape of the lens, which focuses light onto the retina, where the light's energy is converted into nerve impulses. These signals are carried to the brain along the optic nerve.

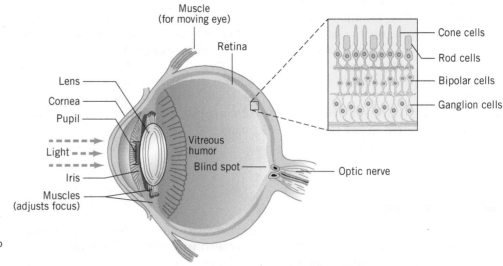

longer ultraviolet waves can cause a chemical change in skin pigments, a phenomenon known as tanning. This lower-energy portion of the ultraviolet is not particularly harmful by itself.

Shorter-wavelength (higher-energy) ultraviolet radiation, on the other hand, carries more energy—enough energy that this radiation, if absorbed by your skin cells, can cause sunburn and other cellular damage. If the ultraviolet wave's energy alters your cell's DNA, it may increase your risk of developing skin cancer (see Chapter 23). In fact, because ultraviolet radiation can damage living cells, hospitals use it to sterilize equipment and kill unwanted bacteria.

The Sun produces intense ultraviolet radiation in both longer and shorter wavelengths. Fortunately, our atmosphere absorbs much of the harmful short wavelengths and thus shields living things. Nevertheless, if you spend much time outdoors under a bright Sun, you should protect exposed skin with a Sun-blocking chemical, which is transparent (colorless) to visible light but reflects or absorbs harmful ultraviolet rays before they can reach your skin (Figure 6-26).

The energy contained in both long and short ultraviolet wavelengths can be absorbed by atoms, which in special materials may subsequently emit a portion of that absorbed energy as visible light. (Remember, both visible light and ultraviolet light are forms of electromagnetic radiation, but visible light has longer wavelengths, and therefore less energy, than ultraviolet radiation.) This phenomenon, called *fluorescence*, provides the so-called black light effects so popular in stage shows and nightclubs. We'll examine the origins of fluorescence in more detail in Chapter 8.

FIGURE 6-26 When you spend time outdoors under a bright Sun, you should protect your skin with sunblock, which is transparent to visible light, but reflects or absorbs harmful ultraviolet rays.

FIGURE 6-27 Internal structures are revealed because bones and different tissues absorb X-rays to different degrees.

X-rays

X-rays are electromagnetic waves that range in wavelength from about 100 nanometers down to 0.1 nanometer, smaller than a single atom. These high-frequency (and thus high-energy) waves can penetrate several centimeters into most solid matter but are absorbed to different degrees by all kinds of materials. This fact allows X-rays to be used extensively in medicine to form visual images of bones and organs inside the body. Bones and teeth absorb X-rays much more efficiently than skin or muscle, so a detailed picture of inner structures emerges (Figure 6-27). X-rays are also used extensively in industry to inspect for defects in welds and manufactured parts.

The X-ray machine in your doctor's or dentist's office is something like a giant lightbulb with a glass vacuum tube. At one end of the tube is a tungsten filament that is heated to a very high temperature by an electrical current, just as in an incandescent lightbulb. At the other end is a polished metal plate. X-rays are produced by applying an extremely high voltage—negative on the filament and positive on the metal plate—so electrons stream off the filament and smash into the metal plate at high velocity. The sudden deceleration of the negatively charged electrons releases a flood of high-energy electromagnetic radiation—the X-rays that travel from the machine to you at light speed.

THE ONGOING PROCESS OF SCIENCE
Intense X-ray Sources

X-rays have become supremely important in many facets of science and industry. X-ray crystallographers use beams of X-rays to determine the spacing and positions of atoms in a crystal (see Chapter 10), physicians use X-rays to reveal bone fractures and other internal injuries, and many industries use X-rays to scan for defects in manufactured products. However, many potential applications, such as structural studies of very small crystals or scans of unusually large manufactured products, are unrealized because of the relatively low intensity of conventional X-ray sources.

A major effort is now underway to develop new, more powerful X-ray sources. One such facility, the Advanced Photon Source (APS) near Chicago, Illinois, generates intense X-ray beams a billion times stronger than conventional sources by accelerating electrons in a circular path (remember, electromagnetic radiation is emitted when charged particles are accelerated). Scientists from around the world converge on the APS to study the properties of matter. Eventually, even more powerful X-ray beams might be produced by an X-ray laser (see Chapter 8), though such a technology is now only a dream.

Gamma Rays

The highest energies in the electromagnetic spectrum are called **gamma rays**. Their wavelengths range from slightly less than the size of an atom (about 0.1 nanometer, or 10^{-10} meter) to the size of a nucleus (less than a trillionth of a meter, or 10^{-12} meter). Gamma rays are normally emitted on Earth only in very high-energy nuclear and particle reactions (see Chapters 12 and 13), but they are produced abundantly in distant energetic stars (see Chapter 14).

Gamma rays have many uses in medicine. Some types of medical diagnosis involve giving a patient a radioactive chemical that emits gamma rays. If that chemical concentrates at places where bone is actively healing, for example, then doctors can monitor the healing by locating the places where gamma rays are emitted. The gamma ray detectors used in this specialized form of nuclear medicine are both large (to capture the energetic waves) and expensive. Doctors also use gamma rays to treat cancer in humans. In these treatments, high-energy gamma rays are directed at tumors or malignancies that cannot be removed surgically. If the gamma ray energy is absorbed in those tissues, the tissues will die and the patient has a better chance to live.

Gamma rays are also studied extensively in astronomy because many of the interesting processes going on in our universe involve bursts of very high energy and, hence, the emission of gamma rays.

THINKING MORE ABOUT ELECTROMAGNETIC RADIATION

Is ELF Radiation Dangerous?

Maxwell's equations tell us that any accelerated charge will emit waves of electromagnetic radiation, not just those that have frequencies of millions or billions of hertz. In particular, the electrons that move back and forth in wires to produce the alternating current in household wiring generate electromagnetic radiation. Every object in which electrical power flows, from power lines to toasters, is a source of this weak, *extremely low-frequency (ELF) radiation.*

For more than a century, human beings in industrialized countries have lived in a sea of weak ELF radiation, but until the late 1980s few questions were raised about whether that radiation might have an effect on human health. Then a series of books and magazine articles created a minor sensation by claiming that exposure to ELF radiation might cause some forms of cancer, most notably childhood leukemia.

Scientists tended to downplay these claims, because the electrical fields most residents experience due to power lines are a thousand times smaller than those due to natural causes (such as electrical activity in nerve and brain cells). They also pointed out that age-corrected cancer rates in the United States (with the exception of lung cancer, which is caused primarily by smoking) have remained constant or dropped over the last 50 years, though exposure to ELF radiation has increased enormously. They also questioned the statistical validity of some studies: more detailed analysis of results did not demonstrate the connection between ELF radiation and disease. In 1995, the prestigious American Institute of Physics reviewed the scientific literature on this subject and concluded that there is no reliable evidence that ELF radiation causes any form of cancer; most funding for research in this area was subsequently cut off.

This situation is typical of encounters at the border between science and public health. Preliminary data indicate a possible

health risk but do not prove that the risk is real. Settling the issue by further study takes years, while researchers carefully collect data and weigh the evidence. In the meantime, people have to make decisions about what to do. In addition, as in the case of ELF radiation, the cost of removing the risk is often very high.

Suppose you were a scientist who had preliminary evidence that some common food—bread, for example, or a familiar kind of fruit—might be harmful. What responsibility would you have to make your results known to the general public? If you stress the uncertainty of your results and no one listens, should you make sensational (perhaps unsupported) claims to get people's attention?

RETURN TO THE INTEGRATED QUESTION

What is color?

- Ancient philosophers and scientists pondered the nature of color. It was not, however, until the seventeenth century that Sir Isaac Newton and others demonstrated that light was the stimulus for the sensation and perception of color. Newton's work was later extended and improved by many other scientists.

- Modern science usually defines color as the human sensation and perception of electromagnetic energy as it interacts with the visual system. Therefore, the color of any object is not a property of that object, but rather the confluence of many factors such as ambient light levels, the reflectivity of the object's surface, and the acuity of the visual system (i.e., the eye and brain) receiving the stimuli. In other words, what we perceive as color is our mind's interpretation of how the eye responds to the background light interacting with the reflective properties of an object's surface.

- The wavelengths of the electromagnetic spectrum perceptible by human beings fall approximately between 400 and 700 nanometers (a nanometer is 10×10^{-9} meter, or about 40 billionths of an inch). The human *eye* has the ability to

distinguish between colors due to the sensitivity of special cells in the retina of the eye. These receptor cells, called cones, react to light of varying wavelengths that correspond to the three primary colors.

- The primary colors are merely different ranges of frequencies, and therefore different energies, of light. Higher frequencies of light correspond to a blue color and lower frequencies to red. Red light has wavelengths corresponding to a range of distances between about 600 and 700 nanometers. Red light includes the longest wavelengths that the eye can see and is the least energetic of the visible electromagnetic waves. Violet light, in contrast, has a range of shorter wavelengths corresponding to about 400–440 nanometers, and includes the most energetic of the visible electromagnetic waves. All of the other colors have ranges of wavelengths and energies between those of red and violet.

- The branch of science that studies the sensation and perception of color is called chromatics. This field encompasses the human perception of color, the properties of materials that lead to color perception and the physics of the visible range of electromagnetic radiation (i.e., light).

SUMMARY

Waves provide a way to transfer energy from one place to another through a medium, without matter traveling across the intervening distance. Every wave can be characterized by a *wavelength*, a velocity, an amplitude, and a *frequency* (measured in cycles per second, or *hertz*). Transverse waves, such as swells on the ocean, occur when the medium moves perpendicular to the direction of the waves. Longitudinal waves, such as sound, occur when the medium moves in the same direction as the wave.

Two waves can interact with each other, causing constructive or destructive *interference*. The observed frequency of a wave depends

on the relative motion of the wave's source and the observer—a phenomenon known as the *Doppler effect*. Waves encountering a surface can be *reflected*, or they may enter the medium moving in a different direction, a process called *refraction*.

The motion of every wave can be described by a characteristic wave equation. James Clerk Maxwell recognized that simple manipulation of his equations that describe electricity and magnetism pointed to the existence of *electromagnetic waves* or *electromagnetic radiation*, alternating electrical and magnetic fields that can travel through a vacuum at the *speed of light*. This discovery solved one of the oldest mysteries of science, the nature of *light*. While visible light was the only kind of electromagnetic radiation known to Maxwell, he predicted the existence of other kinds with longer and shorter wavelengths. Soon thereafter a complete *electromagnetic spectrum* of waves, including *radio waves, microwaves, infrared radiation, visible light, ultraviolet radiation, X-rays,* and *gamma rays,* was recognized.

Electromagnetic radiation can interact with matter in three ways: it can be *transmitted, absorbed,* or *scattered.* We use these properties in countless ways every day—radio and TV, heating and lighting, microwave ovens, tanning salons, medical X-rays, and more. Much of the work in science and technology during the past 100 years has been an effort to find new and better ways to produce, manipulate, and detect electromagnetic radiation.

KEY TERMS

wave
wavelength
frequency
hertz
interference
electromagnetic wave, or
   electromagnetic radiation
light

speed of light, c
Doppler effect
transmission
refraction
absorption
diffuse scattering
reflection
electromagnetic spectrum

radio waves
microwaves
infrared radiation
visible light
ultraviolet radiation
X-rays
gamma rays

KEY EQUATIONS

wave velocity (m/s) = wavelength (m) × frequency (Hz)
wavelength (m) = velocity (m/s)/frequency (Hz)
1 hertz = 1 cycle/second

For light: wavelength (m) × frequency (Hz) = c
Constant: speed of light c = 300,000 km/s = 3×10^8 m/s

DISCOVERY **LAB**

Is frequency related to wavelength of light in the visible spectrum? To find the answer, you will need adding machine tape; a manila folder; red, green, and violet color pencils; masking tape; a timer; and scissors.

Mark off 20 cm from the beginning of the tape and label it START. With a meter stick, measure 100 cm from the START and

label it as END. Leave 20 cm from the END and cut the tape. Draw three evenly spaced lines starting with red, 1 cm away from the top. Divide the red line at an interval of 14 cm and mark it heavy and dark with the red pencil. Draw the middle line green and mark every 10 cm with the green pencil. Draw the bottom line violet and mark every 8 cm.

Adding machine tape

Divide the lines at regular intervals of 14cm (red line), 10cm (green line), and 8cm (violet line)

Start

End

Roll the tape around a pencil

Unroll the tape and move it at a constant rate behind the rectangle

Fasten the END side of the machine tape to a pencil using masking tape. Roll up the machine tape around the pencil. (Have someone hold the pencil.) Cut a rectangle 10 cm by 5 cm from the center of one of the sides of manila folder. The cut side should stand up straight. Lay the uncut side flat on the table and use a book to hold it down. Unroll the machine tape and feed it through the cut in the manila folder so that the word START shows up in the center of the cut. Keep track of time as you slowly begin to pull the tape through the folder from START to the END. One person can tally the wavelength marks while you are pulling the tape and record them in the data table.

Repeat the procedure five times. Make sure to pull the adding machine tape at a constant speed. Use the same steps as above to collect the data for green and violet color. Count the number of tallies for each color separately and divide by the number of trials. Frequency can be found by taking the average of the tallies and dividing them by the average time.

Compare the wavelength and frequency of the three waves. Which color has the longest wavelength and which one has the shortest? Can you determine the relationship between frequency and wavelength?

REVIEW QUESTIONS

1. What is a wave? How do waves transfer energy?
2. Identify five characteristics that can be used to describe a wave. How are these five related?
3. How is the term *hertz* (abbreviated Hz) related to a wave's frequency?
4. Identify everyday examples of waves that travel through solids, liquids, and gases.
5. How is a transverse wave different from a longitudinal wave? Use a Slinky toy to illustrate the difference between these types of waves.
6. How do air molecules move when a sound wave passes by?
7. What is meant by the electromagnetic spectrum? Of what type of waves does it consist?
8. What is the difference between constructive and destructive interference?
9. How are electromagnetic waves produced?
10. What features do all electromagnetic waves share? In what ways might two electromagnetic waves differ?
11. Why did Maxwell think there were kinds of electromagnetic radiation other than visible light?
12. What was meant by "ether"? What prompted the assumption that it existed? What experiment destroyed the idea of its existence?
13. A vat of molten iron is heated until white hot, then poured into a mold. As it cools, its color changes to yellow and then red. Explain why this occurs.
14. Identify three common uses of microwaves.
15. Why is short-wave ultraviolet light more damaging to the skin than long-wave ultraviolet light?
16. What are some uses of gamma rays?
17. What are the longest waves of the electromagnetic spectrum? How large are their wavelengths? Give an example.
18. What kinds of electromagnetic radiation can you detect with your body?
19. In what ways is a water wave like a light wave? In what ways is it different?
20. Describe the Doppler effect. Give an example of how you experience this effect.
21. Identify a substance that:
    a. absorbs radio waves
    b. scatters microwaves
    c. transmits visible light
    d. absorbs X-rays
    e. scatters infrared radiation

DISCUSSION QUESTIONS

1. What are the different kinds of seismic waves? In what ways are they similar to waves on the surface of a body of water and in what ways are they different?
2. An old philosophical question asks, "If a tree falls in a forest and no one hears, does it make a sound?" How do you think a scientist would answer that question?
3. Is your entire body truly transparent to X-rays or does it cast an "X-ray shadow" much as it does when illuminated by visible light?
4. How does sunblock protect against some forms of skin cancer? Against what part of the electromagnetic spectrum does it protect?
5. How do reading glasses work? Describe how the light interacts with the lens.
6. Briefly describe the reasons given for the existence of ether. How did the Michelson-Morley experiment disprove the theory? Is it accurate to say that the Michelson-Morley experiment disproved the existence of ether? Why or why not?
7. Why are X-rays used for medical diagnosis? Why do X-ray technicians leave the room when pictures are taken? What other wavelengths of electromagnetic radiation can you think of that have medical applications?
8. Why do people wear light-colored clothing in summer and dark-colored clothing in winter?

9. If a painted wall reflects light with wavelengths 600 to 700 nm, but absorbs light with wavelengths 400 to 500 nm, what color is it? What if the wall reflects light 400 to 500 nm and absorbs light 600 to 700 nm?

10. Why do different animals "see" in different parts of the electromagnetic spectrum?

11. What causes a rainbow? What is happening to the sunlight to cause us to perceive many individual colors? Why do we not see all the colors all the time?

12. What creates the difference between the waves of an AM radio station and those of a FM radio station?

13. Consider the image of the pencil in Figure 6-14. The part of the pencil under water appears larger and bent along a different line compared to the part outside the water. Is the pencil truly larger when placed in water? Does it bend? What do you think you are seeing?

14. People of the Bedouin tribes in the Arabian Desert adjust to the intensely hot and dry environment by wearing black robes. Given that dark clothing absorbs more heat and therefore has a higher equilibrium temperature than light clothing, how do you think the black robes keep a Bedouin tribesman from overheating?

15. Many species of bee see light in a fashion similar to humans in that the eye has three types of photoreceptors. For humans, those photoreceptors are sensitive to red, green, and blue light. For this species of bee, the photoreceptors are sensitive to green, blue, and ultraviolet light. What colors do you think a bee would see?

16. After enjoying a concert in an auditorium with your friends, one friend to your left complains the music was too loud while a friend to your right complains they could barely hear it. This is an example of the phenomenon known as which of the following?
    a. Spectrum
    b. Interference
    c. Refraction
    d. Radiation

17. An astronomer analyzing light from a distant star similar to the Sun determines that the star's characteristic light pattern has shorter wavelengths than the Sun's. Which of the following is a reasonable conclusion to make about the distant star?
    a. The star is moving away from us.
    b. The star is approaching us.
    c. Light from the star is passing through an interstellar cloud of gas.
    d. It's a normal result of viewing light through the glass optics of the telescope.

18. After undergoing radiotherapy at a hospital, a friend of yours receives an urgent phone call saying they were inadvertently overexposed to radiation with a wavelength of 100 nm. What advice will you offer them?
    a. Don't worry.
    b. Consult a dermatologist about the possibility of skin cancer.
    c. Consult an oncologist about the possibility of cancer in the exposed body part.
    d. Wear stretchable clothing in case you turn big and green when you get angry.

PROBLEMS

1. Consider a 3.09-m long organ pipe that is open at both ends. What is the primary frequency of the sound it produces? Find a table that relates frequencies to musical notes and determine to what pitch this corresponds.

2. While standing at the beach next to the surf, you notice that the waves are coming in at a rate averaging one every 8 seconds. You estimate the separation between wave crests to be 30 m. How fast are the waves traveling?

3. The first person to transmit the sound of their voice over radio in public was the Brazilian inventor Father Roberto Landell de Moura in 1900. Although the signal was weak, the waves associated with that transmission have been traveling outward ever since. How far away is that signal now? Compare that with the distance to Proxima Centauri, the nearest extrasolar star.

4. Satellite radio typically operates with microwaves rather than radio waves owing to radio waves being reflected by the Earth's ionosphere. Suppose a particular satellite uses a wavelength of 7.2 cm. What is the frequency of this signal?

5. The FM radio band in most places goes from frequencies of about 88 to 108 MHz. How long are the wavelengths of the radiation at the extreme ends of this range?

6. The AM radio band in most places goes from frequencies of about 535 to 1610 kHz. How long are the wavelengths of the radiation at the extreme ends of this range?

7. The Cassini spacecraft entered into orbit around the planet Saturn in 2004; as of 2014, it was still in operation. The distance from Earth to Saturn can be as large as 1.67 billion km. How long does it take a radio signal to travel from Cassini to Earth at this distance?

8. When an earthquake occurs, one type of seismic wave travels through Earth. Analysis shows that such a wave travels at a speed of 8 km/s with a frequency of oscillation of 6 Hz. What is its wavelength?

9. Echolocation in animals such as bats requires that the wavelength of the sound be the size of the target or smaller. Consider a bat using echolocation to seek out an insect 0.85 cm

in size. What is the minimum frequency of the sound the bat should emit?

10. An electromagnetic pulse is created and soon detected at a site 450 km away. How long did it take for the pulse to travel to the detector?

a. 1.5 ms

b. 3.0 s

c. about 500 ns

d. 450 s

INVESTIGATIONS

1. Visit a local hospital and see how many types of electromagnetic radiation are used on a regular basis. From radio waves to gamma waves, how are the distinctive characteristics of absorption and transmission for each segment of the spectrum used at the facility?

2. What frequencies of electromagnetic radiation do police, fire, and medivac in your community use for emergency communications? What are the corresponding wavelengths of these signals? What organizations allocate and monitor these frequencies?

3. Look up "cavity magnetron." What role do these devices play in microwave ovens?

4. In large metropolitan areas, a license to broadcast electromagnetic waves at an AM frequency may change hands for millions of dollars.

   a. Why is electromagnetic "real estate" so valuable? Investigate how frequencies are divided up and who regulates the process. Should individuals or corporations be allowed to "own" portions of the spectrum, or to buy and sell pieces of it?

   b. Currently, the only portions of the electromagnetic spectrum that are regulated by national and international law are the longer wavelengths, including radio and microwave. Why are the shorter wavelengths, including infrared, visible light, ultraviolet, and X-ray wavelengths, not similarly regulated?

5. What are the primary colors? Why might there be different definitions for primary colors? What is the difference between additive and subtractive sets of primary colors?

6. Find out how sonar works. Compare it to the use of sound by bats and the use of radar by police. Discuss the similarities and differences among the defenses of submarines against sonar, moths against bats, and motorists against police radar.

7. What does the word "cell" mean when you're referring to your cell phone?

8. Keep an "electromagnetic journal" for one day. What activity makes use of the most electromagnetic energy?

9. When you are at a loud concert, you can actually "feel" the music. What are you feeling? What type of wave is being created?

10. The next time you are driving on a long stretch of road on a hot day, see if you can observe the mirage (i.e., an optical illusion) that is often seen in the distance. Why does it look like water? What causes this illusion?

11. What type of waves can travel through rock? How fast can they travel? Can you outrun an earthquake in a car?

12. Why do you suppose FM radio sounds so much better than AM radio?

7 Albert Einstein and the Theory of Relativity

Can a human ever travel faster than the speed of light, at "warp speed"?

PHYSICS

Particle accelerators that control relativistic charged particles in a closed loop must be designed to correct for change of mass and time experienced by the speeding particles (ch.13)

GREAT IDEA

All observers, no matter what their frame of reference, see the same laws of nature.

TECHNOLOGY

Atomic clocks have been shown to tick slightly slower when strapped aboard a high-speed plane, compared to a stationary clock.

ASTRONOMY

Stars are so massive that they can bend light coming from more distant objects to create a gravitation lens.

 = applications of the great idea discussed in this chapter

 = other applications, some of which are discussed in other chapters

Waiting at the Stoplight

Waiting in your car at a long stoplight, you daydream about the friends you're going to meet. You don't even notice the large bus in the lane next to you.

Suddenly you have the strange sensation that your car is moving backward. But your foot is on the brake—how can that be? You quickly realize that it's the bus that's moving forward, not you moving backward. It was just a brief optical illusion.

For that brief moment you saw the world through eyes unaffected by years of experience. You realized that there is always more than one way to view any kind of motion. One way, of course, is to say that you are stationary and the bus is moving with respect to you. But you could also say that the bus is stationary and you are moving backward relative to it. Which point of view is right?

Almost 100 years ago, Albert Einstein made one of the greatest discoveries of the twentieth century thinking about situations just like this.

Imagemore Co., Ltd./Getty Images, Inc.

◉ 7.1 Frames of Reference

A **frame of reference** is the physical surroundings from which you observe and measure the world around you. If you read this book at your desk or in an easy chair, you experience the world from the frame of reference of your room, which seems firmly rooted to the solid Earth. If you read on a train or in a plane, your frame of reference is the vehicle that moves with respect to Earth's surface. And you could imagine yourself in an accelerating spaceship in deep space, where your frame of reference would be different still. In each of these reference frames you are what scientists call an "observer." An observer looks at the world from a particular frame of reference with anything from casual interest to a full-fledged laboratory investigation of phenomena that leads to a determination of natural laws.

For human beings who grow up on Earth's surface, it is natural to think of the ground as a fixed, immovable frame of reference and to refer all motion to it. After all, train or plane passengers don't think of themselves as stationary while the countryside zooms by. But, as we saw in the opening example, there are indeed times when we lose this prejudice and see that the question of who is moving and who is standing still is largely one of definition.

From the point of view of an observer in a spaceship above the solar system, there is nothing "solid" about the ground you're standing on. Earth is rotating on its axis and moving in an orbit around the Sun, while the Sun itself is performing a stately rotation around the galaxy. Thus, even though a reference frame fixed in Earth may seem "right" to us, there is nothing special about it.

Apparent direction of coin fall

Frame of reference: inside the train   Frame of reference: outside the train

(a)   (b)

- - - - - - - - → **Direction of train movement** - - - - - - - - →

FIGURE 7-1 The path of a coin flipped in the air depends on the observer's frame of reference. (a) A rider in the car sees the coin go up and fall straight down. (b) An observer on the street sees the coin follow an arching path.

Descriptions in Different Reference Frames

Different observers in different reference frames may provide very different accounts of the same event. To convince yourself of this idea, think about a simple experiment. While riding on a train, take a coin out of your pocket and flip it. You know what will happen—the coin will go up in the air and fall straight back into your hand, just as it would if you flipped it while sitting in a chair in your room (Figure 7-1a). But now ask yourself this question: How would a friend standing near the tracks, watching your train go by, describe the flip of the coin?

To that person it would appear that the coin went up into the air, of course, but by the time it came down the car would have traveled some distance down the tracks. As far as your friend on the ground is concerned, the coin traveled in an arc (Figure 7-1b).

So you, sitting in the train, say the coin went straight up and down, while someone on the ground says it traveled in an arc. You and the ground-based observer would describe the path of the coin quite differently, and you'd both be correct in your respective frames of reference. The universe we live in possesses this general feature—different observers will describe the same event in different terms, depending on their frames of reference.

Does this situation mean that we are doomed to live in a world where nothing is fixed, where everything depends on the frame of reference of the observer? Not necessarily. The possibility exists that even though different observers give different descriptions of the same event, they will agree on the underlying laws that govern it. Even though the observers disagree on the path followed by the flipped coin, they may very well agree that motion in their frame is governed by Newton's laws of motion and the law of universal gravitation.

FIGURE 7-2 Albert Einstein (1879-1955).

Bettmann/©Corbis-Bettmann

The Principle of Relativity

Albert Einstein (Figure 7-2) arrived at his theories of relativity by thinking about a fundamental contradiction between Newton's laws and Maxwell's equations. You can see the problem by thinking about a simple example. Imagine you're on a moving railroad car and you throw a baseball. What speed will the baseball have according to an observer on the ground?

If, on the one hand, you throw the ball forward at 40 kilometers per hour while on a train traveling 100 kilometers per hour, the ball will appear to a ground-based observer to travel 140 kilometers per hour—40 kilometers per hour from the ball plus 100 kilometers per hour from the train. If, on the other hand, you throw the ball backward, the ground-based observer will see the ball moving at only 60 kilometers per hour—the train's 100 kilometers per hour minus the ball's 40 kilometers per hour. In our everyday world, we just add the two speeds to get the answer, and this notion is reflected in Newton's laws.

Suppose, however, that instead of throwing a ball you turned on a flashlight and measured the speed of the light coming from it. In Chapter 6 we saw that the speed of light is built into Maxwell's equations. If every observer is to see the same laws of nature, they all have to see the same speed of light. In other words, the ground observer would have to see light from the flashlight moving at 300,000 kilometers per second, and *not* 300,000 kilometers per second plus 100 kilometers per second. In this case, velocities wouldn't add, as our intuition tells us they must.

Albert Einstein thought long and hard about this paradox, and he realized that it could be resolved in only three ways:

1. The laws of nature are not the same in all frames of reference (an idea Einstein was reluctant to accept on philosophical grounds); or,

2. Maxwell's equations could be wrong and the speed of light depends on the speed of the source emitting the light (in spite of abundant experimental support for the equations); or,

3. Our intuitions about the addition of velocities could be wrong, in which case the universe might be a very strange place indeed.

Einstein focused on the third of these possibilities.

The idea that the laws of nature are the same in all frames of reference is called the *principle of relativity,* and can be stated as follows:

● **Every observer must experience the same natural laws.**

This statement is the central assumption of Einstein's **theory of relativity**. Hidden beneath this seemingly simple statement lies a view of the universe that is both strange and wonderful. The extraordinary theoretical effort required to understand the consequences of this one simple assumption occupied Einstein during much of the first decades of the twentieth century.

STOP & THINK It may seem obvious that the laws of nature are the same everywhere in the universe, but how can we know for sure? How might you test this statement?

We can begin to understand Einstein's work by recalling what Isaac Newton had demonstrated three centuries earlier, that all motions fall into one of two categories: uniform motion or acceleration (Chapter 2). Einstein therefore divided his theory of relativity into two parts—one dealing with each of these kinds of motion. The easier part, first published by Einstein in 1905, is called **special relativity** and deals with all frames of reference in uniform motion relative to one another—reference frames that do not accelerate. It took Einstein another decade to complete his treatment of **general relativity,** mathematically a much more complex theory, which applies to any reference frame whether or not it is accelerating relative to another.

At first glance, the underlying principle of relativity seems obvious, perhaps almost too simple. Of course the laws of nature are the same everywhere—that's the only way that scientists can explain how the universe behaves in an ordered way. But once you accept that central assumption of relativity, be prepared for some surprises. Relativity forces us to accept the fact that nature doesn't always behave as our intuition says it must. You may find it disturbing that nature sometimes violates our sense of the "way things should be." But you'll have little problem with relativity if you just accept the idea that the universe is what it is, and not necessarily what we think it should be.

Another way of saying this is to note that our intuitions about how the world works are built up from experience with things that are moving at modest speeds—a few hundred, or at most a few thousand, miles per hour. None of us has any experience with things moving near the speed of light, so when we start examining phenomena in that range our intuitions won't necessarily apply. Strictly speaking, we shouldn't be surprised by anything we find.

Relativity and the Speed of Light

As the example of the train and the flashlight shows, one of the most disturbing aspects of the principle of relativity has to do with our everyday notions of speed. According to the principle, any observer, no matter what his or her reference frame, should be able to confirm Maxwell's description of electricity and magnetism. Because the speed of light is built into these equations, it follows that:

● **The speed of light, c, is the same in all reference frames.**

Strictly speaking, this statement is only one of many consequences of the principle of relativity. However, so many of the surprising results of relativity follow from it that it is often accorded special status and given special attention in discussions of those theories.

◉ 7.2 Special Relativity

Time Dilation

Think about how you measure time. The passage of time can be measured by any kind of regularly repeating phenomenon—a swinging pendulum, a beating heart, or an alternating electrical current. To get at the theory of relativity, though, it's easiest to think of a rather unusual kind of clock. Suppose, as in Figure 7-3, we had a flashbulb, a mirror, and a photon detector. A "tick-tock" of this clock would consist of the flashbulb going off, the light traveling to the mirror, bouncing down to the detector, and then triggering the next flash. By adjusting the distance, *d*, between the light source and mirror, these pluses could correspond to any desired time interval. This unusual "light clock," therefore, serves the same function as any other clock—in fact, you could adjust it to be synchronized with anything from a grandfather clock to a wristwatch.

Now imagine two identical light clocks: one next to you on the ground (Figure7-3a), and the other whizzing by in a spaceship (Figure 7-3b). Imagine further that the mirrors are adjusted so that both clocks would tick at the same rate if they were standing next to each other. How would the moving clock look to you?

Standing on the ground, you would see the ground-based clock ticking along as the light pulses bounce back and forth between the mirror and detector. When you looked at the moving clock, though, you would see the light following a longer zig-zag path. If the speed of light is indeed the same in both frames of reference, it should appear to you that the light in the moving frame takes longer to travel the zig-zag path from light to detector than the light on the ground-based clock. Consequently, from your point of view on the ground, the moving clock must tick more slowly. The two clocks are identical, but the moving clock runs slower. This surprising phenomenon is known as **time dilation**, and it is an essential consequence of relativity.

Remember that each observer regards the clocks in his or her own reference frame as completely normal, while all other clocks appear to be running slower. Thus, paradoxically, although

Stationary light clock

(a)

Moving light clock

(b)

FIGURE 7-3 A light clock incorporates a flashing light and a mirror. A light pulse bounces off the mirror and returns to trigger the next pulse. Two light clocks, one stationary *(a)* and one moving *(b)*, illustrate the phenomenon of time dilation. Light from the moving clock must travel farther, and so it appears to the stationary observer to tick more slowly.

we observe the spaceship clock as slow, observers in the speeding spaceship see the Earth-based clock moving and believe that the Earth-based clock is running more slowly than theirs.

TESTS OF SPECIAL RELATIVITY

Like any other scientific theory, relativity must be tested by comparing its predictions to experiments. The theory has met many such tests, one of which will be seen in our discussion of the GPS system later in this chapter. Historically, two striking experiments verified the theory:

1. In 1971, scientists conducted experiments in which extremely accurate atomic clocks were flown around the world in commercial airliners, and the time they registered was compared to that registered on identical clocks on the ground (Figure 7-4). The results met the predictions of relativity (both special and general).

2. Many of the elementary particles we will meet in Chapter 13 are unstable and decay in a fraction of a second. A particle called the muon (pronounced MEW-on), for example, will decay in a millionth of a second or so in its rest frame. Thus, these particles are a kind of clock that ticks only one time. Because they are continually being produced by the collision of cosmic rays with atoms in the upper atmosphere, we can calculate how many muons would make it to the ground if there were no time dilation. Experiments that measured muon fluxes on mountaintops and then on the ground shows that far too many of the particles reached the ground to be explained by any cause other than time dilation.

FIGURE 7-4 A clock strapped into a flying airplane seat ticks slightly slower than a stationary clock at Earth's surface.

The Size of Time Dilation

We have tried, in general, to talk about science in everyday terms and stay away from formulas in this book. But we have now run into a rather fundamental question that requires some simple mathematics to answer. In this section, you'll be able to follow the kind of thought process used by Einstein when he first formulated his revolutionary theory.

Consider the two identical light clocks in Figure 7-3, one moving at a velocity, v, and one stationary on the ground. Each clock has a light-to-mirror separation distance of d. (The various symbols we are using are summarized in Table 7-1).

The notation for the time it takes for light to travel the distance d from the light to its opposite mirror—that is, one "tick" of the stationary clock—is a little trickier, because we have to keep track of which clock we're looking at and from which reference frame we're looking. We will use two subscripts—the first subscript to tell us if the clock is on the ground (G) or moving (M), and the second subscript to indicate if the observer is one the ground or moving. Thus, t_{GG}

TABLE 7-1 **Symbols for Deriving Time Dilation**

Symbol	Description
v	Velocity of the moving light clock relative to the ground
d	Distance between the clock's light and mirror
t_{GG}	Time for one tick (ground clock, ground mirror)
t_{MG}	Time for one tick (moving clock, ground mirror)
t_{GM}	Time for one tick (ground clock, moving mirror)
t_{MM}	Time for one tick (moving clock, moving mirror)
c	Speed of light, a constant

FIGURE 7-5 Light clocks with dimensions labeled. Both the stationary clock (a) and the moving clock (b) have light-to-mirror distance d. During one tick the moving clock must travel a horizontal distance $v \times t_{MG}$.

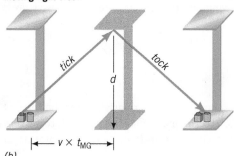

is the time for one tick of the ground-based clock as observed by an observer on the ground. On the other hand, t_{MG} is the time for one tick of the moving clock from the point of view of this ground-based observer. According to the principle of relativity, all observers see clocks in their own reference frames as normal. Or, in equation form,

$$t_{GG} = t_{MM}$$

As ground-based observers, we are interested in determining the relative values of t_{GG} and t_{MG} — what we see as "ticks" of the stationary versus the moving clocks. In the stationary ground-based frame of reference, one tick is simply the time it takes light to travel the distance d:

$$\text{Time} = \frac{\text{distance}}{\text{speed}}$$

Substituting values for the light clock into this equation,

$$\text{Time for one tick} = \frac{\text{light-to-mirror distance}}{\text{speed of light}}$$

or

$$t_{GG} = \frac{d}{c}$$

where c is the standard symbol for the speed of light.

We argued that to the observer on the ground, it appears that the light beam in the moving clock travels on a zig-zag path as shown in Figure 7-3, and that this made the moving clock appear to run more slowly. In what follows, we will show how to convert an intuitive statement like this one into a precise mathematical equation. We begin by labeling the dimensions of our two clocks.

The moving clock travels a horizontal distance of $v \times t_{MG}$ during each of its ticks. In order to determine the value of t_{MG}, we must first determine how far light must travel in the moving clock as seen by the observer on the ground. As illustrated in Figure 7-5, we know the lengths of the two shortest sides of a right triangle. One side has length d, representing the vertical distance between light and mirror (a distance, remember, that is the same in both frames of reference). The other side is $v \times t_{MG}$, which corresponds to the distance traveled by the moving clock as observed in the stationary frame of reference. The distance traveled by the moving light beam in one tick is represented by the hypotenuse of this right triangle and is given by the Pythagorean theorem.

In words: The square of the length of a right triangle's long side equals the sum of the squares of the lengths of the other two sides.

In words (applied to our light clock): The square of the distance light travels during one tick equals the sum of the squares of the light-to-mirror distance and the horizontal distance the clock moves during one tick.

In symbols:

$$(\text{distance light travels})^2 = d^2 + (v \times t_{MG})^2$$

We can begin to simplify this equation by taking the square roots of both sides.

$$\text{distance light travels} = \sqrt{d^2 + (v \times t_{MG})^2}$$

Remember, time equals distance divided by velocity. So the time it takes light to travel this distance, t_{MG}, is given by the distance $\sqrt{d^2 + (v \times t_{MG})^2}$ divided by the velocity of light, c:

$$T_{MG} = \frac{\sqrt{d^2 + (v \times t_{MG})^2}}{c}$$

We now must engage in a bit of algebraic manipulation. First, square both sides of this equation.

$$t_{MG}^2 = t_{GG}^2 + \frac{v^2 \times t_{MG}^2}{c^2}$$

But we saw previously that $t_{GG} = d/c$, so, substituting,

$$t_{MG}^2 = \frac{d^2}{c^2} + \frac{v^2 \times t_{MG}^2}{c^2}$$

Dividing both sides by t_{MG}^2 gives

$$\frac{t_{MG}^2}{t_{MG}^2} = \frac{t_{GG}^2}{t_{MG}^2} + \frac{[v^2 \times t_{MG}^2/c^2]}{t_{MG}^2}$$

or

$$1 = \left(\frac{t_{GG}}{t_{MG}}\right)^2 + (v/c)^2$$

Finally, regrouping yields

$$t_{MG} = t_{GG} / \sqrt{\left[1 - (v/c)^2\right]}$$

This equation expresses in mathematical form what we said earlier in words—that moving clocks appear to run slower. It tells us that t_{MG}, the time it takes for one tick of the moving clock as seen by an observer on the ground, is equal to the time it takes for one tick of an identical clock on the ground *divided by a number less than one*. Thus the time required for a tick of the moving clock will always be greater than that for a stationary one.

The expression $\sqrt{[1 - (v/c)^2]}$ is a number, called the *Lorentz factor*, that appears over and over again in relativistic calculations. In the case of time dilation, the Lorentz factor arises from an application of the Pythagorean theorem.

One important point to notice is that if the velocity of the moving clock is very small compared to the speed of light, the quantity $(v/c)^2$ becomes very small and the Lorentz factor is almost equal to one. In this case, the time on the moving clock is equal to the time on the stationary one, as our intuition demands that it should be. Only when speeds get very high do the effects of relativity become important.

Distance and Relativity

Many results from relativity run counter to our intuition. They can be derived by procedures similar to (but more complicated than) the one we just gave for working out time dilation. In fact, using arguments like those we have presented, Einstein showed that *moving yardsticks must appear to be shorter than stationary ones in the direction of motion* (see Figure 7-6).

The equation that relates the ground-based observer's measurement of a stationary object's length, L_{GG}, to that observer's measurement of the length of an identical moving object, L_{MG}, is

$$L_{MG} = L_{GG} \times \sqrt{\left[1 - (v/c)^2\right]}$$

The term on the right side of this equation is the familiar Lorentz factor that we derived from our study of light clocks. The equation tells us that the length of the moving ruler can be obtained

Spaceship at rest

(a)

Spaceship at high speed

(b)

FIGURE 7-6 A spaceship in motion appears to contract in length, L, along the direction of motion. However, the height, H, and width of the ship do not appear to change.

by multiplying the length of the stationary ruler by a number less than one, and thus must appear shorter. This phenomenon is known as **length contraction**. Note that the height and width of the moving object do not appear to change—only the length along the direction of motion. A moving basketball, then, takes on the appearance of a pancake at speeds near those of light.

Length contraction is not just an optical illusion. While relativistic shortening doesn't affect most of our daily lives, the effect is real. Physicists who work at particle accelerators inject "bunches" of particles into their machines. As these particles approach light speed, the bunches are observed to contract according to the Lorentz factor, an effect that must be compensated for.

STOP & THINK What does the "spaceship at rest" in Figure 7-6 look like to an observer in the "spaceship at high speed?" Does it appear to be normal length, shorter, or longer?

So What about the Train and the Flashlight?

Now that we understand a little about how relativity works, we can go back and unravel the paradox we discussed earlier in this chapter—the problem of how both an observer on the ground and an observer on the train could see light from a flashlight moving at the same speed.

Velocity is defined to be distance traveled divided by the time required for the travel to take place. Since both length and time appear to be different for different observers, it should come as no surprise that the rule that tells us how to add velocities (such as the velocity of the light and the train) might be more complicated than we would expect. The simple intuition that tells us that we should add the velocity of the train to the velocity of the ball, like our notions of time and space, is valid at small velocities but breaks down for objects moving near the speed of light. For those objects, a more complex addition has to be done, and when it is, we find that both observers see the light moving at a velocity of c.

Mass and Relativity

Perhaps the most far-reaching consequence of Einstein's theory of relativity was the discovery that mass, like time and distance, is relative to one's frame of reference. So far we have been faced with three strange ideas:

1. Clocks run fastest for stationary objects; moving clocks slow down. As the speed of light is approached, time slows down and approaches zero.
2. Distances are greatest for stationary objects; moving objects shrink in the direction of motion. As the speed of light is approached, distances shrink and approach zero. Einstein showed that a third consequence followed from his principle:
3. Mass is lowest for stationary objects; moving objects become more massive. As an object's velocity approaches the speed of light, its mass approaches infinity.

Einstein showed that if the speed of light is a constant in all reference frames—which must follow from the central assumption of the theory of relativity—then an object's mass depends on its velocity. The faster an object travels, the greater its mass and the harder it is to deflect from its course. If a ground-based observer measures an object's stationary or "rest" mass, m_{GG}, then the apparent mass, m_{MG}, of that object moving at velocity v is

$$m_{MG} = \frac{m_{GG}}{\sqrt{\left[1 - (v/c)^2\right]}}$$

Once again the Lorentz factor comes into play. As we observe an object approach the speed of light, its mass appears to us to approach infinity.

This property of mass leads to the common misperception that relativity predicts that nothing can travel faster than the speed of light. In fact, the only thing we can conclude is that nothing that is now moving at less than the speed of light can be accelerated to or past that speed. It also says that, should there exist objects already moving faster than light, they could not be decelerated to speeds of less than *c*, and that the only objects that travel at the speed of light (such as photons) are those that have zero rest mass.

Mass and Energy

Time, distance, and mass—all quantities that we can easily measure in our homes or laboratories—actually depend on our frame of reference. But not everything in nature is so variable. The central tenet of relativity is that natural laws must apply to every frame of reference. Light speed is constant in all reference frames in accord with Maxwell's equations. Similarly, the first law of thermodynamics—the idea that total amount of energy in any closed system is constant—must hold, no matter what the frame of reference. Yet here, Einstein's description of the universe seems to run into a problem. He claims that the observed mass depends on your frame of reference. But, in that case, kinetic energy—defined as mass times velocity squared—could not follow the conservation of energy law. In Einstein's treatment, faster frames of reference seem to possess more energy than slower ones. Where does the extra energy come from?

Conservation of energy appeared to be violated because we missed one key form of energy in our equations: mass itself. In fact, Einstein was able to show that the amount of energy contained in any mass turns out to be the mass times a constant.

In words: All objects contain a rest energy (in addition to any kinetic or potential energy), which is equal to the object's rest mass times the speed of light squared.

In equation form:

$$\text{rest energy} = \text{rest mass} \times (\text{speed of light})^2$$

In symbols:

$$E = mc^2$$

This familiar equation has become an icon of our nuclear age, for it defines a new form of energy. It says that mass can be converted to energy, and vice versa. Furthermore, the amounts of energy involved are prodigious (because the constant, the speed of light squared, is so large). A handful of nuclear fuel can power a city; a fist-sized chunk of nuclear explosive can destroy it.

Until Einstein traced the implications of special relativity, the nature of mass and its vast potential for producing energy was hidden from us. Now nearly a quarter of all electrical power in the United States is produced in nuclear reactors that confirm the predictions of Einstein's theory every day of our lives (see Chapter 12).

One way to think about this famous equation is this: before Einstein, scientists thought of the world as being composed of two giant reservoirs—one labeled "mass" and the other labeled "energy." The "mass" reservoir told us that matter couldn't be created or destroyed, and that, for example, the number of atoms on the two sides of a chemical equation have to balance (see Chapter 10). The "energy" reservoir told us energy could not be created or destroyed, as we saw when we discussed the first law of thermodynamics in Chapter 3. Einstein's equation opens a channel between these previously isolated reservoirs, so conversion of mass to energy and energy to mass is allowed to happen.

SCIENCE IN THE MAKING
Einstein and the Streetcar

Newton and his apple have entered modern folklore as a paradigm of unexpected discovery. A less-well-known incident led Albert Einstein, then an obscure patent clerk in Bern, Switzerland, to relativity.

FIGURE 7-7 Albert Einstein, moving away from a clock tower, imagined how different observers might view the passage of time. If Einstein were traveling at the speed of light, for example, the clock would appear to him to have stopped, even though his own pocket watch would still be ticking.

One day, while riding home in a streetcar, he happened to glance up at a clock on a church steeple (Figure 7-7). In his mind he imagined the streetcar speeding up, moving faster and faster, until it was going at almost the speed of light. Einstein realized that if the streetcar were to travel at the speed of light, it would appear to someone on the streetcar that the clock had stopped. The passenger would be like a surfer on a light-wave crest—a crest that originated at 12 noon, for example—and the same image of the clock would stay with him.

However, a clock moving with him—his pocket watch, for example—would still tick away the seconds in its usual way. Perhaps, Einstein thought, *time as measured on a clock, just like motion, is relative to one's frame of reference.*

SCIENCE BY THE NUMBERS

How Important Is Relativity?

To understand why we aren't aware of relativity in our everyday life, let's calculate the size of the time dilation for a clock in a car moving at 70 kilometers per hour (about 50 miles per hour).

The first problem is to convert the familiar speed in kilometers per hour to a speed in meters per second so that we can compare it to the speed of light. There are 3,600 seconds in an hour, so a car traveling 70 kilometers per hour is moving at a speed of

$$70 \text{ km/h} = \frac{70,000 \text{ m}}{3,600 \text{ s}}$$

$$= 19.4 \text{ m/s}$$

For this speed, the Lorentz factor is

$$\sqrt{\left[1 - \left(19.4 / 300,000,000\right)^2\right]} = 0.9999999999999999999$$

Thus, the passage of time for a stationary and speeding car differs by only one part in the sixteenth decimal place.

To get an idea of how small the difference is between the ground clock and the moving one in this case, we can note that if you watched the moving car for a time equal to the age of the universe, you would observe it running *10 seconds slow* compared to your ground clock.

For an object traveling at 99% of the speed of light, however, the Lorentz factor is

$$\sqrt{\left[1 - \left(v / c\right)^2\right]} = \sqrt{\left[1 - \left(0.99\right)^2\right]}$$

$$= \sqrt{(0.0199)}$$

$$= 0.1411$$

In this case, you would observe the stationary clock to be ticking about seven times as fast as the moving one—that is, the ground clock would tick about seven times while the moving clock ticked just once.

This numerical example illustrates a very important point about relativity. Our intuition and experience tell us that the exterior clock on our local bank doesn't suddenly slow down when we view it from a moving car. Consequently, we find the prediction of time dilation to be strange and paradoxical. But all of our intuition is built up from experiences at very low velocities—none of us has ever moved at an appreciable fraction of the speed of light. For the everyday world, the predictions of relativity coincide precisely with our experience. It is only when we get into regions near the speed of light, where that experience isn't relevant, that the "paradoxes" arise.

THE SCIENCE OF LIFE
Space Travel and Aging

Although humans presently do not experience the direct effects of time dilation in their day-to-day lives, at some future time they might. If we ever develop interstellar space travel with near-light speed, then time dilation may wreak havoc with family lives (and genealogists' records).

Imagine a spaceship that accelerates to 99% of the speed of light and goes on a long journey. Although 15 years seem to pass for the crew of the ship, more than a century goes by on Earth. The space explorers return almost 15 years older than when they left, but biologically younger than their great-grandchildren! Friends and family all would be long-since dead.

If we ever enter an era of extensive high-speed interstellar travel, people may drift in and out of other people's lives in ways we can't easily imagine. Parents and children could repeatedly leapfrog each other in age, and the notion of relatedness could take on complex twists in a society with widespread relativistic travel.

⦿ 7.3 General Relativity

Special relativity is a fascinating and fairly accessible intellectual exercise, requiring little more than an open mind and a lot of basic algebra. General relativity, which deals with all reference frames including accelerating ones, is much more challenging in its full rigor. While the details are tricky, you can get a pretty good feeling for Einstein's general theory by thinking about the nature of forces.

The Nature of Forces

Begin by imagining yourself in a completely sealed room that is accelerating at exactly one "g"—Earth's gravitational acceleration. Could you devise any experiment that would reveal one way or the other if you were on Earth or accelerating in deep space?

If you dropped this book on Earth, the force of gravity would cause it to fall to your feet (Figure 7-8a). If you dropped the book in the accelerating spaceship, however, Newton's first law tells us that it will keep moving with whatever speed it had when it was released. The floor of the ship, still accelerating, will therefore come up to meet it (Figure 7-8b). To you, standing in the ship, it appears that the book falls, just as it does if you are standing on Earth.

From an external frame of reference, of course, these two situations would involve very different descriptions. In the one case of the book falls due to the force of gravity; in the other the spaceship accelerates up to meet the free-floating book. But no experiment you could devise *in your reference frame* could distinguish between acceleration in deep space and the force of Earth's gravitational field.

On Earth

(a)

In an accelerating spaceship

(b)

FIGURE 7-8 *(a)* If you drop a book on Earth, the force of gravity causes it to accelerate downward and fall at your feet. *(b)* If you dropped the same book in an accelerating spaceship, the floor of the ship will accelerate upward: the book will appear to fall at your feet.

In some deep and profound way, therefore, gravitational forces and acceleration are equivalent. Newton saw this connection in a way, for his laws of motion equate force with an accelerating mass. But Einstein went a step further by recognizing that what we call gravity versus what we call acceleration is a purely arbitrary decision, based on our choice of reference frame. Whether we think of ourselves as stationary on a planet with gravity, or accelerating on spaceship Earth, makes no difference in the passage of events.

Although this connection between gravity and acceleration may seem a bit abstract, you already have had experiences that should tell you it is true. Have you ever been in an elevator and felt momentarily heavier when it starts up or momentarily lighter when it starts down? If so, you know that the feeling we call "weight" can indeed be affectedly acceleration.

The actual working out of the consequences of this notion of the equivalence of acceleration and gravity is complicated, but a simple analogy can help you visualize the difference between Einstein's and Newton's views of the universe. In the Newtonian universe, forces and motions can be described by a ball rolling on a perfectly flat surface with neatly inscribed grid lines (Figure 7-9a). The ball rolls on and on, following a line exactly, unless an external force is applied. If, for example, a large mass rests on the surface, the rolling ball will change its direction and

Newtonian universe: gravitational forces in a "flat" universe

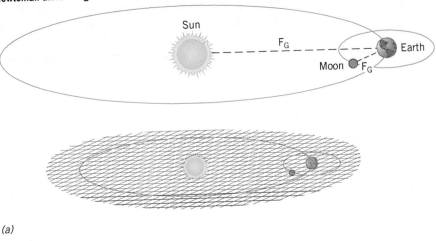

(a)

Einstein's universe: motion in a curved universe.

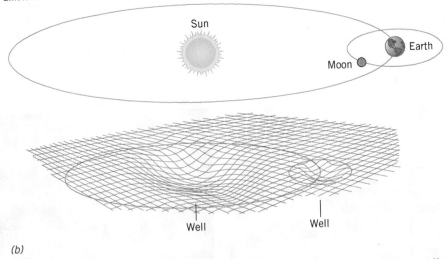

(b)

FIGURE 7-9 Newtonian and Einsteinian universes treat the motion of rolling balls in different ways. In the Newtonian scheme (a), a ball travels in uniform motion unless acted upon by a force; motion occurs along curved paths in a flat universe. In the Einsteinian universe (b), a ball's mass distorts the universe; it moves in a straight line across a curved surface.

speed—it will accelerate in response to the force of gravity. Thus, for Newton, motion occurs along curving paths in a flat universe.

The description of that same event in general relativity is very different. In this case, as shown in Figure 7-9b, we would say that the heavy object distorts the surface. Peaks and depressions on the surface influence the ball's path, deflecting it as it rolls across the surface. For Einstein, the ball moves in a straight line across a curved universe.

Given these differing views, Newton and Einstein would give very different descriptions of physical events. Newton would say, for example, that the Moon orbits Earth because of an attractive gravitational force between the two bodies (Figure 7-9a). Einstein, on the other hand, would say that space has been warped in the vicinity of the Earth–Moon system, and this warping of space governs the Moon's motion (Figure 7-9b). In the relativistic view, space deforms around the Sun, and planets follow the curvature of space like marbles rolling around in the bottom of a curved bowl.

We now have two very different ways of thinking about the universe. In the Newtonian universe, forces cause objects to accelerate. Space and time are separate dimensions that are experienced in very different ways. This view more closely matches our everyday experience of how the world seems to be. In Einstein's universe, objects move according to distortions in space (Figure 7-10), while the distinction between space and time depend son your frame of reference.

You will notice that both Newton and Einstein treat gravity as a force that is always attractive. There's no room for a repulsive force—an "antigravity"—in these theories. In Chapter 15 we discuss some new developments in cosmology that may change this aspect of gravitation. The discovery of what is called "dark energy" indicates that there is another kind of force in the universe—one that, on the scale of galaxies, can be repulsive and play the role of antigravity.

FIGURE 7-10 A computer-generated image of a space–time grid that has been distorted by the presence of mass.

Predictions of General Relativity

The mathematical models of Newton and Einstein are not just two equivalent descriptions of the universe. They lead to slightly different quantitative predictions of events. In three specific instances, the predictions of general relativity have been confirmed.

1. **The Gravitational Bending of Light**

   One consequence of Einstein's theory is that light can be bent as it travels along the warped space near strong gravitational centers such as the Sun (Figure 7-11). Einstein predicted the exact amount of deflection that would occur near the Sun, and his prediction was confirmed by precise measurements of star positions during a solar eclipse in 1919. Today these measurements are made with much more precision by measuring the deflection of radio waves emitted by distant galaxies called quasars (see Chapter 18).

STOP & THINK! Given what you know about electromagnetic waves, do you think general relativity should predict that other waves—radio, for example—should be bent as they come around the Sun?

2. **Planetary Orbits**

   In Newton's solar system, the planets adopt elliptical orbits, with long and short axes that rotate slightly because of the perturbing influence of other planets. Einstein's calculations make nearly the same prediction, but his axes advance slightly more than Newton's from orbit to orbit. In Einstein's theory, for example, the innermost planet, Mercury, was predicted to advance by 43 seconds of arc per century due to relativistic effects—a small perturbation superimposed on much larger effects due to the other planets. Einstein's prediction almost exactly matches the observed shift in Mercury's orbit.

3. **The Gravitational Redshift**

   The theory of relativity predicts that as a photon (a particle of electromagnetic radiation) moves up in gravitational field, it must lose energy in the process. The speed of light is constant, so this energy

FIGURE 7-11 A gravitational lens: A distant massive object bends the light from even more distant objects beyond, causing multiple images.

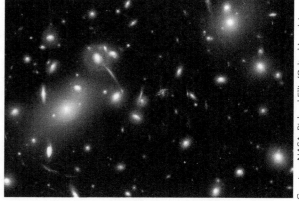

loss is manifest as a slight decrease in frequency (a slight increase in wavelength). Thus, lights on Earth's surface will appear slightly redder than they do on Earth if they are observed from space. By the same token, a light shining from space to Earth will be slightly shifted to the blue end of the spectrum. Careful measurements of laser light frequencies have amply confirmed this prediction of relativity.

These three instances are regarded as the "classical" tests of general relativity. For the greater part of the twentieth century, they were all the experimental evidence that scientists had for general relativity. Over the last several decades, however, we have gotten better at making very precise measurements, so that even tiny differences between Newtonian gravity and general relativity can be probed. For example, general relativity predicts that because of the rotation of Earth, there will be tiny differences in travel time between light going from east to west and light going between the same two points in the opposite direction. Using lasers (see Chapter 8) and atomic clocks, scientists have been able to confirm this prediction.

THE ONGOING PROCESS OF SCIENCE
Gravity Probe B

One of the most interesting modern tests of general relativity, as much for its tortuous political history as for its science, was an experiment called Gravity Probe B. Back in 1959, theorists predicted that Earth, in addition to warping the fabric of space time as described earlier, would drag space time around with it as it rotated. One author compared this effect to what you would see if you twisted a spoon in a jar of honey. This so-called frame-dragging effect could be detected, they pointed out, by the fact that it would produce a very small change in the direction of a gyroscope in orbit. Gravity Probe B was an attempt to confirm both of these predictions by placing such a gyroscope in orbit.

The heart of the experiment was four ping-pong ball-sized quartz spheres rotating in a vacuum in a satellite. These spheres have been called the "roundest objects in the universe," because if they were blown up to the size of Earth, the highest "mountain" would be only 2 feet tall. Developing the technology to produce and monitor these devices taxed the abilities of the scientists involved, and many times the project seemed to be headed to extinction.

Nevertheless, after decades of preparation and testing, Gravity Probe B was launched in 2004 and collected huge amounts of data during its 17-month lifetime. In 2007, the Gravity Probe B team confirmed the warping of spacetime to an accuracy of 1% (later reduced to 0.2% by more analysis). In 2008, NASA cut off funding for further analysis, but a coalition of private sources (including the Saudi royal family) supplied enough money to complete the work. In 2011, the team announced that it had verified the predictions of frame dragging to an accuracy of 19%.

What is perhaps most interesting about this 40-year saga is that while Gravity Probe B was being developed, other experiments using high-precision modern techniques measured both of these effects to higher accuracy. "The project," one commentator noted, "has been a victim of time."

THE ONGOING PROCESS OF SCIENCE
Gravitational Waves

Just as Maxwell's equations predict that accelerating electrical charges will produce electromagnetic waves, the equations of general relativity predict that accelerating masses will produce a phenomenon called gravitational waves. You can think of these waves as ripples in the space-time fabric. They have the effect of stretching out pieces or ordinary matter they encounter. For example, when a gravitational wave passes a basketball, the ball will first be stretched into an ellipse with its long axis in the horizontal direction, then into an ellipse with its long axis in the vertical direction. The primary strategy for detecting gravitational waves is to detect these (very small) oscillations.

The most sensitive system in operation is called LIGO (Laser Interferometer Gravitational Wave Observatory). Picture LIGO as an L-shaped vacuum tube, with each arm of the L being about 4 kilometers long. Lasers monitor the positions of test masses at each end of the L and can detect changes in position as small as 10^{-18} meters (about the distance across a proton). Two identical interferometers, one in Louisiana and the other in Washington State, guard against chance misidentification of small tremors.

After an initial data run begun in 2002, an improved version of LIGO came online in 2014. At present, no gravitational waves have been detected. A major new facility, called eLISA (Laser Interferometer Space Antenna), is on the drawing boards at the European Space Agency. This grand experiment, which is designed to employ a suite of satellites about 100,000 kilometers apart, would be by far the most sensitive gravitational wave detector in existence if it were built.

Who Can Understand Relativity?

Einstein's theory of relativity was extraordinary, but when first introduced it was difficult to grasp in part because it relied on some complex mathematics that were unfamiliar to many scientists at the time. Furthermore, although the theory made specific predictions about the physical world, most of those predictions were exceedingly difficult to test. Soon after the theory's publication it became conventional wisdom that only a handful of geniuses in the world could understand it.

Einstein did make one very specific prediction, however, that could be tested. His proposal that the strong gravitational field of the Sun would bend the light coming from a distant star was different from other theories. The total eclipse of the Sun in 1919 gave scientists the chance to test Einstein's prediction. Sure enough, the apparent position of stars near the Sun's disk was shifted by exactly the predicted amount.

Around the world, front-page newspaper headlines trumpeted Einstein's success. He became an instant international celebrity, and his theory of relativity became a part of scientific folklore. Attempts to explain the revolutionary theory to a wide audience began almost immediately.

Few scientists may have grasped the main ideas of general relativity in 1915, when the full theory was first unveiled, but that certainly is not true today. The basics of special relativity are taught to tens of thousands of college freshmen every year, while hundreds of students in astronomy and physics explore general relativity in its full mathematical splendor.

If this subject intrigues you, you might want to read some more, watch TV specials or videos about relativity, or even sign up for one of those courses!

FIGURE 7-12 The Global Positioning System (GPS) employs a network of 24 satellites that orbit 20,000 miles above Earth's surface.

Detlev van Ravenswaav/Photo Researchers, Inc.

TECHNOLOGY
The Global Positioning System and Relativity

The Global Positioning System (GPS) is one of the marvels of our modern technological society. Today, anyone can walk into an electronic supply store, pay a relatively small amount of money, and walk out with a device that will give his or her position anywhere on the surface of the planet to an accuracy of a few tens of feet. What isn't generally appreciated is that the operation of this system depends on the theory of relativity.

The system consists of 24 satellites orbiting 20,000 km above Earth's surface (Figure 7-12). Each of these satellites carries one or more highly accurate (and highly stable) atomic clocks. These satellite orbits are arranged so that four of them will be above the horizon at any time. A ground observer picks up signals from all four satellites and, by comparing the difference between the time the signal was emitted and the time it was received, determines the distance to each. It is then a simple matter of geometry to get the position of the receiver.

To get the kind of accuracy we need from the GPS system, the times have to be measured to an accuracy of 13 decimal places, an accuracy well within the capability of modern atomic clocks. The problem is that at this level of accuracy the effects of relativity play an important role and have to be taken into account. For example, the satellites are moving at a speed of about 4 kilometers per second with respect to an observer on the ground, which means that even the simple time dilation we derived above will affect the observed time in the 10th decimal place. Other effects predicted by general relativity also have to be taken into account if the comparison of times is to be done accurately. In fact, engineers have found that the effects of relativity in the system are 10,000 times too big to be ignored.

Thus, although the domain of relativity may seem to be a long way from everyday life, you use the theory every time you turn on your car's navigation system or fly in an airplane.

THINKING MORE ABOUT **RELATIVITY**

Was Newton Wrong?

The theory of relativity describes a universe about which Isaac Newton never dreamed. Time dilation, contraction of moving objects, and mass as energy play no role in his laws of motion. Curved space–time is alien to the Newtonian view. Does that mean that Newton was wrong? Not at all.

In fact, all of Einstein's equations reduce exactly to Newton's laws of motion, at speeds significantly less than the speed of light. This feature was shown specifically for time dilation in the "Science by the Numbers" section in this chapter. Newton's laws, which have worked so well in describing our everyday world, fail only when we are dealing with extremely high velocities or extremely large masses. Thus Newton's laws represent an extremely important special case of Einstein's more general theory.

Science often progresses in this way, with one theory encompassing previous valid ideas. Newton, for example, merged discoveries by Galileo of Earth-based motions and Kepler's laws of planetary motion into his unified theory of gravity. And someday Einstein's theory of relativity may be incorporated into an even grander view of the universe.

 RETURN TO THE INTEGRATED QUESTION

Can a human ever travel faster than the speed of light, at "warp speed"?

- The speed of light, denoted by the symbol c, is nearly 300,000 kilometers per second. It is one of the best-known physical constants in science.

- In 1905, Einstein published his theory of special relativity, which asserts that the speed of light is a fundamental constant of nature. It appears the same to all observers in all frames of reference anywhere in space.

- Special relativity asserts that mass is not a constant; as an object increases in speed, it also increases in mass.

- As the mass of an object increases, the energy required to increase its speed also increases.

- Therefore, as an object approaches the speed of light its mass would approach infinity and the energy required to accelerate an infinite mass beyond the speed of light would be infinite.

- Consequently, no physical object such as a human being or spaceship that is moving at less than the sped of light will ever exceed that speed.

SUMMARY

Every observer sees the world from a different *frame of reference*. Descriptions of actual physical events are different for different observers, but the *theory of relativity* states that all observers must see the universe operating according to the same laws. Because the speed of light is built into Maxwell's equations, this principle requires that all observers must see the same speed of light in their frames of reference.

Special relativity deals with observers who are not accelerating with respect to each other, while *general relativity* deals with observers in any frame of reference whatsoever. In special relativity, simple arguments lead to the conclusion that moving clocks appear to tick more slowly than stationary ones—a phenomenon known as *time dilation*. Furthermore, moving objects appear to get shorter in the direction of motion—the phenomenon of *length contraction*. Finally, moving objects become more massive than stationary ones, and an equivalence exists between mass and energy, as expressed by the famous equation, $E = mc^2$.

General relativity begins with the observation that the force of gravity is connected to acceleration, and describes a universe in which heavy masses warp the fabric of space–time and affect the motion of other objects. There are three classic tests of general relativity—the bending of light rays passing near the Sun, the changing orientation of the orbit of Mercury, and the redshift of light passing through a gravitational field.

KEY TERMS

frame of reference
theory of relativity

special relativity
general relativity

time dilation
length contraction

KEY EQUATIONS

Time dilation: $t_{MG} = \dfrac{t_{GG}}{\sqrt{\left[1 - (v/c)^2\right]}}$

Length contraction: $L_{MG} = L_{GG} \times \sqrt{\left[1 - (v/c)^2\right]}$

Mass effect: $m_{GG} = \dfrac{m_{GG}}{\sqrt{\left[1 - (v/c)^2\right]}}$

Rest mass: $E = mc^2$

DISCOVERY LAB

Have you ever wondered if the velocity of a ball you dropped inside an elevator is the same as that when viewed from outside the elevator (i.e., from the ground)? If you think the velocity is different in this circumstance then you are correct. The ball may be falling with respect to the person inside the elevator but actually rising with respect to the person on the first floor.

In this example we have two frames of reference with respect to which motion is measured. By using a stopwatch to measure time and a meter stick to measure distance, you can describe the motion of a person with a frame of reference.

Mark off a distance of 10 meters using a meter stick. If space is limited, you can roll a ball or use a toy car and use shorter distances.

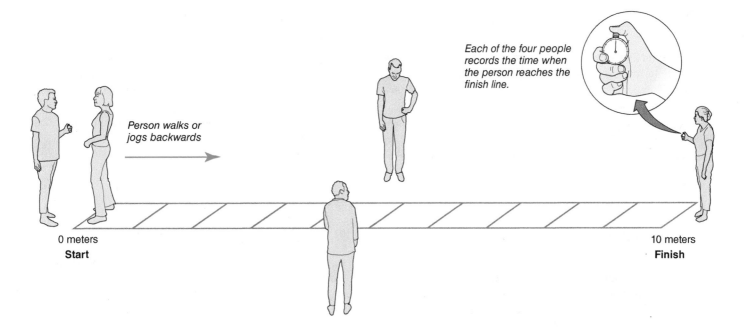

Person walks or jogs backwards

Each of the four people records the time when the person reaches the finish line.

0 meters
Start

10 meters
Finish

Have one person stand behind the starting point and another at the finishing point. One person can stand at the left on the side line and another at the right side. Have them measure the time and distance of another group member who will be walking backward (or jogging, running, hopping, etc.) from the starting point to the finish line.

When the person starts moving backward, each person collecting data at different locations starts his or her stopwatch and records the time when the person reaches the finish line. Repeat the procedure for two more trials and record the data. Reverse the

roles until each person gets a opportunity to walk backward from the starting point. Also make sure to rotate the positions of the people recording the time. The person walking now takes the position of recording data and the person on the right side moves to the left and vice versa.

Calculate the average time of motion from each reference point. Is there a significant difference in the average times from the different frame of reference positions? Do you think frame of reference has an effect on the time of motion? Explain.

REVIEW QUESTIONS

1. What is a frame of reference? Give examples of frames of reference you have been in today.
2. Give an example of how the same event might look different in two frames of reference.
3. What is the central idea of Einstein's theory of relativity?
4. What is the difference between special and general relativity?
5. What is time dilation? How fast does something have to be moving for time dilation to be appreciable?
6. Why don't you notice moving clocks slowing down in your everyday life?
7. What is the Lorentz factor?
8. According to an observer on the ground, how does the length of a moving object compare to the length of an identical object on the ground? How does the mass compare?
9. What is the relation between the mass of an object and its energy?
10. Explain how an observer in an accelerating reference frame cannot distinguish between the effects of gravitational forces and acceleration?
11. Explain three tests of general relativity. Are these the only tests possible?
12. According to Einstein's theory, which of the following factors depend on the frame of reference and which are constant? mass, distance, velocity of light, time, length.

DISCUSSION QUESTIONS

1. Imagine arriving by spaceship at the solar system for the first time. Identify three different frames of reference that you might choose to describe Earth.
2. Did Einstein disprove Newton's laws of motion? Explain your answer.
3. In Chapter 2 we saw that Newton profoundly changed the way people in the seventeenth century thought about the world. How did Einstein change the way people in the twentieth century thought about the world?
4. The twentieth century has been called the age of relativism, where each person has his or her own ethical system and no set of values is absolute. Do you agree? Does the theory of relativity imply that no values are absolute?
5. Is it possible for a massive object now traveling slower than the speed of light to be accelerated past the speed of light? Why or why not?
6. What are the variables in the equation $E = mc^2$? What is the meaning of each quantity in the equation? Can you think of a situation where this equation would not apply?
7. Why did measurements taken during the solar eclipse in 1919 make Einstein an international figure? Can you think of a discovery that could be made today that would have the same effect for a modern scientist? What might that discovery be?

PROBLEMS

1. Suppose you are traveling 100 km/h in your car when you throw a ball 80 km/h forward. What is the speed of the ball as measured by a person standing by the side of the road? How fast would a ground-based person measure the ball to be moving if you threw it backwards at 100 km/h relative to your forward motion?
2. How fast must an object be traveling if its Lorentz factor is 0.50? How fast is it if the Lorentz factor is 0.90?

3. Consider a 20-kg mass moving at $0.99c$, that is, 99% the speed of light. What is its mass in its own frame of reference? What would a nonmoving observer say its mass is?

4. You are testing the theory of relativity by periodically examining a moving clock that seems slow. Each hour, according to you, the clock only ticks off 45 minutes. How fast does special relativity predict the clock to be moving relative to you? (*Hint*: Strangely enough, to solve this problem you need to treat your clock as the moving clock and the clock you're examining as the stationary clock. Why should this be?)

5. Draw a picture illustrating how a spaceship passing Earth might look at 1%, 90%, and 99.9% of light speed.

6. How much total energy is stored in an adult with a mass of 70 kg?

7. You and your friend hop aboard your spaceships, both of you happy that they're fresh-off-the-assembly-line *Relativity 9000s*, capable of any speed up to but not including c. While playing around, you measure your friend's spaceship to be only 78% as long as yours. How long does your friend say your spaceship is? How fast is your friend moving relative to you? Does it matter who is moving?

8. One of the fastest speeds ever achieved by a human-made object was the *Helios 2* probe sent to investigate the Sun. It achieved a speed of 252,000 km/hr (70,000 m/s) relative to the Sun. What was its Lorentz factor at that time? Would you say its Lorentz factor is noticeably different from yours as you drive in your car?

9. Two clocks are moving relative to each other. One clock measures an event to last 14 seconds, and the other measures the same event to be only 6 seconds. What is the Lorentz factor for the relative motion of these clocks?

   a. 0.43

   b. 2.3

   c. 0.65

   d. 0.18

10. You are cooking an egg and it takes 3 minutes. The only clock you have access to is moving at a constant speed of 250,000,000 m/s relative to you. How much time will elapse on that clock before your egg is cooked?

    a. 3 minutes

    b. 0.914 minutes

    c. 5.43 minutes

    d. 1.65 minutes

11. A meter-stick flies past you. You note that its length appears to be 82 cm. How fast is the meter-stick moving compared to you?

    a. $0.42c$

    b. $0.57c$

    c. $0.82c$

    d. $0.33c$

INVESTIGATIONS

1. Read a biography of Albert Einstein. What were his major scientific contributions? For what work did he receive a Nobel Prize?

2. Take a bathroom scale into an elevator in a tall building, stand on it, and record your weight under acceleration and deceleration. Why does the scale reading change?

3. Read the novel *Einstein's Dreams* by Alan Lightman. Each of the chapters explores different time–space relationships. Which chapters teach you something about Einstein's theory of relativity?

4. Investigate the influence of Einstein's theory of relativity on twentieth-century art and philosophy.

5. $E = mc^2$ is a cultural icon. Can you think of any other scientific theories or equations that are as recognizable?

6. If we ever encountered an encompassing, unified galactic civilization then we would almost certainly have to consider adjusting our frame of reference to align our time-keeping system with the rest of the galaxy. What frame(s) of reference do you think a galactic civilization would use?

7. Newton's Laws of Motion were inadequate in explaining the details of the orbit of the planet Mercury, but Einstein's theory of general relativity could explain it in full. Given this and other situations where Newton's laws don't work, does this mean that Isaac Newton was wrong? Why or why not?

8. Upon Isaac Newton's death in 1726, the English poet Alexander Pope wrote:

   Nature and nature's Laws lay hid in night.
   God said, "Let Newton be!" and all was light.

   In 1926, the English poet J. C. Squire followed it up with:

   It did not last: the Devil shouting, "Ho!
   Let Einstein be!" restored the status quo.

   What do you think both Pope and Squire meant?

9. In 1999, when it announced Albert Einstein as the Person of the Century, *Time* magazine said that, "indirectly, relativity paved the way for a new relativism in morality." Moral relativism suggests that there is no absolutely true morality and that the proper moral choice depends on the society and situation in question, which goes against the ideas of many religions about an absolute morality that always applies to everyone. Do you think this is a fair characterization of the theory of relativity? Why or why not?

10. Examine the equation that quantifies the mass of an object as a function of how fast it is traveling. What would happen in the equation if the speed of the object were greater than the speed of light? What would happen if the speed of the object equaled the speed of light? What consequences do you think

this has for the maximum possible speed of an object with mass?

11. What if the speed of light was greater in the distant past than it is now? What would result by applying the equation $E = mc^2$? What effect would this have on the observation of very distant objects in the universe, which we now see as they were billions of years ago?

12. Einstein died in 1955. But 60 years and more after his death, his image remains that of the iconic scientist. Why do you think this is so? When you think of a scientist, are there any other people or images that come to mind?

13. One of the earliest thought experiments related to special relativity was the "twin paradox." Consider two twins, one of whom is whisked away at birth on to a rocket ship that travels at 99.9% the speed of light. Each twin considers the other twin to be aging more slowly because of time-dilation effects. When the twin on the rocket returns to Earth, though, he finds himself younger than his twin. Name at least one reason why this situation doesn't apply to special relativity.

8 The Atom

Why are there so many different materials in the world?

PHYSICS

Experiments reveal that atoms themselves are made of smaller particles.

BIOLOGY

Carbon, the sixth element of the periodic table, forms the backbone of most biological molecules. (Ch. 22)

CHEMISTRY

Elements in the periodic table are arranged according to the structure of their atoms.

GREAT IDEA

All of the matter around us is made of atoms, the chemical building blocks of our world.

TECHNOLOGY

Laser beams are created when a collection of excited atoms releases photons.

ENVIRONMENT

Burning fossil fuels may release compounds of the element sulfur into the atmosphere, which leads to the formation of acid rain. (Ch. 19)

ASTRONOMY

The element helium was first discovered when its spectrum was seen in light from the Sun.

HEALTH & SAFETY

Atoms of heavy metal elements such as lead and mercury, when present in contaminated food and water, can build up gradually in the human body and produce toxic effects. (Ch. 18)

GEOLOGY

Deep within Earth, the element carbon is compressed into its densest form, the diamond. (Ch. 16)

 = applications of the great idea discussed in this chapter

 = other applications, some of which are discussed in other chapters

A Deep Breath

It's a beautiful day. As you drive down the road, into the open countryside, you open the window and take a deep breath of air. It's so relaxing to get away from school and work. Breathing is so instinctive that we seldom stop to think about why we need oxygen. Oxygen is a chemical element, one of about a hundred basic building blocks that make up all the objects around us. With every breath you take, oxygen enters your body and sustains life by participating in chemical reactions that release the energy you use to grow, move, and think. Without an extremely active element such as oxygen, these reactions couldn't take place. So our lives depend on oxygen, as well as many other kinds of atoms.

connare GmbH/Alamy

◎ 8.1 The Smallest Pieces

Imagine that you took a page from this book and cut it in half, then cut the half in half, then cut half of the half in half, and so on. Two outcomes are possible. On the one hand, if paper is smooth and continuous then there would be no end to this process, no smallest piece of paper that couldn't be cut further. On the other hand, you might find that you reach a point where one more cut results in two fragments that are no longer paper. How could you tell if paper has a smallest piece?

The Greek Atom

In about 530 BC, a group of Greek philosophers, the most famous of whom was a man named Democritus, gave this question some serious thought. Democritus argued (purely on philosophical grounds) that if you took the world's sharpest knife and started slicing chunks of matter, you would eventually come to a smallest piece—a piece that could not be divided further (Figure 8-1). He called this smallest piece the "atom," which translates roughly as "uncuttable." He argued that all material is formed from these atoms, and that the atoms are eternal and unchanging, but that the relationships among the atoms are constantly shifting.

STOP & THINK What would happen to Democritus's argument if the dividing process never reached a smallest unit? Is such an outcome logically possible?

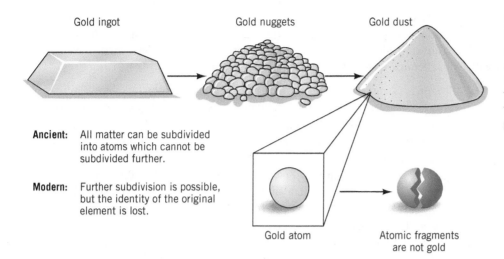

Gold ingot   Gold nuggets   Gold dust

Ancient: All matter can be subdivided into atoms which cannot be subdivided further.

Modern: Further subdivision is possible, but the identity of the original element is lost.

Gold atom   Atomic fragments are not gold

FIGURE 8-1 Repeatedly dividing a bar of gold, just like cutting paper repeatedly, produces smaller and smaller groups of atoms, until you come to a single gold atom. Dividing that atom into two parts produces fragments that no longer have the properties of gold.

Elements

Modern atomic theory is generally attributed to an English meteorologist, John Dalton (1766–1844). In 1808, Dalton published a book called *New System of Chemical Philosophy,* in which he argued that the new knowledge being gained by chemists about materials provided evidence, in and of itself, that matter was composed of atoms. Chemists knew that most materials can be broken down into simpler chemicals. If you burn wood, for example, you get carbon dioxide, water, and all sorts of materials in the ash. If you use an electrical current to break down water, you get two gases, hydrogen and oxygen. Dalton and his contemporaries also recognized that a few materials, called **elements**, could not be broken down into other substances by any chemical means. Wood can be heated to get charcoal (essentially pure carbon), for example; but, try as you might, you can't break the carbon down any further.

The hypothesis that we now call *atomism* was simple in concept. Dalton suggested that for each chemical element there was a corresponding species of indivisible objects called **atoms**. He borrowed the name from the Greeks, but very little else. Two or more atoms stuck together form a **molecule**—the same term applies to any cluster of atoms that can be isolated, whether it contains two atoms or many thousands. Molecules make up most of the different kinds of material we see around us. Water, for example, forms from one oxygen atom and two hydrogen atoms (thus, the familiar H_2O chemical formula). In Dalton's view, atoms were truly indivisible—he thought of them as little bowling balls (Figure 8-2). In Dalton's world, then, indivisible atoms provide the fundamental building blocks of all matter.

FIGURE 8-2 Atoms may be envisioned as solid balls that stack together to form crystals, like fruit at the supermarket. Atomic models are often drawn with spheres, though we now know that atoms are not solid objects.

Discovering Chemical Elements

Describing and isolating chemical elements provided a major challenge for chemists of the nineteenth century. In 1800, fewer than 30 elements had been isolated—not enough to establish any systematic trends in their chemical behavior. In the early 1800s, a new process that broke molecules down into atoms was developed. Called *electrolysis* ("splitting by electricity"), it was facilitated by Volta's invention of the battery (see Chapter 5) and allowed many new elements to be separated by means of electrical current. More than two dozen more elements thus were discovered in the first half of the nineteenth century.

Mitch Diamond/AlamyImages

Most of the materials we encounter in everyday life are not elements, but rather compounds of two or more elements bound together. Table salt, plastics, stainless steel, paint, window glass, and soap are all made from a combination of elements. Nevertheless, we do have experience with a few chemical elements in our everyday lives (Figure 8-3).

- *Helium:* A light gas that has many uses besides filling party balloons and blimps. In liquid form, helium is used to maintain superconductors at low temperatures (see Chapter 11).
- *Carbon:* Pencil lead, charcoal, and diamonds are all examples of pure carbon. The differences between these materials have to do with the way the atoms of carbon are linked together, as we discuss in Chapter 11.
- *Aluminum:* A lightweight metal used for many purposes. The dull white surface of the metal is in fact a combination of aluminum and oxygen, but if you scratch the surface, the shiny material underneath is pure elemental aluminum.
- *Copper:* The reddish metal of pennies and pots. Copper wire provides a cheap and efficient conductor of electricity.
- *Gold:* A soft, yellow, dense, and highly valued metal. For thousands of years the element gold has been coveted as a symbol of wealth. Today it coats critical electrical contacts in spacecraft and other sophisticated electronics.

Although we know of more than 90 different elements in nature, many natural systems are constructed from just a few. Six elements—oxygen, silicon, magnesium, iron, aluminum, and calcium—account for almost 99% of Earth's solid mass. Most of the atoms in your body are hydrogen, carbon, oxygen, or nitrogen, with smaller but important roles played by phosphorus and sulfur. And most stars are formed almost entirely from the lightest element, hydrogen.

FIGURE 8-3 Among the elements used in daily life include are *(a)* helium in balloons, *(b)* carbon in diamond, *(c)* aluminum in cans, *(d)* copper in wires, and *(e)* gold in electronics.

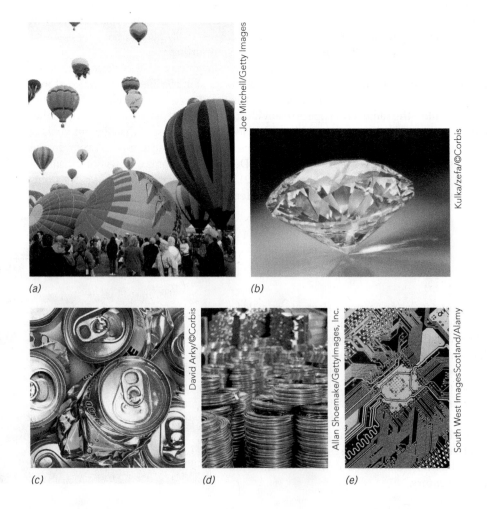

(a)   *(b)*

(c)   *(d)*   *(e)*

STOP & THINK Look around you. How many different elements do you see? How many different compounds? Is it reasonable that there should be so many more compounds than elements? Why or why not?

The Periodic Table of the Elements

Dimitri Mendeleev's 1869 invention of the **periodic table of the elements**, which systematizes all known chemical elements (see Chapter 1), capitalized on the discoveries of new elements and it became a powerful tool for predicting even more new elements. The original table listed several dozen elements on the basis of their atomic weights (in rows from the upper left) and by groups with distinctive chemical properties (in columns). Today, the periodic table lists about 118 elements, of which 92 appear in nature and the rest have been produced artificially (see Figure 8-4). Each element is assigned an integer, called the *atomic number*, which defines the sequence of elements in the table. The atomic number corresponds to the number of protons in the atom, or, equivalently, if the atom is not charged, to the number of electrons surrounding the nucleus. If you arrange the elements as shown in Figure 8-4, with elements getting progressively heavier as you read from left to right and top to bottom as in a book, then elements in the same vertical column have very similar chemical properties.

Periodic Chemical Properties

The most striking characteristic of the periodic table is the similarity of elements in any given column. In the far left-hand column of the table, for example, are highly reactive elements called *alkali metals* (lithium, sodium, potassium, etc.). Each of these soft, silvery elements forms compounds (called *salts*) by combining in a one-to-one ratio with any of the elements in the next-to-last column (fluorine, chlorine, bromine, etc.). Water dissolves these compounds, which include sodium chloride, or table salt.

The elements in the second column, including beryllium, magnesium, and calcium, are metallic elements called the *alkaline earth metals* and they too display similar chemical

FIGURE 8-4 The periodic table of the elements. The weights of the elements increase from left to right. Each vertical column groups elements with similar chemical properties.

properties among themselves. These elements, for example, combine with oxygen in a one-to-one ratio to form colorless compounds with very high melting temperatures.

Elements in the far right-hand column (helium, neon, argon, and so on), by contrast, are all colorless, odorless gases that are almost impossible to coax into any kind of chemical reaction. These so-called *noble gases* find applications when ordinary gases are too reactive. Helium lifts blimps, because the only other lighter-than-air gas is the dangerous, explosive element hydrogen. Argon fills incandescent lightbulbs, because nitrogen or oxygen would react with the hot filament.

In the late nineteenth century, scientists knew that the periodic table "worked"—it organized the 63 elements known at that time and implied the existence of others—but they had no idea *why* it worked. Their faith in the periodic table was buttressed by the fact that, when Mendeleev first wrote it down, there were holes in the table—places where he predicted elements should go, but for which no element was known. The ensuing search for the missing kinds of atoms produced the elements we now call scandium (in 1876) and germanium (in 1886).

SCIENCE IN THE MAKING
Are Atoms Real?

Democritus and other Greek philosophers who speculated on the existence of atoms did not really engage in science—their reasoning lacked the interplay between observation and hypothesis that characterizes the scientific method. No matter how persuasively argued, philosophical speculations on the nature of matter and the existence of atoms were just that—speculations. Over the past three centuries, increasingly convincing evidence has mounted for the reality of atoms. Here are some examples of this growing body of evidence:

1. *The behavior of gas:* The Swiss physicist Daniel Bernoulli (1700–1782) realized that if atoms are real, they must have mass and velocity, and thus kinetic energy. He successfully applied Newton's second law of motion to atoms to explain the behavior of gases under pressure. Doubling the number of gas particles, or reducing the volume by half, doubles the number of collisions between the gas and the confining walls. This increase also doubles the pressure—the force per unit area. Increasing temperature increases the average velocity of the gas particles, also increasing pressure.

2. *Chemical combinations:* English scientist John Dalton advanced the atomic theory based on his observations that for any given compound, elements combine in a specific ratio of weights: water is always eight parts oxygen to one part hydrogen, for example. Furthermore, when two elements combine in more than one way, the ratios of weights for the two compounds will be a small whole number: 12 pounds of carbon can thus combine with either 16 pounds of oxygen or 32 pounds of oxygen (to make the simple molecules CO or CO_2, respectively). Dalton realized, therefore, that compounds don't generally have arbitrary fractional ratios of elements. The implication is that some units of elements are fundamentally indivisible.

3. *Radioactivity:* The discovery in 1896 of radioactivity, by which individual atoms emit radiation, provided a compelling piece of evidence for the atomic theory (see Chapter 12). Certain phosphors flash when hit by this radiation. In 1903, upon seeing the irregular twinkling caused by the radiation emitted from individual atoms, even the most vocal skeptics of the atomic theory had to take pause.

4. *Brownian motion:* Brownian motion is an erratic, jiggling motion observed in tiny dust particles of pollen grains suspended in water. In 1905 Albert Einstein (1879–1955) demonstrated mathematically that such motions must result from a force—the force of random collisions of atoms. Einstein realized that moving atoms constantly bombard any small object suspended in liquid. At any given moment, there will, purely by chance, be more atoms hitting on one side than the other. The object will be pushed toward the side with fewer collisions. A moment later, however, more atoms will be hitting another surface, and the object will change direction. Over time, Einstein argued, atomic collisions would produce precisely the sort of erratic jiggling motion that you see through a

microscope. Einstein used the mathematics of statistics to make a number of predictions about how fast and how far the suspended grains would move – results that convinced many scientists of the reality of atoms.

Note that, in spite of the variety of evidence for atoms, to this point all of this evidence was indirect. Matter was observed to behave *as if* it was made of atoms, but atoms themselves had not been directly observed.

5. *X-ray crystallography:* X-ray crystallography (see Chapter 6), developed in 1912, convinced any remaining skeptics by demonstrating the sizes and regular arrangements of atoms in crystals. X-rays can't bounce off of hypothetical ideas, so these images were further proof that atoms are real physical objects.

6. *Atomic-scale microscopy:* In the early 1980s the first image of an individual atom was produced at the University of Heidelberg in Germany, using an instrument called a scanning tunneling microscope. Now, observational studies of individual atoms are routinely undertaken at many laboratories around the world (Figure 8-5).

Drs. Ali Yazdani & Daniel J. Hor/Photo Researchers, Inc.

FIGURE 8-5 This electronic image representing individual atoms was taken with an instrument called a scanning probe microscope. The "mountains" correspond to individual atoms in a crystal.

STOP & THINK When in the chain of historical events would you have been willing to believe that atoms are real? When Dalton explained the existence of elements? When Einstein explained Brownian motion? When you were shown a picture like the one in Figure 8-5? Never? What does it take to make something "real?" And, finally, does it make a difference to science whether atoms are real?

8.2 The Structure of the Atom

Dalton's idea of the atom as a single indivisible entity was not destined to last. In 1897, English physicist Joseph John (J. J.) Thomson (1856–1940) unambiguously identified a particle called the **electron**. Thomson found that the electron has a negative electrical charge and is much smaller and lighter than even the smallest atom known. Because there was no place from which a particle such as the electron could come other than inside the atom, Thomson's discovery provided incontrovertible evidence for what people had suspected for a long time. Atoms are not the fundamental building blocks of matter, but rather are made up of things that are smaller and more fundamental still. Table 8-1 summarizes some of the important terms related to atoms.

The Atomic Nucleus

The most important discovery about the structure of the atom was made by New Zealand–born physicist Ernest Rutherford (1871–1937), a student of J. J. Thompson, and his coworkers in Manchester, England, in 1911. The basic idea of the experiment is sketched in Figure 8-6. The experiment started with a piece of radioactive material—matter that sends out energetic particles (see Chapter 12). For our purposes, you can think of radioactive materials as sources of tiny subatomic "bullets." The particular material that Rutherford used produced bullets that scientists had named *alpha particles,* which are thousands of times more massive than electrons. By arranging the apparatus as shown, Rutherford produced a stream of these subatomic bullets moving toward the right in the figure. In front of this stream, he placed a thin foil of gold.

The experiment was designed to measure something about the way atoms were put together. At the time, people suspected that the small, negatively charged electrons were scattered around the entire atom, more or less like raisins in a bun. Rutherford was trying to shoot bullets into the "bun" to see what happened.

What the experiment revealed was little short of astonishing. Almost all the subatomic bullets either passed right through the gold foil unaffected or were scattered through very small angles. This result is easy to interpret: it means that most of the heavy alpha particles passed

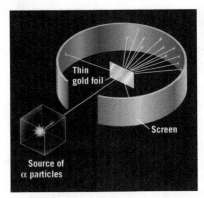

FIGURE 8-6 In Rutherford's experiment, a beam of radioactive particles was scattered by atomic nuclei in a piece of gold foil. A lead shield protected researchers from the radiation.

TABLE 8-1 Important Terms Related to Atoms

Element	A chemical substance that cannot be broken down further
Atom	The smallest particle that retains its chemical identity
Molecule	A collection of two or more atoms bound together; the smallest unit of a substance that has the chemical properties of the substance.
Electron	An atomic particle with negative charge and low mass
Nucleus	The small, massive central part of an atom
Proton	Positively charged nuclear particle
Neutron	Electrically neutral nuclear particle
Ion	An electrically charged atom

through spaces in between gold atoms, and that those that hit the gold atoms were only moderately deflected by the relatively low-density material in them.

Fewer than one alpha particle in a thousand, however, was scattered through a large angle; some even bounced straight back. After almost 2 years of puzzling over these extraordinary results, Rutherford concluded that a large part of each atom's mass is located in a very small, compact object at the center—what he called the **nucleus**. About 999 times out of 1,000 the alpha particles either missed the atom completely or went through the low-density material in the outer reaches of the atom. About 1 time out of 1,000, however, the alpha particle hit the nucleus and was bounced through a large angle.

You can think of the Rutherford experiment in this way. If the atom were a large ball of mist or vapor with a diameter greater than a skyscraper, and the nucleus was a bowling ball at the center of that sphere of mist, then most bullets shot at the atom would go right through. Only those that hit the bowling ball would be bounced through large angles. In this analogy, of course, the bowling ball plays the part of the nucleus, whereas the mist is the domain of the electrons.

As a result of Rutherford's work, a new picture of the atom emerged, one that is very familiar to us. Rutherford described a small, dense, positively charged nucleus sitting at the atom's center, with light, negatively charged electrons circling it, like planets orbiting the Sun. Indeed, Rutherford's discovery has become an icon of the modern age, adorning everyday objects from postage stamps to bathroom cleaners (Figure 8-7). Later on, physicists discovered that the nucleus itself is made up primarily of two different kinds of particles (see Chapter 12). One of these particles carries a positive charge and is called a *proton*. The other, whose existence was not confirmed until 1932, carries no electrical charge and is called a *neutron*.

For each positively charged proton in the nucleus of the atom, there is normally one negatively charged electron "in orbit." Thus the electrical charges of the electrons and the protons cancel out, and every atom is electrically neutral. In some cases, atoms either lose or gain electrons. In this case, they acquire an electrical charge and are called *ions*.

FIGURE 8-7 The Nuclear Regulatory Commission, the U.S. government agency that oversees nuclear power plants and nuclear waste disposal, uses a highly stylized atomic model as its logo.

Why the Rutherford Atom Couldn't Work

The picture of the atom that Rutherford developed is intellectually appealing, particularly because it recalls to us the familiar orbits of planets in our solar system. We have already learned enough about the behavior of nature, however, to know that the atom that is described in the text could not possibly exist in nature. Why do we say this?

We learned in Chapter 2 that an object traveling in a circular orbit is constantly being accelerated—it is not in uniform motion because it is continually changing direction. Furthermore, we learned in Chapter 5 that any accelerated electrical charge must give off electromagnetic radiation, as a consequence of Maxwell's equations. Thus, if an atom were of the Rutherford type, the electrons moving in their orbits would constantly be giving off energy in the form of electromagnetic radiation. This energy, according to the first law of thermodynamics, would have to come from somewhere (remember conservation of energy!), so the electrons would gradually spiral in toward the nucleus as they gave up their energy to electromagnetic radiation. Eventually, the electrons would have to fall into the nucleus and the atom would cease to exist in the form we know.

In fact, if you put in the numbers, the life expectancy of the Rutherford atom turns out to be less than a second. Given the fact that many atoms have survived billions of years, since almost the beginning of the universe, this calculation poses a serious problem for the simple orbital model of the atom.

◉ 8.3 When Matter Meets Light

Almost from its inception, the Rutherford model of the atom encountered difficulties. Some of the problems involved its violations of fundamental physical laws as we have described, whereas others were more mundane—the Rutherford atom simply did not explain all the behavior of atoms that scientists knew about. The first decades of the twentieth century represented a period of tremendous ferment in the sciences as people scrambled to find a new way of describing the nature of atoms.

The Bohr Atom

In 1913, Niels Bohr (1885–1962), a young Danish physicist working in England (Figure 8-8), produced the first model of the atom that avoided the kinds of objections encountered by Rutherford's model. The **Bohr atom** is very strange: it does not match well with our intuition about the way things "ought to be" in the real world. The only thing in the Bohr atom's favor was that it worked.

Bohr's insight began with an educated guess about the distinctive way in which hot hydrogen atoms give off light. Hydrogen gas glows by giving off light in several separate wavelengths, rather than in a continuous range of wavelengths. The young Bohr was deeply immersed in studying this emission of light and the way that atoms interact with light and other forms of electromagnetic radiation. He realized that one way of explaining what he saw in the laboratory was that electrons circling the nucleus, unlike planets circling the Sun, could not maintain their orbits at just any distance from the center. He suggested that there were only certain orbits—he called them "allowed orbits"—located at specified distances from the center of the atom in which an electron could exist for long periods of time *without giving off radiation*. (We prefer to use the terms *electron energy levels* or *electron shells* rather than *allowed orbits* when describing the distribution of electrons in atoms because later work showed that the idea of electron orbits is not a good description of the atom.) Bohr's picture of the atom is shown in Figure 8-9. The idea is that the electron can exist at a specific distance r_1 from the nucleus, or at a distance r_2 or r_3, and so on, each distance corresponding to a different electron energy level. As long as the electron remains at one of those distances, its energy is fixed. In the Bohr atomic model, the electron cannot ever, at any time, exist at any place between these allowed distances.

One way to think about the Bohr atom is to imagine what happens when you climb a flight of steps. You can stand on the first step or you can stand on the second step. It's very hard, however, to imagine what it would be like to stand somewhere between two steps. In just the same way, an electron can be in the first energy level, or in the second energy level, and so on, but it can't be in between these allowed energy levels. In terms of energy, both the steps and the electrons in an atom may be represented by a simple pictorial description (Figure 8-10). Each time you change steps in your home, your gravitational potential energy changes. Similarly, each time an electron changes levels, its energy changes.

An electron in an atom can be in any one of a number of allowed energy levels, each corresponding to a different distance from the nucleus. You would have to exert a force over a distance to move an electron from one allowed energy level to another, just as your muscles have to exert a force to get you up a flight of stairs. Thus, the allowed energy levels of an atom occur as a series of steps as shown in the figure. An electron in the lowest energy level is said to be in the *ground state*, whereas all energy levels above the ground state are called *excited states*.

FIGURE 8-8 Niels Bohr (1885–1962) was awarded the Nobel Prize for his work in physics.

FIGURE 8-9 A schematic diagram of the Bohr atom showing the first three energy levels and respective distances (r_1, r_2, and r_3) from the nucleus.

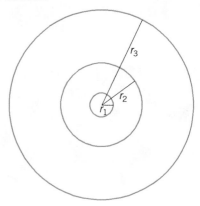

FIGURE 8-10 Stairs provide an analogy to energy changes associated with electrons in the Bohr atom. An electron can be in the ground energy state or any one of several higher energy levels, but never in between energy levels.

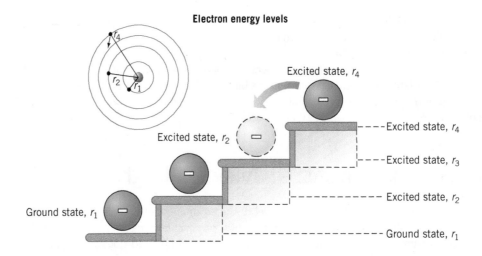

Electron energy levels

FIGURE 8-11 Electrons in an atom may jump between the energy levels shown in (a) and, in the process, (b) absorb or (c) emit energy in the form of a photon.

(a)

(b)

(c)

Photons: Particles of Light

One major feature of the Bohr atom is that an electron in a higher energy level can move down into an available lower energy level. This process is analogous to the process by which a ball at the top of a flight of stairs can bounce down the stairs under the influence of gravity.

Assume that an electron is in an excited state, as shown in Figure 8-11. The electron can move to the lowest state, but if it does, something must happen to the extra energy. Energy can't just disappear. This realization was Bohr's great insight. The energy that's left over when the electrically charged electron moves from a higher state to a lower state is emitted by the atom in the form of a single packet of electromagnetic radiation—a particle-like bundle of light called a **photon**. Every time an electron jumps from a higher to a lower energy level, a photon moves away at the speed of light.

The concept of a photon raises a perplexing question: Is light—Maxwell's electromagnetic radiation—a wave or a particle? We will explore this puzzle at some length in Chapter 9, once we have learned more about the behavior of atoms.

The interaction of atoms and electromagnetic radiation provides the most compelling evidence for the Bohr atom. If electrons are in excited states, and if they make transitions to lower states, then photons are emitted. If we look at a group of atoms in which these transitions are occurring, we will see light or other electromagnetic radiation. Thus when you look at the flame of a fire or the glowing heating coil of an electric stove in your kitchen, you are actually seeing photons that were emitted by electrons jumping between allowed states in that material's atoms.

Not only does the Bohr atom give us a picture of how matter emits radiation, it provides an explanation for how matter absorbs radiation. Start with an electron in a low-energy state, perhaps its ground state. If a photon arrives that has just the right amount of energy so that it can raise the electron to a higher energy (the next step up), the photon can be absorbed and the electron will be pushed up to an excited state. Absorption of light is something like a mirror image of light emission.

This picture of the interaction of matter and radiation is simple, but two key ideas are embedded in it. First, when an electron moves from one allowed state to another, it cannot ever, at any time, be at any place in between. This rule is built into the definition of an allowed energy level. This means that the electron must somehow disappear from its original location and reappear in its final location *without ever having to traverse any of the positions in between*. This process, called a **quantum leap** or **quantum jump**, cannot be visualized, but it seems to be fundamental in nature—an example of the "quantum weirdness" of nature at the atomic scale that we'll discuss in Chapter 9.

The second key idea is that if an electron is in an excited state, it can, in principle, get back down to the ground state in a number of different ways. Look at Figure 8-12a. An electron in the upper energy level can move to the ground state by making one large jump and emitting a single photon with large energy. Alternatively, it can move to the ground state by making two or more smaller jumps, as shown in Figure 8-12b. Each of these jumps emits a photon of somewhat less energy. The energies emitted in the multiple different jumps will generally be different from each other, but the sum of the energies will equal that of the single large jump. If we had a large collection of atoms of this kind, we would expect some electrons to make the large leap while others would make two or more smaller ones. Thus, when we look at a collection of these atoms, we would measure at least three different energies of photons.

This curious behavior of electron energy levels helps to explain the familiar phenomenon of fluorescence that we introduced in Chapter 6. Recall that the energy of electromagnetic radiation is related to its frequency. In fluorescence, the atom in Figure 8-12 absorbs a higher-energy photon of ultraviolet radiation (which our eyes can't detect). The atom then emits two lower-energy photons, at least one of which is in the visible range. Consequently, by shining ultraviolet "black light" on the fluorescent material, it glows with a bright color.

A key point about the Bohr atom is that energy is required to lift an electron from the ground state to any excited state. This energy has to come from somewhere. We have already mentioned one possibility: that the atom will absorb a photon of just the right frequency to raise the electron to a higher energy level. There are other possibilities, however. If the material is heated, for example, atoms will move fast, gain kinetic energy, and undergo energetic collisions. In these collisions, an atom can absorb energy and then use that energy to move electrons to a higher state. This explains why materials often glow when they are heated.

FIGURE 8-12 An electron can jump from a higher to lower energy level in (a) a single quantum leap that is accompanied by the release of one photon, or (b) by multiple quantum leaps that is accompanied by the release of more than one photon.

An Intuitive Leap

Bohr first proposed his model of the atom based on an intuition guided by experiments and ideas about the behavior of things in the subatomic world. In some ways the Bohr model was completely unlike anything we experience in the macroscopic world; indeed, the model seemed to some a little bit "crazy." It took two decades for scientists to develop a theory called *quantum mechanics* that showed why electrons exist only in Bohr's "allowed orbits" and not in between. We will discuss this justification for the Bohr atom in Chapter 9, but it should be remembered that the justification occurred long after the initial hypothesis. Physicists accepted the Bohr atom because it worked—it explained what they saw in nature and allowed them to make predictions about the behavior of real matter.

How could Bohr have come up with such a strange picture of the atom? He was undoubtedly guided by some of the early work that would lead to the theory of quantum mechanics (see Chapter 9). In the end, however, this explanation is unsatisfactory. Many people at the time studied the interactions of atoms and light, but only Bohr was able to make the leap of intuition to his description of the atom. This insight, like Newton's realization that gravity might extend to the orbit of the Moon, remains one of the great intuitive achievements of the human mind.

STOP & THINK How are intuitive leaps, such as the one made by Bohr, consistent or not consistent with the scientific method as described in Chapter 1?

● 8.4 Spectroscopy

Whenever energy is added to a system with many atoms in it, electrons in some atoms jump to excited states. As time goes by, these electrons will make quantum leaps down to the ground

Yoav Levy/Phototake

(a) (b) (c)

FIGURE 8-13 The elements (a) sodium, (b) potassium, and (c) lithium impart distinctive colors to a flame.

state, giving off photons as they do. If some of those photons are in the range of visible light, the source will appear to glow.

You may not realize it, but you have looked at such collections of atoms all your life. Common mercury vapor street lamps contain bulbs filled with mercury gas. When the gas is heated, electrons are moved up to excited states. When they jump down to lower energy states, they emit photons that give the lamp a bluish-white color. Other types of streetlights, often used at freeway interchanges, use bulbs filled with sodium atoms. When sodium is excited, the most frequently emitted photons lie in the yellow range, so the lamps look yellow (Figure 8-13).

Yet another place where you can see photons emitted directly by quantum leaps is in Day-Glo colors, the vivid colors often used in sports clothing and advertising. From these examples, you can draw two conclusions: (1) quantum leaps are very much in evidence in your everyday life, and (2) different atoms give off different characteristic photons.

The second of these two facts is extremely important for scientists. If you think about the structure of an atom, the idea that different atoms emit and absorb different characteristic photons shouldn't be too surprising. Electron energy levels depend on the electrical attraction between the nucleus and the electrons, just as the orbits of the planets depend on the gravitational attraction between the planets and the Sun. Different nuclei have different numbers of protons, so electrons circling them are in different energy levels. In fact, the energy between the allowed energy levels within the atom is different in each of the hundred or so different chemical elements. Because the energy and frequency of photons emitted by an atom depend on the differences in energy between these levels, each chemical element emits a distinct set of characteristic photons.

FIGURE 8-14 A glass prism spreads out the colors of the visible spectrum.

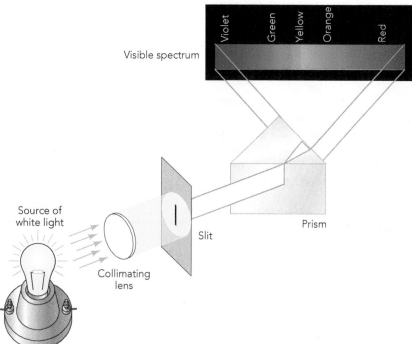

Visible spectrum

Violet Green Yellow Orange Red

Source of white light

Collimating lens

Slit

Prism

You can think of the collection of characteristic photons emitted by each chemical element as a kind of "fingerprint"—something that is distinctive for that chemical element and none other. This feature opens up a very interesting possibility. The total collection of photons emitted by a given atom is called its **spectrum**, a characteristic fingerprint that can be used to identify chemical elements even when they are very difficult to identify by any other means.

In practice, the identification process works like this: Light from the gaseous atoms is spread out by being passed through a prism (Figure 8-14). Each possible quantum jump corresponds to light at a specific wavelength, so each type of atom produces a set of lines, as shown in Figure 8-15. This spectrum is the atomic fingerprint.

The Bohr picture suggests that if an atom gives off light of a specific wavelength and energy, then it will also *absorb* light at that wavelength. The emission and absorption processes, after all, may involve quantum jumps between the same two energy levels but in different directions. Thus if white light shines through a material

EMISSION (BRIGHT LINE) SPECTRA

Lithium

Hydrogen

Sodium

ABSORPTION SPECTRUM
GASES IN SUN'S ATMOSPHERE (PRINCIPAL FRAUNHOFER LINES)

© 1994 Wabash Instrument Corp/Fundamental Photographs

FIGURE 8-15 Line spectra provide distinctive "fingerprints" for different chemical elements, such as lithium, hydrogen, and sodium, as shown in the top three bright line spectra. The bottom spectrum shows dark lines caused by the absorption of photons by these and other elements in the Sun's atmosphere.

containing a particular kind of atom, certain wavelengths of light will be absorbed. Observing that light on the other side of the material, you will see certain colors missing. The dark areas corresponding to the absorbed wavelengths are called *absorption lines*. This set of lines is as much an atomic fingerprint as the set of colors that the atoms emit. And although the use of visible light is very common, these arguments hold for radiation in any part of the electromagnetic spectrum.

Spectroscopy has become a standard tool that is used in almost every branch of science. Astronomers use emission spectra to find the chemical composition of distant stars, and they study absorption lines to determine the chemical composition of interstellar dust and the atmospheres of the outer planets. Spectroscopic analysis is also used in manufacturing to search for impurities on production lines, and by police departments to identify small traces of unknown materials when conducting investigations.

THE SCIENCE OF LIFE
Spectra of Life's Chemical Reactions

In a classic set of experiments in the early 1940s, scientists used spectroscopy to work out in detail how chemical reactions governed by large molecules called enzymes (see Chapter 22) proceed in cells. In these experiments, a fluid containing the materials undergoing the chemical reactions was allowed to flow down a tube. The farther down the tube the fluid was, the farther along the reaction was. By measuring spectra at different points along the tube, scientists were able to follow the change in the behavior of electrons as the chemical reactions went along. In this way, part of the enormously complex problem of understanding the chemistry of life was unraveled.

More recently, scientists have developed instruments that use the principles of spectroscopy to identify pollutants emitted by such diverse sources as power plants, automobiles, and volcanoes. Spectroscopy has thus become a major tool in understanding sources of air pollution and acid rain (see Chapter 19).

SCIENCE IN THE MAKING
The Story of Helium

You have probably experienced helium, perhaps to inflate party balloons. Helium gas turns out to be a very interesting material, not only for its properties (it's less dense than air, so it floats up), but because of the history of its discovery.

The word helium refers to *helios,* the Greek word for Sun, because helium was first discovered in spectral lines in the Sun in 1868 by English scientist Joseph Norman Lockyer (1836–1920). Helium is very rare in Earth's atmosphere, and before Lockyer's discovery scientists were not even aware of its existence. Following the discovery, for a period of about 30 years, astronomers accepted the idea that the element helium existed in the Sun, but they were unable to find it on Earth.

This supposition led to a very interesting problem. Could it be that there were chemical elements on the Sun that simply did not exist on our own planet? If so, it would call into question our ability to understand the rest of the universe, for the simple reason that if we don't know what an element is and can't isolate it in our laboratories, then we can never really be sure that we understand its properties. In fact, the existence of helium on Earth wasn't confirmed until 1895, when Lockyer identified its spectrum in a sample of radioactive material.

TECHNOLOGY
The Laser

The Bohr atom provides an excellent way of understanding the workings of one of the most important devices in modern science and industry—the laser. The word *laser* is an acronym for *l*ight *a*mplification by *s*timulated *e*mission of *r*adiation. At the core of every laser is a collection of atoms—a crystal of ruby, perhaps, or a gas enclosed in a glass tube. The term *stimulated emission* refers to a process that goes on when light and these atoms interact. If an electron is in an excited state, as shown in Figure 8-16, and one photon of just the right energy passes nearby, the electron may be stimulated to make the jump to a lower energy state, thus releasing a

FIGURE 8-16 Lasers produce a beam of light when one photon stimulates the emission of other photons.

Mirror
(100% reflecting)

Electrodes for
optical pumping

Mirror
(95% reflecting)

Tube containing
helium and neon

Coherent light beam

Power supply

Excited atoms

FIGURE 8-17 The action of a laser. Electrons in the laser's atoms are continuously "pumped" into an excited state by an outside energy source, and the beam of photons is released when the electrons return to their ground state.

second photon. By "just the right energy" for the first photon, we mean a photon whose energy corresponds to the energy gap between two electron energy levels in the atom.

Furthermore, the stimulated atom emits photons in a special way. Remember that light is a form of electromagnetic radiation that can be described as a wave. In a laser, the crests of all the emitted photon waves line up exactly with the crests of the first photon, and the signal is enhanced by constructive interference. In the language of the physicists, we say that the photons are "coherent." Thus in stimulated emission, you have one photon at the beginning of the process and two coherent photons at the end.

Now suppose that you have a collection of atoms where most of the electrons are in the excited state, as shown in Figure 8-17. If a single photon of the correct frequency enters this system from the left and moves to the right, it will pass the first atom and stimulate the emission of a second photon. You will then have two photons moving to the right. As these photons encounter other atoms, they, too, stimulate emission so that you have four photons. It's not hard to see that light amplification in a laser will happen very quickly, cascading so that soon a flood of photons is moving to the right through the collection of atoms. Energy added to the system from outside continuously returns atoms to their excited state—a process called *pumping*—so that more and more coherent photons can be produced.

In a laser, the collection of excited atoms is bounded on two sides by mirrors so that photons moving to the right hit the mirror, are reflected, and make another pass through the material, stimulating even more emission of photons as they go. If a photon happens to be lined up exactly perpendicular to the mirrors at the end of the laser, it will continue bouncing back and forth. If its direction is off by even a small angle, however, it will eventually bounce out through the sides of the laser and be lost. Thus only those photons that are exactly aligned will wind up bouncing back and forth between the mirrors, constantly amplifying the signal. Aligned photons will traverse the laser millions of times, building up an enormous cascade of coherent photons in the system.

The mirrors are designed to be partially reflective—perhaps 95% of the photons that hit the mirror are reflected back into the laser. The remaining 5% of photons that leak out form the familiar laser beam, which is made of intense, coherent light.

Laser beams have been applied in thousands of uses in science and industry since their development in the 1960s (Figure 8-18a). Low-power lasers are ideal for optical scanners, such as the ones in supermarket checkout lines, and they make ideal light pointers for lectures and slide shows. The fact that the beam of light travels in a straight line makes the laser invaluable in surveying over long distances—for example, modern subway tunnels are routinely surveyed by using lasers to provide a straight line underground. Lasers are also used to detect movement of seismic faults in order to predict

FIGURE 8-18 Lasers have many uses. (a) Lasers are used by astronomers to align and focus telescopes. (b) Light generated in this argon laser is carried by fiber-optic cable for use in surgery on the human eye.

Ray Nelson/Phototake

Rolf Vennenbernd/dpa/Landov LLC

(a)

(b)

earthquakes (see Chapter 17). In this case, a laser is directed across the fault, so that small motions of the ground are easily measured. Finely focused laser beams have revolutionized delicate procedures such as eye surgery (Figure 8-18b). Much more powerful lasers can transfer large amounts of energy. They are often used as cutting tools in factories, as well as implements for performing some kinds of surgery. The military has also adopted laser technology, in targeting and range finders, and in designs for futuristic energy beam weapons.

From the point of view of science, however, lasers are important because they enable us to make extremely precise measurements of atomic structures and properties. Almost all modern studies of the atom depend in some way on the laser.

Why the Periodic Table Works: Electron Shells

Dimitri Mendeleev could not have known that his periodic table of the elements reveals much about the underlying structure of atoms and their electrons. With the advent of Bohr's atomic model and its modern descendants, we finally have some understanding of why the periodic table works. We now realize that the pattern of elements in the periodic table mirrors the spatial arrangement of electrons around the atom's nucleus—a concentric arrangement of electrons into *shells.*

The atom is largely empty space. When two atoms come near enough to each other to undergo a chemical reaction—a carbon atom and an oxygen atom in a burning piece of coal, for example—electrons in the outermost shells meet each other first. We will see in Chapter 10 that these outermost electrons govern the chemical properties of materials. We have to understand the behavior of these electrons if we want to understand the periodic table.

To gain this understanding, we need to know one more curious fact about electrons. Electrons are particles that obey what is called the *Pauli exclusion principle*, which says that no two electrons can occupy the same energy state at the same time. One analogy is to compare electrons to cars in a parking lot. Each car takes up one space, and once a space is filled, no other car can go there. Electrons behave in the same way. Once an electron fills a particular niche in

FIGURE 8-19 A representation of electrons in a number of common atoms reveals the underlying structure of the periodic table of the elements. The first electron shell can hold one or two electrons, corresponding to the first two elements, hydrogen and helium. The second and third shells each hold eight additional electrons. Atoms in the same column have the same configuration of electrons in their outer shells: the first column has a single electron, the next to the last column is one electron short of a filled shell, and the last column (the noble gases) has completely filled outer shells.

the atom, no other electron can occupy the same niche. A parking lot can be full long before all the actual space in the lot is taken up with cars, because the driveways and spaces between cars must remain empty. So, too, a given electron shell can be filled with electrons long before all the available space is filled.

In fact, it turns out that an electron can fill only two spaces in the innermost electron shell, which corresponds to the lowest Bohr energy level. One of these spaces corresponds to a situation in which the electron "spins" clockwise on its axis, the other to a situation in which it "spins" counterclockwise on its axis. When we start to catalog all possible chemical elements in the periodic table, we have element one (hydrogen) with a single electron in the innermost shell, and element two (helium) with two electrons in that same shell. If we want to add one more electron, it has to go into the second electron shell because the first electron shell is completely filled. This situation explains why only hydrogen and helium appear in the first row in the periodic table.

Adding a third electron yields lithium, an atom with two electrons in the first shell, and a single electron in the second electron shell. Lithium is the element just below hydrogen in the first column of the periodic table, because both hydrogen and lithium have a lone electron in their outermost shell (Figure 8-19).

The second electron shell has room for eight electrons, a fact that is reflected in the eight elements of the periodic table's second row, from lithium with three electrons to neon with ten. Neon appears directly under helium, and we expect these two gases to have similar chemical properties because both have a completely filled outer electron shell.

Thus, a simple counting of the positions available to electrons in the first two electron shells explains why the first row in the periodic table has two elements in it and the second row eight. By similar (but somewhat more complicated) arguments, you can show that the Pauli exclusion principle requires that the third row of the periodic table has 8 elements, the next 18, and so on. Thus, with an understanding of the shell-like structure of the atom's electrons, the mysterious regularity that Mendeleev found among the chemical elements becomes an example of nature's laws at work.

THINKING MORE ABOUT **ATOMS**

What Do Atoms "Look Like?"

Throughout this book you will find drawings of atoms. In this chapter we drew atoms as electrons in circular shells around a central nucleus. In Chapter 10, atoms appear as little spheres in pictures of molecules like H_2O (water) and crystals like NaCl (table salt). In other chapters atoms are portrayed as fuzzy clouds, or waves, or even collections of dozens of smaller sphere-like particles. So, what do atoms really "look like?"

Strictly speaking, we only "see" something when electromagnetic waves from the visible part of the spectrum enter our eyes. We are accustomed, however, to talking about other ways of "seeing." You cannot see X-rays being absorbed by your teeth, for example, unless some intermediary system—film or electronic—converts the X-rays into a pattern that can be detected in the visible region of the electromagnetic spectrum. Similarly, astronomers often convert radio waves, infrared radiation, and other wavelength data into false-color images of distant objects. Scanning tunneling microscope "pictures" of atoms come from another such transformation. The amount of electrical charge at a particular point on a material's surface is converted into the height of the peak you see in the picture.

Is an X-ray picture of your teeth more real than the microscope picture of the atom? Why or why not?

⬅ RETURN TO THE INTEGRATED QUESTION

Why are there so many different materials in the world?

- As we look around our world, we see numerous different materials. Some of these materials, like the sand on the beach or the air we breathe, are naturally occurring, whereas others, like the plastic of our computer keyboard, are "human-made."

- Given the obvious diversity of matter, philosophers and scientists have wondered for millennia if any common fundamental constituents or ultimate building blocks of our natural world existed.

  - Democritus (circa ~530 BC) argued that all matter was constructed of eternal and unchanging particles, which he called "atoms." From a theoretical standpoint, he was correct about the existence of these tiny objects. Nonetheless, the atoms of modern chemistry bear little resemblance to the atoms of Democritus.

  - Over two millennia later, the father of modern chemistry, John Dalton (1766–1844), argued that evidence provided by chemists demonstrated that, although most materials could be broken down into simpler chemicals, some materials resisted further deconstruction.

- For example, if you burn wood you get the gases carbon monoxide and carbon dioxide, as well as numerous other materials found in the leftover ash.

- If you use an electrical current to break down water, you get two gases, hydrogen and oxygen.

- Nevertheless, Dalton and his contemporaries recognized that a few materials, called *elements*, could not be broken down into other substances by any chemical means.

- Today we know that the myriad materials around us are constructed from smaller, more fundamental constituents called atoms, the chemical building blocks of our universe. These chemical building blocks combine to form all the materials in our universe, ranging from simple elements such as helium to incredibly complex organic molecules such as proteins.

- In Chapter 11, you will see that the arrangement of atoms not only creates the diversity of matter, but also the myriad properties that matter exhibits.

SUMMARY

About 100 different *elements* are sufficient to form all the solids, liquids, and gases around us. *Atoms,* the building blocks of our chemical world, combine into groups of two or more; these groups are called *molecules.* For thousands of years atoms were discussed purely as hypothetical objects, but studies of Brownian motion early in the twentieth century and recent imaging of individual atoms in new kinds of microscopes have confirmed the existence of these tiny particles.

Each atom contains a massive central *nucleus* made from positively charged protons and electrically neutral neutrons. Surrounding the nucleus are *electrons,* which are negatively charged particles that have only a small fraction of the mass of protons and neutrons. Early models of this kind of atom treated electrons like planets orbiting around the Sun. Those models were flawed, however, because each electron, constantly accelerating, would have to emit electromagnetic radiation continuously. Niels Bohr proposed

an alternative model in which electrons exist in various energy levels, much as you can stand on different levels of a flight of stairs.

Electrons in the *Bohr atom* can shift to a higher energy level by absorbing the energy of heat or light. Electrons can also drop into a lower energy level and in the process release heat or a *photon,* an individual electromagnetic wave. These changes in electron energy level are called *quantum leaps* or *quantum jumps. Spectroscopic* studies of the light emitted or absorbed by atoms—the atom's spectrum—reveal the nature of each atom's electron energy levels.

Each atom's electrons are arranged in concentric shells. When two atoms interact, electrons in the outermost shell come into contact. This shell-like electronic structure is reflected in the organization of the *periodic table of elements,* which lists all the elements in rows corresponding to increasing numbers of electrons in each shell, and in columns corresponding to elements with similar numbers of outer shell electrons and thus similar chemical behavior.

KEY TERMS

element	**electron**	**quantum leap,** or **quantum jump**
atom	**nucleus**	**spectrum**
molecule	**Bohr atom**	**spectroscopy**
periodic table of the elements	**photon**	

DISCOVERY LAB

Light is a mixture of colors and can be separated into these various colors by using a spectroscope. Each element has its own unique spectrum. Electrons in an atom of an element jump to an excited state when they are given energy. If the energy is removed they return to their ground state, emitting photons or

energy in the process. To build your own spectroscope you will need an old CD, toilet paper roll, two index cards, a permanent marker, and scissors.

Take two index cards and place them side-by-side so that there is a small slit between them. Glue the paper roll to the index cards.

Cut away the excess of index cards; they should be slightly larger than the cylinder base. Put a tape around the border of the tube and the index cards to avoid any light coming into the cylinder. Cut a circle on the CD about the diameter of the toilet paper roll. Peel away the silver-colored film from the CD and glue the CD to the toilet paper roll on the opposite end of the slit. Now you have your spectroscope tube. Point the slit to the source of light and look through the CD. The source of light can be a fluorescent light bulb, an incandescent light, a candle, or glow stick. (Caution! Do not look at the Sun.) Draw the spectrum produced by each source of light and compare them. In what ways do the atomic spectra support Bohr's model of the atom?

REVIEW QUESTIONS

1. Did Democritus use the scientific method to study the existence of atoms?

2. Did Dalton use the scientific method in his studies of the existence of atoms?

3. Review six kinds of observational evidence that were used to support the atomic theory.

4. What three particles make up every atom? What are the major differences among these particles?

5. What is the most massive part of the atom? Of what does it consist? Why are electrons and protons found in different parts of the atom?

6. Why is the smallest unit of an element an atom, but the smallest unit of a compound is a molecule?

7. Approximately how many elements are necessary to form all the solids, liquids, and gases around us?

8. Review the basic elements of Rutherford's experiment. What evidence did Rutherford use to justify his discovery of the nucleus?

9. How does Bohr's model of the atom differ from Rutherford's? How does the interaction of atoms and electromagnetic energy provide evidence for the Bohr model of the atom?

10. What is the relationship between a photon and a quantum leap?

11. How might an emission spectrum and an absorption spectrum of a given element differ in appearance?

12. Cite three examples of everyday objects with vivid emission spectra.

13. How might astronomers on Earth use spectroscopy to determine chemical elements that occur in stars?

14. Describe the basic components of a laser. How does a laser work?

15. How is the periodic table arranged? How do the atomic weights change as you move from the upper left to the lower right of the table?

16. How is the electromagnetic spectrum related to quantum leaps (i.e., electrons moving to lower or higher energy levels)?

DISCUSSION QUESTIONS

1. Which atomic model (i.e., Bohr's or Rutherford's) resembles our solar system of planets orbiting the Sun most closely in structure? How is the degradation of orbiting planets in our solar system like that of the Rutherford atomic model?

2. For what does the acronym "LASER" stand? Why is this acronym representative of what a laser does?

3. What are coherent photons? How are they related to the production of laser emissions?

4. Carbon dioxide lasers are often used for welding and cutting. What other chemical elements are used in lasers and what other applications of lasers are there?

5. Upon analysis of the results of his famous scattering experiment, Ernest Rutherford described his astonishment by stating, "It was almost as incredible as if you fired a 15-inch (artillery) shell at a piece of tissue paper and it came back and hit you." Why do you think he made this particular comparison?

6. What is a quantum leap? How big is a quantum leap? Advertisers often describe improvements in their products as a "quantum leap." Is this an appropriate use of the term?

7. Based on your knowledge of Newton's laws of motion, the laws of thermodynamics, and the nature of electromagnetic radiation, explain why the Rutherford model of the atom couldn't work and the Bohr model does.

8. When you shine invisible ultraviolet light (black light) on certain objects, they glow with brilliant colors. How might this behavior be explained in terms of the Bohr atom?

9. Why do different lasers have different-colored beams?

10. Why is chlorine used in pools and to bleach clothing? What chemical property does chlorine possess that makes it a good chemical for that purpose? Using the periodic table, what other elements might be used instead of chlorine?

11. The number of different stable compounds that can be made with just the elements carbon, hydrogen, oxygen, nitrogen, and fluorine has been estimated to be about 18 billion. Why are there so many different compounds relative to the number of different elements?

12. At the time Mendeleev came up with the idea of the periodic table, and for many years afterwards, no one understood why it worked the way it did. Nevertheless, it came into widespread use even before an explanation was forthcoming. Is it good scientific practice to use something that "works" even if you don't understand why? Can you think of any other thing that "works" even if we don't know why?

13. A typical incandescent lightbulb will be filled with argon. Why do manufacturers use argon when there are plenty of less expensive gases available?

14. Space probes often carry compact spectrometers among their scientific hardware. What kind of spectroscopy might scientists use to determine the surface composition of the cold, outer planets that orbit the Sun? How might they use spectroscopy to determine the atmospheric composition of these planets?

15. In the science fiction series *Star Trek*, there is a weapon called the "photon torpedo." Given what you now know about photons, speculate about how such a weapon might work.

16. If you replaced the tungsten filament of a typical incandescent bulb with an iron filament, would the emission spectrum be the same? Why or why not?

17. How does the Pauli exclusion principle relate to the arrangement of elements in the periodic table?

18. Suppose you were given a sample of an unknown element. How might you determine in which column of the periodic table of elements it belongs?

19. When an element is in a gaseous state and is electrically excited, it emits many different wavelengths of light. Yet when we stare at it, we see only one color. Why is that? Based on Figure 8-15, what do you think the color of electrically excited hydrogen would be?

PROBLEMS

1. How many different wavelengths of light could a hydrogen atom emit if its electron were limited to occupying only four different states, located at radii $r_1, r_2, r_3,$ and r_4? List the different transitions, for example, $r_2 \rightarrow r_1, r_3 \rightarrow r_1,$ etc.

2. A substance is found to contain only carbon and hydrogen. When the substance is separated into its separate elements, it is found that the mass of carbon relative to the mass of hydrogen is in a ratio of 3:1. Given that the mass of a single carbon atom is 12 times more than a single hydrogen atom, what is the ratio of carbon atoms to hydrogen atoms in this molecule?

3. Using the periodic table of elements, determine the result of the following calculations. First, add the number of electrons in the outermost shell of sodium plus the number of electrons in the outermost shell of chlorine. Second, add the number of electrons in the outermost shell of magnesium plus the number of electrons in the outermost shell of oxygen. If sodium and chlorine combine in a 1 to 1 ratio, what do you think is the ratio for the combination of magnesium and oxygen atoms?

4. The width of a human hair has been measured to be as narrow as 17 μm (equivalent to 17×10^{-6} m) and as thick as 181 μm. Given that the diameter of a hydrogen atom is no less than about 1.06 Ångstroms (a distance unit equivalent to 1.06×10^{-10} m), how many hydrogen atoms could fit end-to-end across the width of the thinnest human hair?

5. How many electrons does sulfur have in its outermost shell? If sulfur atom combines one to one with a magnesium atom, how many electrons in total are there in the outermost shells? What single element in that row of the periodic table has the same number of electrons in its outermost shell? How would you characterize that element?

6. If you have 18 kg of water, how many kg of oxygen atoms do you have?

   a. 6 kg

   b. 9 kg

   c. 12 kg

   d. 16 kg

7. Based on a comparison with the elements shown in Figure 8-19 and your understanding of the periodic table of elements, how many electrons would a barium atom have in its outermost shell?

   a. 1

   b. 2

   c. 6

   d. 7

8. Carbon dioxide has the molecular formula CO_2, meaning there are two oxygen atoms for every one carbon atom. If the ratio of the mass of a single oxygen atom to a single carbon atom is 4 to 3, what is the mass ratio of oxygen to carbon in a sample of carbon dioxide?

   a. 8 to 3

   b. 8 to 6

   c. 2 to 1

   d. 2 to 3

9. Examine the periodic table of elements as given in Figure 8-4. If it were discovered, what would be the atomic number of the next element to be considered an alkali metal; that is, what would be the atomic number of the element that would appear below Francium, element number 87?

   a. 88

   b. 112

   c. 113

   d. 119

INVESTIGATIONS

1. Investigate the history of the discovery of chemical elements. What technological innovations led to the discovery of several new elements? What was the most recent element to be discovered, and how was it found? How much time did researchers have to study the most recently developed element? How many elements occur in nature, and how many are human-made?

2. Simple handheld spectroscopes are available in many science labs. Look at the spectra of different kinds of lightbulbs: an incandescent bulb, a fluorescent bulb, a halogen bulb, and any other kinds available to you. What differences do you observe in their spectra? Why?

3. Place pieces of transparent materials between a strong light source and the spectrometer described in Investigation 2. Does the spectrum change? Why?

4. Why do colors look different when viewed indoors under fluorescent light, and outdoors in sunlight? How might you devise an experiment to quantify these differences?

5. Investigate the variety of lasers that are currently available. What is the range of wavelengths available? How are different lasers used in medicine? in industry? in science?

6. At your local hardware store, find "full-spectrum" fluorescent or incandescent bulbs. Read the labels describing their emission spectrum. What wavelengths of electromagnetic energy do the bulbs produce? Are they really "full spectrum"?

7. Many television crime shows depict forensic investigators using spectroscopy to detect the residue of bodily fluids at crime scenes. How does spectroscopy detect this residue?

Quantum Mechanics

How can the electron behave like both a particle and a wave?

PHYSICS

Quantum mechanics requires an entirely new way of describing the state of a system at the level of the atom.

BIOLOGY

Some scientists think that quantum mechanics is intimately involved in the phenomenon of consciousness.

CHEMISTRY

Wave-particle duality explains the shapes of allowed electron orbits, and therefore the chemical reactions of atoms.

GREAT IDEA

At the subatomic scale, everything is quantized. Any measurement at that scale significantly alters the object being measured.

TECHNOLOGY

Sensitive electronic detectors can detect the emission of a single photon from an excited atom.

GEOLOGY

The way that atoms combine to form minerals is governed by the laws of quantum mechanics.

ASTRONOMY

The nuclear reactions that power the Sun are governed by the laws of quantum mechanics. (Ch. 14)

HEALTH & SAFETY

In CAT scans, photoelectric devices convert X-ray photons into electrical currents, whose strength can be used to produce a picture of a patient's internal organs.

 = applications of the great idea discussed in this chapter

 = other applications, some of which are discussed in other chapters

Digital Pictures

It's 9:30 a.m. as you pull into the oceanside parking lot. You've made great time and are eager to hit the beach. You see your friends waiting near the entrance. As you shout and wave a classmate snaps your picture on his new digital camera. Everyone crowds around to see the crisp image on the camera's video monitor.

But how can a little box almost instantaneously capture and display a picture? At the heart of every digital camera is a plate of light-sensitive material called a *photoelectric device*—the same kind of material that converts the Sun's energy into electricity in a solar cell and measures brightness in a light meter. These everyday objects are practical consequences of one of the strangest discoveries in science—the discovery of the quantum world.

Exactostock/SuperStock

◉ 9.1 The World of the Very Small

In Chapter 8 we saw that when an electron moves between energy levels and emits a photon, it is said to make a *quantum leap*. The term **quantum mechanics** refers to the theory that describes this event and other events at the scale of the atom. The word *quantum* comes from the Latin word for "bundle," and mechanics, as we saw in Chapter 2, is the study of the motion of material objects. Quantum mechanics, then, is the branch of science that is devoted to the study of the motion of objects that come in small bundles, or quanta. We have already seen that material inside the atom comes in little bundles—tiny pieces of matter we call electrons travel in orbits around another little bundle of matter we call the nucleus. In the language of physicists, the atom's matter is said to be *quantized*.

Electrical charge is also quantized—electrons have a charge of exactly –1 fundamental unit of charge, and protons have a +1 charge. We've seen that photons emitted by an atom can have only certain values of energy, so that energy levels in the atom and emitted energy are quantized. In fact, inside the atom, in the world of the submicroscopically small, *everything* comes in quantized bundles.

Our everyday world isn't like this at all. Although we've been told since childhood that the objects around us are made up of atoms, for all intents and purposes we experience matter as if it were smooth, continuous, and infinitely divisible. Indeed, for almost any phenomenon in the physical world, the idea of matter existing in continuous form works as well as anyone would want.

The quantum world is foreign to our senses. All of the intuition that we have built up about the way the world operates—all of the "gut feelings" we have about the universe—comes from our experiences with large-scale objects made up of apparently continuous material. If it should turn out (as it does) that the world of the quantum does not match our intuition, we should not be surprised. We have never dealt with this kind of world, so we have no particular reason, based on observations or experience, to believe that it should behave one way or the other.

This warning may not make you feel much better as you learn just how strange and different the quantum world really is, but it might help you come to intellectual grips with a most fascinating part of our physical universe.

Measurement and Observation in the Quantum World

Every measurement in the physical world incorporates three essential components:

1. A sample—a piece of matter to study
2. A source of energy—light, wave, heat, or kinetic energy that interacts with the sample
3. A detector to observe and measure that interaction

When you look at a piece of matter such as this book, you can see it because light bounces off the book and comes to your eye, a very sophisticated detector (see Chapter 6). When you examine a piece of fruit at the grocery store, you apply energy by squeezing it to detect if it feels too ripe.

Many professions employ sophisticated devices to make their measurements. Air traffic controllers reflect microwaves off airplanes to determine their positions (Figure 9-1), oceanographers bounce sound waves off deep-ocean sediments to map the seafloor, and dentists pass X-rays through your teeth and gums to look for cavities. In our everyday world we assume that such interactions of matter and energy do not change the objects being measured in any appreciable way. Microwaves don't alter an airplane's flight path, nor do sound waves disturb the topography of the ocean's bottom. And while prolonged exposure to X-rays can be harmful, the dentist's brief exploratory X-ray photograph has no obvious immediate effects on the tooth. Our experience tells us that a measurement can usually be made on a macroscopic object—something large enough to be seen without a microscope—without altering that object, because the energy of the probe is much less than the energy of the object.

The situation is rather different in the quantum world. If you want to "see" an electron, you have to bounce energy off it so that the information can be carried to your detectors. But nothing at your disposal can interact with the electron without simultaneously affecting it. You can bounce a photon off it, but in the process the electron's energy will change. You can bounce another particle off it, but the electron will recoil like a billiard ball. No matter what you try, the energy of the probe is too close to the energy of the thing being measured. The electron cannot fail to be altered by the interaction.

Many everyday analogies illustrate the process of measurement in the quantum world. It's like trying to detect bowling balls by bouncing other bowling balls off them. The act of measurement in the quantum world poses a dilemma analogous to trying to discover if there is a car in a tunnel when the only means of finding out is to send another car into the tunnel and listen for a crash. With this technique you can certainly discover whether the first car is there. You can probably even find out where it is by measuring the time it takes the probe car to crash. What you *cannot* do, however, is assume that the first car is the same after the interaction as it was before. In the same way, nothing in the quantum world can be the same after the interaction associated with a measurement is as it was before.

In principle, this argument would apply to any interaction, whether it involves photons and electrons or photons and bowling balls. As we demonstrate in the "Science by the Numbers" section in this chapter, however, the effects of the interaction for large-scale objects are so tiny that they can be ignored, while in the case of interactions at the atomic level, they cannot. This fundamental difference between the quantum and macroscopic worlds is what makes quantum mechanics quite different from the classical mechanics of Isaac Newton. Remember that every experiment, be it on planets, or fruit, or quantum objects, involves

FIGURE 9-1 A radar antenna sends out microwaves that interact with flying airplanes, are reflected, and are detected on their return. This allows air traffic controllers to keep track of where airplanes are in the sky.

MAI/NASA/LandovLLC

interactions of one sort or another. The consequences of small-scale interactions make the quantum world different, not the fact that a measurement is being made.

The Heisenberg Uncertainty Principle

In 1927, a young German physicist, Werner Heisenberg (1901–1976), put the idea of limitations on quantum-scale measurements into precise mathematical form. His work, which was one of the first results to come from the new science of quantum mechanics, is called the *Heisenberg uncertainty principle* in his honor. The central concept of the uncertainty principle is simple:

● **At the quantum scale, any measurement significantly alters the object being measured.**

Suppose, for example, that you have a particle such as an electron in an atom and want to know where it is *and* how fast it's moving. The uncertainty principle tells us that it is impossible to measure both the position and the velocity with infinite accuracy at the same time.

The reason for this state of affairs is that every measurement changes the object being measured. Just as the car in the tunnel could not be the same after the first measurement was made on it, so too will the quantum object change. The result is that as you measure one property, such as position, more and more exactly, your knowledge of a property, such as velocity, gets fuzzier and fuzzier.

The uncertainty principle doesn't say that we cannot know a particle's location with great precision. It is possible, at least in principle, for the uncertainty in position to be zero, which would mean that we know the exact location of a quantum particle. In this case, however, the uncertainty in the velocity has to be infinite. Thus, at the point in time when we know exactly where the particle is, we have no idea whatsoever how fast it is moving. By the same token, if we know exactly how fast the quantum particle is moving, we cannot know where it is. It could, quite literally, be in the room with us or in China.

In practice, every quantum measurement involves trade-offs. We accept some fuzziness in the location of the particle and some fuzziness in the knowledge of the velocity, playing the two off against each other to get the best solution to whatever problem it is we're working on. We cannot have precise knowledge of both at the same time, but we can know either one as accurately as we like at any time.

Let's look a little more closely at the differences between the world of our intuition and the quantum world. In the intuition world, we assume that measurement doesn't affect the thing being measured, so that we can have exact, simultaneous knowledge of both the position and velocity of an object such as a car or a baseball. In the quantum world, as Heisenberg taught us, we cannot.

Heisenberg put his notion into a simple mathematical relationship, which is a complete and exact statement of the **uncertainty principle**.

In words: The error or uncertainty in the measurement of an object's position, times the error or uncertainty in that object's velocity, must be greater than a constant (Planck's constant) divided by the object's mass.

In equation form:

$$(\text{uncertainty in position}) \times (\text{uncertainty in velocity}) > \frac{h}{\text{mass}}$$

where h is a number known as Planck's constant (see below).

In symbols:

$$\Delta x \times \Delta v > \frac{h}{m}$$

This equation is a precise, shorthand way of saying that you can never know both the position and velocity of an object with perfect accuracy. The difference between our everyday world and the world inside the atom hangs on the question of the numerical value of h/m, the numbers on the right side of Heisenberg's equation. In SI units (see Appendix A), Planck's constant, h, has a value of 6.63×10^{-34} joule-seconds.

The important point about the Heisenberg relationship is not the exact value of the number, h/m, but the fact that the number is greater than zero. Look at it this way. If you make increasingly precise measurements about the location of a particle, you determine its position more exactly and the uncertainty in position, Δx, gets smaller. In this situation, it follows that the uncertainty in velocity, Δv, has to get bigger. In fact, we can use the uncertainty principle to calculate exactly our uncertainty in velocity for a given uncertainty in position, and vice versa.

SCIENCE BY THE NUMBERS
Uncertainty in the Newtonian World

The best way to understand why we do not have to worry about the uncertainty principle in our everyday life is to calculate the uncertainty in measurements in two separate situations: large objects and very small objects.

1. **Small Uncertainties with Large Objects.** A moving automobile with a mass of 1000 kilograms is located in an intersection that is 5 meters across. How precisely can you know how fast the car is traveling?

   We can solve this problem by noting that if the car is somewhere in an intersection 5 meters across, then the uncertainty in position of the car is about equal to 5 meters. Thus we know the car's mass and uncertainty in position, so we can calculate the uncertainty in velocity:

$$(\text{uncertainty in position}) \times (\text{uncertainty in velocity}) > \frac{h}{\text{mass}}$$

First, we must rearrange this equation to solve for uncertainty in velocity:

$$(\text{uncertainty in velocity}) > \frac{(h/\text{mass})}{\text{uncertainty in position}}$$

$$> \frac{[(6.63 \times 10^{-34}\,\text{J-s})/1000\,\text{kg}]}{5\,\text{m}}$$

$$> \frac{[(6.63 \times 10^{-37}\,\text{J-s})/\text{kg}]}{5\,\text{m}}$$

$$> 1.33 \times 10^{-37}\,\text{m/s}$$

Thus, the uncertainty in the velocity of the automobile is greater than 1.33×10^{-37} m/s (note that the unit J-s/kg-m is equivalent to m/s; see Problem 2 at the end of the chapter). This uncertainty is extremely small. Theoretically, we could know the velocity of the car to an accuracy of 37 decimal places! In practice, however, we have no method of measuring velocities with present or foreseeable future technology to an accuracy remotely approaching this. The uncertainty is, for all practical purposes, indistinguishable from zero. Therefore, for objects with significant mass such as automobiles, the effects of the uncertainty principle are totally negligible. The equation confirms our experience that Newtonian mechanics works perfectly well in dealing with everyday objects.

2. **Large Uncertainties with Small Objects.** Contrast the preceding example with the uncertainty in velocity of an electron in an atom located within an area about 10^{-10} meters on a side. To what accuracy can we measure the velocity of that electron? The mass of an electron is 9.11×10^{-31} kg. If we take the uncertainty in position to be 10^{-10} m, then according to the uncertainty principle,

$$(\text{uncertainty in velocity}) > \frac{(h/\text{mass})}{\text{uncertainty in position}}$$

$$> \frac{[(6.63 \times 10^{-34}\,\text{J-s})/(9.11 \times 10^{-31}\,\text{kg})]}{10^{-10}\,\text{m}}$$

$$> 7.3 \times 10^{6}\,\text{m/s} = 7,300\,\text{km/s}$$

This uncertainty is very large indeed. The mere fact that we know that an electron is somewhere in an atom means that we cannot know its velocity to within about 2.4% of the speed of light.

For ordinary-sized objects such as cars and bowling balls, whose mass is measured in kilograms, the number on the right side of the uncertainty relation is so small that we can treat it as being zero. Only when the masses get very small, as they do for particles such as the electron, is the number on the right large enough to make a practical difference.

STOP & THINK! How massive do you suppose something has to be before we can forget about the effects of the uncertainty principle? As massive as a speck of dust? A baseball? A car?

◎ 9.2 Probabilities

The uncertainty principle has consequences that go far beyond simple statements about measurement. In the quantum world we must radically change the way that we describe events. Consider an everyday example in which the uncertainties are much larger (but easier to picture) than those associated with Heisenberg's equation. Think of a batter hitting a ball during a nighttime baseball game.

Imagine yourself at a big-league ball game under the lights of a great stadium. Cheering fans fill the stands, roving vendors sell their food and drink, and the pitcher and batter play out their classic duel. The pitcher stares the batter down, winds up, and hurls a fastball. But the batter is ready and pounces on the pitch. The ball leaps off the bat with a sharp crack. And then all the lights go out.

Where will the ball be in 5 seconds? If you were an outfielder, this would be more than a philosophical question. You would need to know where to go to make your catch, even in the dark. In a Newtonian world, you would have no problem in doing this. If you knew the position and velocity of the ball at the instant the lights went out, some simple calculations would tell you exactly where the ball would be at any time in the future.

If you were a quantum outfielder in an atom-sized ball field, on the other hand, you would have a much harder time of it. You couldn't know both the position and velocity of the quantum ball when the lights go out; at best you could put some bounds on them. You might, for example, be able to say something like, "It's somewhere inside this 3-foot circle and traveling between 30 and 70 feet per second." This uncertainty means that when you have to guess where the ball will be in 5 seconds, you won't be able to do so with any accuracy. If you were thinking in Newtonian terms, you would have to say that the ball could be 147 feet from the plate (if it were traveling 30 feet per second and located at the back of the 3-foot circle), 353 feet from the plate (if it were traveling 70 feet per second and located at the front of the circle), or anyplace in between. The best you could hope to do would be to predict the likelihood, or **probability**, that the ball would be anywhere in the outfield, and you could present these probabilities on a graph like the one shown in Figure 9-2.

This example shows that the uncertainty principle requires a description of quantum-scale events in terms of probabilities. Just like the baseball in our example of the darkened stadium, there must be uncertainties in the position and velocity for every quantum object when we first start observing it, and hence there will be uncertainties at the end—uncertainties that can be dealt with by reporting probabilities.

This result is extremely important. It tells us that we cannot think of quantum events in the same way that we think of normal events in our everyday world. In particular, we have to rethink what it means to talk about concepts such as regularity, predictability, and causality at the quantum level.

FIGURE 9-2 The position of a "quantum baseball" cannot be precisely determined. Instead, you can predict only the probabilities of the ball being at various distances from home plate, as discussed in the text. The most likely location is at the peak of the curve, but the ball could be anywhere else.

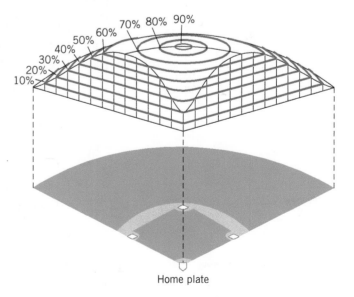

Home plate

● 9.3 Wave-Particle Duality

Quantum mechanics is sometimes called *wave mechanics* because it turns out that quantum objects sometimes act like particles and sometimes like waves. This dichotomy is known as the problem of wave-particle duality, and it is a feature of the quantum world. To understand it, think about how particles and waves behave in our macroscopic world.

The Double-Slit Test

Energy travels either as a wave or as a particle in our everyday world (see Chapter 6). Particles transfer energy through collisions, while waves transfer energy through collective motion of the media or electromagnetic fields. Every aspect of the everyday world can be neatly divided into particles or waves, and many experiments can be used to determine whether something is a particle or wave. The most famous of these experiment uses a two-slit, or double-slit apparatus, which consists of a barrier that has two parallel slits in it (Figure 9-3). If particles such as baseballs are thrown from the left side, a few will make it through the slits, but most will bounce off. If you were standing on the other side of the barrier, you would expect to see the baseballs coming through more or less in the two places shown, accumulating in two piles behind the barrier. You wouldn't expect to see many particles (baseballs) at the spots between the slits.

If, however, waves of water were coming from the left side, you would expect to see the results of constructive and destructive interference (see Chapter 6). Rather than the two piles of baseballs, we would see perhaps half a dozen regions of high waves beyond the barrier, interspersed with regions of still water.

Now, let's use the same arrangement to see whether light behaves as a particle or a wave. In Chapter 8 we learned that light is emitted in discrete bundles of energy called *photons*. On the one hand, photons behave like particles in the sense that they can be localized in space. You can set up experiments in which a photon is emitted at one point, then received somewhere else after an appropriate lapse of time, just as a baseball is "emitted" by a pitcher and "received" later by a catcher (Figure 9-3a). If, on the other hand, you shine light—a flood of photons—on the two-slit apparatus, you will definitely get an interference pattern on the right (Figure 9-3b). In that experiment, photons act like waves. The big question: How can photons sometimes act like waves and sometimes act like particles?

You can make the problem even more puzzling by setting up the barrier so that only one photon at a time comes through the slits. If you do this, you find that each photon arrives at a specific point at the film—behavior you would expect of a particle. If you allow photons to accumulate over long periods of time, however, they will arrange themselves into an interference pattern characteristic of a wave.

You could do a similar series of experiments with any quantum object—electrons, for example (Figure 9-4), or photons, or even atoms. They all exhibit the properties of both particles and waves, depending on what sort of experiment is done. If you perform an experiment that tests the particle properties of these things, they look like particles. If you perform an experiment to test their wave properties, they look like waves. Whether you see quantum objects as particles or waves seems to depend on the experiment that you do.

Some experimenters have gone so far as to try to "trick" quantum particles such as electrons into revealing their true identity by using modern fast electronics to decide whether a particle- or wave-type experiment is being done *after* the quantum object is already on its way into the apparatus. Scientists who do these experiments find that the quantum object seems to "know" what experiment is being done, because the particle experiments always turn up particle properties, while the wave experiments always turn up wave properties.

At the quantum level, the objects that we talk about are neither particles nor waves in the classical sense. In fact, we can't really visualize them at all, because we have never encountered anything like them in our everyday experience. They are a third kind of object, neither particle nor wave, but exhibiting the properties of both.

FIGURE 9-3 The two-slit experiment may be used to determine whether something is a wave or a particle. *(a)* A stream of particles like baseballs striking the barrier will accumulate in the two regions directly behind the slits. *(b)* When waves converge on two narrow slits, however, constructive and destructive interference results in a series of peaks.

Detectors

Number of particles

Particle gun
(shooting baseballs)

Barrier

(a)

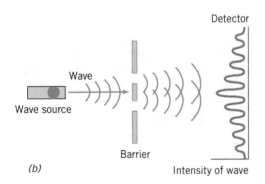

Detector

Wave

Wave source

Barrier

(b)

Intensity of wave

Courtesy Akira tonomura, J. Endo, T. Matsuda and T. Kawasaki, Am. J. Phys. 57 (2): 117, February 1989. Reproduced with permission of American Institute of Physics

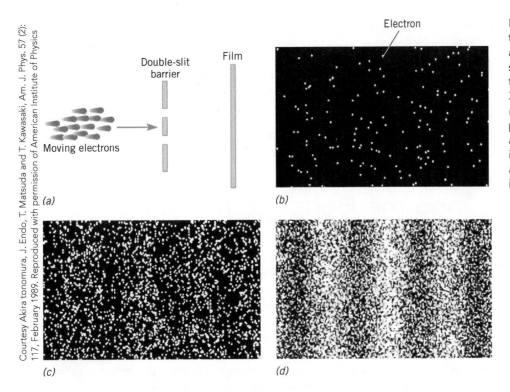

FIGURE 9-4 When electrons pass through a double-slit barrier one at a time (a), they cause 100 single spots on a photographic film (b). As the number of electrons increases to 3000 (c), and then to 70,000 (d), a wave-like interference pattern emerges. The bright areas are places where constructive interference occurs, and the dark areas correspond to destructive interference.

If you persist in thinking about them as if they were baseballs or surf coming onto a beach, you will quickly lose yourself in confusion.

It's a little bit like finding someone who has seen only the colors red and green in her entire life. If she has decided that everything in the world has to be either red or green, she will be totally confused by seeing the color blue. What she has to realize is that the problem is not in nature, but in her assumption that everything has to be either red or green.

In the same way, the problem of wave-particle duality arises from our assumption that everything has to be either a wave or a particle. If we allow ourselves the possibility that quantum objects are things that we have never encountered before, and that they therefore might have properties different from our everyday experience, then the puzzle vanishes. However, it vanishes only if we agree that we won't try to draw a picture of these objects or pretend that we can actually visualize what they are.

TECHNOLOGY
The Photoelectric Effect

When photons of sufficient energy strike some materials, their energy can be absorbed by electrons, which are shaken loose from their home atoms. If the material in question is in the form of a thin sheet, then when light strikes one side, electrons are observed coming out of the other. This phenomenon is called the *photoelectric effect*, and it finds applications in numerous everyday devices.

One aspect of the photoelectric effect played a major role in the history of quantum mechanics. The time between the arrival of the light and the appearance of the electrons is extremely short—far too short to be explained by the relatively gentle action of a wave nudging the electrons loose. In fact, it was Albert Einstein who pointed out that the explanation of this rapid response depended on the particle-like nature of the photon. He argued that the interaction between the light and the electron is something like the collision between two billiard balls, with one ball shooting out instantly after the collision. It was this work, which led to our modern concept of the photon, that was the basis of Einstein's Nobel Prize in 1921.

The conversion of light energy into electrical current is used in many familiar devices. In a digital camera, for example, one photoelectric device measures the amount of light available to determine how wide to open the lens and what the shutter speed should be. Then a photoelectric plate collects the photographic image. In telephone systems that use fiber optics—glass fibers that act like pipes for visible light (see Chapter 6)—light signals strike sophisticated semiconductor devices (see Chapter 11) and shake loose electrons. These electrons form a current that ultimately drives the diaphragm in your telephone and produces the sound that you hear. In CAT scans, photoelectric devices convert X-ray photons into electrical currents whose strength can be used to produce a picture of a patient's internal organs. As all of these examples show, an understanding of the way objects interact in the quantum world can have enormous practical consequences.

● 9.4 Wave-Particle Duality and the Bohr Atom

Treating electrons as waves helps explain why only certain orbits are allowed in atoms (see Chapter 8). Every quantum object displays a simple relationship between its speed (when we think of it as a particle) and its wavelength (when we think of it as a wave). It turns out that for electrons, protons, and other quantum objects, a faster speed always corresponds to a shorter, more energetic wavelength (or a higher frequency).

If you think of an electron as a particle, then you can treat its motion around an atom's nucleus in the same Newtonian way you treat the motion of Earth in orbit around the Sun. That is, for any given distance from the nucleus, the electron must have a precise velocity to stay in a stable orbit. Provided it is moving at such a velocity, it will stay in that orbit just as Earth stays in a stable orbit around the Sun. Any faster and it must adopt a higher orbit; any slower and it will move closer to the nucleus.

If we choose to think about the electron as a wave, however, a different set of criteria can be used to decide how to put the electron into its orbit. A wave on a straight string (on a guitar, for example) vibrates uniformly only at certain frequencies that depend on the length of the string (Figure 9-5). These frequencies correspond to fitting 1/2, 1, and 3/2 wavelengths on the string in the figure. Now imagine bending the guitar string around into a circular orbit. In this case, you will be able to fit only certain standing waves in the orbit, as shown in Figure 9-6.

You can now ask a simple question: Are there any orbits for which the wave and particle descriptions are consistent? In other words, are there orbits for which the velocity of the electron (when we think of it as a particle) is appropriate to the orbit, while at the same time the electron wave (when we think of it as a wave) fits onto the orbit, given the relation between wavelength and velocity?

When you do the mathematics, you find that the only orbits that satisfy these twin conditions are the Bohr orbits. That is to say, *the only orbits allowed in the atom are those for which it makes no difference whether we think of the electron as a particle or a wave.* In a sense, then, the wave-particle duality exists in our minds, and not in nature—nature has arranged things so that what we think doesn't matter.

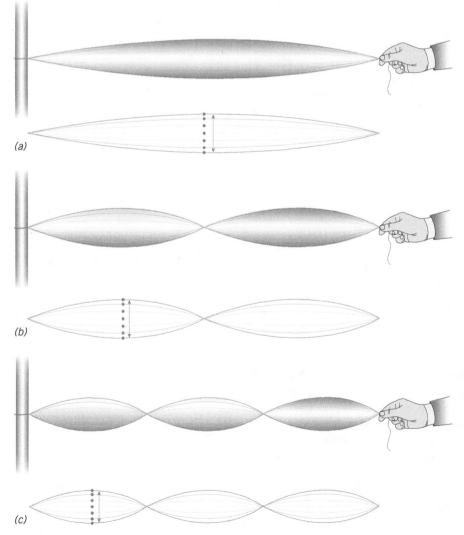

FIGURE 9-5 A vibrating string adopts a regular pattern, known as a standing wave. These diagrams illustrate fixed patterns with (a) 1/2, (b) 1, and (c) 3/2 wavelengths.

(a)

(b)

(c)

Quantum Weirdness

The fact that quantum objects behave so differently from objects in our everyday experience causes many people to worry that nature has somehow become "weird" at the subatomic level. The description of particles in terms of a wave defies our commonsense. Situations in which a photon or an electron seems to "know" how an apparatus will be arranged before the arranging is done seem wrong and unnatural.

Many people, scientists and nonscientists alike, find the conclusions of quantum mechanics to be quite unsettling. The American physicist Richard Feynman stressed this point when he said, "I can safely say that nobody understands quantum mechanics. . . . Do not keep saying to yourself, 'But how can it be like that?' . . . Nobody knows how it can be like that."

In spite of this rather disturbing situation, the success of quantum mechanics provides ample evidence that there is a correct way to describe an atomic-scale system. If you ignore this fact, you can get into a lot of trouble. Newtonian notions such as position and velocity just aren't appropriate for the quantum world, which must be described from the beginning in terms of waves and probabilities. Quantum mechanics thus becomes a way of predicting how subatomic objects change in time. If you know the state of an electron now, you can use quantum mechanics to predict the state of that electron in the future. This process is identical to the application of Newton's laws of motion in the macroscopic world. The only difference is that in the quantum world, the "state" of the system is a probability.

In the view of most working scientists, quantum mechanics is a marvelous tool that allows us to do all sorts of experiments and build all manner of new and important pieces of equipment. The fact that we can't visualize the quantum world in familiar terms seems a small price to pay for all the benefits we receive.

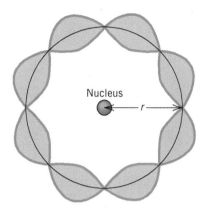

FIGURE 9-6 An electron in orbit about an atom adopts a standing wave like a vibrating string. This illustration shows a standing wave with four wavelengths fitting into the orbit's circumference.

TECHNOLOGY
Quantum Computing

Computers have become a common tool in everyday life—you probably use one routinely in your schoolwork. In Chapter 11 we will see that the basic working unit of a computer is a device known as a transistor, which can be in one of two possible states—on or off. (Think of it as a sort of high-tech lightbulb.) This means that the computer is a device that takes in information in digital form, manipulates it, and sends it back out in the same way. The basic unit of information in this sort of device is called the "bit," with a single bit telling us whether a given transistor is on or off. The computer works by changing bits one at a time (i.e., by switching transistors on and off), and at any moment in time we can characterize the state of the computer by listing the state of each individual transistor.

Scientists have known for decades that quantum mechanics implies the possibility of a radically new type of computer. Because quantum states are described by wave functions or probabilities, you can think of a computer in which the basic device, instead of being "on" or "off," is described as a mix of probabilities of these two states. For example, a particle like the electron can be spinning around its axis in a clockwise direction or in a counterclockwise direction. The wave function of the electron gives us the probability of finding the electron spinning in each direction if we make a measurement, but until that measurement is made, we have to think of the electron as being in both states simultaneously (another bit of quantum weirdness). The unit of information describing this situation is called a "qubit" (for "quantum bit"). Theoretically, a machine that manipulates qubits can be thought of as being in many different states at the same time, instead of in just one state like the conventional computer. This strange circumstance means, theoretically, that a quantum computer could solve certain types of problems much more quickly than a conventional one.

The application of quantum computing that has garnered the most attention is in the field of cryptography. Today, sensitive information sent over the Internet (for example, your credit card number) is protected by the use of codes that involve the multiplication of very large numbers—systems that go by the name of "public encryption codes." They work because it would take an ordinary computer a very long time—perhaps millions of years—to crack the code. In theory, at least, quantum computers could render such codes obsolete.

The main practical problem in building a quantum computer comes from the fact that if the quantum state carrying the qubit interacts with its environment, the system may be forced into a specific state—an electron may be forced into spinning in one direction only, for example. This situation destroys the delicate balance of the quantum state. Scientists refer to this problem as "decoherence," and it is just one roadblock on the way to quantum computing.

Although most of the research on quantum computing has been theoretical in nature, there is at least one quantum computer—the so-called D Wave system—that is commercially available. You won't have it on your desk any time soon, though—the computers go for fifteen million dollars a pop!

◎ 9.5 Quantum Entanglement

One of the strangest features of the quantum world goes by the name *quantum entanglement*. It has no real analog in our everyday experience, but here is an example of something that never happens in our ordinary world, but would demonstrate entanglement if it did. Suppose you had a set of dice, and each die was perfectly normal—if rolled individually, a die shows each face one-sixth of the time. Now suppose you took one of the dice to New York and the other to Los Angeles and rolled them at the same time. Imagine discovering when you did this that whatever showed on the New York die also showed on its partner in Los Angeles. If the New York die came up with a 3, for example, the Los Angeles die would do the same. This would be an example of entanglement—as we said, it never occurs in our ordinary world, but it does happen in the world of the quantum.

The concept of entanglement goes all the way back to 1935, to a paper by Albert Einstein and two of his colleagues, Boris Podolsky and Nathan Rosen. The paper, arguably Einstein's most successful attack on quantum mechanics, was aimed at the notion that the correct way to describe a quantum system is as a wave function representing a mix of all possible states. Their argument was simple: suppose an atom emits two photons at the same time. The two-photon system is then described by a wave function. Now let the two photons travel in opposite directions—traveling so far that there is no possibility that a signal traveling at the speed of light could pass between them in the time that it takes to make a measurement. According to quantum mechanics, measuring one photon would determine the state of the other, even though the unmeasured photon could not know that it's partner had been measured.

For a long time, this was known as the EPR paradox (for Einstein, Podolsky, and Rosen)—it just made no sense. Then, in 1964, Irish theoretical physicist John Bell pointed out that if you actually did the experiment, you would get different results if the photons were described by a wave function with probabilities, or by an equation with an exact solution. When the experiments were done in the 1970s, the quantum-mechanical interpretation was confirmed. In essence, we came to understand that in the quantum world the wave functions of the two photons never really become separated. They remain *entangled* with each other, so that if you measure one photon you know exactly what state the other one is in. Don't try to picture how measuring one photon can change the other, even when the two have no way of communicating with each other. You can't. This is just another example of Feynman's dictum.

TECHNOLOGY

Quantum Teleportation

As strange as quantum entanglement may seem, it actually has practical implications, primarily through a process known as *quantum teleportation*.

Here's how it works: Suppose Bob creates a pair of entangled photons (Figure 9-7). He keeps one and sends the other to Alice. Bob then takes his entangled photon and allows it to interact with

FIGURE 9-7 This is a schematic diagram of the process of quantum teleportation. Bob creates a pair of entangled photons (shown in blue and purple) and sends one to Alice. Alice interacts her entangled photon with the signal photon (red) and communicates the result to Bob, who can then re-create the signal photon in his own laboratory.

Bob

A   B

Entangled photons

C   Signal photon

Bob sends a photon to Alice

Bob keeps a photon

A

B   C

Alice

Information of interaction   Interaction and measurement

C   Photons destroyed   B

A

Reconstructs signal photon

another photon—call this third photon the "signal photon." He then phones Alice and tells her the result of the interaction. Using this information and her entangled photon, Alice can then reconstruct the signal photon. Like the fictional "transporter" in the *Star Trek* science fiction series, quantum teleportation destroys the signal photon in one place and re-creates it in another.

One important aspect of quantum teleportation is that it allows absolutely secure communication between Bob and Alice. If an eavesdropper (usually called "Eve"), on one hand, intercepts the phone conversation it will do her no good because she doesn't have an entangled photon. If, on the other hand, she intercepts Alice's entangled photon, the uncertainty principle guarantees that she will change it, which means that Bob and Alice will know that she is listening.

The quantum teleportation of photons is now a fairly routine laboratory exercise. The next step—the teleportation of atoms—is still in the future, and the teleportation of human beings remains firmly in the realm of science fiction.

STOP & THINK! Is the photon created by quantum teleportation the same photon that was destroyed? If it has all the properties of the original photon, how could you tell the two apart?

SCIENCE IN THE MAKING
A Famous Exchange

Many people are disturbed by the fact that nature must be described in terms of probabilities at the subatomic level. Many scientists were also disturbed when quantum mechanics was first developed in the early twentieth century. Even Albert Einstein, one of the founders of quantum mechanics, could not accept what it was telling us about the world. He spent a good part of the last half of his life trying to refute it. His most famous statement from this period was, "I cannot believe that God plays dice with the universe."

Confronted one too many times with this aphorism, Einstein's lifelong friend and colleague Neils Bohr is supposed to have replied, "Albert, stop telling God what to do."

SCIENCE IN THE MAKING
Teleporting the Venus of Willendorf

In 1997, a group in Vienna headed by physicist Anton Zeilinger sent the first picture through the use of quantum-teleported photons. Zeilinger explained to his team that since this would be a historic event, they would have to be careful in their choice of subject. In fact, he told them, he had two criteria: first, the image had to be peaceful, and second, it had to be Austrian. Their choice: the so-called Venus of Willendorf, a prehistoric statue of a fertility goddess discovered in an Austrian village (Figure 9-8).

FIGURE 9-8 The so-called Venus of Willendorf, a 4-inch (11-centimeter) tall prehistoric statue of a fertility goddess discovered in an Austrian village, was the first picture transmitted through the use of quantum-teleported photons.

THINKING MORE ABOUT **QUANTUM MECHANICS**

Uncertainty and Human Beings

The ultimate Newtonian view of the universe was the concept of the Divine Calculator (see Chapter 2). This mythical being, given the position and velocity of every particle in the universe, could predict every future state of those particles. The difficulty with this concept is that if the future of the universe is laid out with clockwork precision, it allows no room for human action. No one can make a choice about what he or she will do, because that choice is already determined and exists (in the mind of God or the Divine Calculator) before it is made.

Quantum mechanics gives us one way to get out of this particular bind. Heisenberg tells us that, although we might be able to predict the future if we knew the position and velocity of every particle exactly, we can never actually get those two numbers. The Divine Calculator in a quantum world is doomed to wait forever for the input data with which to start the calculation.

One area where the uncertainty principle is starting to play a somewhat unexpected role is in the old philosophical argument about the connection between the mind and the brain. The brain is a physical object—an incredibly complex organ that processes information in the form of nerve impulses. (A more detailed description of the workings of the brain is given in Chapter 11.) The problem: What is the connection between the physical reality of the brain—the atoms and structures that compose it—and the consciousness that we all experience? Philosophers refer to this as the "qualia" problem, and it is centered around the difficulty of going from a description of what the neurons in your brain are doing when you see the color red (for example) and your actual experience of seeing that color.

Many scientists and philosophers have argued that the brain is no more than a physical structure. If this is true, however, the future states of the brain should be predictable. Recently, scientists (most notably Roger Penrose of Cambridge University) have argued that quantum mechanics can introduce a kind of unpredictability into this argument that squares better with our perceptions of our own minds.

Think about how the workings of the brain might be unpredictable at the quantum level. Why might that uncertainty make it difficult (or even impossible) to make precise predictions of the future state of the brain? How does this phenomenon affect our notions of free will?

◀ RETURN TO THE INTEGRATED QUESTION

How can the electron behave like both a particle and a wave?

- Quantum mechanics is also called *wave mechanics* because quantum objects (e.g., electrons or photons) sometimes act like particles and sometimes like waves. This dichotomy is known as the problem of wave-particle duality, and is a feature of the quantum world.

- The problem of duality dates back to at least the seventeenth century, when Christian Huygens and Isaac Newton debated the nature of light and matter.

- In the twentieth century, quantum mechanics offered a unified theoretical framework that afforded an understanding that all matter may exhibit the behavioral characteristics of both particles and waves.

- In Chapter 8, we learned that experiments can be conducted in which photons or electrons will behave like particles in the sense that they can be localized in space. By using the two-slit apparatus, however, an interference pattern will be observed, suggesting that photons and electrons act like waves.

- At the quantum level, subatomic objects are neither particles nor waves in the classical sense. Nevertheless, use of the wave and particle metaphors allows us to visualize discrete facets of the behavior of these phenomena.

- Treating electrons as waves helps explain why electrons will only be found in certain "allowable" orbits (see Chapter 8). Remember that every quantum object displays a simple relationship between its velocity (when we think of it as a particle) and its wavelength (when we think of it as a wave).

- When you think of an electron as a particle, you can treat its motion around an atom's nucleus in the same Newtonian way you treat the motion of Earth in orbit around the Sun. That is, for any given distance from the nucleus, the electron must have a precise velocity to stay in a stable orbit. Conversely, if we choose to think about the electron as a wave, a different set of criteria can be used to decide how to place the electron into its orbit.

- Convincing evidence of the duality of electrons is offered by the fact that the Bohr orbits are the only orbits for which the wave and particle descriptions are consistent. In other words, the Bohr orbits satisfy the relationships between velocity and orbits when the electron is being thought of as a particle, and the relationship between velocity and wavelength when it is being thought of as a wave.

SUMMARY

Matter and energy at the atomic scale come in discrete packets called quanta. The rules of *quantum mechanics,* the laws that allow us to describe and predict events in the quantum world, are disturbingly different from Newton's laws of motion.

At the quantum scale, unlike our everyday experience, any measurement of the position or velocity of a particle causes the particle to change in unpredictable ways. The mere act of measurement alters the thing being measured. Werner Heisenberg quantified this situation in the Heisenberg *uncertainty principle,* which states that the uncertainty in the position of a particle multiplied by the uncertainty in its velocity must be greater than a small positive number. Unlike the Newtonian world, you can never know the exact position and velocity of a quantum particle.

These uncertainties preclude us from describing atomic-scale particles in the classical way. Instead, quantum descriptions are given in terms of the *probability* that an object will be in one state or another. Furthermore, quantum objects are not simply particles or waves—a dichotomy familiar to us in the macroscopic world. They represent something completely different from our experience, incorporating properties of both particles and waves.

KEY TERMS

quantum mechanics **uncertainty principle** **probability**

KEY EQUATIONS

(uncertainty in position) × (uncertainty in velocity) > h/mass

DISCOVERY **LAB**

At times, light behaves as particles, which are packets of energy or photons, but it can also behave as waves. Light has characteristics that any wave would have. Are you surprised at this dual nature of light? To prove this statement, you will need a red laser pointer, aluminum foil, pin, projection screen (wall), a few clips, and a razor.

First, cut 1 square inch of aluminum foil and create pinholes by pressing the pin against the foil. The pinholes should be less than 2 millimeters apart and should be as small as possible. Now make two slits about 4 or 5 millimeters long and 1 millimeter apart. Place the laser about 10 to 12 meters away from the wall in a dark room. Put the foil about 15 centimeters in front of the laser. With the clips, grasp the foil. Shine the laser beam through the pinholes. Make adjustments so that the beam falls on both the pinholes with the same intensity. What is the diameter of the image with the pinholes? What is the length of the image with the slits? What happens when the waves from one slit meet with the waves from the other slit? How does this experiment describe the dual nature of the waves?

You can try different patterns instead of the slits and pinholes. You can also use different color filters and compare the differences.

REVIEW QUESTIONS

1. Explain what the term *quantum mechanics* means?

2. Give three examples of properties that are quantized at the scale of an electron.

3. Every measurement in the physical world requires three components. What are they? Provide an everyday example of each.

4. In what way is a measurement at the quantum scale of an electron different from a measurement at the large scales of everyday objects?

5. There was once a humorous poster showing a picture of a bed with the caption, "Heisenberg may have slept here." In what way is this quote an inaccurate representation of Heisenberg's uncertainty principle?

6. What does it mean to say that quantum measurements involve trade-offs?

7. Why is quantum mechanics sometimes called wave mechanics?

8. Describe what happens when a researcher shines a light on a "two-slit" apparatus. How does this situation demonstrate the wave-like nature of light?

9. What is wave-particle duality?

10. Explain how the photoelectric effect works. Does it depend on the wave or the particle nature of light?

11. How does wave-particle duality explain the Bohr orbits of electrons in atoms?

12. Why did Albert Einstein use playing dice as an analogy for quantum mechanics?

13. How is a quantum computer different from an ordinary computer?

14. What is quantum entanglement?

DISCUSSION QUESTIONS

1. Why is our intuition from our macroscopic understanding of the Newtonian universe insufficient to describe the quantum world? Can you give any examples of measurements on the quantum scale that defy what you would expect on the macroscopic scale?

2. What implications does the act of measurement hold for objects at the subatomic scale that are not observed to occur at the macroscopic scale of everyday life?

3. Identify the sample, the source of energy, and the detector in the following "experiments":
   a. measuring the distance to a remote star
   b. determining the sweetness of a piece of fruit
   c. determining if a piano needs tuning
   d. determining the height of a person
   e. measuring the temperature of a room

4. Imagine experiments that allow us to examine the wave-particle duality of a photon. What experiment tells us information about the photon as a wave, and what experiment tells us about a photon as a particle? What experiments could we do on electrons to give us the same behaviors?

5. Albert Einstein disliked the implications of the probabilistic interpretation of quantum mechanics and is known for saying, "God doesn't play dice with the world." But despite Einstein's negative feelings, this interpretation caught on. Why do you think that occurred?

6. What is quantum teleportation? Is the teleportation of photons possible? How about atoms?

7. What advantages do you think quantum computers would hold compared to the current electronic computers?

8. In Chapter 2 we discussed the fact that chaotic systems are, for all practical purposes, unpredictable. How does this sort of unpredictability differ from that associated with quantum mechanics?

9. Present an argument in terms of the wave nature of the electron that shows why electrons in Bohr orbits cannot emit radiation and spiral in toward the nucleus, as they might be expected to do on the basis of Maxwell's equations. (*Hint*: See "Why the Rutherford Atom Couldn't Work" in Chapter 8.)

10. In what ways are electrons and photons similar? In what ways do you think they are different? Aside from size, what differences are there between a quantum object like an electron and a macroscopic object like a basketball?

11. The very predictable universe envisioned by Isaac Newton was anthropomorphized as the "Divine Calculator." How is the concept of the Divine Calculator affected by the findings of quantum mechanics? Do the results of quantum mechanics influence other aspects such as human behavior or free will?

12. If you threw baseballs through a large two-slit apparatus, would you produce a diffraction pattern? Why or why not? What type of object would you need to produce a diffraction pattern?

13. In order to observe something with any precision, we typically need to use objects that are smaller than the object being observed. For instance, if we want to observe an electron, we need to use a photon with a wavelength smaller than the electron's wavelength. But a photon with a small wavelength has a relatively large energy. What impact do you think this has on the Heisenberg uncertainty principle?

14. An electron microscope uses the wave-like behavior of electrons, which can have wavelengths up to 100,000 times smaller than visible light. What do you think are the advantages and disadvantages of using electrons instead of light?

PROBLEMS

1. A baseball with a mass of 0.145 kg is thrown toward home plate with a speed of 49.05 m/s; knowing the speed to the nearest hundredth typically means our uncertainty in its speed is ±0.01 m/s. Given this level of accuracy, how accurately could its position be determined at any given instant?

2. In the "Science by the Numbers" section in this chapter, we converted the unit J-s/kg-m to the unit of velocity (m/s) without comment. Demonstrate the equivalence of these two units.

3. An atom of gold (mass = 3.27×10^{-25} kg) is accelerated to a speed of 123,901.415 m/s; the accuracy with which the speed is known is ±0.001 m/s. In theory, how accurately could its position be determined? How does this level of accuracy compare to the size of an atomic nucleus? Do you think this level of accuracy in measurement is attainable with current technology?

4. Suppose our particle in Problem 3 is an electron. Would the measuring device need to have a greater level of accuracy, or would a lesser level be sufficient? Why would there be a difference?

5. In the Bohr model of hydrogen, the number associated with the energy level also represents the number of standing waves around the circumference for the electron in that orbit. If the electron is in the r_3 orbit, which has a radius of 4.76×10^{-10} m, what is the wavelength of one of the standing waves?

6. Both a proton and electron are accelerated to a speed of 1.035×10^7 m/s with an uncertainty of ±(0.003×10^7 m/s). Which of them would be harder to pinpoint in terms of location?
   a. The proton
   b. The electron
   c. Both would have the same level of difficulty.
   d. There is insufficient information given in the problem.

7. You need to measure an electron (mass = 9.11×10^{-31} kg) to within a precision equivalent to its wavelength; suppose this value is 3.50×10^{-9} m. What will be the resulting minimum uncertainty in its speed?

a. 2.11×10^{-72} m/s

b. 1.89×10^{-25} m/s

c. 0.000727 m/s

d. 208,000 m/s

INVESTIGATIONS

1. Investigate the doctrine of predestination in an encyclopedia. Does it have a logical connection to the notion of the Divine Calculator? Which came first historically?

2. Werner Heisenberg was a central, and ultimately controversial, figure in German science of the 1930s and 1940s. Read a biography of Heisenberg. Discuss how his early work in quantum mechanics influenced his prominent scientific role in Nazi Germany.

3. Read about the play *Copenhagen* by Michael Frayn. Discuss how World War II changed the relationship between Niels Bohr and Werner Heisenberg.

4. What changes in artistic movements were taking place during the period around 1900 (just before the discoveries of quantum mechanics) and in the mid-twentieth century? Are there any connections between the artistic and scientific movements of those times?

5. Some people interpret the Heisenberg uncertainty principle to mean that you can never really know anything for certain. Would you agree or disagree?

6. Who is Erwin Schrödinger? What was his role in the development of quantum mechanics?

7. What kinds of problems do physicists think that quantum computers will solve? (Hint: One such problem involves encryption.)

8. New age authors sometimes claim that Heisenberg's uncertainty principle demonstrates a cosmic connection between humans and the universe. Do you think this is a valid argument? Why or why not?

10 Atoms in Combination: The Chemical Bond

How does blood clot?

PHYSICS

Atoms bond to each other by the action of electromagnetic forces.

CHEMISTRY

Inert gas elements, including helium and neon, have completely filled electron shells and thus rarely take part in chemical reactions.

BIOLOGY

Living cells break down the chemical bonds in energy-rich molecules such as glucose (a sugar) into water, carbon dioxide, and energy. (Ch. 21)

GREAT IDEA

Atoms bind together in chemical reactions by the rearrangement of electrons.

TECHNOLOGY

Many modern high-strength glues, including epoxy resins and superglue, are liquids that undergo polymerization reactions to produce a solid.

ENVIRONMENT

The national recycling effort involves hundreds of different processes, each one designed for the chemical bonds in specific materials. (Ch. 19)

ASTRONOMY

The predominant state of matter in the Sun and other stars is plasma.

HEALTH & SAFETY

Many types of fire extinguishers blanket flames with a chemical that robs the fire of oxygen, and thus stops the violent flaming reaction.

GEOLOGY

The ionic bonding of most common minerals makes rocks hard and brittle.

 = applications of the great idea discussed in this chapter

 = other applications, some of which are discussed in other chapters

Throwing Things Away

On your way to pick the perfect spot on the beach, you and your friends divide up a heavy load of food and drinks. Your backpack is full, so you decide to discard a couple of old empty soft drink bottles, plastic wrappers, and an old newspaper to make more room. You walk over to the beach house where there are separate receptacles for glass, plastic, paper, and other trash. It seems like a lot of extra work to sort out trash at the beach. Is it really worth the bother? But you dutifully follow the instructions, separate the different materials, and are soon on your way.

Dunstone Images/Alamy Limited

◎ 10.1 Our Material World

Think about all the things you've thrown away during the past month. Every day you toss out aluminum cans, plastic wrappers, glass jars, food scraps, and lots of paper. From time to time you also discard used batteries, disposable razors, dirty motor oil, worn-out shoes and clothes, even old tires, broken furniture, and obsolete electronics. What happens to all that stuff after it becomes trash?

Many communities try to recycle much of their waste. Plastic, glass, aluminum, and newspaper, for example, can be reprocessed and turned into new products and packaging. Old oil can be refined, but most trash ends up in landfills, where, we hope, it will eventually break down into soil.

The situation that faces our society is more than a little ironic. Everything you use and then throw away is made from collections of atoms bonded together. While they are in the store and for as long as we use them, we want these products and their packaging to last and keep looking new. But as soon as we throw them out, we'd like our disposable materials to fall apart and disappear. One way to achieve this end is to engineer biodegradable materials—paper, plastics, fabrics, and other goods designed to break apart when thrown away.

But what holds materials together in the first place? Why do certain atoms, when brought close together, develop an affinity and stick to each other? How do the molecules that play such an important role in our lives retain their identity? And how can we design new materials that will fall apart when their useful lives are over? The answers lie in the nature of the chemical bond.

● 10.2 Electron Shells and Chemical Bonds

The last two chapters have focused on the structure and behavior of individual atoms, but the materials we depend on in day-to-day life are made from combinations of many atoms. The process by which two or more atoms combine is called *chemical bonding*, and the linkage between two atoms is called a **chemical bond**.

Think about how two atoms might interact. You know that the atom is mostly empty space, with a tiny, dense nucleus surrounded by negatively charged electrons. If two atoms approach each other, their outer electrons encounter each other first. Whatever holds two atoms together thus involves primarily those outer electrons. In fact, the outer electrons play such an important role in determining how atoms combine that they are given the special name of *valence electrons* (see Chapter 8). Chemical bonding often involves an exchange or sharing of valence electrons, and the number of electrons in an atom's outermost shell is called its *valence*. Chemists often express the importance of the number of outer electrons by saying that valence represents the combining power of a given atom.

The top three rows of the periodic table of the elements provide the key to understanding the varied strategies of chemical bonding (Figure 10-1). Different electron shells hold different numbers of electrons, which gives rise to the distinctive structure of the periodic table (see Figure 8-4). It turns out that by far the most stable arrangement of electrons—the electron configuration of lowest energy—has completely filled electron shells. A glance at the periodic table tells us that atoms with a total of 2, 10, 18, or 36 electrons (all the atoms that appear in the table's extreme right-hand column) have filled shells and very stable configurations. Atoms with this many total electrons are *inert gases* (also called *noble gases*), which do not combine readily with other materials. Indeed, helium, neon, and argon, with atomic numbers 2, 10, and 18, respectively, have completely filled outer electron shells, and are thus the only common elements that do not ordinarily react with other elements.

Every object in nature tries to reach a state of lowest energy, and atoms are no exception. Atoms that do not have the magic number of electrons (2, 10, 18, etc.) are more likely to react with other atoms to produce a state of lower energy. You are familiar with this kind of process in many other natural systems. If you put a ball on top of a hill, for example, it will tend to roll down to the bottom, creating a system of lower gravitational potential energy. Similarly, a compass needle tends to align itself spontaneously with Earth's magnetic field, thereby lowering its magnetic potential energy. In exactly the same way, when two or more atoms come together the electrons tend to rearrange themselves to minimize the chemical potential energy of the entire system. This situation may require that they exchange or share electrons. Usually, that process involves rearrangements with a total of 2, 10, 18, or 36 electrons.

Chemical bonds result from any redistribution of electrons that leads to a more stable configuration between two or more atoms—especially configurations with a filled electron shell.

FIGURE 10-1 The first three rows of the periodic table, containing elements 1 and 2, 3 through 10, and 11 through 18, respectively, hold the key to understanding chemical bonding.

1 H 1.00794							2 He 4.00260
3 Li 6.941	4 Be 9.01218	5 B 10.811	6 C 12.011	7 N 14.00674	8 O 15.9994	9 F 18.99840	10 Ne 20.1797
11 Na 22.98977	12 Mg 24.3050	13 Al 26.98154	14 Si 28.0855	15 P 30.97376	16 S 32.066	17 Cl 35.4527	18 Ar 39.948

● **Most atoms adopt one of three simple strategies to achieve a filled shell: they give away electrons, accept electrons, or share electrons.**

If the bond formation takes place spontaneously, without outside intervention, energy will be released in the reaction. The burning of wood or paper (once their temperature has been raised high enough) is a good example of this sort of process, and the heat you feel when you put your hands toward a fire derives ultimately from the chemical potential energy that is given off as electrons and atoms are reshuffled. Alternatively, atoms may be pushed into new configurations by adding energy to systems. Much of industrial chemistry, from the smelting of iron to the synthesis of plastics, operates on this principle.

◎ 10.3 Types of Chemical Bonds

Atoms link together by three principal kinds of chemical bonds—ionic, metallic, and covalent—all of which involve redistributing electrons between atoms. In addition, polarization, hydrogen bonding, and van der Waals forces result from shifts of electrons within their atoms or groups of atoms. Each type of bonding corresponds to a different way of rearranging electrons, and each produces distinctive properties in the materials it forms.

Ionic Bonds

We've seen that atoms with the "magic numbers" of 2, 10, 18, or 36 electrons are particularly stable. By the same token, atoms that differ from these magic numbers by only one or two electrons in their outer orbits are particularly reactive—in effect, they are "anxious" to fill or empty their outer orbits. Such atoms tend to form **ionic bonds**, chemical bonds in which the electrical force between two oppositely charged ions holds the atoms together.

Ionic bonds often form as one atom gives up an electron while another receives it. Sodium (a soft, silvery white metal), for example, has 11 electrons in an electrically neutral atom—2 in the lowest orbit, 8 in the next, and a single electron with lots of chemical potential energy in its outer shell. Sodium's best bonding strategy, therefore, is to lose one electron. The seventeenth element, chlorine (a yellow-green toxic gas), on the other hand, is one electron shy of a filled shell. Highly corrosive chlorine gas will react with almost anything that can give it an extra electron (Figure 10-2). When you place sodium in contact with chlorine gas, the result is predictable: in a fiery reaction, each sodium atom donates its extra electron to a chlorine atom.

In the process of this vigorous electron exchange, atoms of sodium and chlorine become electrically charged—they become ions. Neutral sodium has 11 positive protons in its nucleus, balanced by 11 negative electrons in orbit. By losing one electron, sodium becomes an ion with 11 protons but only 10 electrons (a magic number). The resulting sodium ion has one unit of positive charge, shown as Na^+ in Figure 10-2. Similarly, neutral chlorine has 17 protons and 17 electrons. The addition of an extra negative electron creates a chloride ion with 17 protons and 18 electrons (also a magic number). The resulting chlorine ion has one unit of negative charge, shown as Cl^- in the figure. The mutual electrical attraction of positive sodium and negative chloride ions is what forms the ionic bonds between sodium and chlorine. The resulting compound, sodium chloride or common table salt, has properties totally different from either sodium or chlorine.

Under normal circumstances, sodium and chlorine ions will lock together into a crystal, a regular arrangement of atoms such as the one shown in Figure 10-3. Alternating sodium and chloride ions form an elegant repeating structure in which each Na^+ is surrounded by six Cl^-, and vice versa.

Ionic bonds may involve more than a single electron transfer. The twelfth element, magnesium, for example, donates two electrons to oxygen, which has eight electrons. In the resulting compound, MgO (magnesium oxide), both atoms have stable filled shells of 10 electrons, and the ions, Mg^{2+} and O^{2-}, form a strong ionic bond. Ionic bonds involving the negative oxygen ion O^{2-} and positive ions, such as aluminum (Al^{3+}), magnesium (Mg^{2+}), silicon (Si^{4+}), and iron (Fe^{2+} or Fe^{3+}), are found in many everyday objects: in most rocks and minerals, in china and glass, and in bones and eggshells.

Compounds with ionic bonds are often very strong along the direction of the bonds, but they can break easily if the bonds are twisted or bent. As a consequence, ionic-bonded materials such as rock, glass, or eggshells are usually quite brittle. These materials are strong in the

FIGURE 10-2 Sodium, a highly reactive element, readily transfers its single valence electron to chlorine, which is one electron shy of the "magic" number 18. The result is the ionic compound sodium chloride—ordinary table salt. In these diagrams, electrons are represented as dots in shells around a nucleus.

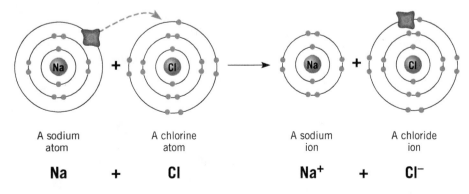

| A sodium atom | A chlorine atom | A sodium ion | A chloride ion |
| Na | + | Cl | Na$^+$ | + | Cl$^-$ |

Sodium ion (Na⁺)

Chloride ion (Cl⁻)

(a)

(b)

FIGURE 10-3 *(a)* The atomic structure of a sodium chloride crystal consists of a regular pattern of alternating sodium and chloride ions. *(b)* This pattern is reflected in the tiny cube-shaped crystals of table salt (magnified 25 times).

EXAMPLE 10-1

IONIC BONDING OF THREE ATOMS

Magnesium chloride, which plays an important role in some batteries, is an ionic-bonded compound with one part magnesium to two parts chlorine ($MgCl_2$). How are the electrons arranged in this compound?

Reasoning: From the periodic table (see Figure 10-1), magnesium and chlorine are elements 12 and 17, respectively. Magnesium, therefore, has 10 electrons $(2 + 8)$ in inner shells and 2 valence electrons. Chlorine has 10 electrons $(2 + 8)$ in its inner shells and 7 electrons in the outer one, meaning that it is 1 electron short of a filled outer shell (Figure 10-4).

Solution: Magnesium has two electrons to give, and chlorine seeks one electron, to achieve stable filled outer orbits. Thus magnesium gives one electron to each of two chlorine atoms, and the resulting Mg^{2+} ion attracts two Cl^- ions to form $MgCl_2$.

FIGURE 10-4 *(a)* Magnesium and chlorine neutral-atom electron configurations (left), and their configurations after electrons have been transferred from the magnesium to the chlorine atoms (right). *(b)* Magnesium chloride, which forms a white powder, is used in the chemical industry.

A magnesium atom	Two chlorine atoms	A magnesium ion	Two chloride ions
Mg	**+** **2 Cl**	**Mg²⁺**	**2Cl⁻**

(a)

Andrew Lambert Photography/Photo Researchers, Inc.

(b)

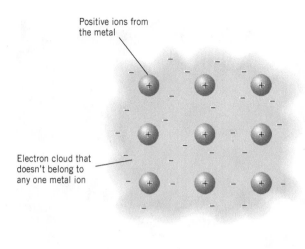

Positive ions from the metal

Electron cloud that doesn't belong to any one metal ion

(a)

Charles D. Winters/Photo Researchers, Inc.

(b)

FIGURE 10-5 *(a)* Metallic bonding occurs when a bond is created by the sharing of electrons among several metal atoms. For example, sodium atoms have 11 electrons, but 10 electrons (a magic number) is much more stable. Therefore, each sodium atom in sodium metal gives up one electron to its surroundings. *(b)* Sodium metal is so soft that it can be cut with a knife, and so reactive that protective gloves must be worn to avoid chemical burns.

sense that you can pile lots of weight on them. But once they shatter and ionic bonds are broken, they can't be put back together again.

Metallic Bonds

Atoms in an ionic bond transfer electrons directly—electrons are on "permanent loan" from one atom to another. Atoms in a metal also give up electrons, but they use a very different bonding strategy. In a **metallic bond**, electrons are redistributed so that they are shared by many atoms.

Sodium metal, for example, is made up entirely of individual sodium atoms. All of these atoms begin with 11 electrons, but they release one to achieve the more stable 10-electron configuration. The extra electrons move away from their parent atoms to float around the metal, forming a kind of sea of negative charge. In this negative electron sea, the positive sodium ions adopt a regular crystal structure, as shown in Figure 10-5.

You can think of the metallic bond as one in which each atom shares its outer electron with all the other atoms in the system. Picture the free electrons as a kind of loose glue in which the metal atoms are placed. In fact, the idea of a metal as being a collection of marbles (the ions) in a sea of stiff, glue-like liquid provides a useful analogy.

Metals, characterized by their shiny luster and ability to conduct electricity, are formed by almost any element or combination of elements in which large numbers of atoms share electrons to achieve a more stable electron arrangement. Some metals, such as aluminum, iron, copper, and gold, are familiar from everyday experience. But many elements can form into a metallic state when the conditions are right, including some that we normally think of as gases, such as hydrogen or oxygen at very high pressure. The great majority of chemical elements are known to occur in the metallic state. In addition, two or more elements can combine to form a metal *alloy*, such as brass (a mixture of copper and zinc) or bronze (an alloy of copper and tin). Modern specialty-steel alloys often contain more than half a dozen different elements in carefully controlled proportions.

The special nature of the metallic bond explains many of the distinctive properties we observe in metals. If you attempt to deform a metal by pushing on the marble-and-glue bonding system, atoms will gradually rearrange themselves and come to some new configuration—the metal is malleable. It's hard to break a metallic bond just by pushing or twisting, because the atoms are able to rearrange themselves. Thus when you hammer on a piece of metal, you often

(a)   *(b)*

FIGURE 10-6 Metals can be molded or hammered into different shapes. *(a)* A construction worker hammers the metal sheeting into position. *(b)* A craftsman hammers sheet metal into a bowl.

FIGURE 10-7 Two hydrogen atoms become an H_2 molecule by sharing each of their electrons in a covalent bond. *(a)* This bonding may be represented schematically in a dot diagram or *(b)* by the merging of two atoms with their electron clouds.

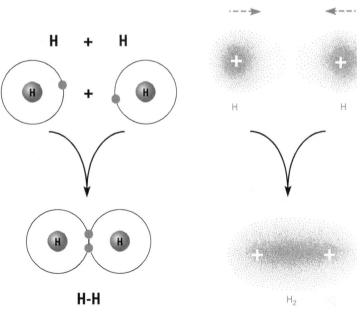

(a)   *(b)*

leave indentations but do not usually break it (Figure 10-6), in sharp contrast to what happens when you hammer on a ceramic plate.

In Chapter 11, we'll examine more closely the electrical properties of materials held together by the metallic bond. We'll see that this particular kind of bond produces materials through which electrons—electrical current—can flow.

Covalent Bonds

In the ionic bond, on one hand, one atom donates electrons to another in a more or less permanent loan. In the metallic bond, on the other hand, atoms share some electrons throughout the material. A third extremely important bonding strategy is the **covalent bond**, in which well-defined clusters of neighboring atoms, called *molecules,* share electrons. These strongly bonded groups may consist of anywhere from two to many millions of atoms.

The simplest covalently bonded molecules contain two atoms of the same element, such as the diatomic gases hydrogen (H_2), nitrogen (N^2), and oxygen (O_2). In the case of hydrogen, for example, each atom has a relatively unstable single electron. Two hydrogen atoms can pool their electrons, however, to create a more stable two-electron arrangement. The two hydrogen atoms must remain close to each other for this sharing to continue, so a chemical bond is formed, as shown in Figure 10-7. Similarly, two oxygen atoms, each with eight electrons, share two pairs of electrons.

(a)

(b)   *(c)*   *(d)*

FIGURE 10-8 Carbon-based molecules may adopt almost any shape. The molecules may consist of *(a)* long, straight chains of carbon atoms that form fibrous materials such as *(b)* nylon or they may incorporate complex rings and branching arrangements that form lumpy molecules such as hexabenzocoronene *(c)*, which is a component of soot *(d)*.

Hydrogen, oxygen, nitrogen, and other covalently bonded molecules have lower chemical potential energy than isolated atoms because electrons are shared. These molecules are less likely to react chemically than the isolated atoms.

The most fascinating of all covalently bonded elements is carbon, which forms the backbone of all life's essential molecules. Carbon, with two electrons in its inner shell and four in its outer shell, presents a case of a half-filled shell. When carbon atoms approach each other, therefore, a real question arises as to whether they ought to accept or donate four electrons to achieve a more stable arrangement. You could imagine, for example, a situation where some carbon atoms give four electrons to their neighbors, while other carbon atoms accept four electrons, to create a compound with strong ionic bonds between C^{4+} and C^{4-}. Alternatively, carbon might become a metal in which every atom releases four electrons into an extremely dense electron sea. But neither of these things happens.

The strategy that lowers the energy of the carbon–carbon system the most is for the carbon atoms to share their outer electrons with other nearby atoms. Once bonds between carbon atoms have formed, the atoms have to stay close to each other for this sharing to continue. Thus the bonds generated are just like the bond in the case of hydrogen. The case of carbon is unusual, however, because a single carbon atom can form covalent bonds with up to four other atoms by sharing one of its four valence electrons with each. A *single bond* (shown as C–C) forms when one electron from each atom is shared, while a *double bond* (shown as C=C) results when two electrons from each atom are shared between one another. By forming bonds among several adjacent carbon atoms, you can make rings, long chains, branching structures, planes, and three-dimensional frameworks of carbon in almost any imaginable shape. There is virtually no limit to the complexity of molecules you can build from such carbon–carbon bonding (Figure 10-8). So important is the study of carbon-based molecules that chemists have given it a special name: *organic chemistry*. In fact, all the molecules in your body and in every

FIGURE 10-9 Each water molecule is formed from two hydrogen atoms and one oxygen atom (H_2O), arranged at a 105° angle. Electrons tend to spend more time on the oxygen side of this polar molecule, which becomes more negatively charged, while the hydrogen side becomes more positively charged.

other living thing are held together at least in part by covalent bonds in carbon chains (see Chapter 22). Covalent bonds also drive much of the chemistry in the cells of your body and play a role in holding together the DNA molecules that carry your genetic code. It would not be too much of an exaggeration to say that the covalent bond is the bond of life. Covalent bonds also play a critical role in the silicon-based integrated circuits that run your computer. The element silicon, like carbon, has four electrons in its outer shell.

STOP & THINK Life on Earth is based on the properties of the element carbon. Looking at the first three rows of the periodic table in Figure 10-1, are there any other candidate elements that might form the basis of life elsewhere?

Polarization and Hydrogen Bonds

Ionic, metallic, and covalent bonds form strong links between individual atoms, but molecules also experience forces that hold one to another. In many molecules, the electrical forces are such that, although the molecule by itself is electrically neutral, one part of the molecule has more positive or negative charge than another. In water, for example, the electrons tend to spend more time around the oxygen atoms than around the hydrogen atoms. This uneven electron distribution has the effect of making the oxygen side of the water molecule more negatively charged, and the two "Mickey Mouse ears" of the hydrogen atom more positively charged (Figure 10-9). Atom clusters of this type, with a positive and negative end, are called *polar molecules.*

The electrons of an atom or molecule brought near a polar molecule such as water will tend to be pushed away from the negative side and shifted toward the positive side. Consequently, the side of an atom facing the negative end of a polar molecule will become slightly positive. This subtle electron shift, called *polarization,* in turn will give rise to an electrical attraction between the negative end of the polar molecule and the positive side of the other molecule. The electron movement thus creates an attraction between the atom and the molecule, even though all the atoms and molecules in this scheme may be electrically neutral. One of the most important consequences of forces due to polarization is the ability of water to dissolve many materials. Water, made up of strongly polar molecules, exerts forces that make it easier for ions such as Na^+ and Cl^- to dissolve.

A process related to the forces of polarization leads to the **hydrogen bond**, a weak bond that may form after a hydrogen atom links to an atom of certain other elements (oxygen or nitrogen, for example) by a covalent bond. Because of the kind of rearrangement of electrical charge described above, a hydrogen atom may become polarized and develop a slight positive charge, which attracts another atom to it. You can think of the hydrogen atom as a kind of bridge in this situation, causing a redistribution of electrons that, in turn, brings larger atoms or molecules together. Individual hydrogen bonds are weak, but in many molecules they occur repeatedly and therefore play a major role in determining the molecule's shape and function. Note that while all hydrogen bonds require hydrogen atoms, not all hydrogen atoms are involved in hydrogen bonds.

Hydrogen bonds are common in biological substances, ranging from everyday materials such as wood and silk, to the complex structures of every cell in your body. As we shall see in Chapter 23, hydrogen bonds in every living thing link the two sides of the DNA double helix together, although the sides themselves are held together by covalent bonds. Ordinary egg white is made from molecules whose shape is determined by hydrogen bonds, and when you heat the material—when you fry an egg, for example—hydrogen bonds are disrupted and the molecules rearrange themselves so that instead of a clear liquid you have a white gelatinous solid.

Van der Waals Forces

The hydrogen bond exists because atoms or molecules can be polarized as their electrons shift to one side or another and thus create local electrical charges that are more or less permanently

(a)

(b)

FIGURE 10-10 Graphite, a form of carbon found in the "lead" in your pencil, contains layers of carbon atoms strongly linked to each other by covalent bonds (represented by solid lines). These layers are held to each other by much weaker van der Waals bonds (represented by dashed lines).

locked into a fixed or static arrangement. Another force between molecules, called the *van der Waals force*, results from the polarization of electrically neutral atoms or molecules that are not themselves polar. (The force is named after the Dutch physicist Johannes van der Waals [1837-1923], the recipient of the 1910 Nobel Prize in physics).

When two atoms or molecules are brought near each other, every part of one atom or molecule feels an electrical force exerted on it by all parts of the other. For example, an electron in one atom will be repelled by the electrons, but attracted to the nucleus, of an adjacent atom. The net result of these forces exerted on the electron may be a temporary shift of the electron. The same thing happens to every electron in any nearby atom or molecule, and the net result is that every electron is shifted because of the presence of other electrical charges in the neighboring atoms. When we balance the attractive and repulsive forces between the distorted atoms, the result can be a net attractive force. In these so-called van der Waals compounds, even if all the molecules are neutral and nonpolar, the sum of attractive forces wins out over repulsive forces and weak bonds are formed.

If you take a piece of clay and rub it between your fingers, your fingers pick up a slick coating of the material, even though the clay crumbles easily. The stain occurs because the clay is made up of sheets of atoms. Within each sheet, atoms hold together by strong ionic and covalent bonds. One sheet is held to another, however, by comparatively weak van der Waals forces. The clay stains on your hands are thin sheets of atoms held together by ionic and covalent bonds, while the crumbling you feel is the breaking of the van der Waals bonds. This situation is not unlike the way a stack of photocopying paper will stick together on a dry day. Each sheet of paper is strong, but the stack of paper sticks together by much weaker electrostatic forces.

Many other examples of van der Waals forces can be seen in everyday life. If you rub talcum powder on your body, for example, you use a layered material not unlike the clay just discussed. Similarly, when you write with a "lead" pencil, you break off van der Waals-bonded layers of graphite (a form of carbon; see Figure 10-10) and leave behind dark graphite sheets on the paper. Van der Waals forces also link molecules in many everyday liquids and soft solids, from candle wax to Vaseline and other petroleum products.

◉ 10.4 States of Matter

So far, we've been looking at the ways in which the limited number of chemical elements in the periodic table can be linked together by a few different types of chemical bonds or attractive

(a) Gas, molecules widely spaced apart

(d) Solid, molecules stay rigidly in place

(c) Liquid, molecules slide past one another

(b)

SOHO (ESA & NASA)

FIGURE 10-11 The different states of matter are distinguished by the arrangements of their atoms (clockwise). *(a)* In a gas, atoms or molecules are not bonded to each other, so they expand to fill any available volume. *(b)* A plasma is like a gas but at a much higher temperature, so electrons are stripped off the atoms. *(c)* In a liquid molecules are bound to each other but they are free to move relative to each other, yielding a material that can change shape but holds its volume. *(d)* In a solid atoms are locked into a rigid pattern that retains its shape and volume.

forces. The everyday materials that we use, however, typically incorporate trillions upon trillions of atoms. Countless linkages among vast numbers of atoms collectively produce the remarkable variety of materials in our world. Depending on how these groups of atoms are organized, they may take on many different forms. These different modes of organization, called the **states of matter**, include gases, plasmas, liquids, and solids (Figure 10-11).

Gases

A **gas** is any collection of atoms or molecules that expands to take the shape of and fill the volume available in its container (Figure 10-11a). Most common gases, including those that form our atmosphere, are invisible, but the force of a gust of wind is proof that matter is involved. The individual particles that make up a gas may be isolated atoms such as helium or neon, or small molecules such as nitrogen (N_2) or carbon dioxide (CO_2). If we could magnify an ordinary gas a billion times, we would see these particles randomly flying about, bouncing off each other and anything else they contact. The gas pressure that inflates a basketball or tire is a consequence of these countless collisions.

Plasma

At extreme temperatures like those of the Sun (Figure 10-11b), high-energy collisions between atoms may strip off electrons, creating a **plasma** in which positive nuclei move about in a sea of electrons. Such a collection of electrically charged objects is something like a gas, but it displays unusual properties not seen in other states of matter. Plasmas, for example, are efficient conductors of electricity and, because they are gas-like, can be confined in a strong magnetic field or "magnetic bottle."

Plasmas are the least familiar state of matter to us, yet more than 99.9% of all the visible mass in the universe exists in this form. Not only are most stars composed of a dense hydrogen- and helium-rich plasma mixture, but several planets, including Earth, have regions of thin plasma in their outer atmospheres. Some gradations exist between gas and plasma. Partially ionized gases in neon lights or fluorescent lightbulbs, for example, have a small fraction of their electrons in a free state. While not a complete plasma, these ionized gases do conduct electricity.

Liquids

Any collection of atoms or molecules that has no fixed shape but maintains its volume is called a **liquid** (Figure 10-11c). Other than water and biological fluids, few liquids occur naturally on Earth. Water, by far the most abundant liquid on Earth's surface, is a dynamic force for geological change (see Chapter 18), and water-based solutions are essential to all life.

At the molecular level, liquids behave something like a container full of sand grains. The grains fill whatever volume they are poured into, freely flowing over each other without ever taking on a fixed shape. Attractive forces between individual atoms or molecules hold the liquid together. At the surface of the liquid, these attractive forces act to prevent atoms or molecules from escaping. In effect, they pull the surface in, giving rise to *surface tension*, the property that causes small quantities of the liquid to form beads or droplets.

Solids

Solids include all materials that possess a more or less fixed shape and volume (Figure 10-11d). In all solid materials the chemical bonds are both strong and directional. In detail, however, solids adopt several quite different kinds of atomic structures.

FIGURE 10-12 (a) The arrangement of atoms in a crystal is regular and predictable over distances of thousands of atoms, a fact reflected in the faceted surfaces that result from the regular repetition of atoms, for example, in (b) this crystal of the mineral quartz, SiO_2. (c) The arrangement of atoms in a glass is regular on a local scale but irregular over a distance of three or four atoms. (d) The curved fracture surfaces of the natural glass obsidian are a consequence of this atomic-scale irregularity.

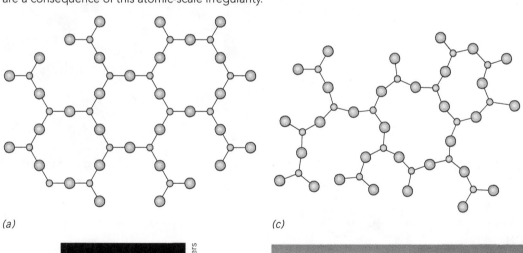

Key:
○ Silicon atom
◯ Oxygen atom

(a)

(c)

(b)

(d)

In **crystals**, groups of atoms occur in a regularly repeating sequence, the same atom or atoms appearing over and over again in a predictable way (Figure 10-12a). A crystal structure can be described by first determining the size and shape of the tiny box-like unit that repeats, then recording the exact type and position of every atom that appears in the box. In common salt (see Figure 10-3), for example, the box is a tiny cube less than a billionth of a meter on an edge. Each box contains chlorine atoms at the cube's corners and face centers, and sodium atoms at the cube's center and at the midpoint of each cube edge. The regular atomic structure of crystals often leads to large single crystals with beautiful flat faces (Figure 10-12b).

Common crystals include grains of sand and salt, computer chips, and gemstones. Most crystalline solids, however, are composed of numerous interlocking crystal grains. The two most important groups of these types of materials in our everyday life are metals and alloys that are characterized by metallic bonds, and most *ceramics,* a broad class of hard, durable solids that includes bricks, concrete, pottery, porcelain, and numerous synthetic abrasives, as well as teeth and bones and most rocks and minerals.

STOP & THINK Crystals, with regular arrangements of atoms, are usually denser than their less-orderly liquid state, yet ice floats on water (a rare instance of the liquid being denser than the crystal). Why might that be? How might life on Earth be affected if ice sank in water?

HINT: What might happen to a shallow lake during a cold winter if ice were denser than liquid water?

FIGURE 10-13 Polymers come in many forms. *(a)* Unbranched polymers form long fibers like nylon *(b)*. By contrast, *(c)* branching polymers can form sturdy solid plastics like the wheels on roller blades *(d)*.

An unbranched polymeric chain

$CH_3 - CH_2 - CH_2 - CH_2 - CH_2 - CH_2 - CH_2 - CH_2 - CH_2 - CH_2 - CH_2 - CH_3$

(a)

A branched polymeric chain

(c)

(b)

(d)

TABLE 10-1 Recycling Plastic

No.	Name	Principal Uses
1	PET	The most common recycled plastic, used for food and beverage containers
2	HDPE	Rigid, narrow-neck containers for detergent and milk; grocery bags
3	PVC	Plastic pipe, outdoor furniture, sturdy containers
4	LDPE	Trash and produce bags, food storage containers
5	PP	Aerosol caps, drinking straws
6	PS	Packing peanuts, cups, and plastic tableware

Glasses, in contrast to crystals, are solids with predictable local environments for most atoms, but no long-range order to the atomic structure (Figure 10-12c). In most common window and bottle glasses, for example, silicon and oxygen atoms form a strong three-dimensional framework. Most silicon atoms are surrounded by four oxygen atoms, and most oxygen atoms are linked to two silicon atoms. If you were placed on any atom in a glass, the chances are good that you could predict the next-door atoms. Nevertheless, glasses have no regularly stacked boxes of structure. Travel more than two or three atom diameters from any starting point, and there is no way that you could predict whether you'd find a silicon atom or an oxygen atom. Consequently, pieces of glass break with sharp, irregular surfaces (Figure 10-12d).

Polymers, which are extremely long and large molecules composed of numerous smaller molecules linked together like a chain, form a variety of important everyday solids. The atomic structure of these materials is often one-dimensional, with predictable repeating sequences of atoms along the polymer chain (Figure 10-13). Common solid polymers include numerous biological materials, such as animal hair, plant cellulose, cotton fibers, and spider's webs.

Polymers include all **plastics**, which are synthetic materials formed primarily from petroleum. They consist of intertwined polymer strands, much like the strands of fiberglass insulation. When heated, these strands slide across each other to adopt new shapes. When cooled, the plastic fiber mass solidifies into whatever shape is available. Though almost unknown a century ago, plastics have become our most versatile commercial materials, providing an extraordinary range of uses: films for lightweight packaging, dense castings for durable machine parts, thin strong fibers for clothing (Figure 10-13a), colorful moldings for toys, and many others. Plastics serve as paints, inks, glues, sealants, foam products, and insulation. New tough, resilient plastics have revolutionized many sports with products such as high-quality bowling and golf balls, and durable football and ice hockey helmets, not to mention a host of completely new products from Frisbees to roller blades.

You've probably noticed the small triangular recycling symbol with a number inside on plastic containers. The numbers refer to common types of plastics, which are separated before reprocessing. Table 10.1 lists the most common plastic varieties and their uses.

SCIENCE IN THE MAKING
The Discovery of Nylon

Nature's success in making strong, flexible fibers inspired scientists to try the same thing. American chemist Wallace Carothers (1896–1937) began thinking about polymer formation while a graduate student in the 1920s. At the time, no one was sure how natural fibers formed, or what kinds of chemical bonds were involved. Carothers wanted to find out.

The chemical company DuPont took a gamble by naming Carothers head of its new "fundamental research" group in 1928. No pressure was placed on him to produce commercial results, but within a few years his team had developed the synthetic rubber neoprene,

FIGURE 10-14 The man-made fiber nylon can be pulled from a liquid.

Charles D. Winters/Photo Researchers, Inc.

and by the mid-1930s they had devised a variety of extraordinary polymers, including nylon, the first human-made fiber (Figure 10-14). Carothers also demonstrated conclusively that polymers in nylon are covalently bonded chains of small molecules, each with six carbon atoms.

DuPont made a fortune from nylon and related synthetic fibers. Nylon was inexpensive to manufacture and had many advantages over natural fibers. It could be melted and squeezed out of spinnerets to form strands of almost any desired size: threads, rope, surgical sutures, tennis racket strings, and paintbrush bristles, for example. These fibers could be made smooth and straight like fishing line, or rough and wrinkled like wool, to vary the texture of fabrics. Nylon fibers could also be kinked with heat, to provide permanent folds and pleats in clothing. The melted polymer could even be injected into molds to form durable parts such as tubing or zipper teeth.

Sadly, Wallace Carothers did not live to see the impact of his extraordinary discoveries. Suffering from increasingly severe bouts of depression, saddened by the death of his sister, and convinced that he was a failure as a scientist, Carothers took his own life in 1937, just a year before the commercial introduction of nylon.

TECHNOLOGY
Liquid Crystals and Your Hand Calculator

Almost every material on Earth is easily classified as a solid, a liquid, or a gas, but scientists have synthesized an odd intermediate state of matter called *liquid crystals*. These materials have quickly found their way into many kinds of electronic devices, including the digital display of your pocket calculator (Figure 10-15a). The distinction between a liquid and a crystal is one of atomic-scale order: atoms or molecules are disordered in a liquid, and ordered in a crystal. But what happens in the case of a liquid formed from very long or very flat molecules? Like a box of uncooked spaghetti or a plate of pancakes, in which the individual pieces may shift around but are well oriented, these molecules may adopt ordered arrangements even in the liquid form.

If the molecules are polar, they may behave like tiny compass needles. Under ordinary circumstances these molecules will occur in random orientations, as in a normal liquid (Figure 10-15b). Under the influence of an electrical field, however, the molecules may adopt a partially ordered structure in which the molecules line up side by side (Figure 10-15c). This change in structure may even change some of the liquid's physical properties—its color or light-reflecting ability, for example. This phenomenon is now widely used in liquid crystal displays in cell phones, computers, and other electronics in which electrical impulses align molecules in selected regions of the screen to provide a rapidly changing visual display.

FIGURE 10-15 (a) Liquid crystal displays are found in many electronic devices. (b) Under normal circumstances, the elongated polar molecules of a liquid crystal display are randomly oriented and the liquid appears transparent, but in an electric field (c) the molecules align in an orderly pattern and the liquid crystal appears darker.

(a)

Random pattern

(b)

Orderly pattern

(c)

(a)

(b)

Paul Souders/©Corbis-Bettmann

Teiji Saga/Photo Researchers, Inc.

FIGURE 10-16 Water displays changes of state. *(a)* Melting water streams from the Jakobshaven Glacier near Ilulissat, Greenland. *(b)* Water condenses from the atmosphere as fog above a cool pond.

Are liquid crystals also found in nature? Every cell membrane is composed of a double layer of elongated molecules, called *lipids* (see Chapter 22). Many scientists now suspect that these "lipid bilayers" originated in the primitive ocean as molecules similar to today's liquid crystals.

Changes of State

Place a tray of liquid water in the freezer and it will turn to solid ice. Heat a pot of water on the stove and it will boil away to a gas. These everyday phenomena are examples of **changes of state**, which are transitions among the solid, liquid, and gas states. *Freezing* and *melting* involve changes between liquids and solids (Figure 10-16a), while *boiling* and *condensation* are changes between liquids and gases (Figure 10-16b). In addition, some solids may transform directly to the gaseous state by *sublimation*.

Temperature induces these transitions by changing the speed at which molecules vibrate. An increase in the temperature of ice to above 0°C (32°F), for example, causes molecular vibrations to increase to the point that individual molecules jiggle loose and the crystal structure starts to break apart. Liquid water forms. Then, above 100°C (212°F), individual water molecules move fast enough to break free of the liquid surface and form water vapor—a gas. These changes require a great deal of energy, because many chemical attractions must be broken to change from a solid to a liquid, or from a liquid to a gas. Thus a pot of water may reach boiling temperature fairly quickly, but it takes a long time to break all the attractions between water molecules and boil the water away. By the same token, a glass of ice water will remain at 0°C for a long time, even on a warm day, until enough energy has been absorbed to break all the ice attractions. Only after the last bit of ice is gone can the water temperature begin to rise.

FIGURE 10-17 On May 6, 1937, the hydrogen-filled German airship *Hindenburg* burst into flame. The rapid reaction of hydrogen plus oxygen produced water and heat.

● 10.5 Chemical Reactions and the Formation of Chemical Bonds

Our world is filled with countless materials—solids, liquids and gases of every description. Where do all these different materials come from? How do new chemical bonds form?

Popperfoto/Getty Images, Inc.

Atoms, as well as smaller molecules, come together to form larger molecules, and larger molecules break up, in processes that we call **chemical reactions**. When we take a bite of food, light a match, wash our hands, or drive a car, we initiate chemical reactions. Earth's chemical reactions include rock formation and rock weathering. Every moment of every day, countless chemical reactions in every cell of our bodies sustain life.

All chemical reactions involve rearrangement of the atoms in elements and compounds, as well as rearrangement of electrons to form chemical bonds. Such reactions can be expressed as a simple equation:

$$\text{reactants} \rightarrow \text{products}$$

All such reactions must balance, so that the total number and kinds of atoms are the same on both sides. For example, oxygen and hydrogen gases can form liquid water by the reaction:

$$2H_2 + O_2 \rightarrow 2H_2O$$

This reaction is balanced because each side has four hydrogen atoms and two oxygen atoms. In the process of this reaction we can observe both chemical changes (the rearrangement of atoms) and physical changes (the gases hydrogen and oxygen transform into liquid water with different properties). The reaction of hydrogen and oxygen to form water is explosively violent. The fiery explosion of the hydrogen-filled airship *Hindenburg* was a dramatic illustration of this chemical reaction (Figure 10-17).

EXAMPLE 10-2

BALANCING CHEMICAL EQUATIONS

Your car battery contains plates of lead (Pb) and lead dioxide (PbO_2) immersed in a solution of sulfuric acid (H_2SO_4). After the battery has been discharged, the lead, the lead dioxide, and sulfuric acid have been converted into lead sulfate ($PbSO_4$) and water (H_2O). Write a balanced reaction that models this process.

Reasoning and Solution: The reactants in this process are Pb, PbO_2 and H_2SO_4, while the products are $PbSO_4$ and H_2O. First write the equation in the simplest form, with one of each reactant and product molecule:

$$Pb + PbO_2 + H_2SO_4 \rightarrow PbSO_4 + H_2O$$

This equation, however, is not balanced. Two lead atoms appear on the left side, for example, whereas only one lead atom is on the right. The only way to make sure that there are as many atoms at the end as at the beginning is to write:

$$Pb + PbO_2 + 2H_2SO_4 \rightarrow 2PbSO_4 + 2H_2O$$

As you can see, on each side of the equation there are now two atoms of lead, two SO_4 groups, four hydrogen atoms, and two oxygen atoms. This balanced equation represents the reshuffling of atoms that goes on when your battery discharges. It tells us that two molecules of sulfuric acid will be used for each atom of lead and that two molecules of water and two of lead sulfate will be produced at the end.

Every chemical reaction, no matter how complex, must balance: you must end with the same number of atoms with which you began. This is an example of the principle (see Chapter 7) that matter cannot be created nor destroyed—a principle that was eventually modified by the theory of relativity.

Chemical Reactions and Energy: Rolling Down the Chemical Hill

Before considering the ways that atoms can combine to form molecules, pause for a moment to think about why these reactions take place at all. The fundamental reason, as so often happens with natural phenomena, has to do with energy, as described by the laws of thermodynamics (see Chapters 3 and 4).

Consider, for example, one of the electrons in the neutral sodium atom shown in Figure 10-2. This electron is moving around the nucleus, so it has kinetic energy. In addition, the electron possesses potential energy because it is a certain distance from the positively charged nucleus. Thus, just by virtue of its position, the electron is capable of doing work (this is the way potential energy was defined in Chapter 3). Finally, the electron has an additional component of potential energy because of the electrical repulsion between it and all of the other electrons in the atom. This is analogous to the small contribution to Earth's gravitational potential energy from the other planets. The sum of these three energies—the kinetic energy associated with orbital motion, the potential energy associated with the nucleus, and the potential energy associated with the other electrons—is the total energy of the single electron in the atom.

The atom's total energy outside the nucleus is the sum of the energies of all of the electrons. For the isolated sodium atom in Figure 10-2, the total energy is the sum of the energy of the 11 electrons; for the chlorine atom, it is the sum of the energies of the 17 electrons. The total energy of the sodium–chlorine system is the sum of the individual energies of the two atoms.

Think about what happens to the energy of the sodium–chlorine system after the ionic bond has formed. The force on each electron is now different than it was before. For one thing, the number of electrons in each atom has changed; for another, the atoms are no longer isolated, so electrons in the sodium can exert forces on electrons in the chlorine and vice versa. Consequently, the orbits of all the electrons will shift a little due to the formation of the bond. This shifting means that each electron will find itself in a slightly different position with regard to the nucleus, will be moving at a slightly different speed, and will experience a slightly different set of forces than it did before. The total energy of each electron will be different after the bond forms, the total energy of each atom will be different, and the total energy of the system will be different.

Whenever two or more atoms come together to form chemical bonds, the total energy of the system will be different after the bonds form than it was before. Two possibilities exist: either the final energy of the two atoms is less than the initial energy, or the final energy is greater than the initial energy.

The reaction that produces sodium chloride from sodium and chlorine is an example of the first kind of reaction, in which the total energy of the electrons in the system is lower after the two atoms have come together (Figure 10-18a). According to the first law of thermodynamics, the total energy must be conserved, and that difference is given off during the reaction in the form of heat, light, and sound (there is an explosion). A chemical reaction that gives off energy in some form is said to be *exothermic*.

Many examples of exothermic reactions occur in everyday life. The energy that moves your car is given off by the explosive chemical combination of gasoline and oxygen in the car's engine. The chemical reactions in the battery that runs your iPhone also produce energy, although in this case some of the energy is in the form of kinetic energy of electrons in a wire. At this moment, cells in your body are breaking down molecules of a sugar known as glucose to supply the energy you need to live (see Chapter 21).

If the final energy of the electrons in a reaction is greater than the initial energy, then you have to supply energy to make the chemical reaction proceed. Such reactions are said to be *endothermic*. The chemical reactions that occur when you cook (poaching an egg, for example, or baking a cake) are of this type (Figure 10-18b). You can put the ingredients of a cake together

(a)   (b)

FIGURE 10-18 Some chemical reactions, such as (a) the formation of table salt from sodium metal and chlorine gas release heat energy— they are exothermic. Other chemical reactions, such as (b) poaching an egg, require heat—they are endothermic.

and let them sit for as long as you like, but nothing will happen until you turn on the oven and supply energy in the form of heat. When the energy is available, electrons can move around and rearrange their chemical bonds. The result: a cake where before there was only a mixture of flour, sugar, and other materials.

As we saw earlier, you can think of chemical reactions as being analogous to a ball lying on the ground. If the ball happens to be at the top of a hill, it will lower its potential energy by rolling down the hill, giving up the excess energy in the form of frictional heat. If the ball is at the bottom of the hill, you have to do work to raise it to the top. In the same way, exothermic reactions correspond to systems that "roll down the hill," going to a state of lower energy and giving off excess energy in some form. Endothermic reactions, on the other hand, have to be "pushed up the hill" and hence absorb energy from their surroundings.

◉ 10.6 Common Chemical Reactions

Many millions of chemical reactions take place in the world around us. Some occur naturally, and some occur as the result of human design or intervention. In your everyday world, however, you are likely to see a few types of chemical reactions over and over again. Let's examine a few of these common reactions in more detail.

Oxidation and Reduction

Perhaps the most distinctive chemical feature of our planet is the abundance of a highly reactive gas, oxygen, in our atmosphere. This trait leads to many of the most familiar chemical reactions in our lives. **Oxidation** includes any chemical reaction in which an atom (such as oxygen or any other atom that will accept electrons) accepts electrons while combining with other elements. The atom that transfers the electrons is said to be *oxidized*. Rusting is a common gradual oxidation reaction in which iron metal combines with oxygen to form a reddish iron oxide, as given by the balanced chemical equation

$$4Fe + 3O_2 \rightarrow 2Fe_2O_3$$

Burning or *combustion* is a much more rapid oxidation, in which oxygen combines with carbon-rich materials to produce carbon dioxide and other byproducts that often pollute. *Hydrocarbons*—chemical compounds of carbon and hydrogen—provide the most efficient fuels for combustion, with only carbon dioxide and water (hydrogen oxide) as products. This reaction is:

In words: Hydrocarbon plus oxygen reacts to form carbon dioxide plus water plus energy.

In chemical notation:

$$C_nH_{2n+2} + \left[\frac{(3n+1)}{2}\right] O_2 \rightarrow nCO_2 + (n+1)H_2O + energy$$

Note that in this rather cumbersome balanced chemical reaction the subscript n indicates the number of carbon atoms in the chain-like hydrocarbon molecule. So, for example, if you heat or cook with natural gas, a hydrocarbon that chemists call *methane* with $n = 1$ (Figure 10-19b), the reaction is written

$$CH_4 + 2O_2 \rightarrow CO_2 + 2H_2O$$

The opposite of oxidation is **reduction**, a chemical reaction in which electrons are transferred to an atom from other elements. The atom that receives the electrons is said to be *reduced*. Thousands of years before scientists discovered oxygen, primitive metalworkers had learned how to reduce metal ores by smelting (Figure 10-20). In the iron-smelting process (typical of the industry carried out at hundreds of North American furnaces 250 years ago), iron makers heated a mixture of ore (iron oxide) and lime (calcium oxide) in an extremely hot charcoal fire.

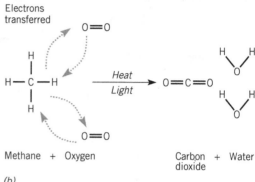

FIGURE 10-19 (a) A forest fire is an oxidation reaction. In pictorial form (b), an oxidation reaction involves the transfer of electrons to oxygen atoms. When natural gas (CH_4) burns, it combines with two oxygen molecules (O_2) to form a molecule of carbon dioxide (CO_2) and two molecules of water (H_2O).

The lime lowered the melting temperature of the entire mixture, which then reacted to produce iron metal and carbon dioxide.

A material that has been oxidized has lost electrons to oxygen or some other atom. A material that has been reduced, on the other hand, has gained electrons. You may find the mnemonic OIL RIG ("oxidation is loss, reduction is gain") useful in keeping the two straight.

FIGURE 10-20 (a) The smelting of iron metal from iron ore is a reduction reaction. (b) In pictorial form, iron ore (an oxide of iron, Fe_2O_3) combines with charcoal (pure carbon) to make iron metal and an oxide of carbon (CO_2).

FIGURE 10-21 The evaporation of salt water leads to the precipitation of large salt flats, such as these deposits at Death Valley National Park in California.

Oxidation and reduction are essential to life, and they define the principal difference between plants and animals. As we shall see in Chapter 21, animals take in carbon-based molecules in their food and allow it to be oxidized in their cells. Carbon dioxide is released as a byproduct. Plants take in carbon dioxide and use the energy in sunlight to reduce it, releasing oxygen as a byproduct.

Precipitation–Solution Reactions

Water and many other liquids have the ability to dissolve solids. You can observe such *solution reactions* when you put salt or sugar into water. You can also watch the opposite process—*precipitation reactions*—occur if you allow ocean water to evaporate. Ocean water contains a rich mixture of elements in solution that precipitate as the water evaporates (Figure 10-21). The complex sequence of precipitation includes calcium carbonate ($CaCO_3$), calcium sulfate ($CaSO_4$), sodium chloride (NaCl), and dozens of other more exotic compounds. In many locations around the world, including the area around Death Valley in California and the Great Salt Lake in Utah, thick deposits of these so-called evaporite chemicals are mined for sodium, potassium, boron, chlorine, and other elements. The next time you're at the ocean, scoop up a handful of salt water and, as the water evaporates, watch as tiny salt crystals precipitate on your palm.

Acid–Base Reactions

Acids are common substances, used by people for thousands of years. The word has even entered our everyday vocabulary; we may refer to someone with an "acid wit" when we mean a sense of humor that is sharp and corrosive. Acids corrode metals and have a sour taste. For our purposes, we can make a technical definition of an acid as follows: An *acid* is any material that, when put into water, produces positively charged hydrogen ions (i.e., protons) in the solution. Lemon juice, orange juice, and vinegar are examples of common weak acids, while sulfuric acid (used in car batteries) and hydrochloric acid (used in industrial cleaning) are strong acids.

Bases are another class of corrosive materials. They taste bitter and generally feel slippery between your fingers. For our purposes, we can define a *base* as any material that, when put into water, produces negatively charged OH^- ions. This ion, consisting of an oxygen atom bound to a hydrogen atom that has an extra electron, is called the hydroxide ion. Most antacids (e.g., milk of magnesia) are weak bases. Cleaning fluids containing ammonia are the strongest of bases we most often encounter, although still relatively weak. Most common drain cleaners are examples of strong bases.

Although the common definitions of acids and bases involve taste and feel, you shouldn't try these tests yourself. Many acids and bases are extremely dangerous and corrosive—for example, battery acid (H_2SO_4) and lye (NaOH).

When acids and bases are brought together in the same solution, the H^+ and the OH^- ions react together to form water, and we say that the substances neutralize each other. For instance, if we mix hydrochloric acid (HCl) and lye (NaOH), we will find a chemical reaction that can be represented as follows:

$$HCl + NaOH \rightarrow H_2O + NaCl$$

This balanced reaction indicates that molecules of HCl and NaOH recombine to form a molecule of water (H_2O) and one unit of common table salt (NaCl). From this equation it appears that the formation of water removes both the positively charged hydrogen ion and the negatively charged hydroxide ion from solution, and the other parts of the original molecules come together to form a new material. Salt is the general name for molecules formed by neutralization of an acid and a base.

The definition of acids and bases leads to a rather odd way of measuring the strength of a solution, called "*pH*," or "power of hydrogen." Although you might not think so at first glance, pure distilled water always contains some protons and some hydroxide groups. A small number of water molecules are always being broken up, and at the same time elsewhere in the liquid, protons and hydroxide groups come together to form new molecules of water. In fact, in pure water there are almost exactly 10^{-7} moles of protons and an equal amount of hydroxide groups per liter. Acids contain more protons than hydroxide groups, whereas bases contain fewer.

This fact is used to set the scale for measuring acids and bases. Pure water has a *pH* of 7. An acid solution that has a larger number of protons than hydroxide groups—a concentration of 10^{-6} moles H^+ per liter, for example—will have a lower pH (a pH of 6 in this example). A base that has a lower concentration of protons than hydroxide groups—10^{-10} moles H^+ per liter, for example—will have a higher pH (a pH of 10 in this example). Here are some common pH values:

Substance	pH
Stomach acid	1.0–3.0
Mean of Adirondack lakes, 1975	4.8
Normal rainwater	5.6
Mean of Adirondack lakes, 1930	6.5
Pure water	7.0
Human blood	7.3–7.5
Household ammonia	11.0

Note in particular the dramatic change in the acidity of lakes in New York's Adirondack Mountains between 1930 and 1975. The cause of this change is acid rain—a phenomenon we will examine in more detail in Chapter 19.

THE SCIENCE OF LIFE
Antacids

The first step of digestion, after the food is chewed and swallowed, takes place when acids in the stomach begin to break up the molecules that you have eaten. Occasionally, the stomach's acidity becomes too high, and we take antacids to feel better.

When you take an antacid, you are running a neutralization reaction in your body. Ordinary over-the-counter antacids contain bases such as aluminum hydroxide [$Al(OH)_3$], sodium bicarbonate ($NaHCO_3$), or magnesium hydroxide [$Mg(OH)_2$, or "milk of magnesia"] which react with some of the acid in the stomach. These products do not neutralize all the stomach's hydrochloric acid—only enough of it to alleviate the symptoms.

Polymerization and Depolymerization

The molecular building blocks of most common biological structures are small (see Chapter 22), consisting of a few dozen atoms at most. Yet most biological molecules are huge, with up to millions of atoms in a single unit. How can small building blocks yield large structures characteristic of living things? The answer lies in the process of polymerization.

A polymer is a large molecule that is made by linking smaller, simpler molecules together repeatedly to build up a complex structure (Figure 10-22). The word comes from the Greek *poly* (many) and *meros* (parts). In spider's webs, clotting blood, and a thousand other processes, living systems have mastered the art of combining small molecules into long chains.

Polymerization reactions include all chemical reactions that form very large molecules from individual small molecules, or *monomers*. Synthetic polymers usually begin in liquid form, with monomers that move freely past their neighbors. Polyethylene, for example, begins as a gas with molecules containing just 6 atoms (2 carbon atoms and 4 hydrogen atoms), whereas the liquid that makes a common nylon contains molecules with 6 atoms of carbon, 11 of hydrogen, 1 of nitrogen, and 1 of oxygen—a combination that chemists write as $C_6H_{11}NO$. Polymers form from the liquid when the ends of these monomers begin to link up. In the case of nylon, polyurethane, and many other common materials, the polymer forms by a *condensation reaction* in

FIGURE 10-22 Polymers form from monomers in two ways. *(a)* Addition polymerization occurs when monomers simply attach end-to-end to produce *(b)* synthetic fibers, as shown here magnified 23 times. *(c)* In condensation polymerization a small molecule is released for each added monomer. *(d)* The tiny bubbles in polyurethane foam insulation are formed by the carbon dioxide molecules released during polymerization.

which each new polymer bond forms by the release of a small molecule such as water or carbon dioxide (Figure 10-22a). Polyethylene, in contrast, forms by *addition polymerization,* in which the basic building blocks are simply joined end to end (Figure 10-22c).

Polymers play an enormous role in our lives. The useful properties of these varied materials are related to the shapes of molecules and the way they come together to form materials (Figure 10-23). In polyethylene, for example, long-chain molecules wrap themselves together into something like a plate of hairy spaghetti. It's hard for water molecules to penetrate into this material, so it is widely used in packaging. The "plastic" on prepackaged fruit or meat at your supermarket may be made from polyethylene. A closely related polymer is polyvinyl chloride (PVC), whose basic building block, vinyl chloride, is just an ethylene molecule in which one of the four hydrogen atoms has been replaced by a chlorine atom. Because the chlorine atom is bigger than hydrogen, the molecules of the polymer are lumpy and cannot pack too closely together. Commercial PVC, widely used in water and sewer pipes, contains other kinds

Linear polymer   Branched polymer   Cross-linked polymer

(a)   (b)   (c)

SUPERSTOCK

(d)

FIGURE 10-23 Polymers can come in many forms: (a) a twisted chain that can form insulating fibers, (b) a branched chain that can form thin, sturdy plastic bags, and (c) chains that are linked together, which are used in solid plastic components. (d) Polymers with coiled and branched chains are typical in the variety of bulk plastics, such as those in these containers.

of molecules that move between the polymers, lubricating the system and making the resulting material highly flexible. Credit cards are also made from this material. Other common polymers include polypropylene (artificial turf), polystyrene ("foam" cups and packaging), and Teflon (nonstick cookware).

Many polymers are extremely long lasting—a situation that presents a growing problem in an age of diminishing landfills. Nevertheless, most polymers are not permanently stable. Given time, they will decompose into smaller molecules. This breakdown of a polymer into short segments is called *depolymerization*.

Perhaps the most familiar depolymerization reactions occur in your kitchen. Polymers cause the toughness of uncooked meat and the stringiness of many raw vegetables. We cook our food, in part, to break down these polymers. Chemicals such as meat tenderizers and marinades can also contribute to depolymerization and can improve the texture of some foods.

Not all depolymerization is desirable. Museum curators are painfully aware of the breakdown process, which affects leather, paper, textiles, and other historic artifacts made of organic materials. Storage in an environment of low temperature, low humidity, and an inert atmosphere (preferably without oxygen) may slow the depolymerization process, but there is no known way to repolymerize old brittle objects.

SCIENCE IN THE MAKING
Polymers and the Origins of Life

Life employs numerous polymers, including long strands of DNA that carry genetic information, proteins that make muscle fibers and spider webs, and the cellulose of leaves and wood (see Chapter 21). A longstanding challenge in studies of the origins of life is how these polymers were synthesized prior to life's emergence.

Two steps must have been involved. First, like all polymers, these biological materials form by linking together numerous monomers—small molecules, such as amino acids to make proteins or sugars to make cellulose. The synthesis of these kinds of small molecules was an early success in origins research (see Chapter 25), and led to eager anticipation that the entire origins of life problem would be solved quickly.

However, the second step—linking the monomers into a functional protein or other polymer—has proven much more difficult and remains a frontier area of origins research. It's difficult to form polymers if the monomers are not highly concentrated, yet all origins scenarios involve a relatively dilute solution of organic molecules—what has been called the "prebiotic soup"—in which monomers rarely interact. To overcome this difficulty, several laboratories are employing minerals such as clay, whose surfaces can attract and concentrate small molecules. Once concentrated on the clay surfaces, the molecules are more likely to polymerize. Keep watching the science news, as many laboratories are hoping to demonstrate this key step in the emergence of life.

◉ 10.7 Building Molecules: The Hydrocarbons

As an example of how a wide variety of materials can be made by assembling the same molecular building blocks in different ways, let's start with the methane molecule shown in Figure 10-19 and build a family of molecules known to chemists as *alkanes*. Alkanes are flammable materials (either gases or liquids) that burn readily and are often used as fuels. Most of the components of the gasoline in your car, for example, are members of this family. Alkanes are one example of **hydrocarbons**, molecules made completely from hydrogen and carbon atoms.

You can think of methane as being composed of a carbon atom and three hydrogen atoms (what chemists call the methyl group) plus a fourth hydrogen atom. We begin by noticing that we can replace the hydrogen in the methane by another methyl group to form a molecule with two carbon atoms in it. This larger molecule is ethane, a volatile, flammable gas (Figure 10-24).

You can keep adding atoms in this way. Adding a third methyl group produces propane, a three-carbon chain. Propane is widely used as a fuel for portable stoves; you may have used it on your last camping trip. The next step is to substitute another methyl group for hydrogen to form a four-carbon chain, a molecule called butane. But there is an ambiguity here. We could, as shown, add the new group at the end of the chain so that all four carbon atoms form a straight line. This process would give us a form of butane known as n-butane (or "normal" butane). However, we could just as well add the methyl group to the interior carbon atom. In this case, the molecule would be known as isobutane. Isobutane and n-butane have exactly the same numbers of carbon and hydrogen atoms but are actually quite different materials. (To give just one example, isobutene boils at –11.6°C, whereas n-butane boils at –0.5°C.) Molecules that contain the same atoms but have different structures are called *isomers*.

As we continue the building process, moving to molecules with five carbons (pentane), six carbons (hexane), seven carbons (heptane), eight carbons (octane), and beyond, the number of different ways to assemble the atoms grows very fast. Octane, for example, has 18 different isomers; some have long chains, others are branched. As we shall see, these structural differences play an important role in a molecule's usefulness as an automotive fuel.

All other things being equal, the carbon chain length affects whether the alkane is a solid, a liquid, or a gas: the longer the chain, the higher the temperature at which that material can

FIGURE 10-24 Hydrocarbons are commonly used as fuels, including *(a)* methane, or natural gas, *(b)* propane in portable metal containers, and *(c)* butane in disposable cigarette lighters. *(d)* These members of the alkane series may be built up by adding methyl groups to methane. The first three members of the group are methane (with one carbon atom), ethane (with two carbon atoms), and propane (with three carbon atoms). The next two members are isomers of butane (n-butane and isobutane, each with four carbon atoms).

remain a solid. If carbon chains are straight, then alkanes with a half dozen or so carbon atoms are liquid, but those with more than 10 carbon atoms are soft solids. Good-quality paraffin candle wax, for example, which melts only near a hot flame of a wick, is composed primarily of chains with 20 to 30 carbon atoms. The presence of branches in the chain, however, makes it more difficult for the molecules to pack together efficiently. One consequence of branching is that the melting points are generally lowered compared to those of straight alkanes.

TECHNOLOGY
Refining Petroleum

Deep underground are vast lakes of a thick, black liquid called petroleum, derived from many kinds of transformed molecules of former life forms. *Petroleum* is an extremely complex mixture of organic chemicals, as much as 98% molecules of hydrogen and carbon (mostly in the

FIGURE 10-25 *(a)* Modern chemical plants bristle with tall distillation columns, in which petroleum products are purified. *(b)* A schematic diagram of a distillation column in a chemical plant shows how a temperature gradient (hotter at the bottom, cooler at the top) is used to separate hydrocarbons into fractions useful as gases, gasoline, kerosene, heating oil, lubricating oils and paraffin, asphalt, and tar.

form of hydrocarbons), with about 2% of other elements. Engineers must separate this mixture into much purer fractions through the process of *distillation*.

Hydrocarbons with different numbers and arrangements of carbon atoms have very different boiling temperatures. The key to distillation, then, is to boil off and collect different kinds of molecules successively, according to their boiling points. The most *volatile* hydrocarbon—the one with the lowest boiling point—is simple methane (CH_4), or natural gas. At the opposite extreme are very-long-chain hydrocarbons with dozens of carbon atoms, as in the molecules that comprise hard waxes, asphalt, and tar.

Modern chemical plants bristle with tall cylindrical towers that distill petroleum. Engineers pump crude oil into a tower, which is heated from below to create a temperature gradient up the tower (see Figure 10-25). At various levels of the tower, useful petroleum products such as gasoline or heating oil are recovered and sent to other parts of the plant for further processing.

The gasoline you buy at a service station is usually rated in "octanes." The octane rating of a gasoline is based on its ability to stand high compression in a cylinder without igniting. A fuel mixture that ignites while the piston is still moving up and compressing the gas in the cylinder will cause the engine to knock—a highly undesirable quality. In general, the more highly branched a molecule is, the better it will perform without knocking.

A particular isomer of octane that has five carbons in a row and three methyl groups on the sides turns out to have very good antiknock properties. This isomer is called isooctane, and an octane rating of 100 for any fuel mixture means that it is as good as pure isooctane. At the opposite extreme, n-heptane is an isomer with seven carbon atoms in an unbranched chain that produces knocking all the time. An octane rating of zero means the fuel mixture is as bad as pure n-heptane. Thus the octane rating of a fuel is simply a statement that it performs as well as a particular mixture of isooctane and n-heptane. A fuel rated at 95 octane, for example, performs as well as a mixture of 95% isooctane and 5% n-heptane.

THE SCIENCE OF LIFE
The Clotting of Blood

Whenever you get a cut that bleeds, your blood begins a remarkable and complex sequence of chemical reactions called *clotting*. Normal blood, a liquid crowded with cells and chemicals that distribute nutrients and energy throughout your body, flows freely through the circulatory system. When that system is breached and blood escapes, however, the damaged cells release a molecule called *prothrombin*.

Prothrombin itself is inactive, but other blood chemicals convert it into the active chemical *thrombin*. The thrombin reacts to break apart other normally stable chemicals that are always present in blood, and thus produces small molecules that immediately begin to polymerize. The new polymer, called *fibrin*, congeals quickly and forms a tough fiber net that traps blood cells and seals the break in minutes (Figure 10-26). Clotting chemical reactions differ depending on the nature of the injury and the presence of foreign matter in the wound. Biologists have discovered that more than a dozen separate chemical reactions may occur during the process. A number of diseases and afflictions may occur if some part of this complex chemical system is not functioning properly. On one hand, hemophiliacs lack one of the key clotting chemicals and so may bleed continuously from small cuts. Some lethal snake venoms, on the other hand, work by inducing dangerous clotting in a closed circulatory system.

FIGURE 10-26: A microscopic view of the clotting of blood reveals the polymerization of thrombin filaments, which trap blood cells (red) and stop bleeding.

Steve Gschmeissner/Photo Researchers

THINKING MORE ABOUT ATOMS IN COMBINATION

Life-Cycle Costs

Every month chemists around the world develop thousands of new materials and bring them to market. Some of these materials do a particular job better than those they replace, some do jobs that have never been done before, and some do jobs more cheaply. All of them, however, share one property—when the useful life of the product of which they are a part is over, they will have to be disposed of in a way that is not harmful to the environment. Until very recently, engineers and planners had given little thought to this problem.

Think about the battery in your car, for example. The purchase price covered the cost of mining and processing the lead in its plates, pumping and refining the oil that was made into its plastic case, assembling the final product, and so on. When that battery reaches the end of its useful life, all of these materials have to be dealt with responsibly. For example, if you throw the battery into a ditch somewhere, the lead may wind up in nearby streams and wells.

One way of dealing with this sort of problem, of course, is to recycle materials—pull the lead plates from the battery, process them, and then use them again. But even in the best system some materials can't be recycled, either because they have become contaminated with other materials through use, or because we don't have the technologies capable of doing the recycling. These materials have to be disposed of in a way that isolates them from the environment. The question becomes, "Who pays?"

Traditionally, in the United States, the person who does the dumping—in effect, the last user—must see to the disposal. In some European countries, however, a new approach is being introduced. Called life-cycle costing, this concept is built around the proposition that once a manufacturer uses a material, he or she owns it forever and is responsible for its disposal. The cost of a product such as a new car, then, has to reflect the fact that someday that car may be abandoned and the manufacturer will have to pay for its disposal.

Life-cycle costing increases the price of commodities, contributing to inflation in the process. What do you think the proper trade-off is in this situation? How much extra cost should be imposed up front compared to eventual costs of disposal?

RETURN TO THE INTEGRATED QUESTION

How does blood clot?

- Blood is a viscous liquid that transports nutrients and oxygen to our tissues. It is pumped by our heart to the millions of cells in our body via the circulatory system's vessels.

  - Blood vessels such as arteries, capillaries, and veins are the conduits that form the "plumbing" of our circulatory system. All blood vessels are comprised of different layers of tissue that serve specific functions. The innermost lining, called the endothelium, allows blood to flow freely and easily. Any damage to the vessel wall and this inner lining (e.g., a small cut or a massive wound) causes blood to flow out of the vessel without restraint (i.e., bleeding).

  - Damage to the endothelium initiates a complex cascade of chemical reactions that attempt to quickly stem the flow of blood. This process is known as hemostasis, and begins with coagulation.

- Coagulation is the process of forming a clot. Blood clots consist of both platelets and fibrous proteins.

  - Platelets are small cell fragments that are continuously circulating in the blood of mammals. They begin to aggregate at the site of injury.

  - Damage to the endothelium also causes the release of prothrombin. Numerous chemical reactions convert prothrombin into an insoluble polymer known as fibrin. This new polymer quickly forms a tough fibrous net that strengthens the platelet plug. This part of the process is known as secondary hemostasis and quickly seals the wound.

    - Once the wound has healed, blood clots are broken down and resorbed by the body.

  - These processes occur in all mammals.

SUMMARY

Atoms link together by *chemical bonds*, which form when a rearrangement of electrons lowers the potential energy of the electron system, particularly by the filling of outer electron shells. *Ionic bonds* lower chemical potential energy by the transfer of one or more electrons to create atoms with filled shells. On the one hand, the positive and negative ions created in the process bond together through electrostatic forces. In *metals*, on the other hand, isolated electrons in the outermost shell wander freely throughout the material and create *metallic bonds. Covalent bonds* occur when adjacent atoms, or groups of atoms called molecules, share bonding electrons. *Hydrogen bonding* is a special case involving distortion of electron distributions to create electrical polarity—regions of slightly positive and negative charge that can bind together.

Atoms combine to form several different *states of matter. Gases* are composed of atoms or molecules that can expand to fill any available volume. *Plasmas* are ionized gases in which electrons have been stripped from the atoms. *Liquids* have a fixed volume but no fixed shape. *Solids* have fixed volume and shape. Solids include *crystals*, with a regular and repeating atomic structure; *glasses*, with a nonrepeating structure; and *plastics*, which are composed of intertwined chains of molecules called *polymers*. The various states of matter can undergo *changes of state*, such as freezing, melting, or boiling, with changes in temperature or pressure.

Chemical bonds break and form during *chemical reactions*, which may involve the synthesis or decomposition of chemical elements or compounds. Reactions in which materials lose electrons to atoms such as oxygen are called *oxidation* reactions. In the opposite reaction, called *reduction*, electrons move onto atoms.

All life depends on *polymerization* reactions, in which small molecules link together to form long polymer fibers such as natural hair, silk, plant fiber, and skin, and synthetic materials such as polyesters, vinyl, cellophane, and other plastics. *Hydrocarbons*, widely used as fuels, are chain-like molecules made of carbon and hydrogen atoms. High temperatures and certain chemicals can cause the breakdown of polymers, or depolymerization, which is often a key objective in cooking.

KEY TERMS

chemical bond	gas	plastic
ionic bond	plasma	changes of state
metallic bond	liquid	chemical reaction
metal	solid	oxidation
covalent bond	crystal	reduction
hydrogen bond	glass	polymerization
states of matter	polymer	hydrocarbon

DISCOVERY LAB

As you may know, acids are substances that taste sour, turn blue litmus red, react with metals, and produce hydrogen gas. Acids remain colorless in the presence of phenolphthalein, they can neutralize bases, and they have a pH between 0 and 7. Bases are substances that taste bitter, are slippery to touch, and turn red litmus blue. In the presence of phenolphthalein, bases turn pink, they can neutralize acids, and they have a pH between 7 and 14. Products of neutralization are salt and water. Neutral substances have a pH of 7.

Now try to identify acids and bases in your home. Gather these materials: water, vinegar, lemon juice, orange juice, soap solution, baking soda in water, milk, glass cleaner, any soft drink, Alka-seltzer in water, and aspirin in water. Make an indicator by using unsweetened grape juice. Put about 10 to 15 milliliters of vinegar in a cup and add a few drops of unsweetened grape juice. If the solution turns red, it is an acid. If it turns green, it is a base. Repeat the same procedure with different solutions and observe the color change. How much vinegar is needed to neutralize a baking soda solution? Take 15 milliliters of baking soda solution and add a few drops of unsweetened grape juice to it. Pour a measured amount of vinegar slowly until the color changes from green to red. Can vinegar neutralize baking soda? How much vinegar did you need? Based on your lab, can you predict if there are more chemicals in your home that are acids or that are bases?

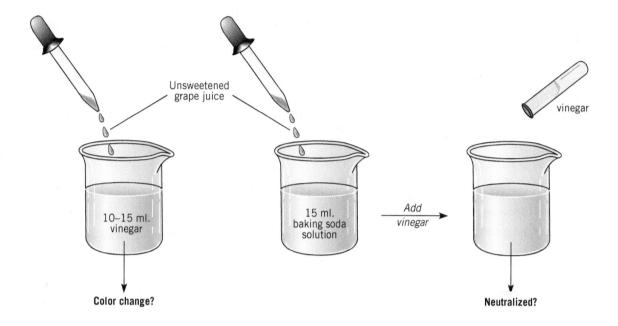

REVIEW QUESTIONS

1. When is an electron a valence electron? Why are valence electrons especially important in chemical reactions?

2. Describe the ionic bond. What sorts of materials have ionic bonds?

3. Describe the metallic bond. What properties of metal follow from the properties of the bond?

4. Describe the covalent bond. Give an example of a material that uses it.

5. Describe the hydrogen bond. Explain how a neutral molecule can become polar.

6. Explain how van der Waals forces can exist between neutral atoms.

7. Describe three everyday states of matter, including differences among them in volume and shape. In which states do the atoms or molecules have the greatest kinetic energy? The least?

8. How is a plasma like a gas? How is it like a metal? Where are plasmas found in the solar system? Where are they found in modern technologies?

9. Explain how a crystalline solid is constructed from individual atoms. How is this different from the structure of a plastic or glass?

10. Identify common changes of state and give examples of each.

11. In what sense are oxidation and reduction reactions opposites?

12. Are the following substances acid, base, or neutral: sodium bicarbonate (pH = 8.3); blood (pH = 7.4); milk (pH = 6.7); orange juice (pH = 3.6); milk of magnesia (pH = 10.5); soda pop (pH = 3.1)?

13. What is polymerization? Give an example.

14. When your body metabolizes the food you eat, are the chemical reactions endothermic or exothermic?

15. Describe how the alkanes are constructed. Why does the construction of alkanes lead you to the consideration of isomers?

16. What is an isomer? Do all isomers have the same chemical properties?

17. What are hydrocarbons? For what are they widely used?

DISCUSSION QUESTIONS

1. Describe the three different ways that atoms can bond together. Identify everyday objects that use each of these three chemical bonds.

2. Why do carbon atoms tend to form covalent bonds? Would you expect a carbon atom under ordinary conditions to form a metallic bond? Why or why not?

3. Classify the solid objects around you as ceramics, metals, glasses, and plastics.

4. When a chemical reaction takes place, it is noted that the temperature in the environment of the reaction drops. Is the chemical reaction endothermic or exothermic?

5. The planet Mars appears to be lifeless, is virtually devoid of liquid water, and its atmosphere is almost entirely carbon dioxide. What common chemical reactions that occur on Earth would be very unlikely to occur on Mars (if at all)?

6. How does cooking affect polymers? Why else might we cook our food?

7. Cooks often tenderize meat by soaking it in a liquid such as lemon juice or vinegar for several hours. What chemical reaction do you think is taking place in the meat? How is this reaction analogous to heating in an oven?

8. During icy winter conditions we often throw salt on sidewalks and streets. What occurs when salt comes in contact with ice? What reaction is involved? How do you think the melting point of saltwater compares to that of pure water?

9. Is the melting of ice an endothermic process? Why or why not? Give everyday examples of endothermic and exothermic processes.

10. Describe the chemical bonds that hold DNA together.

11. What is rust? What substance is typically required for rust to form? What type of reaction leads to the rusting of iron and other metals?

12. What is the maximum number of electrons that an atom can have in its first, second, and third electron shell?

13. Why does a liquid have a fixed volume but not a fixed shape? Why does a liquid have a fixed volume while a gas has a very easily manipulated volume?

14. What is the structural difference between liquid water at 0°C and ice at 0°C? What is the structural difference between liquid water at 0°C and liquid water at 100°C?

15. Why does ice float when placed in water? What roles do hydrogen bonding and polarity play in this phenomenon?

16. What is an isomer? Do all isomers have the same chemical properties? Give examples of different isomers.

17. What is the difference between a solid that is a crystal versus a glass?

18. What information does the octane rating of a fuel provide? When is a fuel with a high octane rating necessary?

19. What is the octane rating of the gasoline that is now in your car's gas tank?

20. Sodium is a metal. Under what conditions would it use the metallic bond? Can a sodium atom bond with another atom with a different kind of bond? If so, which one(s)?

21. How is a hydrogen bond similar to a covalent bond, and how is it different?

22. The molecular structure of the chemical known as benzene was once a mystery to chemists. It was known to be composed of 6 carbon atoms and 6 hydrogen atoms. Around the year 1863, August Kekulé had a dream of a snake eating its own tail that inspired him to arrange the 6 carbons in a ring. Draw a benzene ring with alternating single and double covalent bonds between the carbon atoms.

PROBLEMS

1. As the prefix suggests, hexane is a hydrocarbon with 6 carbon atoms and 14 hydrogen atoms coming together via single covalent bonds. How many different isomers of hexane can we form? Draw them.

2. When you burn methane (CH_4), it unites with oxygen (O_2) to form carbon dioxide (CO_2) and water (H_2O). Write an equation to balance the reactants and products of this reaction.

3. Other hydrocarbons combust with oxygen (O_2) to produce carbon dioxide (CO_2) and water (H_2O). Write balanced chemical reactions for the combustion of ethane (C_2H_6) and propane (C_3H_8).

4. Is $C_4H_{10} + O_2 \rightarrow 4CO_2 + H_2O$ a balanced chemical equation? If not, which are elements are balanced and which elements are out of balance?

5. As the textbook says, there are 18 isomers of octane. Along with the 8 carbon atoms, how many hydrogen atoms are in each isomer?

6. Sometimes when methane burns, instead of creating carbon dioxide it creates the more toxic chemical carbon monoxide, CO. Write a balanced chemical reaction in which methane (CH_4) combusts with oxygen (O_2) to form water (H_2O) and carbon monoxide.

7. When one molecule of methane combusts with oxygen, 5.74×10^{-21} J of energy is released as heat. How many molecules of methane must undergo combustion to heat up 1 gram of water by 1°C? (Note that this process requires 4.184 J.) If one molecule of methane has a mass of 2.66×10^{-23} g, how many total grams of methane are required?

8. Consider the following isomer of heptane (where only the carbon atoms are drawn for the sake of simplicity):

```
C  C     C
|  |     |
C - C - C - C
```

Which of the following patterns represents the same isomer?

a. C - C - C - C - C - C
        |
        C

b. C - C - C - C - C
        | |
        C C

c. C - C - C - C
   | | |
   C C C

d. C - C - C - C - C
       | |
       C   C

9. In the chemical reaction $CH_4 + 2O_2 \rightarrow CO_2 + H_2O$, the hydrogen atoms don't change their oxidation state, but the oxygen atoms each gain electrons. Which of the following scenarios best describes what happens to the carbon and oxygen atoms?

a. Carbon is reduced, oxygen is reduced
b. Carbon is reduced, oxygen is oxidized
c. Carbon is oxidized, oxygen is reduced
d. Carbon is oxidized, oxygen is oxidized

10. What salt forms when hydrobromic acid (HBr) is neutralized by potassium hydroxide (KOH, sometimes known as "potash")?

a. BrK
b. KBr
c. K_2Br
d. KBr_2

INVESTIGATIONS

1. Look around your home and school and list the variety of plastic objects. What strategy might you develop to recycle plastics? Note the numbers surrounded by a triangle on many disposable plastics. What do the numbers mean?

2. Why couldn't they build skyscrapers in America 200 years ago? Look up the Bessemer process.

3. Find out the decomposition rate of materials in landfills. Which materials are likely to be around for 100 years? What are the implications of this result for recycling?

4. Dissect a disposable diaper. How many kinds of materials can you identify? What are the key properties of each? What kind of chemical bonding might contribute to the distinctive properties of these materials? Investigate the arguments for and against using disposable diapers.

5. We often refer to drinking water as being "soft" or "hard," based on the kind of impurities present in the water. Which kind do you have in your community? What kind of chemical reaction can take place if water is too hard? How can you prevent that reaction from occurring?

6. Use a pH meter to measure the acidity of various liquids. What is the pH of lemonade? A soft drink? Milk? How do these liquids compare with stomach acids?

7. New plastics are being created from corn and soybeans, and these plastics break down when exposed to air and water. In what ways will the environment benefit from these biodegradable plastics? Should our government mandate the use of materials that biodegrade once their useful life is over? Why or why not?

8. Why do some experts say that you shouldn't microwave food in plastic containers or microwave food covered by plastic wrap?

Materials and Their Properties

How have computers gotten so much faster?

PHYSICS
Semiconductor diodes control the flow of electrons in modern electronic devices.

BIOLOGY
The human brain is made up of interconnected nerve cells, which are arranged in a complex system that cannot be reproduced artificially.

CHEMISTRY
Metals, in which bonding electrons are shared among many atoms, make the best conductors of heat and electricity.

TECHNOLOGY
High-temperature superconductors, which operate at the temperature of liquid nitrogen, find many applications in high-efficiency magnets and motors.

GREAT IDEA

A material's properties result from its constituent atoms and the arrangements of chemical bonds that hold those atoms together.

ENVIRONMENT
Photovoltaic cells will be used increasingly to convert environmentally safe solar energy into electricity.

ASTRONOMY
Modern telescopes rely on electronic light detectors that use photoelectronic material. (Ch. 14)

HEALTH & SAFETY
Flexible synthetic fibers with high tensile strength are used in automobile seat belts.

GEOLOGY
Rocks tend to be tough and brittle because their atoms are held together primarily by strong ionic bonds.

 = applications of the great idea discussed in this chapter

 = other applications, some of which are discussed in other chapters

Hauling Gear

It's only 10 a.m. but the beach is already starting to get crowded. You and your friends decide to walk a few hundred meters down the beach to a more open stretch. There's a surprising amount of gear to haul across the beach. You carry a Styrofoam cooler filled with aluminum soda cans, while your backpack holds a pile of sandwiches, SPF30 sunblock, a cotton towel, a Frisbee, and your MP3 player with your favorite music.

Without even thinking about it you've loaded up with dozens of amazing high-tech materials, each with its own distinctive and valuable properties: insulating lightweight Styrofoam, shiny strong aluminum, creamy protective lotion, tasty layered sandwiches, soft cool cotton, durable hard plastic, and astonishingly versatile semiconductor devices in your electronic gear. Even your backpack features a score of different sophisticated polymer fibers, plastic zippers, synthetic dyes, and metal alloys. Every one of these distinctive materials has been designed to serve our needs, and every one is crafted from atoms.

Blue Line Pictures/Photographer's Choice/Getty Images, Inc.

◎ 11.1 Materials and the Modern World

The materials people use, perhaps more than any other facet of a culture, define the technical sophistication of a society. We speak of the most primitive human cultures as Stone Age societies, and we recognize Iron Age and Bronze Age peoples as progressively more advanced.

STOP & THINK! Given that historical perspective, in what age are we now living?

Take a moment and look around your room. How many different kinds of materials do you see? The lights and windows employ glass—a brittle, transparent material. The walls may be made out of gypsum, a chalk-like mineral that has been compressed in a machine and placed between sheets of heavy paper. Your chair probably incorporates several materials, including metal, wood, woven fabric, and glues (Figure 11-1).

Many of these materials would have been familiar to Americans 200 years ago, when almost everything was made from less than a dozen common substances: wood, stone, pottery, glass, animal skin, natural fibers, and a few basic metals such as iron and copper. But thanks to the discoveries of chemists and materials engineers, the number of everyday materials has increased a thousand fold in the past two centuries. Cheap and abundant steel transformed the nineteenth-century world with railroads and skyscrapers, while aluminum provided a lightweight metal for hundreds of applications. The development of rubber, synthetic fibers, and a vast array of other plastics affected every kind of human activity from industry to sports. Brilliant new pigments enlivened art and fashion, while new medications cured many ailments and prolonged lives. And in our electronic age, the discovery of semiconductor and superconductor materials has changed life in the United States in ways that our eighteenth-century ancestors could not have imagined.

Chemists take natural elements and compounds that form earth, air, and water and devise thousands of useful materials. They succeed in part because materials display so many different properties: color, smell, hardness, luster, flexibility, density, solubility in water, texture, melting point, strength—the list goes on and on. Each new material holds the promise of doing some job cheaper or safer or otherwise better than any other. Based on our understanding of atoms and their chemical bonding (see Chapter 10), we now realize that the properties of every material depend on three essential features:

1. The kind of atoms of which it is made
2. The way those atoms are arranged
3. The way the atoms are bonded to each other

In this chapter, we look at different properties of materials and see how they relate to their atomic architecture. We examine the strength of materials—how well they resist outside forces. We look at the ability of materials to conduct electricity, and we examine whether they are magnetic. And, finally, we describe what are perhaps the most important high-tech materials in modern society, the semiconductor and the microchip.

FIGURE 11-1 A typical room is filled with high-tech materials: synthetic fibers, specialized glass, colorful plastics, and metal alloys.

◉ 11.2 The Strengths of Materials

Have you ever carried a heavy load of groceries in a thin plastic grocery bag? You can cram a bag full of heavy bottles and cans and lift it by its thin handles without fear of breakage. How can something as light, flexible, and inexpensive as a piece of plastic be so strong?

Strength is the ability of a solid to resist changes in shape. Strength is one of the most immediately obvious material properties, and it bears a direct relationship to chemical bonding. A strong material must be made with strong chemical bonds. By the same token, a weak material, like a defective chain, must have weak links between some of its atoms. While no one type of bond is universally stronger than the other kinds, many strong materials, such as rocks, glass, and ceramics, are held together primarily by ionic bonds. Next time you see a building under construction, look at the way beams and girders link diagonally to form a rigid framework. Chemical bonds in strong materials do the same thing. A three-dimensional network of ionic bonds in these materials holds them together like a framework of steel girders.

The strongest materials we know, however, incorporate long chains and clusters of carbon atoms held together by covalent bonds. The extraordinary strength of natural spider webs, synthetic Kevlar (used to make bulletproof vests), diamonds, your plastic shopping bag, and the muscles in your arm all stem from the strength of covalent bonds among carbon atoms (Figure 11-2).

FIGURE 11-2 The strength of materials is vital to many activities. The strength of muscle fibers (shown magnified on the right) arises in part from strong carbon-carbon bonds.

Muscle fiber

Different Kinds of Strength

Every material is held together by the bonds between its atoms. When an outside force is applied to a material, the atoms must shift their positions in response. The bonds stretch and compress, and an equal and opposite force is generated inside the material to oppose the force that is imposed from the outside, in accordance with Newton's third law of motion. The strength of a material is thus related to the size of the force it can withstand when it is pushed or pulled.

Material strength is not a single property, because there are different ways of placing an object under stress (Figure 11-3). Scientists and engineers recognize three very different kinds of strength when characterizing materials:

1. Its ability to withstand crushing (*compressive strength*)
2. Its ability to withstand pulling apart (*tensile strength*)
3. Its ability to withstand side-to-side shearing, as when you rub your hands together or twist a doorknob (*shear strength*)

Your everyday experience will convince you that these three properties are often quite independent. A loose stack of bricks, for example, can withstand crushing pressures—you can pile tons of weight on it without having the stack collapse. But the stack of bricks has little resistance against pulling apart or twisting. Indeed, it can be toppled by a child. A rope, in contrast, is extremely strong when pulled but has little strength under twisting or crushing.

The point at which a material stops resisting external forces and begins to bend, break, or tear is called its *elastic limit.* We see examples of this phenomenon every day. When you break an egg, crush an aluminum can, snap a rubber band, or fold a piece of paper, you exceed an elastic limit and permanently change the object. When the materials in your body exceed their elastic limit, the consequences can be catastrophic. Our bones may break if put under too much stress, whereas arteries under pressure that is too high may rupture in an aneurysm.

A material's strength is a result of the type and arrangements of chemical bonds. Think about how you might design a structure using Tinkertoys that would be strong under crushing, pulling apart, or twisting. The strongest arrangement would have lots of short sticks with triangular patterns. Nature's strongest structure, diamond, adopts this strategy; it is exceptionally strong under all three kinds of stress because of its three-dimensional framework of strong carbon–carbon bonds (see Figure 11-4). Glass, ceramics, and most rocks, which also feature rigid

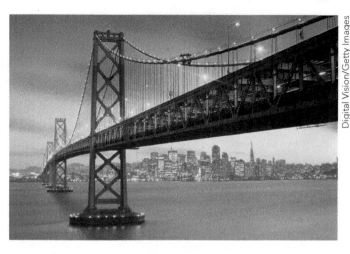

FIGURE 11-3 Suspension bridges feature vertical supports that are extremely strong under compression and massive steel cables that are extremely strong under tension.

FIGURE 11-4 *(a)* The girder framework of a skyscraper and *(b)* a diamond's crystal structure are both strong because of numerous very strong connections. In a building the connections are steel girders; in diamond they are carbon–carbon covalent bonds.

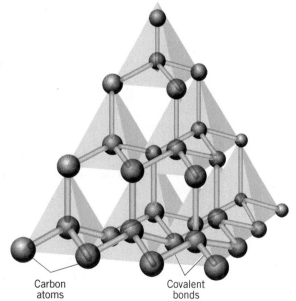

Carbon atoms   Covalent bonds

(a)   *(b)*

FIGURE 11-5 In composite materials, such as reinforced concrete, one material's weakness is compensated by the other's strength.

frameworks of chemical bonds, are relatively strong. Many plastics like the one in your shopping bag, however, have strong bonds in only one direction and thus are strong when stretched, but have little strength when twisted or crushed. Materials with layered atomic structures, in which planes of atoms are arranged like a stack of paper, are generally strong when squeezed but quite weak under other stresses. Thus the strength of a material depends on the kind of atoms in it, the way they are arranged, and the kind of chemical bonds that hold the atoms together.

Composite Materials

Composite materials combine the properties of two or more materials. The strength of one of the constituents is used to offset the weakness of another, resulting in a material whose strengths are greater than any of its components. Plywood, one of the most common composite materials, consists of thin wood layers glued together with alternating grain direction. The weakness of a single thin sheet of wood is compensated by the strength of the neighboring sheets. Not only is plywood much stronger than a solid board of the same dimension, but it can also be produced from much smaller trees by slicing thin layers of wood off a rotating log, like removing paper from a roll.

Reinforced concrete (Figure 11-5) is a common composite material in which steel rods (with great tensile strength) are embedded in a concrete mass (with great compressive strength). A similar strategy is used in fiberglass, formed from a cemented mat of glass fibers, and in new carbon-fiber composites that are providing extraordinarily strong and lightweight materials for industry and sports applications.

The modern automobile features a wide variety of composite materials. Windshields of safety glass are layered to resist shattering and reduce sharp edges in a collision. Tires are intricately formed from rubber and steel belting for strength and durability. Car upholstery commonly mingles natural and artificial fibers, and dashboards often employ complexly laminated surfaces. The bodies of many cars are formed from a fiberglass or other molded lightweight composite. And, as we shall see, all of a modern automobile's electronics, from radio to ignition, depend on semiconductor composites of extraordinary complexity.

● 11.3 Electrical Properties of Materials

Of all the properties of materials, none are more critical to our world than those that control the flow of electricity. Glance around you and tally up the number of electrical devices nearby. Chances are your list will quickly grow to several dozen. Almost every aspect of our technological civilization depends on electricity, so scientists have devoted a good deal of attention to materials that are useful in electrical systems. (See Chapter 5 for a review of electricity and magnetism.) If the job at hand is to send electrical energy from a power plant to a distant city, for example, we need a material that will carry the electrical energy without much loss. If, however, the job is to put a covering over a wall switch so that we will not be endangered by electricity when we turn on a light, we want a material that will not conduct electricity at all. In other words, a large number of different kinds of materials contribute to any electrical device.

Conductors

Any material capable of carrying electrical current—that is, any material through which electrons can flow freely—is called an **electrical conductor**. Metals, such as the copper that carries electricity through the building in which you are now sitting, are the most common conductors, but many other materials also conduct electricity. Saltwater, for example, contains ions of sodium (Na^+) and chlorine (Cl^-), which are free to move if they become part of an electric circuit. We can find out if a material will conduct electricity by making it part of an electric circuit and seeing if current flows through it.

The arrangement of a material's electrons determines its ability to conduct electricity. In the case of metals, you will recall, some electrons are bonded fairly loosely and shared by many atoms. If you connect a copper wire across the poles of a battery, those electrons are free to move in response to the battery's potential. They flow from the negative pole toward the positive pole of the battery.

As we saw in Chapter 5, the motion of electrons in electrical currents is seldom smooth. Under normal circumstances, electrons moving through a metal will collide continuously with the much heavier ions in that metal. In each of those collisions, electrons lose some of the energy they have gotten from the battery, and that energy is converted to the faster vibration of ions—what we perceive as heat. The property by which materials drain the energy away from a current is called **electrical resistance**. Even very good conductors have some electrical resistance. (The inverse of electrical resistance is *electrical conductance,* or the ease with which electrons flow in a material. Resistance and conductance are thus different ways of describing the same property.)

Insulators

Many materials incorporate chemical bonds in which few electrons are free to move in response to the force of an electric field. In rocks, ceramics, and many biological materials such as wood and hair, for example, the electrons are bound tightly to one or more atoms by ionic or covalent bonds (see Chapter 10). It takes considerable energy to pry electrons loose from those atoms—energy that is normally much greater than the energy supplied by a battery or an electrical outlet. These materials will not conduct electricity unless they are subjected to an extremely high voltage, which can pull the electrons loose. If they are made part of an electric circuit, no electricity will flow through them. We call these materials **electrical insulators**.

The primary use of insulators in electric circuits is to channel the flow of electrons and to keep people from touching wires that are carrying current (Figure 11-6). The shields on your light switches and household power outlets and the casings for most car batteries, for example, are often made from plastic, a reasonably good insulating material that has the added advantages of low cost and flexibility. Similarly, electrical workers use protective rubber boots and gloves when working on dangerous power lines. In the case of high-power lines, glass or ceramic components are used to isolate the current because of their superior insulating ability.

Semiconductors

Many materials in nature are neither good conductors nor perfect insulators. We call such materials **semiconductors**, and they form the critical workhorse components of our electronic age. As the name implies, a semiconductor will carry electricity but will not carry it very well. Typically, the resistance of silicon is a million times higher than the resistance of a conductor such as copper. Nevertheless, silicon is not an insulator, because some of its electrons do flow in an electric circuit. Why should this be?

In a silicon crystal (Figure 11-7), all the electrons are taken up in the covalent bonds that hold each silicon atom to its neighbors. At room temperature, the silicon atoms vibrate and a few of the covalent bonding electrons are shaken loose—think of them as picking up a little of the vibrational energy of the atoms. These *conduction electrons* are free to move around the crystal. If the silicon is made part of an electric circuit, a modest number of conduction electrons are free to move through the solid. When a conduction electron is shaken loose, it leaves behind a defect in the silicon crystal—the absence of an electron. This missing electron is called a *hole*. Just as electrons move in response to electrical charges, so too can holes move (see Figure 11-8a).

The motion of holes in semiconductors is something like what you see in a traffic jam on a crowded expressway (Figure 11-8b). A space will open up between two cars, after which one car moves up to fill the space, then another car moves up to fill that space, and so on. You could describe this sequence of events as the successive motion of cars. But you could just as easily (in fact, from a mathematical point of view *more* easily) say that the space between cars—the

FIGURE 11-6 Electrical wiring consists of a conducting metal core surrounded by an insulating layer of plastic.

FIGURE 11-7 A normal silicon crystal displays a regular pattern of silicon atoms. Some of its electrons are shaken loose by atomic vibrations, and these electrons are free to move around and conduct electricity.

Pure material

Silicon atom

Outer-shell electron

(a)

(b)

FIGURE 11-8 (a) A hole in a semiconductor is produced when an electron is missing. Holes can move, just like electrons. As an electron moves to fill a hole, it creates another hole where it used to be. (b) As cars in a traffic jam move slowly forward, "holes" in the traffic can be described as moving backward relative to the flow of cars. This behavior is analogous to holes in a semiconductor.

hole—moves backward down the line. In the same way, you can either describe the effects of the successive jumping of electrons from one atom to another, or talk about the hole moving through the material. Although relatively few semiconducting materials occur in nature, they have played an enormous role in the microelectronics industry, as we shall see later.

Superconductors

Some materials cooled to within a few degrees of absolute zero exhibit a property known as **superconductivity**—the complete absence of any electrical resistance. Below some very cold critical temperature, electrons in these materials are able to move without surrendering any of their energy to the atoms. This phenomenon, discovered in Holland in 1911, was not understood until the 1950s. Today, superconducting technologies provide the basis for a worldwide multibillion-dollar-a-year industry. The principal reason for this success is that once a material becomes superconducting and is kept cool, current will flow in it forever. This behavior means that if you take a loop of superconducting wire and hook it up to a battery to get the current flowing, the current will continue to flow even if you take the battery away.

In Chapter 5, we learned that current flowing in a loop creates a magnetic field. If we make an electromagnet out of superconducting material and keep it cold, the magnetic field will be maintained at no energy cost except for the refrigeration. Indeed, superconductors provide strong magnetic fields much more cheaply than any conventional copper-wire electromagnet because they don't heat up from electrical resistance. Superconducting magnets are used extensively in many applications where very high magnetic fields are essential—for example, in particle accelerators (see Chapter 12) and in magnetic resonance imaging systems for medical diagnosis. Perhaps they will eventually be used in everyday transportation.

How is it that a superconducting material can allow electrons to pass through without losing energy? The answer in at least some cases has to do with the kind of electron–ion interactions that occur. At very low temperatures, heavy ions (atoms with an electric charge) in a material don't vibrate very much and can be thought of as being fixed in more or less one place. As a fast-moving electron passes between two positive ions, the ions are attracted to the electron and start to move toward it. By the time the ions respond, however, the electron is long gone. Nevertheless, when the ions move close together, they create a region in the material with a more positive electrical charge than normal. This region attracts a second electron and pulls it in. Thus the two electrons can move through the superconducting material something like the way two bike racers move down a track, with one running interference for the other.

At the very low temperatures at which a material becomes superconducting, electrons hook up in pairs, and the pairs start to interlock like links of a complex, tangled matrix. While individual electrons are very light, the whole collection of interlocked electrons in a superconductor is quite massive. If one electron in a superconductor encounters an ion, the electron can't be easily deflected. To change the velocity of any electron, something you would have to do to get energy from it, you would have to change the velocity of *all* the electrons. Because this can't be done, no energy is given up in such collisions, and electrons simply move through the material together. If the temperature is raised, though, the ions vibrate more vigorously and are no longer able to perform the delicate minuet required to produce the electron pairs. Thus, above that critical temperature, superconductivity breaks down.

THE ONGOING PROCESS OF SCIENCE
Searching for New Superconductors

Until the mid-1980s, all superconducting materials had to be cooled in liquid helium, an expensive and cumbersome refrigerant that boils at a few degrees above absolute zero, because none of these materials was capable of sustaining superconductivity above about 20 kelvins. Acting on a clever hunch, scientists Karl Alex Müller and George Bednorz of IBM's Zurich, Switzerland, research laboratory began a search for new superconductors. Traditional superconductors are metallic, but Bednorz and Müller decided instead to focus on oxides—chemical compounds, such as most rocks and ceramics, in which oxygen participates in ionic bonds. It was an odd choice, for oxides make the best electrical insulators, although a few unusual oxides do conduct electricity.

Working with little encouragement from their peers and no formal authorization from their employers, the scientists spent many months mixing chemicals, baking them in an oven, and testing for superconductivity. The breakthrough came on January 27, 1986, when a small black wafer of baked chemicals was found to become superconducting at greater than 30 Kelvins—30° above absolute zero—a temperature that shattered the old record and ushered in the era of "high-temperature" (though still extremely cold) superconductors. The scientists' compound of copper, oxygen, and other elements seemed to defy all conventional wisdom, and it began a frantic race to study and improve the novel material.

Today, many scientists are attempting to synthesize new oxides that are closely related to those first described by Bednorz and Müller, while others struggle to devise practical applications for these new materials. Some recently developed compounds superconduct at temperatures as high as 160 Kelvins – still a rather chilly −172° Fahrenheit (see Figure 11-9).

FIGURE 11-9 *(a)* A magnet floats "magically" above a black disk made from a new "high-temperature" superconductor. The clouds in the background form above the cold liquid-nitrogen refrigerant. *(b)* This technology has been used in Japan to float high-speed trains above their tracks.

David Parker/IMI/Univ. Birmingham/
Photo Researchers/Photo Researchers

©AP/Wide World Photos

(a) *(b)*

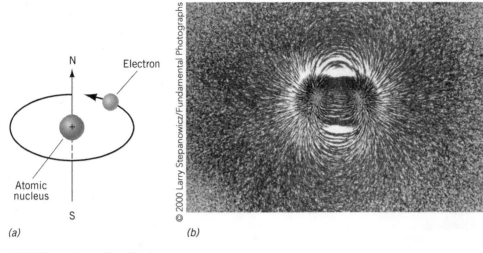

FIGURE 11-10 *(a)* The dipole magnetic field of a single atom takes the same form as that of *(b)* larger magnets. In this image small iron filings align themselves with the dipole magnetic field of a round-shaped permanent magnet.

High-temperature superconductors have taken superconductivity from the domain of a few specialists and have brought it into classrooms around the world. As new generations of scientists grow up with these new superconductors, new questions will be asked and exciting new ideas and inventions are sure to be found. Within the next generation we may have electric motors that rotate a million revolutions per minute on superconducting bearings, superconducting electrical storage facilities that reduce our energy bills, and magnetically levitated trains that travel at jet speeds between cities.

◎ 11.4 Magnetic Properties of Materials

The magnets that lie at the heart of most electric motors and generators, though critical to almost everything we do, are not much evident in our everyday lives. Similarly, we are usually unaware of the magnets that drive our stereo speakers, telephones, and other audio systems, while everyday refrigerator magnets and compass needles are so common that we take them for granted. But why do some common materials such as iron display strong magnetism, while other substances seem to be unaffected by magnetic fields?

In Chapter 5, we learned that one of the fundamental laws of nature is that every magnetic field is due, ultimately, to the presence of electrical currents. In particular, electrons spinning around an atom can be thought of as a small electrical current, so each electron in an atom acts like a little electromagnet. An atom can be thought of as being composed of many small electromagnets, each with different strength and pointing in a different direction. The total magnetic field of the atom arises by adding together the magnetic fields of all the tiny electron electromagnets.

It turns out that many atoms have magnetic fields that closely approximate the dipole type (originally shown in Figure 5-8); thus each atom in the material can be thought of as a tiny dipole magnet (Figure 11-10). The magnetic field of a solid material like a piece of lodestone arises from the combination of all these tiny magnetic fields.

FIGURE 11-11 Different magnetic behavior in materials. *(a)* Nonmagnetic materials have random orientations of atomic spins. *(b)* Ferromagnetic materials with randomly oriented domains are not magnetic. *(c)* A permanent magnet has more uniformly oriented atomic spins.

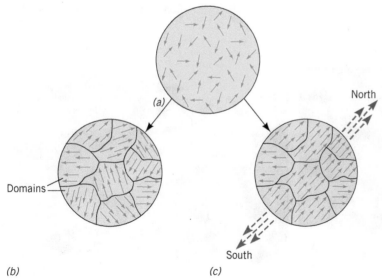

It's somewhat harder to understand why most materials do not have magnetic fields. In Figure 11-11a, we show the orientation of atomic magnets in a typical material. They point in random directions, so at a place outside the material their effects tend to cancel. An observer looking at the material will measure no magnetic field, and a compass placed outside the material will not be deflected. This ordinary situation explains how materials made up of tiny magnets can, as a whole, be nonmagnetic. In a few materials, including iron, cobalt, and nickel metals, the atomic magnets line up—an effect called *ferromagnetism* (Figure 11-11b). In a normal piece of iron, atoms within a specific domain will all be lined up pointing in the same direction, but the orientation of domains is random. Someone standing outside this material will not measure a magnetic field, because the small magnetic fields in different domains cancel each other. In special cases, as when iron cools from very high temperature in the presence of a strong magnetic field, all of the neighboring domains may line up and thus reinforce each other. Only when most of the magnetic domains line up (as shown in Figure 11-11c) do you get a material that exhibits an external magnet field—the arrangement that occurs in permanent magnets.

◎ 11.5 Microchips and the Information Revolution

Every material has hundreds of different physical properties. We have already seen how strength, electrical conductivity, and magnetism all result from the properties of individual atoms and how those atoms bond together. We could continue in this vein for many more chapters, examining optical properties, elastic properties, thermal properties, and so on. But such a treatment would miss another key idea about materials:

● **New materials often lead to new technologies that change society.**

Of all the countless new materials discovered in the last century, none has transformed our lives more than silicon-based semiconductors. From personal computers to auto ignitions, from iPhones to sophisticated military weaponry, microelectronics are a hallmark of our age. Indeed, semiconductors have fundamentally changed the way we manipulate a society's most precious resource—information. The key to this revolution is our ability to fashion complex crystals atom by atom from silicon, a material that is produced from ordinary beach sand.

Doped Semiconductors

The element silicon by itself is not a very useful substance in electric circuits. What makes silicon useful, and what has driven our modern microelectronic technology, is a process known as doping. **Doping** is the addition of a minor impurity to an element or compound. The idea behind silicon doping is simple. When silicon is melted before being made into circuit elements, a small amount of some other material is added to it. One common additive is phosphorus, an element that has five valence (bonding) electrons, as opposed to the four valence electrons of silicon.

When the silicon crystallizes to form the structure shown in Figure 11-12a, the phosphorus is taken into the crystalline structure. However, of the five valence electrons in

FIGURE 11-12 (a) Phosphorus-doped silicon n-type semiconductors have a few extra negatively charged electrons, while (b) aluminum-doped silicon p-type semiconductors have a few extra positively charged holes. Both n- and p-type semiconductors are usually formed from silicon crystals with a few impurity atoms.

(a) (b)

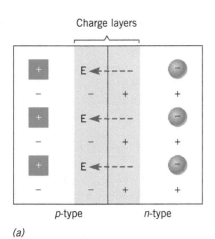

Charge layers

p-type   n-type

(a)

Stockbyte/Getty Images, Inc.

(b)

FIGURE 11-13 *(a)* The semiconductor diode consists of an *n*-type region and a *p*-type region. Electrons in this diode can flow easily from the negative to the positive region. This distribution of electric charge creates a field, labeled *E*, that blocks electrons from flowing the opposite way. The result is a one-way valve for electrons. *(b)* A tiny diode can control a large electric current.

each phosphorus atom, only four are needed to make bonds to silicon atoms in the crystal. The fifth electron is not locked in at all. In this situation, it does not take long for the extra electron to be shaken loose and wander off into the body of the crystal. This action has two important consequences: (1) there are conduction electrons in the material, and (2) the phosphorus ion that has been left behind has a positive charge. A semiconductor doped with phosphorus is said to be an *n-type semiconductor,* because the moving charge is a negative electron.

Alternatively, silicon can be doped with an element such as aluminum, which has only three valence electrons (Figure 11-12b). In this case, when the aluminum is doped into the crystal structure, there will be one less valence electron compared to the silicon atoms it replaced in the crystal. This "missing" electron—a hole—creates a material that can now more easily carry an electrical current. The hole need not stay with the aluminum atom but is free to move around within the semiconductor as described earlier. Once it does so, the aluminum atom, which has now acquired an extra electron, will have a negative charge. This type of material is called a *p-type semiconductor,* because a hole—a missing negative electron—acts as a positive charge.

Diodes

You can understand the basic workings of a microchip by conducting an experiment in your mind. Imagine taking a piece of *n*-type semiconductor and placing it against a piece of *p*-type semiconductor. As soon as the two types of material are in contact, how will electrons move?

Near the contact, negatively charged electrons will diffuse from the *n*-type semiconductor over into the *p*-type, while positively charged holes will diffuse back the other way. Thus, on one side of the boundary there will be a region where negative aluminum ions—ions locked into the crystal structure by the doping process—acquire an extra electron. Conversely, on the other side of the boundary is an array of positive phosphorus ions, each of which has lost an electron but which are nonetheless locked into the crystal.

A semiconducting device like this—formed from one *p* and one *n* region—is called a **diode** (see Figure 11-13). Once a diode is constructed, a permanent electrical field tends to push electrons across the boundary in only one direction, from the *n*-type side to the *p*-type side. As electrons flow "with the grain" in the diode, from negative to positive, the current flows through normally. When the current is reversed, however, the electrons are blocked from going through by the presence of the built-in electrical field. Thus the diode acts as a one-way gate, allowing the electrical current through in only one direction.

The semiconductor diode has many uses in technology. One use, for example, can be found in almost any electronic device that is plugged into a wall outlet. As we saw in Chapter 5, electricity is sent to homes in the form of alternating current, or AC. However, it turns out that most home electronics such as televisions and stereos require direct current, or DC. A semiconductor diode can be used to convert the alternating current into direct current by blocking off half of it. In fact, if you examine the insides of almost any electronic gear, the power cord leads directly to a diode and other components that convert pulsing AC into steady DC, as shown in Figure 11-14.

FIGURE 11-14 A diode converts alternating current to direct current in most electronic devices. Half of the alternating current passes through the diode, but the other half is blocked.

Alternating current

Direct current

n *p*

Negative Positive

Gael Conrad/Corbis Images

FIGURE 11-15 Photovoltaic cells convert the Sun's energy into electricity.

TECHNOLOGY
Photovoltaic Cells and Solar Energy

Semiconducting diodes may play an important role in the energy future of the United States through the use of a device called the photovoltaic cell. A *photovoltaic cell* is nothing more than a large semiconductor diode. A thin layer of *n*-type material overlays a thicker layer of *p*-type. Sunlight striking the top *n*-type layer shakes electrons loose from the crystal structure. These electrons then accelerate through the *n-p* boundary and into an external circuit. Thus, while the Sun is shining, the photovoltaic cell acts in the same way as a battery. It provides a constant force to move electrons through an external circuit. If large numbers of photovoltaic cells are put together, they can generate enormous amounts of current (Figure 11-15)

Photovoltaic cells enjoy many uses today. Your hand calculator, for example, may very well contain a photovoltaic cell that recharges the batteries (it's the small dark band just above the buttons). Photovoltaic cells are also used in regions where it's hard to bring in traditional electricity—to pump water in remote sites, for example, or to provide electricity in backcountry areas of national parks.

Another use of photovoltaics is in cameras. In products from TV cameras to the sensitive detectors that astronomers attach to their telescopes, light strikes a semiconductor rather than film. Using processes slightly more complex than those described for a photovoltaic cell, light striking each part of the semiconductor is converted into an electrical current, with the strengths of the currents from each part depending on the amount of light that falls there. The strength of those currents is then used to reconstruct the visual image.

TECHNOLOGY
Light-Emitting Diodes

Semiconductor devices that produce visible light have become a fast-developing technological frontier. *Light-emitting diodes*, or *LEDs*, exploit the fact that when electrons jump from the *n* to the *p* region of a diode, their energy is reduced and a photon corresponding to that energy difference is emitted. Scientists have learned to "tune" this energy to match the different colors of visible light, so each kind of LED gives off light of a specific color when electrons jump from the negative to the positive.

Modern LEDs provide tiny, but intense, light sources that consume far less electricity per "lumen" (a measure of light intensity) than incandescent bulbs (Figure 11-16a). Though once quite expensive and confined to specialized high-tech applications, LEDs are now used everywhere

FIGURE 11-16 *(a)* Light-emitting diode (LED) bulbs are now widely available for commercial and domestic use. *(b)* The 2014 Nobel Prize in Physics was awarded to Isamu Akasaki, Hiroshi Amano, and Shuji Nakamura of Japan for their advances in LED technology.

(a)

(b)

and are literally changing the lighting scene at work and home, from automobile headlights to video displays to new domestic lighting options. So important are these advances that the 2014 Nobel Prize in Physics was awarded to three Japanese scientists, Isamu Akasaki, Hiroshi Amano, and Shuji Nakamura, for their discoveries of new light-emitting diodes (Figure 11-16b).

The Transistor

The **transistor** is the device that has driven the entire information age, and perhaps more than any other has been responsible for the transformation of our modern society. Invented just two days before Christmas 1947 by Bell Laboratory scientists John Bardeen, Walter Brattain, and William Shockley, the early transistor was simply a sandwich of *n*- and *p*-type semiconductors.

In one kind of transistor, two *p*-type semiconductors form the "bread" of a sandwich, while the *n*-type semiconductor is the "meat." Another kind of transistor uses the *npn* configuration. Both kinds of transistors control the flow of electrons (Figure 11-17). Electrical leads connect to each of the three semiconductor regions of the transistor. An electrical current goes into the region called the *emitter*; the thin slice of semiconductor in the middle is called the *base*; and the third semiconductor section is the *collector*.

Thus the transistor has two built-in electrical fields, one at each *p-n* junction. The idea of the transistor is that a small amount of electrical charge applied to the base can change these electrical fields—in effect, opening and closing the gates of the transistor. The best way to think of the transistor is to make an analogy to a pipe that carries water. The electrical current that flows from emitter to collector is like water that flows through the pipe, and the base is like a valve in the pipe. A small amount of energy applied to turning the valve can have an enormous

FIGURE 11-17 *(a)* A *pnp* and an *npn* transistor. *(b)* Transistors are easily applied to a circuit board.

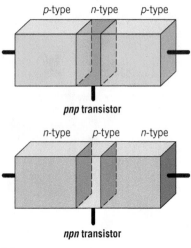

p-type *n*-type *p*-type

pnp transistor

n-type *p*-type *n*-type

npn transistor

(a)

(b)

FIGURE 11-18 A transistor acting as an amplifier. A small amount of energy, supplied by a power source such as a CD player, goes to the base of the transistor, where it is amplified as discussed in the text.

effect on the flow of water. In just the same way, a small amount of charge run onto the base can have an enormous effect on the current that runs through the transistor.

In your cell phone, for example, weak electrical currents are created when your voice sets up vibrations in a small crystal. This weak current can be fed into the base of a transistor, and can thus be impressed on the much larger current that is flowing from the emitter to the collector. A device that takes a small current and converts it into a large one is called an *amplifier* (see Figure 11-18). The amplifier in your cell phone takes the weak current created by your voice and converts it into the much larger current that runs the speakers.

As important as the transistor's amplifying properties are, probably its most important use has been as a switch. If you run enough negative charge onto the base, it can repel any electrons that are trying to get through. Thus moving an electrical charge onto the base will shut off the flow of current through the transistor, whereas running the electrical charge off the base will turn the current back on (Figure 11-19). In this manner the transistor acts as an electron switch and it can be used to process information in computers—arguably the most important device developed in the twentieth century.

Microchips

Individual diodes and transistors still play a significant role in modern electronics, but these devices have been largely replaced by much more complex arrays of *p*- and *n*-type semiconductors, called **microchips** (see Figure 11-20). Microchips may incorporate hundreds or thousands of transistors in one *integrated circuit*, specially designed to perform a specific function. An integrated circuit microchip lies at the heart of your pocket calculator or microwave oven control, for example.

FIGURE 11-19 A transistor acting as a switch. A small current causes the transistor to switch from off (*a*) to on (*b*).

FIGURE 11-20 A microchip incorporates many transistors built into a tiny piece of silicon, as shown here. Fifty years ago, it would have taken several rooms to house the computing power in this single microchip.

Similarly, arrays of integrated circuits store and manipulate data in your personal computer, and they regulate the ignition in all modern automobiles.

The first transistors were bulky things, about the size of a golf ball, but today a single microchip the size of a grain of rice can integrate hundreds of thousands of these devices. California's Silicon Valley has become a well-known center for the design and manufacture of these tiny integrated circuits. Production of thousands of transistors on a single silicon chip requires exquisite control of atoms. One technique is to put a thin wafer of silicon into a large heated vacuum chamber. Around the edges of the chamber is an array of small ovens, each of which holds a different element, such as aluminum or phosphorus. The side ovens are heated in carefully controlled sequence and opened to allow small amounts of other elements—the dopants—to be vaporized and enter the chamber along with silicon.

If you want to make a *p*-type semiconductor, for example, you could mix a small amount of phosphorus with the silicon in the chamber and let it deposit onto the silicon plate at the bottom. Typically, a device called a *mask* is put over the silicon chip so that the *p*-type semiconductor is deposited only in designated parts of the chip. Then the vapor is cleared from the chamber, a new mask is put on, and another layer of material is laid down. In this way, a complex three-dimensional structure can be built up at a microscopic scale. In the end, each microchip has many different transistors in it, connected exactly as designed by engineers.

TECHNOLOGY
Jim Trefil Gives His Car a Tune-Up

As a student, I acquired the first of a long string of Volkswagen Beetles. Now let me tell you, my friends, *that* was a sweet car! There were never any problems with the cooling system, for the simple reason that there wasn't any—the engine was cooled by the air flowing by. And almost any repair could be made by someone with reasonable mechanical ability and a set of tools. While in graduate school, I spent many happy hours under my car, adjusting this or that.

But I never work on my cars any more. When I look under the hood, all I see is a complex array of computers and microchips—nothing a person can get a wrench around (Figure 11-21). Yet the car I drive today, provided everything is working, is much more user friendly than my old Volkswagen. The flow of gasoline to the cylinders, for example, is regulated by a small onboard computer rather than by a clumsy mechanical carburetor.

This personal story about cars turns out to be a pretty good allegory for the way in which the science of materials developed in the second half of the twentieth century and into the twenty-first. Sixty years ago, industry turned out big, relatively simple things that were easy

FIGURE 11-21 Today's automobile engines are controlled by microchips.

to understand and work with—iron wheels for railroads, steel springs for car suspensions, wooden chairs and tables for the home. Today, industry turns out items that perform the same jobs better but that are made from new kinds of materials such as plastics, composites, and semiconductors. Instead of manipulating large chunks of material, we now control the way atoms fit together. Like modern cars, modern materials do their job well, but they cannot be made (or, usually, repaired) by a simple craftsperson working with simple tools.

So, although the materials we use are becoming better at what they do and easier for us to use, it becomes harder and harder for us to understand what those materials are. I might have been able to fix my old Volkswagen myself, but there is no way I can look under the hood and shift atoms around in my modern car's microchip. In a sense, the improved performance of modern materials has been bought at the price of our ability to understand them. To a large extent, the emphasis of modern materials science has shifted away from manipulating large blocks of stuff, which are readily available to our senses, to manipulating atoms in ever-more-complex ways. And, of course, we can't see or taste or feel atoms.

◉ 11.6 Information

The single most important use of semiconducting devices is in the storage and manipulation of information. The modern revolution in information technology—the development of arrays of interconnected computers, global telecommunications networks, vast data banks of personal statistics, digital recording, and the credit card—is a direct consequence of materials science.

All the things we normally consider as conveying information—the printed or spoken word, pictures, or music, for example—can be analyzed in terms of their information content and manipulated by the microchips we've just discussed. The term *information*, like many words, has a precise meaning when it is used in the sciences, a meaning that is somewhat different from colloquial usage. In its scientific context, information is measured in a unit that is called the *binary digit*, or **bit**.

You can think of the bit as the two possible answers to any simple question: yes or no, on or off, up or down. A single transistor being used as a switch, for example, can convey one bit of information—it is either on or off. Any form of communication contains a certain number of bits of information, and the computer is simply a device that stores and manipulates this kind of information.

One way of thinking about information in bits is to imagine a row of lightbulbs. Each bulb can be on or off, so each bulb conveys one bit of information. You could imagine making a code—all lights on is the letter "a", all lights on except the first is the letter "b", and so on. In this way, each on-and-off arrangement of the lights would be a different letter. You could then send a message by flashing different patterns.

If you had only one lightbulb, you could convey only two possibilities—on or off. This would be one bit of information, and would correspond to trying to write a message using only the letters *a* and *b*. (You could, for example, have a code where on meant *a* and off meant *b*.) If you had two lightbulbs, you would have four different configurations—on-on, on-off, off-on, and off-off—and therefore could convey four different possibilities. With two lightbulbs, in other words, you could add *c* and *d* to your list. In fact, you can work out that the number of different arrangements of the on-off signals increases as the number of bulbs in your array grows. The rate of growth is summarized in the following table:

Number of bulbs	Number of configurations
1	2
2	4
3	8
4	16
5	32
6	64
7	128
8	256

Given this table, how many lightbulbs would you need to send any message in the English language? One way to approach this problem is to think about something most of us take for granted—the design of typefaces. There are hundreds of different typefaces, and new ones are being designed all the time. This book, for example, is set in a typeface called Galliard. People who design these typefaces estimate that they need 228 characters to represent a complete message in English. This number includes letters (lowercase and capital), numbers, fractions, punctuation marks, commercial symbols like the $ sign, and what are called "peculiars"—* and %, for example. From the above table, then, we see that in order to have a full representation of the English language, we would need a bank of eight lightbulbs.

Another way of saying this is that it requires 8 bits of information to specify a letter or symbol in English. In computer science, 8 bits is called a **byte**. We can build up a hierarchy of information content as follows:

A six-letter word requires $6 \times 8 = 48$ bits of information

A printed page of 500 words requires $500 \times 48 = 2,400$ bits = 2.4 KB

A 300-page book requires $300 \times 2,400 = 720,000$ bits = 720 KB = 0.72 MB

A million-volume library requires $1,000,000 \times 720,000 = 720$ GB

The size of typical computer files is measured in kilobytes (KB, or thousands of bytes) or megabytes (MB, or millions of bytes), while computer memory devices can hold gigabytes or terabytes (GB or TB, billions or trillions of bytes, respectively).

STOP & THINK! Peoples of the world employ many alphabets besides the Latin alphabet used to write English. How does the number of bits required to designate a letter depend on the number of letters in the alphabet?

SCIENCE BY THE NUMBERS
Is a Picture Really Worth a Thousand Words?

FIGURE 11-22 (a) Digital images are stored in the form of tiny colored squares (b), called pixels. The fewer the pixels per inch the lower the resolution.

(a)

(b)

Christian Petersen/Getty Images, Inc.

Pictures and sounds can be analyzed in terms of information content, just like words. Your television screen, for example, works by splitting the picture into small units called pixels (Figure 11-22). Many high-definition TV sets split the picture into 1920 horizontal and 1080 vertical segments, giving a total of about 2 million pixels (in rounded numbers) for one picture on the TV screen. Your eye integrates these dots into a smooth picture. Every color can be thought of as a combination of the three colors—red, green, and blue—and it is usual to specify the intensity of each of these three colors by a number that requires 10 bits of information to be recorded. (In practice, this means that the intensity of each color is specified on a scale of about 1 to 1000.) Thus each pixel requires 30 bits to define its color. Thus the total information content of a picture on a TV screen is

2,000,000 pixels × 30 bits = about 60 million bits

Thus it requires about 60 megabits, or 7.5 megabytes, to specify a single frame on a TV picture. We should note that a TV picture typically changes 30 times a second, so the total flow of information on a TV screen may approach 2 billion bits per second.

It therefore would appear that a picture is worth not only a thousand words but much more.

In fact, if a word contains 48 bits of information, then the picture will be worth 60 million bits per picture divided by 48 bits per word, which equals about 1.25 million words per picture.

The old saying, if anything, underestimates the truth!

Computers

A **computer** is a machine that stores and manipulates information. The information is stored in the computer in microchips, each of which incorporates many thousands of interconnected transistors that act as switches and carry information. In principle, a machine with a few million transistors could store the text for this entire book. In practice, however, computers do not normally work in this way. They have a *central processing unit (CPU)* in which transistors store and manipulate relatively small amounts of information at any one time. When the information is ready to be stored—for example, when you have finished working on a text in a word processor, or writing a program to perform a calculation—it is removed from the CPU and stored elsewhere. It might, for example, be stored in the form of magnetically oriented particles on a floppy disk or a hard drive. In these cases, a bit of information is no longer a switch that is on or off, but a bit of magnetic material that has been oriented either "north pole up" or "north pole down."

The ability to store information in this way is extremely important in modern society. As just one example, think about the last time you made an airline reservation. You went online and got into communication with the airline's computer. Stored in strings of bits within that computer are the flights, the seating assignments, the ticket arrangements, and often the addresses and phone numbers of every passenger who will be flying on the particular day when you want to fly. When you change your reservation, make a new one, or perform some other manipulation, the information is taken out of storage, brought to the central processing unit, manipulated by changing the exact sequence of bits, and then put back into storage. This process—the storage and manipulation of vast amounts of data—forms the very fabric of our modern society.

You've probably noticed that the speed and information capacity of computers has increased astonishingly over the past few decades (Figure 11-23). Just look at the improvements in the images and action of video games. Gordon Moore, the founder of Intel, first noted this tendency for ever-faster computers in 1965. He pointed to a trend that the number of transistors that can be packed into every square inch of a microchip (a measure of computing power) tends to double about every two years. (Since Moore's time, this number has fallen to 18 months!) "Moore's Law" has held up remarkably for almost half a century, though it can't continue indefinitely. The average size of a single transistor-like region of a microchip is now only a few thousand atoms across, and a semiconductor device can't be much smaller than that.

These advances are primarily the result of many improvements in materials and their processing at the atomic scale—a field called *nanotechnology*. New fine-grained magnetic materials have greatly increased the capacity of information storage devices such as hard disks, while improved semiconductor processing techniques continue to reduce the size of individual *n*- and *p*-type semiconductor domains. The result is smaller, more powerful computers—one of many ways that advances in material science play a direct role in our lives.

FIGURE 11-23 The computer, which has evolved into ever smaller and lightweight devices, plays a wide range of roles in business, education, and entertainment.

Tetra Images/Getty Images, Inc.

FIGURE 11-24 This network of neurons in a human brain (shown magnified) is complexly interconnected. Each of our many billions of neurons is linked to as many as a thousand other brain cells—an architecture beyond the capabilities of modern technology.

Biophoto Associates/Photo Researchers

THE SCIENCE OF LIFE
The Computer and the Brain

When computers first came into public awareness, there was a general sense that we were building a machine that would in some way duplicate the human brain (Figure 11-24). Concepts such as *artificial intelligence* were sold (some would say oversold) on the basis of the idea that computers would soon be able to perform all those functions that we normally think of as being distinctly human. This scenario has not come to pass. The reason has to do with the difference between the basic unit of the computer, which is the transistor, and the basic unit of the brain, which is the nerve cell.

The transmission of electrical signals between the brain's neurons is fundamentally different from that between elements in ordinary electric circuits (see Chapter 5). This difference in signal transmission alone, however, does not make a brain so different from a computer. A computer normally performs a sequential series of operations—that is, a group of transistors takes two numbers, adds them together, feeds that answer to another group of transistors that performs another manipulation, and so on. Many computers are now being designed and built that have some parallel capacity at the same time—machines in which, for example, addition and other manipulations are done in parallel rather than one after the other. Nevertheless, the natural configuration of computers is to have each transistor hooked to, at most, a couple of others.

A nerve cell in the brain, however, operates in quite a different manner. Each of the brain's trillions of nerve cells connects to a thousand or more different neighboring nerve cells. Whether a nerve cell decides to fire—whether the signal moves out along the axon—depends in a complex way on the integration of all the signals that come into that cell from thousands of other cells.

This complex arrangement means that the brain is a system that is highly interconnected, more interconnected than any other system known in nature. In fact, if the brain has trillions of cells and each cell has a thousand connections, there will be on the order of a quadrillion (1,000,000,000,000,000) connections among brain cells. Building a computer of this size and level of connectedness is at present beyond the capability of technology.

THINKING MORE ABOUT PROPERTIES OF MATERIALS

Thinking Machines

One of the most intriguing questions about the ever-increasing abilities of complex computers is whether a computer can be built that is, by general consensus, regarded as alive or conscious. British mathematician Alan Turing proposed a test to address this question. The so-called "Turing test" operates this way: A group of human beings sit in a room and interact with something through some kind of computer terminal. They might, for example, type questions into a keyboard and read answers on a screen. Alternatively, they could talk into a microphone and hear answers played back to them by some kind of voice synthesizer. These people are allowed to ask the hidden "thing" any questions they like. At the end of the experiment, they have to decide whether they are talking to a machine or to a human being. If they can't tell the difference, the machine is said to have passed the Turing test.

As of this date, no machine has passed the test, but in 1990 the Cambridge Center for Behavioral Sciences agreed to sponsor a prize underwritten by American industrialist Hugh Loebner. The prize is an award of $100,000 and a gold medal to the first machine to pass the Turing test. An annual contest looks for the machine that comes closest to this ideal. But what if a machine did actually pass? Would that mean we have invented a truly intelligent machine? John Searle, a philosopher at the University of California at Berkeley, has recently challenged the whole idea of the Turing test as a way of telling if a machine can think by proposing a paradox he calls the "Chinese room."

The Chinese room works like this: An English-speaking person sits in a room and receives typed questions from a Chinese-speaking person in the adjacent room. The English-speaking person does not understand Chinese but has a large manual of instructions. The manual might say, for example, that if a certain group of Chinese characters is received, then a second group of Chinese characters should be sent out. The English-speaking person could, at least in principle, pass the Turing test if the instructions were sufficiently detailed and complex. Obviously, however, the English speaker has no idea of what he or she is doing with the information that comes in or goes out. Thus, argues Searle, the mere fact that a machine passes the Turing test tells you nothing about whether it is aware of what it is doing.

Do you think a machine that can pass the Turing test must be aware of itself? Do you see any way around Searle's argument for the Chinese room? What moral and ethical problems might arise if human beings could indeed make a machine that everyone agreed has consciousness?

⬅ RETURN TO THE INTEGRATED QUESTION

How have computers gotten so fast?

- The properties of any material depend on three essential features: The type, arrangement, and bonding of the atoms that comprise the material.
  - New materials can lead to new technologies (e.g., silicon-based semiconductors), or changes in existing technologies (e.g., increased computing speed).
- Computers are built to store and manipulate vast amounts of information.
  - The basic building block of the computer is the transistor.
  - The first transistors were quite large. Early computers were very slow because space constraints limited the total number of transistors in any circuit.
- Complex arrays of silicon-based semiconductors are called microchips, which may incorporate more than 2 billion transistors in one integrated circuit.
- A measure of computing power is the number of transistors that can be packed onto a microchip. Moore's Law," first noted in 1965, refers to the fact that the number of transistors that can be placed onto a microchip doubles every two years.
- Computers have become faster because the improvement in materials led to an enhancement in computing power by increasing the number of transistors that can be packed onto a single microchip.

SUMMARY

All materials, from building supplies and fabrics to electronic components and food, have properties that arise from the kinds of constituent atoms and the ways those atoms are bonded together. The high *strength* of materials such as stone and synthetic fibers relies on interconnected networks of ionic or covalent bonds. *Composite materials*, such as plywood, fiberglass, and reinforced concrete, merge the special strengths of two or more materials.

The electrical properties of materials also depend on the kinds of constituent atoms and the bonds they form. For example, *electrical resistance*—a material's resistance to the flow of an electrical current—depends on the mobility of bonding electrons. Metals, which are characterized by loosely bonded outer electrons, make excellent *electrical conductors*, while most materials with tightly held electrons in ionic and covalent bonds are good *electrical insulators*. Materials such as silicon that conduct electricity, but not very well, are called *semiconductors*. At very low temperatures, some compounds lose all resistance to electron flow and become *superconductors*.

Magnetic properties also arise from the collective behavior of atoms. While most materials are nonmagnetic, ferromagnets have domains in which electron spins are aligned with each other.

New materials play important roles in modern technology. Semiconductors, in particular, are vital to the modern electronics industry. Semiconductor material, usually silicon, is modified by *doping* with small amounts of another element. Phosphorous doping adds a few mobile electrons to produce an *n*-type semiconductor, while aluminum doping provides positive holes in *p*-type semiconductors. Devices formed by juxtaposing *n*- and *p*-type semiconductors act as switches and valves for electricity. A *diode* joins single pieces of *n*- and *p*-type material, for example, to act as a one-way valve for current flow. *Transistors,* which incorporate a *pnp* or *npn* semiconductor sandwich, act as amplifiers or switches for current. *Microchips* can combine up to billions of *n* and *p* regions in a single integrated circuit.

Semiconductor technology has revolutionized the storage and use of information. Any information can be reduced to a series of simple "yes-no" questions, or *bits*. Eight-bit words, called *bytes*, are the basic information unit of most modern *computers*

KEY TERMS

strength	semiconductor	microchip
composite materials	superconductivity	bit
electrical conductor	doping	byte
electrical resistance	diode	computer
electrical insulator	transistor	

DISCOVERY LAB

You have read that an electrical conductor is any material in which electrons flow freely. It could be a copper wire—or even saltwater! Try this experiment by gathering the following items: one 8.5 × 11 inch piece of poster board, one 6-volt dry cell, three pieces of 12-inch bell wire, scotch tape, spring clothes pin, 2 × 3 inch aluminum strip, 6-volt lamp (bulb), short wide-mouthed plastic cup, one-half cup of table salt, and fingernail clippers.

First, take your aluminum foil and tape the ends down on the poster board. Next, strip 1.5 inches of the insulation off of the wire ends with the fingernail clippers by scoring the plastic in a circular fashion and pulling the insulation off. Then set your 6-volt dry cell down on the poster board and attach one end of the bare wire to the positive terminal and tape the other end down on the aluminum foil. After that, roll a piece of tape and place it on the bottom of the plastic cup, setting the cup near the dry cell. Now take another wire you stripped and place the bare wire end underneath the negative terminal of the dry cell. Follow this up with the other wire end, by placing and taping it into the inside of the cup, about halfway down. After this, wrap one wire end around the lamp base (just below the glass) and stick the lamp into the inside circular part of the clothes pin. Next, set the clothespin down flat on the poster board with the lamp upright and the lamp's contact (metal end) lying against the aluminum foil. Tape both ends of the clothespin down firmly.

Test your connection by taking the other end and touching the bare wire against the other wire's end to see if the bulb lights up and the connection is good. Now place the other end of the wire into the inside of the cup like before and tape it down, leaving some bare wire exposed. Pour warm water into the cup and fill it about 60% full. Then place 6 tablespoons of table salt into the water and slowly stir. Does the lightbulb light? Can you explain why? If the bulb does not light, press down on the clothes pin or add more salt.

REVIEW QUESTIONS

1. What three essential features define the properties of a material?

2. What is strength? What factors determine the strength of a material?

3. Name the three kinds of strength used to characterize materials. Give examples of materials that are strong in each of these modes. What kind of chemical bonding occurs in each of these materials?

4. Diamonds and graphite are both made from carbon atoms. Why is graphite so much weaker?

5. Describe several different kinds of composite materials and explain how each acquires its strength.

6. How do conductors and insulators differ in their atomic structure?

7. Identify the materials that serve as an electrical insulator and an electrical conductor in an electrical device that you use every day.

8. What has to happen to the conduction electrons in a material in order for them to become superconducting?

9. Explain how a semiconductor can carry an electric current.

10. Explain how holes can move in a semiconductor.

11. If all atoms have electrons that are in motion about an atom, why aren't all materials magnetic?

12. Explain how atoms can be arranged in such a way as to create a permanent magnet.

13. What is a semiconductor diode? How do diodes convert AC into DC?

14. What is a transistor? What are the base, emitter, and collector, respectively?

15. How are diodes and transistors similar, and how are they different?

16. What is an integrated circuit? How might one be made?

17. Give an example of a bit of information. What is the difference between a bit and a byte?

18. What is the Turing Test?

DISCUSSION QUESTIONS

1. Give three examples of items people currently use nowadays made from materials that didn't exist 100 years ago. If these materials did not exist, could these items still be constructed? How would life be different without these materials?

2. Identify 10 objects in your home that use semiconductors. What other kinds of materials with special electrical properties are found in all of these 10 objects?

3. If water in a pipe is analogous to electricity in a wire, what is analogous to a diode? A transistor? What electrical device is analogous to a water storage tank?

4. If you repeatedly drop a magnet or hit it with a hammer, it will eventually become demagnetized. Why? Can you think of other ways to demagnetize something?

5. What are microchips and of what materials are they made? How are they related to integrated circuits?

6. Information can come in many complex forms. Consider music. How could music be reduced to binary, yes-no information?

7. Are there any practical limitations on Moore's Law? If so, what are they?

8. Why is the current in household circuits limited by circuit breakers? (*Hint*: Consider the relationship between heat production and current in an electrical resistor.)

9. Would a silicon semiconductor doped with boron be *n* or *p* type? How about one doped with arsenic? (*Hint*: Look at the periodic table.)

10. You have probably seen solar photovoltaic cells in use along highways or other locations. Why do you suppose they were placed at those locations in those positions?

11. How does being able to turn on or shut off a current influence the choice of the binary numerical system for computing?

12. Which do you think is more important for bone to have, high tensile strength or high compressive strength? Why?

13. Why do you think most electronic devices are designed for DC current when the power supply is predominantly AC?

PROBLEMS

1. Some high-definition television sets in use nowadays divide the screen into 1920×1080 pixels. What is the information content delivered in one frame of an HDTV broadcast? If there are 60 frames per second, what is the total information content per second?

2. Construct a set of yes-or-no questions to specify any alphanumeric character; include both upper- and lower-case letters as possibilities. What do you think is the fewest number of questions you need to ask?

3. Construct a set of yes-or-no questions to specify any planet in our solar system.

4. The United States Library of Congress contains in excess of 32 million catalogued books. Estimate the total information contained in 32 million books.

5. The LCD display of a laptop can have a resolution of 1600×900 pixels with a rate of 39 frames per second. How much information must be processed each minute?

6. Construct a *pnp* transistor using the element germanium doped with either gallium or arsenic, as needed.

7. You take a break from studying your 600-page science textbook and play a computer game on your desktop. You have a widescreen monitor measuring 1920×1080 pixels with a rate of 40 frames per second. Based solely on the number of bits of information, how many science textbooks does it take to equal one second of game playing?

8. Semiconductors are non-Ohmic devices in that while they obey Ohm's Law at any given instant, their resistance depends on the applied voltage (Ohmic devices maintain a constant resistance over a range of applied voltages). Given what you know about semiconductors, which of the following graphs of resistance versus voltage do you think best applies to them?

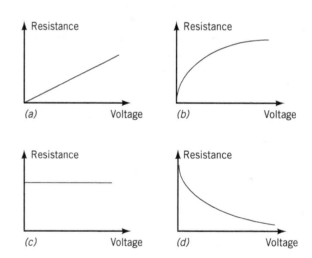

9. If the number of transistors held in a typical integrated circuit in 1971 was 2,000, use Moore's Law, assuming doubling every 2 years, to estimate the number of transistors held in a typical integrated circuit in 2011.

   a. 80,000

   b. 2,000,000,000

   c. 2,000,000,000,000

   d. 2,000,000,000,000,000

10. The Kangxi dictionary compiled in China in 1710 during the Qing dynasty encompasses 46,964 characters. How many bits would it take to specify a specific Kangxi character? Compare this to the number required in languages that have alphabets.

INVESTIGATIONS

1. Shortly after the discovery of high-temperature supercon-ductivity, many newspapers and TV shows ran features on how these new materials would change society. What is the highest temperature at which superconductivity has been demonstrated? In what ways might superconductivity change society? Historically, what other new materials have caused significant changes in human societies? Have all these changes been productive and positive?

2. Every year, one or two promising new materials capture pub-lic attention. Scan recent issues of *Science News* and identify one such material. Who made it? How might it be used?

3. Research the status of magnetically levitated trains like the one now operating in China. How does it operate? How fast might it go?

4. How is a modern radial tire built? Describe the structure in terms of what you know about composite materials.

5. Read the book or watch the 1951 movie *The Man in the White Suit*. What unique material properties are described, and how is the new technology received by society?

6. A class of new materials called fullerenes, including the sub-stance known as buckyballs, was invented in 1985. Investigate these materials and their possible uses.

7. Visit a sports equipment store. Learn about the new materials that are used in tennis rackets, football helmets, and sports clothing.

8. What kinds of materials do surgeons use to replace broken hipbones? What are the advantages of this material?

9. Investigate the use of new materials in sports medicine such as Gore-Tex tendons. What are the ethical implications of using new materials to create athletes who are stronger due to superhuman replacement parts?

10. Police officers routinely wear bulletproof vests. Investigate the properties of Kevlar and explain how the material pro-vides this protection.

11. If you could create a new super-material, what would it be used for? What atomic structure would be necessary to give the material the qualities that you desire? How might this ma-terial change society? Would all the changes be productive?

12. Investigate construction of modern high-tech running shoes. What kinds of new materials are used in these shoes, and how do they support the runner?

12 The Nucleus of the Atom

How do scientists determine the age of the oldest human fossils?

PHYSICS

The nucleus is held together by the strong force.

BIOLOGY

All life on Earth evolved in a radioactive environment. (Ch. 25)

CHEMISTRY

The chemical bonding of an atom's electrons has virtually no effect on what happens in the nucleus.

GREAT IDEA

Nuclear energy depends on the conversion of mass into energy.

TECHNOLOGY

Nuclear reactors produce energy by controlling nuclear fission reactions.

ENVIRONMENT

Wastes from nuclear power generation must be isolated from the environment.

ASTRONOMY

Fusion reactions that combine hydrogen to produce helium plus energy occur in the Sun and other stars. (Ch. 14)

GEOLOGY

All rocks contain a trace of radioactive isotopes, notably those of uranium.

HEALTH & SAFETY

Doctors sometimes rely on radioactive tracers to diagnose injuries and disease.

 = applications of the great idea discussed in this chapter

 = other applications, some of which are discussed in other chapters

It's great to be lying on the beach, lulled by the sound of the surf, soaking up the Sun.

Away from the pressures of school and work, time seems to stand still. In such a relaxing setting it's hard to imagine that hundreds of energetic radioactive particles are tearing through your body every minute. Some of those speeding particles will damage your cells, breaking apart bonds in the molecules that control critical functions of metabolism and cell division. But don't lose a moment worrying about this ubiquitous background radioactivity. Since the dawn of life, low levels of radioactivity in rocks, sand, soils, and the oceans have bathed every living thing. This radioactivity, a natural part of every environment on Earth, reveals much about the inner structure of the atom.

iStockphoto

12.1 Empty Space, Explosive Energy

Imagine that you are holding a basketball, while 25 kilometers (about 15 miles) away a few grains of sand whiz around. And imagine that all of the vast intervening space—enough to house a fair-sized city—is absolutely empty. In some respects, that's what an atom is like, though on a much smaller scale, of course. The basketball is the nucleus, and the grains of sand represent the electrons (remember, though, that electrons display characteristics of both particles and waves). The atom, which has a diameter 100,000 times that of its nucleus, is almost entirely empty space.

Previous chapters explored the properties of atoms in terms of their electrons. Chemical reactions, the way a material handles electricity, and even the very shape and strength of objects depend on the way that electrons in different atoms interact with each other. In terms of our analogy, all of the properties of the atoms that we have studied so far result from actions that are taking place 25 kilometers from the location of the basketball-sized nucleus. The incredible emptiness of the atom is a key to understanding two important facts about the relation of the atom to its nucleus.

1. *The nucleus of an atom is largely unaffected by chemical reactions involving the atom's electrons, and vice versa.* The chemical bonding of an atom's electrons has virtually no effect on what happens to the nucleus. In most situations you can regard the electrons and the central nucleus as two separate and independent systems.

2. *The energies available in the nucleus are much greater than those available among electrons.* The particles inside the nucleus are tightly locked in. Because most of the mass of the atom is in the nucleus, it shouldn't be surprising that most of the energy resides there as well. It takes a great deal more energy to pull a proton or neutron from an atom than it does to remove an electron. The enormous energy we can get from the nucleus follows from the equivalence of mass and energy (which we discussed in Chapter 3). This relationship is defined in Einstein's most famous equation.

In words: Mass is a form of energy. When mass is converted into energy, the amount of energy produced is enormous—equal to the mass of the object multiplied by the speed of light squared.

In equation form:

$$\text{Energy} = \text{mass} \times (\text{speed of light})^2$$

In symbols:

$$E = mc^2$$

Remember that the constant c, the speed of light, is a very large number (3×10^8 meters per second) and that this large number is squared in Einstein's equation to give an even larger number. Thus, even a very small mass is equivalent to a very large energy, as shown in the following "Science by the Numbers" section.

Einstein's equation tells us that a given amount of mass can be converted into a specific amount of energy in any form, and vice versa. This statement is true for any process involving energy. When hydrogen and oxygen combine to form water, for example, the mass of the water molecule is a tiny bit less than the sum of the masses of the original atoms. This missing mass has been converted to binding energy in the molecule. Similarly, when an archer draws a bow, the mass of the bow increases by a tiny amount because of the increased elastic potential energy in the bent material (Figure 12-1).

The change in mass of objects in everyday events such as these is so small that it is customarily ignored, and we speak of the various forms of energy without thinking about their mass equivalents. In nuclear reactions, however, we cannot ignore the mass effects. A nuclear reactor, for example, can transform fully 20% of the mass of a proton into energy in each reaction by a process we will soon discuss. Thus nuclear reactions can convert significant amounts of mass into energy, whereas chemical reactions, which involve only relatively small changes in electrical potential energy, involve only infinitesimal changes in mass. This difference explains why an atomic bomb, which derives its destructive force from nuclear reactions, is so much more powerful than conventional explosives, such as dynamite, and conventional weapons, which depend on chemical reactions in materials such as TNT.

FIGURE 12-1 When a bow is drawn, its mass has increased by a tiny amount.

SCIENCE BY THE NUMBERS
Mass and Energy

On the average, each person in the United States uses about 10,000 kilowatt-hours (kwh) of energy each year, a rate of about one kilowatt-hour each hour. In effect, each individual uses the energy equivalent of a toaster going full blast all the time. How much mass would have to be converted completely to energy to produce your year's supply of energy?

In Appendix B, we find that one kilowatt-hour of energy is the same as 3.6 million joules, so every year each of us uses:

$$\begin{aligned}
\text{Annual energy use} &= (10{,}000 \text{ kwh}) \times (3.6 \times 10^6 \text{ joule/kWh}) \\
&= 36{,}000 \times 10^6 \text{ joule} \\
&= 3.6 \times 10^{10} \text{ joule}
\end{aligned}$$

In order to calculate the mass that is equivalent to this large amount of energy, we need to put this energy into the Einstein equation, which we can rewrite as:

$$mass = \frac{energy}{(speed\ of\ light)^2}$$

Written in this form, the number we seek (the mass) is expressed in terms of two numbers we already know. The speed of light, c, is 3×10^8 m/s, so we find that:

$$mass = \frac{(3.6 \times 10^{10}\ joule)}{(3 \times 10^8\ m/s)^2}$$
$$= \frac{(3.6 \times 10^{10}\ joule)}{(9 \times 10^{16}\ m^2/s^2)}$$
$$= 4.0 \times 10^{-7}\ joule\text{-}second^2/meter^2$$
$$= 4.0 \times 10^{-7}\ kilogram$$

In the last step we have to remember that a joule is defined as a kilogram-meter^2/second^2, so the units "joule-second^2/meter^2" in this answer are exactly the same as kilograms (see Appendix B). Our year's energy budget could be satisfied by a mass that weighs less than a millionth of a kilogram, or about the mass of a small sand grain, if you could unlock that energy!

◉ 12.2 The Organization of the Nucleus

As we saw in Chapter 10, Ernest Rutherford discovered the atomic nucleus by observing how fast-moving particles scatter off gold atoms. In later experiments with even faster atomic "bullets," scientists found that atomic nuclei sometimes break into smaller fragments. Thus, like the atom itself, the nucleus is made up of smaller pieces, most importantly the proton and the neutron. Approximately equal in mass, the proton and neutron can be thought of as the primary building blocks of the nucleus.

The **proton** (from Latin for "the first one)" has a positive electrical charge of +1 and was the first of the nuclear constituents to be discovered and identified. The number of protons determines the electrical charge of the nucleus. An atom in its electrically neutral state will have as many negative electrons outside the nucleus as protons in the nucleus. Thus the number of protons in the nucleus determines the number of electrons and hence the chemical identity of an atom.

When people began studying nuclei, however, they quickly found that the mass of a nucleus is significantly greater than the sum of the mass of its protons. For most atoms the nucleus is more than twice as heavy as its protons. What accounts for this observation of "missing mass?" Scientists concluded that atoms must contain some kind of particle other than the proton or electron, but what is it?

We can identify at least three characteristics of this missing particle. First, it must be relatively massive to account for the observed mass of atoms. Second, it must reside in the nucleus of the atom, in close proximity to the protons. And third, it must be electrically neutral; otherwise it would be easy to identify in an electric field (this observation follows from the fact that charged particles can be manipulated by electrical fields). We now realize that this extra mass is supplied by a particle in the nucleus with no electrical charge called the **neutron** (for "the neutral one"). The neutron has approximately the same mass as the proton. Thus a nucleus with equal numbers of protons and neutrons will have twice the mass of the protons alone.

The mass of a proton or a neutron is about 2,000 times the mass of the electron. Therefore, almost all of the mass of the atom is contained within the protons and neutrons in its nucleus. You can think of things this way: electrons give an atom its size, but the nucleus gives an atom its mass.

Element Names and Atomic Numbers

The most important fact in describing any atom is the number of protons in the nucleus—the **atomic number**. This number defines which *element* you are dealing with.

STOP & THINK Why might electrically charged particles be easier to identify than electrically neutral ones?

All atoms of gold (atomic number 79) have exactly 79 protons, for example. In fact, the name "gold" is simply convenient shorthand for "atoms with 79 protons." Every element has its own atomic number: all hydrogen atoms have just one proton, carbon atoms must have six protons, and so on. The periodic table of the elements that we discussed in Chapter 8 can be thought of as a chart in which the number of protons in the atomic nucleus increases as we read from left to right and top to bottom.

Protons define the chemical behavior of an atom. The fixed number of positively charged protons dictates the number and arrangement of the atom's electrons and thus its chemical properties.

Isotopes and the Mass Number

Each element has a fixed number of protons, but the number of neutrons may vary from atom to atom. In other words, two atoms with the same number of protons may have different numbers of neutrons. Such atoms are said to be **isotopes** of each other, and they have different masses. The total number of protons and neutrons is called the **mass number**. We note in passing that not every isotope of an element is radioactive, although some may be.

Every element exists in several different isotopes, each with a different number of neutrons. The most common isotope of carbon, for example, has 6 neutrons, so it has a mass number of 12 (6 protons + 6 neutrons); it is usually written ^{12}C or carbon-12 and is called carbon twelve. Other isotopes of the carbon nucleus, such as carbon-13 with 7 neutrons, and carbon-14 with 8 neutrons, are heavier than carbon-12, but they have the same electron arrangements and, therefore, the same chemical behavior. A neutral carbon atom, whether carbon-12, carbon-13, or carbon-14, must have 6 electrons to balance the required 6 protons.

The complete set of all the isotopes—every known combination of protons and neutrons—is often illustrated on a graph that plots number of protons versus number of neutrons (see Figure 12-2). Several features are evident from this graph. First, every chemical element has many known isotopes, in some cases, dozens of them. Close to 2,000 isotopes have been documented, compared to the hundred or so different elements. This plot also reveals that the number of protons is not generally the same as the number of neutrons. Although many light elements, up to about calcium (with 20 protons), often have nearly equal numbers of protons and neutrons, heavier elements tend to have more neutrons than protons. This fact plays a key role in the phenomenon of radioactivity, as we shall see.

FIGURE 12-2 A chart of the isotopes. Stable isotopes appear in green, and radioactive isotopes are in yellow. Each of the approximately 2,000 known isotopes has a different combination of protons (Z on the vertical scale) and neutrons (N on the horizontal scale). Isotopes of the light elements (toward the bottom left of the chart) have similar numbers of protons and neutrons and thus lie close to the diagonal $N = Z$ line at 45°. Heavier isotopes (on the upper right part of the chart) tend to have more neutrons than protons and thus lie well below this line.

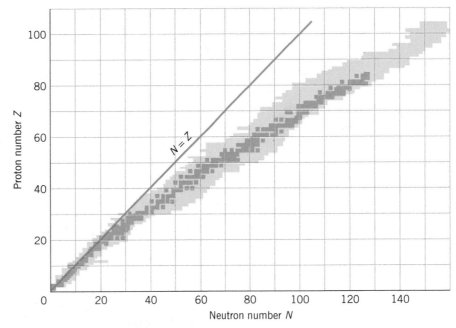

> ### EXAMPLE 12-1
>
> ### INSIDE THE ATOM
>
> We find a nucleus with 9 protons and 8 neutrons surrounded by 10 electrons.
>
> 1. What element is it?
> 2. What is its mass number?
> 3. What is its electrical charge?
> 4. How is it possible that the numbers of protons and electrons are different?
>
> **Reasoning:** We can find the first three answers by looking at the periodic table, but we will refer back to Chapter 10 and the discussion of stable electron states for the last answer.
>
> **Solution:**
>
> 1. The element name depends on the number of protons, which is 9. A glance at the periodic table reveals that element number 9 is fluorine.
> 2. Next, we calculate the mass number, which is the sum of protons and neutrons: $9 + 8 = 17$. This isotope is fluorine-17.
> 3. The electrical charge equals the number of protons (positive charges) in the nucleus minus the number of electrons (negative charges) surrounding the nucleus: $9 - 10 = -1$. The ion is thus F^{-1}.
> 4. The number of positive charges (9 protons) differs from the number of negative charges (10 electrons) because this atom is an ion. Atoms with 10 electrons are particularly stable (see Chapter 11), so fluorine usually occurs as a −1 ion in nature.

> ### EXAMPLE 12-2
>
> ### A HEAVY ELEMENT
>
> How many protons, neutrons, and electrons are contained in the atom ^{56}Fe when it has a charge of +2?
>
> **Reasoning:** Once again we can look at the periodic table for the first two answers, but we will have to do a simple calculation for the last answer. Remember, the number of protons is the same as the atomic number; the number of neutrons is the mass number minus the number of protons; and we compare the number of protons and the +2 charge to determine the number of electrons.
>
> **Solution:** From the periodic table, the element Fe (iron) is element number 26, so it has 26 protons.
>
> The number of neutrons is the mass number, 56, minus the number of protons: $56 - 26 = 30$ neutrons.
>
> The number of electrons surrounding the nucleus is equal to the number of protons minus the charge on the ion, which in this case is +2. Thus, there are $26 - 2 = 24$ electrons.

The Strong Force

In Chapter 5 we learned that one of the fundamental laws of electricity is that like charges repel each other. If you think about the structure of the nucleus for a moment, you will realize that the nucleus is made up of a large number of positively charged objects (the protons) in close proximity to each other. Why doesn't the electrical repulsion between the protons push them apart and disrupt the nucleus completely?

The nucleus can be stable only if there is an attractive force capable of balancing or overcoming the electrical repulsion at the incredibly small scale of the nucleus. Much of the effort of physicists in the twentieth century has gone into understanding the nature of this force that holds the nucleus together. Whatever the force is, it must be vastly stronger than gravity or electromagnetism, the only two forces we've encountered up to this point. For this reason it is called the **strong force**. The strong force must operate only over the very short distances characteristic of the size of the nucleus, because our everyday experience tells us that the strong force doesn't act on large objects. With respect to both its magnitude and its range, the strong force is somehow confined to the nucleus. In this respect, the strong force is unlike electricity or magnetism.

The strong force has another distinctive feature. If you weigh a dozen apples and a dozen oranges, their total weight is simply the sum of the individual pieces of fruit. But this is not true of protons and neutrons in the nucleus. The mass of the nucleus is always slightly less than the sum of the masses of the protons and neutrons. When protons and neutrons come together, some of their mass is converted into the energy that binds them together.

One way of thinking about the nucleus is to realize that there are two competing forces acting—the electrical repulsion between protons tending to tear the nucleus apart, and the strong force, acting between both protons and neutrons, holding it together. The neutrons, then, play a double role—they help to keep the protons separated from each other, which lowers the electrical repulsion, and they contribute to the strong force.

The fact that the nucleus stays together tells us that the strong force wins the competition, but the strength of the force holding everything together varies from one nucleus to the next. This variation is usually expressed in terms of what is called the **binding energy**, which you can think of as the energy that would be required to remove one particle from a nucleus. For light elements, increasing the atomic number generally increases the binding energy—the more protons and neutrons, the more tightly they are bound. When we get past iron in the periodic table, however, this trend changes. The heavier an element gets, the less tightly the protons and neutrons are bound. This variation means that iron is the most tightly bound of all the nuclei—a fact that will become important when we discuss the life cycles of stars in Chapter 14.

● 12.3 Radioactivity

The vast majority of atomic nuclei in objects around you—more than 99.999% of the atoms in our everyday surroundings—are stable. In all probability, the nuclei in those atoms will never change to the end of time. But some kinds of atomic nuclei are not stable. Uranium-238, for example, which is the most common isotope of the rather common element uranium, has 92 protons and 146 neutrons in its nucleus. If you put a block of uranium-238 on a table in front of you and watched for a while, you would find that a few of the uranium nuclei in that block would disintegrate spontaneously. One moment there would be a normal uranium atom in the block, and the next moment there would a couple of smaller atoms, a few fast moving particles, and no uranium. At the same time, fast-moving particles would speed away from the uranium block into the surrounding environment. This spontaneous release of energetic particles is called **radioactivity** or **radioactive decay** (Figure 12-3). The emitted particles themselves are referred to as radiation. The term *radiation* used in this sense is somewhat different from the electromagnetic radiation that we introduced in Chapter 6. In this case, radiation refers to whatever comes out from the spontaneous decay of nuclei, be it electromagnetic waves or actual particles with mass.

FIGURE 12-3 Safety officers in protective clothing use a Geiger counter to examine waste for radioactivity.

Tom Raymond/Stone/Getty Images

> **STOP & THINK** **What might the world be like if most atoms were radioactive?**

What's Radioactive?

Almost all of the atoms around you are stable, but most everyday elements have at least a few isotopes that are radioactive. Carbon, for example, is stable in its most common isotopes, carbon-12 and carbon-13; but carbon-14, which constitutes about a trillionth of the carbon atoms in living things, is radioactive. A few elements such as uranium, radium, and thorium have no stable isotopes at all. Even though most of our surroundings are composed of stable isotopes, a quick glance at the chart of isotopes (Figure 12-2) reveals that most of the 2,000 or so known natural and laboratory-produced isotopes are unstable and undergo radioactive decay of one kind or another.

SCIENCE IN THE MAKING
Becquerel and Curie

The nature of radioactivity was discovered in 1896 by Antoine Henri Becquerel (1852–1908), who studied chemicals that incorporate uranium and other radioactive elements. He placed some of these samples in a drawer of his desk along with an unexposed photographic plate and a metal coin. When he developed the photographic plate some time later, the silhouette of the coin was clearly visible. From this photograph he concluded that some as-yet-unknown form of radiation had traveled from the sample to the plate. The coin seemed to have absorbed the radiation and blocked it off, but the radiation that got through delivered enough energy to the plate to trigger the chemical reactions that normally go into photographic development. Becquerel knew that whatever had exposed the plate must have originated in the minerals and traveled at least as far as the plate.

Becquerel's discovery was followed by an extraordinarily exciting time for chemists, who began an intensive effort to isolate and study the elements from which the radiation originated. The leader in the field we now call radiochemistry was also one of the best-known scientists of the modern era, Marie Sklodowska Curie (1867–1934). Born in Poland and married to Pierre Curie, a distinguished French scientist, she conducted her pioneering research in France, often under extremely difficult conditions because many of her colleagues were unwilling to accept a woman scientist (Figure 12-4). She worked with tons of exotic uranium-bearing minerals from mines in Bohemia, and she isolated minute quantities of previously unknown elements such as radium and polonium. One of her crowning achievements was the isolation of 22 milligrams of pure radium chloride, which became an international standard for measuring radiation levels. She also pioneered the use of X-rays for medical diagnosis during World War I. For her work she became the first scientist to be awarded two Nobel prizes, one in physics and one in chemistry. She also was one of the first scientists to die from prolonged exposure to radiation, whose harmful effects were not known at that time. Her fate, unfortunately, was shared by many of the pioneers in nuclear physics.

FIGURE 12-4 Marie Sklodowska Curie and Pierre Curie received the Nobel Prize in chemistry in 1911 for isolating radium and polonium.

Culture Club/Contributor/Getty Images, Inc.

THE SCIENCE OF LIFE
The CAT Scan

Manipulation of X-rays plays a crucial role in a modern medical technique called the CAT scan. Ordinary X-ray photographs depend on the differences in density (and therefore in the ability to absorb X-rays) of the various materials in the body. In these photographs, the X-rays make one pass through, in one direction only, to produce pictures. They cannot produce a three-dimensional image of the interior of the body, nor can they produce sharp images of organs whose densities are not significantly different from the densities of their surroundings. These shortcomings are overcome by a different X-ray technique known as *computerized axial tomography (CAT)*.

The easiest way to visualize a CAT scan is to imagine dividing the body into slices perpendicular to the backbone, with each slice being a millimeter or so in width. The material in each slice is probed by successive short bursts of X-rays, lasting only a few milliseconds each, that cross the slice in different directions. Each part of the slice is thus traversed by many different X-ray bursts. Each burst of X-rays contains the same number of photons when it starts, and the ones that go all the way through the body (i.e., those not absorbed by material along their path) are measured by a photoelectric device. Once all the data on a given slice have been

TABLE 12-1 **Types of Radioactive Decay**

Type of Decay	Particle Emitted	Net Change
alpha	alpha particle	new element with two fewer protons and two fewer neutrons
beta	electron	new element with one more proton and one fewer neutron
gamma	photon	same element, less nuclear energy

FIGURE 12-5 A CAT scan of a human skull and brain.

obtained, a computer works out the density of each point of the body based on the transmission counts and produces a detailed cross section along that particular slice (Figure 12-5). A complete picture of the body (or a specific part of it) can then be built up by combining successive slices.

The Kinds of Radioactive Decay

Physicists who studied radioactive rocks and minerals soon discovered three different kinds of radioactive decay, each of which changes the nucleus in its own characteristic way, and each of which plays an important role in modern science and technology (Table 12-1). These three kinds of radioactivity were dubbed alpha, beta, and gamma radiation to emphasize that they were unknown and mysterious when first discovered.

1. Alpha Decay

Some radioactive decays involve the emission of a relatively large and massive particle composed of two protons and two neutrons. Such a particle is now known to be exactly the same as the nucleus of a helium-4 atom, although this fact was not known to early experimenters—hence the use of the Greek letter alpha to describe it. The process by which it is emitted is called **alpha decay**. (An alpha particle is often represented in equations and diagrams by the Greek letter α.)

The nature of alpha decay was discovered by Ernest Rutherford, the discoverer of the nucleus, in the first decade of the twentieth century. His simple and clever experiment, sketched in Figure 12-6, began with a small amount of radioactive material known to emit alpha particles in a sealed tube. After a number of months, careful chemical analysis revealed the presence of a small amount of helium in the tube, helium that hadn't been present when the tube was sealed. From this observation, Rutherford concluded that alpha particles must be associated with the helium atom. Today we would say that Rutherford observed the emission of the helium nucleus in radioactive decay, followed by the acquisition of two electrons to form an atom of helium gas. Rutherford received the Nobel Prize in chemistry for his chemical studies and his work in sorting out radioactivity. He is one of the few people in the world who made his most important contributions to science—in this case the discovery of the nucleus—*after* he received the Nobel Prize.

When the nucleus emits an alpha particle, it loses two protons and two neutrons (Figure 12-7a). This loss of nuclear particles means that the daughter nucleus will have two fewer protons than the original. If the original nucleus is uranium-238 with 92 protons, for example, the daughter nucleus will have only 90 protons, which means that it is a *completely different chemical element* called thorium. The total mass of the new atom will be 234, so alpha decay causes uranium-238 to transform to thorium-234. The thorium nucleus with 90 protons can accommodate only 90 electrons in its neutral state. This means that, soon after the decay, two of the original complement of electrons will wander away, leaving the daughter nucleus with its allotment of 90. The

FIGURE 12-6 The Rutherford experiment led to the identification of the alpha particle, which is the same as a helium nucleus.

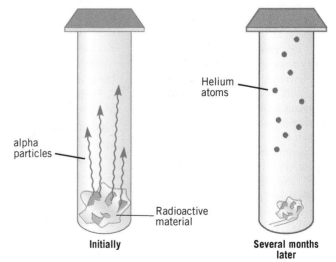

Helium atoms

alpha particles

Radioactive material

Initially

Several months later

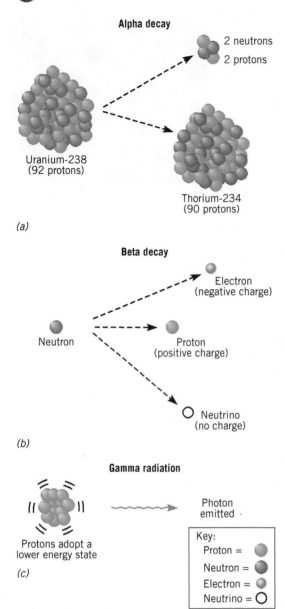

Alpha decay

2 neutrons
2 protons

Uranium-238
(92 protons)

Thorium-234
(90 protons)

(a)

Beta decay

Electron
(negative charge)

Neutron

Proton
(positive charge)

Neutrino
(no charge)

(b)

Gamma radiation

Photon
emitted

Protons adopt a
lower energy state

(c)

Key:
Proton =
Neutron =
Electron =
Neutrino = O

FIGURE 12-7 The three common types of radioactive decay involve the spontaneous release of energetic particles from an atom. In alpha decay *(a)* an atom emits an alpha particle with two protons and two neutrons. In beta decay *(b)* a neutron in the atom's nucleus transforms to a positively charged proton, which remains in the nucleus, plus an energetic negatively charged electron and a neutrino, which are emitted as radiation. In gamma decay *(c)* an energetic gamma ray (a photon) is emitted as positively charged protons adopt a lower energy state.

process of alpha decay reduces the mass and changes the chemical identity of the decaying nucleus.

Radioactivity is nature's "philosopher's stone." According to medieval alchemists, the philosopher's stone was supposed to turn lead into gold. The alchemists never found their stone because almost all of their work involved what we today would call chemical reactions; that is, they were trying to change one element into another by manipulating electrons. Given what we now know about the structure of atoms, we realize that they were approaching the problem from the wrong end. If you really want to change one chemical element into another, you have to manipulate the nucleus—which is precisely what happens in the process of radioactivity.

When the alpha particle leaves the parent nucleus, it typically travels at a very high speed (often at an appreciable fraction of the speed of light) so it carries a lot of kinetic energy. This energy, like all nuclear energy, comes from the conversion of mass: the mass of the daughter nucleus and the alpha particle, added together, is somewhat less than the mass of the parent uranium nucleus. If the alpha particle is emitted by an atom that is part of a solid body, then it will undergo a series of collisions as it moves from the parent nucleus into the wider world. In each collision it will share some of its kinetic energy with other atoms. The net effect of the decay is that the kinetic energy of the alpha particle is eventually converted into heat, and the material warms up. About half of Earth's interior heat comes from exactly this kind of energy transfer. As we shall see in Chapter 17, this heat is ultimately responsible for many of Earth's major surface features.

2. Beta Decay

The second kind of radioactive decay, called **beta decay**, involves the emission of an electron. (Beta decay and the electron it produces are often denoted by the Greek letter β.) While bound neutrons in stable nuclei are stable, free neutrons are not. The simplest kind of beta decay that can be observed is for a single neutron (Figure 12-7b). If you put a collection of neutrons on the table in front of you, they would start to disintegrate, with about half of them disappearing in the first 10 minutes or so. The most obvious products of this decay are a proton and an electron. Both particles carry an electrical charge and are therefore very easy to detect. This production of one positive and one negative particle from a neutral one does not change the total electrical charge of the entire system.

In the 1930s, when beta decay of the neutron was first seen in a laboratory, the experimental equipment available at the time easily detected and measured the energies of the electron and proton. Scientists looking carefully at beta decay were troubled to find that the process appeared to violate the law of conservation of energy, as well as some other important conservation laws in physics. When they added up the mass and kinetic energies of the electron and proton after the decay, the total amounted to less than the mass tied up in the energy of the original neutron. If only the electron and proton were given off, the conservation law of energy, as well as other important laws of nature, would be violated.

Rather than face this possibility, physicists at the time followed the lead of Wolfgang Pauli (see Chapter 8) and postulated that another particle had to be emitted in the decay—a particle that they could not detect at the time, but that carried away the missing energy and other properties. It wasn't until 1956 that physicists were able to detect this missing particle—the *neutrino*, or "little neutral one"—in the laboratory. This particle has no electrical charge, travels close to the speed of light, and, if modern theories are correct, carries a very tiny mass. Today, at giant particle accelerators (see Chapter 13), neutrinos are routinely produced and used as probes in other experiments. When beta decay takes place inside a nucleus, one of the neutrons in the nucleus converts into a proton, an electron, and a neutrino. The lightweight electron and the neutrino speed out of the nucleus, while the proton remains. The electron that comes off in beta decay is not one of the electrons that was originally outside the nucleus in a Bohr electron shell. The electrons emitted from the nucleus come out so fast that they are long gone from the atom before any of the electrons in shells have time to react. The new atom has a net positive charge, however, and eventually may acquire a stray electron from the environment.

The net effect of beta decay is that the daughter nucleus has approximately the same mass as the parent (it has the same total number of protons and neutrons), but has one more proton and one less neutron. It is therefore a different element than it was before. Carbon-14, for example, undergoes beta decay to become an atom of nitrogen-14. If you were to place a small pile of carbon-14 powder—it would look like black soot—in a sealed jar and come back in 20,000 years, most of the powder would have disappeared and the jar would be filled with colorless, odorless nitrogen gas. Beta decay, therefore, is a transformation in which the chemical identity of the atom is changed, but its mass is virtually the same before and after. (Remember, the electron and neutrino that are emitted are extremely lightweight and make almost no difference in the atom's total mass.)

What force in nature could cause an uncharged particle such as the neutron to fly apart? The force is certainly not gravitational attraction between masses, nor is it the electromagnetic force that causes oppositely charged particles to fly away from each other. And beta decay seems to be quite different from the strong force that holds protons together in the nucleus. In fact, beta decay is an example of the operation of the fourth fundamental force in nature, the *weak force*.

3. Gamma Radiation

The third kind of radioactivity, called **gamma radiation**, is different in character from alpha and beta decay. (Gamma decay and gamma radiation are often denoted by the Greek letter γ.) A "gamma ray" is simply a generic term for a very energetic photon—electromagnetic radiation (Figure 12-7c). In Chapter 6 we saw that all electromagnetic radiation comes from the acceleration of charged particles, and that is what happens in gamma radioactivity. When an electron in an atom shifts from a higher energy level to a lower one, we know that a photon will be emitted, typically in the range of visible or ultraviolet light. In just the same way, the particles in a nucleus can shift between different energy levels. These shifts, or nuclear quantum leaps, involve energy differences thousands or millions of times greater than those of an atom's electrons. When particles in a nucleus undergo shifts from higher to lower energy levels, some of the emitted gamma radiation is in the range of X-rays, while others are even more energetic.

A nucleus emits gamma rays any time its protons and neutrons reshuffle. Neither the protons nor the neutrons change their identity, so the daughter atom has the same mass, the same isotope number, and the same chemical identity as the parent. Nevertheless, this process produces highly energetic radiation.

Radiation and Health

The most important thing to realize about radiation is that it is a natural part of our environment. Life on our planet evolved in a radioactive environment, and radiation did not suddenly appear when we were able to detect and measure it in the twentieth century. Cosmic rays from space are passing through your body as you read this paragraph, for example.

As we shall see in Chapter 25, living things evolve in such a way as to adapt to their environment. This adaptability means that cells in organisms (including humans) have, over the ages, developed mechanisms for repairing the damage caused by radiation. In fact, there is a long-standing debate between scientists on the question of whether or not small amounts of radiation, by stimulating the immune system, actually improve an organism's overall health.

Now that we understand what radiation is, we can understand how it might harm living tissue. The basic process, called *ionization*, involves fast moving alpha, beta, or gamma rays stripping electrons from atoms as they pass by (Figure 12-8). If the damaged atom happens to be in a molecule, the radiation might cause essential functions of the cell to be disrupted.

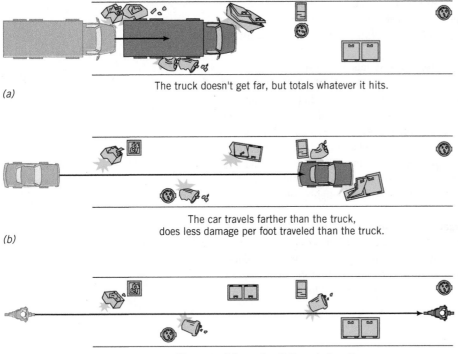

(a)

The truck doesn't get far, but totals whatever it hits.

(b)

The car travels farther than the truck,
does less damage per foot traveled than the truck.

(c)

The motor bike makes it through the alley,
doing less damage per foot traveled.

FIGURE 12-8 The damage to atoms and molecules from different kinds of radiation can be compared to the damage to objects in an alleyway caused by different types of vehicles. The massive, lumbering truck is analogous to an alpha particle (a), the smaller, faster car is analogous to a beta particle (b), and the small, swift motorcycle is analogous to a gamma ray (c). Although you might conclude that the gamma ray does the least amount of damage, its high kinetic energy and ability to penetrate deeply makes it especially dangerous in large quantities.

The three types of radiation have different penetrating powers. Alpha radiation can be stopped by a sheet of paper, beta rays can penetrate a few millimeters of aluminum, and gamma rays can pass through several centimeters of lead. It is alpha radiation, however, that can cause the most damage once it is inside the human body.

Large doses of radiation, such as those encountered by some people in the nuclear attacks of Hiroshima and Nagasaki in World War II or the Chernobyl reactor accident in Ukraine in 1986, can cause serious illness or death. More significant, however, is the possibility that exposure to radiation can result in cancer or birth defects years after exposure. The 23,797 survivors of Hiroshima and Nagasaki who received significant non-fatal doses and were followed by doctors for years thereafter, for example, contracted about three more cases of leukemia a year than were seen in a similar group that was not exposed.

THE SCIENCE OF LIFE
Robert Hazen's Broken Wrist

I once had an experience that gave me a whole new perspective on radioactivity. Years ago while playing beach volleyball I dove for a ball and bent back my wrist. It hurt a lot, but it was early in the season, so I taped up the wrist and kept on playing. After a couple of weeks it didn't hurt too much, so I forgot about the injury.

Years later, when the wrist started hurting again, I saw a doctor, who said, "Your wrist has been broken for a long time. When did it happen?" Because the break was so old, my doctor had to find out whether the broken bone surfaces were still able to mend. They sent me to a specialized hospital facility where I was given a shot of a fluid containing a radioactive phosphorus compound—a compound that concentrates on active growth surfaces of bone. After a few minutes this radioactive material circulated through my body, with some of the phosphorus compound concentrating on unset regions of my wrist bones. Radioactive molecules constantly emitted particles that moved through my skin to the outside; as I lay on a table, my broken wrist glowed on the overhead monitor. The process produced a clear picture of the fracture, so my doctor was able to reset the bones. My wrist has healed, and I'm back to playing volleyball.

Today numerous different radioactive materials are useful in medicine and industry because all radioactive isotopes are also chemical elements. Electrons govern the chemistry of atoms, whereas the radioactive properties of a material arise from the nucleus and are totally unrelated to the chemical properties. This fact means that a radioactive isotope of a particular chemical will undergo the same chemical reactions as a stable isotope of that same element. If a radioactive isotope of iodine or phosphorus is injected into your bloodstream, for example, it will collect at the same places in your body as stable iodine or phosphorus.

Medical scientists can use this fact to study the functions of the human body and to make diagnoses of diseases and abnormalities (Figure 12-9). Iodine, for example, concentrates in the thyroid gland. Instruments outside the body can study the thyroid gland's operation by following the path of iodine isotopes that are injected into the bloodstream. Radioactive or nuclear tracers are also used extensively in the Earth sciences, in industry, and in other scientific and technological applications to follow the exact chemical progressions of different elements.

Small amounts of radioactive material will produce measurable signals as they decay and move through a system, allowing scientists and engineers to trace their pathways.

Half-Life

A single nucleus of an unstable isotope left to itself will eventually decay in a spontaneous event. That is, the original nucleus will persist up until a specific time, then radioactive decay will occur, and from that point on you will see only the fragments of the decay.

Watching a single nucleus undergo decay is like watching one kernel in a batch of popcorn. Each kernel will pop at a specific time, but all the kernels don't pop at the same time. Even though you can't predict when any one kernel will pop, you can predict the time during which the popping will go on. A collection of radioactive nuclei behaves in an analogous way. Some nuclei decay almost as soon as you start watching; others persist for much longer times. The percentage of nuclei that decay in each second after you start watching remains more or less the same.

Physicists use the term **half-life** to describe the average time it takes for half of a batch of radioactive isotopes to undergo decay. If you have 100 nuclei at the beginning of your observation and it takes 20 minutes for 50 of them to undergo radioactive decay, for example, then the half-life of that nucleus is 20 minutes. If you were to watch that sample for another 20 minutes, however, not all the nuclei would have decayed. You would find that you had about 25 nuclei at the end, then at the end of another 20 minutes you would most likely have 12 or 13, and so on (Figure 12-10).

Saying that a nucleus has a half-life of an hour does *not* mean that all the nuclei will sit there for an hour, at which point they will all decay. The nuclei, like the popcorn kernels in our example, decay at different times. The half-life is simply an indication of how long on average it will be before an individual nucleus decays.

Radioactive nuclei display a wide range of half-lives. Some nuclei, such as uranium-222, are so unstable that they persist only a tiny fraction of a second. Others, such as uranium-238, have half-lives that range into the billions of years, comparable to Earth's age. Between these two extremes you can find a radioactive isotope that has almost any half-life you wish.

We do not yet understand enough about the nucleus to be able to predict half-lives. On the other hand, the half-life is a fairly easy number to measure and therefore can be determined experimentally for any nucleus. The fine print on most charts of the isotopes (expanded versions of Figure 12-2) usually includes the half-life for each radioactive isotope.

Radiometric Dating

The phenomenon of radioactive decay has provided scientists who study Earth and human history with one of their most important methods of determining the age of materials. This remarkable technique, which depends on measurements of the half-life of radioactive materials, is called **radiometric dating**.

The best-known radiometric dating scheme involves the isotope carbon-14. Every living organism takes in carbon during its lifetime. At this moment, your body is taking the carbon in your food and converting it to tissue, and the same is true of all other animals. Plants are taking in carbon dioxide from the air and doing the same thing. Most of this carbon, about 99%, is in the form of carbon-12, while perhaps 1% is carbon-13. But a certain small percentage, no more than one carbon atom in every trillion, is in the form of carbon-14, a radioactive isotope of carbon with a half-life of about 5,700 years. Carbon-14 is routinely created by the collisions of high-energy cosmic rays with nitrogen atoms in Earth's upper atmosphere.

As long as an organism is alive, the carbon-14 in its tissues is constantly renewed in the same small proportion that is found in the general environment. All of the isotopes of carbon behave the same way chemically, so the proportions of carbon isotopes in the living tissue will be nearly the same everywhere, for all living things. When an organism dies, however, it stops taking in carbon of any form. From the time of death, therefore, the carbon-14 in the tissues is no longer replenished. Like a ticking clock, carbon-14 disappears, atom by atom, to form

FIGURE 12-9 Radioactive tracers at work. The patient has been given a radioactive tracer that concentrates in the bone and emits radiation that can be measured on a film. The dark spot in the front part of the skull indicates the presence of a bone cancer.

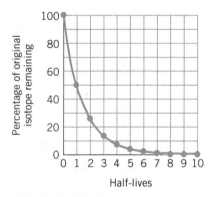

FIGURE 12-10 The graph shows the number of radioactive nuclei left in a sample as the number of half-lives increases.

an ever-smaller percentage of the total carbon. We determine the approximate age of a bone, piece of wood, cloth, or other object by carefully measuring the fraction of carbon-14 that remains and comparing it to the amount of carbon-14 that we assume was in that material when it was alive. If the material happens to be a piece of wood taken out of an Egyptian tomb, for example, we have a pretty good estimate of how old the artifact is and, by inference, when the tomb was built.

Carbon-14 dating often appears in the news when a reputedly ancient artifact is shown to be from more recent times. In a highly publicized experiment, the Shroud of Turin, a fascinating cloth artifact reputed to be involved in the burial of Jesus, was shown by carbon-14 techniques to date from the thirteenth or fourteenth century AD (Figure 12-11).

FIGURE 12-11 The Shroud of Turin, with its ghostly image of a man, was dated by carbon-14 techniques to centuries after the death of Jesus.

STOP & THINK In Chapter 2 we described the monument known as Stonehenge and gave an age for it. This age came from the carbon dating technique we've just described. Because the monument we see today is made of stone (which has no carbon), how do you suppose this dating was done?

Carbon-14 dating has been instrumental in mapping human history over the last several thousand years. When an object is more than about 50,000 years old, however, the amount of carbon-14 left in it is so small that this dating scheme cannot be used. To date rocks and minerals that are millions of years old, scientists must rely on similar techniques that use radioactive isotopes of much greater half-life (Figure 12-12). Among the most widely used radiometric clocks in geology are those based on the decay of potassium-40 (half-life of 1.25 billion years), uranium-238 (half-life of 4.5 billion years), and rubidium-87 (half-life of 49 billion years). In these cases, we measure the total number of atoms of a given element, together with the relative percentage of a given isotope, to determine how many radioactive nuclei were present at the beginning. Most of the ages that we will discuss in the chapters on the Earth sciences and evolution are ultimately derived from these radiometric dating techniques.

SCIENCE BY THE NUMBERS
Dating a Frozen Mammoth

FIGURE 12-12 The oldest human fossils are too ancient to be dated by carbon-14 methods. An alternative technique, called potassium-argon dating, is employed for dating the rocks in which these skulls, which are up to 3.7 million years old, were found.

Russian paleontologists occasionally discover beautifully preserved mammoths frozen in Siberian ice. Carbon isotope analyses from these mammoths often show that only about one-fourth of the original carbon-14 is still present in the mammoth tissues and hair. If the half-life of carbon-14 is 5,700 years, how old is the mammoth?

To solve this problem it's necessary to determine how many half-lives have passed, with the predictable decay rate of carbon-14 serving as a clock. In this case, only one fourth of the original carbon-14 isotopes remain ($1/4 = 1/2 \times 1/2$), so the carbon-14 isotopes have passed through two half-lives. After 5,700 years about half of the original carbon-14 isotopes will remain. Similarly, after another 5,700 years only one-half of those remaining carbon-14 isotopes (or one-fourth of the original amount) will remain. The age of the mammoth remains is thus two half-lives, or about 11,400 years.

Decay Chains

When a parent nucleus decays, the daughter nucleus will not necessarily be stable. In fact, in the great majority of cases, the daughter nucleus is as unstable as the parent. The original parent will decay into the daughter, the daughter will decay into a second daughter, on and on, perhaps for more than a dozen different radioactive events. Even if you start with a pure collection of atoms of the same isotope of the same chemical element, nuclear decay will guarantee that eventually you'll have many different chemical species in the sample. A series of decays of this sort is called

FIGURE 12-13 The uranium-238 decay chain. The nuclei in the chain decay by both alpha and beta emission until they reach lead-208, a stable isotope. Some isotopes may undergo either alpha or beta decay, as indicated by splits in the chain. Nevertheless, all paths eventually arrive at lead-208 after 14 decay events.

a *decay chain*. The sequence of decays continues until a stable isotope appears. Given enough time, all of the atoms of the original element will eventually decay into that stable isotope.

To get a sense of a decay chain, consider the example we used at the beginning of this chapter—uranium-238, with a half-life of approximately 4.5 billion years. Uranium-238 decays by alpha emission into thorium-234, another radioactive isotope. In the process uranium-238 loses 2 protons and 2 neutrons. Thorium-234 undergoes beta decay (half-life of 24.1 days) into protactinium-234 (half-life of about 7 hours), which in turn undergoes beta decay to uranium-234. Each of these beta decays results in the conversion of a neutron into a proton and an electron. After three radioactive decays we are back to uranium, albeit a lighter isotope with a 247,000-year half-life.

The entire uranium decay chain is shown in Figure 12-13. It follows a long path through eight different elements before it winds up as stable lead-206. Given enough time, all of Earth's uranium-238 will eventually be converted into lead. Since Earth is only about 4.5 billion years old, however, there's only been time for about half of the original uranium to decay, so at the moment (and for the foreseeable future) we can expect to have all the members of the uranium decay chain in existence on Earth.

Indoor Radon

The uranium-238 decay chain is not an abstract concept, of interest only to theoretical physicists. In fact, the health concern over indoor radon pollution is a direct consequence of the uranium decay chain. Uranium is a fairly common element—about 2 grams out of every ton of rocks at Earth's surface are uranium. The first steps in the uranium-238 decay chain produce thorium, radium, and other elements that remain sealed in ordinary rocks and soils. The principal health concern arises from the production of radon-222, about halfway along the path to stable lead. Radon is a colorless, odorless, inert gas that does not chemically bond to its host rock.

As radon is formed, it seeps out of its mineral host and moves into the atmosphere, where it undergoes alpha decay (half-life of about 4 days) into polonium-218 and a dangerous sequence of short-lived, highly radioactive isotopes. Historically, radon atoms were quickly dispersed by winds and weather, and they posed no serious threat to human health. In our modern age of well-insulated, tightly sealed buildings, however, radon gas can seep in and build up, occasionally to hundreds of times normal levels, in poorly ventilated basements. Exposure to such high radon levels is dangerous because each radon atom will undergo at least five more radioactive decay events in just a few days.

The solution to the radon problem is relatively simple. First, any basement or other sealed-off room should be tested for radon. Simple test kits are available at your local hardware store. If high levels of radon are detected, then the area's ventilation should be improved.

◉ 12.4 Energy from the Nucleus

Most scientists who worked on understanding the nucleus and its decays were involved in basic research (see Chapter 1). They were interested in acquiring knowledge for its own sake. But, as frequently happens, knowledge pursued for its own sake is quickly turned to practical use. Such applications certainly happened with the science of the nucleus.

The atomic nucleus holds vast amounts of energy. One of the defining achievements of the twentieth century was the understanding of, and subsequent ability to harness, that energy. Two very different nuclear processes can be exploited in our search for energy: processes called nuclear fission and nuclear fusion.

Nuclear Fission

Fission means splitting, and nuclear fission means the splitting of a nucleus. In most cases, energy is required to tear apart a nucleus. Some heavy isotopes, however, have nuclei that can be split apart into products that have less mass than the original. From such nuclei, energy can be obtained from the mass difference.

The most common nucleus from which energy is obtained by fission is uranium-235, an isotope of uranium that constitutes about 7 of every 1,000 uranium atoms in the world. If a neutron hits uranium-235, the nucleus splits into two roughly equal-sized large pieces and a number of smaller fragments. Among these fragments will be two or three more neutrons. If these neutrons go on to hit other uranium-235 nuclei, the process will be repeated and a *chain reaction* will begin, with each split nucleus producing the neutrons that will strike other uranium atoms, causing them to split. To sustain this sort of chain reaction we need to have other uranium atoms nearby. The amount of uranium-235 that has to be assembled to support a chain reaction is the *critical mass*. For a sphere of uranium-235, the critical mass is a little over 50 kilograms.

By this basic process, large amounts of energy can be obtained from uranium. The device that allows us to extract energy from nuclear fission is called a **nuclear reactor** (Figure 12-14). The uranium in a reactor contains mostly uranium-238, but it has been processed so it contains much more uranium-235 than it would if it were found in nature. This uranium is stacked in long fuel rods, about the thickness of a lead pencil, surrounded by a metallic protector. Typical reactors will incorporate many thousands of fuel rods. Between the fuel rods is a fluid called a *moderator*, usually water, whose function is to slow down neutrons that leave each rod.

The nuclear reactor works like this: A neutron strikes a uranium-235 nucleus in one fuel rod, causing that nucleus to split apart. These fragments include several fast-moving neutrons. Fast neutrons are very inefficient at producing fission, but as the neutrons move through the moderator they slow down. In this way, they can initiate other fission events in other uranium atoms. A chain reaction in a reactor proceeds as neutrons cascade from one fuel rod to another. In the process, the energy released by the conversion of matter goes into heating the fuel rods and the water. The hot water is pumped to another location in the nuclear plant, where it is used to produce steam.

The steam is used to run a generator to produce electricity as described in Chapter 5 (see Figure 5-24). In fact, the only significant difference between a nuclear reactor and a coal-fired generating plant is the way in which steam is made. In the nuclear reactor, the energy to produce steam comes from the conversion of mass in uranium nuclei; in the coal-fired plant, it comes from the burning of coal. Nuclear reactors must keep a tremendous amount of nuclear potential energy under control while confining dangerously radioactive material. Modern reactors are thus designed with numerous safety features. Devices called control rods that can be raised or lowered between the fuel rods regulate the rate at which fission occurs. Control rods are made from the metal element cadmium, which absorbs neutrons and becomes a slightly heavier isotope of cadmium in the process, so the position of those rods determines how many neutrons are left to take part in the chain reaction.

The water that is in contact with the uranium in a reactor is sealed in a self-contained system and does not touch the rest of the reactor. Another built-in safety feature is that nuclear reactors cannot function without the presence of the moderator. If there should be an accident in which the water evaporates from the reactor vessel, the chain reaction shuts off. Thus a reactor cannot explode and is *not* analogous to the explosion of an atomic bomb.

FIGURE 12-14 A nuclear reactor, shown here schematically, produces heat that converts water to steam. The steam powers a turbine, just as in a conventional coal-burning plant.

Reactor Accidents

The most serious accident that can occur at a nuclear reactor involves processes in which the flow of water to the fuel rods is interrupted. When this happens, the enormous heat stored in the central part of the reactor can cause the fuel rods to melt. Such an event is called a *meltdown*. In 1979, a nuclear reactor at Three Mile Island in Pennsylvania suffered a partial meltdown but caused only a slight release of radiation—only about 1% of the allowed daily dosage (Figure 12-15). In 1986, a less carefully designed reactor at Chernobyl, Ukraine, underwent a meltdown accompanied by dangerously large releases of radioactivity.

The largest nuclear reactor accident since Chernobyl occurred at Fukushima, Japan, northeast of Tokyo, on March 11, 2011. On that date a major earthquake rocked the western Pacific. There were six reactors at Fukushima, making it one of the largest nuclear installations in the world. At the time of the earthquake, three were shut down for routine maintenance. The remaining three reactors shut down when the earthquake hit, and diesel generators took over the job of pumping water through the reactor cores and pools holding spent fuel rods to keep them from overheating. So far so good.

Then disaster struck. A tsunami almost 50 feet high swept in from the Pacific, easily coming over the 20-foot seawall protecting the plant. It flooded the rooms holding the diesel generators and destroyed the power lines connecting the plant to the Japanese power grid. The flooding and lack of power triggered a series of

FIGURE 12-15 On March 11, 2011, an earthquake and tsunami hit the coast of Japan, damaging the nuclear power facility at Fukushima. Three reactors experienced partial meltdown, while explosions caused by hydrogen gas (shown here) rocked the plant.

events that taxed the skill of the engineers. Because there was no water to cool the reactor cores, three of the reactors went through the meltdown process described above. In addition, old fuel rods that were stored in pools in the reactor buildings began to heat up when their supply of cooling water was cut off. Reactions between the zirconium fuel rod containers and heated water released hydrogen, causing several explosions. Radioactive material was released to the environment, and as a precaution the Japanese government evacuated people from a 12-mile radius around the reactor plant.

After about a week, outside power was brought to the site and the reactors were cooled. However, the extensive job of repair and cleanup may take years.

Fusion

Fusion refers to a process in which small atoms combine together, or fuse, to form a larger atom. Under special circumstances it is possible to push two small nuclei together and make them fuse in a way that produces energy. When elements with low atomic numbers fuse under these special circumstances, the mass of the final nucleus is less than the mass of the elements that started the reaction, with the difference appearing as energy. In these cases, it's possible to extract energy from the fusion reaction by conversion of that "missing" mass to other forms of energy.

The most common fusion reaction in nature combines four hydrogen nuclei to form a helium nucleus (Figure 12-16). (Remember that an ordinary hydrogen nucleus is a single proton, with no neutron. Thus we use the terms *hydrogen nucleus* and *proton* interchangeably.) This nuclear reaction powers the Sun and other stars and thus is ultimately responsible for all life on Earth.

FIGURE 12-16 A fusion reaction releases energy as individual protons combine to form larger nuclei. Hydrogen nuclei enter into a multistep process whose end product is a helium-4 nucleus. The red balls are positively charged protons, the blue ones are electrically neutral neutrons, and "other particles" include positrons and neutrinos that don't form part of nuclei. "Deuterium," with one proton and one neutron, is another name for a hydrogen-2 nucleus. Helium-3 and helium-4 nuclei both have two protons plus one or two neutrons, respectively. The helium-4 nucleus is also known as an alpha particle when it is emitted from a larger atomic nucleus as alpha radiation.

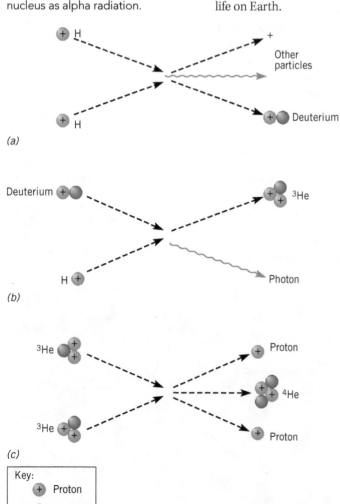

(a)

(b)

(c)

Key:
(+) Proton
● Neutron

You cannot just put hydrogen in a container and expect it to form helium, however. Two positively charged protons must collide with tremendous force in order to overcome their electrostatic repulsion and allow the strong force to kick in (remember, the strong force operates only over extremely short distances). In the Sun, high pressures and temperatures in the star's interior trigger the fusion reaction. The sunlight falling outside your window is generated by the conversion of 600 million tons of hydrogen into helium each second. The helium nucleus has a mass about half a percent less than the original hydrogen nuclei. The "missing" mass is converted to the energy that eventually radiates out into space.

Since the 1950s, many attempts have been made to harness nuclear fusion reactions to produce energy for human use. The problem has always been that it is very difficult to get protons to collide with enough energy to overcome the electrical repulsion between them and initiate the nuclear reaction. These reactions typically do not start with hydrogen, but with the hydrogen isotope deuterium, which has one proton and one neutron in its nucleus. The main reason that scientists pursue the dream of fusion power is that there is enough deuterium in the world's oceans to supply a virtually limitless source of energy for humanity.

One promising but technically difficult method is to confine protons in a very strong magnetic field while heating them with high-powered radio waves. This is the technique used in the world's largest fusion reactor, now being built in France (see the accompanying "Technology" section). Another technique, being explored at the National Ignition Facility at the Lawrence Livermore Laboratory in California, is to use powerful lasers to crush a pellet of frozen hydrogen isotopes, producing temperatures and pressures high enough to achieve fusion. In 2015 modest progress was made toward this goal, but scientists agree that "ignition" (producing more energy from fusion that is put into the apparatus) is a long way off.

TECHNOLOGY
ITER: The Future of Fusion

The technique of using magnetic fields to contain hydrogen plasma while it is heated to fusion temperatures is the main principle behind the operation of a major fusion reactor now being built near the town of Cadarache in southern France—a site chosen after extended international negotiations in which sites on three continents were considered. The machine, originally scheduled to come on line in 2019, is called ITER (Figure 12-17). Originally the name was an acronym for "International Thermonuclear Experimental Reactor," but it is now used as a single word that means "forward" in Latin.

The main working unit will be a doughnut-shaped vacuum chamber enclosed by magnets. The plasma circles around the doughnut as it is heated by a radio frequency field. When its temperature gets high enough, fusion reactions will be initiated.

Although other fusion reactors of this type have been built in various laboratories around the world, ITER will be the first to generate more power than it uses. It is, in fact, designed to produce 500 megawatts of electricity—enough to power a small town. It is important to remember, however, that ITER is not being built as a commercial reactor, but as what engineers call a "proof of concept," a machine that will act as a model for future commercial applications.

Unfortunately, massive cost overruns and delays have caused some countries to doubt the value of the project, with cost estimates of about $5 billion in 2003 now topping $21 billion. Current estimates are that ITER will start running with ordinary hydrogen in 2024 and shift to hydrogen isotopes 10 years later.

SCIENCE IN THE MAKING
Superheavy Elements

Uranium, with 92 protons, is the heaviest element commonly found in nature, but ever since the mid-twentieth century scientists have been able to build heavier ones in the laboratory. If you look at the periodic table of the elements in Chapter 8, all of the elements past uranium occur only as transient byproducts of specialized experiments. The general technique used by groups trying to produce superheavy nuclei is to use an accelerator to get a heavy ion (gold, for example, or krypton) moving fast and then allow it to collide with a heavy target nucleus. In the resulting nuclear maelstrom, it sometimes happens that enough protons and neutrons stick together to create a short-lived superheavy nucleus. Using this technique, scientists have created nuclei up to element 118. In 2011, the international body in charge of naming chemical elements gave the name of Darmstadtium to element 110, Roentgenium to element 111, and Copernicium to element 112. The first of these honors the city in Germany where these elements were first produced, and the other two follow the long tradition of naming elements after important scientists.

Although these heavier atoms are unstable and decay quickly, they can last long

FIGURE 12-17 This cutaway view of the proposed ITER reactor shows the large coils that will be used to produce the magnetic field needed to confine the plasma during the fusion process.

ITER/Photo Researchers, Inc.

enough to be identified by their spectra. Scientists predict that when we get to atomic numbers around 126, we will find an "island of stability"—nuclei that, once created, will not decay. If this prediction turns out to be correct, you can imagine these new nuclei forming the basis for a whole new branch of chemistry.

THINKING MORE ABOUT THE NUCLEUS

Nuclear Waste

When power is generated in a nuclear reactor, many more nuclear changes take place than those associated with the chain reaction itself. Fast-moving debris from the fission of uranium-235 strike other nuclei in the system—both the ordinary uranium-238 that makes up most of the fuel rods, and the nuclei in the concrete and metal that make up the reactor. In these collisions, the original nuclei may undergo fission or absorb neutrons to become isotopes of other elements. Many of these newly produced isotopes are radioactive. The result is that even when all of the uranium-235 has been used to generate energy, a lot of radioactive material remains in the reactor. This sort of material is called *high-level nuclear waste*. (The production of nuclear weapons is another source of this kind of waste.) The half-lives of some of the materials in the waste can run to hundreds of thousands of years. How can we dispose of this waste in a way that keeps it away from living things?

The management of nuclear waste begins with storage. Power companies usually store spent fuel rods at a reactor site for tens of years to allow the short-lived isotopes to decay. At the end of this period, long-lived isotopes that are left behind must be isolated from the environment.

Until recently, plans in the United States called for incorporating these nuclei into stable solids, such as glass. The idea was that the electrons in radioactive isotopes form the same kind of bonds as stable isotopes, so that with a judicious choice of materials, radioactive nuclei will be locked into a solid mass for long periods of time. The glass was to be surrounded by successive layers of steel and concrete, and these stable containers were to be buried deep under Earth's surface in stable rock formations. A site at Yucca Mountain repository, in a remote desert region of Nevada, was chosen as the burial site where long-lived wastes would be sequestered from the environment until after they are no longer dangerous to human beings. In 2009, however, the Obama administration terminated support for the project, and at the moment the United States has no plan to deal with nuclear waste.

Supporters of the Yucca Mountain site argue that a single, remote, long-term site is vastly preferable to the present 131 temporary repositories now located in 39 different states. Such scattered sites are difficult to monitor and protect from terrorist threats. Opponents of Yucca Mountain counter that hauling thousands of tons of nuclear waste on interstate highways poses a far greater danger to the public than the present sites. Furthermore, some geologists fear that Yucca Mountain may be subject to occasional earthquakes and volcanic activity, and that its location, less than 100 miles from Las Vegas, is not sufficiently remote.

What should we do with our increasing quantities of nuclear waste? What responsibility do we have to future generations to ensure that the waste we bury stays where we put it? Should the existence of nuclear waste restrain us in our development of nuclear energy? Should we, as some scientists argue, keep nuclear waste materials at the surface and use them for applications such as medical tracers and fuel for reactors?

RETURN TO THE INTEGRATED QUESTION

How do scientists determine the age of the oldest human fossils?

- Radiometric dating uses the phenomenon of radioactive decay and measurements of the half-life of radioactive elements to determine the age of materials.

- This method provides scientists who study Earth and human history with one of their most important methods of establishing the age of materials from both the near and distant past.

- Radiocarbon dating is one of the most useful radiometric dating methods. It uses the naturally occurring isotope carbon-14 to determine the age of carbonaceous materials up to about 50,000 years.

  - Carbon-14 is a radioactive isotope of carbon with a half-life of about 5,700 years. It is produced continuously as solar radiation enters Earth's atmosphere.

- As long as an organism is alive, it will continuously be taking in carbon-14 along with other forms of carbon. Plants absorb it through photosynthesis, and animals acquire it from the consumption of plants and other animals. When an organism dies, it stops absorbing all forms of carbon from the environment, including carbon-14.

- The passage of time and the process of radioactive decay cause the amount of carbon-14 in the remains of the organism to diminish faster than other more stable forms of carbon. The proportion of carbon-14 left in the remains provides an indication of the time that has passed since its death. The approximate age of any former living object, be it a bone, piece of wood, cloth, is determined by carefully measuring the fraction of carbon-14 that remains and comparing it to the amount of carbon-14 that we assume was in that material when it was alive.

- Radiometric dating using the carbon-14 method has a limit of approximately 50,000 years because the amount of carbon-14 left after this period of time will be quite small. Therefore, the oldest known human remains (which may be as old as 200,000 years) are much too ancient to use carbon-14 techniques.

- To date the most ancient of human fossils, scientists must determine the geological age of surrounding rock. This age is determined using techniques similar to the carbon-14 method, but radioactive isotopes with much greater half-lives are used. Among the most widely employed radiometric clocks in geology are those based on the decay of potassium-40 (half-life of 1.25 billion years), uranium-238 (half-life of 4.5 billion years), and rubidium-87 (half-life of 49 billion years). In these cases, we measure the total number of atoms of a given element, together with the relative percentage of a given isotope, to determine how many radioactive nuclei were present at the beginning.

SUMMARY

The nucleus is a tiny collection of massive particles, including positively charged *protons* and electrically neutral *neutrons*. The nucleus plays a role independent of the surrounding electrons that control chemical reactions, and the energies associated with nuclear reactions are much greater. The number of protons—the *atomic number*—determines the nuclear charge and therefore the type of element; each element in the periodic table has a different number of protons. The number of neutrons plus protons—the *mass number*—determines the mass of the *isotope*. Nuclear particles are held together by the *strong force*, which operates only over extremely short distances.

While most of the atoms in objects around us have stable, unchanging nuclei, many isotopes are unstable—they spontaneously change through *radioactive decay*. In *alpha decay*, a nucleus loses two protons and two neutrons. In *beta decay*, a neutron spontaneously transforms into a proton, an electron, and a neutrino. A third kind of radioactivity, involving the emission of energetic electromagnetic radiation, is called *gamma radiation*. The rate of radioactive decay is measured by the *half-life*, which is the time it takes for half of a collection of isotopes to decay. Radioactive half-lives provide the key for *radiometric dating* techniques based on carbon-14 and other isotopes. Unstable isotopes are also used as radioactive tracers in medicine and other areas of science. Indoor radon pollution and nuclear waste are two problems that arise from the existence of radioactive decay.

There are two forms of nuclear energy. On one hand, *fission* reactions, as controlled in *nuclear reactors,* produce energy when heavy radioactive nuclei split apart into fragments that together weigh less than the original isotopes. *Fusion* reactions, on the other hand, combine light elements to make heavier ones, as in the conversion of hydrogen into a smaller mass of helium in the Sun. In each case, the lost nuclear mass is converted into energy.

KEY TERMS

proton	binding energy	radiometric dating
neutron	radioactivity or radioactive decay	fission
atomic number	alpha decay	critical mass
isotope	beta decay	nuclear reactor
mass number	gamma radiation	fusion
strong force	half-life	

DISCOVERY LAB

Radiometric dating is the process of finding the age of rocks using the time it takes for the radioactive substances in the rock to decay. Have you ever wondered how scientists determine the age of the rocks? You can try this activity by gathering 100 M&M candy pieces, a stopwatch, and a Styrofoam cup.

Put the M&M's (representing the rock) in a cup and record the total number of parent isotope (M&M's). Empty the contents of the cup on a table. Any "M" of M&M's that is face-down will represent a decayed nucleus. Remove all the decayed nuclei and count the total number decayed (this represents the parent isotope). Count the number of M&M's with the other side up (daughter isotope). Now you have gone through one half-life. Repeat the procedures every 2 minutes for five trials or until all the M&M's are gone. Find the total number of half-lives the parent isotope went through. Find the age of the rock (M&M's) by calculating the parent-to-daughter ratio. At every step find the percent of the parent atom remaining in the rock. (Number of half-lives × length of half-life = age of the sample) In what ways is using the M&M's similar to radioactive decay?

REVIEW QUESTIONS

1. By what order of magnitude is an atom larger than its nucleus?
2. What equation describes the relationship between mass and energy?
3. Why do we say that most of the mass of an atom is in the nucleus?
4. Which particles determine the atomic number of the nucleus? Which determine the atomic weight?
5. Why did scientists postulate the existence of the neutron?
6. What is an isotope?
7. What is the strong force? How is the strong force different from gravity and electromagnetism?
8. What is alpha decay? Beta decay? Gamma decay? How does each of these processes change the nucleus?
9. Explain the term *half-life.*

10. What is radiometric dating? What is the most commonly used isotope in the radiometric dating of previously living organisms? Why must geologists use potassium-40 and uranium-238 instead of carbon-14 to date the oldest fossils?
11. What led physicists to hypothesize the existence of the neutrino?
12. What form of indoor air pollution is the result of naturally occurring radioactive decay?
13. How can we obtain energy from nuclear fission?
14. What is a chain reaction? What is a critical mass?
15. How does a nuclear reactor work?
16. How do fusion reactions produce energy?
17. How are radioactive tracers useful in medicine? Give an example.
18. What is nuclear waste? Why is it a serious problem for society?

DISCUSSION QUESTIONS

1. Does a spring have more mass when it is compressed compared to when it is relaxed? Why or why not?
2. What prompted theorists to propose the existence of the strong nuclear force, and what evidence is there for it?
3. One of the largest explosions from a non-nuclear source occurred in 1969 when a Soviet prototype rocket exploded during testing, releasing an estimated equivalent of 7,000 tons of TNT. The smallest nuclear explosives produced were estimated to yield 10,000 tons of TNT. Why is the destructive force of conventional explosives much less than that of nuclear explosives?
4. What are the potential benefits and risks in using nuclear tracers in medical diagnosis?
5. *Critical mass* is a term that is widely used outside of nuclear science. What is its everyday meaning, and how does that relate to its scientific meaning?
6. What types of researchers and scientists use carbon-14 radiometric dating? What type of researcher would use other isotopes such as uranium-238?
7. Discuss the pros and cons of nuclear power. Why is the possibility of sustained nuclear fusion as a source of power explored with such determination?
8. Under what conditions can radiation escape from a power plant?
9. What do you think the prospects are of having commercial energy from nuclear fusion in your lifetime?

10. Suppose you are a scientist from the distant future who has discovered the ruins of the Empire State Building. Which isotopes do you think would exist in the ruins that would allow you to estimate the date that the building was constructed?
11. Why must uranium be enriched in order to be used in a nuclear power plant? What is changed in the process of enrichment?
12. How would you characterize the effect that electrons have on the interactions occurring in the nucleus of the atom? Why?
13. What is a decay chain and why is it important?
14. The electron, originally called a cathode ray, was identified as a particle in 1897. Subsequently, the proton was identified as a particle in 1919 and a neutron in 1932. What do you think were the challenges that led to these particles being discovered in this order?
15. Mount St. Helens in the state of Washington erupted in 1980. Some rocks taken from the eruption were analyzed using potassium-argon dating, which indicated that these rocks were over 100,000 years old when they were clearly "fresh." Do you think this fact means that radioisotope dating is untrustworthy? Why or why not?
16. Which do you think would incur higher health risks: an amount of radioactive material with a short half-life, or the same amount of radioactive material with a relatively long half-life? Why?

PROBLEMS

1. Use the periodic table to identify the element, atomic number, mass number, and electrical charge of the following combinations:

   a. 1 proton, 0 neutrons, 1 electron
   b. 8 protons, 8 neutrons, 8 electrons

c. 17 protons, 18 neutrons, 18 electrons

d. 36 protons, 50 neutrons, 36 electrons

2. Use the periodic table to determine how many protons and neutrons are in each of the following atoms:

a. carbon-14

b. iron-56

c. silver-110

d. gold-160

3. What are the letter abbreviations for the elements in Problems 1 and 2? Where did they come from?

4. On average, an atom of cobalt weighs more than an average atom of nickel. However, a cobalt atom has 27 protons and a nickel atom has 28 protons. How could this situation arise?

5. Potassium-40 decays into argon-40 with a half-life of 1.2 billion years. A particular mineral grain is known to have had a million potassium atoms in its crystal structure when it formed. When the grain was ground up, scientists discovered 750,000 atoms of argon-40. When did the grain form?

6. Imagine that at Earth's formation 4.5 billion years ago a million atoms of uranium-238 were collected and placed in a box where they couldn't interact with anything else. Estimate the number of uranium-238 atoms that would still be in the box. What other elements would you likely find in the box (see Figure 12-13)?

7. Isotope X has a half-life of 100 days. A sample is known to have contained about 10 million atoms of isotope X when it was put together but is now observed to have only about 100,000 atoms of isotope X. Estimate how long ago the sample was assembled. Explain the relevance of this problem to the technique of radiometric dating.

8. Uranium-238 is a radioactive isotope, so why hasn't all the uranium-238 in Earth decayed? Estimate how much time must elapse for there to be only 10% of the current amount of uranium-238 left in Earth. Considering that we anticipate the Sun to start dying in about 5 billion years, and probably destroy Earth in the process, do you think Earth will be around to see this happen?

9. A pot of water contains 500 g of water at 3°C. The water is heated to the boiling point at 100°C, taking 203,000 J of energy. By how much does the mass of the water change due to this addition of energy? Do you think you would notice this change in mass? Why or why not?

10. Carbon-14 decays into nitrogen-14 via beta decay with a half-life of 5,740 years. If we have an archaeological sample that appears to have initially had 100 mg of carbon-14 but is found to have 6 mg of carbon-14 and 94 mg of nitrogen-14, how old would we estimate it to be?

11. You are told that a particular atom has 11 protons and 10 electrons. Which of the following best describes this?

a. Neon, charge = +1

b. Neon, charge = −1

c. Sodium, charge = +1

d. Sodium, charge = −1

12. Suppose isotope A decays with a half-life of 50 years into isotope B. Isotope B then decays with a half-life of only 5 minutes into stable nucleus C. If we start with 10 mg of isotope A, which of the following choices is the best estimate of the quantities of A, B, and C that we would have after 50 years?

a. 5 mg of A, 5 mg of B, 0 mg of C

b. 5 mg of A, 0 mg of B, 5 mg of C

c. 5 mg of A, 2.5 mg of B, 2.5 mg of C

d. 3.33 mg of A, 3.33 mg of B, 3.33 mg of C

INVESTIGATIONS

1. Read a historical account of the Manhattan Project, which resulted in the first atomic bombs. What was the principal technical problem in obtaining the nuclear fuel? Why did chemistry play a major role? What techniques are now used to obtain nuclear fuel?

2. Read about the life of Marie Curie. What were her major scientific accomplishments? How did her gender affect her scientific career?

3. What is the current status of U.S. progress toward developing a depository for nuclear waste? How do your representatives in Congress vote on matters relating to this issue?

4. What sorts of isotopes are used for diagnostics in your local hospital? Where are supplies of those radioisotopes purchased? What are the half-lives of the isotopes, and how often are supplies replaced? What is the hospital's policy regarding the disposal of radioactive waste?

5. How much of the electricity in your area comes from nuclear reactors? What fuel do they use? Where are the used fuel rods taken when they are replaced? If the facility offers public tours, visit the reactor and observe the kinds of safety procedures that are used.

6. Obtain a radon test kit from your local hardware store and use it in the basement of two different buildings. How do the values compare? Is either at a dangerous level? If the values differ, what might be the reason?

7. Read an account of the so-called cold fusion episode. At what point in this history were conventional scientific procedures bypassed? Ultimately, do you think that the scientific method worked or failed?

8. What do you think is the best policy for dealing with nuclear waste in the United States?

9. Investigate the Three Mile Island nuclear power accident and compare it to the Fukushima disaster. What design flaws caused Fukushima to be deadly, while the Three Mile Island accident was relatively benign?

10. What are the half-lives of isotopes employed in medical research (e.g., strontium-89, yttrium-90, iodine-103, and thallium-201)? In what procedures are these and other specific isotopes used?

11. What countries generate the majority of their electric power using nuclear energy? Do these countries have higher rates of cancer or other diseases? Why isn't the United States generating more electricity from nuclear energy?

12. Do you think that nuclear power is a productive idea, or a danger to the environment? Try to find as much information as possible to support the opposing viewpoint (i.e., if you think nuclear power is dangerous, find all relevant scientific publications that suggests its relative safety, and vice versa).

The Ultimate Structure of Matter

How can antimatter be used to probe the human brain?

PHYSICS

Matter is composed of six kinds of quarks and leptons, whose actions are governed by a single unified force.

BIOLOGY

Positrons, a form of antimatter, play an important role in the study of the living brain.

CHEMISTRY

Elementary particles can be detected by measuring the changes they cause in stable atoms.

GREAT IDEA

All matter is made of quarks and leptons, which are the most fundamental building blocks of the universe that we know.

TECHNOLOGY

The largest particle accelerators use electromagnets with superconducting wire.

GEOLOGY

Earth's structure is stable because of the balance between chemical and gravitational forces.

ASTRONOMY

The Sun and other stars produce cosmic rays, which gave scientists their first view of elementary particles.

HEALTH & SAFETY

Particle accelerators are now used in the treatment of some types of cancer.

 = applications of the great idea discussed in this chapter

 = other applications, some of which are discussed in other chapters

Looking at Sand

As you lie on the beach you let a handful of sand sift through your fingers. Look at a single tiny grain, and think about its microscopic structure. Imagine that you could magnify that grain a thousand-fold, a million-fold, even more. What would you see?

At a thousand magnification the rounded grain would appear rough and irregular, but no hint of its atomic structure could be seen. At a million magnification individual atoms, each about a ten-billionth of a meter across, would begin to be visible. And at a trillion magnification the atomic nuclei would appear as tiny points, surrounded by almost nothing.

But is that it? Or is there even more to the submicroscopic structure of the atom? What are the ultimate building blocks of matter?

iStockphoto

◎ 13.1 Of What Is the Universe Made?

The Library

The next time you head over to the library, wander through the stacks and think about what constitutes the fundamental building blocks of the library. Your first reaction might be to say that books are fundamental building blocks—row after row, shelf after shelf, of bound volumes (Figure 13-1). But a library is not just a collection of books; the volumes are arranged with an order to them. You could describe the set of rules that dictates how books are arranged in libraries—the Dewey decimal system or the Library of Congress classification scheme, for example. Thus a complete description of a library at this most superficial level includes two things: books as the fundamental building blocks and rules about how the books are organized.

Inside a book, the various volumes are not as different from each other as they might seem at first. They are all made of an even more fundamental unit—the word. You could argue that the word is the fundamental building block of the library; and, as was the case for cataloged books, we require a set of rules, called grammar, that tells us how to put words together to make books. Words and grammar, then, take you down to a more basic level in your probe of a library's reality.

You probably wouldn't be content very long with the notion of the word as the fundamental building block, because all of the thousands of words are different combinations of a small number of more fundamental things—letters. Only 26 letters (at least in the English alphabet) provide the building blocks for all the thousands of words on all the pages in all the books of the library. Furthermore, we need a set of rules (spelling) that tells us how to put letters together into words. The discovery of letters and spelling would constitute perhaps the next deepest description of a library and its organization. Recalling from Chapter 11 that letters can be represented in binary form—that is, by strings of 0's and 1's—we would realize that these bits would be the ultimate building blocks of the library.

So the library can be described in this way: We use the bits to give us letters, then use spelling to tell us how to put letters together into words. Grammar then tells us how to put words together into books. Finally, we use organizing rules to tell us how to put books together into a library.

And this organization, as we shall see, is how scientists attempt to describe the entire physical universe.

Reductionism

How many different kinds of material can you see when you look up from this book? You may see a wall made of cinder block, a window made of glass, or a ceiling made of fiberglass panels. Outside the window you may see grass, trees, blue sky, and clouds. We encounter thousands of different kinds of materials every day. They all look different—what possible common ground could there be between a cinder block and a blade of grass? They all look different, but are they really?

FIGURE 13-1 In a library, letters form words and words form books. Letters can thus be thought of as the fundamental unit of the library.

For at least two millennia, people who have thought about the physical universe have asked this question. Is the universe just what we see, or is there some underlying structure, some basic stuff, from which it's all made? You could even say that herein lies one of the most fundamental scientific questions.

Philosophers refer to the quest for the "ultimate building blocks" of the universe as *reductionism*. Reductionism is an attempt to reduce the seeming complexity of nature by first looking for underlying simplicity, and then trying to understand how that simplicity gives rise to the observed complexity. This pursuit is a continuation of an old intellectual belief that the appearances of the world do not tell its true nature, but that its true nature can be discovered by the application of thought and, in the case of science, experiment and observation.

The Greek philosopher Thales (c.625–546 BC) suggested that all materials are made of water. This supposition was based on the observation that, in everyday experience, water appears as a solid (ice), a liquid, and a gas (water vapor). Thus, alone among the common substances, water seemed to exhibit all the states of matter (see Chapter 10). To Thales, this observation suggested that water was in some sense fundamental. We no longer accept the idea that water is the fundamental constituent of matter, but we do believe that we can find other fundamental constituents.

The Building Blocks of Matter

To many people, the library analogy presents a profoundly satisfying way of describing complex systems. Some would even argue that everything you could possibly want to know about the library is contained in letters and their organizing principles. In just the same way, scientists want to describe the complex universe by identifying the most fundamental building blocks and deduce the rules by which they are put together.

At first, you might say the most fundamental building block of the universe is the atom. All the myriad solids, liquids, and gases are made of just 100 or so different kinds of chemical elements. The complexity of materials that appears to the senses results from the many combinations of these relatively few kinds of atoms. The rules of chemistry tell us how atoms bind together to make all of the materials we see.

Early in the twentieth century, scientists learned that atoms are not really fundamental, but rather they are made up of smaller, more fundamental bits—nuclei and electrons. These particles arrange themselves according to their own set of rules, with massive neutrons and protons in the positively charged nucleus, and negatively charged electrons in shells around

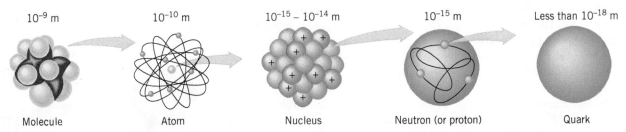

10^{-9} m 10^{-10} m $10^{-15} - 10^{-14}$ m 10^{-15} m   Less than 10^{-18} m

Molecule   Atom   Nucleus   Neutron (or proton)   Quark

FIGURE 13-2 The modern picture of the fundamental building blocks of the universe. Molecules are made from atoms, which contain nuclei, which are made from elementary particles, which in turn are made from quarks. In some modern theories, the quarks are thought to be made from still more elementary objects called strings.

the nucleus. A picture of the universe with only three fundamental building blocks—protons, neutrons, and electrons—is very simple and appealing. Protons and neutrons together form nuclei, and electrons surround the nucleus to form atoms. Atoms combine and interact with each other to form all the materials we know about.

But just as words and grammar gave us a false level of simplicity in the analogy of the library, this simple picture of the universe didn't stand up to more detailed experiments and observations. As we have hinted, the nucleus contains much more than just protons and neutrons, although this fact did not become clear to physicists until the post–World War II era. If we are going to follow the reductionist line in dealing with the universe, we have to start thinking about what makes up the nucleus. By common usage, the particles that make up the nucleus, together with particles such as the electron, were called *elementary particles* to reflect the belief that they comprised the basic building blocks of the universe (Figure 13-2). The study of these particles and their properties is the domain of a field known as **high-energy physics,** or **elementary-particle physics**. Today physicists realize that what were called elementary particles are made of entities more elementary still—entities called "quarks."

● 13.2 Discovering Elementary Particles

Nowhere in nature is the equivalence of mass and energy more obvious than in the interactions of elementary particles. Imagine that you have a source of protons traveling at very high velocities, approaching the speed of light. This source might be astronomical in nature, or it might be a machine that accelerates particles. Once the proton has been accelerated, it has a very high kinetic energy. If this high-energy proton collides with a nucleus, the nucleus can be split apart. In this process, some kinetic energy of the original proton can be converted into mass according to the equation $E = mc^2$. When this happens, new kinds of particles that are neither protons nor neutrons can be created.

Cosmic Rays

During the 1930s and 1940s, physicists used a natural source of high-energy particles, so-called **cosmic rays,** to study the structure of matter. Cosmic rays are particles (mostly protons) that rain down continuously on Earth's atmosphere after being emitted by stars in our galaxy and in other galaxies.

Space is full of cosmic rays. When they hit the atmosphere, they collide with molecules of oxygen or nitrogen and produce sprays of fast-moving secondary particles. These secondary particles, in turn, can make further collisions and produce even more particles, building up a cascade in the atmosphere. It is not uncommon for a single incoming particle to produce billions of secondary particles by the time the cascade reaches Earth's surface. Indeed, on average, several of these rays pass through your body every minute of your life.

Physicists in the 1930s and 1940s set up their apparatus on high mountaintops and observed what happened when fast-moving primary cosmic rays or slightly slower-moving secondary particles collided with nuclei. A typical apparatus incorporated a gas-filled chamber several centimeters across (Figure 13-3). Midway in the chamber was located a thin sheet of target material—lead, for example. Cosmic rays occasionally collided with one of the nuclei in the piece of lead, producing a spray of secondary particles. By studying particles in that spray, physicists hoped to understand what was going on inside the nucleus.

By the early 1940s, when the international effort in physics research shut down temporarily because of World War II, physicists working with these cosmic ray experiments had discovered particles in addition to the proton, neutron, and electron. And when the research effort started up again after the war, these discoveries multiplied as more and more particles were found in the debris of nuclear collisions, both by cosmic ray physicists and by those working at the new particle accelerators we will discuss shortly.

The net result of these discoveries was that the nucleus could no longer be considered as a simple bag of protons and neutrons. Instead, we had to think of the nucleus as a very dynamic place. All kinds of newly discovered elementary particles in addition to protons and neutrons were found there. These exotic particles are created in the interactions inside the nucleus, and they give up their energy (and, indeed, their very existence) in subsequent interactions to make other kinds of particles. This constant dance of the elementary particles inside the nucleus has been well documented since these early explorations.

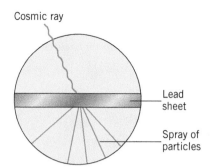

FIGURE 13-3 In a typical cosmic ray experiment, cosmic rays hit a lead nucleus, producing a spray of particles.

 ## TECHNOLOGY
Detecting Elementary Particles

If elementary particles are smaller even than an individual nucleus, how do we know they are really there? Experimental physicists have raised detection of elementary particles to a fine art over the years. Nevertheless, the basic technique used in any detection process is the same: the particle in question interacts with matter in some way, and we measure the changes in matter that are the effects of that interaction.

If an elementary particle has an electrical charge, it may tear electrons loose as it goes by an atom. Thus, a charged elementary particle moving through material such as a photographic emulsion will leave a string of ions in its wake, much as a speedboat going across a lake leaves a trail of troubled water.

A more modern detection method is to allow the particles to pass though a grid of thin conducting wires (usually made of gold). As a particle passes a wire, it exerts a force on the electrons in the metal, creating a small pulse of current. By measuring the time that this pulse arrives at the end of the wire, and by putting together such information from many wires, a computer can reconstruct the particle's path with high precision.

Uncharged particles such as neutrons are much more difficult to detect because they do not leave a string of ions in their path. Typically, the passage of an uncharged particle cannot be detected directly; instead, we wait until it collides with something. If that collision produces charged particles, then we can detect them by the techniques just outlined and can work backward and deduce the property of the uncharged particle.

Particle Accelerators: The Essential Tool

For a time, physicists had to sit around and wait for nature to supply high-energy particles (in the form of cosmic rays) so that they could study the fundamental structure of matter. The arrival of cosmic rays could not be controlled, and it could be very time consuming waiting for one to hit. Physicists quickly realized that they had to build machines that could produce streams of "artificial cosmic rays"—**particle accelerators** that scientists could turn on and off at will and that would take the place of the sporadic cosmic rays in experiments. At the beginning of the 1930s at the University of California at Berkeley, Ernest O. Lawrence began producing a new kind of accelerator called a *cyclotron*—an invention for which he won the 1939 Nobel Prize in Physics (Figure 13-4).

FIGURE 13-4 Ernest O. Lawrence posed in the 1930s with his invention, the cyclotron, which was the first particle accelerator.

One aspect of Maxwell's equations that we didn't talk about in Chapter 5 is that when a charged particle moves in a magnetic field, that field exerts a force on the particle. The effect of the force is to make the particle move in a circular path, and this alteration in direction is the basic working principle behind the operation of the cyclotron. As the particles move in a circular path between two large disk shaped magnets, at one point in their path, they encounter intense radio waves producing a large acceleration according to Newton's second law (force = mass × acceleration; see Chapter 2). The radio waves are encountered over and over again, and the particles are accelerated almost to the speed of light. Once they have acquired this much kinetic energy, they are allowed to collide with other particles. Those collisions provide the interactions that scientists wish to study.

Lawrence's first cyclotron was no more than a dozen centimeters (about 5 inches) across and produced energies that were pretty puny by today's standards. A modern particle accelerator called a **synchrotron** is a huge, high-tech structure capable of producing energies as high as all but the most energetic cosmic rays. The main working part of the synchrotron is a large ring of magnets that keep the accelerated particles moving in a circular track.

As a particle in a synchrotron moves around the circle, the large electromagnets are adjusted to keep its track within a small chamber (typically several centimeters on a side) in which a near-perfect vacuum has been produced. This chamber, in turn, is bent into the large circle that marks the particle's orbit. Each time the particles come around to a certain point, an electric field boosts their energy. As the velocity increases, the field strength in the magnets is also increased to compensate, so that the particles continue around the circular track. Eventually, the particles reach the desired speed, and they are brought out into an experimental area where they undergo collisions. The machine gets its name because the magnetic field has to be synchronized with the particle speed during acceleration.

As the energy required to stay at the frontier of particle physics increases, so too does the size of accelerators (Figure 13-5). Today, the world's highest energy accelerator is the Large Hadron Collider (LHC) located at the European Center for Nuclear Research (CERN) in Geneva, Switzerland.

FIGURE 13-5 Giant particle accelerators like these are the main working tool of particle physicists. We show (a) Fermilab, (b) apparatus inside the new Large Hadron Collider outside of Geneva, Switzerland, and (c) the Stanford Linear Accelerator Center.

Courtesy Fermi National Accelerator Laboratory

CERN

CERN

Particle accelerator

(a)

(b)

(c)

SCIENCE IN THE MAKING
CERN

In the aftermath of World War II, the nations of Europe came together to create a joint institution devoted to forefront physics. In 1951 the *Conseil Européen pour la Récherché Nucleaire* (European Council for Nuclear Research) met, eventually selecting Geneva, Switzerland, as the site for their major research installation and chose to designate themselves with the letters CERN. Today, with 2,500 staff members and scientists representing over 110 countries, CERN is the world's foremost high-energy physics research center. The Large Hadron Collider (see below) is just the most recent of a long series of machines that have defined the forefront of elementary particle physics for over half a century.

The basic operating principle of CERN has always been simple: countries contribute to the organization, and, in return, scientists from contributing countries can participate in experiments. One of the detectors involved in the discovery of the Higgs Boson (which we will discuss below) was built by the United States, for example.

As much as any place in the world, CERN embodies the international nature of the scientific community. One of the authors (JT) spent a year there as a postdoctoral fellow and still has fond memories of the cafeteria patio, where you could hear a dozen different languages being spoken while you enjoyed a view of the Swiss Alps.

FIGURE 13-6 The Large Hadron Collider is the world's most powerful particle accelerator.

TECHNOLOGY
The Large Hadron Collider

The **Large Hadron Collider** is surely the largest and most complex technological project ever undertaken (Figure 13-6). Located in a 27-kilometer (about 15-mile) long tunnel that runs between 50 and 175 meters underneath the Swiss-French border near Geneva, this machine provides scientists with their first look at collisions whose energy is almost 10 times that found in previous accelerators.

The main ring of the machine works on the same principle as an ordinary synchrotron. In the ring are two beams of counter-rotating protons, each accelerated to an energy equivalent to 7 trillion volts. (The protons move at 99.9999991% of the speed of light). At four places around the ring the proton beams are allowed to collide head-on. Each of these intersection points is surrounded by a huge apparatus designed to detect particles produced in the collisions.

Because of the extreme cost involved in building a machine like the LHC, countries throughout the world (including the United States) contributed to the construction of the ring and its detectors, and scientists from over 100 countries will participate in the experiments there.

The machine accelerated its first protons in September 2008, but after only a few days of operation a major problem developed with the magnets and the entire operation shut down for an extended period of repairs. In November 2009, the machine started up again and began taking data. In 2012, as discussed below, physicists at CERN announced the discovery of the Higgs particle. In 2015 the machine is scheduled to be taken up to its full design energy of 14 trillion volts, and it is expected to keep operating until at least 2030.

THE SCIENCE OF LIFE
Accelerators in Medicine

The ability to build machines that accelerate charged particles has had an important effect in many areas of medicine, most notably in the treatment of cancer. Often the goal of this treatment is to destroy malignant cells in tumors, subjecting those cells to high-energy X-rays or gamma rays is a particularly effective way of doing this for some cancers.

To produce a beam of gamma rays for cancer therapy, a small accelerator produces an intense beam of high-speed electrons. These electrons are then directed into a block of heavy metal such as copper, where they are stopped abruptly. As we learned in Chapter 5, electrically charged objects that are accelerated (or, in this case, decelerated) emit electromagnetic waves.

In the case of electrons accelerated to an appreciable fraction of the speed of light and suddenly stopped, those waves will be in the form of gamma rays. The direction of the electron beam is arranged so that the gamma rays pass through the tumor, killing cells as they pass through.

● 13.3 The Elementary Particle Zoo

At the beginning of the 1960s, the first generation of modern particle accelerators began to produce copious results, and the list of elementary particles known to reside inside the nucleus began to grow rapidly. The list now numbers in the hundreds. A few important groups of particles are summarized in the following sections and in Table 13-1.

Leptons

Leptons are elementary particles that do not participate in the strong force that holds the nucleus together, and they are not part of the nuclear maelstrom. We have encountered two leptons so far—the *electron*, which is normally found outside the nucleus rather than in the nucleus itself, and the *neutrino*, a light neutral particle that hardly interacts with matter at all. Since the 1940s, physicists have discovered four additional kinds of leptons, for a total of six. If you keep in mind that the electron and the neutrino are typical leptons, you will have a pretty good idea of what they're like. The six leptons seem to be arranged in pairs—in each pair there is a particle like the electron, which has a mass, and a specific kind of neutrino.

Hadrons

All of the different kinds of particles that exist inside the nucleus are referred to collectively as **hadrons**, or "strongly interacting ones." The array of these particles is truly spectacular. Hadrons include particles that are stable like the proton, particles that undergo radioactive decay in a matter of minutes like the neutron (which undergoes beta decay), and other particles that undergo radioactive decay in 10^{-24} seconds. The last-named particles do not even live long enough to travel across a single nucleus! Some hadrons carry an electrical charge, whereas others are neutral. But all of these particles are subject to the strong force, and all participate in holding the nucleus together; thus they help make the physical universe possible.

Antimatter

For every particle that we see in the universe, it is possible to produce an antiparticle. Every particle of **antimatter** has the same mass as its matter twin, but the particles have opposite charge and opposite magnetic characteristics. The antiparticle of the electron, for example, is a positively charged particle known as the *positron*. It has the same mass as the electron but a positive electrical charge. Antinuclei, composed of antiprotons and antineutrons and surrounded by positrons, can form antiatoms.

TABLE 13-1 **Summary of Elementary Particles**

Type	Definition	Examples
leptons	do not take part in holding together the nucleus	electron, neutrino
hadrons	participate in holding nucleus together	proton, neutron, roughly 200 others
antiparticles	particles with same mass, but opposite charge and other properties	positron

When a particle collides with its antiparticle, both masses are converted completely to energy in a process called *annihilation,* the most efficient and violent process that we know in the universe. The original particles disappear, and in their place energy appears as a spray of rapidly moving particles and electromagnetic radiation. Science fiction writers have long appropriated this fact in their descriptions of futuristic weapons and power sources. (The starship *Enterprise* on *Star Trek,* for example, has matter and antimatter pods as its power source.)

Although antimatter is fairly rare in the universe, it is routinely produced in particle accelerators. High-energy protons or electrons strike nuclear targets, and the energy of the particles is converted to equal numbers of other particles and antiparticles. Thus the existence of antimatter is verified daily in laboratories.

SCIENCE IN THE MAKING
The Discovery of Antimatter

In 1932, Carl Anderson, a young physicist at the California Institute of Technology, was performing a rather straightforward cosmic ray experiment of the type described in the text. Cosmic rays entered a type of detector called a cloud chamber. In Anderson's cloud chamber, a cosmic ray particle would move through a moisture-laden gas, leaving behind a string of ions. By pulling out a piston at the bottom of the chamber, Anderson lowered the gas pressure and the liquid (usually alcohol) that had been in gaseous form condensed out into droplets. The ions acted as nuclei for the condensation of these droplets, so that the path of the particle was marked by a string of droplets in the chamber.

The key innovation in Anderson's experiment was the positioning of the cloud chamber between the poles of powerful magnets. These magnets caused electrically charged cosmic rays to move in curved tracks, with the amount of curving dependent on the particle's mass, speed, and charge. Furthermore, the tracks of positively and negatively charged particles curved in opposite directions under the influence of the magnetic field.

Soon after he switched on his apparatus, Anderson saw tracks of particles whose mass seemed to be identical to that of the electron, but whose tracks curved in the opposite direction from those of electrons being detected (Figure 13-7). This feature, he concluded, had to be the result of a "positive electron," a phrase he contracted to positron. Although no one realized it at the time, Anderson was the first human being to see antimatter.

FIGURE 13-7 Carl Anderson identified the positron (the antiparticle of the electron) from the distinctively curved path left in a bubble chamber. In Anderson's original photograph *(a)* the positron path curves upward and to the left. In a more recent photograph *(b)* an electron (e⁻) and a positron (e⁺) curve opposite directions in a magnetic field.

(a)

(b)

STOP & THINK How might Anderson have interpreted his results if he had seen tracks of particles curving the same direction as electrons, but curving a different amount? (*Hint: Remember Newton's second law of motion.*)

 ## THE ONGOING PROCESS OF SCIENCE
How Does the Brain Work?

The study of elementary particles often seems quite abstract, but situations do arise in which elementary particles play a very important role in understanding the real world. The fascinating technology of positron emission tomography (PET), for example, helps scientists probe the mysterious workings of the brain. In this medical technique, molecules such as glucose (see Chapter 22) that have been made using an unstable isotope of an element such as oxygen (an isotope produced in nuclear reactors) are injected into a patient's bloodstream. Organs in the body, including the brain, take up these molecules. They will go to the parts of the brain that need it—the parts that require extra energy at the time (see Figure 13-8). Alternatively, they may be molecules shaped in such a way that they attach to specified spots on the cells in the brain (see Chapter 21).

The isotopes are chosen for this technique because they emit a positron, the antiparticle of an electron, when they decay. These positrons quickly annihilate with nearby electrons, emitting energetic gamma rays in the process. These gamma rays are relatively easy to detect from outside the body. A PET scan works like this: After the material is injected into the bloodstream, the patient is asked to do something—talk, read, do mathematical problems, or just relax. Each of these activities uses a different region of the brain. Scientists watching the emission of positrons can see those regions of the brain "light up" as they are used. In this way, scientists use antimatter to study the normal working of the human brain without disturbing the patient, as well as to detect and study abnormalities that can perhaps be treated.

Quarks

When chemists understood that the chemical elements could be arranged in the periodic table, it wasn't long before they realized what caused this regularity. Different chemical elements were not "elementary," as Dalton had suggested, but were structures made up of things more elementary still. The same kind of organization is true of the hundreds of elementary hadrons, or nuclear particles. They are not themselves elementary but are made up of units

FIGURE 13-8 Positron emission tomography, commonly called the PET scan, reveals activity in the human brain. (*a*) A patient undergoing a PET scan. (*b*) A scan of a normal brain is seen at the left of the figure. The bright spots are places where large amounts of glucose (a simple sugar used by most cells for energy) are being used by the brain. The right half of the figure shows a scan of a person suffering from Alzheimer's disease.

(a)   (b)

Hank Morgan/Photo Researchers/Photo Researchers

Dr. Robert Friedland/SPL/Photo Researchers, Inc.

more elementary still—units that are given the name **quark** (pronounced "quork)." First suggested in the late 1960s, quarks have come to be accepted by physicists as *the* fundamental building blocks of hadrons. Even though they never have been (and probably cannot be) seen in the laboratory, the concept of quarks has brought order and predictability to the complex zoo of elementary particles. (It is important to remember that only hadrons, not leptons, are made from quarks.)

Quarks are different from other elementary particles in a number of ways. Unlike any other known particle, they have fractional electrical charge, equal to $\pm\frac{1}{3}$ or $\pm\frac{2}{3}$ of the charge on the electron or proton. In this model of matter, quarks and antiquarks in pairs or triplets make up all the hadrons, but once they are locked into these particles, no amount of experimental machination will ever pry them loose. Quarks existed as free particles only briefly in the very first stages of the universe (see Chapter 15).

In spite of these strange properties, the quark picture of matter is a very appealing one. Why? Because instead of dealing with numerous hadrons, only six kinds of quarks (and six antiquarks) occur in the universe. The quarks, like many phenomena in elementary-particle physics, have been given fanciful names: *up, down, strange, charm, top, and bottom* (see Table 13-2). Scientists have now found elementary particles that contain all six different kinds of quarks. (The last piece of this puzzle—experimental confirmation of the top quark—was announced in May 1994.)

From these six simple particles, all of the hadrons that we know about—all those hundreds of particles that whiz around inside the nucleus—can be made. The proton, for example, is the combination of two up quarks and one down quark, while the neutron is the combination of two down quarks and one up quark. In this scheme, the charge on the proton, equal to the sum of the charges on its three quarks, is:

$$\frac{2}{3}+\frac{2}{3}+\left(-\frac{1}{3}\right)=+1$$

whereas the charge on the neutron is:

$$\frac{2}{3}+\left(-\frac{1}{3}\right)+\left(-\frac{1}{3}\right)=0$$

In the more exotic particles, pairs of quarks circle each other in orbit, like some impossible star system.

TABLE 13-2 **Quark Properties**

Name of Quark	Symbol	Electrical Charge*
down	d	$-\frac{1}{3}$
up	u	$+\frac{2}{3}$
charm	s	$-\frac{1}{3}$
strange	c	$+\frac{2}{3}$
bottom	b	$-\frac{1}{3}$
top	t	$+\frac{2}{3}$

* Quarks with the same charge differ from each other in mass and other properties.

Quarks and Leptons

The quark model gives us a picture of the universe that restores the kind of simplicity that was brought by both Dalton's atoms and Rutherford's nucleus. All of the elementary particles in the nucleus are made from various combinations of six kinds of quarks. These elementary particles are then put together to make the nuclei of atoms. The six different leptons—primarily the electrons—are stationed outside the nucleus to make the complete atoms, and different atoms interact with each other to produce what we see in the universe. In this scheme, the quarks and leptons are the 0's and 1's of the universe; they are the basic stuff from which everything else is made. The fact that there are six leptons and six quarks has not escaped the notice of physicists. This phenomenon is built into almost all theories of elementary particles. The question of *why* nature should be arranged this way remains unanswered.

● 13.4 The Four Fundamental Forces

In our excursion into the library, finding the letters of the alphabet wasn't enough to explain what we saw. We had to know the rules of spelling and grammar by which letters are converted into words and then books. In the same way, if we are going to understand the fundamental nature of the universe, we have to understand not only the quarks and leptons, but also the forces that arrange them and make them behave the way they do.

TABLE 13-3 **The Four Forces**

Force	Relative Strength*	Range	Gauge Particle
gravity	10^{-39}	infinite	graviton
electromagnetic	1/137	infinite	photon
strong force	1	10^{-13} cm	gluon
weak force	10^{-5}	10^{-15} cm	W and Z

* Relative to the strong force.

One useful analogy is to think of the quarks and leptons as the bricks of the universe. The universe appears to be built of these two different kinds of bricks that are arranged in different ways to make everything we see. But you cannot build a house using bricks alone: Something like mortar has to hold the bricks together. The "mortar" of the universe—the things that hold the elementary particles together and organize the physical universe into the structures we know—are the forces. At the moment, we know of only four fundamental forces in nature. Two of these, *gravity* (Chapter 2) and *electromagnetism* (Chapter 5), were known to nineteenth-century physicists and are part of our everyday experience. They are forces with infinite range—that is, objects such as stars and planets can exert these forces on each other even though they are very far apart.

The other two forces are less familiar to us because they operate in the realm of the nucleus and the elementary particle. They have a range comparable to the size of the nucleus (or smaller) and hence play no role in our everyday experience. The *strong force* holds the nucleus together, whereas the *weak force* is responsible for processes such as beta decay (see Chapter 12) that tear nuclei and elementary particles apart.

Each of the four fundamental forces is different from the others in both strength and range (see Table 13-3). The important point about the four forces is that whenever anything happens in the universe, whenever an object changes its motion, it happens because one or more of these forces is acting.

Force as an Exchange

We know that forces cause matter to accelerate—nothing happens without a force. We have talked about the gravitational force, the electromagnetic force, the strong force, and the weak force. Each has its own distinctive effects on nature. We have not, however, asked how these forces work.

The modern understanding of forces may be thought of schematically as illustrated in Figure 13-9. Every force between two particles corresponds to the exchange of a third kind of particle, called a *gauge particle* for historical reasons. That is, a first particle (an electron, for example) interacts with a second particle (say another electron) by the exchange of a gauge particle. The gauge particles produce the fundamental forces, such as electricity, that hold everything together.

In Chapter 2 we used the analogy of someone standing on skates throwing baseballs to explain Newton's third law of motion. Suppose a person on skates throws a baseball, and another person standing on skates catches the baseball some distance away. The person who threw the baseball would recoil, as we discussed. The person who subsequently caught the baseball would also recoil. We could describe the situation this way: Two people stand still before anything happens. After some time, the two people are moving away from each other. From Newton's first law, we conclude that a repulsive force had acted between those two people. Yet it's very clear in this analogy that that repulsive force is intimately connected with (a physicist would say "mediated by") the exchange of the baseball.

In just the same way, we believe that every fundamental force is mediated by the exchange of some kind of gauge particle (Figure 13-10). For example, the electrical force is mediated by the exchange of *photons*. That is, the magnet holding notes onto your refrigerator is exchanging huge numbers of photons with atoms inside the refrigerator metal to generate the magnetic force.

FIGURE 13-9 The exchange of a baseball between two skaters provides an analogy for the exchange of a gauge particle. Skater A, who throws the ball, recoils, and skater B recoils when the ball reaches her. Thus both skaters change their state of motion, and, by Newton's first law, we say that a force acts between them.

In the same way, in unified field theories the gravitational force is thought to be mediated by as yet undiscovered particles called *gravitons*. In this picture you are exchanging large numbers of gravitons with Earth, an exchange that prevents you from floating up into space. The four fundamental forces and the gauge particles that are exchanged to generate each of them are listed in Table 13-3.

In general, the heavier a gauge particle is, the shorter the distance it can travel between the time it is emitted and the time it is absorbed. Thus, the weak force acts only over distances appropriate to the nucleus of the atom and plays no role in our everyday experience. The gluons, like the quarks they govern, cannot exist outside of the nucleus either, so the strong force is also not part of our everyday experience. Only gravity and electromagnetism, mediated by the exchange of massless particles unconstrained by quantum mechanical rules, can act over distances associated with ordinary experience.

The two familiar forces of gravity and electromagnetism act over long distances because they are mediated by massless, uncharged particles (of which the familiar photon is one). The weak interaction, in contrast, has a short range because it is mediated by the exchange of very massive particles—the W and Z *particles*—that have masses about 80 times that of the proton. Like the photon, the W and Z are particles that can be seen in the laboratory—they were first discovered in 1983 and are now routinely produced at accelerators around the world.

The situation with the strong force is a bit more complicated. The force that holds quarks together is mediated by particles called *gluons* (they "glue" the hadrons together). These particles are supposed to be massless, like the photon, but, like the quarks, they are confined to the interior of particles.

(a)

(b)

FIGURE 13-10 *(a)* Exchange diagram, introduced by *(b)* physicist Richard Feynman (1918–1988), provides a model for particle interactions and the fundamental forces. Two incoming particles (such as two electrons) exchange a gauge particle (a photon) and thus are deflected by the force.

AIP Emilio Segre Visual Archives, Physics Today Collection

Labels on figure (a): Deflected by force; Exchange of gauge particle; Incoming particles

Unified Field Theories

Although a universe with six kinds of quarks, six kinds of leptons, and four kinds of forces may seem to be a relatively simple one, physicists have discovered an even greater underlying simplicity. The four fundamental forces turn out not to be as different from each other as their properties might at first suggest. The current thinking is that all four of these "fundamental" forces may simply be different aspects of a single underlying force.

Scientists suggest that the four forces appear to be different because we are observing them at a time when the universe has been around for a long time and is at a relatively low temperature. The situation is somewhat analogous to freezing water. When water freezes it can adopt many apparently different forms—powdered white snow, solid ice blocks, delicate hoarfrost on tree branches, or a slippery layer on the sidewalk. You might interpret these forms of frozen H_2O as very different, and in some respects they are distinct. But heat them up, and they are all simply water.

Similarly, the four forces look different at the relatively low temperatures of our present existence, but heat matter up to trillions of degrees and the different forces are not really different at all. Theories in which fundamental forces are seen as different aspects of one force are called **unified field theories**.

The first unified field theory in history was Isaac Newton's synthesis of earthly gravity and the circular motions observed in the heavens. To medieval scientists, earthly and heavenly motions seemed as different as the strong and electromagnetic forces do to us. Nevertheless, they were unified in Newton's theory of universal gravitation. In the same way, scientists today are working to unify the four fundamental forces.

The general idea of these theories is that if the temperature can be raised high enough—that is, if enough energy can be pumped into an elementary particle—then the underlying unity of the forces will become clear. At a few laboratories around the world, it is possible to take protons and antiprotons (or electrons and positrons), accelerate them to extremely high

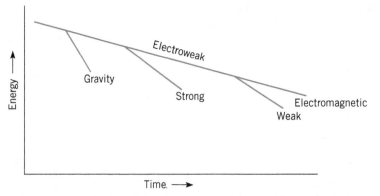

FIGURE 13-11 The four forces become unified at extremely high energy or high temperatures, equivalent to those at the beginning of the universe. At 10^{-43} second after the moment of creation, the universe had already cooled sufficiently for gravity to have separated from the other three forces. The strong force separated at 10^{-33} second, while the weak and electromagnetic forces separated at 10^{-10} second.

energies, and let them collide. (As we have noted, proton–antiproton collisions involve the process of annihilation between particle and antiparticle.) When these collisions occur, for a brief moment the temperature in the volume of space about the size of a proton is raised to temperatures that have not been seen in the universe since it was less than a second old. In the resulting maelstrom, particles are produced that can be accounted for only if the electromagnetic and weak forces become unified.

In 1983, experiments at CERN and the Stanford Linear Accelerator Center demonstrated that this kind of unification does occur. When protons and antiprotons (at the former laboratory) or electrons and positrons (at the latter) were accelerated and allowed to collide head-on, W and Z particles were seen in the debris of the collisions. Not only were the reactions seen, but the properties of the resulting particles and their rates of production were exactly those predicted by the first unified field theories.

The Standard Model

At energies now available in our accelerators, we can see the unification of the electromagnetic and weak forces into what is called the *electroweak* force (Figure 13-11). At still higher energies, energies much higher than those that might be reached by any foreseeable accelerator, we expect the strong and electroweak forces to unify. The theory that describes this unification has been given the somewhat prosaic name of the "Standard Model." Although we cannot test the unification of strong and electroweak forces directly, the theory makes many predictions of the details of interactions we can test in our laboratories. Since the theory has proved to be remarkably successful in its predictions, scientists feel that it gives us the correct description of the last-but-one unification of forces. This understanding of the relationships among the four forces will be important in Chapter 15, when we discuss the earliest stages in the evolution of the universe.

One prediction of the Standard Model is that there is yet another kind of particle in nature. It is called the Higgs, after Scottish physicist Peter Higgs, the man who first predicted its existence (Figure 13-12). The best way to think about Higgs particles is to imagine them as a kind of thin molasses pervading all of space. According to the Standard Model, other particles acquire their mass by interacting with this background. Some particles have a big interaction with the Higgs and are slowed down a lot by the "molasses," a fact that we interpret as the particle having a large mass. Similarly, other particles interact less strongly with the Higgs, are slowed down less, and are perceived to have a small mass. Thus, the Higgs particle is thought to explain the existence of mass. The discovery of the Higgs particle at the Large Hadron Collider in 2012 was a major milestone on the road to understanding the ultimate nature of matter.

FIGURE 13-12 Scottish physicist Peter Higgs, who first suggested the existence of the particle that bears his name.

◉ 13.5 Quantum Gravity, Strings, and Theories of Everything

As things stand now, we have a successful theory that describes the unification of the strong, electromagnetic, and weak forces. This leaves only the force of gravity to be incorporated into the unification scheme. The search for such a theory involves an area that physicists call "quantum gravity," and would require that we understand gravity as arising from the exchange of gravitons, just as the electrical force arises from an exchange of photons. Nobel Laureate Steven Weinberg calls this the "Final Theory," and other scientists often refer to it as a "Theory of Everything" (TOE). In spite of the best efforts of theoretical physicists over the past several decades, we do not yet have such a theory. It remains the final goal of our theory of the structure of the universe.

The leading candidates for the TOE are called **string theories**. In these theories the quarks and leptons are seen as being made from tiny vibrating strings, with different quarks corresponding to different vibration modes of the string (think of a violin string with its overtones). These types of theories turn out to be very difficult mathematically, and they have not yet been developed to the point where they can make experimentally verifiable predictions.

String theories have the unusual feature that, unlike a violin string that vibrates in three dimensions, the theories demand that the fundamental strings vibrate in 11 or more dimensions (don't try to picture this—you can't). One way to think about the question of how our ordinary four-dimensional world (three space dimensions plus time) could arise from a world in which the fundamental materials have many more dimensions is to consider a simple analogy. If you look at an ordinary garden hose close up, you see it as a three-dimensional object. There is the length of the hose, which is basically a two-dimensional line, and there is the roundness of the hose, which can be thought of as a third dimension. If you look at the same hose from far away, however, you don't see that third dimension—all you see are the single dimension that describes the length of the hose. In just the same way, scientists argue, when we look at an 11-dimensional world from the human viewpoint, all the dimensions but 4 are basically invisible, and we have to get down inside the elementary particles before we see them.

Another candidate for the TOE is called quantum loop gravity. In these theories, the space-time grid in which we exist becomes granular when we look at it closely enough—picture it as being something like a sheet of chain mail. Which, if either, of these two candidates will prevail depends on how future experiments turn out.

THINKING MORE ABOUT **PARTICLE PHYSICS**

Basic Research in Particle Theory

One aspect of research in elementary particle physics should be obvious from our description of the current generation of particle accelerators—it is expensive. The cost of the giant machines needed to probe into the heart of matter runs into billions of dollars, and this high price tag creates problems. In 1993, for example, the United States Congress terminated a project called the Superconducting Supercollider, a machine even bigger than the Large Hadron Collider (LHC). At the time, the machine was under construction south of Dallas and had a price tag of over $10 billion.

Are projects of this magnitude justified? On one hand, some people argue that with all the problems in the world—hunger, poverty, terrorism—it makes no sense to spend large amounts of money on machines that will produce no immediate benefit, or whose benefits may be far off.

On the other hand, others point out that in the past money spent on apparently useless basic research has resulted in huge benefits to humanity. The development of the theory of electromagnetism in the nineteenth century and quantum mechanics in the twentieth, for example, have both changed the human condition for the better. It's hard to put a price tag on something like the ability to generate electricity or to process information in a computer. Basic research has always paid off big in the past, they argue, so we should support it now.

How much money do you think the federal government should spend on research like this, whose benefits may be a generation in the future? What percentage of your tax dollars would you be willing to allocate to this task?

← RETURN TO THE INTEGRATED QUESTION

How can antimatter be used to probe the human brain?

- As we saw in Chapter 8, matter is composed of particles. For every particle in the universe, it is possible to produce an antiparticle. These antiparticles are known as *antimatter*. Every particle of antimatter has the same mass as its matter twin, but the antimatter particle has the opposite charge and magnetic characteristics. The antiparticle of the electron, for example, is a positively charged particle known as the *positron*. It has the same mass as the electron but a positive electrical charge.

  - When a particle (e.g., an electron) collides with its antiparticle (e.g., a positron), both masses are converted completely to energy in a process called *annihilation,* the most efficient and yet violent process that we know in the universe. Nothing from the collision of the original particles exists except energy.

- Matter–antimatter reactions have practical application in a number of domains, including medical imaging. For example, three-dimensional images of functional processes within the human body and brain are possible with a nuclear medicine imaging technique known as positron emission tomography (PET).

  - In PET, a positron-emitting radionuclide (i.e., a radioactive tracer) is injected into the body. Three-dimensional computer images are generated via the gamma ray emissions of the tracer.

- Many newer PET systems incorporate X-ray Computed Tomography (PET-CT). Computer-generated images from both technologies are systematically combined into a single image. With this combined system, the metabolic activity captured with the PET is aligned with the precise anatomic imaging obtained by CT scanning. This technology offers dramatic diagnostic benefits compared with imaging technologies only a decade old.

SUMMARY

High-energy physics, or elementary-particle physics, deals with bits of matter that we cannot see, and forces and energies that we can barely imagine. Nevertheless, the study of the subatomic world holds the key to understanding the structure and organization of the universe.

All matter is made up of atoms, which are made up of even smaller particles—electrons and the nucleus—but these are not the most fundamental building blocks of the universe. Physicists originally examined collisions between energetic *cosmic rays* and nuclei to study elementary particles. They now employ *particle accelerators,* including *synchrotrons* and *linear accelerators,* to collide charged particles at near-light speeds. These scientists have discovered hundreds of subatomic particles.

One class of particles, the *leptons* (including the electron and neutrino), are not subject to the strong force and thus do not participate in holding the nucleus together. Nuclear particles called *hadrons* (including the proton and neutron), according to present theories, are made from *quarks*—odd particles that have fractional electrical charge and cannot exist alone in nature. Together, leptons and quarks are the most fundamental building blocks of

matter that we know. Each of these particles has an *antimatter* particle, such as the positron, the positively charged antiparticle of the electron.

The four known forces—gravity, electromagnetism, the strong force, and the weak force—cause particle interactions that lead to all of the organized structures we see in the universe. Particle interactions are mediated by the exchange of gauge particles, with a different gauge particle for each of the different forces. Two masses, for example, will exchange gravitons (the gauge particle of gravity) as they attract each other, and two charged particles will exchange photons, much the same way that two skaters will be "repelled" by each other if a mass is thrown (exchanged) from one to the other.

Although the four known forces appear to us to be quite different from each other, scientists speculate that early in the universe, when temperatures were extremely high, the four forces were unified into a single force. At the forefront of modern physics research is the search for a *unified field theory* that describes this single force. *String theories*, the most prominent type of unified field theory, envision quarks as made of fundamental units called strings.

KEY TERMS

high-energy physics, or elementary
   particle physics
cosmic rays
particle accelerator
synchrotron

Large Hadron Collider
leptons
hadrons
antimatter

quarks
unified field theory
string theories

DISCOVERY **LAB**

When subatomic particles are made to pass through detectors, they can be identified by their speed, mass, and charge. To simulate how particle detectors work, you will need two shoebox lids, small objects to lift the lids up, iron filings, and ordinary and magnetic marbles.

Shoebox lid

Iron filings

Magnetic marble

Roll the magnetic marble under the lid.

To make the simulated detector, set one lid of the shoebox upside down on the table high enough for the marbles to easily roll under the lid. Sprinkle iron filings all over the lid to evenly cover the surface. Roll a magnetic marble under the lid and record your observations. What property of the marble is being detected?

Repeat the process by rolling an ordinary marble under the lid and write down your observations. Which particle would behave in this manner?

Put another lid next to the first one. This looks like a two-part detector to track neutral particles. Place three to four magnetic marbles underneath the edge of the second lid. Sprinkle iron filings evenly on both of the lids. Roll a magnetic marble beneath the first lid. If it hits the magnetic marble what can you

infer from the tracks in the second lid? Which particles behave in this way? How does this experiment show how particle detectors work?

REVIEW QUESTIONS

1. What is reductionism?

2. What are the building blocks of matter?

3. What are "cosmic rays"? How were they used to study the structure of matter?

4. What is a particle accelerator? How do scientists use particle accelerators to study subatomic particles?

5. What is the difference between a hadron and a lepton?

6. What are the basic building blocks of hadrons?

7. What is antimatter, and how do we know it exists? What is the antiparticle of an electron?

8. How do quarks differ from other elementary particles? Can quarks ever be seen as free particles?

9. Describe how quarks and leptons are put together to make all the matter we see.

10. Explain what it means for quarks to be confined.

11. List the four fundamental forces from strongest to weakest.

12. Under what conditions do scientists speculate that the four fundamental forces were unified into a single force?

13. What particle is exchanged to generate each of the four fundamental forces?

14. What is a unified field theory? Give an example.

15. What is string theory?

DISCUSSION QUESTIONS

1. What allows for a relatively small number of particles to give rise to all the complexity we observe in our universe?

2. What are the roles of experimentation and observation in reductionist science? Identify what might be considered the "fundamental units" and rules of organization of: (a) a large

city, (b) the human body, and (c) a family. How many levels of organization can you identify? (Remember, not all questions have only one correct answer.)

3. Which particle–antiparticle interaction releases more energy: an electron–positron annihilation or a proton–antiproton

annihilation? In what form do you think this energy is generally released?

4. Consider the atomic theory of the ancient Greeks. What was their justification for assuming the existence of atoms? How is that similar to or different from our current understanding of the fundamental particles of nature?

5. Why is a universe composed of six types of quarks and six types of leptons more appealing to physicists than a model built up from hundreds of particles?

6. Describe Carl Anderson's experiment, and the observations that led him to conclude that he had discovered a particle with the same mass as the electron, but with a positive electrical charge.

7. Was there ever a point in the history of the universe in which all four fundamental forces were unified? If so, when? Furthermore, what does it mean to say these forces were unified?

8. How might you detect the presence of a charged elementary particle?

9. Some theorists have speculated on the existence of "preons" as particles that make up quarks and leptons. Supposing these

particles actually exist, how would we know if preons are the ultimate building blocks of matter or if there is something even more fundamental?

10. What medical technologies (e.g., PET) rely on the physics of elementary particles? What are the benefits of noninvasive procedures such as PET?

11. Why is "big science" needed in the study of elementary particles? Who provides the funding for "big science"? Does "big science" stimulate economic growth? If so, in what ways?

12. What elementary particles do you interact with on a regular basis? Which ones are they, and how do you interact with them?

13. In describing his efforts at developing the theory of quantum mechanics, Nobel laureate Paul Dirac once said, "It seems that if one is working from the point of view of getting beauty in one's equations, and if one has really a sound insight, one is on a sure line of progress." How do you think this statement fits in with the philosophy behind reductionism?

14. Discuss how Isaac Newton's theory of gravity is a unification theory combining Galileo's theories of terrestrial motion with Kepler's theories of celestial motion.

PROBLEMS

1. What is the electrical charge of an anti-proton? What are the constituent quarks of an antiproton? What are the electrical charge and constituent quarks of an antineutron?

2. What is the electrical charge of a positron? How does this particle differ from a proton?

3. A hadron known as the "sigma particle" has two down quarks and a strange quark. What is the charge of this sigma particle?

4. A particle known as the "charmed sigma particle" is composed of two up quarks and a charm quark. What is its electrical charge?

5. A hadron called the lambda particle is made from two down quarks and one strange quark. What is the charge of the lambda particle?

6. A particle called the delta is made from three up quarks. What is the charge of this particle?

7. The proton is a combination of which quarks? Calculate the charge of a proton based on its constituent quarks. (*Hint*: See page 297)

8. Within a nucleus of helium, the two protons can be 1.0 femtometer (10^{-15} meter) from each other. Ignoring the effect

of the neutrons in the nucleus, what must be the minimum strength of the strong force that keeps the protons from flying apart?

9. Devise three different particles each with a total charge of zero and each composed of one up quark and two other, different quarks (do not include anti-quarks in your particles).

10. A particle called a "pi-meson" is composed of an up quark and an anti-down quark. What is the charge of this particle?

   a. 0

   b. +1

   c. −1

   d. +2

11. Which of the following combinations of quarks would result in a particle with a charge of −2?

   a. up, up, charm

   b. anti-up, anti-up, down

   c. anti-up, anti-charm, anti-bottom

   d. anti-up, anti-up, anti-charm

INVESTIGATIONS

1. Read Michael Riorden's book, *The Hunting of the Quark*. How does the discovery of quarks illustrate the scientific method? What experimental evidence convinced scientists of the existence of quarks?

2. Watch an episode of *Star Trek* and discuss the use of matter and antimatter in the propulsion system of the *Enterprise*. Can you find any other uses of antimatter in science fiction stories?

3. What does it mean that the fundamental building blocks of the universe are things we can never isolate and study? Does that mean they aren't real? You might want to think about the question of the reality of atoms (see Chapter 8) for a historical precedent to this situation.

4. Investigate the philosophies of Thales and Democritus. What questions did they seek to answer? Has modern science answered the questions that they posed?

5. Read Brian Greene's book *The Fabric of the Cosmos.* How do the ideas discussed in Greene's book connect to what you have learned from this chapter?

6. In what ways has modern physics improved our ability to study and understand our behavior and our brains? Investigate the underlying physics of fMRI, MRI, EEP, and PET technologies.

7. Go to the Large Hadron Collider homepage and see what is happening in high-energy physics today.

14

The Stars

How much longer can the Sun sustain life on Earth?

PHYSICS

The Sun's heat energy flows outward from its core into space first by conduction, then primarily by convection, and finally by radiation.

CHEMISTRY

All chemical elements heavier than hydrogen are being produced in the nuclear reactions of stars.

BIOLOGY

The Sun provides virtually all of the energy for life on Earth. (Ch. 21)

GREAT IDEA

The Sun and other stars use nuclear fusion reactions to convert mass into energy. Eventually, when a star's nuclear fuel is depleted, the star must burn out.

ENVIRONMENT

Since the Sun first entered its main sequence, the total amount of energy generated has increased slowly, providing a stable energy supply for life on Earth.

TECHNOLOGY

A variety of satellite observatories detect a wide range of electromagnetic radiation from stars.

ASTRONOMY

A star's life cycle can be measured in stages that correspond to the way the energy is generated.

HEALTH & SAFETY

Exposure to ultraviolet radiation emitted by the Sun increases the risk of skin cancer. (Ch. 24)

GEOLOGY

The Sun's radiant energy drives Earth's weather patterns. (Ch. 18)

 = applications of the great idea discussed in this chapter

 = other applications, some of which are discussed in other chapters

Sunshine

The glaring Sun blazes down with midday brilliance. You make sure to use sunblock before stretching out on the beach towel. It's hot, but that's the way it's supposed to be at the beach. And the cooling ocean is just a few steps away. What is the Sun— this distant glowing object that gives our planet light and warmth? Is the Sun unique? Has it always graced Earth's sky? Will it ever stop shining?

◉ 14.1 The Nature of Stars

Astronomy, the study of objects in the heavens, is perhaps the oldest science. When you examine the night sky, the most striking feature is the thousands of visible stars (Figure 14-1). Each **star** is an immense fusion reactor in space—a large ball of gas, consisting mostly of hydrogen and helium, which are the two most abundant elements in the universe. Every star is held together by gravity, and every star radiates energy that is generated via nuclear fusion. The Sun, the nearest star to Earth, is just one of countless trillions of stars in our universe.

You have already learned enough about the way the universe works to understand some of the implications of your nighttime view of the stars. The fact that you can see the stars, for example, means that they are emitting electromagnetic radiation in the form of photons (see Chapter 6). Every star you see sends this radiant energy into space—energy that provides the essential data for all astronomers. Your eye intercepts a tiny fraction of that energy and converts it into the image you see, but similar amounts of energy radiate out in every direction from the star.

The laws of nature, including the laws of thermodynamics that describe the behavior of energy, apply everywhere in the universe. If a star sends radiant energy out into space, then the star must have a source of that energy. Furthermore, because every star is a finite object, it must have a finite store of energy. This simple observation leads to perhaps one of the most profound insights about the universe.

● **All stars have a beginning and an ending.**

In other words, the magnificent display that we see in the nighttime sky is a temporary phenomenon. It has lasted from the time that stars first formed until the present, a span of about

FIGURE 14-1 Thousands of stars are visible in the night sky.

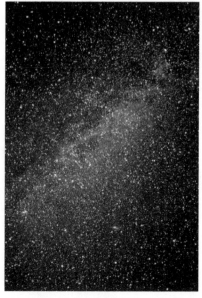

13.8 billion years. However, the view we see in the heavens will not last forever. Each star will eventually run out of energy. Before we look at the life cycle of stars, it's worth examining the kinds of data that astronomers use to understand the history and dynamic processes of stars.

Measuring the Stars with Telescopes and Satellites

Our primary source of data on distant stars is electromagnetic radiation—energy in the form of photons streaming through space at 3×10^8 meters per second. The art and science of astronomy lies in the collection, analysis, and interpretation of these data. Most astronomers spend their lives measuring four aspects of photons from space:

1. Their wavelength, which is measured by spectroscopy
2. Their intensity, which is measured by a device like a light meter
3. Their direction, which is measured by recording two angles—one up from the horizon (called the altitude) and the other around from north (called the azimuth)
4. The variations of these wavelengths, intensities, and positions with time

These data, in turn, enable astronomers to understand many aspects of stars, including their distribution in space, their physical characteristics such as mass and composition, and their histories and future behavior. For example, astronomers find that many stars possess spectra that are virtually identical to that of the Sun. The fact that the intensity of light from these stars is many orders of magnitude weaker than the Sun indicates that they are very far away.

Telescopes

To collect and analyze radio waves, microwaves, light, and other radiation, astronomers have devised a variety of **telescopes**, which are devices that focus and concentrate radiation from distant objects.

The first telescopes could examine only visible light, and when most people use the word "telescope" today, they mean an instrument for gathering and concentrating this form of radiation. The classic reflecting telescope (see Figure 14-2a) has a large mirror that reflects and

FIGURE 14-2 Schematic diagrams of telescopes. *(a)* In an optical telescope, light strikes a curved mirror at the back and is focused on a light-sensitive detector such as the eye or a piece of film. *(b)* In a radio telescope, radio waves from space strike a metal dish that focuses the waves onto an antenna. Signals are amplified and processed by computer.

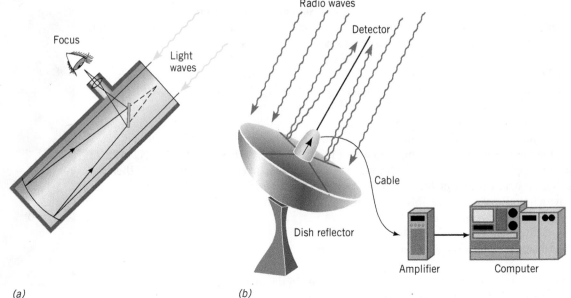

(a)   *(b)*

focuses light to produce an image of the object being studied. (See Chapter 6 for a review of the reflection and refraction of light.)

Many modern light-gathering telescopes are built differently. Instead of having a solid block of glass for a mirror, they have an array of small, independently controlled, lightweight mirrors that, taken together, produce an image. The Keck Telescope on Mauna Kea in Hawaii is an example of this sort of construction (Figure 14-3). It is a collection of more than a dozen mirrors that, taken together, give it a collecting surface of about 10 meters (30 feet) in diameter.

The location of telescopes has also changed. Observatories are usually built on high mountains, which places them above the main part of the atmosphere. In the mid-twentieth century, the world's largest telescope was on Mount Palomar in California. Later, the largest telescope was located on Mauna Kea in Hawaii, as mentioned earlier. Today, the main site of telescope construction is at the Las Campanas Observatory in the Andes Mountains in northern Chile, a site that already has several other telescopes in operation. In addition to being high, this observatory is located in one of the driest spots on Earth, which means that absorption by water vapor in the air does not affect it very much.

Northern Chile is also the site of another major observatory, the Atacama Large Millimeter Array (ALMA), which came online in 2013. Located on a plateau with an elevation of 5,000 meters (about 15,000 feet), this facility hosts an array of 66 detectors designed to measure radiation in the microwave and infrared range which, with no fewer than 21 countries involved in its construction, represents the first truly international telescope ever built.

The next optical telescope that will claim the title of "world's largest" is under construction at Las Campanas. The Giant Magellan Telescope (Figure 14-4) is scheduled for completion in 2018; it will have a collecting surface with a diameter equivalent to more that 24 meters (80 feet) and will produce images 10 times sharper than the Hubble Space Telescope (see below). Other factors being equal, the larger a telescope is the more light it will gather and the more detailed the data it will produce. Finally, in 2014 the European Space Agency began construction on the next major instrument in Chile, the European Extremely Large Telescope (E-ELT). When it is operational in 2024, the E-ELT will have a main mirror 39 meters across and will be composed of 798 component mirrors. It will then be the world's largest "eye in the sky."

In the 1930s, astronomers built radio receivers that did for radio waves what the reflecting telescope did for light waves (see Figure 14-2b). For the first time, they could look at another kind of electromagnetic radiation. Today, large radio telescope facilities can be found all around the world.

(a)

(b)

FIGURE 14-3 *(a)* The Keck Telescopes in Hawaii are the world's largest. *(b)* The ALMA array.

Orbiting Observatories

Except for visible light and radio waves, Earth's atmosphere is largely opaque to the electromagnetic spectrum. Most infrared and all ultraviolet radiation, short-wavelength microwaves, X-rays, and gamma rays entering the top of the atmosphere are absorbed long before they can reach instruments at the surface. The use of satellite observatories during the last half of the twentieth century has ushered in a golden age of astronomy. In this period, we have been able to put instruments into orbit far above the atmosphere and, for the first time, record and analyze the entire flood of electromagnetic radiation coming to us from the cosmos. NASA (the National Aeronautic and Space Administration) has created a fleet of observatories high above the atmosphere that will allow astronomers to probe every part of the electromagnetic spectrum. Some important observatories in orbit today are the following:

- *Hubble Space Telescope (HST)*. Launched in 1990, HST is a reflecting telescope with a 2.4-meter mirror designed to give unparalleled resolution in the visible and ultraviolet wavelengths (Figure 14-5). Despite a troubled beginning, the HST has proven to be one of the greatest scientific instruments in history. The HST was designed so that astro-

FIGURE 14-4 Artist's rendering of the Giant Magellan Telescope (GMT) in its enclosure.

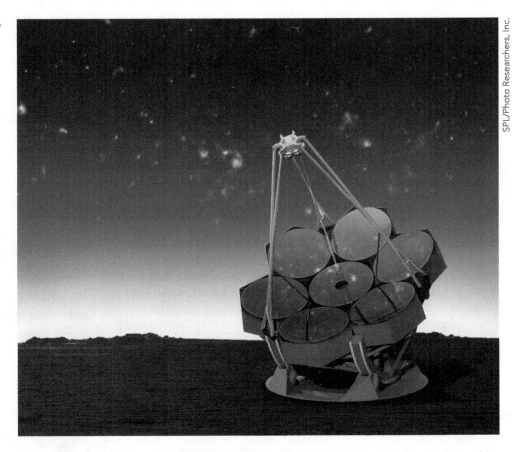

nauts in the Space Shuttle could visit it periodically and install updated equipment, most recently in 2009. Thus, although the telescope has been in orbit for over two decades, it continues to be the premier astronomical instrument in the world. (Indeed, in 2008 the HST completed its 100,000th orbit around Earth, having logged 2.7 *billion* miles.) HST accomplishments include photographs of the comet Shoemaker-Levy hitting Jupiter in 1994, detection of the most distant supernovae and most distant quasars (1997), and accurate determination of the Hubble constant (2001). The servicing of the HST in 2009 was the last scheduled maintenance for the instrument, and it will be retired at the end of its current tour of duty.

- *Chandra X-Ray Observatory.* Launched in 1999, the Chandra produces high-resolution X-ray images of objects in the sky. Its orbit carries it high above the belts of charged particles that surround Earth, giving it a clear view of the X-ray sky. It is named for the Indian-American astrophysicist Subramanian Chandrasekar, the first scientist to understand the final stages in the lives of stars such as the Sun. Although Chandra was designed to have a five-year lifetime, astronomers now hope it will continue to return data until 2015.

- *Fermi Gamma Ray Telescope.* In 2008 NASA launched a large orbiting observatory whose goal was to explore the highest energy part of the electromagnetic spectrum. It was named after the Italian American physicist Enrico Fermi, who was responsible for producing the first controlled nuclear fission reactor in 1942. This instrument explores the most energetic events in the universe, such as the regions around supermassive black holes and collisions between neutron stars.

FIGURE 14-5 The Hubble Space Telescope.

- *Gaia,* launched by the European Space Agency in 2013, will measure the precise location of over a billion stars in the Milky Way, allowing astronomers to have data of unprecedented accuracy in tracing the movements of stars within the galaxy.

- *James Webb Space Telescope* The designated successor to the Hubble, JWST has been in the planning stage since the mid-1990s. Its main instrument will be a 6.5-meter-diameter mirror, with a collecting area about five times larger than that of the Hubble. It will be put in orbit a point between Earth and the Sun, where the gravitational forces create a point of stability. This so-called LaGrange point is 1,500,000 kilometers (930,000 miles) from

Earth. The launch date of JWST is 2019, and when it is launched it will explore the creation of the first galaxies and the details of the formation of planetary systems.

- *Kepler Observatory* Launched by NASA in 2009, the Kepler was designed to search for planets circling other stars by monitoring the light from over 150,000 stars and looking for small changes in brightness as planets pass in front of them. After finding over 2,000 planets, the spacecraft encountered mechanical problems in 2013 and is now returning data in a restricted mode. Results from the Kepler Observatory are discussed in more detail in Chapter 16.

14.2 The Anatomy of Stars

Astronomical observations reveal that stars are much more than uniform balls of gas. They have a complex and dynamic interior structure that is constantly changing and evolving. The Sun is the only star that is near Earth, and thus it's the only star for which we have the kind of detailed knowledge that allows us to talk about how the various parts function. In this sense, the Sun is not only the giver of life on our planet, but also the giver of knowledge.

The Structure of the Sun

Based on comparisons with literally millions of other, more distant stars, the Sun appears to be a rather ordinary star. Although we can't peer into the Sun's center, theorists have learned to apply the principles of nuclear reactions to model processes deep inside stars. At its center is the stellar core, comprising about 10% of the Sun's total volume. This core is the Sun's furnace, where nuclear reactions rage and energy generated in the core streams out from the center. Deep within the Sun, this energy transfer takes place largely through collisions of high-energy particles—gamma rays and X-rays, for example—that are generated by the core's nuclear reactions. About four-fifths of the way out, however, the energy-transfer mechanism changes, and the hydrogen-rich material in the Sun begins to undergo large-scale convection. This outer region, comprising the turbulent upper 200,000 kilometers (about 125,000 miles) of the Sun, is called the *convection zone.* Thus energy is brought from the core to the surface in a stepwise process, first by collisions, then by convection.

The only part of the Sun that we actually see is a thin outer layer (Figure 14-6). We can observe perhaps 150 kilometers (about 100 miles) into the Sun; any deeper and the stellar material becomes too dense to be transparent. The outer part of the Sun, the part that actually emits most of the light we see, is called the *photosphere.* The Sun does not have a sharp outer boundary, but it gradually becomes thinner and thinner farther away from the surface. These gaseous layers are not usually visible from Earth. During a total eclipse of the Sun, however, when the Moon passes in front of the Sun, the Sun's spectacular halo, called the *chromosphere* and the *corona,* may become visible for a few minutes (Figure 14-7).

FIGURE 14-6 The surface of the Sun, showing hot material following magnetic field lines.

Courtesy NASA

The Sun constantly emits a stream of particles—mainly ions (electrically charged atoms) of hydrogen and helium—into space around it. This stream of particles, called the **solar wind**, blows by Earth and the other planets all the time. Because the particles are charged, they affect the magnetic fields of the planets, compressing the fields on the "upstream" side and dragging them out on the "downstream" side (Figure 14-8a). The interaction of the solar wind with the outer reaches of Earth's atmosphere also gives rise to the aurora borealis, or northern lights (Figure 14-8b).

The flow of energy from the Sun is a complex affair. Beginning with the conversion of mass in fusion reactions, the energy slowly percolates outward, first in collisions and later in great convection cells under the solar surface. It takes a few tens of

FIGURE 14-7 The Sun's chromosphere and corona become visible during a total eclipse. This halo of incandescent plasma is normally blotted out by light from the Sun's main disk.

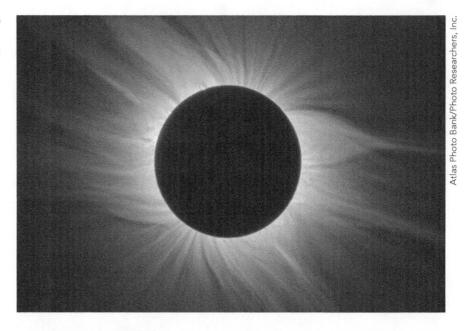

Atlas Photo Bank/Photo Researchers, Inc.

George Lepp/Stone/Getty Images

(a)

(b)

FIGURE 14-8 (a) Earth's magnetic field is swept out into a long tail by the solar wind. (b) Northern lights result from interactions of the solar wind with Earth's magnetic field.

thousands of years for the energy to work its way to the photosphere but only 8 minutes for photons to cover the distance between the Sun and Earth.

Once the sunlight reaches our planet, a tiny fraction of it is converted by the process of photosynthesis in plants into chemical energy stored in large molecules (see Chapter 21). This solar radiation is the primary source of energy for most living things on the planet. Another fraction of the energy in sunlight heats the air at the equator and, as we shall see in Chapter 18, drives Earth's weather patterns.

 THE SCIENCE OF LIFE
Why Is the Visible Spectrum Visible?

In Chapter 5 we saw that, of all the possible waves in the electromagnetic spectrum, the human eye can detect only the small interval of wavelengths between red and violet. One reason why the human eye is made this way was discussed in Chapter 5—Earth's atmosphere is transparent to these wavelengths, so it is possible for the waves to travel long distances through the air. But there is another aspect to the development of the human eye that has to do not with Earth, but with the Sun. Because of the fusion reactions at its core, the temperature of the outer part of the Sun is quite high, about 5500°C (for reference, gold melts at about 1065°C). Every object above absolute zero radiates electromagnetic waves, and both the total amount of energy and the wavelengths of the radiation depend on the body's temperature.

In Figure 14-9, we show the amount of energy that the Sun radiates at each wavelength, with the visible spectrum represented by the vertical lines. We see that the Sun's peak output of energy is in the middle of the visible spectrum. Thus, the wavelengths between red and violet are visible for two reasons: the air is transparent to them, and the Sun, our main source of light, emits the greatest proportion of its energy in that form.

Science fiction writers often use this fact when they portray imaginary beings from other planets. Those from planets around cooler stars than the Sun may be given large eyes so they can absorb more of the scarcer photons. For the reasons we have cited, however, humans don't require such large optical collectors.

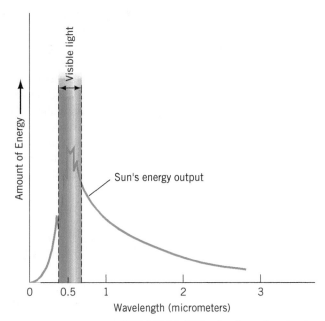

FIGURE 14-9 The Sun's peak output of energy is in the middle of the visible spectrum, with lesser amounts of energy emission at different wavelengths.

TECHNOLOGY
Space Weather

We are used to thinking of the Sun as a steady, reliable source of heat. But there is another side to our star, as is shown by the existence of the solar wind. The intensity of that wind can vary, and occasionally it can spike in a solar flare or a massive burst of plasma and radiation known as a coronal mass ejection. Such events can have an impact on both space and ground-based equipment on Earth.

The varying intensity of solar emissions is known as "space weather." The effect of high-energy particles striking spacecraft is easy to understand because the particles can damage sensitive electronic equipment. Shielding is routinely installed in spacecraft to protect such components, and considering that communication systems, the Internet, and GPS systems all depend on satellites, such protection is vital to our economy.

The terrestrial effect of space weather is more indirect. An intense stream of charged particles will change the shape of Earth's magnetic field, compressing it on the sunward side. We learned in Chapter 5 that changing magnetic fields can produce electrical currents. Consequently, when this distortion occurs (an event known as a "geomagnetic storm"), unexpected electrical currents can flow in equipment on Earth's surface. Such storms disrupt communication systems, and large-scale structures such as power grids and pipelines are particularly susceptible. The Sun is constantly monitored with both satellite and ground-based systems to warn of impending storms.

The first recorded geomagnetic storm occurred on September 2, 1859. It interfered with telegraph operations all over Earth and even produced currents that shocked some telegraph operators. On July 23, 2012, NASA satellites reported a coronal mass ejection that narrowly missed Earth. Scientists estimate that there is a 12% chance that such an injection will cause a major geomagnetic storm by 2022.

The Sun's Energy Source: Fusion

Once people came to understand conservation of energy—that energy has to come from somewhere and that the total amount of energy in a closed system is constant—two key questions about the stars arose naturally: What is their energy source? How can they continue to burn, emitting huge amounts of energy into space, yet remain seemingly unchanged for such long periods of time?

In the nineteenth century, several scholars attempted to explain the Sun's energy source. One astronomer, for example, calculated how long the Sun could burn if it were composed entirely of the best fuel available at that time—anthracite coal. (The answer turns out to be about 10,000 years.) The Sun's energy source also figured in the famous debate at the end of the nineteenth century regarding Earth's age (see Chapter 3).

Today, we understand that the Sun is indeed using a fuel but that fuel is hydrogen, which is consumed through nuclear fusion reactions (see Chapter 12). Stars are made primarily of the element hydrogen, the most common element in the universe. As a star forms, gravity pulls the hydrogen into a dense ball that heats up. Electrons are torn from the hydrogen and other atoms, creating a plasma (see Chapter 10) made up primarily of protons (the nucleus of the hydrogen atom) and electrons. (The process of star formation will be discussed in more detail below.)

Normally, protons would repel each other (see Chapter 5). As matter accumulates in the new star, however, the protons move faster as the temperature increases. Eventually, they acquire enough energy to overcome the electrical repulsion between them and they start to fuse.

The nuclear fusion process in the Sun's core does not take place all at once, with four particles suddenly coming together to make a helium-4 nucleus. Instead, it takes place in three steps.

$$\text{Step 1: } P + P \rightarrow D + e^+ + \text{neutrino} + \text{energy}$$

Two protons *(P)* come together to form a deuterium nucleus (*D,* the isotope hydrogen-2, made up of one proton and one neutron), a positron (*e^+*, the antiparticle of the electron as described in Chapter 13), and a neutrino.

$$\text{Step 2: } D + P \rightarrow {}^3\text{He} + \text{photon} + \text{energy}$$

Another proton collides with the deuterium produced in the first step to form the isotope helium-3, which has two protons and one neutron in its nucleus. A photon in the form of an energetic gamma ray is also produced.

$$\text{Step 3: } {}^3\text{He} + {}^3\text{He} \rightarrow {}^4\text{He} + 2 \text{ protons} + \text{photon} + \text{energy}$$

Two helium-3 nuclei collide to form helium-4, two protons, and a photon (another gamma ray).

This three-step fusion process is called *hydrogen burning* (though these nuclear reactions *are not* the same as the chemical reactions that we commonly call burning). The net effect of this process is that four protons are converted into a helium-4 nucleus with a few extra particles thrown in. As we saw in Chapter 12, the sum of the masses of all the particles produced in this reaction amounts to *less* than the mass of the original four protons. The lost mass has been converted into energy—the nuclear energy that powers the Sun and eventually radiates out into space.

How long could the Sun consume hydrogen at its present rate? If you simply add up all the hydrogen in the Sun and ask how long it could last, the answer turns out to be something like 75 billion years. Actually, no star ever consumes all of its hydrogen in this way. The hydrogen-burning process is generally confined to a small region in the center of the star called the core. The best current estimate of the total lifetime of our Sun is about 11 billion years—that is, our star is almost halfway through its hydrogen-burning phase.

STOP & THINK Why do you suppose fusion proceeds in a stepwise manner rather than having four protons come together all at once?

THE ONGOING PROCESS OF SCIENCE
The Solar Neutrino Problem

Our explanation of the Sun's energy source is a theory—a very plausible one—that is subject to experimental verification. In fact, a great deal of observational evidence supports the notion that hydrogen-burning reactions account for the Sun's energy. One crucial piece of evidence, however, seemed to indicate that we might not have known as much about the interior of the Sun as we'd like to think. Beginning in the early 1970s, a large experiment located a mile underground in a gold mine in Lead, South Dakota, has been returning results that are puzzling, to say the least.

The idea behind this experiment is that, as we have just seen, nuclear fusion reactions in the Sun's core produce neutrinos. Most of these neutrinos escape from the Sun without being absorbed or changed, and they arrive at Earth unchanged. Most of them will pass through Earth as well, but occasionally one will interact with an atom in the apparatus of this experiment, so that it can be detected. Thus, the experiment provides us with a "telescope" that can "see" right down to the center of the Sun. If we believe we know what reactions are going on there, we should be able to predict how many neutrinos should be seen.

When these measurements were taken, scientists saw only about one-third to one-half of the number of neutrinos they had expected to see. Other experiments of this type, run in Europe, the former Soviet Union, and Japan (Figure 14-10), bore out this same result. Explaining the missing one-half to two-thirds of the expected neutrinos became known as the "solar neutrino problem."

Today we understand that this result has to do with the fact that, as we saw in Chapter 13, there are actually three different types of neutrinos. If one type of neutrino is produced in nuclear reactions in the Sun, by the time those original neutrinos get to Earth some will have changed identity—roughly speaking, only a third will still be of the type produced in the Sun. Thus, the "solar neutrino problem" turns out to tell us something about the nature of neutrinos rather than the nature of the Sun.

TECHNOLOGY
The IceCube Neutrino Detector

Today, the attention of scientists has turned to looking at neutrinos given off in all sorts of violent cosmic events, as well as from the Sun. The world's premier neutrino detector is called IceCube (Figure 14-11a). Located at the South Pole, this is a cubic kilometer of instrumented ice that came online in 2011 and is producing data as you read this. The way it's built is simplicity itself—hot water is used to create a mile-deep hole in the ice, a cable (string) with 60 detectors attached is lowered into the hole, and the ice is allowed to freeze up around it. The final target of 80 strings and 4,800 sensors will detect light emitted from particles with which the passing neutrinos have interacted (Figure 14-11b).

The idea is that this huge instrument will not be looking up into the sky but down, finding neutrinos that have come through the entire Earth before interacting with atoms in the rocks underneath the ice cap (or with the ice cap itself). It is projected that during its lifetime (about 10 years), IceCube will log over a million neutrino collisions—thousands of times our current inventory.

FIGURE 14-10 Scientists inspect the Super Kamiokande neutrino detector in Japan.

FIGURE 14-11 (a) A view of the research station at the South Pole, where IceCube is located. (b) In the IceCube array, instruments are lowered into a hole drilled by hot water, which then freezes around them. Neutrinos interact, and they produce particles that give off light that is seen by the detector array.

This material is based upon work supported by the National Science Foundation under Grant Nos. OPP-9980474 (AMANDA) and OPP-0236449 (IceCube),

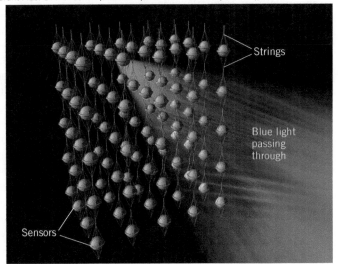

Strings

Blue light passing through

Sensors

(a)

(b)

Remote stars

Nearby star

Sun

Earth

First photograph of stellar region

Second photograph of same stellar region, six months later

FIGURE 14-12 The triangulation of stellar distances. By measuring the angle of sight to a given star from two points of known separation, we can determine the star's distance from us.

FIGURE 14-13 Annie Jump Cannon (*left*) and Henrietta Swan Leavitt (*right*) contributed important studies of the spectroscopy of stars at Harvard College Observatory.

Topham/The Image Works

On January 3, 2012, the IceCube detected a neutrino with the incredible energy of 1140.8 trillion electron volts—the most energetic neutrino ever seen. The IceCube scientists were so impressed with this event that they gave the neutrino a nickname—Ernie.

◉ 14.3 The Variety of Stars

Knowing how one star, our own Sun, works should help us understand the variety of other stars we see. When you look at the stars in the night sky, one of the first things you notice is that they don't all look the same. For example, some stars appear reddish, while others are almost blue. Your everyday experience with flames provides a simple explanation: different stars must be at different temperatures. Very hot flames, such as a gas burner, emit a greater percentage of high-energy blue photons; cooler fires feature lower-energy orange and red photons.

Stars also differ in their brightness; some appear as brilliant points of light, whereas others are barely visible. Differences in brightness arise from two factors—distance and energy output. Brightness varies in part because the stars are different distances from Earth. An unusually bright star located far away will appear dim to us, whereas an average star located nearby might appear relatively bright. The brightness of a star is also related to the amount of energy it produces. Astronomers often refer to the total energy emitted by a star as its *luminosity*. These differences in a star's appearance are taken into account by distinguishing between a star's *apparent brightness,* which is the brightness it appears to have when viewed from Earth, and its *absolute brightness,* which is the brightness it would have if viewed from a standard distance.

Much of the differences in the stars' appearances arise from the many varieties of stars themselves. Some stars shine a thousand times brighter than the Sun, while others are a thousand times dimmer. Some stars contain 40 times more mass than the Sun, while others have much less. As we shall see, we can bring order to this tremendous diversity of stars by recognizing that the behavior of every star depends primarily on just two factors: its total mass, and its age.

The Astronomical Distance Scale

When we look at the sky, we see a two-dimensional display—all stars look equally distant. Before characterizing the different varieties of stars, we need to add the third dimension to determine their distances. Only then can we relate apparent brightness (what we see from Earth) to absolute brightness (the luminosity or energy output of the star). Astronomers customarily measure these great distances in **light-years**, which is the distance light travels in 1 year, or about 10 trillion kilometers (about 6.2 trillion miles).

In practice, no single method can be used to find the distance to every star. Just as you might use a ruler, a tape measure, and a surveyor's tape to measure successively larger distances, astronomers measure distances to stars with a series of "yardsticks," each appropriate to a particular distance scale.

For short distances (up to a few hundred light-years), several different methods involving simple geometry can be used. For nearby stars, the angle of sight to the star measured at opposite ends of Earth's orbit (Figure 14-12) can be used to work out the distance. For centuries, navigators on Earth's surface have used a similar method, called *triangulation,* to determine the position of ships.

For greater distances, a standard type of star called a *Cepheid variable* is used. These stars, the first of which was discovered in the constellation of Cepheus, show a regular behavior of steady brightening and dimming over a period of weeks or months. Henrietta Leavitt (1868–1921) of Harvard College Observatory showed that the absolute magnitude of these stars is related to the time it takes for them to go through the dimming–brightening–dimming sequence (Figure 14-13). Thus, we can watch a Cepheid variable for a while and deduce how much energy it is pouring into space. This measurement, together with knowledge of how much energy we actually receive, tells us how far away it is.

The method of Cepheid variables can be used to measure distances of many millions of light-years. As we shall see in Chapter 15, it was a crucial ingredient in the birth of modern cosmology.

The Cepheid variable scale is an example of what astronomers call a "standard candle." The idea is that if you know how much energy an object is giving off and compare that with how much energy you are actually receiving, you can figure out how far away from you the object is. The development of other kinds of standard candles is a major thrust of modern research.

Although this discussion of the distance scale makes the process sound simple, in point of fact establishing the distance to the stars was one of the most difficult problems in the history of science. It was not until 1828 that the task was actually accomplished.

The Hertzsprung-Russell Diagram

Early in this century, two astronomers, Ejnar Hertzsprung of Denmark and Henry N. Russell of the United States, independently discovered a way to find order among the diversity of stars. The product of their work, called the *Hertzsprung-Russell (H-R) diagram,* is a simple graphical technique widely used in astronomy. It works like this: On a graph's vertical axis, astronomers plot the amount of energy given off by a star, as measured by estimating the star's distance and brightness. On the graph's horizontal axis, they plot the star's surface temperature, as determined by its color, or spectrum (see Chapter 6). Each star has its own characteristic combination of energy and temperature, and so it appears as a single point on the Hertzsprung-Russell diagram. The Sun, for example, is one of the points highlighted in Figure 14-14.

When stars are plotted this way, the majority (the ones like the Sun) fall on a band that stretches from the upper left to the lower right in the diagram. That is, most stars conform to a trend from very hot stars emitting lots of energy, down to relatively cool stars emitting less energy. Objects in this grouping are called **main-sequence stars**. All of these stars are in the hydrogen-burning phase of their lives, and their energy is produced in the fusion reactions that we described earlier in this chapter.

Two additional clumpings of stars appear in the H-R diagram. One clumping, in the upper-right corner, corresponds to stars that emit a lot of energy but whose surfaces are very cool. These stars must be very large—many times the size of our Sun—so that the low temperature (and thus the low-energy emission of each square foot of surface area) is compensated by the large surface area. Stars of this type are called **red giants**, and they often do appear somewhat reddish in the sky.

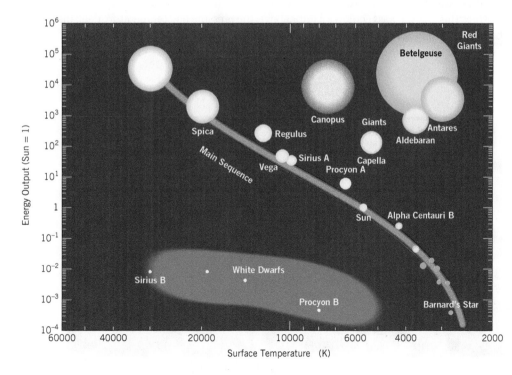

FIGURE 14-14 A Hertzsprung-Russell diagram plots a star's temperature versus its energy output. Stars in the hydrogen-burning stage, including the Sun, lie along the main sequence, while red giants and white dwarfs represent subsequent stages of stellar life.

Another grouping of stars appears in the lower-left corner of the H-R diagram. These stars, called **white dwarfs**, have very low emission of energy but very high surface temperatures. Consequently, white dwarf stars must be very small, typically about the size of Earth. Both red giants and white dwarfs play crucial roles in the life cycles of stars, as we shall see shortly.

◉ 14.4 The Life Cycles of Stars

Every star passes through a cycle that includes formation from dust and gas, a period of nuclear fusion, and an end to nuclear reactions. As we shall see, the duration and violence of that cycle depend almost entirely on the initial mass of the star.

The Birth of Stars

All stars are born in the depths of space, in clouds of gases and other debris. The modern theory of star and planet formation was first put forward by the French mathematician and physicist Pierre Simon Laplace (1749–1827). His was a simple idea that takes into account many of the distinctive characteristics of our solar system, which contains both the Sun and planets (see Chapter 16). According to the model, called the *nebular hypothesis,* long ago (about 4.5 billion years ago based on radiometric dating) a large cloud of dust and gas collected in the region now occupied by the solar system. Such dust and gas clouds, called **nebulae**, are common throughout our galaxy, the Milky Way (Figure 14-15). They typically contain more than 99% hydrogen and helium, with lesser amounts of all the other naturally occurring elements.

Under the influence of gravity, a nebula slowly, inexorably, collapses on itself. This collapse causes the cloud to spin faster and faster. The rapid spin means that some of the material in the outer parts of the nebula begins to spin out into a flat disk. This common consequence of fast rotation is familiar to anyone who has watched a pizza maker create a flat disk of dough by spinning a mass overhead. You can imagine a nebula at this stage of its formation as a large pancake with a big lump in the middle. The big lump represents material that eventually will become a star, and the material in the thin flattened disk eventually will become the planets and the rest of the solar system (Figure 14-16). As a new star begins to form, and as more and more mass pours into it from the surrounding region of the nebula, the pressure and temperature at the center of the proto-star begins to climb.

Once this central mass achieves a critical size, the pressure and temperature deep inside will become high enough to initiate nuclear fusion reactions. At that moment, a star is born.

Courtesy NASA

FIGURE 14-15 The Eagle Nebula, an immense cloud of dust and gas, is a birthplace of stars. Our solar system would appear as a small dot next to this nebula.

FIGURE 14-16 As the nebula that formed the solar system collapsed, it began to rotate and flatten into a disk. The stages in solar system formation include *(a)* a slowly rotating nebula, *(b)* a flattened disk with massive center, *(c)* planets in the process of birth represented as mass concentrations in the nebula, and *(d)* the solar system.

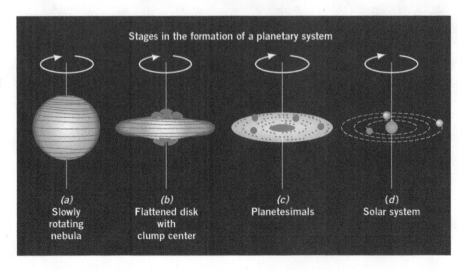

Stages in the formation of a planetary system

(a) Slowly rotating nebula

(b) Flattened disk with clump center

(c) Planetesimals

(d) Solar system

The Main Sequence and the Death of Stars

Every star begins as an immense ball of hydrogen and helium, formed by the gravitational collapse of a nebula. The ultimate fate of any given star, however, depends on the total mass of hydrogen and helium. The Hertzsprung-Russell diagram provides the key to understanding the very different fates of stars.

Stars Much Less Massive Than the Sun

All stars begin their lives in the hydrogen-burning stage—the stage represented by main sequence stars on the Hertzsprung-Russell diagram. If a star is much less massive than the Sun—perhaps only 10% of the Sun's mass—it will be just barely large enough to begin hydrogen burning in its core. Such a small star, called a *brown dwarf*, shines faintly compared to the Sun, with surface temperatures of only a few thousand degrees. Nuclear fusion proceeds relatively slowly, so such a star will continue to glow steadily for a hundred billion years without any significant change in size, temperature, or energy output.

Stars about the Mass of the Sun

The Sun and other stars of similar mass enjoy a more central position on the Herzsprung-Russell main sequence (Figure 14-17). The greater mass of the Sun, relative to brown dwarf stars, means that core temperatures and pressures are much higher and hydrogen burning proceeds at a much faster rate. Consequently, the Sun has a higher surface temperature, and it completes its hydrogen-burning phase much more quickly—in a matter of a few billion years.

One way to look at the life of a star like the Sun is to think of it as a continual battle against the force of gravity. From the moment when the Sun's original gas cloud started to contract, the force of gravity acted on every particle, forcing it inward and trying to make the entire structure collapse on itself. When the nuclear fires ignited in the core of the Sun 4.5 billion years ago, gravity was held at bay. The increase in temperature in the center raised the pressure in the star's interior and balanced the inward pull of gravity. But in the long view of things, this balance can be only a temporary state of affairs. The Sun can stave off the inward tug of gravity only as long as it has hydrogen to consume. When hydrogen fuel in the core is depleted, the amount of energy generated in the core will decrease, and gravity will begin to take over. The Sun will begin to contract and heat up.

This dramatic situation will have two effects. First, the temperature in the region immediately surrounding the core will begin to rise. Any remaining hydrogen in that region, which had not been consumed because it had been at too low a temperature, will begin to undergo nuclear fusion reactions. Thus a hydrogen-burning shell will begin to form around the extinguished core. The second effect is that the temperature in the core will rise until helium, the "ash" of hydrogen burning, will begin to undergo nuclear fusion reactions. The net reaction will be:

$$^4\mathrm{He} + {}^4\mathrm{He} + {}^4\mathrm{He} \rightarrow {}^{12}\mathrm{C} + \text{energy}$$

This process is called *helium burning,* in which the helium in the core undergoes nuclear fusion reactions to make carbon. The Sun will then resemble an onion, with a helium-burning core surrounded by a layer where hydrogen is being fused. At this stage the Sun will begin to move off of the main sequence (Figure 14-17, point 2).

This notion that the "ashes" of one nuclear fusion process serve as fuel for the next fusion process is central to an understanding of what goes on in stars. In stars like the Sun, the temperature never gets high enough to initiate fusion of the carbon, so helium burning is the final energy-producing stage. In more massive stars, this process of successive nuclear fusion cycles can go on for quite a while, as we shall see.

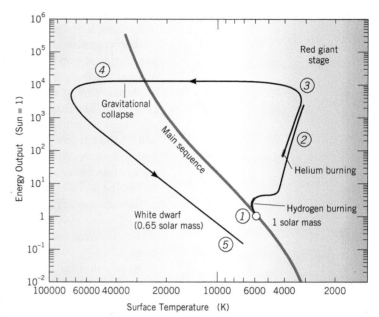

FIGURE 14-17 The life cycle of the Sun on a Hertzsprung-Russell diagram. The Sun started hydrogen burning in its core more than 4.5 billion years ago on the main sequence (at point 1), and it will remain near that point on the diagram for several billion years more. As the hydrogen in the core is consumed, however, a short period of helium burning (point 2) will move the Sun's position on the diagram rapidly upward toward the red giant stage (point 3). Once the helium is consumed, the nuclear fusion reactions will cease and gravitational collapse will cause the Sun to heat up (point 4). Eventually, the Sun will cool to a white dwarf (point 5).

The Sun will maintain more or less its present size and temperature for billions of years more. Since it first entered the main sequence 4.5 billion years ago, for example, the amount of energy generated by the Sun has increased by only about 30%. This long-term stability has important implications for the development of life on this planet. But in its final stages, our star will undergo dramatic changes. When the core consumes all of its nuclear fuel, the hydrogen-burning shells surrounding the central region will be pulled in. This temporary collapse will increase the amount of energy generated by fusion, and the increased energy will cause the surface of the Sun to balloon out. At its maximum expansion, the dying Sun will extend out past the orbit of Venus. Because the solar wind will also increase during this period, however, the Sun's mass will drop, its gravitational force will decrease, and the planets will move outward. In the end, only Mercury will be swallowed up. During this phase of its life, the Sun will emit almost 10,000 times more energy than it does today, but it will do so through a much larger surface. Consequently, that surface will appear to be very cool—red hot to our eyes. Our Sun will become a red giant, and the helium in the Sun's core will undergo nuclear fusion reactions to produce an inner core primarily of carbon (Figure 14-17, point 3).

As carbon accumulates in the core, a slow collapse will ensue until some other force intervenes. In the case of the Sun, that force will come from the Pauli principle—the principle (see Chapter 8) that tells us that no two electrons can occupy the same state. As the core starts to collapse, its electrons will be compressed into a smaller and smaller volume. For a time the Sun will continue to emit prodigious amounts of energy through a shrinking surface that reaches temperatures in excess of 70,000 degrees (Figure 14-17, point 4). Ultimately, the electrons will reach the point (what we called the "full parking lot" in Chapter 8) where they can no longer be pushed together. At this point, the Pauli principle will take over, and the collapse will stop for the simple reason that the electrons can't be pushed together any closer than they already are. A permanent outward force will be exerted on every element in the star, an outward force that will balance the inward force of gravity.

When the Sun reaches this stage, it will be rather small—probably about the size of Earth (though still hundreds of thousands of times more massive than Earth)—and it will no longer be generating energy through nuclear reactions. It will be very hot and will take a long time to cool off. During this phase, the temperature of each part of the Sun's surface will be very high, but, because the Sun will be so small, the total amount of radiation coming from it will not be very large. It will be, in other words, a white dwarf (Figure 14-17, point 5). Most of the carbon that is the end product of helium burning will remain locked in the white dwarf and will not be returned to the cosmos.

Stars up to five or six times the mass of the Sun will follow approximately the same path on the H-R diagram (Figure 14-17). Such stars will have different lifetimes; one of the paradoxes of astronomy is that larger stars—those with the most hydrogen fuel—have the shortest lifetimes. This paradox arises because the largest stars have to burn hydrogen at a prodigious rate in order to overcome the intense force of gravity. Thus, a star 4 times as massive as the Sun will complete its cycle in a relatively short time, less than a billion years, compared to the Sun's 11-billion-year span. But all of these stars will have essentially the same life history: main sequence → red giant → white dwarf.

Very Large Stars

Stars more than 10 times as massive as the Sun end their lives quite differently, in explosions of unimaginable power. For these stars, the pressure exerted by gravity is high enough so that the helium in the core not only burns to carbon, but the carbon can also undergo fusion reactions to produce oxygen, magnesium, silicon, and other larger nuclei. For such a star, the successive collapses and burnings produce a layered, onion-like structure such as that shown in Figure 14-18.

In the largest stars, this chain of nuclear burning goes on until iron, the element with 26 protons, is produced. As we noted in Chapter 12, iron is the most tightly bound nucleus. The addition of energy is required to break

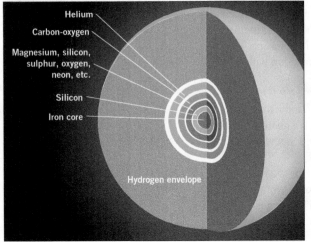

FIGURE 14-18 The interior of a large star displays concentric shells of fusion reactions, yielding progressively heavier elements toward the core.

Helium
Carbon-oxygen
Magnesium, silicon, sulphur, oxygen, neon, etc.
Silicon
Iron core
Hydrogen envelope

the iron nucleus apart (nuclear fission) and to add more protons and neutrons to it (nuclear fusion). Thus, it is impossible to extract energy from iron by any kind of nuclear reaction.

The cores of large stars will eventually fill up with iron "ash," and, no matter how high the pressure and temperature get, iron simply will not burn to produce a countervailing force to gravity. In fact, the iron core builds up until the force of gravity becomes so great that even the pressure of the electrons pushing for elbow room cannot prevent collapse. At the incredible pressures and temperatures at the center of the star, the electrons combine with protons inside the iron nuclei, forming neutrons—a process that is the exact opposite of radioactive beta decay (see Chapter 12). Within a second or so, all of the protons in the iron nuclei are turned into neutrons, and all of the electrons disappear. At this point, the core of the star begins a catastrophic collapse. The collapse will go on until another force appears on the scene to counteract gravity. In this case, the force is provided by the degeneracy pressure of the neutrons, which, like electrons, are subject to the Pauli exclusion principle.

The core collapses so fast that it falls inward beyond the point where the degeneracy pressure of the neutrons can balance gravity. Like an acrobat jumping on a trampoline, the star's falling matter first bounces inward and then rebounds as the neutrons exert a counterpressure. Meanwhile, the outer gaseous envelope of the star has suddenly lost its support and begins a free-fall toward the interior of the star. When the collapsing envelope of dense gas meets the rebounding core of neutrons, intense shock waves are set up in the star, and the entire outer part of the star literally explodes. From a distance the star suddenly appears to brighten in the sky, usually in a matter of a day or so. We call this dramatic event a **supernova**.

During the explosion, intense shock waves tear back and forth across the exploding star, raising the temperature enough to form all of the chemical elements in the periodic table. In a complex set of collisions, some of the nuclei up to iron that have been created by the successive fusion reactions soak up neutrons and undergo beta decay (see Chapter 12) to form nuclei up to uranium and beyond. All elements beyond iron are created in the short-lived maelstrom of the supernova explosion.

Supernovas probably happen about every 30 years in our own Milky Way galaxy. We don't see most of these events because of intervening dust, but we do see them in neighboring galaxies. On February 23, 1987, for example, a supernova was seen in the Large Magellanic Cloud, a small galaxy-like structure near the Milky Way galaxy. Although the supernova was 170,000 light-years from Earth, it caused a great stir in science because it was the first supernova to be measured with modern observatories, including satellites. It was seen by large neutrino detectors and many ordinary telescopes on Earth, and by X-ray and gamma-ray observatories above the atmosphere. Because it was the first supernova observed in 1987, it was given the name "1987A" (Figure 14-19). Perhaps the biggest surprise to come out of the experience was that there were so few surprises. The intricate theories of nuclear reactions that take place in those incredibly complex few hours when a star explodes were largely confirmed.

Neutron Stars and Pulsars

For a while after a star explodes, the supernova is surrounded by a cloud of ejected material. This expanding cloud dissipates into interstellar space, leaving behind the core of neutrons that was created in the collapse. A star that is being held up by degeneracy pressure of neutrons, called a **neutron star**, is in essence a giant nucleus—incredibly dense and very small. A typical neutron star might be 10 miles across, small enough to fit within the city limits of even a moderate metropolis. Several significant changes occur when a large star shrinks down into something the size of a city. For one thing, the rate of rotation of the star goes up substantially. Just as an ice skater increases her spin when she pulls in her arms, a star rotates faster and faster as it contracts. Some neutron stars in our galaxy rotate 1,000 times a second. Compare this to the sedate motion of the Sun, which rotates once every 26 days.

Neutron stars do not give off much light, and they would probably have gone undetected if some of them didn't exhibit unusual behavior in the radio part of the spectrum. The reason for this behavior can be understood if you follow the collapse that leads to the neutron star. As the star collapses, the strength of its magnetic field increases. If a normal star has a dipole field (see Chapter 5), for example, then during the collapse the field lines are

FIGURE 14-19 The striking NASA Hubble Space Telescope picture shows three rings of glowing gas encircling the site of supernova 1987A, a star that exploded in February 1987.

Courtesy NASA

dragged in with the material of the star so that the field becomes much more concentrated and intense. Some neutron stars in our galaxy possess fields as much as a trillion times that of the magnetic field at Earth's surface.

These two effects—a strong magnetic field and rapid rotation—may combine to produce a special kind of neutron star, which astronomers call a **pulsar**. The first pulsars were discovered in 1967 by Jocelyn Bell (see Figure 14-20). Fast-moving particles speed out along the intense magnetic field lines of the rotating neutron star, and these accelerating particles give off electromagnetic radiation, as shown in Figure 14-21. Most of this radiation is in the radio range, so the neutron star's signal is seen primarily with radio telescopes.

One way of thinking about a pulsar is to imagine it as being somewhat like a searchlight in the sky. Radio waves are continuously emitted along an axis that goes between the north and south magnetic poles of the neutron star, and this line describes a circle in space as the neutron star rotates. If you are standing in the line, you will see a burst of radio waves every time the north or south pole of the pulsar is pointing toward you, and nothing when it's not. You will, in other words, see a series of pulses of radio waves. The signature of a pulsar in the sky is a series of regularly spaced pulses, typically some tens to thousands per second. The pulsar represents one possible end state of a supernova. All pulsars are neutron stars, although all neutron stars are probably not seen as pulsars by earthbound astronomers.

We know of several pulsars that are the remnants of previous supernovas. One of the first pulsars discovered lies at the core of the Crab Nebula, a supernova seen from Earth in AD 1054. Likewise, Supernova 1987A is also expected to reveal a pulsar when all the dust clears.

Our current theories of stellar evolution say that stars more than 10 times as massive as the Sun will go through the supernova process we've just described and eject large amounts of heavy elements into space.

Black Holes

Occasionally, a large star may die in a way that does not lead to the formation of a pulsar. If a star is large enough—perhaps 50 or more times as massive as the Sun—there may be processes, as yet only imperfectly understood, by which even the degeneracy pressure of neutrons is overcome and the star collapses. The result is the ultimate triumph of gravity, a **black hole**. A black hole is an object so dense, a mass so concentrated, that nothing, not even light, can escape from its surface. A black hole formed from the collapse of a star is called a "stellar" black hole.

The first black holes found were not of the stellar type, but were in the center of most galaxies, including our own. We can't see that object, but it causes nearby stars to careen wildly in tight orbits, some of which take only a dozen years to complete. It appears that our own black hole, with a mass millions of times that of the Sun, is rather typical of those found in other galaxies.

The search for stellar black holes concentrates on double star systems in which one star has evolved into a black hole. This type of black hole is much smaller than the galactic black hole described earlier. The idea is that even though we can't see these black holes themselves,

FIGURE 14-20 Jocelyn Bell Burnell detected the first pulsars in 1967.

FIGURE 14-21 A schematic diagram of a pulsar reveals its two key attributes—rapid rotation and an intense magnetic field. This combination of traits produces a pulsing, lighthouse-like pattern of energetic radiation.

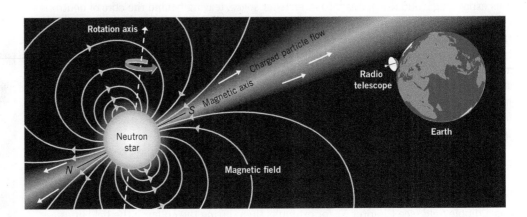

we can see their effects on partner stars and surrounding material. The best candidate for a nearby stellar black hole is Cygnus X-1, a star in the constellation Cygnus (The Swan). The black hole affects the orbit of its companion star, and material falling into the black hole emits X-rays that can be detected by orbiting satellites described above.

THINKING MORE ABOUT **STARS**

Generation of the Chemical Elements

Think about the remarkable range of elements you can buy at your local shopping center. The hardware store stocks aluminum siding, copper wire, and iron nails. The drugstore sells iodine for cuts, zinc and calcium compounds as dietary supplements, and perhaps bottles of oxygen for patients with breathing difficulties. The jeweler displays rings and necklaces of silver, gold, and platinum set with diamonds, a form of carbon. And your local electronics dealer offers an amazing assortment of audio and video equipment made possible by integrated circuits of silicon, perhaps doped with small amounts of aluminum or phosphorus.

It may come as a surprise to you that almost everything you see about you was made in a supernova. Your body, for example, is made primarily from elements that formed in some distant exploding star more than 4.5 billion years ago. We say this because, as we shall see in Chapter 15, the universe began its life with only light elements—hydrogen, helium, and small amounts of lithium. These elements formed the first stars and were processed in the first stellar nuclear fires. In stars like the Sun, elements heavier than helium may be made, but they remain in that star and never return to the cosmos.

In large stars, however, all the elements up to uranium (the element with 92 protons) and beyond are made and spewed back into the interstellar medium in the titanic explosions we call supernovas. These heavy elements enrich the surrounding galaxy, and when new stars are formed these elements are incorporated into them. The Sun, which formed fairly late in the history of our own galaxy, thus incorporated many heavy elements that had been made in previous supernovas.

You can think of the history of our galaxy as successive and cumulative enrichments by nuclear processing in large, short-lived stars. These stars, with lifetimes as short as tens of millions of years, take the original hydrogen in the galaxy and convert it into heavier elements. Except for hydrogen and helium, then, every chemical element in your life was made in a star. Thus we expect that older, smaller stars that have been shining since the early history of the universe will have fewer heavy elements than relatively young stars like the Sun—a prediction that is borne out by astronomical observations.

Think about what this means as you look around you. All the objects in your life—this book, your clothes, even your skin and bones—are made of atoms that formed in the hearts of giant stars long ago.

 ## RETURN TO THE INTEGRATED QUESTION

How much longer can the Sun sustain life on Earth?

- The star at the center of our solar system, which we call the Sun, provides the energy for Earth's living systems (Chapter 3). Without the Sun, our planet would be unable to sustain complex forms of life.

- As a star, the Sun has a finite life span. Like the billions of other stars in the universe, the Sun began as an immense sphere of hydrogen and helium formed by the gravitational collapse of a nebula.

- In many ways, the life of a star may be viewed as a continual struggle against the force of gravity. From the moment the Sun's original cloud of gas and dust began to contract 4.5 billion years ago, gravity forced it to collapse on itself. As it collapsed, the intense pressure caused hydrogen to begin to burn in its core. The extreme temperatures produced by the burning hydrogen increased the outward pressure and balanced the inward pull of

gravity. The interplay of gravity and expansion will only continue as long as the Sun's core has hydrogen to consume.

- Ultimately, the life span of any star depends on its mass. The more massive a star, the faster it burns its fuel and the hotter it gets. The hotter it gets, the quicker it exhausts its fuel supply. The quicker it exhausts its fuel supply, the faster it begins to die. The Sun, which is approximately 4.5 billion years old, has used about half of its nuclear fuel (i.e., hydrogen) and will survive another 5 billion years.

- The Sun will maintain its present size and temperature for billions of years. Since it first entered the main sequence 4.5 billion years ago, the amount of energy generated by the Sun has increased by only 30%. This long-term stability has important implications for the development and continuance of life on this planet. Nevertheless, in its final stages our star will undergo dramatic changes that will lead to the extinction of all living systems on Earth.

SUMMARY

Astronomy is the study of objects in the heavens. Astronomers have discovered much about the nature and origins of *stars*. We study stars with *telescopes,* instruments that gather and focus electromagnetic radiation. Earth-based telescopes detect visible and radio waves, while orbiting observatories detect all other regions of the electromagnetic spectrum. The most powerful telescopes can detect stars that are hundreds of millions of *light-years* away.

Extreme temperatures and pressures deep inside a star cause its hydrogen core to undergo nuclear fusion reactions, burning to create helium and heat energy. Ignition of these nuclear fires creates an outward flow of particles, called the *solar wind.* The fusion reaction proceeds in three steps, in which: (1) two protons come together to form deuterium, (2) a proton and a deuterium nucleus come together to form helium-3, and (3) two helium-3 nuclei fuse to make helium-4. This energy creates the pressure that balances the force of gravity that pulls the star inward.

Stars such as our own Sun form from giant clouds of interstellar dust called *nebulae*—clouds that gradually collapse under the force of gravity. This collapse subjects the star's atoms, primarily hydrogen, to tremendous temperatures and pressures. The life of a star is a continuous struggle against this gravitational force.

Stars that are burning hydrogen to produce energy are said to be *main-sequence stars*. Larger stars burn hotter and emit more energy, whereas smaller stars are cooler and radiate less energy. Main-sequence stars are found in a simple band-like pattern on a Hertzsprung-Russell diagram, which graphs a star's energy output versus its temperature.

When a star like the Sun consumes most of its core hydrogen, a helium-rich central region remains. The star once again begins to collapse under gravity, and internal temperatures rise again. Hydrogen burning begins in shells outside the core, whereas the core's helium may also combine in nuclear fusion reactions to form carbon. These new nuclear processes may cause a star like the Sun to expand briefly and become a *red giant*, a star whose relatively cool outer layers glow red. Eventually, however, nuclear fuel must be exhausted. Gravity will dominate and the carbon-rich star will collapse to a very small, very hot *white dwarf.*

Stars much larger than the Sun may evolve beyond hydrogen and helium burning. If temperatures and pressures are high enough, carbon can undergo additional nuclear reactions to form elements as heavy as iron, the ultimate nuclear ash. Once iron is formed, however, these reactions cannot produce any more energy, and so burning will cease. The sudden extinguishing of a star causes a catastrophic gravitational collapse and rebound—a *supernova*, in which the star literally explodes and spews all the chemical elements into the heavens. A dense, spinning *neutron star* or *pulsar* may be the only remnant of the original star. The largest stars may collapse into a *black hole,* an object so massive that not even light can escape its gravitational pull.

KEY TERMS

astronomy	main-sequence star	neutron star
star	red giant	pulsar
telescope	white dwarf	black hole
solar wind	nebulae	
light-year	supernova	

DISCOVERY LAB

You have learned about reflecting telescopes and orbiting observatories in this chapter. A reflective telescope concentrates radiant energy to a focal point with a large bowl-shaped mirror. In this experiment you will need an umbrella, a roll of aluminum foil, and a hand-held AM/FM radio with a built-in antenna.

First, line the entire inside of the umbrella with aluminum foil, folding the excess foil down over the edge of the umbrella's rim. Next, turn the radio on and find a weak station. Hold the radio in one hand, extending that arm out from your chest. Now take the umbrella and hold it upside down with your other hand. Slowly bring the umbrella toward and underneath the radio. The signal should get stronger and the sound should be louder. Experiment with different umbrella angles, holding the umbrella in various positions and directions. Move the radio near the handle and stem area in various positions until you hear the strongest signal. Can you explain and demonstrate on paper how the radio signal gets stronger? Can the same basic result be reached, with radiant energy from the stars being focused into a reflective telescope?

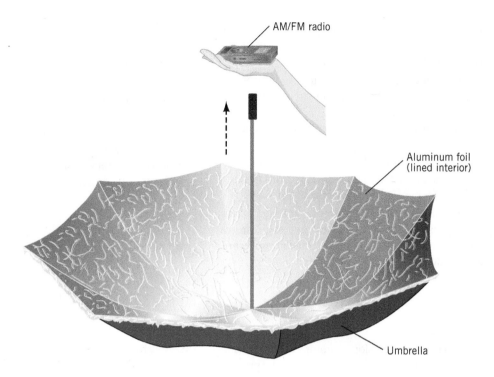

AM/FM radio

Aluminum foil
(lined interior)

Umbrella

REVIEW QUESTIONS

1. What is a star? Is the Sun a star?
2. What kinds of radiation allow us to study distant stars?
3. What conditions are present in stars that cause hydrogen to form helium? What is this process called?
4. What are the major layers of the Sun? Which layer produces most of the light we see?
5. How long does it take for the energy produced in the Sun's core to reach the photosphere? How long does it take a photon at the edge of the photosphere to reach Earth?
6. What two properties of stars do scientists plot on a Hertzsprung-Russell diagram? Why do they choose these properties?
7. In what ways is the Sun a typical star?
8. What are the effects of the solar wind on Earth?
9. What is a neutrino? What happens to some of them as they travel to Earth?
10. What forms of radiation do ground-based telescopes examine?
11. What parts of the electromagnetic spectrum are absorbed in the atmosphere before they reach the surface of Earth?

12. What causes stars to vary in brightness? In color?
13. What are the advantages of placing a telescope in orbit?
14. What is a "standard candle" in astronomy?
15. What is a "light-year"?
16. Describe two ways to determine the distance to another star.
17. Describe the process by which stars are formed.
18. Why must the Sun eventually burn out? What changes will the Sun undergo before it burns out?
19. Why don't larger stars burn longer than smaller stars?
20. What is a black hole? Why is it difficult to detect a black hole from Earth?
21. Why won't the Sun become a supernova or a black hole?
22. Explain how supernovae produce neutron stars and pulsars.
23. If iron is the ultimate nuclear ash, where do elements heavier than iron come from?
24. Explain how supernovae create the heavy chemical elements.

DISCUSSION QUESTIONS

1. Neutrinos are produced in the nuclear reactions at the core of the Sun. Based on what we know about neutrinos, do you suppose that they are like photons in that they take tens of thousands of years to percolate through the Sun's convection zone? Why or why not?

2. Do stars shine during the day? If yes, why do we not see them? Is it possible to "see" them during the day using other wavelengths of light?
3. How are light telescopes similar to radio telescopes? How are they different? Can you think of other types of telescopes that might yield more information?

4. What assumptions are made when astronomers determine the age of a star while observing from Earth? What measurements do they make to help them determine the age?

5. How do you think eyesight would evolve in life on a planet orbiting a red dwarf? Would visible light for such life forms be in the same set of wavelengths as for us? If not, where do you think the set of wavelengths would lie? Would you expect any overlap?

6. How can we speak with so much confidence about the life span of stars, which can be measured in millions to trillions of years, while having observed them for only a few thousand years?

7. Look around you and try to identify materials made of atoms that were formed mainly before there were any stars, atoms formed in the cores of stars during normal fusion processes, and atoms formed during supernova explosions.

8. Most stars we see are on the main sequence. Stars spend most of their lives consuming their initial stock of hydrogen. Is there a connection between these two statements? If so, what is it?

9. How do we know what stars are made of?

10. What are nebulae? Why are they mostly light elements such as hydrogen and helium? What force causes them to collapse?

11. What is the Sun's source of energy? What "fuel" is being "burned"? Why you think the words "fuel" and "burned" are placed in quotation marks in this context?

12. How does the energy produced at the core of the Sun reach the photosphere?

13. What are the roles of gravity, temperature, and pressure in the formation and death of a star?

14. Describe the effects, if any, of solar winds on Earth. If there are no effects, explain why.

PROBLEMS

1. The process that describes the fusion of protons ultimately into a helium nucleus is outlined in three steps. How many protons are used to produce each helium nucleus? What other particles are also produced in the total reaction?

2. In a process typically found in stars older than the Sun, helium nuclei can fuse together. Predict the nucleus that results when two helium nuclei, ^{4}He, come together. Many times, that resulting nucleus fuses with a third helium nucleus. What is the nucleus that results from that reaction?

3. All known nuclear reactions conserve the electric charge and the number of baryons (for simplicity's sake, consider the number of baryons to be equal to the number of protons + number of neutrons). Consider the reaction: $D + D \rightarrow {}^3He + ? + e^- +$ antineutrino. Predict what the missing product is.

4. The radius of the Sun is about 7×10^8 m. If a photon could travel from the core to the surface of the Sun without being hindered by the convection zone, how long would it take?

   a. 2.3 s

   b. 4.7 s

   c. 8 minutes

   d. 1 year

5. You detect a star and determine its mass to be four times that of the Sun's. What is your prediction for the ultimate fate of this star?

   a. Red Giant

   b. White Dwarf

   c. Neutron Star

   d. Black Hole

6. Each formation of a helium nucleus in the core of the Sun releases a total of 4.2×10^{-12} J of energy. If the Sun emits 3.8×10^{26} J of energy each second, how many nuclear reactions are taking place each second?

   a. 1.1×10^{-38}

   b. 8.0×10^{14}

   c. 4.6×10^{14}

   d. 9.0×10^{37}

7. In the formation of a single helium nucleus, 4.2×10^{-12} J of energy are released. If this energy results from the conversion of mass to energy, how much mass does the Sun lose each time a helium nucleus forms?

   a. 4.7×10^{-29} kg

   b. 1.4×10^{-20} kg

   c. 5.9×10^{-32} kg

   d. 3.8×10^5 kg

8. How far away is Alpha Centauri, the nearest star? How long would it take to get there at a speed of 2,000 miles per hour (the speed of a fast jet plane?)

9. How much more light-gathering ability does the Giant Magellan telescope with its 80-meter diameter mirror array have than the 2.5-meter Hubble Space Telescope? (*Hint:* Light-gathering ability is proportional to the area of the mirror.)

INVESTIGATIONS

1. Locate some stars in the sky and find out their apparent magnitude. (You might want to start with some familiar stars such as those in the Big Dipper.)

2. The Crab Nebula formed from a supernova event that was sighted on Earth almost 1,000 years ago. It must have been visible as a brilliant object for several days. What cultures left a record of this astronomical event? How did they explain what they saw?

3. Astronomers often debate the relative merits of Earth-based versus orbiting telescopes. What are some of the arguments on both sides of this issue?

4. You can set up an analog to the astronomical distance scale by using two "yardsticks"—a ruler and a tape measure, for example—to measure distances. Measure the dimensions of your classroom this way. How would you make sure that distances on each yardstick were the same? Does this exercise suggest a way for astronomers to check the consistency of their distance scale?

5. The nineteenth-century American poet Walt Whitman (1819–1892) wrote the following poem about astronomy:

When I Heard the Learn'd Astronomer
When I heard the learn'd astronomer,
When the proofs, the figures,
were ranged in columns before me,
When I was shown the charts and diagrams,
to add, divide, and measure them,

When I sitting heard the astronomer where he
lectured with much applause in the lecture-room,
How soon unaccountable I became tired and sick,
Till rising and gliding out I wander'd off by myself,
In the mystical moist night air, and from time to time,
Look'd up in perfect silence at the stars.

Although Whitman was unimpressed by the facts and figures of the "learn'd astronomer," astronomers of the past century have changed the way we think about our place in the universe. In this respect, how does science complement poetry? How do poetry and astronomy differ as ways of understanding why we are here? How would you answer the poet today?

6. Investigate the effects of light pollution in your area. Is it a major problem for amateur astronomers?

7. Is there an astronomical observatory within 100 miles of your home? What is it, and what aspects of astronomy do they study?

8. Find out when the next meteor shower or solar eclipse in your area is due. Grab a blanket and some friends and enjoy one of nature's finest exhibitions.

9. Investigate the concept of a Dyson sphere. Is it a practical idea for energy conservation? Why or why not?

10. Read about an object known as a Brown Dwarf. How does it differ from our Sun?

Cosmology

Will the universe end?

GREAT IDEA

The universe began billions of years ago in the big bang, and it has been expanding ever since.

PHYSICS

At the moment of creation, the four fundamental forces were unified as a single force. They have subsequently "frozen" into the forces we see today.

CHEMISTRY

The relative cosmic abundances of the elements hydrogen, helium, and lithium were established before the universe was 500,000 years old.

TECHNOLOGY

The Hubble Space Telescope and other orbiting observatories have provided key data for understanding the origin of the universe.

ASTRONOMY

The cosmic microwave background, the universal expansion, and the abundance of light elements provide strong evidence for the big bang theory.

 = applications of the great idea discussed in this chapter

 = other applications, some of which are discussed in other chapters

A Glowing Charcoal Fire

While you were lying down, soaking up the Sun's rays, a couple of your friends started a charcoal fire on a small grill. If you observe closely, you may notice that the color of the coals in the fire changes, depending on how hot the fire is. The coals are ordinarily red, but in a roaring blaze they can glow blue-white. Then, as the fire starts to go out, they glow a dull orange and eventually stop glowing altogether.

But even when the coals aren't glowing, they are giving off energy in the form of infrared radiation, which you can feel if you put your hand out to the dying fire. Even the next day, you might still be able to feel the radiation given off by the cooling embers.

Believe it or not, a phenomenon like this campfire experience led twentieth-century scientists to a completely new understanding of the structure and history of the universe in which we live.

◉ 15.1 Edwin Hubble and the Discovery of Galaxies

On any given night, as we look into the sky with modest-sized telescopes, we can see that the hazy band of the **Milky Way** is composed of countless millions of stars. Those stars appear as tiny pinpricks of light. But there are lots of other less distinct objects that appear as fuzzy masses, too distant to resolve. And those cloudlike objects, called *nebulae,* were the subject of intense debate in the early twentieth century.

The Nebula Debate

Some astronomers thought nebulae were nearby dust clouds that are illuminated by other stars. In that case, they would be fairly close by and have no resolvable structures, even in the most powerful telescope. Other astronomers suggested that nebulae were much more distant clusters of stars. They're composed of lots of individual stars but are much too far away for those stars to be resolved.

As so often happens in science, improved instruments were the key to discovery. In this case a larger telescope, quite literally, resolved the issue. In 1900, the world's largest telescopes were reflectors with mirrors in the range of 50 or 60 inches in diameter—not large enough to reveal nebular structure. So it was that the Carnegie Institution of Washington decided to build a mammoth new telescope with an unprecedented 100-inch diameter mirror on Mount Wilson, near Los Angeles, California. At the time, Mount Wilson was a lonely

FIGURE 15-1 Edwin Hubble (1889–1953) at the 100-inch telescope of California's Mount Wilson Observatory.

outpost on the outskirts of a small city. Today it has been engulfed by the Los Angeles metropolitan area, but in those days it afforded astronomers a chance to look at the sky through clear, unpolluted air.

In 1919, the young American astronomer Edwin Hubble (1889–1953), fresh from distinguished service in World War I, went to work at Mount Wilson and used this magnificent instrument to tackle the mystery of the nebula (Figure 15-1). Because his new telescope allowed him to see individual Cepheid variable stars in some nebulae, which no one had been able to do before, Hubble was able to measure the distance to them. (Recall from Chapter 14 that Cepheid variable stars can be used as standard candles.) It turned out that the Cepheid variable stars were extremely faint, so the distance to the nearest one, located in the Andromeda nebula, was some 2 million light-years, far outside the bounds of the Milky Way. Thus, with a single observation, Hubble established one of the most important facts about the universe we live in: it is made up of billions of galaxies, of which the Milky Way is but one.

We now know that each of these countless **galaxies** is an immense collection of millions to hundreds of billions of stars, together with gas, dust, and other materials, that is held together by the forces of mutual gravitational attraction. In making these discoveries, Hubble set the tone for a century of progress in the new branch of science called **cosmology**, which is devoted to the study of the structure and history of the entire universe.

Kinds of Galaxies

The Milky Way is a rather typical galaxy. As shown in Figure 15-2, it is a flattened disk about 100,000 light-years across. A central bulge known as the nucleus holds most of our galaxy's hundreds of billions of stars. Bright regions in the disk, known as spiral arms, mark areas where new stars are being formed (Figure 15-3). About 75% of the brighter galaxies in the sky are of this spiral type.

> **STOP & THINK** What is the connection between the flat, spiral shape of our galaxy and the appearance of the Milky Way in the night sky?

FIGURE 15-2 A map of the Milky Way galaxy, showing the nucleus and spiral arms.

Top view

Cygnus arm
Perseus arm
Orion arm
Sun
Sagittarius arm
Norma arm

30,000 ly
Disk
Sun
Nucleus (core)
Nuclear bulge
120,000 ly
Halo
Side view
Globular cluster

FIGURE 15-3 A typical spiral galaxy, with a bright core and spiral arms where new stars are forming.

Other galaxies, known as ellipticals, resemble cosmic footballs. The brightest elliptical galaxies tend to have more stars than spiral galaxies do and comprise about 20% of bright galaxies (Figure 15-4). In addition to the relatively large and bright elliptical and spiral galaxies, the universe is littered with small collections of stars known as irregular and dwarf galaxies. Even though these galaxies are faint and therefore difficult to detect, many of them have been identified. Astronomers thus think that these are probably the most common galaxies in the universe.

The total number of galaxies in the universe has been estimated by taking long-exposure photographs of small regions in the sky with no stars—regions that would appear as black voids in smaller telescopes. The results of these so-called deep-field images are astonishing (Figure 15-5). The more we look, the more galaxies we see—more than 100 billion galaxies, each with countless stars.

Larger elliptical and spiral galaxies and smaller irregular and dwarf galaxies can be thought of as quiet, homey galaxies, where the process of star formation and death goes on in a stately, orderly way. But a small number of galaxies—perhaps 10,000 among the billions known—are quite different and are referred to collectively as active galaxies. The most spectacular of these unusual objects are the *quasars* (for quasi-stellar radio sources). Quasars are wild, explosive, violent objects, where as-yet-unknown processes pour vast amounts of energy into space each second from an active center no larger than our solar system. Astronomers suggest that the only way to generate this kind of energy is for the center of a quasar to be occupied by an enormous black hole (with masses, in some cases, millions of times greater than that of the Sun) and for the energy to be generated by huge amounts of mass falling into this center. Because they are so bright, quasars are the most distant objects we can see in the universe.

FIGURE 15-4 A typical elliptical galaxy. This one is known as M84 and is located in the constellation Virgo.

FIGURE 15-5 This "deep-field" image of galaxies depicts a tiny patch of apparently "empty" sky (i.e., with no stars). Several hours of exposure by the powerful Hubble Space Telescope reveals more than 100 galaxies—evidence that the universe holds more than 100 billion galaxies, each with hundreds of billions of stars.

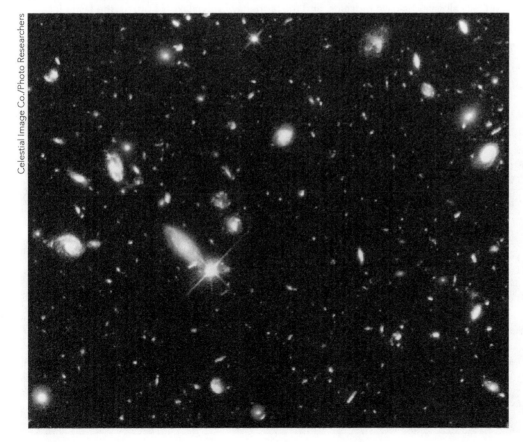

◎ 15.2 The Redshift and Hubble's Law

Hubble's recognition of galaxies other than our own Milky Way wasn't the end of his discoveries. When he looked at the light from nearby galaxies, he noticed that the distinctive colors emitted by different elements seemed to be shifted toward the red (long-wavelength) end of the spectrum, compared to light emitted by atoms on Earth. Hubble interpreted this **redshift** as an example of the Doppler effect (see Chapter 6), the same phenomenon that causes the sound of a car whizzing past to change its pitch. Hubble's observation meant that distant galaxies are moving away from Earth. Furthermore, Hubble noticed that the more distant a galaxy, the faster it moves away from us (Figures 15-6 and 15-7).

On the basis of measurements of a few dozen nearby galaxies, Hubble suggested that a simple relationship exists between the distance of an object from Earth and that object's speed away from Earth. Comparing two galaxies—one twice as far away from Earth as the other—the farther galaxy moves away from us twice as fast. This statement, which has been amply confirmed by measurements in the subsequent half-century, is now called **Hubble's law**. Hubble's law states:

In words: The farther away a galaxy is, the faster it recedes.

In equation form:

$$\text{galaxy's velocity} = (\text{Hubble's constant}) \times (\text{galaxy's distance})$$

FIGURE 15-6 In the upper view, Earth and a distant galaxy are stationary with respect to each other; therefore, the characteristic lines in the spectrum from that galaxy are not shifted. In the middle example, the galaxy is moving away from us, so the characteristic spectral lines are shifted toward the red end of the spectrum. In the lower view, the galaxy is moving toward us, so we observe a blue shift of the spectral lines. Edwin Hubble discovered that virtually all galaxies have redshifts, and the farther away a galaxy is from us, the faster it is moving way.

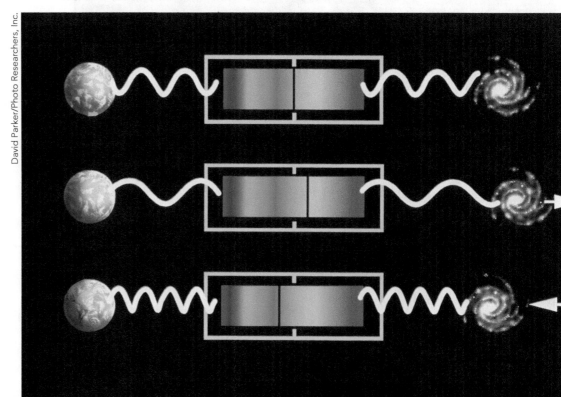

David Parker/Photo Researchers, Inc.

In symbols:

$$v = H \times d$$

Hubble's law tells us that we can determine the distance to galaxies by measuring the redshift of the light we receive, whether or not we can make out individual stars in them. Most astronomers now accept a value of close to 70 kilometers per second per megaparsec (a megaparsec, or Mpc, is a distance of a million parsecs or 3.3 million light-years). In this view of the cosmos, the redshift becomes the final "ruler" in the astronomical distance scale (see Chapter 14).

One way of interpreting Hubble's constant is to notice that if a galaxy were to travel from the location of the Milky Way to its present position with a velocity v, then the time it would take to make the trip would be distance divided by speed:

$$t = \frac{d}{v}$$

Substituting for v from Hubble's law:

$$t = \frac{d}{H \times d}$$
$$= \frac{1}{H}$$

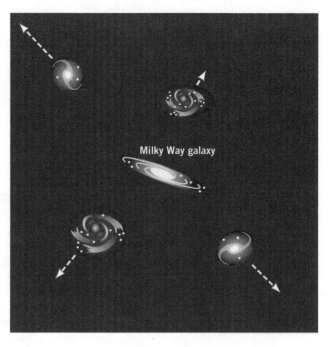

FIGURE 15-7 Illustration of Hubble expansion. The more distant a galaxy is from Earth, the faster it moves away from us.

Thus, the Hubble constant provides a rough estimate of the time that the expansion has been going on and, hence, of the age of the universe. A Hubble constant of 70 km/s/Mpc corresponds to an age of the universe of about 14 billion years.

EXAMPLE 15-1

THE DISTANCE TO A RECEDING GALAXY

Astronomers discover a new galaxy and determine from its redshift that it is moving away from us at approximately 100,000 kilometers per second (about one-third the speed of light). Approximately how far away is this galaxy?

Reasoning: According to Hubble's law, a galaxy's distance equals its velocity divided by the Hubble constant.

Solution:

$$\text{Distance (in Mpc)} = \frac{\text{velocity (in km/s)}}{[\text{Hubble's constant (in km/s/Mpc)}]}$$
$$= \frac{(100,000 \text{ km/s})}{(70 \text{ km/s/Mpc})}$$
$$= \frac{100,000}{70} \text{ Mpc}$$
$$= 1,429 \text{ Mpc}$$

Remember, a megaparsec equals about 3.3 million light-years, so this galaxy is almost 5 billion light-years away. The light that we observe from such a distant galaxy began its trip about the time that our solar system was born.

TABLE 15-1 **Some of Hubble's Data**

Distance to Galaxy (in megaparsecs)	Velocity (in km/s)
1.0	620
1.4	500
1.7	960
2.0	850
2.0	1,090

SCIENCE BY THE NUMBERS
Analyzing Hubble's Data

In his original sample, Hubble observed 46 galaxies but was able to determine distances to only 24. Some of his data are given in Table 15-1.

How does one go about analyzing data like these? One common way is to make a graph. In this case, the vertical axis is the velocity of recession of the galaxy, and the horizontal axis is the distance to the galaxy. In Figure 15-8a we show the data as originally plotted by Hubble, and in Figure15-8b we present a more recent compilation of many galaxies.

Looking at the original data, we find that the general trend of Hubble's law is obvious: the farther you go to the right (i.e., the farther away the galaxies are), the higher the points (i.e., the faster the galaxies are moving away). You also notice, however, that the points do not fall on a straight line but are scattered. Confronted with this sort of situation, you can do one of two things. You can assume that the scattering is due to experimental error and that more accurate experiments will verify that the points fall on a straight line; or you can assume that the scatter is a real phenomenon and try to explain it. Hubble took the first alternative, so the only problem left was to find the line about which experimental error was scattering his data.

This analysis is usually done by finding the line for which the sum of the distances between the line and each data point is smaller than for any other line. In effect, you find the line that comes closest to all the data points. The slope of this line, which measures how fast the velocity increases for a given change in distance, is the best estimate of Hubble's constant.

◉ 15.3 The Large-Scale Structure of the Universe

The Milky Way is part of a group of galaxies known as the Local Group, made up of ourselves, the Andromeda galaxy, and perhaps a dozen small "suburban" galaxies. The Andromeda galaxy is visible with the naked eye from Earth—you can see it from a dark spot on a clear summer night as a fuzzy patch of light in the northeast. The Local Group, in turn, is part of the Local Supercluster, a collection of galaxies about 100 million light-years across.

We now know that more than 100 billion galaxies populate the universe, each a collection of many millions or billions of stars. Like the Milky Way, most galaxies seem to be clumped together into *groups* and *clusters,* many of which, in turn, are grouped into larger collections called *superclusters* of thousands of galaxies.

FIGURE 15-8 *(a)* Hubble's original distance versus velocity relationship. *(b)* Modern graphs of distance versus velocity record data from hundreds or thousands of galaxies.

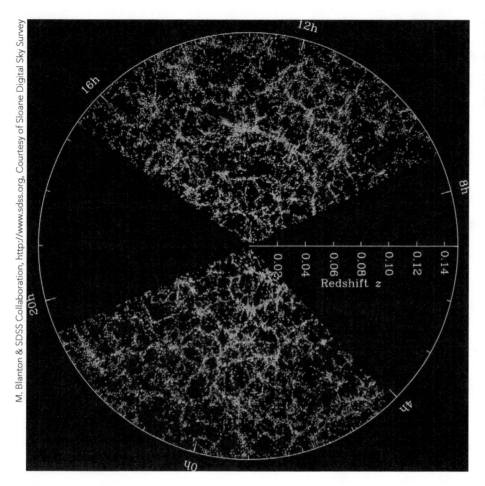

FIGURE 15-9 Results from the Sloan Digital Sky Survey showing how galaxies are distributed in space. Each dot is a galaxy of about 100 billion stars, and the clustering of galaxies can be seen.

In the 1980s, astronomers began to make "redshift surveys" of the sky, in which they observe distant galaxies and measure their redshifts so that we know how far the galaxies are. In this way, it is possible to construct a full, three-dimensional picture of the distribution of matter in the cosmos. With the results from these observations, originally led by the team of Margaret Geller and John Huchra at the Harvard-Smithsonian Astrophysical Observatory, astronomers have put together a picture of the universe that is very different from what you might expect.

Instead of finding galaxies scattered more or less at random through space, they find that galaxies are collected into large structures that run for billions of light-years across the sky. You can get an excellent picture of the structure of the universe by imagining the distribution of galaxies as something like a big pile of soapsuds. The result will give you a structure in which large empty spaces are surrounded by soap film. In exactly the same way, matter in the universe seems to be concentrated in superclusters on the surfaces of large empty areas called voids (Figure 15-9). Attempting to understand the reason for this very complex structure in the universe remains one of the major tasks of modern cosmology.

In 1998, a major multiyear mapping project got underway when a 2.5-meter telescope located at Apache Point in New Mexico saw first light, initiating the Sloan Digital Sky Survey (Figure 15-10). The ultimate goal of this project is to produce detailed maps of at least a quarter of the sky, detecting and measuring the redshift for more than a million galaxies. The project requires massive data

FIGURE 15-10 Apache Point Observatory in the Sacramento Mountains of New Mexico. The Sloan Digital Sky Survey's 2.5-meter telescope is on the left.

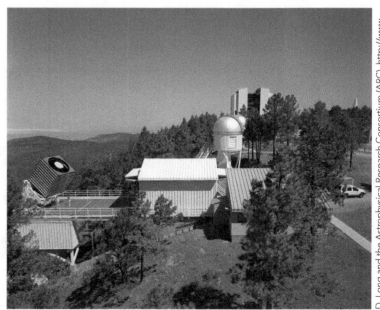

management capability as well as more traditional astronomical skills. As its data becomes available, it is posted on the project's website for public use. The detailed information coming from the survey has already produced a number of surprises in the astronomical community, including the discovery of several dwarf companion galaxies to the Milky Way.

The Big Bang

Hubble's law reveals an extraordinary aspect of our universe: it is expanding. Nearby galaxies are moving away from us, and far-away galaxies are moving away even faster. The whole thing is blowing up like a balloon. This startling fact leads us, in turn, to perhaps the most amazing discovery of all. If you look at our universe expanding today and imagine moving backward in time (think of running a videotape in reverse), you can see that at some point in the past the universe must have started out as a very small object. In other words:

● **The universe began at a specific time in the past, and it has been expanding ever since.**

This picture of the universe—that it began as an infinitely hot, dense concentration of energy and has been expanding ever since—is called the **big bang theory**. This theory constitutes our best idea of what the early universe was like.

Think how different the big bang theory of the universe is from the theories of the Greeks or the medieval scholars, or even the great scientists of the nineteenth century whose work we have studied. To them, Earth went in stately orbit around the Sun, and the Sun moved among the stars, but the collection of stars you can see at night with your naked eye or with a telescope was all that there was. Suddenly, with Hubble's work, the universe grew immeasurably. Our own collection of stars, our own galaxy, is just one of more than 100 billion known galaxies in a universe in which galaxies are flying away from each other at incredible speeds. It is a vision of a universe that began at some time in the distant past and will, presumably, end at some time in the future.

Some Useful Analogies

FIGURE 15-11 The raisin-bread dough analogy of the expanding universe. As the dough expands, all raisins move apart from each other. The farther apart two raisins are, the faster the distance between those two raisins increases.

The big bang picture of the universe is so important that we should spend some time thinking about it. Many analogies can be used to help us picture what the expanding universe is like, and we'll look at two. Be forewarned, however: none of these analogies is perfect. If you pursue any of them far enough they fail, because none of them captures the entirety and complexity of the universe in which we live. And yet each of the analogies can help us understand aspects of that universe.

1. The Raisin-Bread Dough Analogy

One standard way of thinking about the big bang is to imagine the universe as being analogous to a huge vat of rising bread dough in a bakery (Figure 15-11). If raisins scattered through the dough represent galaxies, and if you're standing on one of those raisins, then you would look around you and see other raisins moving away from you. You could watch as a nearby raisin moves away because the dough between you and it is expanding. A nearby raisin wouldn't be moving very fast because there isn't much expanding dough between you and that raisin, while more distant raisins would be moving faster because there is more dough between them and you.

STOP & THINK Compared to a nearby raisin, how fast would a raisin that is three times farther away from you appear to be traveling?

The raisin-bread dough analogy is very useful because it makes it easy to visualize how everything could seem to be moving away from us, with objects that are farther away moving faster. If you stand on any raisin in the dough, all the other raisins look as though they're moving away from you. This analogy thus explains why Earth seems to be the center of the universe. It also explains why this fact isn't significant—every point appears to be at the center of the universe.

But the expanding dough analogy fails to address one of the most commonly asked questions about the Hubble expansion: What is outside the expansion? A mass of bread dough, after all, has an inside and an outer surface; some raisins are nearer the center than others. But we believe that the universe has no surface, no outside and inside, and no unique central position. In this regard, the surface of an expanding balloon provides a better analogy.

2. The Expanding Balloon Analogy

Imagine that you live on the surface of a balloon in a two-dimensional universe. You would be absolutely flat, living on a flat-surface universe (similar to the way we are three-dimensional, living in a three-dimensional universe). Evenly spaced points cover the balloon's surface, and one of these points is your home. As the inflating balloon expands, you observe that every other point moves away from you—the farther away the point, the faster away it moves (Figure 15-12).

Where is the edge of the balloon? What are the "inside" and "outside" of the balloon in two dimensions? The answers, at least from the perspective of a two-dimensional being on the balloon's surface, are that every point appears to be at the center, and the universe has no edges, no inside, and no outside. The two-dimensional being experiences one continuous, never-ending surface. We live in a universe of higher dimensionality, but the principle is the same: our universe has no center and no inside versus outside.

The balloon analogy is also useful because it can help us visualize another question that is often asked about the expanding universe: What is it expanding *into*? If you think about being on the balloon, you realize that you could start out in any direction and keep traveling. You might come back to where you started, but you would never come to an end. There would never be an "into." The surface of a balloon is an example of a system that is bounded (in two dimensions) but that has no boundaries.

Evidence for the Big Bang

In Chapter 1 we pointed out that every scientific theory must be tested and have experimental or observational evidence backing it up. The big bang theory provides a comprehensive picture of what our universe might be like, but are there sufficient observational data to support it? It turns out that three lines of evidence make the big bang idea extremely compelling to scientists.

1. The Universal Expansion

Edwin Hubble's observation of universal expansion provided the first strong evidence for the big bang theory. If the universe began from a compact source and has been expanding, then you would expect to see the expansion going on today. The fact that we do see such an expansion is taken as evidence for a big bang event in the past. It is not, however, conclusive evidence. Many other theories of the universe have incorporated an expansion but not a specific beginning in time. During the 1940s, for example, scientists proposed a *steady-state universe*. Galaxies in this model move away from each other, but new galaxies are constantly being formed in the spaces that are being vacated. Thus, the steady-state model describes a universe that is constantly expanding and forming new galaxies, but with no trace of a beginning.

Because of the possibility of this kind of theory, the universal expansion, in and of itself, does not compel us to accept the big bang theory.

2. The Cosmic Microwave Background

In 1964, Arno Penzias and Robert W. Wilson, two scientists working at Bell Laboratories in New Jersey, used a primitive radio receiver to scan the skies for radio signals. Their motivation was a simple one. They worked during the early days of satellite broadcasting, and they were measuring microwave radiation to document the kinds of background signals that might interfere with radio transmission. They found that whichever way they pointed their receiver they heard a faint hiss in their apparatus. There seemed to be microwave radiation falling on Earth from all directions. We now call this radiation the **cosmic microwave background radiation**.

At first they suspected that this background noise might be an artifact—a fault in their electronics, or even interference caused by droppings from a pair of pigeons that had nested inside their funnel-shaped microwave antenna. However, a thorough testing and cleaning made no

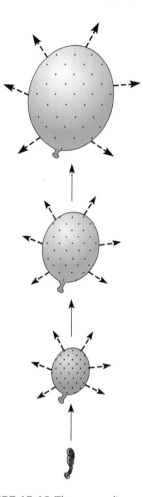

FIGURE 15-12 The expanding-balloon analogy of the universe. All points on the surface of the expanding balloon move away from each other. The farther apart the points, the faster they move apart.

difference in the odd results. A constant influx of microwave radiation of wavelength 7.35 centimeters flooded Earth from every direction in space. And so the scientists asked: Where is this radiation coming from?

In order to understand the answer to their question, you need to remember that every object in the universe that is above the temperature of absolute zero emits some sort of radiation (see Chapter 6). As we saw in the "Science Through the Day" that opened this chapter, a coal on a fire may glow white-hot and emit the complete spectrum of visible electromagnetic radiation. As the fire cools, it will give out light that is first concentrated in the yellow, then orange, and eventually dull red range. Even after it no longer glows with visible light, you can tell that the coal is giving off radiation by holding out your hand to it and sensing the infrared or heat radiation that still pours from the dying embers. As the coal cools still more, it will give off wavelengths of longer and longer radiation.

One way to think about the cosmic microwave background, then, is to imagine that you are inside a cooling coal on a fire. No matter which way you look, you'll see radiation coming toward you, and that radiation will shift from white to orange to red light and eventually all the way down to microwaves as the coal cools.

In 1964, a group of theorists at Princeton University (not far from Bell Laboratories) pointed out that if the universe had indeed begun at some time in the past, then today it would still be giving off electromagnetic radiation in the microwave range. The best calculations at the time indicated that the radiation would be characteristic of an object at a few degrees above absolute zero. When Penzias and Wilson got in contact with these theorists, the reason they couldn't get rid of the microwave signal became obvious. Not only was it a real signal, it was evidence for the big bang itself. For their discovery, Penzias and Wilson shared the Nobel Prize in physics in 1978—not a bad outcome for a measurement designed to do something else entirely!

We said before that it is possible to imagine theories, such as the steady-state theory, in which the universe is expanding but has no beginning. However, it is difficult to imagine a universe that does not have a beginning but that produces the kind of microwave background we're talking about. Thus Penzias and Wilson's discovery put an end to the steady-state theory.

In 1989, a satellite called the Cosmic Background Explorer was launched with the express purpose of making extremely accurate measurements of the comic microwave background (Figure 15-13). Data from this satellite established beyond any doubt that we live in a universe where the average temperature is 2.7 kelvins (K). This finding reaffirmed the validity of the big bang theory in the minds of scientists.

FIGURE 15-13 *(a)* Artist's conception of the Cosmic Background Explorer, which first made detailed measurements of the microwave background. *(b)* WMAP (see text) produced this map of microwave radiation from the entire sky. Blue indicates regions that are 0.01% cooler than average, whereas red indicates 0.01% warmer regions. This map indicates that the early universe was not perfectly uniform, a situation that led to the present "clumpiness" of the universe.

(a) *(b)*

In 2001 another NASA satellite, the Wilkinson Microwave Anisotropy Probe (WMAP) was launched. It eventually went into orbit at what is called the Lagrange Point, a spot about 1.5 million kilometers from Earth where the Sun's gravity balances that of Earth, creating a spot where satellites can be in stable orbit. WMAP produced a map of the microwave sky of unprecedented accuracy. WMAP stopped operation and went into a "graveyard orbit" in 2010. In 2009, the European Space Agency (ESA) launched the Planck Observatory, which by 2012 had completed an even more detailed mapping of the microwave sky (see Chapter 14).

3. The Abundance of Light Elements

The third important piece of evidence for the big bang theory comes from studies of the abundances of light nuclei in the universe. For a short period in the early history of the universe, as we'll see at the end of this chapter, atomic nuclei could form from elementary particles. Cosmologists suggest that the only abundant nuclei that could have formed in the big bang are isotopes of hydrogen, helium, and lithium (the first three elements, with one, two, and three protons in their nuclei, respectively). All elements heavier than lithium were formed primarily later in stars, as discussed in Chapter 14.

The conditions necessary for the formation of light elements were twofold. First, matter had to be packed together densely enough to allow enough collisions to produce fusion reactions. Second, the temperature had to be high enough for those reactions to happen, but not so high that nuclei created by fusion would be broken up in subsequent collisions. In an expanding universe, the density of matter will decrease rapidly because of the expansion, and each type of nuclei can form only in a very narrow range of conditions. Calculations based on density and collision frequency, together with known nuclear reaction rates, make rather specific predictions about how much of each isotope could have been made before matter spread too thinly. Thus, the cosmic abundances of elements such as deuterium (the hydrogen isotope with one proton and one neutron in its nucleus), helium-3 (the helium isotope with two protons and one neutron), and helium-4 (with two protons and two neutrons) comprise another test of our theories about the origins of the universe.

Studies of the abundances of these isotopes find that they agree quite well with the predictions made in this way. The prediction for the primordial abundance of helium-4 in the universe, for example, is that it cannot have exceeded 25% of helium atoms. Observations of helium abundance are quite close to this prediction. If the abundance of helium differed by more than a few percent from this value, the theory would be in serious trouble.

◉ 15.4 The Evolution of the Universe

Our vision of an expanding universe leads us to peer back in time, to the early history of matter and energy. What can we say about the changes that must have taken place during the past 14 billion years?

Some General Characteristics of an Expanding Universe

Have you ever pumped up a bicycle tire with a hand pump? If you have, you may have noticed that after you've run the pump for a while, the barrel gets very hot. All matter heats up when it is compressed.

The universe is no exception to this rule. A universe that is more compressed and denser than the one in which we live would also be hotter on average. In such a universe, the cosmic radiation background would correspond to a temperature much higher than 2.7 K (where it is today), and the wavelength of the background radiation would be shorter than 7.35 centimeters.

When the universe was younger, it must have been much hotter and denser than it is today. This cardinal principle guides our understanding of how the universe evolved. In fact, the big bang theory we have been discussing is often called the "hot big bang" to emphasize that the universe began in a very hot, dense state and has been expanding and cooling ever since.

In Chapter 10 we saw that changes of temperature may correspond to changes of state in matter. If you cool water, for example, it eventually turns into ice at the freezing point. In just the same way, modern theories claim, as the universe cooled from its hot origins it went through changes of state very much like the freezing of water. We will refer to these dramatic changes in the fabric of the universe as *freezings,* even though they are not actually changes from a liquid to a solid state.

We can identify six such "freezings" in the history of the universe (Figure 15-14). On the one hand, the most recent three involve changes in the predominant state of matter. In essence, as we go back in time and the temperature increases, matter is stripped down to its most fundamental constituents. The earliest three "freezings," on the other hand, involve the kind of unification of forces discussed in Chapter 13. Going from the most recent freezing to the earliest, we have the following important events in the evolution of the universe:

Several Hundred-Thousand Years: Atoms

Before this time, the temperature was so high that if an electron attached itself to a nucleus to form an atom, it would be torn loose in the next collision. After this time, the temperature had dropped to the point that if an electron attached to a nucleus, the atom would survive subsequent collisions. Thus, the predominant form of matter in the universe became the atom. The most important consequence of this freezing was that matter became transparent to light. The photons that form the cosmic microwave background were emitted at this time and have been traveling through the expanding universe ever since.

Three Minutes: Nuclei

Before 3 minutes, if a proton and a neutron came together to form a simple nucleus, subsequent collisions would tear them apart. Only after the universe was about three minutes old could the nuclei of atoms be stable. As we pointed out earlier, there was only a short period when nuclei could form because the Hubble expansion quickly carried elementary particles away from each other. The only abundant nuclei formed in the big bang were isotopes of hydrogen and helium, along with a small amount of lithium.

10^{-5} Seconds: Elementary Particles

We are now back to the first second of the life of the universe. Before this time, matter existed only in the form of quarks and leptons (see Chapter 13). At this point, when the universe was

FIGURE 15-14 The sequence of "freezings" in the universe since the big bang. The earliest freezings involve the splitting of forces, whereas later freezings involve forms of matter.

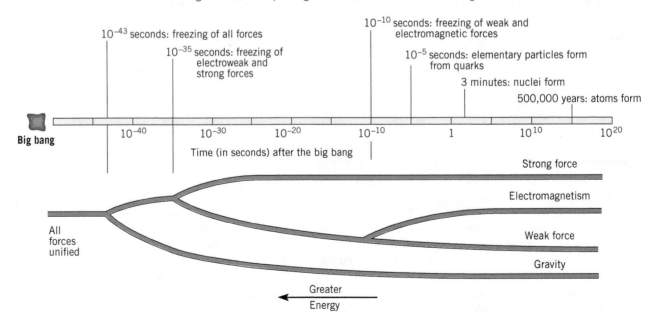

10^{-43} seconds: freezing of all forces

10^{-35} seconds: freezing of electroweak and strong forces

10^{-10} seconds: freezing of weak and electromagnetic forces

10^{-5} seconds: elementary particles form from quarks

3 minutes: nuclei form

500,000 years: atoms form

Big bang

10^{-40} 10^{-30} 10^{-20} 10^{-10} 1 10^{10} 10^{20}

Time (in seconds) after the big bang

Strong force

Electromagnetism

All forces unified

Weak force

Gravity

← Greater Energy

about one hundred-thousandth of a second old, the quarks coalesced into the elementary particles that would eventually form nuclei and atoms.

10^{-10} Seconds: The Unification of the Electromagnetic and Weak Forces

At this point, the "freezings" involve forces rather than the state of matter. Before this time, there were only three forces—strong, gravitational, and the unified electroweak. Ever since this time, the four forces with which we are familiar operated in the universe.

This milestone is important for another reason. It represents the farthest back we can go in time and still be able to reproduce the state of the universe in our laboratories. At particle accelerators such as the Large Hadron Collider (see Chapter 13), particles are smashed together at such high energies that for a fleeting moment, the temperature in a volume the size of a proton approaches what it was at this moment in the life of the universe. Thus, this freezing is the limit beyond which direct experimental verification of our theories is possible.

10^{-35} Seconds: The Unification of the Strong and Electroweak Forces

The theories that describe the fundamental forces—what we called the "Standard Model" in Chapter 13—tell us that prior to this time the temperature of the universe was high enough so that the strong and electroweak forces were unified. Before this time, only two forces operated in the universe: the strong-electroweak force and gravity. After this time, there were three forces: the strong, the electroweak, and gravity.

This is also the time when our theories tell us that two other important events took place:

1. Inflation—an extremely rapid expansion of the universe, taking it (roughly) from something smaller than a proton to something about the size of a grapefruit (Figure 15-15).

2. Elimination of antimatter—small differences between the production of matter and antimatter in accelerator experiments indicate that it was at this time that antimatter was removed from the universe. The theories tell us that for every 100,000,000 antimatter particles produced in the inflationary period, there were 100,000,001 particles of ordinary matter. When these large numbers of matter and antimatter particles annihilated each other, only one particle of ordinary matter was left, and this remnant is what we see in the universe today. This time also represents the farthest back we can go in time using our best theory—the Standard Model.

10^{-43} Seconds: The Unification of All Forces

When we finally find a theory in which gravity is unified with the other forces of nature, this is the time we expect that it happened. Because we do not have such a theory, however, descriptions of events at this so-called Planck time and of earlier events remain in the realm of speculation.

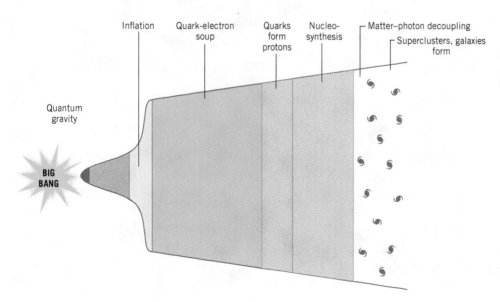

FIGURE 15-15 The evolution of the universe through the succession of freezings discussed in the text. Note the rapid expansion associated with the inflationary period.

◎ 15.5 Of What Is the Universe Made?

Looking out at the starry sky, with or without a telescope, it is natural to assume that the splendid display you are seeing is pretty much all there is. After all, we are made from quarks and leptons, as are our planet and our star, so what else could everything else be made of? Over the last quarter century, however, scientists have made two discoveries that not only call this easy assumption into question, but show that it is simply not true. In a series of observations that many have compared to Copernicus's removal of Earth from the center of the universe, these scientists have shown that ordinary matter—the sort of stuff with which we are familiar and which we have been discussing in this book—makes up only a small fraction of the universe. In fact, we now know that most of the universe is made up of two mysterious substances called, respectively, *dark matter* and *dark energy*. (Keep in mind that in spite of their similar names, these two phenomena are very different from each other.)

Dark Matter

In the early 1970s, astronomer Vera Rubin of the Carnegie Institution of Washington (Figure 15-16) was making some rather mundane measurements of distant galaxies. Using recently developed instruments, she was trying to find what astronomers call the rotation curve of those galaxies. Basically, this is a measurement of how fast stars and other objects are moving at different distances as they orbit around the galactic center.

Close in to the galactic center the results were what astronomers expected: gravity locks the stars tightly together, and the entire stellar assemblage turns together, like an impossibly gigantic wheel. In this central region of galaxies, therefore, the farther from the center a star is, the faster it must be moving to keep pace with the assemblage.

Farther out from the galactic center a different kind of rotation was seen. In this region, all the stars were moving at the same speed, like runners in different lanes on a curved track. Because stars farther from the center had farther to go, they tended to fall behind stars located closer to the center.

FIGURE 15-16 Vera Rubin of the Carnegie Institution of Washington discovered dark matter by studying the rotation of galaxies.

Zuma Press/NewsCom

STOP & THINK How does the fact that stars far from the galactic center move at the same speed produce the familiar spiral pattern of galaxies like the Milky Way?

Most astronomers expected that if you looked still farther out, you would see yet another pattern. Kepler's laws of planetary motion (see Chapter 2) tell us that if objects are in orbit around a massive central object (like the planets in the solar system orbiting the Sun), then the farther away from that central object something is, the slower it will move. Rubin expected that when she looked at the thin hydrogen gas located outside the place where stars were found in her galaxies, she would see the velocity falling off as Kepler had predicted. After all, in this case each individual hydrogen molecule could be thought of as a small "satellite" of the distant galaxy.

Much to Rubin's surprise, she saw nothing of the kind. Instead of dropping off, the velocity of the hydrogen gas stayed the same as far out as her instruments would take her (Figure 15-17). This surprising result has been duplicated hundreds of times since her first measurement, on many galaxies. The question: why should the far reaches of the visible galaxy behave this way?

We can understand the rotation curve only if we assume that the entire galaxy—stars as well as hydrogen gas—is locked into a massive sphere of material that we can't see. This material doesn't interact with electromagnetic radiation (otherwise we'd see it emitting or absorbing that radiation) but would make its presence known only because it exerts a gravitational force. The material came to be called **dark matter**.

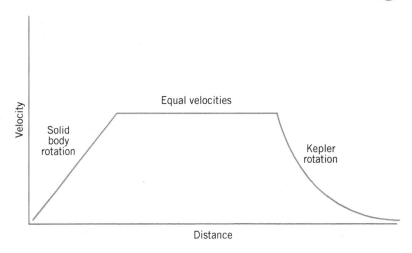

FIGURE 15-17 The speed of stars in a galaxy as you move away from the center should follow this pattern. Near the center, there is "wheel flow," with stars farther away from the center moving faster than stars close in. At intermediate distances, all the stars should move at the same speed. Finally, there should be a situation where the farther away a star is, the more slowly it moves. The failure to see this sort of rotation led to the discovery of dark matter.

 ## THE ONGOING PROCESS OF SCIENCE
Dark Matter Searches

We now estimate that 90% of the mass of galaxies like the Milky Way is composed of dark matter, and this matter forms a sphere in which the familiar starry spirals are embedded. We see further evidence for dark matter in large galactic clusters, where it seems to provide a kind of gravitational glue to keep the galaxies from flying away from each other. The best current estimate is that dark matter makes up about a quarter of the mass of the universe.

But what is it? It turns out that a number of particles could play the role of dark matter. The current favorites are a group known as "weakly interacting massive particles," or **WIMPs**. "Weakly interacting" refers to the fact that whatever particles make up dark matter, they do not interact with electromagnetic radiation—that's what "dark" means, after all—so that their interaction with all types of matter must be very weak. This characteristic, in turn, means that detecting dark matter is very difficult.

The basic idea behind the searches is that if the galaxy is really embedded in a sphere of dark matter, then the motion of Earth in its orbit must create a dark matter "wind," just as a moving car creates a wind on a still day. This dark matter wind is sweeping through your body as you read this chapter, but because the particles in the wind interact only through the (very weak) force of gravity, most of the dark matter particles pass on through without having an effect.

The world's most sensitive dark matter search is going on in what was once a gold mine in Lead, South Dakota. In a chamber 4,850 feet below the surface, a phone booth-sized container of liquid xenon is being monitored for evidence of the rare interactions of the dark matter wind with the nuclei of xenon atoms. Called the LUX (for large underground xenon) experiment, the apparatus is shielded from cosmic rays by the overlying rock. At the time of this writing, LUX has not detected a dark matter signal.

The location of the experiment has an interesting history. In the nineteenth century, the Homestake Gold Mine was one of the most successful mining operations in the United States. In the latter part of the twentieth century, unused chambers in the mine began to be used for physics experiments—see, for example, the discussion of the solar neutrino problem in Chapter 14. The mine closed in 2002, and eventually South Dakota businessman and philanthropist T. Denny Sanford provided funds to reopen the mines as the Sanford Underground Research Facility, continuing its contribution to science.

Dark Energy

Like dark matter, dark energy came on the scene because of an expected observational result. The basic question that scientists were trying to solve involved the future of the Hubble expansion. As galaxies move outward as part of the expansion, you can see that other galaxies will exert a gravitational force on them. This force will act to pull the outward moving galaxy back toward other massive galaxies. Thus, if gravity is the only force acting, we would expect the Hubble expansion to slow down over time.

Traditionally, astronomers have distinguished between three different scenarios when thinking about the future of the universe:

Open universe: In this case, the mass of the universe (and hence the gravitational force exerted on the outward-moving galaxies) isn't large enough to stop the expansion. Therefore, the future of the universe is an eternal expansion, but an expansion that slows with time.

Closed universe: At the same time, the gravitational force may be big enough to stop and reverse the Hubble expansion. In this case, the current expansion is a temporary phase and will be replaced in the future by a contraction, perhaps even a return to the original hot, dense state with which everything began. Astronomers call this situation a closed universe, and refer, somewhat facetiously, to the coming "big crunch."

Flat universe: A flat universe is one that has just enough mass to stop the Hubble expansion after an infinite time, but not enough to reverse it. You can think of the flat universe as the boundary between the open and closed cases discussed earlier. Most modern cosmological theories predict that the universe is flat.

With these options for the future, the task of the astronomer is clear: he or she has to go out and count up all the matter in the universe and see if there is enough to make the universe flat. (Aastronomers say that they are looking for enough mass to "close" the universe.) This is why the discovery of dark matter was greeted with such excitement, because the gravitational effects of dark matter have to be taken into account when you add up the forces acting to slow the expansion.

As we have pointed out, if gravity is really the only force acting on the expansion, then it should slow down over time. In particular, the rate of expansion billions of years ago should have been higher than the rate of expansion today. This means that if we look at distant galaxies, galaxies whose light has been traveling through space for billions of years, we should be able to see that slowdown.

The problem is that to get the expansion rate, we have to be able to measure both the distance to the galaxy and its speed. The speed is easy—we just need to look at the redshift. Getting the distance, however, is a different story. If we look at a distant galaxy, our telescopes aren't good enough to allow us to pick out individual Cepheid variable stars, so we can't use the standard candle that Hubble used to establish the expansion in the first place.

During the 1990s, astronomers at the University of California at Berkeley and the University of Michigan worked to establish a new standard candle that could be used for very distant galaxies. They settled on an event known as a Type Ia supernova. These events occur in double star systems in which one of the partners is a white dwarf (see Chapter 14). If the two stars in the system are close enough together, the dwarf will pull hydrogen away from its partner, and over time a layer of hydrogen will build up on its surface. When this layer is thick enough, the pressure ignites a fusion reaction and the entire star explodes like a giant hydrogen bomb. Since all white dwarves are the same size, all Type Ia supernovae will, in principle, give off the same amount of light, which means that they can be used as a standard candle. They also give off a tremendous amount of light, so that they are easily visible in even the most distant galaxies.

It took the researchers some time to work out all the details of this scheme, but by 1998 they announced their first results for the rate of expansion of the universe billions of years ago. To everyone's amazement, they found that the expansion was not slowing down at all. Actually, the rate of expansion early in the history of the universe was less than it is today. The Hubble expansion is speeding up!

Other astronomers quickly verified this remarkable finding, which has only one possible explanation: the attractive force of gravity cannot be the only force acting in the universe. There must be another force—a sort of antigravity—acting to push the galaxies apart. Astrophysicist Michael Turner of the University of Chicago gave it the name **dark energy**.

You can think of the universal expansion, then, as being something like your car. Gravity is acting to slow the expansion down—the brake—and dark energy is acting to speed it up—the gas pedal. In this scheme the flat universe, where neither brake nor gas pedal is engaged, can be thought of as "coasting."

Detailed studies show clear evidence for the interplay between dark energy and gravity. For the first five million years of the existence of the universe, when galaxies were close together, gravity overcame dark energy. The universal "brakes" were on, and the expansion actually did slow down. After about five billion years, when galaxies were much farther apart, gravity became weaker than dark energy and the universe tromped on the gas pedal. The expansion started to accelerate.

One result of the discovery of dark energy is that we now have a clear picture of the composition of the universe (Figure 15-18). It is 74% dark energy, 22% dark matter, and only 4% ordinary matter. The stuff we're made of, in other words, makes up only a very small part of the universe. Taken together, this particular collection of materials seems to be enough to "close" the universe. In the words of Michael Turner, we now have all the ingredients we need to make the cake, and all we have to do is figure out how they're supposed to be put together.

The inclusion of dark energy gives rise to two related questions: (1) What is it? And (2), what effect will it have on the fate of the universe?

For cosmologists, finding the answer to the first question is the most important task facing scientists in the early twenty-first century. Unlike the situation we saw for dark matter, there are no experimental programs under way to detect dark energy. The primary theoretical idea is that it is, in some way, a property of space and time—the "cost of having space" as one astronomer put it.

As far as the future of the universe is concerned, it depends on the properties of dark energy. We can imagine several scenarios:

1. There is a fixed amount of dark energy. In this case, the Hubble expansion will eventually dilute it, gravity will reassert itself, and we'll be back in a universe whose expansion is slowing. The brakes, in other words, will eventually come on again.

2. The density of dark energy in the universe stays the same. In this case, new dark energy will be created as the universe expands and the current acceleration will continue more or less at its present rate. The gas pedal will stay down as matter thins out.

3. The density of dark energy increases with time. If this happens, then the future will be truly spectacular as the repulsive force grows. It could even get to the point where expansion would overcome not just gravity, but electromagnetism as well. In this case, you can imagine a future in which atoms themselves are torn apart.

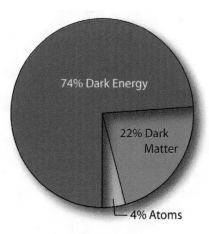

FIGURE 15-18 The composition of the universe, with ordinary matter being only a small fraction of the whole.

THINKING MORE ABOUT **COSMOLOGY**

The History of the Universe

The story of the big bang that we have just recounted has one clear feature: there were no human beings around to observe any of the events we've just described. In 1999, creationists on the Kansas Board of Education used this fact as a reason to ban questions about the big bang from statewide high school scientific achievement tests. Let's think for a moment about the kind of evidence we require to establish the existence of events in the past.

How do you know there was an event called the American Civil War? No one alive today actually took part in the Civil War, yet no one suggests that we should doubt its existence. The reason is that all sorts of evidence exists in the form of texts, artifacts, documents, and even recorded stories told by survivors before they died. The weight of this evidence is so overwhelming that the existence of the war is universally accepted.

But what about events farther back in time—the Crusades, for example, or the Thirty Years' War? The evidence here is weaker than that for the Civil War. What about events that occurred before the invention of writing—the arrival of the first humans in North America, for example? Here the evidence is exclusively in the form of archaeological data. And what about geological events where the evidence is in the rocks themselves?

The evidence for the big bang has been outlined in this chapter. How does it compare to the evidence for other events in the past? How much evidence is required to establish the existence of such events? Why do you suppose so few scientists agree with the decision of the Kansas School Board?

◀ RETURN TO THE INTEGRATED QUESTION

Will the universe end?

- In 1931, Edwin Hubble published his data and observations of Cepheid variable stars. His work, in concert with evidence of cosmic background radiation, provides support for the theory that our universe began with the big bang and has been expanding for billions of years.

- Because most scientists agree that the universe as we know it has a beginning, the ultimate fate of the universe (i.e., its end) is both a logical and valid question for cosmologists.

- The answer to the question of how the universe will end will depend on the physical properties of the universe, such as its mass and overall density, its rate of expansion, and the total amount of energy contained within it.

- Many theories have been proffered about the nature and probable future of our universe. Most scientifically sound theories depend on the properties of dark energy. Several scenarios are possible:
  - In a closed universe, there is a fixed amount of dark energy. Over time, the Hubble expansion will eventually dilute it, gravity will reassert itself, and we will be back in a universe whose expansion is slowing. The brakes, in other words, will eventually come on again.
    - Consequently, if the mass and density of the universe are both great enough to overcome the amount of dark energy present, gravity will stop the expansion and eventually force the universe to contract back into a single hot, dense point in space.
    - This scenario is known as the "big crunch."
  - If we live in an open universe, the density of dark energy stays the same. Therefore, new dark energy will be created as the universe expands. This scenario would mean that the current acceleration of expansion will continue more or less at its present rate. In other words, the gas pedal will stay down as matter thins out.
  - If the density of dark energy increases with time, then the future will be truly spectacular. As the repulsive force grows, it could reach the point where it would overcome not just gravity, but electromagnetism as well. In this case, you can imagine a future in which atoms themselves are torn apart. This scenario is known as the "big rip."

SUMMARY

Early in the twentieth century, Edwin Hubble made two extraordinary discoveries about the structure and behavior of the universe, the science we call *cosmology*. First, he demonstrated that our home, the collection of stars known as the *Milky Way*, is just one of countless *galaxies* in the universe, each containing many millions or billions of stars. By measuring the *redshift* of galaxies, he also discovered that these distant objects are moving away from each other. According to *Hubble's law*, the farther the galaxy, the faster it is moving away. This relative motion implies that the universe is expanding.

One theory that accounts for universal expansion is the *big bang*, the idea that the universe began at a specific moment in time and has been expanding ever since. Evidence from the *cosmic microwave background radiation* and the relative abundances of light elements, in addition to expansion, supports the big bang theory.

At the moment of creation, all forces and matter were unified in one unimaginably hot and dense volume. As the universe expanded, however, a series of six "freezings" led to the universe we see today. Freezings at 10^{-43} second, 10^{-35} second, and 10^{-10} second caused a single unified force to successively split into the four forces we observe today: the gravitational, strong, electromagnetic, and weak forces. At that early stage of the universe, when all matter and energy were contained in a volume no larger than a grapefruit, matter was in its most elementary form of quarks and leptons.

At 10^{-5} second, the quarks bonded together to form heavy nuclear particles such as protons and neutrons. Subsequent freezings saw these particles first fuse to nuclei at 3 minutes and ultimately join with electrons to form atoms when the universe was several hundred thousand years old. Stars, which formed from those atoms, then could begin the processes that provided all the other chemical elements.

The search for *dark matter*—mass that we cannot see with our telescopes—is a research frontier that may help us determine whether the universe will continue expanding forever. Recent data tells us that the expansion of the universe is accelerating, an effect that scientists attribute to something called *dark energy*.

KEY TERMS

Milky Way
galaxy
cosmology
redshift

Hubble's law
big bang theory
cosmic microwave background
   radiation

dark matter
WIMPs
dark energy

DISCOVERY LAB

The universe is constantly expanding and changing. To create a model of the expanding universe, you will need a balloon, a tape measure, a binder clip, and a marker.

Inflate the balloon to the size of a grapefruit, then clamp the balloon neck with a binder clip. Mark a point "S" as the starting point near the equator of the balloon. Measure 5-mm intervals along the equator and mark 10 to 15 dots evenly spaced. Label the dots with numbers. Measure the distance from S to point 1 and record the distance. Now measure the distance between S and the other points. Record the data.

Inflate the balloon until it is twice its size and clamp the neck of the balloon. Repeat the process of measuring the distance between the starting dot and the other dots using the same technique, recording the distance from S to each of the points.

Calculate the distance the point moved by finding the initial distance from dot 1 and the final distance from dot 1. Calculate the change from before to after by subtracting initial distance from dot 1 from final distance from dot 1. Follow the procedure to calculate the distance traveled by all the points.

Measure the distance between "S" dot and all of the other dots.

Inflate the balloon to twice its size.

Measure the distances again.

Do the dots get larger or smaller as the balloon expands? What do the dots represent? What is expanding—the galaxies or the space between galaxies? Compare this to the idea of the expanding universe.

What is the relationship between the points on the balloon and the galaxies in space? What pattern do you see?

When you deflate the balloon what happens? List some of the evidence on the origin of universe.

REVIEW QUESTIONS

1. What is cosmology? How does cosmology differ from astronomy?

2. What is a galaxy? How are galaxies distributed in the universe?

3. How did Edwin Hubble discover that there are galaxies in the universe other than the Milky Way?

4. Name the different types of galaxies and their distinguishing characteristics.

5. How do astronomers estimate the number of galaxies in the universe?

6. Describe Hubble's law. How did Hubble discover it?

7. How does the abundance of light elements provide support for the big bang picture of the universe?

8. Why does the existence of the cosmic redshift lead to the big bang picture of the universe?

9. What is the cosmic microwave background and what role does it play in cosmology?

10. Is the universe getting warmer or colder? Give evidence to support your answer.

11. What are "freezings," and why are they important?

12. What is dark matter, and what evidence exists for it?

13. What effect does dark energy have on the expansion of the universe?

DISCUSSION QUESTIONS

1. What was the nebula debate? What role did technology play in resolving it?

2. Is there a center to the universe? Why or why not?

3. What are the limitations of the raisin-bread dough and expanding balloon analogies of the universe?

4. If the "big crunch" scenario is the correct one for our universe, what does this portend for the cosmic microwave background?

5. Why was the steady-state theory of the universe abandoned? How does this episode fit into the discussion of the scientific method in Chapter 1?

6. Atoms didn't form until several hundred thousand years after the big bang. Yet, which atoms would form was decided just a few minutes after the big bang. Why? How did this lead to an abundance of the lightest elements in the universe?

7. Louis Pasteur once said, "chance favors only the mind that is prepared." Apply this saying to the discoveries of Edwin Hubble and of Penzias and Wilson.

8. Many advances in our knowledge only occurred after more sophisticated technological developments, such as the 100-inch Hooker telescope used by Edwin Hubble to measure the expansion of the universe. What other advances in cosmology have been spurred by technological developments?

9. How can we determine the existence of something we can't see? What is the evidence for dark matter and dark energy? How can we learn more about these phenomena?

10. What is the ultimate fate of a closed universe? An open universe? A flat universe? What data do we need to determine which kind of universe we have?

11. Many religions have beliefs about the "birth" and "death" of the universe. For example, some religions believe that the universe has a cyclic nature in which all matter is destroyed and re-created over and over again for all eternity. Which type of universe is consistent with this belief? What is the difference between scientific theories and these religious beliefs?

12. Telescopes designed to observe photons will be unable to see into the past any further than 500,000 years after the big bang. Suppose a telescope that observed neutrinos were constructed. How far back in time could such a telescope see?

13. If we extend the expanding balloon analogy to our universe, it would seem to indicate that our universe is expanding into a fourth dimension. If we are unable to physically enter this dimension, does the idea of a fourth spatial dimension go beyond the testable bounds of science?

PROBLEMS

1. Assuming a Hubble constant of 70 km/s/Mpc, at what rate is a galaxy 200 Mpc away moving from us? 3000 Mpc away?

2. If a galaxy is moving away from us at 80% the speed of light, how far away is it? Assume the Hubble constant is 70 km/s/Mpc.

3. An observer on one of the raisins in our bread-dough analogy measures distances and velocities of neighboring raisins. The data look like the following:

Distance (cm)	Velocity (cm/hr)
0.9	1.02
1.9	2.0
5.1	4.05
0	0
3.4	2.90
7.0	5.90
9.4	7.10

Plot these data on a graph and use the plot to estimate a "Hubble constant" for the raisins.

4. From the data in Problem 3, estimate the time that has elapsed since the dough started rising. Estimate the largest and smallest values of this number consistent with the data.

5. Some theories say that in the inflationary period, the scale of the universe increased by a factor of 10^{50}. Suppose your height were to increase by a factor of 10^{50}. How tall would you be? Express your answer in light-years and compare it to the size of the observable universe.

6. Suppose a proton (diameter about 10^{-13} cm) were to inflate by a factor of 10^{50}. How big would it be? Convert the answer to light-years and compare it to the size of the observable universe.

7. The earliest galaxies appear to be about 13.1 billion light-years away. How many Mpc is this? How fast are these galaxies moving away from us? What percentage of the speed of light is this?

8. The average temperature of the universe is 2.7 K. What is that temperature in degrees Fahrenheit? How far above absolute zero is that?

9. If we scaled the universe so that the distance from Earth to the Sun, 1.5×10^{11} m, was the thickness of a dollar bill, how high would a stack of dollar bills be to represent a distance of one light-year? How high would the stack be to represent the distance to the nearest major galaxy, Andromeda (2.2 million light-years away)?

10. The Milky Way galaxy is estimated to have a mass equivalent to about 1 trillion Suns. If the Andromeda Galaxy has an identical mass and is 2.2 million light-years away, what is the strength of the gravitational attracted between the two? Assume the mass of the Sun is 2.0×10^{30} kg.

11. The Andromeda galaxy is 2.2 million light-years away. At what rate is the overall expansion of the universe separating the Andromeda galaxy from the Milky Way galaxy?

12. There is a large region of space with a dearth of galaxies known as the "Boötes Void." Its center is about 700,000,000 light-years away. How fast is the Boötes Void moving from us? Assume the Hubble Constant is 70 km/s/Mpc.

   a. 4700 km/s
   b. 15,000 km/s
   c. 49,000 km/s
   d. 10,000,000 km/s

13. If we imagine dark energy converted into mass, then the density of dark energy throughout the universe is estimated to be 1.7×10^{-27} kg/m^3. Earth has a radius of 6.4×10^6 m. What is the equivalent mass of dark energy contained in Earth? [*Note:* The formula for the volume of a sphere is $(4/3)\pi r^3$.]

   a. 1.9×10^{-6} kg
   b. 4.6×10^{-20} kg
   c. 4.5×10^{-7} kg
   d. 6.5×10^{47} kg

INVESTIGATIONS

1. The Milky Way is a band of stars that, seen from Earth in the summer months, stretches all the way across the sky. Given what you know about galaxies, why do you suppose that our own galaxy appears this way to us? Who was the first natural philosopher to figure this out?

2. Will the constellation of Andromeda be above the horizon tonight? If so, go out and try to spot the Andromeda Galaxy.

3. Look up the "Great Attractor." How does the existence of such an object fit in with the concept of the Hubble expansion? How would you modify the raisin-bread dough analogy to put in the Great Attractor?

4. Investigate the creation stories of other societies. How do they differ from the big bang?

5. What agencies or organizations fund cosmological research? What was the role of the Carnegie Institution of Washington in Edwin Hubble's research?

6. Visit the NASA website, nasa.gov. What new astronomical satellites are being developed, and when will they be launched?

7. The computer and the Hubble telescope were major advancements in technology. What new advances in technology may prove useful for astronomy and cosmology?

Earth and Other Planets

Is Earth the only planet with life?

PHYSICS

The force of gravity caused the solar nebula to collapse on itself, forming our solar system.

BIOLOGY

The ancestors of living things could not have come into existence until after the great bombardment.

CHEMISTRY

Earth's early atmosphere was rich in the elements carbon, hydrogen, oxygen, and nitrogen.

GREAT IDEA

Earth, one of the planets that orbit the Sun, formed 4.5 billion years ago from a great cloud of dust.

TECHNOLOGY

Scientific instruments on board the *Voyager 1* and *2* satellites have provided detailed images and information about the outer planets in our solar system.

ENVIRONMENT

Large meteors or comets, left over from the initial period of planetary formation, still occasionally hit Earth and may cause mass extinctions. (Ch.25)

ASTRONOMY

Earth and the other planets in our solar system orbit in the same direction around the Sun and are more or less in the same plane.

HEALTH & SAFETY

The low force of gravity in space may cause gradual bone deterioration and thus limit the duration of long space voyages.

GEOLOGY

Differentiation caused Earth's interior to become layered into the core, mantle, and crust.

 = applications of the great idea discussed in this chapter

= other applications, some of which are discussed in other chapters

The Sun and the Moon

It's shortly after noon; the Sun is blazing overhead. As you scan the horizon you see a perfect half Moon rising in the east. The rough, cratered surface stands out even in daylight. But you recall that just a few days ago you saw the Moon as a thin crescent in the evening sky. And a couple of weeks before that, the night's full Moon was so bright you could almost read by it. The Moon, like other objects in our solar system, is constantly changing in the sky.

As you stare at our nearest neighbor in space, it's amazing to think that a few decades ago humans actually walked on that hostile world and brought precious pieces of its surface back to Earth. What did scientists learn from those alien rocks? What do they tell us about the ancient origin and dynamic state of our home, the solar system?

◉ 16.1 The Formation of the Solar System

Walk outside and look at the sky tonight just after sunset. Chances are you will find two or three particularly bright objects that stand out among the stars, even in the haze and illumination of a city. They don't seem to twinkle like stars but shine steadily. If you look at them through binoculars, they appear to be small disks.

If you look at the same bright objects on successive nights, you'll notice that over a period of weeks or months they seem to wander among the stars, never appearing in exactly the same place two nights in a row. The Greeks called them "wanderers," or planets, and assigned them the names of the gods (although today we use the Roman names). In the evening and morning, for example, you are likely to see Venus, named for the goddess of love, or swift-moving Mercury, the messenger of the gods. And the night sky is often dominated by Jupiter, the king of the gods.

Today we know that those disks of light in the sky are objects similar in many ways to our own planet, Earth. They show us that we are part of a system that includes not only Earth, but the Sun, the other planets, dozens of moons, and innumerable other smaller objects as well. Our probes have visited most of them and landed on several, including Mars and Venus. Visionaries talk of the day when science fiction will become reality and human beings will work and live on these, our nearest neighbors in the cosmos. In every sense of the word, the planets are the next frontier.

FIGURE 16-1 The solar system.

Clues to the Origin of the Solar System

The Copernican revolution radically altered human perceptions of our place in the universe (see Chapter 2). Rather than occupying what was assumed by many to be the center of creation, Earth became just one of a number of planets orbiting the Sun. The **solar system**, which includes many worlds—the Sun, the planets, and their dozens of moons, plus all other objects gravitationally bound to the Sun—displays several distinctive characteristics. Describing these features and explaining in detail how they came to be remains one of the main challenges faced by planetary scientists today. Indeed, the study of these many other worlds helps us to understand the origin and evolution of our own planet.

How can we deduce the origin and present state of the solar system? Until recently, all our observations of the Sun and planets had been made from Earth's surface. We see points of light moving in the sky, but how can that information be translated into a vivid picture of a dynamic system?

Humans have studied the solar system for thousands of years, making observations and proposing models. Ancient scholars recorded the changing positions of the brightest planets, such as Venus and Jupiter. Application of the telescope by Galileo and many subsequent astronomers (see Chapter 2) led to the discovery of numerous new, faint objects, including several moons and other small bodies. More recently, orbiting space probes and flyby missions have returned close-up photographic images of several planets, while spacecraft have landed on Venus, Mars, Saturn's large moon Titan, Pluto, and even a comet. Our present understanding of the solar system, therefore, represents the cumulative effect of centuries of observation.

As astronomers gathered data on the solar system, they noticed several striking regularities regarding the orbits of planets and the distribution of mass—patterns that provide clues to understanding the evolution of our home (Figure 16-1).

Clue #1: Planetary Orbits

Think about what Newton's laws tell us regarding satellites orbiting a central body. A satellite can go in any direction: east to west or west to east, around the equator or over the poles. There are no constraints regarding the orientation of the orbit, and planets could orbit any which way around the Sun. Yet in our solar system we see three very curious features:

1. All planets, and most of their moons, orbit in the same direction around the Sun, and this direction is the same as that of the rotation of the Sun.

2. All orbits of planets and their larger moons are in more or less the same plane. The solar system resembles a bunch of marbles rolling around on a single flat dish.

3. Almost all planets and moons rotate on their axes in the same direction as the planets orbit the Sun.

STOP & THINK If you had only the preceding information, what scenarios for the origin of the solar system would you construct?

Clue #2: The Distribution of Mass

You could imagine a solar system in which mass is evenly distributed, with all planets more or less the same size and same chemical composition. But our solar system is not that way at all (Figure 16-2). Instead:

• Virtually all of the material of the solar system is contained within the Sun, with only a small fraction in the planets and other objects in orbit.

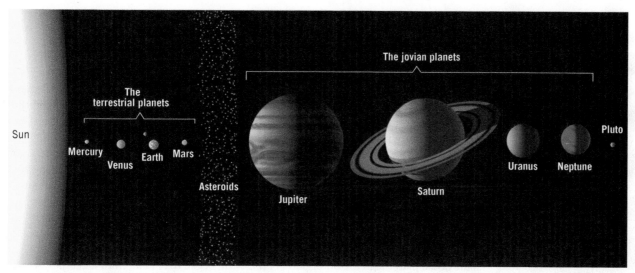

FIGURE 16-2 Most of the mass in the solar system is in the Sun, and most of the rest is in the Jovian planets. (Distances in this figure are not to scale.)

- Planets are divided into two distinct types. Near the Sun, in the "inner" solar system, are planets like Earth—relatively small, rocky, high-density worlds. These are called the **terrestrial planets** and include **Mercury, Venus, Earth, Mars,** and (although it isn't really a planet) **Earth's Moon**.
- Farther out from the Sun, in the "outer" solar system, are huge worlds made primarily of hydrogen and helium. We call them "gas giants," or **Jovian planets**, and they are **Jupiter, Saturn, Uranus,** and **Neptune**. (The question of how to categorize Pluto, long considered to be the outermost planet, is still a subject of debate among astronomers, but in 2006 the International Astronomical Union defined it to be the first of a new class of objects in the outer solar system, as discussed below.) The eight planets of the solar system and some of their characteristics are listed in Table 16-1.

These regularities in the distribution of the solar system's mass, combined with data on terrestrial and Jovian planetary orbits, add support to the nebular hypothesis—our best model of how the solar system was formed.

TABLE 16-1 **The Planets and Their Characteristics**

	Mercury	Venus	Earth	Mars	Jupiter	Saturn	Uranus	Neptune
Diameter (km)	4,880	12,104	12,756	6,787	142,800	120,000	51,800	49,500
Mass (Earth = 1)	0.0558	0.815	1.0	0.108	317.8	95.2	14.4	17.2
Density (gm/cm^3; water = 1)	5.44	5.20	5.52	3.93	1.30	0.69	1.28	1.64
Number of Moons	0	0	1	2	61	30	21	11
Length of day (Earth hours)	1,416	5,832	24	24.6	9.8	10.2	17.2	16.1
Period of one revolution around Sun (Earth years)	0.24	0.62	1.00	1.88	11.86	29.50	84.00	164.90
Average distance from Sun (millions of km)	58	108	150	228	778	1427	2870	4497

● 16.2 The Nebular Hypothesis

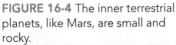

Spencer Sutton/Science Source Images

In Chapter 14 we examined the modern theory of star formation—the *nebular hypothesis,* which was first put forward by the French mathematician and physicist Pierre Simon Laplace (1749–1827). His model of star formation also helps to explain many of the distinctive characteristics of the solar system—the rotation of the Sun, the orbits of the planets, and the distribution of mass into one large central object and lots of much smaller orbiting bodies. According to the nebular hypothesis, long ago (about 4.5 billion years ago based on radiometric dating) a large cloud of dust and gas collected in the region now occupied by the solar system. Such dust and gas clouds, called **nebulae**, are common throughout our galaxy, the Milky Way. They typically contain more than 99% hydrogen and helium, with lesser amounts of all the other naturally occurring elements.

Under the influence of gravity, the nebula slowly, inexorably, started to collapse on itself. As was the case for the formation of stars from a nebula, the collapse caused the cloud to spin faster and faster. The rapid spin had several consequences. For one thing, it meant that some of the material in the outer parts of the cloud began to spin out into a flat disk. As we saw in the previous chapter, the solar system at this stage of its formation can be thought of as a large pancake with a big lump in the middle. The big lump represents the material that will eventually become the Sun and the material in the thin, flattened disk will eventually become the planets and the rest of the solar system (Figure 16-3).

The flattening of the nebula into a disk explains another feature of the solar system. The planets had to form in this rotating disk of material, and hence their eventual orbits had to lie close to the disk's plane. The fact that all planetary orbits lie near the same plane, then, is a simple consequence of the solar system's rapid rotation as the nebular cloud began to contract.

In any clump of matter such as the spinning disk, by chance, matter is more densely collected in some regions than elsewhere. These regions exert a stronger gravitational force than their neighbors, so that nearby matter tends to gravitate to them. Once the nearby matter has come in, the concentration of matter at that point is even greater, and it will pull even more material into it. As material accumulates, solid grains start to stick together.

This ultimate consequence of gravitational force leads to the rapid breakup of the disk into small objects called *planetesimals*, which range in size from boulders to masses several kilometers across. Once this segregation has happened, the process of gravitational attraction goes on at a grander scale. Planetesimals collide with each other; larger objects capture smaller ones and continue growing.

FIGURE 16-3 As the nebula that formed the solar system collapsed, it began to rotate and flatten into a disk. The stages in solar system formation include: (a) a slowly rotating nebula, (b), a flattened disk with massive center, (c) planets in the process of birth represented as mass concentrations in the nebula, and (d) the solar system.

FIGURE 16-4 The inner terrestrial planets, like Mars, are small and rocky.

Courtesy NASA

Our primary method of investigating this phase of the formation of the solar system is through the use of computer models. Many of these models describe an early solar system with many Mars-sized objects hurtling around, colliding with each other, breaking up, re-forming, and even being completely ejected from the solar system before things settled down to something like our present state of affairs.

About the time that this process was going on in the early solar system, the material at the center—more than 99% of the nebula's original mass—began to turn into a star. Light energy began to radiate out from the Sun, and large temperature differences began to develop in the disk. Those parts nearest the Sun were heated to temperatures above 1,000° Celsius, whereas those farther out warmed only a little—think of these two regions being separated by a "frost line" somewhere outside the orbit of Mars, beyond which liquid water did not form. As a result, the inner and outer solar systems developed differently. In the hot inner system, compounds such as water, methane, and carbon dioxide were in gaseous form, whereas farther out they were frozen into solids.

Thus, everyday physical processes having to do with phases of matter and the response to temperature—processes as familiar as boiling water and making ice—explain one of the crucial facts about the solar system. The terrestrial planets, including Mercury, Venus, Earth, and Mars, were formed from those materials that could remain solid at high temperatures. Consequently, they are small, rocky worlds (Figure 16-4).

Farther out in the solar system we find the Jovian planets, including Jupiter, Saturn, Uranus, and Neptune. The compositions of those planets are essentially the same as the material concentrated in the original nebula; that is, they contain large amounts of hydrogen and helium (Figure 16-5). These planets formed from material that condensed and accumulated under the condition of lower temperatures far from the Sun. Consequently, these outer Jovian planets have a markedly different chemical composition from the inner terrestrial planets of the solar system.

In passing, we should note that the Jovian planets probably had their own complement of high-density materials. Scientists suspect that beneath the thousands of kilometers of helium, hydrogen, and other condensed gases on these planets is concealed a core like a small terrestrial planet, whose composition is much like that of Earth and its neighbors, but this rocky matter represents only a small fraction of these planets' total mass.

Computer models give us a complex picture of the formation of the outer planets. It used to be assumed that these planets formed more or less where they are now found. The best current models tell us that Uranus and Neptune formed much closer to the Sun than they are now, and that gravitational forces associated with Jupiter and Saturn pushed them out to their present orbits about 4 billion years ago. This scenario would explain the difference in composition between the various outer planets, since Uranus and Neptune would have formed in a region where much of the hydrogen had been blown away by particles streaming out from the Sun, leaving those planets with less of the lighter elements than Jupiter and Saturn.

Just as any construction site has a pile of leftover materials lying around when the building is finished, so too does the solar system have its "scrap pile." These leftovers take the form of the rocky asteroids and icy comets that still orbit the Sun (see below), which represent some of the matter that never got taken up into planets.

FIGURE 16-5 Gas giant planets, like Jupiter, are large and are composed mainly of hydrogen and helium. Note the Great Red Spot—a storm that has raged on Jupiter for centuries.

THE SCIENCE OF LIFE
Gravity and Bones

The planets in our solar system vary greatly in mass, from "little" Mercury with only 1/20th the mass of Earth to Jupiter, which is 317 times more massive than our own planet. Consequently, the force of gravity at the surface of each planet is different; you would weigh a small fraction of what you do now on the surface of Mercury, but many times your present weight on Jupiter. (The connection between mass and weight is reviewed in Chapter 2.)

In humans, bones in the skeleton support our weight (Figure 16-6). Bone is not as rigid a material like concrete; rather, it must be flexible in response to its environment. It constantly rebuilds itself, replacing the calcium-rich minerals that form the solid structure. In fact, you can think of what goes on in bones as being analogous to the remodeling of a house. First, the old material is removed (a process called resorption), then new material is added. If a bone is subject to unusual stress (or lack of it), it will change gradually in response, adding or subtracting mass.

On the surface of the Moon, for example, you would weigh one-sixth of your Earth weight. Your bones would start to remodel themselves in response to the lower force of gravity, unless you kept them under stress by an extended program of vigorous exercise. Astronauts spending a few weeks or months in the weightless environment of space have experienced significant bone loss that, fortunately, is eventually made up after they return to Earth. Scientists are less certain, however, of the long-term effects of low gravity on bone loss. What might happen during the long months of a space flight to Mars, for example? Studies on astronauts now may well determine whether such ambitious interplanetary flights take place in the foreseeable future.

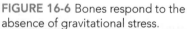

FIGURE 16-6 Bones respond to the absence of gravitational stress.

STOP & THINK What advantages to a living thing do you suppose arise from the features of bones we've just discussed? Why do you suppose bones aren't built like bridges, which are designed to carry the heaviest load possible?

FIGURE 16-7 An artist's impression of Earth's surface during the great bombardment.

The Formation of Earth

The gravitational collapse of the solar nebula into the Sun and planetesimals began the solar system's evolution. Each object that we now recognize as a planet grew in its own distinctive way. For Earth and the other terrestrial planets, this history had to do with the violent collisions of planetesimals, which quickly led to the formation of planets. Larger planetesimals swallowed smaller planetessimals as they moved in their crowded, competing orbits. The largest planetesimals eventually won, coalescing into the planets we see today. As the process of accumulation went on, each growing planet gradually swept up most of the debris that lay near its orbit.

If you had been standing on the surface of the newly forming planet Earth during this stage, you would have seen a spectacular display. A constant rain of debris left over from the initial period of planetary formation fell to the surface, steadily adding mass to the planet. During this period, called the **great bombardment**, the large amounts of kinetic energy carried by the shower of stones were converted into heat, which was added to the newly forming planet (Figure 16-7). By some accounts, much of the planetary surface would have glowed bright red from this accumulating heat and each large impact would have been accompanied by a spectacular splash of molten rock. Although in the case of Earth the addition of material has slowed considerably since the beginning, it has not stopped. Every time you see a meteor (often called a shooting star), for example, you are seeing an object roughly the size of a grain of sand being added to our planet. Scientists estimate that Earth's mass grows by about 20 metric tons (20,000 kg, or 2×10^7 g) per day by accretion of material falling from space.

When the nebular hypothesis was first proposed in the eighteenth century, there seemed little chance that any direct observational evidence could be found to support it. In 1992 astronomers using the Hubble Space Telescope (see Chapter 14) detected thick masses of dust encircling newborn stars in a region of space called the Orion nebula. Subsequent observations have confirmed the existence of numerous disks around young stars (Figure 16-8). It appears that in these cases we are seeing distant solar systems in the process of being born—observations that give us a measure of confidence in our model of how planets come into existence.

FIGURE 16-8 These Hubble Space Telescope pictures show a disk around a young star.

SCIENCE BY THE NUMBERS
Earth's Growth

Earth's mass is approximately 6×10^{27} grams. If 2×10^7 grams are added per day, how long would it take to double Earth's mass?

Reasoning and Solution: First, we have to calculate how many grams are added to Earth each year by multiplying the daily added mass by the number of days in a year. Earth's total mass, divided by the mass added each year, gives us the time it would take to double the present mass.

First we determine the yearly mass added to Earth.

$$\text{mass added per year} = (365 \text{ days/year}) \times (2 \times 10^7 \text{ g/day})$$
$$= 730 \times 10^7 \text{ g/year}$$
$$= 7.3 \times 10^9 \text{ g/year}$$

Then, divide Earth's total mass by the mass added every year.

$$\text{number of years} = \frac{(6 \times 10^{27} \text{g})}{(7.3 \times 10^9 \text{ g/year})}$$
$$= 0.82 \times 10^{18} \text{ years}$$
$$= 8.2 \times 10^{17} \text{ years}$$

This number is the time (in years) that would be required to double Earth's mass at its present rate of growth. This immense time, nearly a billion-billion years, is vastly greater than the lifetime of our planet, which is only 4.5 billion years. From this calculation we see that the total amount of mass now being added to Earth is trivial, so that most of the planet's mass must have accumulated in the beginning.

Differentiation

Each time another planetesimal hit the young Earth, all of its kinetic and potential energy was converted into heat. That heat diffused through the planet. Earth's surface glowed red-hot, and the deep interior reached temperatures of thousands of degrees. Eventually, Earth either melted completely or else was heated to high enough temperatures so that it was very soft all the way through. Heavy, dense materials (like iron and nickel) sank under the force of gravity toward the center of the planet, while lighter, less dense materials floated to the top. The result of this process, called **differentiation**, is that the present-day terrestrial planets have a distinctively layered structure. (Earth's structure is shown in Figure 16-9.)

In a sense, what happened to these planets long ago isn't too different from what happens to a mixture of oil and water that is shaken up and then allowed to stand. Eventually, the lighter oil will float to the top and the heavier water will sink to the bottom under the influence of gravity. Earth also separated into layers of different density when it underwent differentiation.

At Earth's center, with a radius of about 3,400 kilometers (2,000 miles), is the **core**, made primarily of iron and nickel metal. Temperatures at Earth's center are believed to exceed 5,000°C, but pressures are so high—about 3.5 billion grams per square centimeter (almost 50 million pounds per square inch)—that the iron–nickel inner core is solid. A little farther out the pressures are somewhat lower, so that the outer region of the iron–nickel core is a liquid.

The metal core is overlain by a thick layer, the **mantle**, which is rich in the elements oxygen, silicon, magnesium, and iron. Metallic bonding predominates in the core, but the mantle features minerals with primarily ionic bonds between negatively charged oxygen ions and positively charged silicon, magnesium, and other ions. Mantle rocks are similar in composition to some familiar surface rocks, but the atoms in these high-pressure materials are packed together in much denser forms.

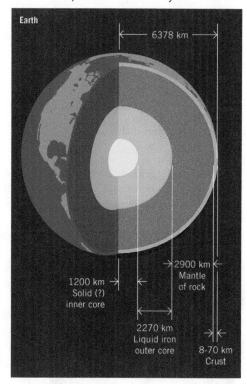

FIGURE 16-9 The layered Earth. The principal layers, which differ in chemical composition and physical properties, are the core, the mantle, the crust, and the atmosphere (not shown). When looked at in detail, each of these layers is itself composed of smaller layers.

At Earth's very outer layer is the **crust**, which is made up of the least dense materials. The crust's thickness ranges from less than 10 kilometers (about 6 miles) in parts of the oceans to as much as 70 kilometers (about 45 miles) beneath parts of the continents. The crust is the only layer of the solid Earth with which human beings have had contact, and it remains the source of almost all the rocks and minerals that we use in our lives.

You might wonder how scientists could describe parts of Earth's interior that no human being has ever seen. In the next chapter we introduce seismology, a branch of science that has provided (among other things) our present picture of Earth's interior.

TECHNOLOGY
Producing World-Record High Pressures

The force of gravity, pulling inward on all of Earth's layers, results in immense internal pressures, exceeding 3 million times the atmospheric pressure at Earth's center. What changes affect rocks and minerals at these extreme conditions? High-pressure researchers, who have learned to sustain laboratory pressures greater than those at Earth's center, are providing surprising answers.

Of all the materials from Earth's deep interior, none holds more fascination than diamond, the high-pressure form of carbon. This magnificent gemstone is also the hardest known substance and the most efficient abrasive for shaping the tough metal parts of modern industrial machines. Until the mid-1950s, diamonds were available only from few natural sources, but in 1954 scientists at General Electric discovered how to manufacture diamonds by duplicating the extreme temperatures and pressures that exist hundreds of kilometers beneath Earth's surface. The researchers squeezed carbon between the jaws of a massive metal vise and heated their sample with a powerful electrical current. Early experiments yielded only a fraction of a carat of diamond, but large factories now produce more than 100 tons of diamonds annually—an output exceeding the total amount of diamonds mined since biblical times.

Earth taught us how diamonds are made, and now scientists use diamonds to learn how Earth was made. The highest sustained laboratory pressures available today are obtained by clamping together two tiny pointed anvils of diamond. Samples squeezed between the diamond-anvil faces are subjected to pressures of several million kilograms per square centimeter, greater than at Earth's center. At such extreme conditions, rocks and minerals compress to new, dense forms occupying less than half their original volumes (Figure 16-10). Dramatic changes in chemical bonding are also observed, with many ionically and covalently bonded compounds transforming to metals at high pressure.

The Formation of the Moon

The origin of the Moon, the only large body in orbit around Earth, poses one of the oldest puzzles in planetary science. The Moon is one of the largest bodies in the solar system—larger than Mercury and almost as large as Mars. The Moon's density and chemical composition, subjects of intense study by the astronauts of the *Apollo* lunar missions, are quite different from Earth as a whole, though they are remarkably similar to those of Earth's mantle. (Roughly speaking, Earth as a whole has a density about five times that of water, whereas that of the Moon is only three times that of water). The problem of the Moon's origin can be stated simply: How could such a large body have arisen in the same region of space as Earth, when its composition is so different?

Computer models suggest a solution to this puzzle. In these models, Earth underwent differentiation as described earlier, so that the heaver material sank to the core and the lighter material floated up into the mantle. At this point, a Mars-sized planet that was competing with Earth for a similar orbit around the Sun smashed into Earth in an immense collision, which blasted a large amount of Earth's mantle material (but not the dense metal core) into space (Figure 16-11). Some of this material went into orbit around Earth and, in a process much like that which formed the planets, formed the Moon. In this scheme, the Moon's low density can be understood as a consequence of the process of Earth's differentiation.

FIGURE 16-10 Researchers attain high pressures, equivalent to those deep inside Earth and other planets, using the diamond anvil cell. Looking through such diamond cells, you can observe pressurized samples such as this high-pressure ice crystal that was formed at room temperature by squeezing water.

Photo by Alvin Van Valkenburg, courtesy of Robert Hazen

Stocktrek/Getty Images, Inc.

FIGURE 16-11 An artist's conception of the impact that led to the formation of Earth's Moon.

As for Earth, the theories predict that, as a result of the collision, large-scale melting occurred so that Earth's surface re-formed without any crater. When the planet cooled off, no trace of the mammoth impact was left.

EXAMPLE 16-1

THE DENSITY OF THE MOON

Scientists can measure the mass of the Moon by observing satellites in orbit or by measuring tides on Earth. This mass is approximately 7.4×10^{22} kg. They can also measure the radius of the Moon by observing its apparent size in the sky. Its radius is approximately 1.7×10^6 km. What is the average density of Earth's nearest neighbor?

Reasoning: The density of an object is defined to be its mass divided by its volume. The first step, then, is to find the volume of the Moon. Once we have the volume, the density will be given by:

$$\text{density} = \text{mass of Moon/volume of Moon}$$

The volume of a sphere of radius R is given by:

$$\text{volume of sphere} = 4/3 \times \pi \times \text{radius}^3$$

Solution: The volume of the Moon is then:

$$\text{volume} = 4/3 \times 3.14 \times (1.7 \times 10^6)^3$$
$$= 2 \times 10^{19} \text{ m}^3$$

So that the density is:

$$\text{density} = \frac{7.4 \times 10^{22} \text{kg}}{2 \times 10^{19} \text{m}^3}$$
$$= 3{,}700 \text{ kg/m}^3$$

For reference, the density of water is $1{,}000$ kg/m^3 and Earth's average density is about $5{,}500$ kg/m^3. Thus, the overall density of the Moon is considerably less than that of Earth. It is about the same as the comparatively light material in Earth's mantle, a fact that plays an important role in our theories of the Moon's formation, as we saw earlier.

Planetary Idiosyncrasies

The natural processes that occurred during Earth's formation affected the other planets as well. Mercury, Mars, and the Moon, for example, display surface cratering that suggests that large chunks of rock bombarded all of these bodies late in their formation. On Mercury and the Moon, which have no atmosphere, no weathering has affected the craters and so they are still there.

The early bombardment may also have affected other characteristics of the terrestrial planets. The direction of rotation of Venus, for example, is opposite that of Earth. (Planets revolve around the Sun, but rotate about their axes.) Earth's axis of rotation, furthermore, is tilted at 23° to the plane of its orbit, whereas Uranus has its axis of rotation close to the plane of its orbit, a full 90° from an upright orientation. Current thinking is that these differences resulted from the more or less random collisions with large objects, perhaps hundreds of kilometers in diameter, which marked the very end of the main phase of planetary formation. You might expect that the details of these late-stage collisions between very large objects were different for each planet. Thus, the nebular hypothesis not only explains how it is that the planets all have their orbits in the same plane and move in the same direction around the Sun, but also allows us to explain why the rotations of individual planets can be so different.

THE SCIENCE OF LIFE
When Could Life Begin?

This scenario for Earth's formation also has important implications for the origins of life on our planet. During the period of the great bombardment, Earth was constantly being hit by huge objects—chunks of rock the size of a city or even a state (Figure 16-12). At the very least, the tremendous energy released by such collisions would be enough to vaporize most of any oceans that had formed, sterilizing most of the planet. Even if life had come into existence during this period, it would have been wiped out by the impacts. Thus, the ancestors of modern living things may not have gotten their start until the end of the bombardment, which occurred between 4.2 and 3.8 billion years ago. This fact will become important when we discuss the origins of life in Chapter 25.

The Evolution of Planetary Atmospheres

Earth didn't always have the kind of atmosphere it has today. Scientists now suggest that originally it had no atmosphere at all, and that once an atmosphere formed, its chemical composition gradually evolved to its present form. The question of how Earth's atmosphere arose and changed is extremely important because this history is inseparable from understanding the origin and evolution of life on our planet.

During the early formation of the Sun, large amounts of material and radiation were thrown off. This flood of materials would have blown off any atmosphere Earth might have accumulated. Thus, for all intents and purposes, early Earth was an airless ball of hot (or even molten) rock floating in space.

During the period of cooling that followed the great bombardment and melting, large amounts of water vapor, carbon dioxide, and other gases would have been released from deep within Earth's solid interior in a process called *outgassing*. Some of these materials may also have been brought in by impacts during the last part of the great bombardment. In other words, the gases that formed the ancestor of today's atmosphere were probably originally locked into the rocks near Earth's surface or in orbiting debris when the original atmosphere was swept away.

Outgassing, which was violent and rapid early in Earth's history, has not ended today. We tend to think of volcanic eruptions as involving the flow of red-hot lava, but if you remember pictures of eruptions, you probably recall large clouds of smoke and steam that accompany the glowing lava flows. Even today, more than 4.5 billion years after the planet's formation, volcanoes release

FIGURE 16-12 The 1,200-meter-wide Meteor Crater in Arizona formed from a collision about 20,000 years ago. The meteorite was approximately the size of a small car.

large amounts of gases from Earth's interior. Presumably, the same sort of process occurred on the other terrestrial planets. For a time, Earth's atmosphere was probably too hot for water to condense from a gas to a liquid, but eventually the atmospheric temperature dropped and torrential rains began to fill the ocean basins.

Once a planet has acquired an atmosphere by outgassing and impact, that atmosphere can evolve and change in several ways. The simplest mechanism is *gravitational escape.* The molecules in an atmosphere heated by the Sun may move sufficiently fast so that appreciable fractions of them can escape the gravitational pull of their planet. The Moon, Mercury, and Mars are examples of bodies that had denser atmospheres early in their history, but lost much of these gases through gravitational escape long ago. Most of the light elements such as hydrogen and helium were presumably lost in the same way from Earth, but the heavier gases such as carbon dioxide and water vapor remained because they were too heavy to escape Earth's gravitational force.

A second cause of atmospheric change that operates only on Earth is the effect of living things. To the best of our knowledge, no life exists anywhere else in the solar system (although some scientists argue that simple forms of life might exist beneath the surface of Mars or in the oceans on Jupiter's moon, Europa). By the time Earth was 2 billion years old, photosynthetic organisms had evolved to use the Sun's energy to power the chemical reactions essential for life. As life flourished on the planet, the amount of free oxygen increased as well, until today it comprises about 20% of the atmosphere.

We tend to think of oxygen as a benign and beautiful substance, but from a chemical point of view it's really rather nasty stuff. As we saw in Chapter 8, oxygen reacts violently with many materials (think of fire burning or the explosion of hydrogen or gasoline). In fact, the production of oxygen by living things on early Earth can be thought of as the first global pollution event. Thus, life forms both affect and are affected by the atmosphere of the planet on which they reside. Many scientists now suggest that you can tell whether a planet has life on it simply by looking at its atmosphere.

◎ 16.3 Exploring the Solar System

We live in a time of intense exploration of our planetary neighbors. Dozens of missions by NASA and agencies in other countries have led to remarkable discoveries of new objects and unexpected features in our solar system. Let's look at just a few of these efforts.

The Inner Solar System

Space probes have visited all of our nearest neighbors—the terrestrial planets Mercury, Venus, and Mars. Mercury and Venus, the two planets closest to the Sun, are too hot to sustain life. Thus, of the terrestrial planets, the exploration of Mars continues to generate the greatest interest. Of all our planetary neighbors, Mars is the body most likely to have harbored life (Figure 16-13). For the last two decades NASA has sent a veritable flotilla of probes to the Red Planet, including devices that have landed and explored the Martian surface. Over the years the "rovers," which can be thought of as remote-controlled mobile laboratories, have grown from something the size of a large suitcase to vehicles the size of a small car.

These missions have shown that there was once liquid water on the Martian surface—even a large ocean—and have provided evidence that a substantial quantity of water remains locked in the Martian crust. For example, the *Phoenix Mars Lander* (Figure 16-14) landed in the north polar region of the planet in 2008 and found water ice (i.e., ice made by the freezing of ordinary water) mixed with Martian soil. In August 2012, the car-sized *Curiosity* rover made a spectacular landing on Mars and continues to collect information about Martian rocks, soil, ice, and atmosphere composition, including unambiguous evidence that water once flowed on the martian surface.

FIGURE 16-13 The surface of Mars might have been covered by an ocean at one time.

NASA/JPL–Caltech/MSSS

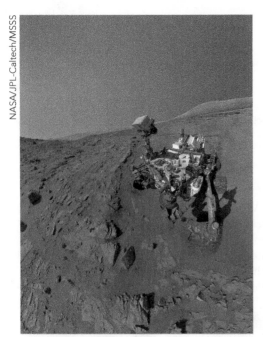

The Mars *Curiosity* rover

FIGURE 16-14 *(a)* An artist's conception of the *Phoenix Lander* on Mars. *(b)* The lander dug into the Martian surface and found ice. *(c)* The ice evaporated after several days.

The current thinking is that early in its history, before it lost its atmosphere to gravitational escape, Mars would have looked much like Earth. And, so the reasoning goes, because life seems to have developed quickly on Earth, it may well have done the same on Mars. Even if the cooling and loss of atmosphere wiped out that early life, we should be able to find evidence for it in the form of fossils.

Projecting beyond 2020, NASA scientists have aspirations for both detection of life on Mars and sample return missions. NASA planners are working closely with the Centers for Disease Control to ensure that these samples neither contaminate, nor are contaminated by, microbes from Earth. A high-security containment structure will be constructed to house the Mars samples when they return.

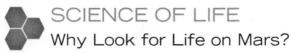

SCIENCE OF LIFE
Why Look for Life on Mars?

The idea that life exists on Mars has been a staple of science fiction for decades, with writers depicting Martian life either as immensely threatening to Earth (Figure 16-15) or as something like one of our own ancient civilizations. In the early part of the twentieth century, the American astronomer Percival Lowell even claimed that he could see "canals" on the Red Planet, which he took to be proof positive of life.

As we have learned more about our neighbor, however, we have seen that these ideas are simply not true. Lowell's "canals," for example, turned out to be a combination of optical illusions and wishful thinking. Nevertheless, the hope persisted that some sort of microbial life might exist on Mars, and every Mars lander has carried equipment designed to detect signs of living organisms. To date, no such signals have been seen.

The consensus view today is that microbial life may have existed on Mars early on, when it had oceans on its surface. The surface is now inhospitable, but warm and wet environments may persist underground and hardy microbes may survive to this day. As a result, one of the prime goals of the sample return mission will be to bring back drill cores that can be examined for signs of life, past or present (see Chapter 25). And this pursuit raises the question of why we should care that life once existed on our neighbor.

The reason is simple. As we shall see in Chapter 25, all living things on our planet descended from a single common ancestor and share the same chemical makeup. All living things that we know about, in other words, are the result of a single experiment. We have no idea whether life is common in the universe or whether what we see around us is the result of some sort of cosmic fluke. If we found evidence that life had evolved independently on Mars, even if it is now extinct, it would tell us that we can expect to find it elsewhere in the galaxy.

FIGURE 16-15 Science fiction writers have often thought of Mars as the home of an advanced civilization, as in this old 1940 Buck Rogers movie showing "Ming the Merciless" as the ruler of the imaginary planet Mongo.

The Outer Solar System

A number of space probes sent out from Earth since the 1970s have visited most of the outer planets and provided a new view of the outer solar system. The distances to the giant outer planets are immense. The closest gas giant, Jupiter, orbits at five times the Earth–Sun distance, over 800 million kilometers away. Saturn is twice that far, while Uranus and Neptune are several billion kilometers away and Pluto and the Kuiper Belt objects are farther still. This far out in the system, the Sun looks like a small marble in the sky, and its warming effects are feeble indeed. Compounds that are normally gases on Earth, such as carbon dioxide, nitrogen, and methane, are found in liquid or even solid form under the intense pressures that exist in the interiors of the Jovian planets.

The structure of the outer giant planets is layered, like that of the terrestrial planets, but they do not have a well-defined solid surface like Earth and the Moon. Moving down from space into the body of Jupiter or Saturn would be a strange experience. You would move through progressively denser and denser layers of clouds and then pass imperceptibly into a layer where the gases change into liquids because of the high pressure. Landing on Jupiter would be more like landing on a giant ice cream sundae than landing on Earth or the Moon. In Figure 16-16, we show a typical structure for one of the Jovian planets.

During the mid-1990s, astronomers got two unique opportunities to study the atmosphere of Jupiter. One of these was fortuitous. From July 16 to 22, 1994, a string of objects known collectively as Comet Shoemaker-Levy collided with Jupiter (Figure 16-17). The effect of these collisions was to bring gases that normally lie hundreds of miles deep up to the top of the atmosphere where scientists could see them. The net effect of the impacts, other than providing a spectacular show, was to allow astronomers to fine-tune their notions about the composition of the Jovian atmosphere.

In December 1995, the spacecraft *Galileo* arrived in orbit around Jupiter to begin a study of the planet. *Galileo* was launched on October 18, 1989. Its orbit took it around the Sun and Earth for an extra boost from gravity. When it arrived at Jupiter, the satellite launched a small probe into the Jovian atmosphere. Its descent slowed by a parachute system, the probe sank into the atmosphere, sending back information about the material through which it was passing. After 57 minutes of operation, the probe (as expected) was destroyed, but during its brief lifetime it gave scientists a library of new information about the atmosphere of the largest planet. After that, *Galileo* spent several years in orbit around Jupiter, sending back a treasure trove of information about that planet and its moons. On September 21, 2003, the aging spacecraft was deliberately plunged into the atmosphere of Jupiter to guard against possible future contamination of Europa.

Then, in June 2004, NASA's *Cassini* became the first spacecraft to enter orbit around Saturn, where it continues to return spectacular images and measurements of the beautiful ringed planet (Figure 16-18). At more that 5,000 kilograms, *Cassini* is by far the largest and most complex space probe ever launched. As we shall see, its main task has been a detailed exploration of Saturn's moon, particularly Titan.

FIGURE 16-16 A theoretical view of the interior of Jupiter, one of the Jovian planets. Most of the planet's volume is highly compressed hydrogen and helium.

FIGURE 16-17 This infrared image of Jupiter shows the many impact sites, or splashes, due to fragments of Comet Shoemaker-Levy 9 in July 1994.

FIGURE 16-18 The ringed planet Saturn has numerous moons, including Titan (foreground) and other smaller moons. In this composite photograph the objects are not shown to scale.

Moons and Rings of the Outer Planets

Astronomers have found dozens of moons circling Jupiter, Saturn, Uranus, and Neptune. These bodies range from small rocks to planet-sized objects. Each of these moons is its own world, with its own history and formed by its own unique collection of physical processes. Each can be thought of as a small laboratory that sheds some light on the formation of terrestrial planets, but three are of special interest.

Io

The moon Io, which circles close to Jupiter, is the only moon in the solar system known to have active volcanoes. Scientists think that Jupiter's powerful gravitational forces flex and twist the moon to produce the energy to drive those volcanoes.

Europa

Jupiter's second moon has become one of the most studied objects in the solar system because the *Galileo* spacecraft results suggest the possibility that conditions there may be appropriate for the development of life. The *Voyager* spacecraft photographs of Europa showed a smooth surface made of water ice. The relative absence of craters means that the surface must have formed recently, which would be puzzling in a moon in the frigid outer depths of the solar system.

STOP & THINK Why should the absence of craters indicate a young surface on Europa?

When *Galileo* arrived at Jupiter, it sent back close-up photographs of the surface of Europa that looked more like the Arctic ice pack than a perpetually frozen world. Giant blocks of ice seemed to be jumbled together, welded together at their boundaries by what looked like ridges of freshly frozen material. Scientists began to speculate that under Europa's icy surface, heated by the same kind of gravitational twisting that powers Io's volcanoes, there might be liquid water—an entire ocean, in fact (Figure 16-19). Later measurements showed that Europa has a magnetic field that could arise from a salty ocean in its interior, and pictures of craters were produced that look as if they had been filled in by a slushy fluid after impact. Europa was the first nonterrestrial ocean seen in the solar system, and recent results from the *Cassini* spacecraft show that Saturn's moon Enceladus has a similar structure. Because life on Earth probably developed in the oceans, the possibility exists that life (in microbial form, at least) might have arisen on Europa.

TECHNOLOGY
Drilling Through Europa's Ice

Although any attempt to search for life in Europa's oceans is decades away, scientists are starting to design and test instruments that might be able to penetrate the outer layer of ice. Two competing technologies are on the drawing boards. The first method involves an apparatus called a penetrator that would melt surface ice, then heat the resulting water to melt its way down through the thick ice layer. When the penetrator reached the liquid ocean, it would release a small submarine that would explore the new environment. An alternative possibility involves the development of a lightweight drill that could be lowered by a tether until it had penetrated to the ocean. Which, if either, of these approaches will work is still very much an open question.

We should note that scientists believe that the ice of Europa is very thick in places, with the ocean lying an average of 20 kilometers (13 miles) or more beneath the surface. Some theorists have suggested, however, that the ice sheet might be as thin as a few hundred meters in spots. Like settling on the design of the apparatus, developing a more detailed understanding of Europa's ice is a task for the future.

Titan

Scientists believe that Saturn's moon Titan, which is about the same size as the planet Mercury, may well serve as a laboratory for chemical reactions that took place billions of years ago on Earth. One of the first tasks of the *Cassini* space probe when it arrived at Saturn in 2004 was to drop a probe into Titan's atmosphere. The probe, named *Huygens*, after the seventeenth-century Dutch astronomer Christiian Huygens (1629–1695), who discovered Titan, descended on a parachute and broadcast data back to *Cassini* for over three hours before it succumbed to the cold and the pressure. As a result, we now know that Titan is made primarily of rock and water ice, with liquid methane (CH_4, or natural gas) raining down and forming large lakes. On top of this surface in places is black goo, suggesting to scientists that the chemical reactions that form organic compounds take place on Titan, albeit slowed down by the cold. The thought is that these reactions happened much more quickly in the balmy oceans of early Earth and that Titan thus constitutes a kind of museum of Earth's early chemistry.

Rings

In addition to these numerous moons, each of the four Jovian planets has a system of rings formed from countless fragments of ice and rock. Saturn features the most spectacular of these ring systems—an array of dozens of fine bands formed from small, highly reflective ice crystals, separated by larger objects called shepherd satellites. Uranus and Neptune have their own complex ring systems, though apparently composed of automobile-size chunks of dark carbon-rich material, quite unlike the luminous particles that comprise the icy rings of Saturn.

Pluto and the Kuiper Belt

Pluto has traditionally been regarded as the outermost planet, but it is really not like planets in the inner solar system. For one thing, Pluto is small—it has only about 0.3% of Earth's mass. For another, its orbit is tilted out of the plane of other planetary orbits, and it spends part of each of its "years" inside the orbit of Neptune. Finally, Pluto is circled by a moon, Charon, which is almost as large as Pluto itself (Figure 16-20).

During the last half of the twentieth century, scientists discovered that a large disk-shaped collection of comets and rocky objects left over from the formation of the solar system lies outside the orbit of Pluto. This collection is called the **Kuiper Belt**, after Gerard Kuiper (1905–1973), the Dutch astronomer who first suggested its existence. The discovery of the Kuiper Belt led to a new understanding of Pluto. Instead of being an oddball last planet in the solar system, it is now recognized as the first typical object in the Kuiper Belt. In 2006 the International Astronomical Union recognized this new status by conferring the name **plutoid** on any large planet-like object orbiting farther out than Pluto.

Small objects in the Kuiper belt were observed in the 1990s, but it wasn't until 2005 that another Pluto-sized object was identified. Since then, a number of these objects have been found and named (including one called Eris, which is more massive than Pluto), and scientists expect more to be seen in the future. Thus, the Kuiper Belt promises to be a treasure trove of new planetary discoveries.

In 2006 NASA launched the *New Horizons* space probe. After having passed by Jupiter in 2007, this probe flew by Pluto in 2015—the first human-made object to visit this mysterious body. *New Horizons* has since gone on to explore the Kuiper Belt.

FIGURE 16-19 An artist's conception of the oceans of Europa. It shows the rocky ocean floor on the bottom, the liquid ocean, and, on top, the thick layer of ice covering the water.

FIGURE 16-20 Artist's conception of Pluto (in back) orbited by its large moon, Charon.

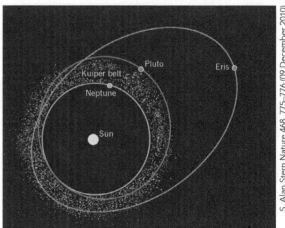

The Kuiper Belt planets and Pluto

Detlev van Ravenswaay/Photo Researchers, Inc.

S. Alan Stern Nature 468, 775–776 (09 December 2010) doi:10.1038/468775a

SCIENCE IN THE MAKING
The Discovery of Pluto

Five of the planets—Mercury, Venus, Mars, Jupiter, and Saturn—are easily visible to the naked eye and have been known from ancient times. The other two,

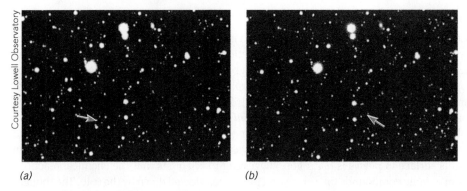

(a)   *(b)*

FIGURE 16-21 The discovery photos for Pluto reveal the shift of one point of light between January 23, 1930 *(a)*, and January 29, 1930 *(b)*. The red arrows point to Pluto.

most distant planets—Uranus and Neptune—were discovered after the invention of the telescope. A more recent discovery of the first plutoid occurred on February 18, 1930, by 23-year-old Clyde Tombaugh (1906–1997), who had been brought up on a Kansas farm. Employed as a technician at Lowell Observatory in Flagstaff, Arizona, Tombaugh uncovered convincing evidence for the existence of a new planet.

As a teenager, Tombaugh had built a small telescope, using parts from an old cream separator to make its stand. He drew sketches of the surface of Mars and sent them to Lowell Observatory, which was then engaged in observations of the red planet. The sketches, made with a small amateur's instrument, corresponded so well to what astronomers at Lowell were seeing through their state-of-the-art telescope that Tombaugh received a job offer by return mail.

At Lowell, he began a systematic search for what was then called Planet X. The founder of the observatory, American astronomer Percival Lowell, had predicted the existence of such a planet based on some rather questionable data on variations in the orbit of Neptune. Tombaugh's task was straightforward, if tiring. He would take photographs of each section of the sky, then a second photograph of the same section a few days later. The two photographs were then put into a machine that would show first one photograph, then the other, in an eyepiece (Figure 16-21). As the photographs were "blinked," any object that had moved between the time of the two photographs would appear to jump back and forth, while stars would remain stationary.

The main problem is that the plane of the solar system is littered with other large objects called asteroids and comets (see below), each of which could show up as a moving light on such photos. The key point wasn't that Tombaugh found something out there that moved—there were plenty of such objects. The point was to find a point of light that moved by as much as Kepler's laws tell us that a planet out beyond Neptune would move in a few days. That is exactly what Tombaugh found on that day in February, some 10 months into his search.

After becoming the first human to discover what we now call a plutoid, Tombaugh went back to college. Much to his surprise, he was not allowed to take introductory astronomy. "They cheated me out of 4 hours!" he said. And his old telescope? When one of the authors (J.T.) asked him before his death a few years ago whether he was going to donate it to the Smithsonian Institution, the 83-year-old astronomer replied, "They want it, but they can't have it. I'm not through using it yet!"

SCIENCE IN THE MAKING
The *Voyager* Satellites

On August 20, 1977, a rocket blasted off from Cape Canaveral in Florida, to set a small space probe on its course. Sixteen days later, another rocket did the same. These two probes, called *Voyager 1* and *2*, respectively, spent the next 15 years moving past the planets of the outer solar system, providing scientists with their first close-up look at the Jovian planets and their moons.

Each spacecraft had 10 scientific instruments on board, each designed to measure a different aspect of the deep-space environment. The ones that had the greatest public impact were the cameras that took pictures of moons, rings, and planets, but measurements were also made of magnetic fields, cosmic ray abundances, and infrared and ultraviolet radiation. Taken together, the *Voyager* probes produced a good deal of the detailed information about the outer solar system contained in this chapter.

One interesting feature of spaceflights like this is that by the time a spacecraft has been in flight for a while, all of its instrumentation has become obsolete. Between its encounters with Jupiter and Neptune, for example, the computers on *Voyager 2* were reprogrammed to make significant changes in the way they analyzed and transmitted data. As a result, the rate of transmission during the Neptune flyby in 1989 was not significantly different from that of the Jupiter encounter in 1979, despite the greater distance and lower light levels at Neptune.

Among their discoveries, the *Voyagers* found ring systems around all the Jovian planets, recorded a volcanic eruption on Io, tripled the number of known moons around Uranus, and clocked record winds on the surface of Neptune. Today, both *Voyagers,* together with a couple of earlier space probes called *Pioneers,* have moved out of the solar system and into interstellar space, passing what scientists call the "termination shock," where the solar wind blends with the interstellar medium of the galaxy. *Voyager 2* is expected to keep returning data until its plutonium power supply runs down, sometime around 2020. By that time, it may have reached the place where the Sun's magnetic field blends into the magnetic field of our galaxy, thereby becoming the first human-made object to have broken free from all the dominant influences of the Sun.

Asteroids, Comets, and Meteors

As the solar system formed, not all the material in the planetary disk was taken up into the bodies of the planets and moons. Even after hundreds of millions of years of accumulation and bombardment, a lot of debris was still floating around out there and remains even today. This debris comes in two main forms, asteroids and comets, which in a sense mimic the compositional differences of the inner and outer planets.

Asteroids

Asteroids are small rocky bodies in orbit around the Sun and are like miniature versions of the inner terrestrial planets. Most asteroids are found in a broad, circular **asteroid belt** between Mars and Jupiter—material thought to be a collection of planetesimals that never managed to collect into a stable planet. The most likely explanation is that the nearby planet Jupiter had a disrupting gravitational effect. In addition, many asteroids possess orbits that cross Earth's orbit, and they produce occasional large impacts on our planet.

Because the asteroids never underwent the process of differentiation discussed earlier, they tend to be rich in minerals. Starting in 2013, commercial companies have been formed to develop the technology needed to exploit that resource. In addition, NASA is planning what is called the Asteroid Redirection Mission (ARM) to capture an asteroid and move it into orbit around the Moon where it can be studied. This mission could fly as early as 2024.

FIGURE 16-22 A comet develops a tail as it approaches the Sun.

Friedrich Saure / Science Source Images

Comets

Comets can best be thought of as "dirty snowballs." Unlike asteroids, they consist of chunks, sometimes many miles in diameter, of material such as water ice and methane ice in which a certain amount of solid, rocky material or dirt is embedded. Also, unlike asteroids, most of the comets in the solar system circle the Sun outside the orbit of Pluto. Two main reservoirs of comets are found in the solar system. One of these is a large spherical array called the *Oort cloud* (named after Dutch astronomer Jan Oort, 1900–1992, who first postulated its existence), located far from the solar system. The other is part of the Kuiper Belt.

Occasionally, when the orbit of a comet is disturbed, the comet will be deflected so that it falls toward the Sun. When this happens, the increasing temperature of the inner solar system begins to boil off materials, and we see a large "tail," blown away from the Sun by the solar wind, that reflects light to us (Figure 16-22).

Sometimes a comet will be captured and fall into a regular orbit around the Sun. The most famous of these periodic comets is Halley's Comet (see Chapter 2), which returns to the vicinity of Earth about every 76 years. Halley's return in 1910 was quite spectacular because the comet passed near Earth when it was at its highest temperature and therefore had its largest and most spectacular tail. The return in 1986 was much less spectacular because the comet was on the far side of the Sun when it was at its brightest. The next predicted return in 2061, unfortunately, will probably be just as unspectacular.

STOP & THINK **How do you suppose astronomers knew that the Oort cloud and Kuiper Belt existed before objects in the latter could actually be seen?**

Scientists have long observed comets with telescopes and other instruments. Recently, they have also enlisted space probes to get even more detailed information. In 1999 NASA launched the probe *Stardust*, which collected material from the tail of comet Wild 2 (pronounced "Vild," after its discoverer, Paul Wild, 1934–2008). In 2005, NASA's *Deep Impact* mission dropped a projectile into the nucleus of comet Tempel 1 and monitored the material that came out.

One of the most ambitious projects was the European Space Agency's probe *Rosetta*, launched in 2004. The spacecraft went into orbit around comet Churynumov-Gerasimeno in 2014, dropped a probe onto its surface, and followed it as it went around the Sun. The mission collected detailed data on the comet's structure.

THE SCIENCE OF LIFE
Comets and Life on Earth

In addition to providing us with one of the first historical tests of the law of universal gravitation, comets may have had an important effect on the evolution of life on Earth. Many scientists suspect that the impacts of comets or asteroids may have drastically altered Earth's climate and produced mass extinctions, or killings, at various times in Earth's history (see Chapter 25). Most Earth scientists, for example, now suspect that the dinosaurs and other life forms that thrived 65 million years ago were driven to extinction following the impact of a large comet or asteroid that hit Earth at a site near Mexico's Yucatán Peninsula.

Meteoroids, Meteors, and Meteorites

© Xinhua/RIA/Xinhua Press / Corbis Images

Meteoroids are small pieces of ancient space debris in orbit around the Sun. Occasionally, one of these bits, perhaps the size of a sand grain, will fall into Earth's atmosphere where it becomes briefly visible as a **meteor**. Most meteors burn up completely to microscopic particles of ash that slowly, imperceptibly, rain down on Earth. The meteors' bright streaks of light record the path of this burning. Occasionally, if the object is big enough so that only the outer surface burns, a piece of rock may actually reach Earth's surface. Any such rock that has fallen to Earth from space is called a **meteorite**. The most recent meteorite impact occurred near the city of Cheyabinsk, Russia, in 2013.

Meteor showers are spectacular, regularly occurring events in the night sky. During a shower, every minute or so you can see brilliant streaks in the sky, each one caused by the collision of Earth with swarms of small debris that travel around the orbits of comets. Some of these swarms may be comets that were broken up by the gravitational pull of one of the planets. Table 16-2 lists some of the most spectacular meteor showers.

Meteorites are extremely important in the study of the solar system because they represent the material from which the system was originally made. They are analyzed intensely by scientists, both to get a notion of how and when Earth was made and to learn what kinds of materials human beings will find when they leave Earth to explore the rest of the solar system.

TABLE 16-2 Major Annual Meteor Showers

Name	Date for Maximum	Extreme Limits	Hourly Rate of Meteors
Quadrantid	January 3	January 1–4	30
Aquarid	May 4	May 2–6	5
Perseid	August 12	July 29–August 17	40
Orionid	October 22	October 18–26	13
Taurid	November 1	September 15–December 15	5
Leonid	November 17	November 14–20	6
Geminid	December 14	December 7–15	5

● 16.4 Extrasolar Planets

For centuries astronomers wondered whether other stars have planets circling them. Because planets shine only by reflected light from their star, direct detection is very difficult. One astronomer compares it to the problem of seeing a birthday candle next to a searchlight in Boston by looking through a telescope in Washington, DC. Consequently, astronomers had to develop indirect ways of finding "extrasolar" planets (the term simply means "planets outside the solar system" and is often shortened to "exoplanets").

One way to search for these planets is to use the Doppler effect (see Chapter 6). Imagine that you are looking at a star that has a planet in orbit. When the planet lies between the star and you, its gravity will pull the star toward you. Half a "year" later, however, when the planet is on the far side of the star, that same gravity will pull the star away from you. Consequently, you will see the star executing a regular back and forth motion as the planet moves in orbit. When the star moves toward you, the frequency of the light it emits will be shifted toward the blue, but when it moves away from you, the light will be shifted toward the red. Thus, as you observe the star, you will see a regular change in the frequency of the light, as illustrated in Figure 16-23.

Alternatively, if the plane of the planet's orbit lies directly in our line of sight from Earth, the planet will pass in front of the star and we will be able to detect a slight drop in the intensity of the emitted light (Figure 16-24).

The first extrasolar planet, discovered in 1994, was a planet circling a pulsar (see Chapter 14), and changes in the pulsar's radio emissions were monitored. Because pulsars are what is left after a supernova, this particular planet was completely unexpected.

The first normal extrasolar planet, discovered in 1995 by a team of Swiss astronomers, circles a star called 51 Pegasi, located about 42 light-years from Earth. Since then. over a thousand exoplanets have been found, particularly those discovered by the Kepler satellite (see below). Most of the earliest planets found by the Doppler technique were large planets orbiting close to their stars, planets that were dubbed "hot Jupiters." Typically, they moved well inside what would correspond to the orbit of Mercury.

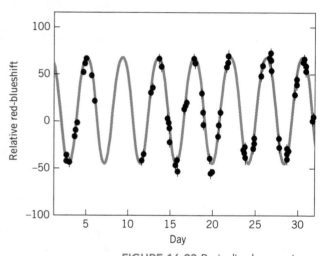

FIGURE 16-23 Periodic changes in the redshift or blueshift of light may reveal the presence of a planet. This graph illustrates such a red-blueshift versus time for a nearby star. These data indicate a planet that orbits the star every 4.4 days.

STOP & THINK Why should the fact that we detect planets through the use of the Doppler effect make it more likely that we will detect hot Jupiters than planets like Earth? (*Hint:* What kind of planet will exert the largest gravitational force on its star?)

The search for extrasolar planets based on transits—the temporary dimming of a star when its planet passes between it and Earth—received a tremendous boost with the launch of NASA's Kepler satellite in 2009 (Figure 16-25). Kepler monitored more than 150,000 stars to look for this effect, and it found thousands of probable planets. Some of these objects appear to be Earth-sized

FIGURE 16-24 Artist's conception of the transit of a planet in front of a star in a distant solar system.

Lynette Cook/Photo Researchers, Inc.

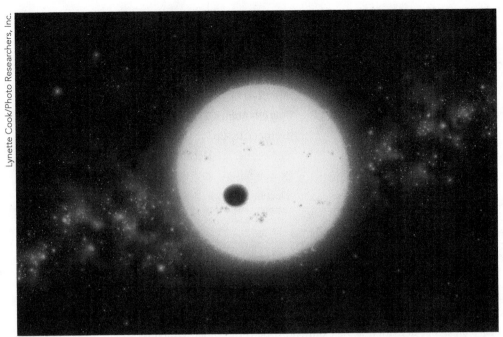

bodies in distant star systems with several other planets, much like our own solar system. In order to keep the Earth from blocking part of its view of the sky, Kepler is in orbit around the Sun, trailing along behind Earth.

The massive data collection capability of the Kepler telescope has revolutionized our view of the formation of planetary systems. One of the most important early conclusions of the Kepler mission was the realization that hot Jupiters are not all that common in the galaxy—they were simply the first exoplanets to be seen by Doppler searches. Scientists on the Kepler team are very careful to point out that the thousands of signals they have detected represent "candidates" and that some may not be planets at all. A complex verification process involving Doppler measurements made by ground-based telescopes is required to promote an object from "candidate" to "planet." The Kepler spacecraft has identified over 2,000 extrasolar planets to date.

FIGURE 16-25 The Kepler satellite was launched in 2009 and has monitored more than 100,000 stars to find those that dim temporarily as planets pass in front of them. Kepler has already identified thousands of likely extrasolar planets.

Courtesy NASA

STOP & THINK Can you think of any processes that might cause a signal like that in Figure 16-24 but that do not involve planets?

Kepler has provided two important lessons. First, planets are common—we live in a galaxy that has more planets than stars. Second, planets in our own solar system are a small subset of the total collection of strange worlds out there. Some examples follow:

- A planet orbiting so close to its star that rocks vaporize on the star-facing side and then, when the vaporized rock moves to the cooler side, it experiences a "snowfall" of solid rock.
- Rogue planets that move around the galaxy unattached to any star.
- "Styrofoam worlds"—planets whose density is so low that we can't understand why they don't collapse under their own gravity.

The list could go on, but the message is clear: when we move into the area of exoplanets, we should be prepared for surprises.

SCIENCE OF LIFE
The CHZ and the "Goldilocks Planet"

In Chapter 25 we will see that current theories about the origin of life require that the appropriate chemical reactions take place in liquid water. One way to have such an environment is for a planet to have liquid water on its surface for billions of years, as Earth has had. The region around a star where the temperature stays in the right range for water to be in its liquid form is called the Continuously Habitable Zone, or CHZ. In our solar system, only Earth is in the Sun's CHZ.

One important goal of exoplanet searches is to find what is nicknamed the "Goldilocks planet"—a planet that is not too hot, not too cold, but just right. Such a planet would probably have to be a terrestrial planet in the CHZ of its star. As this search continues, it is important to remember that there is a distinction between "Earth-sized" and "Earth-like." As astronomer Sara Seager of MIT has pointed out, "Venus is Earth-sized, but it is not Earth-like."

STOP & THINK How does the discovery of Europa's oceans affect the search for the Goldilocks planet?

THINKING MORE ABOUT **PLANETS**

Human Space Exploration

Since before astronaut Neil Armstrong became the first human to walk on the surface of the Moon in 1969, the scientific community has debated the question of how the exploration of the solar system should be carried out. The question is this: Should future missions to the planets carry people, or should they carry only machines?

Those who advocate exploration by machines point to the enormous technical difficulties involved in providing a safe habitat for human beings in the harsh environment of space. Why, they ask, should we make the enormous, expensive effort to put a human being on the surface of Mars, for example, when just as much can be learned by sending instrument packages and robots controlled from Earth?

On the other side of the issue, scientists advocating space exploration by astronauts argue that no machine has the flexibility and ingenuity of a human being. They note that no matter how well designed a machine might be, when it is millions of miles from Earth things can go wrong, and only a trained astronaut can salvage the mission. They point out that even a mammoth project such as the Hubble Space Telescope needed astronauts to replace flawed optical systems. Besides, they argue, if one goal of the space program is to establish human colonies on other bodies in the solar system, you can't do that with machines.

One idea that is gaining traction in the scientific community, though has yet to catch on at NASA, is the possibility of one-way human space travel. Were we to send a Mars expedition with years of supplies instead of fuel, with sturdy shelter and a greenhouse, with seeds, with a lot of oxygen and water and tools to extract more life-giving resources from the red planet, then an expedition might just make it. It would be unbelievably dangerous, but so were many of the pioneering human voyages of discovery. Humans have not lost their urge to engage in such risky ventures. If NASA posted a sign-up sheet for the chance at a one-way trip to Mars, thousands of scientists would sign up in a heartbeat.

What do we hope to learn from our studies of the solar system? Is colonization of the rest of the solar system the real long-term goal of the space program? How much extra effort (and taxpayers' dollars) is it worth expending to put people instead of machines on the surface of Mars?

RETURN TO THE INTEGRATED QUESTION

Is Earth the only planet with life?

- Astrobiology (Chapter 25) is the study of life originating outside of Earth (i.e., extraterrestrial life). Although there is no credible evidence that extraterrestrial life exists, the possibility remains an interesting hypothetical question.
  - All forms of life on Earth require carbon, hydrogen, oxygen, nitrogen, and a number of other elements (e.g., sulfur, phosphorus).

- In addition to these elemental constituents, life on Earth also requires the most ubiquitous solvent known to science.
  - Liquid water provides an ideal medium for chemical reactions, as well as the transport of life-sustaining oxygen and vital energy substrates.
  - As we saw in Chapter 14, the heating of Earth's surface during the death of our Sun will boil off all liquid water, and consequently cause the demise of all terrestrial life in roughly one billion years.

- Because all planets, including Earth, were formed from the same foundational materials (i.e., interstellar dust from collapsing nebulae), the relative abundance of the building blocks of organic matter may exist throughout the universe.

- As we will see in Chapter 25 (evolution), Miller and Urey's experiment in 1953 demonstrated that organic compounds such as amino acids, carbohydrates, and other essential building blocks of life (Chapter 22) can be synthesized via naturally occurring processes. These organic compounds serve as structural elements for more advanced forms of life, or provide the chemical energy for all metabolic reactions (Chapter 3).

- Many of the processes that produced organic molecules during the formation of our planet may have occurred as other planets were formed elsewhere in the universe.

- Nevertheless, the most important facet in the development of life on Earth, and perhaps elsewhere in the universe, is the evolution of Earth's atmosphere.

  - Scientists now suggest that initially there was no atmosphere at all and that once an atmosphere formed, its chemical composition gradually evolved to its present form.

  - The question of how Earth's atmosphere arose and changed is extremely important because this history is inseparable from understanding the origin and evolution of life on our planet.

- Given the nearly infinite nature of our universe, it could be that extraterrestrial life exists. Nonetheless, the development and evolution of life on Earth is the culmination of myriad multifactorial and interdependent processes that have yet to be observed elsewhere in our universe.

SUMMARY

Earth formed along with the Sun and other planets in our *solar system* from a *nebula*—a large gas and dust cloud rich in hydrogen and helium—approximately 4.5 billion years ago. As that cloud began to contract as a result of gravitational forces, it also began to rotate and flatten out into the disk that now defines the planetary orbits. More than 99% of the original nebula's mass concentrated at the center, which became the Sun.

Gradually, the matter in the flat disk began to form clumps under the influence of its own local gravitational forces. The largest of these masses swept up more and more debris as they orbited the early Sun, and they began to define a string of planets. *Terrestrial planets*, those nearest the Sun, were subjected to high temperatures and strong solar winds, so that most gases such as hydrogen, helium, and water vapors were swept out into space. Thus, the inner four planets, including *Mercury, Venus, Earth*, and *Mars*, are dense, rocky places with a relatively low content of gaseous elements.

Earth's formation was probably typical of these planets. After most of Earth's mass had been collected together, additional rocks and boulders showered down in the *great bombardment*, adding matter and heat energy to the planet. Dense iron and nickel separated from lighter materials by the process of *differentiation* and sank to the center to form a metallic *core*. Most of Earth's mass concentrated in the thick *mantle*, while the lightest elements formed a thin *crust*. The *Moon*, Earth's only large satellite, may have formed when a planet-sized body hit Earth early in its history.

The solar system's outer *Jovian planets*, including *Jupiter, Saturn, Uranus*, and *Neptune*, are quite different from the inner planets. Lying beyond the strong effects of solar heat and wind, they accumulated large amounts of gases such as hydrogen, helium, ammonia, and water. These outer planets are thus giant balls of ice, with thick atmospheres and great frigid oceans of nitrogen, methane, and other compounds that are gases on Earth. All of the planets except Mercury and Venus, the two closest to the Sun, have *moons* in orbit.

Beyond the Jovian planets lies a disk of debris left over from the formation of the solar system known as the Kuiper Belt. *Pluto*, traditionally thought of as the outermost planet, is now seen as the first *plutoid* in the Kuiper Belt.

Interspersed with the planets and their moons are many other kinds of objects. Small, rocky *asteroids,* most of which are concentrated in an *asteroid belt* between Mars and Jupiter, circle the Sun like miniature planets. Far outside the solar system, swarms of "dirty snowballs" called *comets* are concentrated in the Oort cloud. If a comet's distant orbit is disturbed, it may fall toward the Sun and create a spectacular display in the night sky. When a piece of interplanetary debris hits Earth's atmosphere, it creates a *meteor,* sometimes called a shooting star, which burns up with a fiery trail. Occasionally, a meteor fragment will hit Earth and become a *meteorite.*

KEY TERMS

solar system

terrestrial planets (Mercury, Venus, Earth, Earth's Moon, Mars)

Jovian planets (Jupiter, Saturn, Uranus, Neptune)

nebulae

great bombardment

differentiation

core

mantle

crust

Pluto

Kuiper Belt

plutoid

asteroids

asteroid belt

comet

meteor

meteorite

DISCOVERY **LAB**

Are you curious to measure the position of the Moon and stars? You need to make an astrolabe, which is an instrument used to measure altitudes above the horizon. To make an astrolabe, you will need a plastic protractor; a drinking straw; invisible tape; a weight such as a nut, washer, or fishing weight; and string about 30 centimeters or a foot long.

Thread one end of the string to the hole in the middle of the straight edge of the protractor and tie a weight to the other end. Tape the straw to the straight edge of the protractor. Cut the two ends of the straw so that the ends are the same size as the straight edge.

Hold the protractor so that the curved part is down and the straight edge is on top with the string hanging down. Use one eye to look through the straw at any celestial object of your choice; when the object is in sight, hold the string against the protractor. Note the position of the string and record the degree mark. This number gives you an estimate of how many degrees above the horizon your object is.

Take several readings every 30 minutes of the celestial object. What do you notice about the pattern of the object as it moves across the sky? Use the same procedure to take readings for different celestial objects and compare your findings.

Tape

Drinking straw

Protractor

Using one eye, look through the straw at a celestial object of your choice.

Note the position of the string and record the degree mark.

Moon

Weight

REVIEW QUESTIONS

1. What does the fact that all the planets in the solar system are in the same plane tell you about the formation of the solar system?

2. Why are the Jovian planets larger than the terrestrial planets?

3. What are nebulae? What forms of matter are found in nebulae? How are nebulae related to the formation of planetary systems such as the solar system?

4. What are planetesimals, and what role do they play in the formation of planets?

5. What is differentiation? How has this process affected Earth?

6. How does the high pressure in the core affect chemical bonds?

7. What is Earth's mantle? Of what elements is it made?

8. Describe the "big splash" theory of the Moon's origin.

9. Explain the importance of outgassing to Earth's history. Is it still going on today?

10. Explain the role of gravity in the evolution of a planet's atmosphere.

11. How are comets different from asteroids? Of what are comets made? And asteroids?

12. What is the asteroid belt? Where is it located?

13. What determines the orbit of a comet?

14. How have asteroids and comets affected life on Earth?

15. How many planets in the solar system have moons?

16. What is the difference between the Kuiper Belt and the Oort cloud?

DISCUSSION QUESTIONS

1. How do you think the formation of Earth was similar to that of other planets in the solar system, and how may have it been different?

2. What are the characteristics of Earth that allowed for life to develop so extensively compared to the rest of the solar system? How has Earth itself responded to the development of life?

3. What is the best explanation we have for why the direction of rotation of Venus is opposite to the direction of Earth's (as well as all the other planets)?

4. The temperature of Earth's core is estimated to be greater than 5,000°C. Is the core temperature of a planet such as Jupiter hotter or colder? Why? Does the distance from the Sun affect the core temperature?

5. Why do Mercury and the Moon lack an atmosphere? Titan, Saturn's largest moon, possesses an atmosphere despite being roughly the same size as Mercury. Why does it have an atmosphere when Mercury doesn't?

6. What sources of data might help us determine more about how Earth's Moon formed?

7. How does Clyde Tombaugh's work fit into the scientific method?

8. In the best models to describe the formation of planets, the formation of Saturn and Jupiter are more like the Sun's than Earth's. Why?

9. Could material from Earth contaminate planets visited by our spacecraft? What might be the consequences?

10. What is the point of sending humans into space? Do you foresee positive economic effects in the short term? What about long-term economic effects?

11. Jupiter is known as a gas giant planet. What are the most common gases near the surface in Jupiter's atmosphere? Which of those gases occur in molecular form, and which occur in elemental form?

12. How would the structural stability of your bones be different if you were growing up on the Moon compared to growing up on Earth?

13. How do you suppose astronauts deal with bone loss during extended stays in space?

14. Given the nearly 90° tilt in the axis of Uranus, do you think there would be different seasons on the planet? How would they occur relative to the northern and southern hemispheres of the planet (e.g., on Earth if it's spring in the northern hemisphere, then it's autumn in the southern)? If it takes Uranus 84 years to orbit the Sun, how long would a single season last?

15. Many stars in the galaxy exist in a binary system; that is, two stars in relatively close gravitational orbit about each other. Assuming the nebular hypothesis of planetary formation operates under these conditions, what do you think would be the distribution of terrestrial planets versus gas giant planets in such a system?

PROBLEMS

1. Given the diameters of the planets in Table 16-1, what are the relative volumes of Earth, Mercury, Saturn, and Jupiter? From the same table, what are the relative masses? Which planets are most similar? Why?

2. From the values of mass in Problem 1, calculate the densities (mass divided by volume) for Earth, Mercury, Saturn, and Jupiter. Why do you think they are different? Which planets are most similar? Why?

3. The total mass of the asteroid belt is approximately 3×10^{21} kg. Assuming the average density of the asteroids is the same as the average density of Mercury, what would be the diameter of the planet they would form if they came together? (The formula for the volume of a sphere is $(4/3) \pi r^3$, where r is the radius.) How does this value compare to the diameter of Mercury?

4. If Earth's diameter and rotation rate were the same as Jupiter's, how fast would an object at the equator be traveling? By what factor is that different from what the speed of an object at Earth's equator really is?

5. If the average thickness of Earth's crust is 30 kilometers, what fraction of the solid Earth's total volume is in the crust? What fraction is in the mantle? And the core?

6. Because of tidal effects, the Moon is receding from Earth at a rate of 3.8 cm per year. If the Moon is currently 3.84×10^8 m away and if the recession rate stays constant, how long would it take for the Moon's orbital radius about Earth to double from what it is now?

7. A "brown dwarf" is a failed attempt at the formation of a star owing to insufficient mass. A typical brown dwarf may have a mass about 50 times that of the planet Jupiter. How many brown dwarfs of this mass would it take to equal the same mass as the Sun?

8. The exact amount of time it took for sufficient mass to accrete to the size of Earth is unknown, but some models indicate that it took around 20 million years for most of Earth's mass to accumulate. Assuming these models are correct, how many kilograms were being added to Earth each second during the accretion period to achieve its full mass of 6×10^{24} kg?

9. Many Kuiper Belt objects are found to be concentrated at a distance of about 45 times Earth's orbital radius from the Sun. How many millions of kilometers is this distance?

   a. 0.57 million km

   b. 45 million km

   c. 95 million km

   d. 6,750 million km

10. Consider the change in redshift of a distant star as plotted in the graph below. What is a good estimate of the orbital period of the planet orbiting this star causing the variation?

   a. 1 day

   b. 2.5 days

   c. 3.5 days

   d. 10.5 days

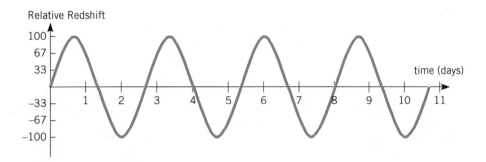

INVESTIGATIONS

1. Investigate the history of unmanned planetary probes. What are the names, dates, and target planets of these probes? What countries sponsored them? What kinds of data did they return?

2. Look up the *New Horizons* space probe. Where is it heading, and where is it right now?

3. Read a history of the *Apollo* missions to the Moon. What theories about the Moon's origins prevailed before these missions? What new data changed theories about the origin of the Moon?

4. Investigate the discovery of the planet Neptune. What role did the ability to calculate planetary orbits play in this discovery?

5. How would you respond to an argument that goes as follows: No one was present when Earth was formed, so how can scientists talk about the details of the formation process?

6. Listen to *The Planets*, a suite for orchestra by the British composer Gustav Holst. In what ways do the musical descriptions of each planet reflect the physical characteristics of that planet? What other sources of inspiration, besides scientific data, did Holst use in creating these pieces? Which planets did he omit and why?

7. There are many more meteor showers than the ones listed in Table 16-2. Find out which ones may be coming in the next month or two and plan a meteor-watching party.

8. Scientists are attempting to document the paths of asteroids with Earth-crossing orbits. Investigate this research and comment on the probability that a large asteroid might hit Earth. Should we increase funding for asteroid monitoring?

9. How do modern space probes use the gravity of planets that they pass by to get them to their destinations? How did *New Horizons* do this?

10. Research the intended path of an unmanned planetary probe. Why do the probes circle the Sun and Earth a number of times before venturing out into deep space?

11. How many satellites are orbiting Earth? What are the purposes of most of these devices? What equipment do you use in your daily life that depends on satellites?

PHYSICS
Heat energy moves from Earth's core to the surface primarily by the process of mantle convection.

CHEMISTRY
Chemical processes contribute to the gradual weathering of rocks. (Ch. 18)

BIOLOGY
The shifting of continents has affected the distribution of land animals on Earth.

TECHNOLOGY
Sensitive instruments developed to detect submarines during World War II were later used to measure the magnetism of rocks on the seafloor.

GREAT IDEA
Earth is changing due to the slow convection of soft, hot rocks deep within the planet.

ENVIRONMENT
Scientists have speculated that giant volcanic eruptions 250 million years ago caused mass extinctions of life on Earth. (Ch. 25)

ASTRONOMY
Radio astronomers have used distant quasars to measure the slow process of seafloor spreading.

HEALTH & SAFETY
New buildings in earthquake-prone regions are designed to withstand violent wave-like motions of the ground.

GEOLOGY
New crustal rocks are created at divergent plate boundaries.

 = applications of the great idea discussed in this chapter

 = other applications, some of which are discussed in other chapters

Windblown Sand

Early afternoon at the beach: A cooling breeze has picked up off the water. The steady flow of air is wonderfully refreshing, though occasional gusts of wind kick up sand and grit. Some of that sand blows onto your beach towel and into your hair.

The wind constantly moves soil at Earth's surface, slowly altering the landscape. Shifting sand may seem a trivial phenomenon, but such gradual tiny daily changes add up to extraordinary transformations of the land over countless millions of years. Similar gradual movements of matter deep within our planet accomplish even more remarkable changes. Earth's seemingly permanent continents and oceans are also in constant motion. The continent of North America is about a meter farther from Europe than it was when you were born, the result of forces deep within Earth's interior.

Earth's surface is always changing. No feature of our planet—no desert or broad plain, no mountain or ocean—is permanent. Every feature is constantly evolving into something different.

Adelman-Cohen/Taxi/Getty Images Inc.

◉ 17.1 Dynamic Earth

Think about the last time that you passed a new construction site after a rain shower. You could probably see little valleys freshly carved by water running over the bare earth, and shallow pools where fine-grained material collected in layers—features that are small-scale examples of the erosion of soil by rain. If the earthmovers had dug a deep pit, you might have noticed different layers of soil and rock freshly exposed—layers that represent sediments deposited by water long ago.

These sorts of small-scale changes in Earth's surface are mirrored by much more dramatic large-scale changes. When Mount St. Helens, a volcano in Washington State, erupted in 1980, the entire side of a mountain was blown away and many square kilometers of forest were flattened. And when a major earthquake struck off the coast of Japan on March 11, 2011, more than 15,000 people died. Large volcanoes and earthquakes will continue to change the course of rivers and destroy villages and towns.

But how do we know that Earth's surface is changing at larger scales? We rarely observe significant changes in the landscape, but you can make a simple estimate that will convince you that Earth must be a very dynamic planet. Mountains appear to be as permanent as anything could be, yet, as we see in the following section, it's easy to convince yourself that mountains must wear away in times much shorter than Earth's 4.5- billion-year age. We'll also see that the arrangement of our planet's great continents is not as permanent as it appears to be.

SCIENCE BY THE NUMBERS
How Long Could a Mountain Last?

Although there is no such thing as a "typical" mountain (Figure 17-1), for the purposes of this rough estimate let's think of a mountain as a rectangular mass about 2 kilometers high, 4 kilometers long, and 4 kilometers wide (that's about 1.2 miles by 2.5 miles by 2.5 miles). The volume of this midsized mountain is

$$\text{volume} = \text{length} \times \text{height} \times \text{width}$$
$$= 2\,\text{km} \times 4\,\text{km} \times 4\,\text{km}$$
$$= 32\,\text{km}^3$$

Expressed in cubic meters, that is

$$2000\,\text{m} \times 4000\,\text{m} \times 4000\,\text{m} = 3.2 \times 10^{10}\,\text{m}^3$$

Think about a stream running down a mountainside. You know that such a stream carries a certain amount of sand, silt, and dirt with it. You can see this movement of sediment because the stream has a sandy bottom, and you can watch it depositing sand in little eddies and still water along its side. You might also see gravel and boulders in the stream—evidence that, from time to time, heavy rains cause much more violent movement of material down the mountainside. That material had to be worn off of materials higher up on the mountain, so the existence of the stream means that the mountain is constantly being eroded away.

You can estimate how long a mountain might survive against erosion by a stream. Suppose, for example, that four principal streams run off the sides of the mountain and that each stream carries an average of one-tenth of a cubic meter of sediment per day off the mountain. (The actual amount would vary from day to day depending on the kind of rock, the amount of water flowing downhill, and other factors.) One-tenth of a cubic meter per day is not very much material. It's like a pile of sand, dirt, and gravel about 50 centimeters (a foot and a half) on a side—a pile that could fit under an ordinary kitchen chair. If you think about the amount of material you might collect if you put your hand down into a stream for a while, you'll see that the number is reasonable. Over a period of a year, the four streams might thus remove

$$4\,\text{streams} \times 0.1\,\text{meter}^3/\text{stream-day} \times 365\,\text{days/year} = 146\,\text{meter}^3/\text{year}$$

Every year, therefore, close to 150 cubic meters of material—about six dump-trucks full—could be removed from a mountain by normal erosional processes of streams.

If the mountain streams remove about 150 cubic meters each year, then the lifetime of the mountain can't be much longer than the volume of the mountain divided by the volume lost each year:

$$\frac{3.2 \times 10^{10}\,\text{m}^3}{(150\,\text{m}^3/\text{year})} = 0.0213 \times 10^{10}\ \text{years}$$
$$= 213,000,000\ \text{years}$$

This estimate, though very rough and not directly applicable to any specific mountain, tells us that under normal circumstances mountains can't last more than a few hundred million years. All mountains must disappear and be eroded away to low, rounded hills in times much shorter than Earth's 4.5-billion-year age.

The Case of the Disappearing Mountains

We must conclude that if the erosion of mountains takes a few hundred million years, then any mountain that existed when

FIGURE 17-1 Pike's Peak near Colorado Springs, Colorado, may be approximated as a 2 × 4 × 4 km rectangular block of rock.

©AP/Wide World Photos

(a)   (b)

FIGURE 17-2 Steep slopes and angular peaks characterize young mountains such as the 65-million-year-old Rocky Mountains in Alberta, Canada (a) photographed from Mount Rae. The 400-million-year-old Great Smoky Mountains in Tennessee (b) display the rounded character of older mountains.

Earth first formed 4.5 billion years ago would have been worn away long ago, and Earth's surface by now should be smooth and featureless. The only way that mountains could still exist on Earth is for mountains to be continuously formed.

Everyday observations of erosion and some very simple arithmetic thus lead us to a startling conclusion: tremendous forces must be acting on Earth, creating new mountain chains as the old ones are worn down. Earth's surface cannot be static. Although mountains seem to human beings to symbolize eternal solidity, they are transitory. Geologists who map the distribution and ages of rocks have shown that the Appalachian Mountains were formed a few hundred million years ago, and the Rocky Mountains only about 60 million years ago (Figure 17-2).

Newton's laws of motion (Chapter 2) tell us that nothing happens unless a force acts. What forces could create entire mountain ranges? Until recently, this question remained one of the greatest puzzles in geology.

Volcanoes and Earthquakes— Evidence of Earth's Inner Forces

Most geological processes such as mountain building and erosion are slow by human standards and take thousands or millions of years to produce noticeable change. But volcanoes and earthquakes may transform a landscape in an instant, thus revealing the tremendous energy stored in our dynamic planet (Figure 17-3).

Volcanic eruptions provide the most spectacular process by which new mountains are formed. In a typical **volcano**, subsurface molten rock called *magma*, concentrated in Earth's upper mantle or lower crust, breaks through to the surface, as shown in Figure 17-4. This breakthrough may be sudden, giving rise to the kind of dramatic events seen when Mount St. Helens exploded in 1980, or it may be relatively slow, with a stately surface flow of molten rock, known as *lava*. In both cases, however, magma eventually breaches the surface and hardens into new rock.

An **earthquake** occurs when rock suddenly breaks along a more or less flat surface, called a *fault*. Have you ever stretched a thick, strong elastic band, only to have it snap back painfully against your hand? You gradually added elastic potential energy to the band, and that energy was suddenly released—converted to violent kinetic energy. The same thing happens in an earthquake when stressed rock suddenly snaps (Figure 17-5).

(a)

(b)

(c)

US Geological Survey/SPL/Photo Researchers, Inc.

Science Source/USGS/Photo Researchers, Inc.

Calvin Larsen/Photo Researchers, Inc.

FIGURE 17-3 Mount St. Helens is an active volcano in Washington State. *(a)* In March 1980, prior to the eruption, the volcano displayed a large bulge caused by a buildup of internal pressure. *(b)* The violent eruption that took place on May 18, 1980, killed 57 people. *(c)* The eruption literally blew the top off the mountain.

FIGURE 17-4 A cross section of a volcano reveals a magma chamber, which stores molten rock, and a system of pipes, cracks, and vents that lead to the surface. The terms in the orange area refer to the kinds of rock formations resulting from cooled magma. Xenoliths are the original rocks encased in this cooled magma.

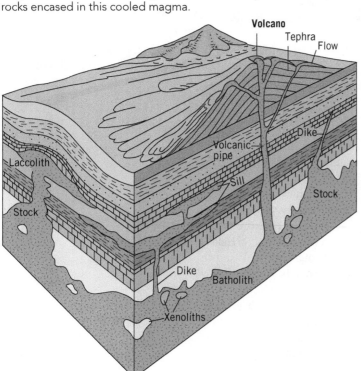

When a brittle rock breaks, tremendous amounts of potential energy are released. The two sides of a fault can't fly apart like an elastic material can, so the energy is transmitted in the form of a sound wave or seismic wave (see Chapter 6). These waves, traveling at speeds of several kilometers per second, cause the ground to rise and fall like the surface of the ocean. Normally "solid" ground sways and pitches in a motion that can cause severe damage to buildings and other structures.

If an earthquake occurs under or near a large body of water, violent motions of the ground can transfer energy into great ocean waves that can travel thousands of miles and devastate low-lying coastal areas. Such waves are often referred to as "tidal waves," though they aren't caused by tides. A more correct term is *tsunamis*, a Japanese word for harbor or bay waves.

On March 11, 2011, a devastating earthquake occurred off the coast of Japan. The event was stronger than any previously recorded quake and in the end wound up shifting the coast of Japan up to 5 meters eastward. The sudden motion of the seafloor created a huge tsunami that inundated hundreds of miles of the Japanese coastline. Waves up to 15 meters high swept ashore, killing in excess of 15,000 people and displacing nearly half a million from their homes. In addition, as we saw in Chapter 12, the tsunami caused a major disaster at the Fukushima nuclear reactor facility. It was a deadly reminder that the forces of nature can still wreak havoc with human societies (Figure 17-6).

Fortunately, such destructive earthquakes and tsunamis are relatively rare, but smaller earthquakes, barely noticeable to the average person, occur every day by the thousands. Earthquakes were traditionally rated on the *Richter scale*, named after Charles Richter, the American geologist who devised it. Technically, the Richter scale refers to the amount of ground motion that would be measured by an instrument a fixed distance from the center of the earthquake. The scale is such that each increase of 1 unit corresponds to 10 times more ground motion. Thus, an earthquake that measures 7 will have 100 times more ground motion than one that measures 5, and so on. Today, a similar magnitude scale, based on energy release, is used.

Earthquakes that measure around 5 on the magnitude scale will be felt by most people but will do little damage in areas with well-constructed buildings. An earthquake between 6 and 7 will do considerable damage to buildings, and a magnitude 8 earthquake will level large areas. The earthquake that occurred in the San Francisco Bay area in October 1989 measured 7.1 and was dubbed the "Pretty Big One" by Californians who are waiting for what they call the "Big One." The powerful March 2011 earthquake that triggered the Japanese tsunami measured 9.0 on the magnitude scale. No earthquakes greater than 9.5 on the magnitude scale have ever been recorded, probably because no rocks can store that much energy before they rupture.

The puzzle remains, however: Where does all the energy that powers volcanoes and earthquakes come from?

FIGURE 17-5 Earthquakes, which occur when Earth's crust fractures, can cause extensive damage.

SCIENCE IN THE MAKING
Robert Hazen and the Japanese Earthquake

On March 11, 2011, Robert Hazen was at Tokyo's Narita Airport in a travel lounge when the great earthquake hit. At magnitude 9.0, it was the largest recorded earthquake ever to strike Japan and the fourth largest in world history. Even though Tokyo is many miles from the quake's epicenter, the event was frighteningly intense.

The earthquake started suddenly with moderate shaking, accompanied by a roaring sound not unlike an approaching railroad train. The intensity of the shaking increased quickly, and soon it was impossible to stand. Many of us held onto a solid doorway or just sat on the floor. Ceiling tiles came crashing down, as glass panes shattered and dishware and glasses flew from shelves of the lounge. The intense shocks lasted for a full 2 minutes.

We were quickly evacuated to the runways, away from the damaged terminal buildings. Severe aftershocks occurred every few minutes and continued for several hours. As evening fell and temperatures dropped, we were ushered to a relatively safe low building—perhaps 2,000 travelers occupying every square foot of the facility. Remarkably, we never lost electrical power. The efficient Japanese airport employees distributed blankets, water, and Ritz crackers, as we watched overhead monitors that displayed televised scenes of the great tsunamis washing ashore, swallowing many square miles of the Japanese countryside. Gasps of horror and muted sobs accompanied the images, as we realized the great loss of life that was occurring so nearby.

We all eventually made it home safely, but the experience of the great Japanese earthquake of 2011 will stay with us forever.

FIGURE 17-6 The March 2011 tsunami, which hit the Japanese coast, was triggered by an underwater earthquake and caused great damage and loss of life.

The Movement of the Continents

Geologists have faced other mysteries as well. Think about a large map of the world. In your mind, move North and South America eastward toward Eurasia and Africa. Have you ever noticed how the two coastlines seem to fit together (Figure 17-7)?

English statesman and natural philosopher Francis Bacon (1561–1626) pointed out this fact in 1620, though he had no simple explanation for the observation. It wasn't until the beginning of the twentieth century, however, that anyone took the parallel coastlines seriously enough to ask about the origin of this pattern. In 1912, a German meteorologist named Alfred Wegener (1880–1930) proposed that Earth's continents are in motion. The reason that the Americas fit so well into the coastline of Europe and Africa, he suggested, is that they were once joined and have since been torn apart.

Wegener's theory, called *continental drift*, was eventually dismissed by most Earth scientists. He amassed some geological evidence to back it up, such as the matching locations of distinctive rock formations and fossils on opposite sides of the Atlantic Ocean. But most of this evidence was fragmentary and unconvincing to other scientists; indeed, some of Wegener's arguments later turned out to be wrong. More importantly, he failed to provide any reasonable mechanism by which continents could move. For most of the twentieth century, continental drift was regarded as a far-fetched exercise in theory, and few geologists paid much attention

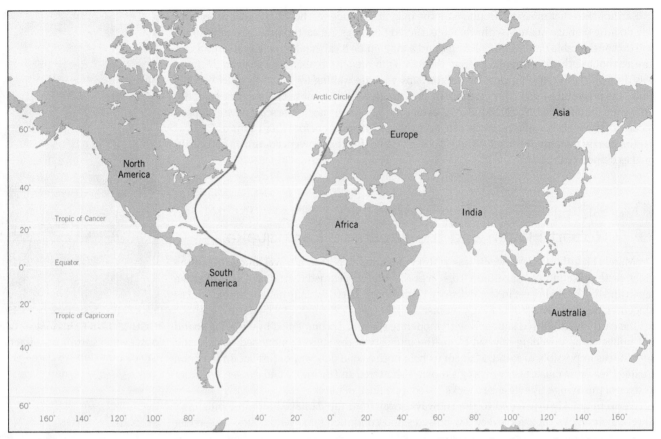

FIGURE 17-7 A map of the world's continents reveals the similar shapes of coastlines on the two sides of the Atlantic Ocean.

to it. Beginning about 1960, however, geologists and oceanographers obtained new evidence to support one aspect of Wegener's notion—the idea that the continents are not fixed.

The discovery that continents do indeed move required the merging of very different kinds of newly acquired geological evidence—topographic profiles of the oceans' floors, maps of rock magnetism, and data on rock ages.

1. Ocean Floors

When the contours of ocean floors were mapped in the years following World War II, oceanographers discovered remarkable, unsuspected features. Most scientists thought that the deep-ocean bottoms were simply flat plains, passively collecting the sediments that gradually eroded off the ancient continents. Instead they found steep-walled canyons and lofty mountains, indicating that the seafloor is as dynamic and changing as the continents themselves (Figure 17-8). The longest mountain range on Earth, for example, is not on a continent, but in the middle of the Atlantic Ocean. Called the *Mid-Atlantic Ridge,* this feature extends from Iceland in the North Atlantic to the South Sandwich Islands in the South Atlantic. Similar long ridges, which are found beneath all of Earth's oceans, are sites of continuous geological activity, including numerous earthquakes, volcanoes, and lava flows. In fact, oceanographers have now mapped more than 85,000 kilometers of ocean ridges.

2. Magnetic Reversals

To understand the nature of magnetic data, the second kind of evidence that pointed to continental motion, you have to recall that Earth has a magnetic field with north and south magnetic poles. For reasons that are not fully understood, this field changes direction sporadically over time—something like an electromagnet in which the direction of current in the coils changes occasionally (see Chapter 5). More than 300 reversals of Earth's magnetic field have been recorded in ancient rocks spanning about 200 million years. During recent episodes of reversed fields, Earth's north magnetic pole was located somewhere in what is now Antarctica, and the south magnetic pole somewhere above the Arctic Circle in the Canada–Greenland region.

When lava flows out of a fissure, it contains small crystals of natural iron oxides, including the naturally magnetic mineral magnetite. Magnetite cannot sustain a magnetic field at the extreme temperatures of molten rock. However, once the rock hardens and cools and the bits of magnetite are frozen in place, each magnetite grain acquires a magnetic field from Earth. If we measure rocks that hold those tiny magnetite grains, we can tell whether Earth's magnetic field was oriented as it is today or whether it was reversed. The field devoted to the study of this sort of effect is called *paleomagnetism,* and it came into maturity in the early 1960s.

In the mid-1950s, an oceanic exploration ship named *Pioneer* began taking magnetic measurements near the ocean floor off the coast of Washington State. At first the data made little sense, but as more and more profiles were obtained, a puzzling pattern of stripes on the ocean floor began to emerge. It seemed that there were parallel strips of rock in which the magnetic direction in neighboring strips alternated. (We show some of the original data in Figure 17-9.) Through the mid-1960s, Earth scientists collected more and more data of this type, and it soon became clear that the Mid-Atlantic Ridge, the East Pacific Rise, and many other places on ocean floors show the same pattern of alternating magnetic stripes.

How could these magnetic stripes be explained? In an environment in which the orientations of north and south magnetic poles were switching back and forth over time, the only way to get the observed striping is shown in Figure 17-10. The seafloor must be getting wider, a process called *seafloor spreading,* as new molten rock comes from deep within Earth and erupts through fissures on the ocean bottom. Over time, this new rock will be pushed aside as the continents move apart and as more magma comes up to take its place. The magnetite grains in this newer rock will point to the location of the magnetic north pole when their rock host cooled and hardened. Each new batch of magma will solidify and lock in the current magnetic orientation, despite any further reversals. Each time Earth's magnetic field reverses, the dipole direction of the planet's magnetic field changes and gets locked into the newly formed rock. Thus, over long periods of time, we would expect to see alternating bands of magnetic orientation—exactly the kind of zebra-striped pattern of alternating north and south compass orientations shown in Figure 17-10.

FIGURE 17-8 A topographic map of ocean floors reveals dramatic mountain chains, deep flat plains, canyons, and trenches. These features suggest that ocean basins are active geological regions.

3. Rock Ages

The conclusions from magnetic data were reinforced by studies of the age of volcanic rocks in the oceanic crust. Volcanic rocks contain radioactive isotopes that can be used to measure how long ago they erupted (see Chapter 12). Rocks near the Mid-Atlantic Ridge and other similar features were found to be quite young, a few million years old or less. Rocks collected successively farther away from the ridge proved to be successively older.

STOP & THINK Given what you know about the scientific method, why do you suppose scientists accept the movement of continents as a fact today but didn't accept it in Wegener's time?

New Support for the Theory

The new data on the topography of ocean floors, as well as the magnetic properties and ages of its rocks, suggested to many scientists that the width of the Atlantic Ocean must be increasing yearly as the seafloor spreads. Eurasia and North America, it appears, are moving apart. Could the hypothesis that this distance is increasing be tested by an experimental measurement?

FIGURE 17-9 Measurements in the late 1950s and early 1960s revealed magnetic stripes running nearly parallel to the coastlines of Vancouver Province in Canada and Washington State.

Up until the late 1980s, no one was able to measure the motion of continents directly. The breakthrough came from an unexpected source—radio astronomy. Astronomers in North America and Europe trained radio telescopes on distant quasars (see Chapter 15). By measuring the times of arrival of the crests of the same radio wave, astronomers were able to get very accurate measurements of the distance between their telescopes. By repeating these sorts of experiments over a period of a few years, they were able to measure exactly the separation of the continents. Their work shows that North America is separating from Europe at the rate of about 5 centimeters (about 2 inches) a year.

SCIENCE BY THE NUMBERS

The Age of the Atlantic Ocean

If continents are constantly moving at speeds up to several centimeters per year, what would a map of Earth's surface have looked like millions of years ago? We can make an educated guess by using present rates of movement and "reversing the tape," so to speak. We know, for example, that the floor of the Atlantic Ocean is spreading at about 5 centimeters per year. Assuming that the rate of spreading has remained more or less constant, how old is the Atlantic Ocean?

To calculate the answer, we need to apply the familiar equation for travel time:

$$\text{time of travel} = \frac{\text{distance}}{\text{speed}}$$

You use the same relationship every time you estimate the driving time for a vacation. The speed in this equation is the spreading rate, 5 cm per year, and the present width of the Atlantic is approximately 7,000 kilometers, or 7×10^8 cm. The Atlantic Ocean began to open, therefore, at

$$\text{time} = \frac{7 \times 10^8 \text{ cm}}{(5 \text{ cm/yr})}$$
$$= 1.4 \times 10^8 \text{ years}$$
$$= 140 \text{ million years}$$

By this calculation, 140 million years ago Europe and the Americas must have been joined together because there was no Atlantic Ocean! By retracing the wandering paths of continents, Earth scientists have discovered that 200 million years ago what we now call the continents of

FIGURE 17-10 Magnetic stripes that parallel ocean ridges must form as new magma wells up from the fissure and pushes out to the sides. In this cross-sectional view, older rocks lie farther from the ridge. The "lithosphere" is the relatively cool and rigid outer portion of Earth's surface that includes the uppermost mantle and all of the crust. It moves as a unit because of its rigidity.

North America, South America, Eurasia, and Africa were locked together in one giant continent, now called *Pangaea* (Figure 17-11). A map of that ancient Earth would be all but unrecognizable, with a huge landmass on one side of the globe and a giant ocean on the other.

By the same token, 100 million years from now Earth's continents will have moved thousands of kilometers and appear completely different from today's arrangement.

STOP & THINK How much farther apart are Europe and North America since you were born?

◉ 17.2 Plate Tectonics: A Unifying View of Earth

The compelling model of the dynamic Earth that has emerged from studies of the ocean floor, paleomagnetism, rock dating, and much other data is called **plate tectonics**. "Tectonics" is related to the word "architect" and carries the connotation of building or putting things together. The plate tectonic theory provides a picture of the world that explains many of Earth's large-scale surface features and related phenomena.

The central idea of the plate tectonics theory is that Earth's surface is broken up into about a dozen large pieces (as well as a number of smaller ones) called **tectonic plates** (Figure 17-12). Each plate is a rigid, moving sheet of rock up to 100 kilometers (60 miles) thick, composed of the crust and part of the upper mantle. Oceanic plates have an average 8 to 10 kilometer thickness of dense rock known as *basalt* on top of the mantle rock. Continental plates have an average 35-kilometer thickness of lower density rock, such as *granite,* capping the basalt.

The tectonic plate boundaries are not the same as those of the continents and oceans. Some plates have continents on all or part of their surface, whereas some are covered only by oceanic crust. Most of the North American continent, for example, rests on the 8,000-kilometer-wide North American Plate, which extends from the middle of the Atlantic Ocean to the Pacific Plate on the West Coast.

About one quarter of Earth's surface is covered by continent; the rest is ocean. On timescales of millions of years, the plates shift about on the planet's surface, carrying the continents with them like passengers on a raft. Thus, it's not the motion of the continents themselves that is fundamental to understanding Earth's dynamics, but the constant motion of the underlying plates. Continental motion (what Wegener called continental drift) is just one manifestation of that plate motion.

The Convecting Mantle

Nothing happens without a force. What force could possibly be large enough to move not only the continents, but also the plates of which they are a part? Many geophysicists accept the theory that continents move as a result of the forces generated by **mantle convection** deep within Earth—motions driven by our planet's internal heat energy.

Two sources of energy contribute to Earth's interior heat. Some of this heat energy is left over from the gravitational potential energy released during the great bombardment and differentiation of the mantle and core as Earth formed (see Chapter 16). The decay of uranium and other radioactive elements (see Chapter 12), which are fairly common throughout Earth's core and mantle, provides a second important source of heat energy. These radioactive elements decay over time and produce energetic, fast-moving decay products—particles that collide with atoms and molecules in surrounding rocks and give up their energy as heat. Deep inside Earth, all this heat energy softens rocks to the point that they can flow slowly like hot taffy.

In Chapter 4 we saw that heat energy, once generated, must move spontaneously toward cooler regions. The heat generated in Earth's interior, for example, must eventually be radiated into space. If Earth were somewhat smaller, or if only small amounts of heat were generated, the energy could be carried to the surface entirely by conduction—the movement of heat by atomic collisions. This process operates in the Moon and Mars, for example. In the case of Earth, however, there is too much internal heat to be carried by conduction alone. Rocks in the mantle have been heated to the point where they are able to flow slowly, and immense

240 million years ago

120 million years ago

Present

FIGURE 17-11 Once the motion of continents was determined, scientists could predict how Earth's surface might have looked in the past. More than 200 million years ago, the present-day continents were joined together as the ancient continent Pangaea.

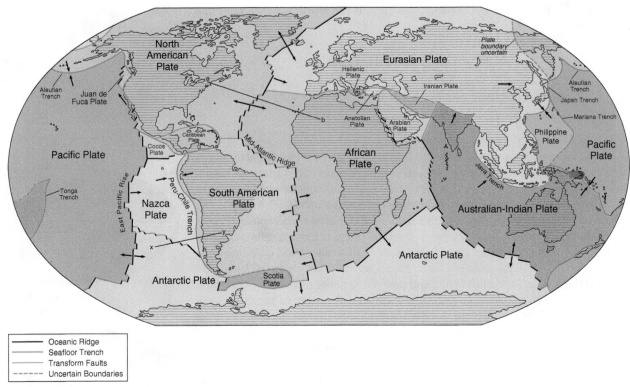

	Oceanic Ridge
	Seafloor Trench
	Transform Faults
	Uncertain Boundaries

FIGURE 17-12 Earth's major tectonic plates form a jigsaw puzzle of our planet's surface. The arrows show the relative directions and magnitudes of plate motions.

FIGURE 17-13 Heat moves through Earth's interior through the process of convection in the mantle. Hot magma rises, cools off, and sinks, moving the plates and their continental passengers as it does so.

convection cells are set up deep within Earth's mantle. According to this model, mantle rocks behave something like water in a boiling pot (see Chapter 4).

There are, of course, very important differences between Earth's mantle and a boiling pot—in particular, the timescales. Solid rock cannot flow significantly on timescales comparable to human lifetimes. But give soft, hot rocks a few hundred million years and they can move large distances. Earth scientists now estimate that Earth's convection cells go through a full cycle—with hot rocks rising from the lower mantle, cooling near the surface, and falling back to be replaced by other, warmer rocks—on a timescale of about 200 million years. In effect, Earth behaves something like a giant spherical stove, with burners on the inside and circulating rocks bringing the heat to the surface (Figure 17-13).

At the very top, these partially molten, circulating mantle rocks encounter the comparatively thin plates that cover the surface in a relatively cool, brittle layer. Along the oceanic ridges the brittle plates fracture and basaltic lava erupts, initiating seafloor spreading and plate motion. The plates move along with the convection cells underneath them, more or less as a film of oil on boiling water would move along on top of the water. The plates shift around, bash into each other, join each other, and are split apart in a constant dance. And on top of these plates, floating along like a thin scum, with no control whatsoever over their destiny, are the continents—the places that we call the "solid Earth."

The theory of plate tectonics caused a revolution in the Earth sciences. For the first time, evidence from many different Earth science disciplines had been brought together to form a single, coherent picture of our planet. This theory includes the oceans, the landmasses, the planet's deep interior, and the interconnections among all these systems. There was a time when geologists of different specialties—women and men who studied the ocean currents or ancient fossils, ore deposits or the planet's deep interior—had little to say to each other. That situation is no longer true. All of these different disciplines now share a common way of looking at Earth and thus are able to give each other ideas and gain breadth and depth from interactions with each other. It may be that your college or university no longer has a department of geology but instead has a department called Earth sciences or environmental sciences. These changes in name are more than just bureaucratic shufflings. They represent a very real change in the way scientists view and study planet Earth.

SCIENCE IN THE MAKING
Reactions to Plate Tectonics

At first, geologists confronted by the observations of magnetic stripes on the ocean floors, rock ages, and other seemingly odd data tried to find an explanation that did not require new seafloor to be created. All geologists had been taught a "fixed Earth" model in their college courses, and that was the standard picture of our planet they used in their work. Most of these scientists were not prepared to accept this radical new idea that the continents might actually move without a fight.

Some experts questioned the statistical significance of the magnetic data, and they wondered whether the distinctive striped patterns weren't the result of some as-yet unknown effect (such as small electrical currents running around the ocean floor). Others simply tried to ignore the whole thing. But as geologists and oceanographers collected more data—as new measurements of magnetic patterns and more precise rock ages were obtained—the evidence for seafloor spreading simply became overwhelming.

In a very short time, less than a decade from the time the first puzzling data from the *Pioneer* expedition came in, geologists had for the most part accepted a theory that radically changed many of the central principles of their discipline. This dramatic change in perspective brings us back to a point we made in Chapter 1. Good scientists will eventually accept the implications of their observations, regardless of whether those implications violate conventional ideas. A scientist can't look at data without some preconceived notions. Few scientists, for example, took the original continental drift arguments of Wegener seriously, in part because no obvious mechanism could cause entire continents to move.

We should note in passing that, although Wegener's theory contained one feature of modern theories, namely moving continents, continental drift was not plate tectonics. Wegener predicted, for example, that the average elevation of continents would increase with time—a prediction not confirmed by careful measurements. But as more and more data supported the more convincing plate tectonics model, the majority of Earth scientists readily changed their notions as the data demanded it.

The fact that the fixed Earth—one of the most revered and widely accepted geological theories—could be abandoned in the space of a few years when confronted by powerful contrary evidence indicates that the scientific method works. It also shows that many of the arguments one hears from the proponents of pseudosciences such as UFOs, astrology, creation science, and the like—arguments to the effect that the scientific community routinely closes its mind to new ideas and will not accept them—are simply wrong. Scientific theories, unlike the untestable claims of pseudoscience, are subject to repeated scrutiny and can be falsified. When confronted with overwhelming evidence, scientists are indeed prepared to accept new ideas and abandon the old "conventional wisdom."

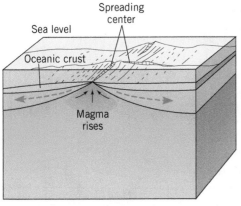

FIGURE 17-14 A divergent plate boundary defines a line along which new plate material is formed from volcanic rock.

Plate Boundaries

The boundaries between Earth's tectonic plates are active sites that determine much of the geological character of the surface. Three main types of boundaries separate Earth's tectonic plates: divergent plate boundaries, convergent plate boundaries, and transform plate boundaries.

1. Divergent Plate Boundaries

We saw one aspect of plate motion when we talked about seafloor spreading at the Mid-Atlantic Ridge, where new plate material is formed. We can now understand how such a spreading feature arises. In Figure 17-14, we show what happens when plates lie above a zone where magma comes to the surface. Not only does the volcanic action form a chain of mountains, but the motion of the magma also pushes the two adjoining plates farther and farther away from each other. The newly erupted molten material cools to rock and becomes new plate material. As the brittle tectonic plates crack and separate, shallow earthquakes of relatively low energy occur. This mechanism drives the seafloor spreading that gave us our first indication of the nature of continental motion. Such a spreading zone of crustal formation is called a **divergent plate boundary**.

When a divergent plate boundary occurs on the ocean floor, the seafloor spreads, basalt lava erupts from the newly created fissures, the two plates are pushed apart, and any continents that might be located on other portions of those plates are pushed apart as well. Eurasia and North America, for example, are separating right now at the rate of about 5 centimeters per year; consequently, the Atlantic Ocean is getting wider. Note that old spreading centers, such as the Mid-Atlantic Ridge, are always located in the middle of an ocean.

New spreading centers, in contrast, may begin anywhere, even in the middle of a continent. If a continent happens to be sitting above what will eventually become a divergent plate boundary, then the continent itself will be literally torn apart. The Great East African Rift Valley, which extends south from Ethiopia, along the east coastal interior of central Africa to the coast of Mozambique, and north into Israel and Syria, is a modern-day example of this motion. Millions of years in the future, an ocean may separate the western part of Africa from the eastern part. In fact, at the point where the Great Rift Valley crosses the African coast, this sea is already beginning to form. Look at the Dead Sea, Red Sea, and Gulf of Aqaba and you will see this rift in progress (Figure 17-15).

2. Convergent Plate Boundaries

Earth is not getting any larger. If new material pushes tectonic plates apart at places such as the oceanic ridges, then old plate material must be pushed together and taken into Earth's interior somewhere else. A place where two plates are coming together is called a **convergent plate boundary**.

At most convergent plate boundaries, one plate sinks beneath another to form a **subduction zone**. The plate that is subducted, or "taken beneath," in this way sinks down to rejoin the mantle material from which it came.

FIGURE 17-15 A satellite photograph of a portion of Africa's Great Rift Valley. The narrow body of water defines a divergent plate boundary where new plate material is being created and plates are moving out to either side.

Earth scientists observe three broadly different kinds of surface features associated with convergent plate boundaries, all shown in Figure 17-16. First, if no continents are on the leading edge of either of the two converging plates, the result will be a *deep-ocean trench*. As one plate penetrates into Earth's interior, it can bend and buckle the adjacent plate to produce a deep furrow in the ocean floor (Figure 17-16a). Melting of the subducting slab at depths of 100 or 200 kilometers can generate magma. The hot magma slowly rises toward the surface, and, if the magma penetrates the overlying ocean crust, continuing eruptions of lava will build a chain of volcanic islands adjacent to the trench. The Marianas Trench, the deepest point in the world's oceans (11 kilometers or about 7 miles deep, 2 kilometers deeper than Mount Everest is high) near the volcanic coastline of the Philippines, is an example of just such a subduction zone and volcanic terrain (Figure 17-16b).

A very different situation occurs if continents ride on top of both converging plates: they will collide. Continental material will be compressed together like crumpled cloth and pushed up to form a high, jagged mountain chain (Figure 17-16c). The Himalayas, for example, which began to form about 30 million years ago, are still growing taller at about 1 centimeter per year as the once-separate Indian subcontinent collides with Asia (Figure 17-16d). Similarly, the Ural

Ocean-Ocean

Deep-ocean trench

Peter Hendrie/Lonely Planet Images/Getty Images, Inc

(a)

(b)

Continent-Continent

Nonvolcanic mountains

Lithosphere

Christophe Boisvieux/AGE Fotostock

(c)

(d)

Ocean-Continent

Deep-ocean trench

Volcanic mountains

Oceanic plate

Marc Adamus/Aurora/Getty Images, Inc.

(e)

(f)

FIGURE 17-16 Convergent plate boundaries may display a variety of surface features, depending on the distribution of continental material. *(a)* When neither tectonic plate carries continental material at the convergent boundary, then a subduction zone is formed. A deep-ocean trench and chain of island volcanoes *(b)* are often created in this case. *(c)* When both tectonic plates carry continental material at the boundary, the continental materials buckle and fold *(d)* to form nonvolcanic mountains. *(e)* When only one tectonic plate carries continental material at the boundary, the oceanic plate will subduct beneath the continent. A deep trench may form offshore, and a coastal mountain range will form on land. *(f)*

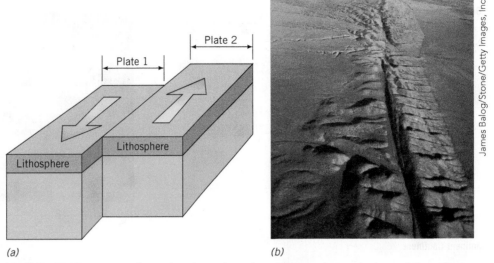

(a) (b)

FIGURE 17-17 *(a)* A transform plate boundary, showing the relative motions of the adjacent plates. *(b)* The San Andreas Fault in California marks the transform boundary between the North American Plate and the Pacific Plate.

Mountains mark the point at which Europe and Asia were welded together, and the Alps mark the point at which the Italian peninsula was joined to Europe. All of these geological processes involve the production of midcontinent mountain chains.

Finally, if a continent rests at the leading edge of only one of the two colliding plates, the denser oceanic plate will subduct beneath the continent (Figure 17-16e). Just as in the case where two oceanic plates converge, a deep trench may form a short distance offshore, while the continental material may be crumpled into a coastal mountain range. In addition, the subducting tectonic slab may partially melt and thus provide magma that rises to form a chain of volcanic mountains parallel to the coast. The Andes Mountains of South America and the Cascade Mountains of the northwestern United States are spectacular examples of this phenomenon (Figure 17-16f).

Roughly speaking, Earth's oceanic plate material renews itself about every 200 million years. The process of seafloor spreading and subduction is constantly replacing the ocean crust, whereas the lower-density continental plate material experiences no subduction. This process explains why, although some rocks on ancient continents formed billions of years ago and are still preserved there, no rocks on the ocean floor are older than about 200 million years.

3. Transform Plate Boundaries

The third kind of boundary between plates occurs when one plate scrapes past the other, with no new plate material being produced. This kind of plate contact is called a **transform plate boundary** and is shown in Figure 17-17a. The most famous transform boundary (and the only active plate boundary in the continental United States) is the San Andreas Fault in California. At the San Andreas Fault, the Pacific Plate is moving northwestward with respect to the North American Plate at the rate of several centimeters a year (Figure 17-17b).

The process by which two plates slide past each other is not smooth. Over time, the motion of plates compresses and strains rocks at the boundary. Friction normally prevents the stressed rocks from moving, but periodically the rocks simply break, moving as much as several meters in one sudden burst. When they do so, an earthquake occurs. No mountain building or volcanism is associated with transform boundaries.

THE SCIENCE OF LIFE
Upright Posture

Have you ever wondered why human beings are among the very few animals on Earth that walk upright? Some scientists speculate that it was the adaptation of upright walking that freed our hands. That innovation led eventually to the use of tools and development of increased brain size in humans. Richard Leakey, a well-known anthropologist, has suggested that our upright posture might have resulted indirectly from movements of Earth's tectonic plates.

His argument goes like this: 30 million years ago, a lush jungle covered most of eastern Africa. No fewer than 20 different species of apes, including our ancestral species, flourished in that environment and were especially well adapted to living in trees. When a divergent boundary started to pull the continent apart along the East African Rift Valley, the environment started to change. The forest began to disappear, to be replaced first by open plains dotted with stands of trees, and finally, 3 million years ago, by the savannah that exists there today. Most of the apes became extinct long before our 3-million-year-old ancestors, but Leakey argues that walking upright and being able to get rapidly from one forest "island" to another would have been a distinct advantage in that sort of environment. The result, according to Leakey, is that today there are only three kinds of descendants from those apes in Africa—gorillas, chimpanzees, and human beings.

The Geological History of North America

The epic movements of tectonic plates provided geologists with a new way of thinking about the history of Earth's surface. Earth scientists now use our understanding of plate tectonics to tell us something about the formation of our own continent. The oldest parts of the North American continent are in northeastern Canada and Greenland. Here we find large geological formations of rocks several billion years old that form the core of the continent (see Appendix C for the geological timescale). Over long periods of time, land was added to this continent by tectonic activity. Most of the western part of the United States, for example, is made up of small chunks of land called *terranes*—masses of rock several hundred kilometers across (Figure 17-18). Originally, these terranes were large islands in the Pacific Ocean, but they were carried toward the North American continent by plate activity and added to the mainland as tectonic plates converged. The hills near Wichita, Kansas, for example, are old mountains that once marked the addition of a large South American terrane onto what then comprised North America. (The idea that Wichita might have once had oceanfront property is one of the strange discoveries that comes out of plate tectonics.)

The Appalachian Mountains, which may at one time have rivaled the Himalayas in majesty, were formed over a period from about 450 to 300 million years ago when the continents that are now Eurasia and Africa slowly converged into the continent that is now North America. A series of long folds and fractures—structures that formed the present-day Appalachian

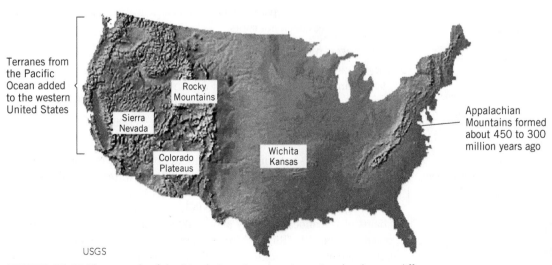

Terranes from the Pacific Ocean added to the western United States

Rocky Mountains

Sierra Nevada

Colorado Plateaus

Wichita Kansas

Appalachian Mountains formed about 450 to 300 million years ago

USGS

FIGURE 17-18 The growth of the North American continent involved many different geological processes, as discussed in the text.

Mountains—appeared in the surface rocks. This process explains, for example, why roads in the mountainous regions of the eastern part of the United States tend to run from southwest to northeast. They follow the mountain valleys that were created by erosion of these folded rocks. Thick wedges of sediments eroded off the mountains, forming the Coastal Plains of eastern North America and contributing to the sediments of the Great Plains.

The dramatic geological features of the western United States record a great variety of mountain-forming events. The Rocky Mountains rose approximately 60 million years ago from a broad warping and subsequent folding and fracturing of continental material. The Colorado Plateau, comprising parts of the states of Colorado, Arizona, Utah, and New Mexico, experienced a more gentle uplift, as rivers incised features such as the Grand Canyon. The Sierra Nevada range formed more recently when molten rock pushed up a huge block of sediments. These processes of uplift and erosion continue to this day in many places around the world.

◉ 17.3 Another Look at Volcanoes and Earthquakes

Plate tectonics provides us with a dynamic picture of our planet. Plates continually move over the hot, partially molten rocks in the mantle. They converge, move apart, and scrape by each other. In the process, tall mountain chains are slowly and steadily uplifted and worn down, and wide ocean basins are opened and closed as continents come together and split apart. Nothing on Earth is permanent because heat continuously flows from the hot interior to the cooler surface, and mantle convection provides the primary mechanism for that heat transfer. The scale of these ongoing processes is vast, nearly outside our ability to comprehend, but we are occasionally reminded of the power of geological processes.

For thousands of years humans have realized that Earth's most violent events—volcanoes and earthquakes—do not occur randomly. Earthquakes are common in California and Alaska but extremely rare in Kansas or Florida. Volcanoes are commonplace in Hawaii and the Pacific Northwest but never appear in New York or Texas. Why should this be? Plate tectonics provides an answer.

FIGURE 17-19 Volcanoes form above a subduction zone when heated plate material partially melts. The hot magma rises through the overlying crust to form a chain of volcanic islands.

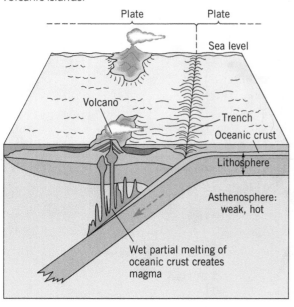

Plates and Volcanism

The global distribution of volcanoes may be understood in terms of the principles of plate tectonics. Volcanoes are common in three geological situations: along divergent plate boundaries, near convergent plate boundaries, or above places called hot spots.

1. Divergent Plate Boundaries

The formation of new crust along volcanic spreading ridges of divergent plate boundaries is the principal way that new crustal rocks are formed (see Figure 17-14). New basaltic plate material forms at the rate of a few centimeters per year along about 85,000 kilometers of oceanic ridges around the world.

2. Convergent Plate Boundaries

Volcanoes are also common near subduction zones, except in the case where two continental tectonic plates collide. As water-rich crustal material plunges into the mantle, it becomes hotter and may partially melt. This magma, which is highly mobile fluid rock, rises to the surface to form chains of volcanoes, typically about 200 kilometers inland from the line of subduction. The "Ring of Fire," a dramatic string of volcanoes that borders much of the Pacific Ocean, is a direct consequence of plate subduction (Figure 17-19).

(a)

(b)

FIGURE 17-20 (a) The Hawaiian Islands stretch along a northwest-southeast line. (b) The ages of these islands reveal the northwesterly motion of the Pacific Plate over a fixed hot spot. As the Pacific Plate moves, new volcanic islands are created to the southeast, while older islands erode away. The island of Kauai, currently the oldest, is between 3 and 5.5 million years old, while Hawaii, the youngest island, is less than 0.8 million years old.

The volcanoes that form the Cascade Mountain chain along the northwestern coast of the United States (including Mount Rainier and Mount St. Helens) are striking examples of the processes associated with subduction of an oceanic plate beneath a continent (see Figure 17-16e). Frequent dramatic eruptions of similar volcanoes in Central America, Japan, and the Philippines point to other places where subduction and volcanism occur in tandem.

3. Hot Spots

Finally, **hot spots** are a dramatic type of volcanism indirectly associated with plate tectonics. Earth scientists recognize dozens of hot spots around the world, including Hawaii, Yellowstone Park, Iceland, and others where large isolated chimney-like columns of ascending hot rock, also known as *mantle plumes*, rise to the surface more or less like bubbles coming to the surface in water being heated on a stove. These plumes may originate in the lower mantle or even at the core–mantle boundary. On a geological timescale, sources of hot spots are relatively stationary, so if a tectonic plate slowly moves over the fixed hot spot, the result will be a chain of volcanoes like the Hawaiian Islands that are built through a series of basaltic lava eruptions (Figure 17-20). These islands were created one at a time as the Pacific Plate moved above the localized hot spot.

The present-day volcano Kilauea on the "big island" of Hawaii, the site of most of the island chain's active volcanism, is directly over a hot spot. The volcanic islands to the northwest are progressively older as well as smaller owing to erosion, revealing that the motion of the Pacific Plate is also toward the northwest. In fact, a series of eroded submarine peaks that were islands millions of years ago stretch hundreds of kilometers farther to the northwest. In several million years, the most northwesterly of the present Hawaiian Islands will have been eroded beneath the waves, but new volcanic activity has already begun on the ocean floor southeast of Kilauea, promising a new island that has already been given the name "Loihi" by islanders.

Earthquakes

Stress builds up in brittle rock for several reasons. Heated rock expands and cooling rock contracts—changes that cause a solid formation to warp and distort. Rock may also become stressed in response to changes in pressure, as overlying mountains wear away or new layers of sediment weigh down. And stress builds up to extreme levels as two tectonic plates attempt to move past each other at a transform plate boundary.

Earthquakes may be felt near any plate boundary. Minor shallow earthquakes occur near divergent plate boundaries as two oceanic plates move apart. Stronger earthquakes, including "deep-focus" earthquakes originating more than 100 kilometers down, occur near subduction zones. Many of the most destructive shocks in Japan are of this type. In the United States, earthquakes at the transform plate boundary along the San Andreas Fault receive the most attention because of the fault's unusual activity, length, and proximity to major population centers. There are, however, occasional earthquakes in the middle of plates—in Missouri or Virginia, for example. Such events may arise from gradual warping of the wide, brittle North American Plate, though the origins of these earthquakes are still not fully understood.

FIGURE 17-21 Seismic waves passing through Earth can take a variety of paths. The speeds of compressional waves (shown in red, dashed lines) and shear waves (in black, dashed lines) are different depending on the type of rock, its temperature, and the pressure. Shear waves, furthermore, cannot travel through the liquid outer core, which results in a "shadow zone" that reveals the size of the liquid outer core.

Seismology: Exploring Earth's Interior with Earthquakes

Scientists who study earthquakes have discovered that these violent events provide the best means for exploring the deep interior of our planet. Geologists can't get their hands on much more than the outer 10 kilometers or so of rock layers. Almost everything we know about Earth's interior deeper than a few kilometers has to be obtained by indirect means. The science of **seismology**, the study and measurement of sound vibrations within Earth, is dedicated to deducing our planet's inner structure.

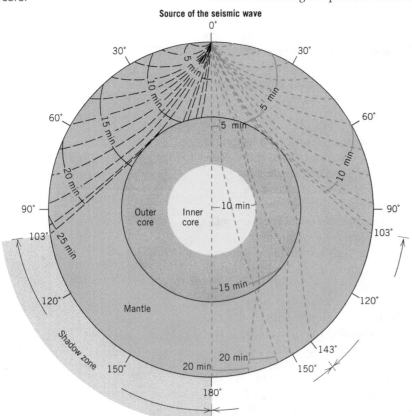

Source of the seismic wave

The basic idea of seismology is simple. When an earthquake or explosion occurs, waves of vibrational energy (see Chapter 5) move out through the rocks. Some of these waves travel through Earth's center, others move along the surface, and still others bounce off layers deep within the planet.

So-called seismic waves come in two principal types (see Chapter 6). *Compressional* or *longitudinal waves*, on the one hand, are like sound—the molecules in the rock move back and forth in the same direction as the wave. *Shear waves*, on the other hand, are *transverse waves*, like water waves in which the molecules move up and down perpendicular to the direction of wave motion. These kinds of waves travel through rock at different velocities depending, among other things, on the rock type, its temperature, and the pressure. After a major earthquake, scientists at laboratories around the world record the intensity and time of arrival of the various kinds of waves, both those that pass along the surface and those that pass through Earth's interior (Figure 17-21). By comparing the arrival behavior of waves from the same earthquake at many different sites on Earth's surface, a computer can construct a picture of the material through which those waves passed.

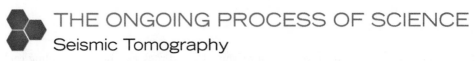

THE ONGOING PROCESS OF SCIENCE
Seismic Tomography

The picture of Earth we give in Chapter 16, in which we talk about the solid and liquid core, the layered mantle, and the thin brittle crust, comes from studies of seismic waves. Now, as more and more seismic data are collected, and ever-faster computers permit new ways those data, a new branch of Earth science called *seismic tomography* is enabling geophysicists to obtain astonishing three-dimensional pictures of Earth's deep interior, including deep regions of different rock types and magma (Figure 17-22). We are now able to document the basic movements of cold subducting slabs, hot upwelling mantle plumes, and the convection cells that characterize plate tectonics.

STRUCTURE OF THE BASE OF EARTH'S MANTLE

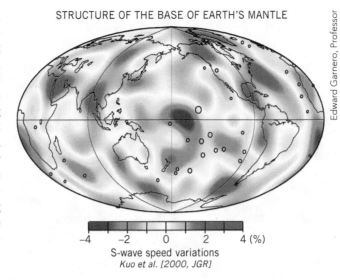

Edward Garnero, Professor

−4   −2   0   2   4 (%)
S-wave speed variations
Kuo et al. [2000, JGR]

FIGURE 17-22 A seismic tomograph provides a picture of Earth's deep interior, based on millions of individual measurements of seismic wave velocities. This image reveals hot rocks (red) around the Pacific Ocean rim and cooler rocks (blue) under the continents.

TECHNOLOGY
The Design of Earthquake-Resistant Buildings

Most of the people who die in earthquakes die because of falling buildings, not because of the violent shaking. Over the past few decades, structural engineers have learned a great deal about how to design buildings so that they do not collapse during an earthquake (Figure 17-23). The basic problem they face is how to construct a building that will maintain its integrity when the ground on which it sits moves. Two general solutions can solve this problem—make it flexible or make it rigid.

The first strategy, widely used in designing tall buildings, is best typified by a tree bending in the wind. A building with a specially reinforced steel skeleton can be designed so that it will bend and vibrate as the ground shakes, but come back to its original orientation without damage when the quake stops.

The second approach is widely used in individual houses and apartment buildings. The idea is to construct the building so that it tosses about on the moving surface like a ship on the ocean. The main preoccupation of the engineers is to guarantee that the building's corners are maintained at 90 degrees, no matter how much it moves around, by reinforcement of corners and rigid connections to the foundation and roof. Sometimes this rigidity can be obtained simply by covering all the walls of the building with plywood sheets before the outer siding is installed.

FIGURE 17-23 This experimental house in Japan is made from Styrofoam. It is designed to be resistant to both earthquakes and high winds.

Kyodo/Landov

THINKING MORE ABOUT **PLATE TECTONICS**

Earthquake Prediction

One of the most important roles scientists can play in modern society is to provide warnings of natural disasters such as earthquakes, volcanic eruptions, and large storms. In the fall of 1999, for example, early warnings allowed thousands of Florida residents to escape the path of Hurricane Andrew. The storm caused billions of dollars of property damage, but surprisingly little loss of life. Similarly, volcanic eruptions, which are usually preceded by numerous small earthquakes, also can be forecast with some certainty. The successful prediction of Mount Pinatubo's 1991 eruption in the Philippines gave thousands of people living on the flanks of the long-dormant volcano time to flee.

Earthquake prediction is another story, however. Earthquakes occur because of the predictable and measurable gradual buildup of stresses in Earth's crust. But the sudden failure of rock is not so predictable. You are familiar with this situation if you've ever gradually bent a pencil to the breaking point. It's easy to predict that a bent pencil will eventually break, but it's very hard to say exactly at what point the failure will occur. Much of the scientific effort related to earthquake prediction centers on the careful documentation of stress buildup in earthquake-prone areas. But these measurements alone tell us little about the exact time when failure will occur.

In their efforts to predict earthquakes, many scientists search for "precursor events"—measurable phenomena that precede a quake. A lot of anecdotal evidence suggests that such events may indeed occur. Folklore has it that some domesticated animals become highly agitated before a strong earthquake or that changes are seen in the flow of well water or hot springs. Recognition of such changes enabled Chinese scientists to save many lives prior

to a major earthquake in 1975. Similarly, scientists have noticed changes in the regularity of geysers and have recorded swarms of minor quakes just prior to some big earthquakes. Nevertheless, no reliable methods for predicting earthquakes have yet been devised. At best, we can reliably predict the probability that a large earthquake might occur in a given area during a period of a few decades.

Ironically, if we do develop a way to predict the timing of earthquakes precisely, a whole new series of problems could arise. Suppose you could predict with 80% certainty that a major earthquake will strike the Los Angeles Basin sometime in the next 30 days. Would you then announce it? What would happen in the Los Angeles Basin if you made such an announcement? What would happen if you made the announcement and the earthquake never occurred? What would happen if you didn't make the announcement and the earthquake did occur? These are not easy subjects to deal with.

◀ RETURN TO THE INTEGRATED QUESTION

Can we predict destructive earthquakes?

- As you learned in Chapter 1, a scientific perspective requires that every idea must be tested by using it to make predictions about how a particular system will behave, and then observing nature to see if the system behaves as predicted.

- In their efforts to predict earthquakes, many scientists search for "precursor events" (i.e., measurable phenomena that precede a quake). The goal is that with enough observation and measurement of precursor events, a system may be devised to predict earthquakes in order to minimize their destructive consequences.

- For thousands of years, many cultures have believed that unusual animal behavior is a "precursor event." For example, in Japanese folklore, catfish behavior has been used for prediction. Nonetheless, scientific inquiry has failed to demonstrate any correlation between the behavior of catfish and the occurrence of earthquakes.

- Nevertheless, the Chinese government has used a quasi-scientific study of changes in animal behavior, groundwater levels, and foreshocks for prediction over many years. In 1975, recognition of such changes enabled Chinese scientists to save thousands of

lives prior to a major 1975 earthquake. Unfortunately, this same system failed to predict the deadly Tangshan earthquake 1 year later that killed nearly 250,000 people.

- A great deal of seismographic research on earthquake prediction revolves around detailed observations and measurements of the stress buildup in earthquake-prone areas. The measurement of the gradual buildup of stresses in Earth's crust that lead to earthquakes is both simple and accurate. Nevertheless, predicting the moment in time that the sudden failure in rock will occur is not.

- At the present time, no reliable method for the prediction of earthquakes has been developed. However, this does not mean that scientific progress is halted. In 2004, DEMETER (Detection of Electro-Magnetic Emissions Transmitted from Earthquake Regions), a microsatellite, was launched by the French equivalent of NASA. Its mission over the past few years was to gain information for earthquake prediction. Using sophisticated sensors, it detects changes in Earth's magnetic field and disturbances in the ionosphere. Perhaps in the near future, messages from satellites in space will inform us of "precursor events" and hopefully save lives.

SUMMARY

Earth's surface constantly changes. Mountains are created and worn away, while entire continents slowly shift, opening up oceans and closing them again. *Plate tectonics,* a relatively new theory that explains how a few thin, rigid *tectonic plates* of crustal and upper mantle material are moved across Earth's surface by *mantle convection,* provides a global context for these changes. According to this theory, plates move over partially molten underlying sections of Earth's mantle, like rafts on the ocean, in response to convection of hot mantle rocks.

Three different kinds of observations—the geological features of ocean floors, parallel stripes of magnetic rocks situated symmetrically about volcanic ridges on the ocean floor, and the ages of these rocks—provided direct evidence that new crust is being created at *divergent plate boundaries.* Meanwhile, old crust returns to the mantle in *subduction zones,* where plates converge. *Convergent plate boundaries* in the ocean create deep trenches and associated volcanic islands. When an oceanic plate subducts beneath a plate carrying a continent, an offshore trench and chain of continental volcanoes parallel to shore result. The collision of two plates that carry continents at their margins produces mountain ranges of crumpled continental rocks. *Transform plate boundaries* occur where two plates scrape past each other.

Most *volcanoes* form near plate boundaries, either along the volcanic ridges of diverging plates or above subducting plates. Other volcanoes such as the Hawaiian Islands form above *hot spots* originating in Earth's mantle. *Earthquakes* occur when stressed rock ruptures. Earthquakes may be felt at all plate boundaries. The only plate boundary in the United States, California's San Andreas Fault, is a transform boundary in which one block of crust moves horizontally past the opposing block. The science of *seismology,* which documents the passage of earthquake-generated waves through Earth, is providing new insights into the dynamic processes that drive plate tectonics.

KEY TERMS

volcano
earthquake
plate tectonics
tectonic plates

mantle convection
divergent plate boundary
convergent plate boundary
subduction zone

transform plate boundary
hot spots
seismology

DISCOVERY LAB

Viscosity is the resistance of a liquid to flow. Why are some liquids more viscous than others? How do these liquids behave?

You can check the viscosity of various commonly seen liquids. You will need the following materials: a large dropper, a drinking straw, a stopwatch, four containers for the liquids, a fizzy drink, chocolate syrup, ketchup, and honey.

Draw two lines on the dropper, one at the lower level and the other at the higher level. The exact level is not important. Fill in the liquid to the top line (read at the bottom of the meniscus). Squeeze the bulb of the dropper. Record how long it takes for the liquid to drain to the bottom line. Keep the dropper upright because if the dropper inclines, it will increase the time it takes to drain the

liquid. Repeat the procedure until you have collected data for all four liquids.

Put a straw into the liquids and blow bubbles. How does viscosity affect gases in liquids? In liquids with low viscosity, gases can escape easily; in more viscous liquids, gases find it harder to escape; and in most viscous liquids, gases cannot escape. How did your test liquids behave?

Apply what you know about liquid viscosity and gases to volcanic activity on Earth. The behavior of magma depends on the composition of magma—the amount of gas dissolved and if it reacts with water. What makes magma erupt? Does all magma rise to Earth's surface? Which type of magma will create the most explosive volcanoes? Why don't all volcanoes look and erupt the same way?

Large dropper

Draw two lines on the dropper.

Squeeze the bulb of the dropper.

Record how long it takes to drain to the bottom line.

Put straw into liquids and blow bubbles.

Fizzy drink   Chocolate syrup   Ketchup   Honey

REVIEW QUESTIONS

1. What evidence suggests that Earth's surface is dynamic and ever changing?

2. Describe geological processes that can alter landscapes over long periods of time.

3. Give an example of a mountain created by a volcano.

4. What evidence suggests that Europe, Africa, and North and South America were once joined?

5. Explain how the magnetism of seafloor rocks was the first evidence for plate tectonics.

6. Describe the three kinds of plate boundaries.

7. Describe the three different kinds of surface features that might occur at a convergent boundary.

8. Explain how mountain ranges might form as a result of plate motions. Give an example of one such mountain range.

9. Identify a mountain range in North America that formed as a result of plate motions.

10. What does the "Ring of Fire" (i.e., a string of volcanoes that surrounds much of the Pacific Ocean) suggest about the type of geologic activity in that area?

11. Describe the geological processes that produced the Appalachian Mountains.

12. How do we know that tectonic plates move? Describe how transform plate boundaries differ from divergent plate boundaries. What form of geologic activity is exhibited along transform boundaries?

13. What is the Richter scale? Where might you read about it?

14. How do the ages of rocks on the ocean floor help support the theory of seafloor spreading?

DISCUSSION QUESTIONS

1. Where are the tallest and longest mountain chains on Earth? How were they formed?

2. On what tectonic plate do you live? How many adjacent plates are there? What kinds of boundaries do you find to the north, south, east, and west? In which direction are these plates moving?

3. If you got a lucrative job offer that required you to live near the San Andreas Fault, would you take it? Would you build a house in that area? Why or why not?

4. Based on your understanding of plate tectonics, will the California coast eventually "slide into the ocean?" Why or why not?

5. Why are all three types of plate boundaries essential if plate tectonics is to work? What is occurring at each type of boundary?

6. How would you explain the difference between Earth's crust and tectonic plates?

7. Why is it so difficult to explain earthquakes that occur in the middle of tectonic plates, such as those that occur in places such as Missouri and the East Coast of the United States.

8. The continent of Antarctica has rocks with plant and animal fossils that suggest the Antarctic climate was once temperate. Explain at least two different ways in which these warm-climate fossils might have ended up in what is now a polar region. How might you test your hypotheses?

9. What are the geological forces that give rise to volcanoes? Why aren't volcanoes found in all places on the surface of Earth?

10. A number of portions of the Mid-Atlantic Ridge are high enough to extend above sea level, forming islands such as Ascension Island and the Azores. If you were to use radioisotope dating on rocks from these islands, what pattern do you think you would find?

11. Geology has been called an integrated science because it calls on several scientific disciplines to help explain features and processes of Earth. Explain how geologists have used other sciences to answer the following questions:

    a. How old is a piece of rock?

    b. How is heat transferred from Earth's deep interior to the surface?

    c. How does Earth's magnetic field change over time?

    d. What is the structure of Earth's interior?

    e. What is the topography of the seafloor?

12. What was Pangaea? How does plate tectonics explain what happened to it? Could Earth's continents form into a single, Pangaea-like mass again? Why or why not? If they could, can you estimate how long it would take for them to do so?

13. At some convergent plate boundaries, deep-ocean trenches lie a relatively short distance from tall mountains; one such example is the Peru–Chile Trench running parallel to the Andes Mountains. How are these contrasting features related to each other?

14 Why do most volcanoes form near the boundaries of diverging or subducting plates?

15. Is it possible to outrun an earthquake in a car? Why or why not?

16. Explain the stresses that build up in rocks prior to an earthquake.

17. The meteor that slammed into the Yucatán Peninsula 65 million years ago is estimated to have induced an earthquake of magnitude 13.0, compared to the 9.5 magnitude of the strongest recorded earthquake. Why would such a powerful earthquake not happen without such external mechanisms?

18. The islands making up Hawai'i have resulted from active volcanoes such as Mauna Loa and Kilauea. Yet Hawai'i is in the

middle of the Pacific Plate rather than along the edges. What do you think is responsible for the presence of these volcanoes? Are there other islands around the world that have risen through similar mechanisms?

19. The Appalachian Mountains formed when the plates came together to form the supercontinent Pangaea. Which present-day continent collided with what was to become North America to form these mountains?

   a. Africa

   b. Asia

   c. Europe

   d. South America

PROBLEMS

1. If the Mid-Atlantic Ridge continues spreading at a rate of 5 centimeters per year, how much farther apart will New York and Paris be from each other over the course of an average human life (80 years)? How far apart have they separated since the Declaration of Independence was signed?

2. Assuming it is undergoing the process of erosion rather than uplifting, estimate the probable lifetime of your favorite mountain. (*Hint:* Get its dimensions from a map and then estimate its volume.)

3. Mount Everest is now approximately 8,850 meters tall, and it has been growing taller at a rate of about 2 centimeters per year. Estimate the approximate age of the mountain.

4. An earthquake occurs at a particular location. If compressional waves travel at a speed of 5,000 meters per second and shear waves travel at a speed of 500 meters per second, how far apart will the signals arrive at a seismic station 2,000 miles from the earthquake?

5. Make a bar graph of the thickness of Earth's core, mantle, and crust. Make a graph of the densities of the core, mantle, and crust. What do these graphs portray about the interior of our planet?

6. Compare the amount of ground motion in an earthquake that measures magnitude 2.0 versus an earthquake of magnitude 5.0, which is strong enough for people to notice.

7. The volcanoes forming the chain of islands of Hawai'i are estimated to have produced 750,000 km^3 of rock over 85 million years. On average, how much lava has been flowing out each second during this time? If the lava has a density of 2,700 kg/m^3, how many kg/s is this?

8. Traveling halfway around the world is a trip of 20 million meters. If the tectonic plates have consistently moved at a rate of 5 centimeters per year, how many years do you think would elapse between the formation of supercontinents?

9. If Earth's magnetic field has reversed orientation 300 times in the past 200 million years, how many years elapse on average between reversals?

   a. 670,000 years

   b. 1.5 million years

   c. 60,000 years

   d. 100 million years

INVESTIGATIONS

1. Examine original sources related to Wegener's continental drift theory. Why was this theory rejected by the majority of Earth scientists in the 1920s? Compare and contrast the major features of the continental drift theory with plate tectonics theory.

2. Investigate the destruction of the city of Pompeii in AD 79. What tectonic processes led to its destruction?

3. Does plate tectonics operate on any other planet or moon in our solar system? Why or why not?

4. In your library, examine newspaper reports of major volcanoes and earthquakes during the past 20 years (each student could take one year). Plot these events on a world map. Do you see any obvious geographic patterns? How do the locations of these events relate to the plate boundaries shown in Figure 17-12?

5. Jupiter's moon Io is thought to be the most volcanically active object in the solar system. How does the energy source of the volcanoes on Io differ from the energy source of volcanoes on Earth?

6. Investigate the history of predictions of earthquakes at the New Madrid Fault in Missouri. Why do you suppose those predictions were never borne out?

7. Scientists have discovered astonishing deep-ocean communities of life forms associated with plate boundaries. Investigate the nature and distribution of these deep ecosystems. Why are they found close to these boundaries and not elsewhere? What energy source do they utilize to survive?

8. Investigate the history of the formation of the Hawaiian Islands. When is a new island expected to appear?

9. What major cities in the United States are affected by earthquakes? What type of early warning systems are in place to help protect inhabitants of these cities? Would you buy a piece of property a few miles from the San Andreas Fault? Why, or why not?

10. How many volcanoes are there in the United States? How many are active?

11. Where is the safest place on Earth to live? The safest in the United States? Research the various natural phenomena that affect ecosystems worldwide (e.g., earthquakes, tornadoes, hurricanes) and decide where you would like to live. What are the probabilities of these phenomena affecting your life? Which has killed more people in the last 100 years: hurricanes or volcanic eruptions?

18 Earth's Many Cycles

Will we ever run out of fresh water?

PHYSICS

The movement of heat by convection drives ocean currents.

BIOLOGY

Coral reefs are limestone deposits built by the gradual action of microscopic plants and animals; each generation grows on the remains of the previous one.

CHEMISTRY

Earth has a finite number of atoms, which are constantly moving and recycling in repositories of rocks, water, and air.

TECHNOLOGY

Doppler radar measures the motions of air currents and thus can detect the approach of violent weather.

GREAT IDEA

All matter above and beneath Earth's surface moves in cycles.

ENVIRONMENT

Humans are removing water from aquifers faster than they can be replenished, depleting the supply of available freshwater.

ASTRONOMY

Variations in Earth's rotation and orbit are partly responsible for our planet's cycle of ice ages.

HEALTH & SAFETY

Elements move through the human body in cycles; your body depends on a regular intake of elements to help replace dying cells.

GEOLOGY

The rock cycle creates, alters, and destroys Earth's solid materials.

 = applications of the great idea discussed in this chapter

 = other applications, some of which are discussed in other chapters

A Seaward Breeze

The beautiful day continues, bright and clear. As the Sun gradually arcs overhead into the western sky, the afternoon shadows begin to lengthen and the cool wind picks up off the water. By 2 p.m. there's a steady seaward breeze blowing close to 20 miles per hour.

Day after summer day it's the same story at the shore: refreshing offshore breezes pick up during the day, while warm onshore breezes blow in the evening. This familiar atmospheric behavior is just one of Earth's countless cycles.

Alan Sirulnikoff / Photo Researchers, Inc.

◉ 18.1 Cycles Small and Large

Every place we go, every day of our lives, we experience Earth's cycles. A day may start out clear and sunny, with mild temperatures and gentle breezes. But, suddenly, the wind picks up as a line of dark clouds presses in from the west. With the wind comes the first threatening rumble of thunder, flashes of distant lightning, and spurts of rain. A heavy downpour and powerful gusts of wind follow, as thunder booms and lightning illuminates the gray sky around us. Trees sway, windows rattle, and old dead limbs come crashing down at the height of the storm.

Within an hour skies are sunny again, though the temperature is noticeably cooler. The air has a fresh, clean smell, and the sky seems more deeply blue than before. In the span of a few hours we have experienced one of Earth's many cycles—the atmospheric cycle called weather.

Day and night, summer and winter, life and death—these and many other cyclical changes characterize our dynamic planet. As the author of the *Book of Ecclesiastes* wrote 3,000 years ago:

> One generation passeth away, and another generation cometh: but the earth abideth forever;
> The sun also ariseth, and the sun goeth down, and hasteth to the place where he arose;
> The wind goeth toward the south, and turneth about unto the north; it whirleth about
>   continually, and the wind returneth again according to his circuits;
> All the rivers run into the sea; yet the sea is not full; unto the place from whence the rivers
>   come, thither they return again...
> The thing that hath been, it is that which shall be; and that which is done is that which shall be
>   done: and there is no new thing under the sun.

John Wood Photography/Getty Images, Inc.

FIGURE 18-1 Recycling cans saves the energy required to mine and smelt aluminum.

Recycling

Think about the last time that you drank a can of soda. What did you do with the aluminum can when you were through? You may have taken the time to place the can in a recycling bin. Alternatively, you may have tossed it into a trash container, or even by the side of the road. What difference does it make? Where do the aluminum atoms end up?

The atoms that make up Earth, with the exception of a few radioactive isotopes (Chapter 12), will last virtually forever. A single aluminum atom, for example, will appear in many different guises during its lifetime. It may form part of a swirling lava flow in which it is tightly bonded to oxygen atoms. It may then be incorporated with those oxygen atoms into a solid rock. As the rock weathers away, the atom may wind up in soil and become concentrated with other aluminum atoms, where it is mined. Giant smelters separate the aluminum atom—a process that consumes prodigious amounts of energy—to produce the aluminum metal that made your soda can. Once discarded, the atom may be recycled into new cans, or it may go back to the soil where it once again bonds to oxygen.

STOP & THINK One of the main points in Chapter 3 is that energy flows into and out of the Earth system. Does matter flow in the same way through Earth? Explain.

Earth has a vast, though finite, number of aluminum atoms that take part in the aluminum cycle. The advantage to recycling aluminum is that we save all the energy that went into finding concentrated aluminum sources and breaking aluminum-to-oxygen bonds (Figure 18-1). But no matter what you do with your can, the aluminum atoms still are part of our planet.

The Nature of Earth's Cycles

The history of an aluminum atom is just one example of the many paths within the three great cycles of Earth materials: the oceans, the atmosphere, and rocks. Two central ideas frame our understanding of the movement of matter in our changing planet:

● **Earth materials move in cycles.**

 and

● **A change in one cycle affects the others.**

The story of the aluminum atom suggests a useful two-step strategy for analyzing any of the many cycles by which each type of Earth material moves. The first step is to make an inventory of all the different **reservoirs** in which that substance is found. Earth's water, for example, is found in oceans, lakes, rivers, ice caps, and several other reservoirs. The second step is to identify the varied ways that the material is transferred from one reservoir to another. In the case of water, for example, movement may occur by precipitation, evaporation, or gravity.

Each of Earth's cycles illustrates a central theme: our planet's atoms are constantly moving and recycling. Water moves from rivers to oceans to glaciers and to clouds as it takes part in Earth's dynamic hydrologic cycle. Above Earth's surface, the gases of the atmosphere flow in the great cycles of weather, the seasons, and global climate. And the solid surface of Earth slowly alters, erodes away, and forms again in the stately rock cycle.

Many of Earth's cycles are driven by the tendency of heat to spread out—to flow from hot to cold in what we described as the second law of thermodynamics in Chapter 4. Earth has two primary sources of heat energy: the Sun and its own geothermal processes, each of which drives its own cycles of heat transfer. More heat energy from the Sun falls at the equator than at the poles, and heat transfer by convection thus moves gases in the atmosphere and water in the oceans in the great cycles from equator to poles, a process that controls weather and climate. Similarly, heat energy in Earth's core and mantle drives the convection cycles that move the tectonic plates.

Thus, Earth's cycles reflect the most basic properties of matter and energy. These cycles may be studied at many levels, from an atomic scale for an individual element such as aluminum, to the global cycles involved in plate tectonics. We find it especially useful to consider Earth in terms of the three most familiar cycles around us: the cycles of water, air, and rock.

◉ 18.2 The Hydrologic Cycle

Water plays a vital role in the unique chemistry of Earth's outer layers. Water saturates the air, falls to the ground as precipitation, moves through a complex system of rivers and streams, and is stored for long periods in underground reservoirs, oceans, and ice. Water shapes the surface of our planet, and it provided the medium in which life began. The combination of processes by which water moves from repository to repository above, below, and on Earth's surface is called the **hydrologic cycle**.

Reservoirs of Water

The total amount of water near Earth's surface has stayed roughly the same from very early times. Water first reached the surface during the outgassing of the young, volcano-covered Earth, and, possibly, by a late bombardment during the formation of the planet by the assembly of planetesimals (see Chapter 16). When the planet's surface temperature finally fell below 100°C, this water condensed into liquid form and began to fill the ocean basins. Relatively minor processes still add and remove small amounts of water from Earth. High in the atmosphere, ultraviolet rays from the Sun break up water molecules, freeing hydrogen atoms, which may escape into space because of their low mass. At the same time, at converging and diverging plate boundaries and other sites of volcanism, small amounts of new water are emitted from Earth's deep interior. These losses and gains are in rough equilibrium, and in any case both are rather small—by one estimate, no more than one or two Olympic-sized swimming pools of water per year. Thus, for all intents and purposes, we can treat Earth as if it has had a fixed amount of water at its surface for billions of years. The water that we have now is all there is.

Earth boasts several major water repositories, as summarized in Table 18-1. In addition to oceans, lakes, and rivers, significant amounts of water are locked into Earth's polar ice caps and glaciers, bodies of ice that form in regions where snowfall exceeds melting. **Ice caps** are layers of ice that form at Earth's north and south polar regions.

Glaciers are large bodies of ice that slowly flow down a slope or valley under the influence of gravity (Figure 18-2). Approximately 96% of glaciers (by volume) are found in Antarctica and Greenland, while the rest are widely scattered in mountainous areas. All of these places where water occurs tap into the same central supply. During its lifetime, a given molecule of water will cycle through many different reservoirs, over and over again.

A vast part of the hydrologic cycle remains unseen. Some of the water that falls on the continents does not immediately return to the ocean; rather, it seeps into the soil to become **groundwater**. There, it goes into large *aquifers*—reservoirs that are, in effect, underground storage tanks of water. By some estimates, more than 99% of the world's fresh water is stored as groundwater. Water typically percolates into the ground and fills the tiny spaces between grains of sandstone and other porous rock layers. Impermeable materials, such as clay, which keeps the water from seeping away, often bound these layers of water-saturated rock.

TABLE 18-1 Reservoirs of Water*

Reservoir	Percent of Earth's Supply
Oceans	96.5
Lakes, rivers, and streams	0.013
Ice caps and glaciers	1.74
Groundwater	1.7
Clouds, atmosphere	0.001
Living things	0.0001

*Data from the United States Geological Survey

John Hyde/Perspectives/Getty Images, Inc.

FIGURE 18-2 Glaciers and ice caps store a small percentage of Earth's water. In this image a killer whale surfaces below Chilkat Glacier, Alaska.

Movements of Water Between Reservoirs

Earth's water is in constant motion both within and between reservoirs—a process that may gradually change the distribution of water near Earth's surface. The hydrologic cycle with which most of us are familiar involves the short-term back-and-forth transfer of water molecules between the oceans and the land. Water evaporates off the surface of the oceans, forms into clouds, falls as rain on the land, and then returns to the oceans via rivers and streams. Most terrestrial life depends on this simple cycle (Figure 18-3).

Much of the movement of Earth's water occurs within the oceans, which are far from static. Each ocean basin has great **currents**, which are like rivers of moving water within the larger ocean (see Figure 18-4). These currents play a vital role in redistributing heat across the surface of the planet, and thus in determining climate. Some surface currents carry warm water from the equator, where a large amount of heat energy from the Sun is absorbed, toward the cooler poles. At the same time, other surface currents carry cold water from the poles back to the equator to be heated and cycled again. These great gyres as they are called have a profound effect on the weather of the land they flow past. In the North Atlantic, for example, the Gulf Stream current starts in the Caribbean and flows past the eastern coast of the United States. It comes near England, making the British Isles much warmer than you might expect them to be based on their latitude, which is farther north than Maine. A much colder current flows along the western coast of Europe back to the tropics to complete the cycle.

In addition to this rather rapid circulation of water at the surface, we find deeper three-dimensional circulation of water in the ocean. When the effects of surface currents and wind along a coast act in such a way as to push surface water away from the land, colder water from the depths comes up to create an area of upwelling. The waters along the coast of California

FIGURE 18-3 A diagram of the hydrologic cycle showing the transfer of water molecules between oceans and land. The numbers in parentheses show the volume of water that cycles through the continental United States in millions of cubic meters each day.

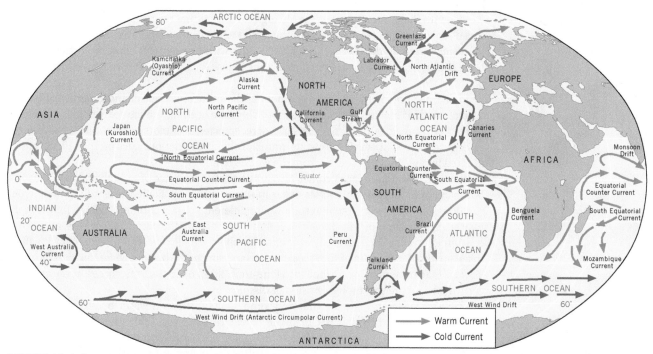

FIGURE 18-4 Ocean currents play a major role in redistributing Earth's heat. Surface currents that tend to carry warmer (less dense) water from the equator toward the poles are shown in red, whereas deeper colder currents that tend to carry water from the poles toward the equator are shown in blue.

display this phenomenon, which helps explain why the ocean there is so cold. On a larger scale, water from the Arctic and Antarctic, which is both cold and salty because so much fresh water is removed to form ice, sinks to the bottom of the sea and rolls sluggishly toward the equator. This dense, cold water forms the slow, deep flow that characterizes much of the bottom currents in the world's ocean basins.

Humans also participate in the water cycle by tapping into deep aquifers when they drill wells to supply water for cities and agriculture. One problem with using aquifers as a water supply is that it may take many thousands of years to fill them but only a few years to drain them. For example, when farmers in the central United States take water from the Ogallala aquifer, one of North America's great underground reservoirs, they are in effect mining the water. Underground water is not a renewable resource except over very long timescales.

THE SCIENCE OF LIFE
Sobering Facts about Water

Although Earth's supply of water is vast, about 97.5% is salty and most of the remaining fresh water is locked into ice caps and glaciers. Thus, much less than 1% of Earth's water is readily available for human use.

Modern society places tremendous demands on this limited resource. Agriculture, industry, and personal needs result in an average daily water consumption of more than 2,000 gallons per person in North America. As supplies of groundwater are reduced and pollution contaminates other reservoirs, shortages of fresh water may become a serious concern in the future.

Chemical Cycles in the Oceans

Just as the water in the oceans is in constant physical motion, so too are the chemicals that make it salty. Scholars once thought that the oceans were passive receptacles for materials washed into them from the land. The old argument went that rivers flowing into the ocean carried dissolved minerals and salts with them, and when water evaporated, these minerals were left behind, leaving the oceans saltier and saltier with time. In this view, the extremely salty Dead Sea in Israel was always cited as a place where salts had accumulated over the longest period of time.

In fact, we now know that the saltiness of the oceans has not changed appreciably over several hundred million years, and they probably have been salty since soon after they formed. Instead of thinking of the oceans as passive receptacles, it is more accurate to think of them as large test tubes in which a constant round of chemical reactions goes on that affects and is affected by the input of minerals from the world's rivers.

The saltiness of the oceans comes primarily from the presence of sodium and chloride ions, but many other dissolved minerals occur in seawater as well. Each element follows different reactions, and each will remain in solution for different periods of time. Calcium, for example, may be dissolved out of limestone by water and carried into the ocean. Once there, an average calcium ion can be expected to float around for about 8 million years, but eventually it will be taken up into the skeleton of some sea creature and sink to the bottom when that creature dies. There it may once more be formed into limestone, lifted up by tectonic forces, and eventually carried back to the sea through erosion or dissolution.

The average length of time that an atom will stay in ocean water before it is removed by some chemical reaction is called the *residence time* (see Table 18-2). Sodium (one of the atoms that gives seawater its distinctive taste) enters the ocean after dissolving out of various kinds of rocks. A sodium ion will stay in suspension on average for about 260 million years before it is incorporated again into various kinds of clay and mud on the ocean bottom. Once so incorporated, it can go through the same cycle of uplift and erosion as limestone.

Chloride ions, in contrast, tend to stay in the ocean almost forever, though these atoms may leave the ocean for short periods of time in tiny droplets, or aerosols, of ocean spray. Only when a body of salt water is evaporated, forming dry salt deposits like those surrounding the Great Salt Lake in Utah, is chlorine removed from its water environment for any appreciable length of time (Figure 18-5). But even these deposits, slowly buried and compressed, could eventually (in perhaps a few hundred million years) rise to the surface as salt domes, where they would weather away, returning the salt once again to the sea.

TABLE 18-2 Some Typical Residence Times for Elements in the Ocean

Element	Concentration (parts per million)	Residence Times (millions of years)
Sodium	10,800	260
Calcium	413	8
Chlorine	19,400	infinite
Gold	0.00005	0.042
Potassium	387	11
Copper	0.003	0.05

Thus chemical cycles in the ocean can be simply pictured. Earth's many rivers continuously transport various elements into the sea. Each of these elements resides for a certain amount of time in the ocean and then is removed by chemical reactions. The supply of every kind of atom is being constantly renewed, and the oceans may never be any less salty than they are today.

THE SCIENCE OF LIFE
Element Residence Times

Your body, like the oceans, constantly recycles atoms. Some of your body's cells, such as the lining of the intestines, are replaced every few days. You need fresh supplies of carbon, oxygen, and nitrogen every day to help replace these cells. Red blood cells last much longer—120 days on average—but you need a regular intake of iron to produce these important cells. Failure to digest

FIGURE 18-5 Dry salt deposits, such as these at the Great Salt Lake in Utah, occur when a body of salt water evaporates.

William Belknap / Science Source Images

enough iron can lead to anemia, a condition characterized by fatigue due to insufficient red blood cells.

Atoms in your bones and tendons last much longer—a decade or more, on average—but even those atoms are constantly being replaced. Gradual loss of calcium in bone, for example, is of special concern in older people who may not consume enough replacement calcium. Osteoporosis, a disease in which bones become weak and brittle, may result from this calcium deficiency (Figure 18-6). A similar loss of bone calcium affects astronauts who spend more than a few days in the weightless environment of space.

Some harmful elements, including lead, mercury, and other so-called heavy metals, do not easily recycle once taken into the body because we have no effective biological process to remove them. Their average residence times, in other words, are much longer than a human lifetime. Concentrations of these atoms can thus build up over time and can result in sickness or even death. You may hear about local efforts to test drinking water for high concentrations of lead that are sometimes found in old plumbing systems.

(a)

(b)

FIGURE 18-6 *(a)* Healthy porous bone requires constant replacement of calcium atoms, which recycle over periods of a decade or more. *(b)* Brittle bone disease (osteoporosis) occurs when calcium is not replaced and bones lose mass.

SCIENCE BY THE NUMBERS
The Ocean's Gold

We've just said that every element can be found in seawater. How much gold is there in a cubic kilometer of seawater?

According to Table 18-2, gold is present in the ocean at a concentration of 0.00005 parts per million (ppm). A concentration of 1 ppm corresponds to 1 milligram (mg) of a solid dissolved in a liter (l) of water. A liter is a volume measurement equal to a thousandth of a cubic meter (10^{-3} m³). The total amount of gold in a cubic meter of seawater, therefore, is 0.00005 milligrams per liter times 1,000 liters per meter cubed:

$$(0.00005 \text{ mg/l}) \times (1,000 \text{ l/m}^3) = 0.05 \text{ mg/m}^3$$

A gram contains 1,000 milligrams, so

$$(0.05 \text{ mg/m3}) \times (1 \text{ g/1,000 mg}) = 0.00005 \text{ g/m}^3$$

A cubic kilometer contains $(1,000 \text{ m}) \times (1,000 \text{ m}) \times (1,000 \text{ m}) = 10^9$ m³, so the total amount of gold in a cubic kilometer of seawater is

$$(10^9 \text{ m}^3) \times (0.00005 \text{ g/m}^3) = 5 \times 10^4 \text{ gm}$$

Every cubic kilometer of ocean water holds about 50,000 grams (about 100 pounds) of gold. At $1,500 an ounce, that much gold is worth close to three million dollars.

The total amount of gold dissolved in the world's oceans is vast, but no economical way to extract these riches is known. The equipment and energy required to process that much water would cost far more than the value of any gold recovered.

Ice Ages

From time to time, much of Earth's water supply becomes locked into glaciers that advance across land from the poles—a period called an **ice age**. We are now in the middle of an ice age, a period of several million years during which glaciers have repeatedly advanced and retreated. Within the present ice age we are living in an *interglacial period,* which is occurring between two major advances of glaciers. About 20,000 years ago, massive glaciers began to spread down from eastern and central Canada, covering a good deal of northern North America and reaching their maximum extent about 18,000 years ago. These glaciers then gradually receded to Greenland by about 10,000 years ago, as illustrated in Figure 18-7. Glaciers have come and gone many times, and periods of cyclic glaciation like the one in which we now live have occurred relatively often during the past 2 million years of Earth history.

The total amount of Earth's water is fixed, so as ice caps and glaciers grow, the amount of water available to fill the ocean basins decreases and the sea level drops. During the most recent maximum advance of glaciers about 18,000 years ago, for example, as much as 5% of Earth's water was locked into ice. Sea level dropped by more than 200 feet, to the point that the eastern coast of what is now the United States was about 150 miles (250 kilometers) farther east than it is today. A land bridge joining western North America and eastern Asia made it possible to walk from Alaska to Siberia. This land bridge provided a route that was taken by the ancestors of many Native Americans when they moved into the Americas from Siberia.

Milankovitch Cycles

Earth's rotation and orbit around the Sun determine both long-term and short-term variations in the climate. The single most important aspect of Earth's orbit is that the rotation axis is not perpendicular to its orbital plane but is tilted at an angle of 23.5°. This tilt is the cause of the seasons. We experience summer in the Northern Hemisphere when the North Pole is tilted toward the Sun, and winter when the North Pole is tilted away. That's why it's summer in the Southern Hemisphere when it's winter in the Northern Hemisphere (Figure 18-8).

FIGURE 18-7 This map shows the maximum extent of the most recent North American glaciation, approximately 18,000 years ago, as it appeared looking down on the North Pole. Arrows indicate the direction of the glaciers' advances across North America, Europe, and Asia. Because of the lower sea level a land bridge connected what is now Russia and North America.

The main causes of periodic glaciations, which occur on much longer timescales than the seasons, were first explained by Milutin Milankovitch (1879–1958), a Serbian civil engineer, in the early part of the twentieth century. His theory was simple: The relationship between Earth and Sun is affected by a number of variations in Earth's rotation and its orbit. These variations cause slight changes in the amount of solar radiation absorbed by Earth.

Perhaps the easiest of the orbital effects to understand is the precession of Earth's axis of rotation. If you have ever watched a child's top spinning, you know that sometimes as the top spins rapidly around its axis, the axis itself describes a lazy circle in space. This circular motion is called a *precession*. In the same way that a top may precess every second or two, Earth's tilted axis precesses once every 23,000 years (Figure 18-9a).

A second important factor in cycles of glaciation involves a slow change in the angle of the axis of rotation (it rocks back and forth by about a degree and a half every 41,000 years; Figure 18-9b). These changes affect the contrast in temperatures between summer and winter months: The bigger the tilt, the greater the contrast.

Additional effects have to do with Earth's slightly elliptical orbit. At present, Earth is closest to the Sun (about 91.5 million miles away) in early January and farthest away (about 94.5 million miles) in early July. That means Earth's axis is now oriented such that the Northern Hemisphere is tilted away from the Sun during the winter months (the period in which Earth is actually closest to the Sun). But this slightly elliptical orbit changes in two ways. First, the long axis of Earth's elliptical orbit slowly moves around the Sun owing to the gravitational effects of the other planets. Consequently, in about 11,500 years the Northern Hemisphere will be tilted toward the Sun when the Sun is closest to Earth, causing a larger contrast between average summer and winter temperatures than we experience today. In addition, the shape of Earth's elliptical orbit changes in a complex way as the result of gravitational effects from other planets. The orbit thus varies somewhat erratically over hundreds of thousands of years, from nearly circular to almost twice as elongated as the present orbit.

Milankovitch recognized all of these variables, and he proposed that the global climate varies in cycles (now called *Milankovitch cycles*) when these effects reinforce each other. If we find ourselves in a period of decreasing solar energy absorption and increased precipitation, more snow will fall in the winter and it will stay on the ground longer in the summer. Snow and ice reflect sunlight, so this extra snow and ice further cool Earth's surface, causing more snow to fall and snow to stay on the ground even longer. Thus, a decline in absorption of sunlight may trigger a sequence of events that can lead eventually to glacial advance. By the same token, a period of increased absorption of sunlight will result in warmer periods during which glaciers will tend to retreat.

FIGURE 18-8 Earth's orbit showing the relationship of tilt to the seasons. Summer occurs in the Northern Hemisphere when that hemisphere is tilted toward the Sun.

FIGURE 18-9 (a) The precession of Earth's axis and (b) small changes in the tilt of the axis contribute to recurring ice ages.

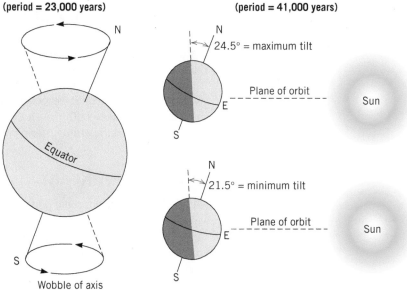

(a)

(b)

Several other factors play a role in controlling the extent and distribution of glaciers. Large glaciers can form only on landmasses, which gradually shift because of tectonic motion. The locations of mountain chains also play a significant role by altering wind and precipitation patterns. Recent evidence also suggests that the amount of volcanic dust and gases in the atmosphere can cause short-term changes in global temperatures. Finally, some scientists suspect that the energy output of the Sun is cyclical and that variations in the Sun's energy output impose a cyclical variation in Earth's temperature.

For the record, most scientists think that we are heading into a new phase of glacial advance within the next 10,000 years. This cooling trend may be offset for a time, however, by global warming that results from an enhanced greenhouse effect (see Chapter 19).

SCIENCE IN THE MAKING
Milankovitch Decides on His Life's Work

Milutin Milankovitch didn't seem to be headed toward a career in the sciences. Trained in Vienna as a civil engineer, he designed reinforced-concrete structures in central Europe prior to becoming a professor of mathematics in his native Belgrade just before World War I. Swept up in the nationalistic movements that were then (as now) prominent in the Balkans, he became friendly with some poets who specialized in writing patriotic verse. One evening, drinking coffee to celebrate a new book of verse, Milankovitch and his friends came to the attention of a banker at a neighboring table. The banker was so taken with the poems that he bought 10 copies on the spot.

With new money in their pockets, the friends celebrated with wine. After the first bottle, Milankovitch says in his journal, "I looked back on my earlier achievements and found them narrow and limited." By the third bottle, he had decided to "grasp the entire universe and spread light to its farthest corners."

He then methodically set apart a few hours each day to study and interpret climate records. Even during World War I, when he served as an engineer on the Serbian general staff and became a prisoner of war, he kept at it. A member of the Hungarian Academy of Sciences arranged for him to have a desk at the Academy after he gave his word of honor that he would not try to escape, and a good deal of the work described in the text was done under those conditions. The final work, published in 1920, was quickly recognized and accepted by the scientific community.

◉ 18.3 The Atmospheric Cycle

Earth's atmosphere and oceans play the most important role in redistributing heat across our planet's surface. The atmosphere also has chemical cycles involving oxygen and carbon, but those cycles are intimately bound up with the presence of living things on Earth, and we will wait to discuss them until we look at Earth's ecosystems (Chapter 19). The circulation of gases near Earth's surface—both the short-term variations of weather and the longer patterns of climate—is called the **atmospheric cycle**.

Air Masses: Reservoirs of the Atmosphere

At first glance, it might seem odd to speak of an atmospheric cycle. After all, the atmosphere appears to be one continuous mass of air rather than several different reservoirs. However, at any one time the atmosphere can be divided into many separate "air masses," each of which has more or less uniform properties. Each air mass can be thought of as a separate reservoir of air, and adjacent air masses differ in physical properties. Adjacent air masses may occupy different regions close to the ground, such as a low-pressure system in the Midwest and an adjacent high-pressure system off the New England coast. On the other hand, adjacent air masses may represent different atmospheric layers high above the surface.

In order to understand the properties of air masses, we need to define two closely related terms—weather and climate. **Weather**, on one hand, is the state of the atmosphere at a given time and place. At any given place, the weather is influenced by many factors and may be highly variable from day to day, not to mention from season to season. **Climate**, on the other hand, is a long-term average of weather for a given region. A regional climate may be hot or cold, wet or dry, though the weather on any given day might be quite different. Climate may remain unchanged for centuries, or it may shift quite dramatically, often for reasons that are as yet uncertain.

Weather

Five variables define the state of the atmosphere: temperature, air pressure, humidity, cloudiness, and prevailing winds. Your local weather report typically covers all of these variables.

FIGURE 18-10 A satellite photo of a low-pressure system that is centered over Ireland and moving toward the European continent. Notice the counterclockwise rotation of the air.

1. The *temperature* reported in daily weather predictions refers to temperature at ground level. Temperature varies strongly with altitude above the ground. In fact, the major layers of the atmosphere—regions such as the stratosphere and troposphere—are defined by these temperature variations.

2. The second variable that defines the state of the atmosphere is *pressure,* which decreases significantly with altitude because air is compressed by its own weight. At a height of 5.5 kilometers (about 3.5 miles or 18,000 feet), air pressure is only half of its value at sea level, whereas in the deepest South African gold mines air pressure approaches twice that of the surface. Pressure also varies laterally because air masses tend to move and rotate with respect to each other. Air piles up in some places to form a high-pressure system, while it stretches out in other places to form a low-pressure system (Figure 18-10). Air in low-pressure systems tends to rise, which causes cooling and increased clouds; conversely, high-pressure systems tend to feature warmer, dry air. Significant air pressure differences, which can arise at boundaries between layers high in the atmosphere, cause high-speed air currents called the **jet stream** (Figure 18-11). The jet stream moves west to east across the United States; it causes flights from New York to Los Angeles to average almost an hour longer than flights from Los Angeles to New York.

3. The third atmospheric variable is *humidity,* which is a measure of the atmosphere's highly variable water content. The bulk composition of the atmosphere is remarkably uniform;

FIGURE 18-11 The jet stream is a fast-moving, high-altitude air current above North America. (a) The jet stream often follows a relatively straight path, with minor undulations. (b) Strongly developed undulations may pull a mass of cold arctic air to the south.

Jet stream with small undulations

Strongly-developed undulations pull a trough of cold air south

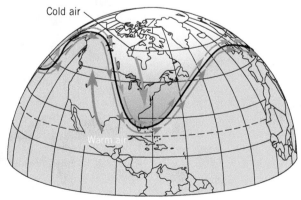

(a)

(b)

nitrogen and oxygen make up 99% of dry atmosphere. The atmosphere also always contains some water vapor, though the amount is highly variable, depending on the temperature and relative humidity. Air on a cold, dry winter day might hold less than 0.1% water by volume, whereas air on a hot, humid summer day may contain several percent water by volume.

4. *Cloudiness,* the fourth weather variable, is closely tied to humidity. Clouds are a concentration of tiny water droplets or ice crystals. These substances scatter light, so clouds appear white. Clouds form when air becomes saturated with water—a process that often occurs when a mass of air rises and cools. Clouds often dramatically outline the contact between two adjacent air masses. A band of clouds may mark a front, where two air masses at different temperatures collide near ground level. Dramatic anvil-shaped thunderhead clouds often form when a warmer air mass contacts a cooler air mass. The warmer air mass is less dense, and so it rides up over the cooler air. This increase in elevation cools the warm, wet air, causing clouds and rain. Large gradients in temperature and pressure generate strong winds and violent lightning. Similarly, clouds and rain often form on the windward side of mountain ranges as an air mass is forced to rise up the mountain flanks. The side of the island away from the wind, for example, is usually much drier (Figure 18-12). Some mountainous areas of Hawai'i receive more than 400 inches of rain per year on the eastern side, while experiencing near-arid conditions a few kilometers away on the western slopes.

5. The fifth atmospheric variable is the direction and strength of *winds.* Winds are a consequence of atmospheric convection—a process that helps to redistribute heat. Ocean breezes on a tranquil summer day illustrate how winds can occur. During a sunny day, the land heats up more than water, so warmer air rises from the land and cooler air flows in from the water, producing a refreshing sea breeze. In the evening, as the land cools, the pattern reverses; warmer air over the water rises and the breeze comes from the land.

The General Circulation of the Atmosphere

The atmosphere circulates in vast rivers of air that cover the globe from the equator to the poles. These prevailing winds arise in much the same way as local winds, though on a much larger scale. As in local winds, this circulation is powered by the energy of the Sun. Air in the tropics is heated and rises. If Earth did not rotate, we would expect to have a situation like the one shown in Figure 18-13. Warm air would rise at the equator, cool off, and sink at the poles. This pattern of flow is the familiar convection cell we saw in Chapter 4. Such a pattern arises whenever a fluid is heated nonuniformly in a gravitational field.

FIGURE 18-12 Clouds and rain often form on the windward side of mountain ranges as an air mass is forced to rise up the mountain flanks (blue arrows). The side of the island away from the wind is usually much drier (red arrow).

Gary Hincks/SPL/Photo Researchers, Inc.

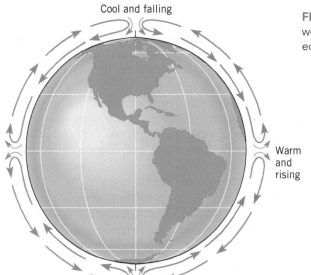

Cool and falling

Warm and rising

FIGURE 18-13 If Earth did not rotate, the circulation of the atmosphere would take place in convection cells that create high-altitude winds from equator to pole, and low-altitude winds from pole to equator.

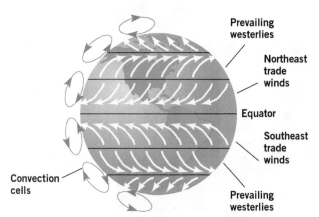

Prevailing westerlies

Northeast trade winds

Equator

Southeast trade winds

Prevailing westerlies

Convection cells

FIGURE 18-14 Atmospheric convection on the rotating Earth contrasts with that for a nonrotating planet (see Figure 18-13). A series of band-like air circulation cells develop. Compare this diagram with the photograph of Jupiter in Chapter 16.

If Earth did not rotate, prevailing winds in the Northern Hemisphere would flow from north to south. Actually, they do nothing of the kind. The weather patterns in much of the Northern Hemisphere, including North America, move, in general, from west to east—we live in a region of what meteorologists call *prevailing westerlies*. This behavior of Earth's atmosphere results from the fact that Earth rotates. This rotation breaks the north–south atmospheric convection cell that would exist in its absence into three cells in each hemisphere, as shown in Figure 18-14. In addition, the rotation "stretches out" the shape of the air circulation pattern in each cell. In the cell nearest the equator, the winds at the surface tend to blow from east to west—the so-called *trade winds* that drove sailing ships from Europe to North America. In temperate zones, the effect is to cause the winds to blow from west to east, creating regions in which weather patterns also usually move from west to east. Finally, in the Arctic and Antarctic, the winds blow once again from east to west.

Similar patterns of atmospheric motion can be seen on all the planets in the solar system that have atmospheres. In some cases, like the planet Jupiter, the rapid rotation of the planet and the atmospheric dynamics cause more than three convection cells. Rapidly rotating Jupiter has no fewer than 11 separate east–west bands between its north and south poles.

Common Storms and Weather Patterns

Many kinds of severe weather conditions affect our world. *Tropical storms* are severe storms that start as low-pressure areas over warm ocean water. They draw energy from the warm water, growing and rotating in great *cyclonic* patterns hundreds of kilometers in diameter. Tropical storms that begin in the Atlantic Ocean off the coast of Africa or in the Caribbean Sea and affect North America are called *hurricanes;* those that begin in the North Pacific were once called *typhoons,* though they are often now called hurricanes by weather forecasters (Figure 18-15). Until recently, these violent weather systems frequently hit unprotected coastlines with little warning. Today, weather satellites spot and track tropical storms long before they approach land. In 2005, when Hurricane Katrina approached the New Orleans area, residents received several days' warning, allowing many of them to get out of the way of the storm.

Tornadoes, much smaller-scale phenomena than hurricanes, are rotating air funnels some tens to hundreds of meters across. Tornadoes descend from storm clouds to the ground, causing intense damage along the path where the funnel touches the ground (Figure 18-16). The largest tornadoes, with air speeds in excess of 500 kilometers (about 300 miles) per hour, are the most violent weather phenomenon known.

El Niño, a weather cycle that recurs every four to seven years, affects weather from the Pacific Basin to the Atlantic Coast. The name means Christ Child and comes from the fact that the

FIGURE 18-15 Satellite photo of Hurricane Wilma entering the Gulf of Mexico, taken in October 2005. Mexico's Yucatán Peninsula is at the lower left of the photo. Wilma was a category 5 hurricane, the strongest and most damaging type of storm.

Science Source/Photo Researchers, Inc.

FIGURE 18-16 Tornadoes descend from violent storm clouds to the ground, causing intense damage along the path where the funnel touches the ground.

phenomenon, when it happens, usually begins around Christmastime. El Niño can cause severe storms and flooding all along the western coast of the Americas, and drought from Australia to India. El Niño, which requires both winds and ocean currents to develop, is an example of a coupling between two of Earth's cycles—in this case, the atmospheric and water cycles. Here's what happens: Normally, the winds off the coast of Peru blow westward. They move the warm ocean water westward, like water sloshing in a bathtub, to the western Pacific. As the surface water moves west, the colder, nutrient-rich water from the deep ocean wells up and supports marine life and fish-eating birds. Because the eastern Pacific is cooler, the atmosphere cools and descends there, forming a zone of high pressure and dry weather off the coast of South America. Meanwhile, the western Pacific is warmer, so air warms and rises above that region in a rainy, low-pressure zone.

Every 4 to 7 years, however, this pattern changes, signifying the beginning of an El Niño event. Warm surface water sloshes to the east, the water temperature in the eastern Pacific increases by a few degrees, and the normal atmospheric patterns switch places. Westerly winds replace the normally easterly flowing trade winds. This wind reversal reinforces the movement of warm water eastward to the coast of South America, where air warms and rises, creating rainy conditions. The marine life and birds are no longer supported by the nutrients of the cold, deep water. The western Pacific becomes relatively cool and dry. Eventually, the water sloshes back and the whole cycle repeats itself. Historical records tell us that this cycle has been repeating in the Pacific Basin since the 1600s and may have been going on since the last ice age.

Climate

Climate, as opposed to weather, seldom changes much on the scale of human lifetimes. In spite of many uncertainties about climate change, several factors that strongly influence regional climate are now well documented. Large bodies of water and ocean currents, such as the Gulf Stream, can greatly change a region's climate by transferring heat. Oceans and large lakes can also add moisture to an air mass. Northwest New York State, for example, receives heavy rains and snows as Canadian air masses pass over the Great Lakes. Mountain ranges disrupt the movement of air masses and can efficiently remove moisture from an air mass. We have seen how tall mountains on Hawai'i affect rainfall; nearby locations on opposite sides of a volcanic mountain can have radically different rainfalls.

These effects of oceans and mountains on climate reveal that movements of tectonic plates play a major long-term role in Earth's climate. As plates move, bodies of water open and close and mountain ranges are formed. In addition, the presence of continents near one or both poles strongly influences the severity of ice ages because thick accumulations of ice require a solid base. Thus, Earth's atmospheric cycle is strongly influenced by other global cycles.

 THE ONGOING PROCESS OF SCIENCE
How Steady Is Earth's Climate?

Through most of recorded history, Earth's climate has been pretty much as we know it today, but recorded history covers only 4,000 years—a blink of an eye in geological time—and detailed records of weather have been kept for only a few centuries. Until recently, scientists assumed that climate change always happened slowly in response to factors such as the tectonic movement of the continents. However, since the early 1990s thinking on this subject has started to change. It turns out that Earth's climate can change more drastically, and more quickly, than anyone had realized.

Key evidence came from deep-sea cores drilled in the floor of the North Atlantic Ocean. During times corresponding to the last ice age, scientists found layers of rocks in these cores, spaced between 7,000 and 11,000 years apart, that are identical to rocks found in northern Canada. The first clue as to what these layers might mean came from geophysicist Douglas MacAyael at the University of Chicago. His explanation was based on the behavior of the ice sheets that covered North America and the rock underneath them. Over most of northeastern Canada, the underlying rock is hard and strong. In Hudson Bay, however, the rock is softer. MacAyael's calculations showed that when the ice over Hudson Bay piled up several miles deep, the soft underlying rock would fracture and, when mixed with melted water, turn into a layer about the consistency of toothpaste. When this happened, the ice sheet would slide out to sea and huge armadas of glaciers would sail out into the North Atlantic. In this scheme, the mysterious Canadian rocks were simply material incorporated into the icebergs that dropped to the ocean floor whenever the iceberg melted.

However, from the point of view of climate stability, the important thing about these events is that they are accompanied by huge swings in temperature—the data seem to indicate that the average temperatures changed by 5°C (9°F) in a matter of 10 years or so. For reference, this change would be roughly like suddenly moving the climate of Florida to Boston. The most likely explanation is that the fresh water added to the North Atlantic by melting ice temporarily shut down the ocean currents that distribute heat around the globe and that these currents stayed "off" until the water had been mixed and become salty again.

Since the discovery of the first of these sudden climate swings during the last ice age, scientists have found evidence for many more. Today, scientists are trying to understand how sudden changes in climate can be caused not only by glaciers, but also by changes in the brightness of the Sun and a host of other effects. It appears that our comfortable view of a stable Earth won't survive long as we unravel the history of the climate.

Understanding Climate

Although the daily weather is often dominated by the position of the jet stream and the creation of high- and low-pressure zones, the long-term climate depends on more lasting features of Earth's surface. These factors include the distribution of heat due to the stabilizing temperature of oceans, and the presence of mountains, which force air masses up over them. The climate is also extremely sensitive to the amount of sunlight that falls on the atmosphere and the amount of heat that is radiated back to space.

At the moment, our best attempts at predicting long-term climate depend on complex computer models of the atmosphere called *global circulation models (GCMs)*. In a typical GCM, a computer splits the world's surface into squares ranging from 250 to 600 kilometers on a side, slices the atmosphere into 10 to 20 vertical compartments and the oceans into as many as 30 layers. In each of these boxes, the laws of motion and thermodynamics are used to calculate the amount of heat that flows in and out, how much water vapor comes out of the air, and so on. The computer balances the inflow and outflow from all of the boxes in the atmosphere and projects forward in time to try to predict long-term climate trends. Our current models are still rather crude (they have a great deal of difficulty accounting for the effects of clouds, for example), but they represent the best attempts to date to understand what factors affect Earth's climate. These models also play a critical role in discussing various types of ecological changes such as global warming (see Chapter 19).

TECHNOLOGY
Doppler Radar

Radar has been a vital tool for weather forecasters for decades, and you may see radar maps of local weather conditions on TV every night. The way radar works is simple. A central antenna sends out microwaves, which are reflected back if they encounter objects such as raindrops, snowflakes, or ice in the air. Each kind of material produces a distinct pattern of reflected waves because its density is different from that of the surrounding air. These reflection patterns are used to assemble a map of local storm activity.

Ordinary radar, however, cannot detect winds, even winds of high velocity, because the densities of moving air and stationary air are usually not very different. Therefore, the same reflection pattern occurs, whatever the wind speed. But in many situations it's important to detect

FIGURE 18-17 A computerized radar weather map shows areas of cloud cover and precipitation.

air currents. Near airports, for example, sudden downdrafts create violent air turbulence called *wind shear*, an extremely dangerous condition that we need to be able to detect.

Doppler radar is designed to detect motions of the air by using the Doppler effect (see Chapter 6). It works like this: Reflected waves are analyzed not only for their intensity, as in ordinary radar, but for their frequency as well. From the difference between the emitted and reflected frequencies, an analysis of the Doppler effect yields the velocity of the object from which the wave was reflected. In this way, high winds and atmospheric turbulence can be detected at a safe distance (Figure 18-17). As you might expect, Doppler radar requires powerful computers and is much more expensive than ordinary radar, but the increased safety is well worth the expense.

◉ 18.4 The Rock Cycle

When Earth formed there were no rocks. About 4.5 billion years ago, the great bombardment—the process that built Earth from the solar nebula (see Chapter 16)—released prodigious amounts of energy as swarms of meteorites crashed into the growing planet, converting gravitational potential energy into heat. That heat produced a molten ball orbiting the Sun. There was no land, no oceans, and no atmosphere. Only when the bombardment subsided and Earth began to cool did rocks appear. First, as the temperature dropped below the melting point of surface rocks, the outer crust of Earth gradually solidified like the first layer of ice on a pond in winter. Then, when surface temperatures dropped below the boiling point of water, the first rains must have fallen. Together, these two events began the **rock cycle**, a cycle of internal and external Earth processes by which rock is created, destroyed, and altered (Figure 18-18).

Rock *formations,* which are bodies of rocks that form as a continuous unit, may be thought of as the "reservoirs" of the rock cycle. The atoms that make up the solid Earth spend most of their lives cycling among igneous, sedimentary, and metamorphic rocks—three principal types of rocks that differ in the processes by which they are formed.

Igneous Rocks

Igneous rocks, which solidify from a hot liquid and thus were the first solids to appear on Earth's ancient surface, come in two principal types. **Volcanic** or **extrusive rocks** solidify on the surface in what are by far the most spectacular of all rock-forming events, volcanic eruptions. Red-hot fountains and flows of lava ooze down the slopes of the growing volcanic cone. The most common variety of volcanic rock is *basalt,* a dark, even-textured rock rich in oxides of silicon, magnesium, iron, calcium, and aluminum (Figure 18-19). Basalt makes up most of the rock in Hawaii, as well as most of the new material formed at mid-ocean ridges. Other volcanoes feature rocks richer in silicon; if these magmas mix with a significant amount of water or other volatile (easily boiled) substance, the volcanic rock can become the frothy rock called *pumice.*

Igneous rocks that harden underground are called **intrusive rocks.** Dark-colored basalt often exploits underground cracks near volcanoes to form layers or sheets of igneous rock. The Palisades on the Hudson River near New York City formed in this way. Lighter in color and density, *granite* is perhaps the most common intrusive rock in Earth's crust (Figure 18-20). Hard, durable granite, with its attractive pink or gray colors and speckled array of light and dark minerals, makes an ideal ornamental building stone. New England is particularly famous for its many fine granite quarries.

Igneous rocks are still being formed on Earth—for example, when new plate material is formed at diverging boundaries (see Chapter 17) or in active volcanoes. In other places, such as the Yellowstone Park region, hot springs and geysers reveal hidden sources of underground heat and may indicate places where intrusive igneous rocks are forming today.

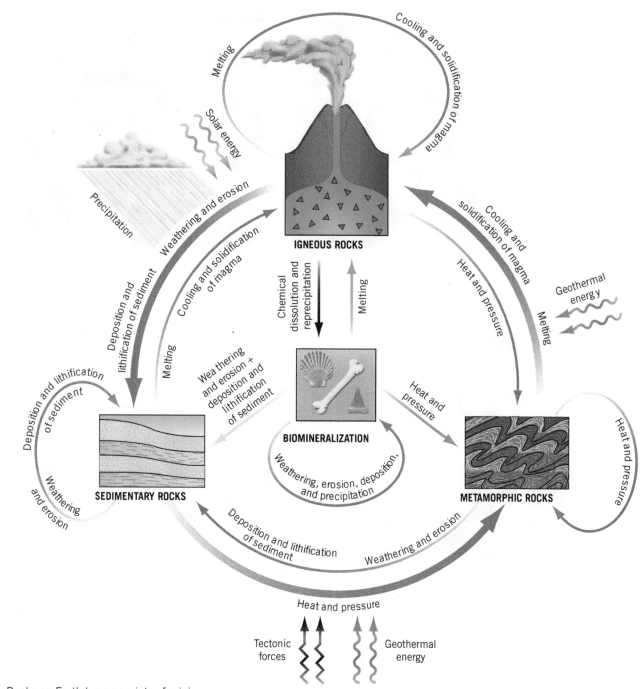

Rocks on Earth have a variety of origins:
- Crystallization of magma (**IGNEOUS**),
- Deposition of particles weathered and eroded from preexisting rocks (**SEDIMENTARY**),
- Biologic precipitation (**BIOMINERALIZATION**),
- Alteration of preexisting rocks (**METAMORPHISM**).

Biomineralization is commonly considered a sedimentary process.

FIGURE 18-18 The rock cycle.

Sedimentary Rocks

When the first rains began to fall on the first igneous rocks, the process of *weathering* began. Small grains washed off the recently hardened volcanic rocks, flowed down through streams and rivers toward the seas, and were deposited in shallow lakes and on the ocean floor. Weathering also occurred as water dissolved rocks and by the mechanical action of water freezing in

FIGURE 18-19 (a) Devil's Tower in Wyoming represents the neck of a would-be volcano that may have never quite reached the surface. The surrounding sediments have subsequently eroded away. (b) Igneous rocks solidify from molten rock.

(a)   (b)

FIGURE 18-20 Granite from a quarry in Barre, Vermont, solidified from magma deep underground.

cracks. Over time, layers of sediment accumulated, especially at the mouths of rivers near the shores of Earth's new oceans. As more and more sediment collected, these layers became thicker and thicker. In many places on Earth right now—the Mississippi River Delta that extends into the Gulf of Mexico, for example—layers of sediment may reach several kilometers in thickness.

As the first sediments were buried deeper, they were subjected to increased temperature and pressure. In addition, water flowed through the layers of sediments, dissolving and redepositing glue-like chemicals—something like the crusty deposits that can build up on an ordinary faucet when water drips continuously. The net result of all of these processes—pressure, heat, and the effects of mineral-laden water—was to weld the bits of sediment together into new layered rocks. This kind of rock, appropriately called **sedimentary rock**, is made up of grains of material worn off previous rocks. Other common sedimentary rocks, including salt deposits, may form from layers of chemical precipitates.

Although uniform sedimentary rocks can form at the base of a single mountain or cliff, the collection of grains often comes together from many different places. The grains in a single fragment of sedimentary rock being formed in the Mississippi Delta, for example, may have come from a cliff in Minnesota, a valley in Pennsylvania, and a mountain in Texas. Similarly, sediments deposited near the mouth of the Colorado River carry bits of history from much of the North American West. Deltas inevitably contain particles from all rocks in their rivers' drainage area.

As you travel across the United States, you will encounter many common varieties of sedimentary rock (Figure 18-21a). They're easy to spot in road cuts and outcrops because of their characteristic layered appearance, like the pages of a book or a many-layered cake. *Sandstone* forms mostly from sand-sized grains of quartz (silicon dioxide or SiO_2), the most common mineral at the beach, and from other hard mineral and rock fragments. Sandstone often formed from ancient beaches, deserts, or streambeds—places where concentrations of sand are found today. Sandstone usually feels rough to your touch, and you can just barely see the individual grains that have been cemented together.

Shale and *mudstone* form from sediments that are much finer grained than sand. These rocks commonly accumulate beneath the calm waters of lakes or in the deep-ocean basins—places often teeming with life. There organisms, both large and small, die and are buried in muddy ooze, where they may eventually form into fossils that provide us with much information about the evolution of life on Earth (see Chapter 25).

Limestone, another distinctive type of sedimentary rock, forms from the calcium carbonate ($CaCO_3$) skeletons of sea animals or from chemical precipitation directly from ocean water.

(a)

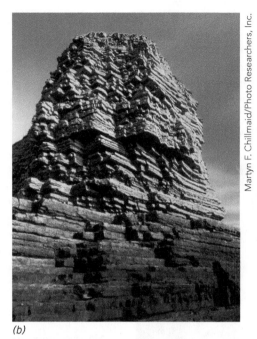
(b)

FIGURE 18-21 (a) A spectacular example of sedimentary rocks in Utah. The different colored bands correspond to layers of different kinds of materials that were deposited on the floor of a long-vanished ocean. The surrounding sediments have been eroded away to provide material for new sedimentary rocks downstream. (b) Limestone is a distinctive type of sedimentary rock that forms from the calcium carbonate shells of sea animals or by chemical precipitation from ocean water. These deposits are located in Chattanooga, Tennessee, far from the nearest ocean.

Some limestone grows from a gradual rain of microscopic debris or broken shells, whereas others represent a coral reef that spreads across the floor of a shallow sea. Like shale and mudstone, limestone commonly bears fossils.

Given what we know about plate tectonics and about the constant movement of materials around Earth's surface, it should come as no surprise that just because sedimentary rocks originally formed at the bottom of the ocean, they have not necessarily stayed there since their formation. Indeed, it's not at all unusual to see sedimentary rocks in mountain passes thousands of meters above the ocean, or in the middle of continents thousands of kilometers from the nearest open water. Spectacular limestone formations form cliffs above Chattanooga, Tennessee, mountains near El Paso, Texas, and the heart of the Canadian Rockies, all far removed from the ocean (Figure 18-21b).

One of the best places to get an appreciation of sedimentary rocks is at the beach. If you pick up a handful of sand, you'll notice that each grain is different. Some are dark colored, some are light. Some have sharp, angular edges, some are smooth and worn down (Figure 18-22). Each of these grains of sand was once was part of a rock in a drainage system of the rivers that feed into the ocean. As the rock weathered away, each grain was chipped off and carried to the sea by wind and water. Eventually, the grains of sand you hold in your hand will be formed into solid rock and subjected to the forces of plate tectonics. That sandstone may someday be uplifted to an altitude far above sea level, where the grain may be weathered again and start the whole cycle all over. Each grain of sand in your hand, then, may have made the trip from rock to beach to sandstone many times in its history.

The story of the grain of sand provides a good model for the way materials move about Earth's surface. The atoms of rocks, just like those of the air, water, or your body, are always shifting around, but it is always the same matter—the same atoms—recycling.

FIGURE 18-22 A microscopic view of a handful of sand, here magnified approximately 50 times, reveals grains of many different sizes, shapes, and colors.

THE SCIENCE OF LIFE
Coral Reefs

Coral reefs are the abodes of countless billions of creatures that build their homes, bit by bit, from calcium carbonate (Figure 18-23). Reefs thrive in shallow, clear, ocean water with temperatures above 18°C (about 64°F). *The Pelican Island* by British poet James Montgomery (1771–1854) captures the extraordinary phenomenon of entire oceanic islands rising from this biological process:

I saw the living pile ascend,
The mausoleum of its architects,
Still dying upwards as their labours closed;
Slime the material, but the slime was turn'd
To adamant, by their petrific touch;
Frail were their frames, ephemeral their lives,
Their masonry imperishable. . . .
Atom by atom, thus their burthen grew,
Even like an infant in the womb, till Time
Deliver'd ocean of that monstrous birth,
— A coral island, stretching east and west.

Massive limestone reefs like the one in Montgomery's poem once thrived in ancient shallow seas of New York, Illinois, Montana, Texas, and many other places where limestone ridges or mountains now stand.

FIGURE 18-23 Coral reefs form in the shallow waters around many Pacific islands.

Metamorphic Rocks

It may happen that sedimentary rocks are slowly buried deep within our planet, where they are subjected to intense pressure and heat. There they will be turned into yet another kind of rock, transformed by Earth's extreme conditions into **metamorphic rock**. If a shale or mudstone formation is buried like this it may eventually turn into a brittle, hard *slate*, the kind of rock from which roofing shingles (Figure 18-24a) and school blackboards used to be made. Even higher temperatures and pressures can transform slate into spectacularly banded rocks, called *schists* and *gneisses*, which often boast fine crystals of garnets and other high-pressure minerals.

FIGURE 18-24 *(a)*. Slate is a brittle, layered metamorphic rock that is commonly used for roofing material. *(b)* The Grand Teton Mountains in Wyoming feature intensely folded metamorphic rocks. These rocks have been altered by high pressure and temperature deep within Earth's crust, and then uplifted and eroded into mountains.

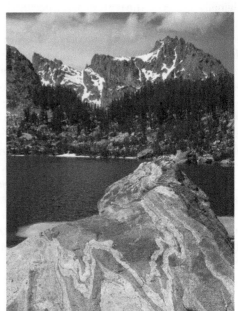

(a)   *(b)*

Roadcuts and outcrops of these metamorphic rocks can look like an intensely folded cloth or a giant cross section of swirled marble cake (Figure 18-24b). Sandstone, when exposed to high temperature and pressure, also metamorphoses, recrystallizing to a durable rock in which the original sand grains fuse into a solid mass known as *quartzite*.

The Story of Marble

Of all the metamorphic rocks, none tells a more astonishing tale than *marble*, a rock of extraordinary beauty. If you ever travel the roads of Vermont, chances are you will pass an outcrop or roadcut of distinctive greenish-white cast, a rock with intricate bands and swirls. These marbles take a high polish and have been prized for centuries by sculptors and architects (Figure 18-25). But no works of humans can match the epic process that formed the stone.

Most marble began as limestone, which is a rock type that originates primarily from the skeletal remains of sea life. Over the ages, limestone in the area we now call Vermont was buried deeper and deeper, crushed under the weight of many kilometers' thickness of sand, shale, and more limestone in an ancient sea. But no ocean or sea can last forever on our dynamic planet. An ancient collision of the Eurasian and North American Plates compressed and deformed this ocean basin, crumpling the layered rock into tight folds and subjecting the sedimentary pile to intense temperatures and pressures. The buckled and contorted formations were uplifted to high elevations when the Appalachian Mountains formed several hundred million years ago. During the intense pressures and high temperatures associated with the converging tectonic plates, the limestone was metamorphosed to the marble that we use today. Many millions of years of erosion and uplift have exposed these ancient rocks, which are gradually weathering away to begin the cycle again. And humans, in a futile quest for immortality, quarry the marble for their monuments and tombstones and other transient reminders of Earth's incessant change.

Igneous, sedimentary, and metamorphic rocks all participate in the rock cycle. Igneous rocks, once formed, can be weathered to form sedimentary rocks, or they can undergo metamorphism. Layers of sedimentary rocks also can be transformed into metamorphic rocks. All three kinds of rocks can be subducted into Earth's interior, partially melted, and re-formed as new igneous rocks. Thus the rock cycle never ceases.

FIGURE 18-25 The Lincoln Memorial is one of many famous monuments carved from marble, a metamorphosed limestone.

SCIENCE IN THE MAKING
Hutton and the Discovery of "Deep Time"

Near the town of Jedburgh in Scotland is a curious cliff that reveals vertical layers of rock overlain by horizontal layers (Figure 18-26). How could such a sequence have occurred? In the last decades of the eighteenth century, Scottish scientist James Hutton (1726–1797), a man who is often called "the father of modern geology," studied this remarkable cliff and realized that he was seeing the result of an incredibly long period of geological turmoil.

Knowing what you now know about sedimentary rocks, you will realize when you look at this cliff that you are seeing the end product of a long chain of events (Figure 18-27). First, a series of sedimentary rocks was laid down in the usual horizontal fashion, one flat layer on top of another. Then some tectonic activity disrupted those layers, breaking and folding them until they were tilted nearly vertically. Then, after still more tectonic activity, the rocks found themselves at the bottom of an ocean and another layer of sedimentary rocks formed on top of them. Finally, an episode of uplift and erosion has brought the rocks to our view.

Hutton realized that geological forces must have been operating for very long times indeed. Each step of the formation process—gradual sedimentation, burial, folding, uplift, more sedimentation, and so on—would require countless generations, based on observations of ongoing geological processes. In the words

FIGURE 18-26 James Hutton recognized the immense spans of time required to form this spectacular outcrop at Siccar Point, near Jedburgh in Scotland.

Gradual sedimentation

(a)

Burial and deformation

(b)

Uplift and erosion

(c)

Gradual sedimentation

(d)

FIGURE 18-27 This series of diagrams shows several stages in the history of the Jedburgh outcrop. *(a)* Layers of sediment were gradually deposited in water. *(b)* Those sediments, deeply buried, were compressed and tilted during tectonic activity. *(c)* Uplift brought the tilted sediments to the surface, where they were partly eroded. *(d)* The rocks subsided, and a new cycle of sedimentation began.

of nature writer John McPhee, Hutton had discovered "deep time." In order for a formation like the one at Jedburgh to exist, Earth had to exist not for thousands of years or even hundreds of thousands of years, but for many millions of years.

Today, we know that Earth's age is calculated in billions of years, and the existence of structures like the one at Jedburgh is not surprising. At the time of its interpretation by James Hutton, however, the rocks at Jedburgh provided a totally new insight into the inconceivable antiquity of our planet.

In the words of Hutton himself, the testimony of the rocks offered "no vestige of a beginning, no prospect of an end."

The Interdependence of Earth's Cycles

We have described the hydrologic, atmospheric, and rock cycles as if they were largely independent of each other, as if they operated alone in splendid isolation. In fact, each cycle affects and is affected by the others.

The amount of rainfall in a given location affects the rate of erosion and thus the amount of sediment being deposited in deltas—and therefore the amount of sedimentary rock being formed. In this way, the atmospheric and water cycles affect the rock cycle. In the same way, the breakdown of rock is essential to the formation of soils in which plants grow. The presence of plants, in turn, affects the absorption of sunlight at Earth's surface and thus the energy balance that controls the movement of the winds and ocean currents. And, over hundreds of millions of years, the global cycle of plate tectonics, which controls the distribution of Earth's mountains and oceans, influences all other cycles. Thus, although Earth's cycles operate on very different timescales, they constantly influence each other.

THINKING MORE ABOUT CYCLES

Beach Erosion

Something about the shore appeals to people. Beachfront property is considered to be highly desirable, and over the past half-century America's prosperity has resulted in large-scale development of the Atlantic, Pacific, and Gulf of Mexico coastlines. As a result, Americans are becoming very aware of the effects of natural cycles on property values.

Beaches, like all other systems in nature, are not static but change in response to environmental forces. The action of waves transports sand grains from one place and deposits them somewhere else. Large waves tend to move sand away from a beach and deposit it in offshore bars, whereas smaller waves tend to move the sand back toward the beach. Thus, a seasonal movement of sand occurs on many beaches—offshore in the winter (when storms send in large waves) and onshore during the summer. In addition, waves normally strike a beach at a slight angle, a phenomenon that moves sand along the beachfront. Large storms may completely destroy beaches and dunes, which are rebuilt farther inland over time. Thus every beach is a dynamic, shifting system. Left to itself, a beach will move around in response to the forces of wave and storm.

If the beach were left to itself, this cycle of change would cause no problems. If, however, waterfront properties worth many millions of dollars have been developed on or near the beach, such movements have enormous economic consequences for homeowners and developers (Figure 18-28). Should governments use public funds to try to protect such homes? Should the government provide low-cost insurance to indemnify the owners for loss? Should insurance be issued to allow people to rebuild beachfront homes after a storm?

FIGURE 18-28 Large coastal storms cause millions of dollars in damage to shorefront homes every year.

The News & Observer, Robert Miller/©AP/Wide World Photos

← RETURN TO THE INTEGRATED QUESTION

Will we ever run out of fresh water?

- The term *fresh water* refers to any source of water that contains low concentrations of dissolved salts. Fresh water includes bodies of water such as lakes and rivers, as well as the polar ice caps and glaciers.

- Fresh water is a vitally important renewable natural resource. Because most species cannot drink salt water, it is an indispensable ecological component for the continued survival of terrestrial organisms (i.e., land-dwelling plants and animals).

- Although Earth's water supply is vast, only a small portion is available for human use. Approximately 97.5 % of the world's water is either brackish or saline (i.e., salty). Most of the remaining 2.5% is locked in glaciers and ice caps. This leaves less than 1% that can be accessed for human needs.

  - Fresh water is used for many human activities ranging from drinking to agriculture.

  - The United Nations estimates that over one billion people do not have access to fresh drinking water.

- The ultimate source of fresh water is the hydrologic cycle. Evaporation from the oceans, rivers, and streams eventually falls to Earth as precipitation, usually in the form of rain, sleet, or snow.

  - Some of this precipitation returns to the oceans relatively quickly via rivers and streams. The rest percolates into the ground and becomes part of groundwater aquifers. It is estimated that 99% of the nonglacial fresh water is contained in underground aquifers.

- Modern society places tremendous demands upon these aquifers.

  - We often drill deep into these aquifers to supply water for human and livestock consumption, industry, and agriculture.

  - In North America, total per capita water consumption is well over 500,000 gallons per year.

  - These aquifers are a renewable, but limited resource. They may have taken thousands of years to fill, and yet can be drained in a few decades.

  - As more freshwater is extracted each year, the potential for a shortage of freshwater becomes a distinct and troubling possibility.

SUMMARY

Matter that forms Earth's outer layers follows many cycles, driven by the energy of the Sun and Earth's inner heat energy. Each cycle can be analyzed in terms of *reservoirs* that hold matter and by the movement of matter between reservoirs.

The *hydrologic cycle* traces the path of water as it evaporates from the oceans, falls back to Earth as rain, and forms lakes, rivers, *ice caps, glaciers,* and *groundwater* reservoirs. During unusually cold climatic periods, more water falls as snow, creating a white reflective blanket that further reduces the amount of absorbed solar radiation. This situation, if prolonged, can lead to an *ice age,* during which ocean levels drop significantly and great sheets of ice cover the land at high and middle latitudes. Temperatures in these latitudes may be moderated, however, by ocean *currents* that are important in redistributing temperatures at Earth's surface.

The *atmospheric cycle* of the *weather* redistributes solar energy from the warmer equatorial regions to higher latitudes through the development of global convection cells of air. The prevailing westerly flow of weather across North America marks one of these large cells, while the *jet stream* delineates the boundary between this flow and the contrary cell to our north. *Climate,* in contrast to weather, varies much more slowly in response to ocean circulation, the Sun's energy output, the positions of continents and mountain ranges, and other relatively fixed conditions.

The solid materials of Earth's crust are subject to the *rock cycle.* The first solids to form on the cooling planet were *igneous rocks,* which are formed from hot, molten material. *Volcanic* or *extrusive* igneous rocks solidify on the surface, while *intrusive* igneous rocks cool underground. The first igneous rocks were subjected to weathering by wind and rain, which eventually produced layers of sediment and the first *sedimentary rocks.* Sandstone, shale, limestone, and other sedimentary rocks were deposited in ocean basins, layer upon layer, in sequences often many kilometers thick. Igneous and sedimentary rocks were subsequently buried and transformed by Earth's internal temperature and pressure to form *metamorphic rocks.* Each of the three major rock types—igneous, sedimentary, and metamorphic—can be converted into the others by the ongoing processes of the rock cycle.

KEY TERMS

reservoirs	current	jet stream	sedimentary rock
hydrologic cycle	ice age	rock cycle	metamorphic rock
ice caps	atmospheric cycle	igneous rock	
glaciers	weather	volcanic or extrusive rock	
groundwater	climate	intrusive rock	

DISCOVERY LAB

The hydrological cycle is a continuous process in which water moves between Earth's surface and atmosphere. For simulating the water cycle, you will need a 1-liter plastic soda bottle (or any 1-liter plastic juice bottle), a heat lamp with a 40-watt bulb, ice in a Ziploc bag, a 100- or 250-milliliter beaker, and food coloring.

Make a 1-inch hole about halfway in the bottle. Put about 200 mL of water in the bottle and close the cap tightly. Position the bottle with the help of support at an angle of 30°. (Tilt the side of the bottle with the hole.) Put the beaker under the hole of the bottle. Focus the lamp so that it heats the water in the bottle. Place ice cubes in the Ziploc bag. Put the bag with ice on the top end of the bottle and secure it. Make initial observations.

Place the lamp at a safe distance from the bottle so that there is no fire hazard. Turn on the lamp. When the water cycle starts, make your observations again. It will take several hours for the process to begin.

After observing the entire cycle, add food color to the water. Make observations before and after adding food color.

What process is started when you place ice at the mouth of the bottle? What process is demonstrated by the heat lamp? What processes are involved in the water cycle? How is this a simulation of the water cycle?

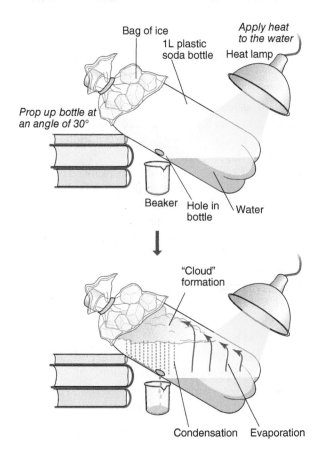

REVIEW QUESTIONS

1. Describe one cyclical process that happens on Earth.

2. Explain how the temperature difference between the poles and the equator drives the motion of the oceans and the atmosphere.

3. What are the principal repositories of water on Earth? How does water move between them?

4. What role does evaporation play in the hydrologic cycle?

5. By what processes does the amount of water on Earth change from year to year? What is the magnitude of this change from year to year?

6. Describe the processes that lead to an ice age. What effect does the formation of large glaciers have on the hydrologic cycle?

7. What are the differences between ice caps and glaciers?

8. What factors might cause glaciers to advance from polar areas to more temperate zones?

9. How do ocean currents affect local climate?

10. Why do we call groundwater in most areas a "nonrenewable resource?"

11. What is the difference between weather and climate? Describe the weather and climate of your area.

12. Explain what is meant by the statement, "Earth's climate is always changing." Give examples.

13. In what ways are air masses like reservoirs of the atmosphere?

14. What are the five variables that describe the weather?

15. Why does air pressure vary from place to place?

16. What is the jet stream? What is the prevailing direction of the jet stream? How does it influence your weather?

17. Explain the difference between prevailing westerlies and trade winds.

18. How is a volcanic eruption part of the "rock cycle?" What other cycles might an eruption affect?

19. Why were igneous rocks Earth's first rocks?

20. What are three main kinds of rocks? How do they form?

21. If you were driving past a large road cut through rock, what features might you observe that would tell you its origin?

DISCUSSION QUESTIONS

1. Describe how a large volcanic eruption can affect global temperatures. How might a supervolcano—a volcano that can eject hundreds to thousands of times more material than a "regular" volcano—affect global climate?

2. What do geologists mean when they refer to "deep time?" What evidence suggested deep time in the first place? Are any untestable assumptions made when considering deep time?

3. In the case of the cycle of an aluminum atom, what are some of the reservoirs of aluminum?

4. Describe three places where you might find volcanic rocks forming today. Describe three places where you could watch sedimentary rocks forming today. Where would you have to go to watch metamorphic rocks form?

5. Is it possible that when you pick up sand at the beach you are holding the first grain of sand ever created? Why or why not?

6. What are three places around the world where you can find volcanic rocks forming? Where could you go to see the formation of sedimentary rocks? Metamorphic rocks? Which do you think would be the most dynamic process and which one the least? Why?

7. Why does temperature vary with latitude and altitude?

8. How do oceans redistribute Earth's heat? How does the atmosphere accomplish this? Which of these, the oceans or the atmosphere, moves more heat toward the poles? Why?

9. At the beach during the day, breezes tend to blow from the shore to the ocean but during the night the prevailing breezes are from the ocean to the shore. Review the idea of heat capacity from Chapter 4 and use that material to predict the relative heat capacities of land versus ocean. Which do you think has the higher heat capacity? Why?

10. What are the building blocks of coral reefs? Would you categorize a coral reef as a living organism? Why or why not?

11. Imagine a terrestrial planet far out in the solar system that generates heat from its own core. Suppose it generates enough heat to have a surface temperature comparable to Earth's. Would you expect there to be a temperature difference between the equator and the poles? Would the atmosphere circulate around the planet? Why or why not?

12. Why is draining an aquifer akin to mining water? How is the water in an aquifer replaced? How long does this process take?

13. How would our weather patterns be affected if Earth stopped rotating?

14. What is the Gulf Stream? What countries are directly affected by the path that it takes?

15. The village of Plockton on the west coast of Scotland is at latitude 57° north. The city of Riga, situated on the eastern side of the Baltic Sea, is also about the same latitude. The average high temperature in Plockton in January is 45°F, while the average high in Riga in January is 28°F. Why do you think there is such a difference in climate?

16. In 2012, pseudoscience advocates were saying that Earth was passing through the plane of the Milky Way galaxy and that this would lead to calamitous effects. It wasn't true—Earth won't be passing through the plane of the galaxy for another 30 million years—but even if it were true, explain why the effects would have been unnoticed.

17. The Gaia hypothesis is the idea that life interacts with the surrounding system and both shape each other to form a self-regulating system that supports life. What evidence can you think of that supports this hypothesis? What scientific criticisms can you come up with regarding the Gaia hypothesis?

PROBLEMS

1. How much potassium is in 5 cubic kilometers of seawater? (*Hint:* Refer to Table 18-2.)

2. An unusually large limestone deposit in north-central Montana is 2,500 meters thick. If the thickness of this deposit increased at a rate of 1.25 millimeter per year, how long did it take for this deposit to form?

3. If copper is worth $7 per kilogram, what is the value of the copper in 1 cubic kilometer of seawater? Historically, the price of copper has gone up 4% per year since 1900. If this continues, how much will it be worth in 2050?

4. Record the temperature, atmospheric pressure, and percent cloudiness at both noon and at midnight in your area each day for at least 15 days.

   a. Make a graph of temperature versus pressure for the noontime measurements and for the nighttime measurements. Do you see any systematic trends?

   b. Make a graph of percent cloudiness versus pressure. Do you see a trend between the two? If so, what do you observe and why do you think it is happening?

   c. Is there a correlation between cloudiness and the difference between temperatures at noon and midnight? Why?

   d. Try graphing your data again with a different type of graph (e.g., bar, line, pie). Did your original choice of graph affect how easily you could interpret the data and results?

5. Some types of rock undergo the metamorphic process at a rate of 1 centimeter of thickness every 8 years. How long would it take a 500-meter-thick slab of such rock to undergo the full process of metamorphism?

6. After 1 residence time, half of a material originally in the ocean has been removed. After another residence time, half of the remainder is removed; this process continues indefinitely. Suppose 10 kilograms of copper atoms is distributed throughout the ocean. After a period of time, 1.25 kilograms is left. How many years have elapsed?

7. Some coral reefs grow at a rate of 2 centimeters per year. The Belize Barrier Reef is 300 kilometers long. If it grew at a rate of 2 centimeters/year, for how long has it been growing?

   a. 6,000 years

   b. 600,000 years

   c. 15,000,000 years

   d. 300,000,000 years

8. On average, a person in the United States uses about 570 liters of water per day. If the United States has 310 million people, how many days would it take to use up water equivalent to the volume of Lake Michigan (4,900 km^3 of water)?

   a. 16 days

   b. 28 days

   c. 8.6 days

   d. 9,000 days

INVESTIGATIONS

1. Look at some weather maps in your local newspaper over a period of several weeks and see if observing weather patterns to the west of your location is a good predictor of your weather. Why should this be so?

2. Where does water come from at your college? Is the water processed or treated in any way? How long might that source of water last? What alternatives exist if that supply is depleted?

3. Find out what kind of rock is below the soil at your college. How do you know?

4. Investigate the biological cycle of calcium in your body. Where in your body is calcium used? How often is it replaced? How much calcium do you need to consume each day? What are the best food sources of this element?

5. What are the "doldrums," and how do they form? What are the "horse latitudes," and how did they get that name?

6. Many movies have been made about weather disasters—hurricanes, tornadoes, blizzards, and so on. Watch one of these movies and comment on the accuracy of the science portrayed.

7. Investigate all the possible sources for global warming. What do we know about the Sun's energy output? Is it stable? Does the core of Earth supply any energy to the surface?

8. How many ice ages have there been? How many periods of increasing temperature are associated with interglacial periods?

9. The next time you walk past a large building, see if you can identify the different types of stone that were used in the construction.

10. Why would a sculptor use a metamorphic rock such as marble for a detailed sculpture rather than an igneous rock like granite?

11. What is the possible major natural disaster that people worry about in your area? What causes it? How do precautions differ for various possible disasters?

Ecology, Ecosystems, and the Environment

Are human activities affecting the global environment?

PHYSICS

Smokestacks equipped with electrostatic precipitators rely on electromagnetic forces to collect ash and soot particles.

BIOLOGY

Energy in ecosystems flows from the Sun through plants to herbivores, then carnivores.

CHEMISTRY

Burning fossil fuels releases nitrogen and sulfur compounds, which react with water in the air to form acid rain.

GREAT IDEA

Ecosystems are interdependent communities of living things that recycle matter while energy flows through.

TECHNOLOGY

New methods of recycling, such as the use of surfactants, play a significant role in reducing solid waste in the United States.

ENVIRONMENT

A gradual buildup of atmospheric carbon dioxide may lead to global warming caused by the greenhouse effect.

ASTRONOMY

The intense output of ultra-violet radiation from the Sun is largely absorbed by Earth's ozone layer.

GEOLOGY

Acid rain has increased the rate of weathering of rocks, most notably limestone and other sedimentary rocks used in buildings and statues.

HEALTH & SAFETY

The release of CFCs into the atmosphere has caused a decrease in the concentration of protective ozone and may contribute to an increase in skin cancer.

 = applications of the great idea discussed in this chapter

 = other applications, some of which are discussed in other chapters

Life Under the Sand

Y ou and a friend decide to take a walk down the beach, away from the crowd. Along a deserted stretch you watch as dozens of small shorebirds scurry back and forth, poking their long pointed bills into the wet sand. They seem to be searching for food. A closer look reveals tiny air holes in the sand—the telltale signs of tiny crustaceans. Farther down the beach, the sand is littered with small shiny shells; a golf ball-sized crab scurries by, and smelly strands of seaweed wash up onto the shore.

But those life forms are only the most obvious members of the oceanside community. If you could take a small sample of beach sand and examine it under a microscope, you would observe countless bacteria and other tiny organisms that thrive in the tidal environment. The beach turns out to be a richly varied community of organisms. In much the same way, a full understanding of our living planet will come if you view it not as a series of isolated individuals but as one vast interconnected community.

◉ 19.1 Ecology and Ecosystems

Think about the wonderful communities of living things that you've seen in your travels—deep woods and flowering meadows, shallow ponds and ocean beaches, dry deserts and stagnant swamps. Perhaps you've been lucky enough to hike in high-mountain tundra or go snorkeling at a coral reef (Figure 19-1). Each of these places boasts a collection of interdependent living organisms in a distinctive physical environment.

STOP & THINK What characteristics do all the living communities that we have just listed have in common?

The word **ecology**, derived from the Greek word for household or housekeeping, is the branch of science that focuses on natural living systems in the broadest sense. An **ecosystem** includes all the different kinds of living things that live in a given area, together with their physical surroundings. In every ecosystem, some organisms, such as plants, act as producers; they obtain atoms and energy from their physical surroundings and convert them into the essential carbon-based molecules of life. These biomolecules then sustain other organisms, such as animals, which act as *consumers* in ecosystems. In addition, still other life forms, including bacteria and fungi, act as *decomposers* that renew the raw materials of life. Together, these diverse organisms form an interdependent *community*.

An ecosystem can be as small as a single community of organisms on and near a bush in a tropical forest. It can be an aquarium in your living room, or a lake, including all the fish, insects, plants, and microorganisms in it. Or an ecosystem can be a mountain meadow, a salt marsh, a continent, even an entire planet. No matter what size ecosystem we talk about, however, the

Georgette Douwma/The Image Bank/Getty Images

Wildlife Pictures/Age Fotostock America, Inc.

Gerald C. Kelley/Photo Researchers, Inc.

(a)

(b)

(c)

FIGURE 19-1 *(a)* Complex coral reef ecosystems are extremely sensitive to changes in local conditions, such as salinity and water temperature. Large areas of coral near the coasts of North and South America are endangered by human activity. Other examples of ecosystems include a pond *(b)* and the desert *(c)*.

emphasis of ecology is on looking at the system—its matter and its energy—as a whole, rather than as a group of independent parts.

Every living organism, from single cells to complex animals and plants, relies on its ecosystem to sustain life. Indeed, the continuance of life on Earth is not a property of isolated individual organisms or even of species, but rather of ecosystems. One key to understanding living organisms, therefore, is to examine the ecosystems in which they survive.

Much can be learned from looking at living things as part of integrated natural systems, but this realization is relatively recent. Throughout the nineteenth century, for example, biologists were concerned with cataloging living things and paid little attention to how they were affected by (and, in turn, how they affected) their environment. Only within the last few decades have many of the insights discussed in this chapter come to be recognized as different aspects of the study of ecology.

Characteristics of Ecosystems

Ecosystems are richly varied. They occur on virtually every body of water and parcel of land on Earth, from the deepest ocean trench to the highest mountain range to the soil in your backyard.

Scientists often classify ecosystems by using units called **biomes** (pronounced bi-ohms), which are defined as the assembly of species found together in a particular climate region. So, for example, moving southward from the pole in the Northern Hemisphere, we would encounter the arctic tundra, evergreen forests, and deciduous forests as the temperature increased. We might pass through grasslands or deserts, and we would eventually wind up in a tropical rain forest. Each of these (any many others) is an example of different biomes.

Yet, in spite of this diversity, all ecosystems share a few basic characteristics. As you read about these characteristics, think about how they apply to an ecosystem near your home.

1. Every Ecosystem Consists of Both Living and Nonliving Parts

Nonliving or *abiotic* parts form the chemical and physical **environment** of the ecosystem—the water, soil, atmosphere, and so forth. Local climate conditions, including average temperature, rainfall, winds, and Sun exposure, are important physical properties of land ecosystems, whereas water temperature, pressure, salinity, and acidity help to characterize ecosystems in oceans, lakes, and other bodies of water.

Living organisms form the *biotic* part of an ecosystem; they form an *ecological community,* which may be defined as all the individuals in an area that interact with each other to maintain life. In a forest ecosystem, for example, an ecological community will include trees, shrubs, insects, birds, snakes, and squirrels, as well as fungi, bacteria, and a host of other microscopic organisms in the soil.

2. Energy Flows Through Ecosystems

The most important interactions of organisms in an ecological community are by way of a *food chain* or *food web,* which indicates who feeds on whom. Each species in a food web obtains energy and chemicals from its environment, including from other organisms; in turn, each species provides energy and chemicals for other organisms. Insects eat plants, birds eat insects, bacteria and fungi in the soil decompose birds and other organisms when they die, and plants obtain vital nutrients from the soil. Food webs for ecological communities may be extremely complex.

The flow of energy between *trophic levels* (see Chapter 3) is an important unifying characteristic of all ecosystems. The first trophic level of photosynthetic plants, which use only the Sun's energy, provides energy for herbivores in the second trophic level. Herbivores, in turn, pass some of their energy to carnivores of the third trophic level and so on. Decomposers, including bacteria and fungi, obtain energy from all other trophic levels. In each energy transfer from one trophic level to another, most of the available energy cannot be recovered in a useful form; it eventually radiates into space as waste heat (see Chapter 4). In fact, only about 10% of the energy available at one trophic level normally finds its way to the next. Thus, as energy flows through an ecosystem, it must be replaced continuously.

3. Matter is Recycled by Ecosystems

Atoms continuously cycle from one part of Earth to another. Perhaps the easiest way to understand the cycling of atoms through Earth's biosphere is to follow the *carbon cycle.* This cycle can be illustrated by looking at the possible path of a single atom of carbon that leaves your lungs the next time you breathe out a molecule of carbon dioxide. This carbon atom enters the atmosphere, where many different things can happen to it. It can, for example, be taken up by a plant during photosynthesis and then be incorporated into the tissues of a tree or a blade of grass (Figure 19-2a). The plant can then be eaten so that the carbon atom becomes part of the tissue of an herbivore. Alternatively, the carbon can simply return to the atmosphere if the plant dies and rots without being eaten.

If the carbon atom is taken into the tissue of an herbivore, then it may show up on your dinner plate one day and be taken into your body as part of some food you eat. It might even be incorporated into your own body to stay there until you die or to move through the chemical cycles described in Chapter 21. In either case, the carbon atom, in time, will enter the atmosphere again.

Another possible track for a carbon atom is shown in Figure 19-2b. It can enter the ocean by being added to a mollusk shell or the skeleton of a microscopic organism. Upon the death of the organism, these hard parts sink to the ocean bottom, where, in the form of calcium carbonate, they are turned into limestone. In this case, the carbon atom can remain locked up

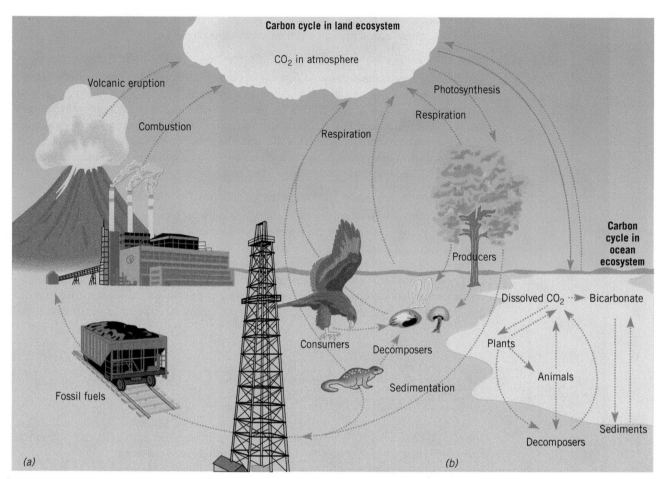

FIGURE 19-2 The carbon cycle. *(a)* Carbon atoms cycle through both living (biotic) and nonliving (abiotic) parts of Earth's ecosystem. They are found in carbon dioxide in the air, then taken into plants to become part of their structure. If a plant is eaten, the carbon may be returned to the air through respiration or become part of an animal's tissue. When the animal dies, the carbon dioxide returns to the air. Carbon atoms may also be locked into sedimentary rocks such as shale and limestone. *(b)* Another part of the carbon cycle involves the oceans, for example, as dissolved CO_2 in ocean water or as the shells of marine animals.

for hundreds of millions of years until the limestone is weathered and the carbon is released into the atmosphere.

A single atom of carbon, in other words, may have gone through many different chemical reactions during the 4.5-billion-year life of the planet and will continue to do so as long as Earth has living things on it. The one thing it will not do, however, is leave the planet. A similar story can be told for an atom of nitrogen or phosphorus or any other chemical element.

STOP & THINK Some toxic chemicals, such as the heavy metal mercury and the pesticide DDT, may gradually concentrate to harmful levels in living things because cells have no mechanisms to remove them. These dangerous substances are observed to be most concentrated in species at the top of the food chain—a phenomenon known as *bioconcentration* or *biological magnification*. Based on the characteristics of ecosystems, why should this phenomenon occur?

4. Every Organism Occupies an Ecological Niche

The **ecological niche**, a central concept in ecology, refers to a particular mode of survival—a particular way of obtaining matter and energy—within an ecosystem. In a forest ecosystem, there may be a niche that can be filled by one or more kinds of warm-blooded, insect-eating, nocturnal animals—bats, for example. Mushrooms growing in shaded wooded areas may fill another niche. Each plant or animal in an ecosystem fills an ecological niche, and different organisms compete for dominance in their preferred ecological niche.

5. Stable Ecosystems Achieve a Balance among Their Populations

This balance, called *homeostasis,* reflects the fact that matter and energy are limited resources that must be shared among all individuals of an ecosystem. An ecosystem in homeostasis will exhibit some variations in population sizes, as food supplies and other factors vary from season to season and year to year. But the overall distribution of species is usually relatively constant. A one-acre sunny meadow, for example, will boast a large but limited amount of grasses, flowering plants, and other vegetation. Year in and year out, those plants support a limited population of insects, which in turn will feed perhaps a few dozen birds.

6. Ecosystems are not Permanent, but Change over Time

Although ecosystems may appear to be stable, we know for a certainty that they change over time. On the longest timescales, the effects of plate tectonics will change the climate in a given area, converting a desert into a fertile plain, for example. On shorter timescales, the advance and retreat of glaciers can have a similar effect, as can changes in patterns of precipitation. Even on very short timescales, the introduction of a new species, by humans or by other natural processes, can profoundly change the pattern of life in a given area. As the science of ecology progresses, understanding and predicting these sorts of changes is becoming a major research goal.

◉ 19.2 The Law of Unintended Consequences

The complex interweaving of living things in their environment leads to a central insight in the science of ecology, an idea called the **law of unintended consequences**.

● **It is virtually impossible to change one aspect of a complex system without affecting other parts of the system, often in as-yet unpredictable ways.**

Whenever we alter something in an ecosystem other changes will follow, and we have to consider what those changes might be. Examples of this "law" appear in the news almost daily: building levees on the Mississippi River has caused unintended intensification of flooding; extracting petroleum and water from underground reservoirs has caused unintended land subsidence; building jetties into the ocean has resulted in unintended erosion of beaches. Each of these systems is interdependent, so the whole responds to every stimulus.

As often happens when scientists and engineers encounter complex systems for the first time, a good deal of observation and trial and error has to take place before an understanding of the system begins to emerge. Unfortunately, during that period of study serious mistakes can be made (see the discussion of the Aral Sea in the following section). Eventually, however, people learn how to proceed and begin to undertake large-scale projects with some confidence. At the moment, for example, the largest reconstruction project ever attempted is being undertaken in the Everglades of South Florida. The Everglades Restoration Plan is designed to restore the Everglades by changing the flow of water in the entire southern part of the state. As the plan proceeds, you can be sure that everyone—engineers and environmentalists alike—will have the law of unintended consequences firmly in mind.

⬡ SCIENCE IN THE MAKING
The Aral Sea Disaster

The Aral Sea is a large body of water located in Central Asia. In the mid-twentieth century it was ranked among the four largest lakes in the world, boasting an area of 68,000 square kilometers (about 26,000 square miles)—roughly the size of West Virginia (Figure 19-3a). The Aral Sea is

(a)   (b)

FIGURE 19-3 *(a)* The Aral Sea in Central Asia. *(b)* The result of the shrinking of the Aral Sea.

fed by two large rivers that flow into it through land that is largely arid desert. In the 1960s, the government of the then Soviet Union decided to divert some of the water in those rivers to irrigation systems that would, they believed, produce large crops of cotton for export.

Unfortunately, the irrigation system was poorly designed, with water being sent through unlined ditches and disappearing into the ground—some estimates place the loss of water between the river and the field being irrigated as high as 75%. As a result, more water was diverted and the Aral Sea began to shrink. By 2007, it was only a tenth of the size it had been a few decades earlier.

The results of the shrinkage were striking (Figure 19-3b). The Aral Sea fishing industry, which had employed tens of thousands of people, disappeared. Industrial waste and agricultural run-off that had been carried into the Sea became incorporated into the large salt flats that were left behind by the receding waters. These pollutants were picked up by the wind and breathed in by people living in the area, causing major health problems. In 2010, the Secretary General of the United Nations declared the Aral Sea one of the planets "most shocking disasters."

Fortunately, in the twenty-first century the countries in the Aral Sea region began a program to restore the Aral Sea, and the results of their efforts are encouraging. A system of dams has allowed sea level to increase, and there has been a modest restoration of the fishing industry.

Who would have thought, however, that a plan to grow cotton would have such far-reaching consequences?

 The ecologist Garrett Hardin has stated as a principle of ecology that "We can never do merely one thing." What do you think he meant by this?

SCIENCE IN THE MAKING
Island Biogeography

Because ecosystems are so complex, it's sometimes difficult to draw unambiguous conclusions from field studies. In 1963, however, American ecologists Robert MacArthur and Edward O. Wilson looked at the populations on islands, small ecosystems separated from the rest of

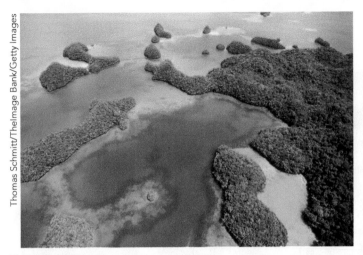

FIGURE 19-4 New species migrate to islands like this, reestablishing ecosystems.

the terrestrial world by water (Figure 19-4). From their study, they were able to frame a hypothesis: Whenever a new species migrates to an island that already has a thriving and stable ecosystem, it will flourish only if another species becomes extinct. According to this so-called equilibrium hypothesis, only a fixed number of species exist in any ecosystem, and if a new species invades, one of the old species will be driven to extinction.

The hypothesis was supported a few years later by Wilson and Daniel Simberloff in a classic ecological experiment. They first surveyed all the insects and crustaceans on a series of small mangrove islands off the coast of southern Florida. They then removed all living animals on the islands by draping large plastic sheets over them and fumigating. Over a period of years, they watched the islands undergo the process of repopulation as new animals migrated from the mainland or from other islands. As expected, the total number of species on each island at the end was about the same as it had been at the beginning. Perhaps less expected, however, was the fact that the kinds of animals on the repopulated islands were often quite different from those that had been there before. New species that happened by chance to be carried to an island on the tides were able to establish themselves in particular ecological niches, which were then unavailable to competitors that arrived later.

In 1995, nature began a similar experiment on its own. A violent hurricane propelled a large raft of fallen trees along with 15 green iguanas—spiny lizards up to 4 feet in length—from the Caribbean island of Guadeloupe to the island of Anguilla, 200 miles away. A new colony of green iguanas has begun to breed on Anguilla, and it soon will be competing for resources with the native species of brown iguanas. Ecologists are keeping close tabs on this dramatic example of changing island ecology.

● 19.3 Threats to the Global Ecosystem and Environment

The resources of our global ecosystem are vast but limited, and we often don't know enough about them to predict accurately how they will respond to change. These two inescapable facts, coupled with the growing pressure of human populations for energy and material goods, have led to a number of large-scale environmental problems. We are going to look at four of those problems—the disposal of solid waste, acid rain, the degradation of the ozone layer, and the greenhouse effect. All of these problems are serious, but their solutions entail different levels of national and international commitment. Taken together, they provide a sense of how ecosystems respond to human activities, as well as the difficulties that will have to be solved in order for our industrial society to keep functioning.

The Problem of Urban Landfills

Garbage (so-called solid waste) is generated at an enormous rate in American cities today (Figure 19-5a). New York City alone adds 17,000 tons of solid waste to its landfill every day (Figure 19-5b).

In a landfill, solid waste is dumped on the ground and compacted, then covered with a layer of dirt, then another layer of compacted waste, then another layer of dirt, and so on. Material in such a landfill is cut off from air and water, and the bacteria that normally operate to decompose the waste cannot thrive. Archaeologists digging into landfills have discovered, for example, that newspapers from the 1950s are still readable after having been buried for over a half century! This situation means that, unlike an ordinary garden compost pile, in which materials are quickly broken down by the action of bacteria, the landfill is really more like a burial site.

(a) *(b)*

FIGURE 19-5 *(a)* Typical percentages of different kinds of trash in urban landfills. *(b)* New York City produces immense quantities of solid waste.

One strategy to deal with this problem is recycling; every aluminum can that is recycled is one that won't be taking up space in a landfill.

SCIENCE BY THE NUMBERS
Trash

How much solid waste is produced in the United States every year? Engineers estimate that the average American each year is responsible for about 40 tons (80,000 pounds) of trash, including everything from disposable containers, newspapers, and mail-order catalogs to old automobiles and appliances, as well as the industrial wastes necessary to manufacture the things we buy. What is the total volume of this waste? Compacted trash typically weighs about 80 pounds per cubic foot—somewhat denser than water but less dense than rock (of course, it takes up much more volume before it's compacted). Forty tons, therefore, is equivalent to a volume of

$$\frac{80{,}000 \text{ pounds}}{80 \text{ pounds per cubic foot}} = 1{,}000 \text{ cubic feet}$$

That's enough compacted trash to fill two large dump trucks for every man, woman, and child in the United States every year. Thus, 300 million Americans produce a total annual volume of trash of

$$300{,}000{,}000 \text{ people} \times 1{,}000 \text{ cubic feet/person} = 3 \times 10^{11} \text{ cubic feet}$$

That's almost two cubic miles of trash every year, enough to build a solid 500-foot-wide wall across the Grand Canyon at its widest and deepest point.

TECHNOLOGY
The Science in Recycling

Because the environmental cost of using materials once and then throwing them away is growing steadily, governments have recently begun to pay more attention to recycling. Every recycled plastic milk jug or sheet of paper means less material in landfills, as well as less petroleum taken from the ground or less energy used to convert wood pulp to paper.

But recycling is not as easy as it sounds. A great deal of science and engineering has to be done before even the simplest materials can be reused. In addition, the processes that have to take place to recover one kind of material are, in general, different from those needed to recover another. The recycling of different kinds of plastics (see Chapter 10), for example, requires different kinds of chemical reactions, and processes that work for plastic soft-drink bottles will not necessarily work for ketchup containers. As a result, each kind of material that is to be recycled poses its own unique problems to an engineer.

Take white paper, for example (Figure 19-6). The average office worker generates about 250 pounds of high-grade paper waste per year, and many offices around the country have paper recycling programs. The first step in this process is simple: the paper is sorted, shredded, and ground up into a pulp and added to water to make a slurry. Copying machines and laser printers work by melting bits of carbon mixed with resins onto the paper. That sort of ink makes heavier particles when the paper is ground up, and those particles do not separate easily from the paper fibers.

The technology for dealing with this problem involves the addition of substances called surfactants to the pulp. The molecules in these substances bind to the heavier ink particles on one

FIGURE 19-6 The process of recycling paper involves several physical and chemical procedures.

Paper waste is collected

Sorted and shredded

Recycled paper rolls are manufactured

Ink is skimmed off the water

Ground into pulp and water added

Surfactant

Slurry

Gas bubbles

Added

Surfactant binds

Added

Clean paper pulp

Ink   Paper pulp

end and to bubbles of gas on the other. Once the molecules are attached to the ink, various gases are bubbled through the slurry. The surfactants and their load of ink rise to the surface with the bubbles and are skimmed off, leaving clean paper fibers for reuse.

Modern electronic equipment also poses special recycling problems. Consider the printed circuit board, a component of almost every electronic device. The board consists of copper circuits plated onto a material made of fibers held together by resins. Grinding up the board will allow quick recovery of the copper, but the remaining material, which used to be thrown away, can be heated and mixed with other resins to make things like fences and park benches—you may have sat on one of these benches yourself without knowing it.

A national recycling effort will involve hundreds of different processes such as these, each geared to a specific material, but each doing its part to make a coherent whole.

Acid Rain and Urban Air Pollution

Burning—the chemical reaction of oxidation—inevitably introduces chemical compounds into the atmosphere. For example, carbon dioxide and water vapor, the common products of hydrocarbon combustion (see Chapter 11), are always released. But burning produces three other significant sources of pollution: nitrogen oxides, sulfur compounds, and hydrocarbons.

1. *Nitrogen oxides.* Whenever the temperature of the air is raised above about 500°C, nitrogen in the air combines with oxygen to form what are called NOx compounds (pronounced "nox"): nitrogen monoxide (NO), nitrogen dioxide (NO_2), and others. The "x" subscript indicates that these compounds contain different numbers of oxygen atoms.

2. *Sulfur compounds.* Petroleum- and coal-based fossil fuels usually contain small amounts of sulfur, either as a contaminant or as an integral part of their structure. The result is that chemical combinations of sulfur and oxygen, particularly sulfur dioxide (SO_2), are released into the atmosphere as well.

3. *Hydrocarbons.* The long-chain molecules that make up hydrocarbons are seldom burned perfectly in any real-world situation. As a result, a third class of pollutants, bits and pieces of unreacted hydrocarbon molecular chains, enters the atmosphere.

FIGURE 19-7 A comparison of Los Angeles *(a)* during a clear day and *(b)* on a smoggy day.

©Guido Alberto Rossi/Age Fotostock America, Inc.

(a)

The Effects of Air Pollution and Acid Rain

The emission of NO_x compounds, sulfur dioxide, and hydrocarbons gives rise to a number of serious environmental problems. One of these problems, which has immediate consequences for urban residents, is **air pollution** (Figure 19-7). Sunlight hitting nitrogen compounds and hydrocarbons in the air triggers a set of chemical reactions that, in the end, produce **ozone**, a molecule made up of three oxygen atoms instead of the usual two. And whereas ozone in the stratosphere is essential to life on Earth (see the following section on the ozone problem), ozone at ground level is a caustic, stinging gas that can cause extensive damage to the human respiratory system. This "bad ozone" is a major product of modern urban air pollution associated with photochemical *smog*—the brownish stuff that you often see over major cities during the summer.

Urban air pollution is a serious problem, but it can sometimes seem to be an immediate and transitory one. If the air quality in a city declines, then people can be alerted about it immediately as part of the weather forecast. Just like the

David R. Frazier/Photo Researchers, Inc.

(b)

FIGURE 19-8 Acid rain originates from burning in one area, while its major effects are often felt in faraway ecosystems. Pollutants from urban and industrial areas can travel great distances, affecting lakes and forests hundreds of miles away.

weather, the intensity of air pollution varies on a daily basis, and it can change swiftly with the arrival of a thunderstorm or stiff winds.

However, long-term problems are associated with the presence of nitrogen and sulfur compounds in the air; these problems may not have an immediate effect on the place where the emissions occur. When these compounds are in the air, they interact with water, sunlight, and other atmospheric chemicals to form tiny droplets of nitric and sulfuric acid. (Sulfuric acid is the type of acid normally used in automobile batteries.) When it rains, these droplets of acid wash out and they become, in effect, a rain of dilute acid rather than water. This phenomenon is known as **acid rain** (Figure 19-8). (Rain is normally slightly acid because carbon dioxide dissolves in raindrops to make a weak solution of carbonic acid. The term *acid rain* refers to the considerable extra acidity produced by human activities.)

You can see one effect of this sort of acid rain in cities. Many of the great historical monuments in European cities, for example, are made from limestone, which is particularly susceptible to the effect of acid. Over the years, the acid rain simply dissolves the fabric of the building (Figure 19-9).

In the mid-twentieth century, the local effects of acid rain and other kinds of pollution in the United States were dealt with by the construction of tall smokestacks, particularly in the industrial parts of the Midwest. The effect was to put the pollutants high enough in the atmosphere to be taken away by the prevailing winds. But, in keeping with our dictum, "you can't throw anything away," that approach didn't really solve the problem. It merely displaced it. The nitrogen and sulfur compounds emitted in Midwestern smokestacks fell as acid rain on the forests of New England, and increased the acidity of lakes in places such as the Adirondack Mountains.

Acid rain may not be the only cause of damage to forests and lakes. Other agents, such as local climate changes, may be responsible in some cases. As in other ecosystems, scientists cannot be sure of every cause and effect. Nevertheless, in a society that is more and more concerned with preserving nature, the added stress on forests and lakes due to acid rain receives a great deal of attention.

FIGURE 19-9 One of the dramatic effects of acid rain is the slow dissolution of some kinds of rocks. Over a period of 60 years, this sandstone statue on a castle in Germany has been completely destroyed.

TopFoto/The Image Works

Dealing with Air Pollution

The response of governments to urban air pollution has centered on reducing the levels of emissions associated with burning fossil fuels. In many states large facilities such as power plants, which emit huge amounts of pollutants, are required to use coal with low sulfur content or to install complex engineering devices known as scrubbers, whose job it is to remove the sulfur compounds from the smokestack before they become part of the atmosphere (Figure 19-10). Controlling emissions from automobiles is a more complex task. In most urban areas cars are required to undergo emissions testing in order to be licensed, a program that has been successful. Mandating the sale of so-called zero emission vehicles—electric cars (see Chapter 3)—has been less successful. In 1990 California imposed such a mandate, saying that 2% of the cars sold in the state by 1998 had to be zero emission, with the percentage rising to 10% in 2003. Faced with the unwillingness of consumers to invest in an unproven technology, however, the mandate has been revised over the years, with the 2% mandate being dropped in 1996 and other mandates being lowered in 2003. More recently, California required that 2,500 zero emission vehicles be sold in the state between 2012 and 2014.

Acid rain and air pollution are examples of moderate environmental problems. We understand in a general way what the problems are, what at least some of the consequences of pollution are, and what has to be done to prevent the pollution. The costs of dealing with these problems, however, are high, so that political and economic questions become very important. How much are we willing to pay for clean air? This is not an easy question, nor is it a question answerable by science alone.

The Ozone Problem

In Chapter 14 we pointed out that, although the Sun gives off most of its radiation in visible light, a certain amount of that radiation comes in the form of ultraviolet light from the higher-energy part of the spectrum. Ultraviolet radiation can be very damaging to living organisms; indeed, it is routinely used to sterilize equipment in hospitals. If Earth's surface were not shielded in some way from the Sun's ultraviolet rays, life on land would be very different, if not impossible.

Ozone, which as we saw in the previous section contributes to urban air pollution near the ground, plays a beneficial role in absorbing ultraviolet radiation high in the atmosphere. If enough ozone molecules exist in the atmosphere, they will absorb most of the ultraviolet

FIGURE 19-10 *(a)* An electrostatic precipitator creates an electric field that attracts ash and soot and collects them before they can pollute the atmosphere. *(b)* Smokestacks connect to the electrostatic precipitator."

(a)

(b)

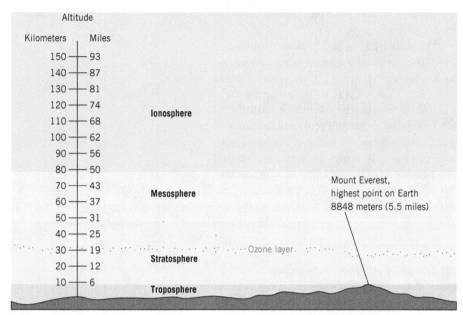

FIGURE 19-11 The ozone layer. Although ozone is found everywhere in the atmosphere, even at ground level, it is concentrated in a layer some 20 miles above Earth's surface. The labels in the middle are the standard terms scientists use to describe different levels of the atmosphere.

radiation from the Sun and keep it from reaching the ground. A protective shield of ozone formed high in Earth's atmosphere several hundred million years ago, and it was only after this shield formed that life moved onto land.

The Ozone Layer

Scientists detect ozone in the atmosphere by using several techniques. One is simply to fly specialized aircraft into the region where ozone is common and collect samples. For the past several decades this kind of sampling has been done routinely by organizations such as the National Oceanic and Atmospheric Administration (usually called "Noah" after its acronym NOAA) and its counterparts in other countries. Another way to detect ozone is to measure characteristic spectral lines given off by the ozone molecule (see Chapter 8). These measurements can be made from satellites, from aircraft, or by ground-based observers. In general, all these techniques are now used to give us a picture of the health of the ozone layer.

Measurements reveal that ozone is a trace gas that constitutes less than one molecule in a million in Earth's upper atmosphere. Although ozone is found at every altitude (you are breathing a small amount even as you read this), most of the ozone is found some 30 kilometers (about 20 miles) up in a region called the stratosphere (Figure 19-11). In this region, concentrations of ozone are significantly higher than they are in other parts of the atmosphere, although even here the amounts are very small. This region of enhanced ozone concentration is called the **ozone layer**. Most of the absorption of ultraviolet radiation goes on in this layer, but it should not be thought of as anything analogous to a cloudbank in the sky.

The Ozone Hole

In 1985, British scientists working in Antarctica noticed that during the Antarctic spring (roughly the months of September through November) the amount of ozone in the ozone layer over Antarctica dropped significantly. Later studies from satellites and ground-based experiments confirmed these results. During this period of the year, the concentration of ozone falls by different amounts in different years. The region over the Antarctic where this phenomenon occurred was dubbed the **ozone hole** (see Figure 19-12). The ozone hole is not a place where the atmosphere has disappeared, but a volume of the atmosphere in which the concentration of the trace gas ozone has declined significantly. Scientists became concerned about the appearance of the ozone hole because the ozone layer worldwide is so vital to the existence of life on our planet.

FIGURE 19-12 The dark area marks a region of lower ozone concentration over Antarctica—the ozone hole.

Courtesy NASA

In the 1950s, scientists introduced a new class of chemicals, called *chlorofluorocarbons* or *CFCs*, that were a boon to industry. Chlorofluorocarbons are very stable and nontoxic gases; they last a long time and do not break down readily when they are released into the atmosphere. Inexpensive CFCs were ideal for increasingly popular aerosol spray products, and they were valued replacements for rather nasty chemicals such as ammonia that had been used in refrigerators and air conditioners. Thus, CFCs played a key role in the great air-conditioning boom that made the southern part of the United States comfortably habitable during the summer.

In the mid-1970s, before the ozone hole was discovered, a group of researchers realized that CFCs might cause destruction of ozone in the atmosphere. Once the annual appearance of the ozone hole was firmly established in the 1980s, concerns over the role of CFCs increased. In a classic example of the law of unintended consequences, seemingly benign

CFCs turned out to present a very real danger to Earth's ozone layer. Over periods of time that range into the decades, molecules of CFCs work their way into the upper regions of the atmosphere, where they can be broken apart by high-energy ultraviolet radiation from the Sun. The chlorine atoms that are freed in this way act as a catalyst in a reaction that can be written as follows:

In words: (ozone plus chlorine plus sunlight) become (ordinary oxygen plus chlorine)

In symbols: $2O_3 + Cl + \text{sunlight} \rightarrow 3O_2 + Cl$

Although this reaction proceeds very slowly, each chlorine atom liberated from a CFC can, over time, destroy millions of ozone molecules before it is safely locked into another chemical species in the atmosphere.

Over most of Earth's surface, the effect of the chlorine atoms is not striking because new ozone molecules are being created all the time. In the Antarctic, however, a number of unusual circumstances come together to create the ozone hole. For one thing, during the months immediately preceding the hole, no sunlight falls in the Antarctic region of Earth. This period of darkness leads to the appearance of high clouds made entirely of ice crystals, the so-called polar stratospheric clouds. Crystals of ice in these clouds provide sites on which molecules that contain chlorine atoms undergo a series of chemical reactions. These chemical reactions proceed up to the final step before ozone molecules are actually broken down. As soon as high energy in the form of ultraviolet sunlight returns in the Antarctic spring, the destruction of ozone proceeds very quickly because large quantities of ozone-destroying chlorine atoms are released all at once. The ozone is destroyed in a matter of days or weeks, and the ozone hole results.

You might think that the disappearance of the ozone shielding in the Antarctic spring would not be a major environmental problem. After all, life is sparse on the Antarctic continent. The real danger of the ozone hole, however, is that it points to chemical reactions that could have long-term effects on the entire ozone layer.

Dealing with the Threat to the Ozone Layer

In 1986, an international congress meeting in Montreal produced a treaty by which all the industrial nations of the world agreed first to limit, then to eliminate, their production of CFCs. This decision triggered a lot of activity in major chemical companies, where people started looking to find replacement substances. In 1992, the reduction of CFCs was proceeding so quickly that the target date for elimination of most CFCs was set at 1996. Government mandates prohibited use of Freon in automobile air-conditioning systems by 1994 and called for its complete elimination by 1996. Current calculations suggest that, while the ozone hole still forms over Antarctica during the fall months, these restrictions in CFC use are having the desired effect and that the ozone layer will return to normal by the second half of the twenty-first century.

The ozone hole is an example of a serious environmental concern but one that has a relatively straightforward solution. Scientists have established the cause of the problem. The effects of the ozone hole, though serious, are not totally devastating to life on Earth, and the cost of solving the problem is relatively low. The problem of ozone depletion appears to be well on its way to being solved.

The Greenhouse Effect

The temperature at Earth's surface is determined primarily by the extent to which gases in the atmosphere absorb outgoing infrared radiation (see Chapter 6). The atmosphere is largely transparent to the Sun's incoming visible and ultraviolet radiation that warms the surface, but it is somewhat opaque to the infrared (heat) energy that radiates out into space (Figure 19-13). If it were not for the trapping of heat by the atmosphere, the average temperature of Earth's surface (i.e., the average day–night, winter–summer temperature) would be about −20°C. Thus, like a greenhouse, the atmosphere raises Earth's temperature from an inhospitable −20°C to its

FIGURE 19-13 The greenhouse effect. Just as the Sun's energy passes through the glass of a greenhouse and becomes trapped inside as heat, the atmosphere acts as a greenhouse to warm up Earth's surface.

Solar radiation passes through the greenhouse glass and is converted to heat, which is trapped within the greenhouse.

Solar radiation passes through the atmosphere and is converted to heat, which is trapped within the planetary atmosphere.

Solar radiation

Atmospheric shell of CO_2 and other greenhouse gases

Panes of greenhouse glass

present more temperate temperature distribution. This natural temperature increase associated with atmospheric trapping of heat is the so-called **greenhouse effect**.

In today's news, "greenhouse effect" refers to projected increases in global temperatures—both a change in average global temperature and a change in the temperature contrast between equator and poles. Three points of general agreement frame debates about global warming.

1. All scientists agree that carbon dioxide absorbs infrared radiation and acts as a greenhouse gas. Our neighboring planet, Venus, which has a thick carbon dioxide atmosphere and surface temperature exceeding 460°C (see Chapter 16), demonstrates this effect most dramatically. In fact, many atmospheric gases contribute to Earth's less severe greenhouse effect, and CO_2 accounts for only about 10% of the total infrared absorption. Water vapor, especially in clouds, is the dominant greenhouse gas, whereas the trace gases methane and CFCs, which make up less than a few millionths of the atmosphere, are molecule-for-molecule the most efficient infrared absorbers.

2. All scientists agree that the burning of fossil fuels by human beings has increased the amount of carbon dioxide in Earth's atmosphere. This dramatic trend is illustrated in Figure 19-14, which is a graph of the amount of carbon dioxide in Earth's atmosphere as measured at a high mountaintop observatory in Hawaii during the past several decades. The small wiggles in the graph correspond to annual cycles by which carbon dioxide is taken into leaves in the spring and then returned to the atmosphere in the fall.

FIGURE 19-14 Measurements of atmospheric CO_2 concentrations reveal an annual cycle, as well as a gradual increase.

3. And scientists agree that the average global temperature has been increasing since the middle of the nineteenth century, with 25 of the 30 warmest years in recorded history occurring since 1980. Against all expectations, however, the first decade of the twenty-first century saw no increase in average global temperatures.

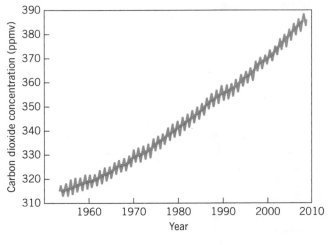

◉ 19.4 Debates about Global Climate Change

Global warming debates focus on whether increased CO_2 is entirely responsible for the observed increase in global temperature. These uncertainties stem from the fact that the only way we can predict the behavior of Earth's atmosphere is through global circulation models (see Chapter 17). These models are at best imperfect ways of predicting changes in climate.

One of the most important areas of difficulty in the models has to do with the effect of clouds. We simply don't know enough about the complex problem of cloud formation to incorporate them accurately into the models. Add to this the fact that high clouds reflect sunlight, and therefore cool the planet, while low clouds trap heat and warm it, and you can see that this is an important gap in our ability to predict climate change.

The world's oceans are another important effect that is difficult to incorporate in global circulation models. A constant interplay takes place between water and atmosphere at an ocean's surface, and carbon dioxide moves into and out of the oceans all the time. The amount of carbon dioxide locked in the oceans and their sediments is much greater than that stored in the atmosphere. Even small changes in the way that oceans interact with atmospheric carbon dioxide can thus have huge effects on the world's climate. In addition, as we saw in Chapter 17, ocean currents are instrumental in spreading heat around Earth's surface. Small changes in those currents could have enormous effects on Earth's climate, causing some regions to become warmer and other regions to experience lower average temperatures.

It has become standard practice in the climate change debate to make all calculations and predictions about Earth's temperature for the case in which atmospheric carbon dioxide doubles. A group called the Intergovernmental Panel on Climate Change (IPCC), which shared the 2007 Nobel Peace Prize with former U.S. Vice President Al Gore, relies on the participation of thousands of scientists around the world and issues reports every few years. Their most recent report, issued in 2014, states that warming of the global climate is unequivocal, and suggests that Earth's temperature will increase between 2°C and 6°C over the next century, with a "best guess" of about 4°C. The panel also estimates that this rise in average global temperature will be accompanied by glacial melting and an average rise in sea level of 2 feet or more over the next century.

The range of possible consequences of greenhouse warming in North America is also the subject of debate. As a general rule, for every 0.5°C of greenhouse warming, a global line of a given temperature will move about 100 miles northward. Thus, for 2°C warming, temperatures in Washington, DC, will become comparable to those in Atlanta, and temperatures in Minneapolis will be comparable to those in St. Louis. The effects on Earth's biosphere and ecosystems might be large or small depending on the magnitude and rate of warming. The total warming in the Northern Hemisphere after the last ice age, for example, was about 5°C and took place over a period of several thousand years. We know from studies of pollen deposited in the bottom of lakes that this warming, though large, was sufficiently gradual that plant populations were able to adapt and migrate north with the retreat of the glaciers. More recently, studies of the northern Atlantic Ocean have indicated that there have been periods in which the temperature in that region has changed by 5°C over a much shorter period, perhaps as little as a few decades. No known ecological disasters appear to be associated with these events. The predictions of consequences of greenhouse warming, should it occur, thus are also surrounded with a great deal of uncertainty (Figure 19-15).

Whatever the consequences, a growing international consensus holds that global warming is real and should be a matter of concern. From the point of view of government policy, the central question remains: What will be the social and economic consequences of climate change? Unfortunately, it is extraordinarily difficult to answer this question with the scientific knowledge we now have. Global warming could cause dramatic changes in coastal flooding, agricultural production, distribution of infectious diseases, rainfall, number and intensity of hurricanes, and other factors that influence the well-being of societies (Figure 19-16). But how much will it cost in social and economic terms to wean ourselves from the fossil fuels that emit carbon dioxide? Any effort to reduce drastically the consumption of

FIGURE 19-15 During a period known as the "Little Ice Age" from about 1645 to 1715, Earth's temperature was lower than it is now, and canals like this one in Holland froze over all winter.

FIGURE 19-16 Global warming could result in dramatic changes in rainfall, and consequent flooding.

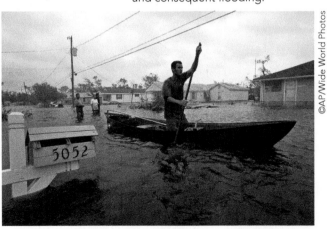

fossil fuels will cost consumers money, and they might require significant changes in lifestyles as well. Just think about all the ways we use carbon-based fuels. They're the basic energy source for automobiles, jet planes, ships, and most of our electric power plants. Thus, finding ways out of this dilemma is not easy.

THE ONGOING PROCESS OF SCIENCE
Dealing with Climate Change

Climate change is both the most difficult and the most potentially alarming of the many environmental problems that face the global ecosystem. It is the most difficult to model because the effect of adding carbon dioxide to the atmosphere is uncertain, and the cost of doing something about it is very high. The idea that you can take the world economy, which now runs almost entirely on fossil fuels, and change it over to other sources of energy in a very short period of time is unrealistic. In the past, it has taken many decades to make similar changes in a society's energy use and consumption. Figure 19-17, for example, shows the transitions from wood to coal and from coal to oil and gas in the U.S. economy. As you can see, it takes 30 to 50 years for a new fuel to work its way into the economy. If the more disastrous predictions of greenhouse warming are true, in about 50 years the warming will already have occurred, and it will be too late to do anything about it.

In addition, the best scientific estimates now indicate that if warming occurs, it will not cause severe environmental changes for several decades, far beyond the planning horizon of corporations, governments, and other major institutions in any society. The question comes down to something like this: Are you willing to change your driving habits now because a possibility exists that global warming will adversely affect the lifestyles of your grandchildren? Human beings find it difficult to suffer real hardship in the present to prevent an uncertain event from happening in the future.

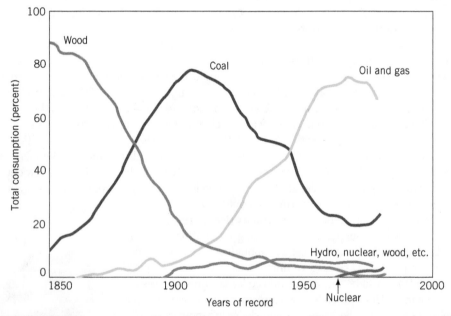

FIGURE 19-17 U.S. energy transitions. In the past, it has taken 30 to 50 years to make transitions from one type of fuel to another. We could expect a transition to solar energy (as an example) to take about this long.

THINKING MORE ABOUT **GLOBAL WARMING**

How Certain Do You Have to Be?

As we've seen, the problem of global warming is a complex one. There is no debate within the scientific community that global temperatures are rising and that human use of fossil fuels is at least partially to blame. Uncertainties remain about what the effects of the continued use of fossil fuels will be, and whatever those effects are, they are unlikely to be made manifest for decades. Nevertheless, decisions will be made over the next decade that will, at least potentially, have enormous consequences for future generations. In this situation, even doing nothing—pursuing business as usual—is a decision with consequences.

On the one hand, if the lower-level predictions of the GCM turn out to be correct—if Earth warms only 2 or 3 degrees—the consequences will be relatively mild. On the other hand, if the higher-end predictions turn out to be true, the consequences could be severe and far-reaching, and include effects such as increased droughts in many areas of the world and extensive flooding of low-lying coastal areas.

The problem is that we may have to act now, and incur real costs, to prevent something that might happen in the future. How much sacrifice should people be willing to make today to reduce risks for the next generation? On one hand, what sorts of sacrifices are you individually willing to make? Would you give up driving your car a couple of days a week? Would you buy a lower-performing but more efficient vehicle, or lower the thermostat in your house during the winter? Would you pay more for heating and electricity?

On the other hand, are you willing to ignore the risks of global climate change and rising sea levels? Unfortunately, this is a problem for which there are no easy answers.

RETURN TO THE INTEGRATED QUESTION

Are human activities affecting the global environment?

- Alterations of the global environment (e.g., climate change) result from a confluence of natural and human processes. Human activities will at times be the driving force behind some biophysical changes while playing little or no role in other worldwide changes.

- There is little scientific doubt that human activities play a central role in environmental change on the local and regional scale. The consumption of natural resources and energy demands are the main forces behind this anthropogenic environmental change.

  - As the world becomes increasingly more populated, the pressures on local ecosystems will increase concomitantly.

  - Current anthropogenic alterations in local ecosystems include:

    - Slash-and-burn agriculture that leads to deforestation and the loss of biodiversity via habitat loss.

    - The burning of fossil fuels that leads to acid rain and air pollution.

    - Groundwater pollution from the landfilling of solid waste.

  - In addition to the local effects, some human activities may affect the global or worldwide environment.

    - Burning fossil fuels increases levels of atmospheric carbon dioxide (CO_2) and particulate matter.

    - CO_2 is a potent "greenhouse" gas. As such, increasing levels may play a role in increasing global temperatures. These increases in temperature may cause an increase in sea levels and atmospheric water vapor via the melting of polar glaciers and ice caps.

    - Water vapor in the form of clouds is one of the most powerful of the greenhouse agents. Any significant increase in atmospheric water vapor could create a dramatic increase in global warming.

- Despite the fact of global warming, the consequences of this large-scale alteration in worldwide ecosystems are unknown.

- The popular media tends to oversimplify the scientific debate surrounding global warming and often seeks dramatic headlines in lieu of informed scientific debate. Drama and sensationalism are rarely antecedents to productive scientific inquiry, as they tend to confuse rather than illuminate the topic at hand.

- Given the complex interweaving of living things in their environment that is the foundation of the science of ecology, scientists and policy makers should heed the law of unintended consequences as they attempt to direct the flow of socioeconomic and biophysical forces.

SUMMARY

Ecology is the branch of science that studies interdependent groups of living things, called *ecosystems.* Each ecosystem is characterized by its physical *environment* and its community of living organisms. In every ecosystem many different organisms, each competing for matter and energy, occupy their own *ecological niches.* Photosynthetic plants in the first trophic level use energy from the Sun; these plants provide the energy for animals in higher trophic levels. In this way, energy flows through an ecosystem. Matter, in contrast, is constantly recycled as atoms are used over and over again.

Although these principles seem simple, the actual behaviors of ecosystems are extremely complex and unpredictable. It's virtually impossible to change one aspect of such a complex interdependent network without affecting something else, often inadvertently—a phenomenon often called the *law of unintended consequences.*

Human actions are causing changes in Earth's global environment—changes that may affect ecosystems. Burning coal and other fossil fuels, for example, releases sulfur and nitrogen compounds into the atmosphere—chemicals that contribute to *air pollution* and *acid rain.* Dealing with acid rain will require cleaning up emissions from automobiles and power-generating plants.

The use of chlorofluorocarbons (CFCs) during the past several decades is having a pronounced effect on *ozone,* a molecule of three oxygen atoms found as a trace gas in the *ozone layer* of the upper atmosphere. Ozone provides important protection on Earth from the Sun's harmful ultraviolet radiation, but chlorine atoms from CFCs hasten the breakdown of ozone molecules, thus creating a growing *ozone hole.*

Carbon dioxide, a necessary product of all combustion of carbon-based fuels, adds to the atmosphere's store of infrared-absorbing gases and thus contributes to the *greenhouse effect.* At present, scientists are not able to predict the consequences of these global changes with absolute certainty.

KEY TERMS

ecology	ecological niche	acid rain
ecosystem	law of unintended consequences	ozone layer
biome	air pollution	ozone hole
environment	ozone	greenhouse effect

DISCOVERY LAB

We have seen that when certain compounds such as nitrogen and sulfur pollute the air, they interact with sunlight, water, and other atmospheric chemicals to form tiny droplets of sulfuric and nitric acid. When it rains, these acids in the air will wash out in a diluted acid form we call *acid rain.* However, even natural rain is slightly acidic because of the carbon dioxide present in the air, which dissolves in rain to make carbonic acid. Statues, tombstones, and other monuments are often made from sedimentary rock, such as sandstone or limestone, and are gradually destroyed by either natural or acid rain because of this acidic factor. We can simulate this acidic effect on sedimentary rocks by simply taking a tall transparent glass, a small bottle of white vinegar, and some good sedimentary teacher's chalk, for an interesting experiment. Wear your safety goggles for this!

First, fill the glass with white vinegar (a mild acid). Next, slowly drop the chalk into the vinegar. Observe the effect of the mild acid on the chalk, which disintegrates the chalk within the hour. How would this accelerated effect compare to a sandstone statue or to a limestone monument dissolving over 60 years or more?

Slowly drop in chalk

White vinegar

Chalk

REVIEW QUESTIONS

1. What is ecology? How is this branch of science related to other branches such as biology and geology?

2. Give an example of an ecosystem near your home. Describe how energy "flows though" this ecosystem.

3. What is an ecological niche? Give an example. Within any given ecological niche, for what resources are organisms competing?

4. What is a biome?

5. How many different trophic levels were represented in your last meal?

6. In what ways can an ecosystem be stable? In what ways can it be unstable?

7. State the law of unintended consequences. Give an example of the law in operation.

8. How does carbon cycle through Earth's ecosystem? What other elements undergo a similar kind of cycle?

9. Why doesn't trash decompose in a modern landfill? What is needed for the process of decomposition to begin?

10. What is the ozone layer? Where is it located? Why is it important to life on Earth?

11. What is the ozone hole? What chemical processes produced it? How have governments responded to the discovery of the ozone hole?

12. Why is ozone in the upper atmosphere considered beneficial, whereas ozone at ground level is not?

13. What three pollutants are produced via the combustion of hydrocarbons? What effect do these have on the environment?

14. What is photochemical smog? How is it produced? Why is the smog in Los Angeles worse during the summer months?

15. What is acid rain? What steps would have to be taken to solve the acid rain problem?

16. What is the greenhouse effect? What are the most potent greenhouse gases? Are these produced naturally, or are they strictly anthropogenic?

17. Why are the predictions of the global circulation models uncertain? What would have to be done to reduce this uncertainty?

18. What steps would have to be taken to reduce the severity of the greenhouse effect?

DISCUSSION QUESTIONS

1. How do you think the size of an island affects the number of species and number of ecological niches on it?

2. How variable is solar energy output? How is this measured? How might variations in the Sun's energy production affect Earth's climate?

3. What environmental changes might result from a global increase in the average temperature of 2°C? What countries would be most negatively affected? What countries might be positively affected? Would having longer growing seasons sufficiently offset lands lost via rising oceans?

4. Do you think Wilson and Simberloff's experiment was ethical? Why or why not? Was there any other way to get this information?

5. One of the challenges in understanding the workings of ecosystems is that in most cases it is impossible to change only one independent variable while keeping the others constant. What examples can you think of where you might try to change only one variable in an ecosystem? How do you think this would affect other variables you wish to remain constant?

6. How does driving a car on a daily basis affect the environment? What other modes of transportation exist to try to lessen this effect?

7. What would the political, social, and economic consequences be in your community if serious steps were taken to reduce acid rain or air pollution?

8. If you apply the so-called law of unintended consequences to legislation designed to limit greenhouse effects, what do you think might happen? Why? Could these effects intrude on your day-to-day life?

9. Does the production of ethanol, an alternative fuel, still produce greenhouse emissions? If so, how is it an improvement over petroleum products?

10. Based on previous transitions in the nation's infrastructure, if the United States committed itself to a complete overhaul from fossil fuels to solar energy, how long do you think it would take? Who would be hurt by such a change? Who would benefit?

11. Of what ecosystem is the squirrel on your lawn or the bird flying across your campus a part? Are there any threats to the well-being of that ecosystem?

12. Where do electric cars obtain their energy? Is it true that they do not generate pollution because they have batteries?

13. If global warming were found to be almost entirely attributable to natural processes such as increased radiation from the Sun or greater thermal venting from Earth's interior, how do you think the current debate on climate change would be affected?

14. What are the nonliving components of an ecosystem or environment? How do the nonliving components limit the living components?

15. How might changes in climate affect the relative distribution of organisms in an ecosystem? Can you think of an example to discuss?

16. Why is there so much concern over the level of carbon dioxide in the atmosphere nowadays when there were naturally occurring higher levels in Earth's atmosphere in the past?

17. What is the most efficient greenhouse gas? What does cow flatulence, which produces methane, have to do with global warming?

18. What is a microclimate? How does the presence of microclimates enhance an ecosystem in terms of biodiversity?

19. Does an average increase of 2°C result in a decrease in the number of snowy days? Why might there be an increase?

PROBLEMS

1. The warming from the last glacial period had the temperature rise by 5°C over 8,000 years. If the temperature during the twenty-first century rises by 4°C over 80 years, how many times faster is the temperature change in the twenty-first century compared to the temperature rise after the last glacial period?

2. A typical passenger vehicle emits 4,700 kilograms of carbon dioxide into the air each year. Estimate the total number of cars in the United States and then determine the mass of carbon dioxide released into the atmosphere by those vehicles.

3. If your town were to experience an average increase of 2°C, how might the climate in your town be affected? (*Hint:* Find a town closer to the equator than yours that sits in a similar part of land; e.g., if you live in a coastal town, then pick another coastal town, but if you live inland in a hilly region, then find another town in the hills.)

4. If there are 310 million Americans each producing an average of 28 cubic meters of compacted garbage per year, how many years would it take to fill the Grand Canyon (4.17 trillion cubic meters), which has taken over 17 million years to form?

5. In 2011, fossil fuel emissions are estimated to account for 34.8 billion tons of carbon dioxide added to the atmosphere. Coal burning accounted for 43% of those emissions. How many tons of carbon dioxide were added to the atmosphere in 2011 because of coal burning?

   a. 15.0 billion tons
   b. 8.2 billion tons
   c. 19.8 billion tons
   d. 26.6 billion tons

6. Between 2005 and 2012, carbon dioxide emissions in the United States fell by a total of 12%. If the yearly carbon dioxide emission per capita in the United States in 2005 was 20,000 kilograms of carbon dioxide, how much was it in 2012?

   a. 12,000 kg
   b. 17,600 kg
   c. 2,400 kg
   d. 8,000 kg

INVESTIGATIONS

1. Do commercial jet airliners fly through the ozone layer? What effects might this have?

2. How are solid wastes such as plastics handled in your community? Does that method represent a long-term or short-term solution to the problem? What other options are available to your community?

3. Look up the Lake Victoria disaster. How does it illustrate the law of unintended consequences?

4. What is an environmental impact statement? Are there any projects in your area that have required environmental impact statements? Where should they be required?

5. Identify an environmental law or court ruling that has been enacted in the last year. What impact will this law have? Who benefits from the decision? Will anyone lose his or her job as a result?

6. What happens to your garbage? Is there a recycling program in your town? What materials can be recycled?

7. Read about the "pea-soup fogs" that used to plague London. What caused them? How many people could be killed in one?

8. Investigate the controversy over the environmental impacts of "fracking" (hydraulic fracturing) as a way of producing natural gas. What sort of government oversight is appropriate for this technique?

9. What chemicals are used in recycling paper? Different types of plastics? Are the chemicals that are used in the recycling of various products more harmful to the environment than the original waste material? What happens to these chemicals?

10. Look up the 2009 controversy known as "ClimateGate." How has this event influenced public attitudes toward global warming predictions?

11. What is the current state of the international negotiations on limiting carbon emissions? What will the next step in these negotiations be?

12. Watch the film *Darwin's Nightmare.* How does the "law of unintended consequences" come into play?

Strategies of Life

PHYSICS
Stems and trunks support plants and allow them to grow upward against the force of gravity.

BIOLOGY
Living things are classified according to their shared physical characteristics.

CHEMISTRY
All life depends on chemical reactions that take place in cells. (Ch. 21)

TECHNOLOGY
Microscopes play an important role in the discovery of new life-forms. (Ch. 21)

GREAT IDEA
Living things use many different strategies to deal with the problems of acquiring and using matter and energy.

ENVIRONMENT
Evidence from fossils suggests that the average lifetime of a species on Earth is a few million years. (Ch. 25)

ASTRONOMY
The Sun provides energy for life on Earth.(Ch. 3)

HEALTH & SAFETY
The common mold *Penicillium* was found to secrete a substance that kills bacteria, making it the first effective antibiotic.

GEOLOGY
Lichens often grow on rocks to absorb the minerals they need, and thus play an important role in the breakdown of rock into soil.

 = applications of the great idea discussed in this chapter

 = other applications, some of which are discussed in other chapters

The Diversity of Life

Look at how many different living objects you can find at the beach. You've already seen birds, seaweed, crustaceans, a variety of shells, and a crab near the water's edge. Higher up the beach you notice an abundance of dune grasses and small weeds, along with countless flies, ants, and other insects. A rocky tidal pool holds starfish, sea urchins, and myriad tiny swimming creatures. Schools of fish roil the surface of the water close to shore, while a few jellyfish (fortunately, not the stinging kind) also inhabit the shallow water. You even remember seeing a majestic whale spouting far offshore during an earlier trip to this very beach.

There's not a place on Earth's surface where you won't find living things. The frigid Arctic seas teem with life, whereas the frozen wastes of Antarctica yield up hardy lichens and single-celled organisms. Living things may be found in the deepest, darkest parts of the ocean and in the most dry and forbidding deserts. You could argue that what makes Earth different from every other place we know in the solar system (and perhaps even every other place in the galaxy) is the existence of varied and abundant life.

◉ 20.1 The Organization of Living Things

Biology is the branch of science devoted to the study of living things, by far the most complex systems that scientists study. Every single cell is astonishingly complex—vastly more intricate than the most advanced machines—and each human being contains tens of trillions of cells. Yet, despite this complexity, living things operate according to the same laws of nature as everything else we've studied. The laws of motion, energy conservation, the laws of electricity and magnetism, and the chemical bonding of atoms, for example, all operate in and govern the behavior of all living things. We have underscored this point by using examples from biology to illustrate all of the preceding chapters.

Ways of Thinking about Living Things

An ant provides a useful way to begin thinking about the study of living things. We can study the ant in many ways (Figure 20-1). We can, for example, examine it as an individual organism, in which case we ask questions such as: "How big is it?" "How much food does it consume?" "Where does it get its energy?" We could take a more reductionist or microscopic view and consider the individual ant as a collection of specialized organs. In this case we might ask about how the ant moves oxygen from the air to its cells, or how its hard outer covering protects it and supports its weight. Penetrating still deeper, we could look at the ant as a collection of

(a)

(b)

(c)

FIGURE 20-1 An ant can be studied at many scales, from individual microscopic molecules and cells to the structure of individual organs and structures, as shown in (a) this micrograph of the powerful overlapping serrated jaws, to (b) close-up of a solitary ant, to (c) the complex interactions of an ant colony.

cells and ask how a single one of those cells operates. Questions such as: "How does this cell carry out its chemical functions?" and "What are the pieces from which this cell is made?" would then be appropriate. Finally, we could look inside the cell and think about its ultimate constituents—the atoms and molecules that combine and react chemically to make the cell what it is. Here we would ask, "What are the molecules that operate in a cell?" and "How do they interact as chemicals?"

We could also choose to look at the big picture. Instead of probing ever-smaller parts of the ant, we could choose to view the ant as part of larger and larger structures. The single ant, for example, is part of the social organization of an ant colony, which in turn forms part of an ecosystem of living and nonliving things—a sand dune or a field or a patch of forest. This small community, in turn, represents part of the great global system that encompasses all living things on the planet.

Learning about a single living thing such as an ant can therefore take place on many levels. Different branches of biology deal with these levels, which we will discuss in the following chapters. The important point to remember, however, is that all of these ways of viewing the ant are important. Each approach complements, and is complemented by, the others.

In spite of this range of approaches, a profound change occurred in the life sciences during the last half of the twentieth century. Traditional biology concerned itself largely with discovering, understanding, and cataloging organisms and their interactions. Beginning in the nineteenth century, however, chemists began increasingly to study the cells and molecules found in living systems. This work culminated in the 1950s, when scientists discovered the singular role played by the molecule deoxyribonucleic acid (DNA) in determining what traits living organisms inherit from their parents (see Chapter 23). This discovery opened up an entire new world in the life sciences. As a result, during the past few decades the study of living things has undergone a fundamental realignment. Today the great majority of biologists are studying living systems at the level of molecules rather than at the level of the organism. Why this should be so will become clear in the following chapters.

◎ 20.2 What Is Life?

We all have a sense of what it means to be alive. We recognize some living things by their use of energy to grow and repair themselves, their response to external stimuli, and their ability to reproduce. But the more we learn about the world around us, the harder it becomes to provide a precise definition of life. Some objects, such as the mule, are clearly alive but are usually unable to reproduce. Certain seeds may lie dormant for centuries without any sign of life but then suddenly awaken. Furthermore, as technology advances, machines take on more and more of the qualities we usually associate with life. As a result of these sorts of problems, most scientists prefer not to try to define what life is in the abstract, but rather to describe the collective properties of living systems at some level, as we will do.

Other medical, legal, and ethical questions relating to the definition of life concern when life begins and when it ends. How should our society define human life? Is it possible that we could develop machines that are in some way alive? These are ethical questions that must take scientific knowledge into account, but their ultimate answers lie outside the realm of scientific inquiry.

The Characteristics of Life

The diversity of living things is truly staggering. You have only to think of whales, palm trees, mold, and mosquitoes to recognize this fact. Yet biologists have found that beneath this diversity many characteristics link all life together. In fact, the general principles that govern all living things will occupy us for most of the rest of this book. We list them here, however, to make the point that, despite their seeming diversity, living things are really not that different from one another.

FIGURE 20-2 The chameleon gets its energy like all animals—by eating other living things.

1. *All living things maintain a high degree of order and complexity.* Objects can be ranked according to their *complexity,* which is related to the number of different parts that are organized to make the whole. In this sense, a jet airplane is more complex than a wristwatch, which is more complex than a pencil. Even the simplest living thing is vastly more complex than any object ever constructed by humans.

2. *All living things are part of larger systems of matter and energy.* Living things and their surroundings form complex ecosystems (see Chapter 19). Matter continuously recycles in a given system, while energy flows through it. All organisms need energy to continue living (Figure 20-2). Plants, on one hand, use photosynthesis, by which the Sun's radiant energy is used to produce energy-rich molecules from water and carbon dioxide. Animals and fungi, on the other hand, obtain energy-rich molecules from plants and other animals.

3. *All life depends on chemical reactions that take place in cells.* As we shall see in Chapters 21 and 22, most living things share a basic set of

molecular building blocks and chemical reactions. By the same token, specific chemical reactions are what make one living thing different from another—what makes you different from a kumquat. Cells, the chemical factories of life, are the highly organized building blocks of life. Many organisms such as bacteria and blue-green algae are single-celled, whereas larger organisms such as human beings may incorporate trillions of interdependent cells.

4. *All life requires liquid water.* Liquid water possesses several unusual properties, including its ability as a solvent (see Chapter 10) and its high heat capacity (see Chapter 4), which make it an essential medium in the cells of all living things.

5. *Organisms grow and develop.* All organisms change in form and function at different stages in their lifetimes (Figure 20-3). In this chapter we will survey some of the varied ways that organisms accomplish these changes.

FIGURE 20-3 All organisms, from single-celled microbes to these complex hummingbirds, grow and develop.

6. *Living things regulate their use of energy and respond to their environments.* During periods of extreme cold or dryness, for example, many plants will lie dormant, and animals will become sluggish. During warmer or wetter periods, however, plants may flower and animals may enter their reproductive cycle. You experience this kind of change all the time. When your body temperature increases significantly, you sweat and heat is removed from the body as the sweat evaporates from your skin. When you get cold, you shiver and the extra heat generated by your muscles warms you up.

7. *All living things share the same genetic code, which is passed from parent to offspring by reproduction.* The chemical reactions in a cell are governed by a code written in the language of the molecule DNA (see Chapter 23). Just as all books in English are written with the same alphabet, so too the hereditary information that passes traits from parents to offspring uses a single genetic language. Sometimes the process of reproduction can be as simple as the splitting of a single cell into two offspring, and other times as complex as human sexual reproduction. In all cases, though, life consists of a chain of parents and offspring moving through time.

8. *All living things are descended from a common ancestor.* In Chapter 25 we will review the long chain of evidence that led Charles Darwin and others to recognize the evolution of life. We will see that the many similarities among living things arise from their common ancestry.

SCIENCE IN THE MAKING
Measuring Plant Growth

We can see the similarity between biology and the other sciences by looking at how the scientific method was used to answer an old question. All animals derive their nourishment from the food they eat, but where do plants get theirs? Throughout most of recorded history, people thought that plant nourishment must come from the soil—that plants "eat" soil in the same way that animals eat meat or fruit.

Jan Baptiste Van Helmont (1579–1644), a Flemish physician and the discoverer of carbon dioxide, reported an experiment that changed this view. He planted a willow tree weighing five pounds in a pot containing 200 pounds of soil and watered it for 5 years as it grew. At the end of that time, he weighed the tree and found that its weight had increased to 169 pounds while the amount of soil in the pot had decreased by at most a few ounces. He concluded that all the material used to construct the fabric of the willow tree came from the water.

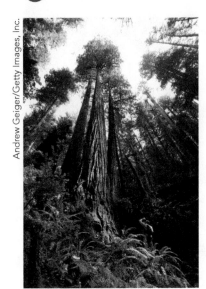

FIGURE 20-4 Most of the tissues of trees, such as these giant sequoias, comes from carbon dioxide in the air.

Subsequent experiments showed that he was wrong; much of the tissue in plants comes from carbon dioxide in the air (Figure 20-4). The point of the Van Helmont story, however, is that in science a good quantitative experiment, even one with an incorrect conclusion, can clear the way for progress. In this case, Van Helmont's proof that plants did not take their fabric from the soil led eventually to our present understanding of the role of plants in removing carbon dioxide from the atmosphere and producing oxygen.

◉ 20.3 Classifying Living Things

In Chapter 1 we saw that science begins with observation. People must start their exploration of a new area by looking to see what's there. Astronomers watched the skies for thousands of years and named many celestial objects before Newton could explain the motion of the solar system. Alchemists mixed chemicals and observed countless chemical reactions long before modern ideas of the atom or chemical bonding were developed. Similarly, humans spent thousands of years observing and naming living things before they could begin to recognize order in the variety of organisms they encountered. **Taxonomy**, the field devoted to cataloging living things, describing them, and giving them names, plays a central role in science because our search for patterns in the universe depends on recognizing similarities and differences.

Classification provides us with more than just a way of describing our world. It helps us fit new objects and phenomena into an existing framework. Classification enables a biologist who finds a new organism to group it with similar organisms and thereby to make a number of intelligent conjectures about that organism—about its diet, for example, or its mating habits. The same holds true of classification schemes for nonliving objects. Astronomers who classify stars, for example, know by systematic comparisons that a Sun-like star will have a lifetime of about 10 billion years and will eventually become a white dwarf (Chapter 15).

Cataloging Life

Biologists, confronted by the amazing variety of living things, realized that they had to find some systematic way of cataloging life's diversity. Indeed, the earliest attempts to classify life must extend back to the origins of language itself. In ancient times, the Greek philosopher Aristotle (384–322 BC) tackled this problem in his extensive biological writings. He noted, for example, that whales and dolphins, though fish-like, are actually not fish.

The most successful attempt to devise a systematic classification scheme was begun by Swedish naturalist Carolus Linnaeus (1707–1778). His work was based on observation. When you look at living things, it becomes obvious that some characteristics are shared but others are not. A human being, for example, is more like a squirrel than like a blade of grass; a sparrow is more like a fish than like algae in a pond. The purpose of the **Linnaean classification** was to group all living things according to their shared characteristics so that each organism would be as close as possible to those other organisms that it resembles and as far as possible from those it does not (Figure 20-5).

The basic unit of the classification scheme is the **species**, which we define today as an inter-breeding population of individual organisms that produces fertile offspring. Linnaeus, who worked at a time when European scientific institutions were being flooded with new types of plants from around the world, realized that simply describing species would not be enough. Instead, he introduced a system in which all species can be placed into a *hierarchy*—a sequence of categories that places all species into a larger framework based on similarities and differences among organisms.

Linnaeus's original goal was to organize the entire structure of nature, and to this end he published classification schemes for three "kingdoms" of plants, animals, and minerals. As you might expect in the first attempt to achieve such an ambitious goal, there were some errors in his work. (For example, he mistakenly classified the rhinoceros as a rodent.) But Linnaeus's work showed that it is possible to define relationships among different species.

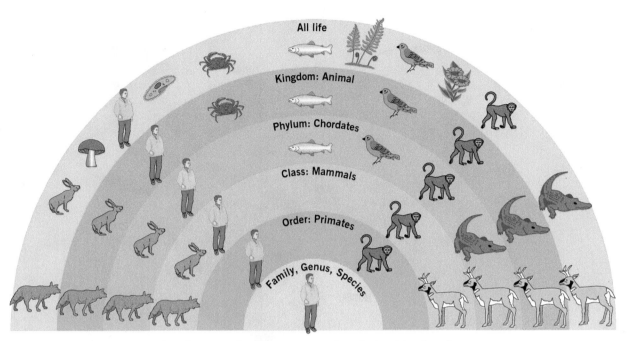

FIGURE 20-5 The Linnaean classification scheme recognizes the relationship of each living thing to every other. We can arrange species into groups that are more and more closely related. Although human beings are not treated differently from other organisms in this classification system, we are naturally more familiar with our own species than with any other.

The task of classifying living things is something like the problem of pinpointing one particular building in the entire world—a problem you face every time you mail a letter. You might start by specifying the continent on which the building stands, then the country, then the state or province, the town, the street, and finally the street number. Each step in this list of designations represents a separation, a splitting off. Houses on different continents are more distant than those on the same continent, houses in different towns more distant than those in the same town, and so on. Eventually, you get to an exact designation—a street address in a given town—that specifies the building uniquely.

The modern biological classification scheme uses the same kind of hierarchical scheme, with narrower and narrower divisions. However, instead of political and geographical distinctions such as city or country, the Linnaean scheme uses divisions based on the biological similarities of different species—similarities that point to common evolutionary pathways (see Chapter 25).

The main categories that biologists use, going from broadest to narrowest, are *kingdom, phylum, class, order, family, genus,* and *species.* (A useful mnemonic to help you remember this sequence is the sentence "King Phillip Came Over For Good Spaghetti.") As the number of known species has grown to more than a million, additional divisions such as suborder (a subdivision of an order) and superfamily (a few closely related families) have been added to the Linnaean scheme. You can think of this classification as being represented by a series of ever-smaller circles, with the specifications of kingdom, phylum, class, order, family, genus, and species serving to guide you to ever-smaller groupings. At the end, you come to a single kind of organism sitting in a circle all its own. Each step in this narrowing process involves a judgment about which organisms are like each other and which organisms are not.

This narrowing leads ultimately to the familiar two-part scientific names of organisms. When you go to a zoo or read a biology textbook, you will probably notice that the scientific names of plants and animals are given in terms of two Latin words—*Homo sapiens* or *Tyrannosaurus rex,* for example—that indicate the genus and species. (By convention, the two words are italicized and the genus is capitalized.) This *binomial nomenclature* is an important legacy of Linnaeus's work.

FIGURE 20-6 The five kingdoms of the biological classification system are illustrated by this diagram, which also suggests the progression from simple monera to more complex life forms.

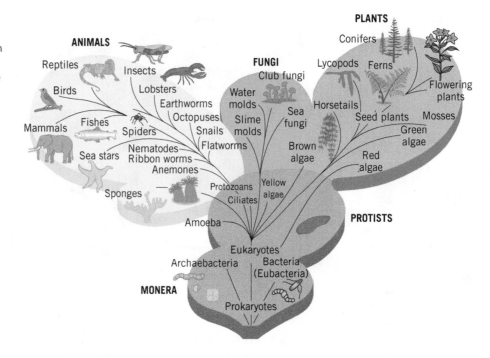

Biologists have traditionally considered the **kingdom** to be the broadest classification, corresponding to the coarsest division of living things. Until the 1960s, most biologists recognized only two kingdoms—plants and animals. In subsequent decades, most biologists classified living things into five kingdoms (Figure 20-6), though, as we shall see, this view is also changing as new data come to light. In the five-kingdom scheme, two of the kingdoms consist primarily of single-celled organisms.

1. *Monera.* Single-celled organisms without an internal structure called the *cell nucleus* (see Chapter 21). Monera are the most primitive living things (Figure 20-7).
2. *Protista.* Mainly single-celled organisms with a cell nucleus, but also a few multicellular organisms that have a particularly simple structure (Figure 20-8).

The remaining three kingdoms in this classification scheme include *multicellular* organisms, in which several different kinds of interdependent cells combine in a single species. Members of these kingdoms are distinguished primarily by the way that they obtain energy.

(a)   *(b)*   *(c)*

FIGURE 20-7 Monera—single-celled organisms without a nucleus—come in a variety of shapes. These microscope photographs show bacteria in the shape of: *(a)* spheres, *(b)* rods, and *(c)* spirals.

3. **Fungi**. Multicellular organisms that get their energy and nutrients by absorbing materials from their environment.

4. **Plants**. Multicellular organisms that get their energy directly from the Sun through photosynthesis. (This process will be described in detail in Chapter 21. For now, all you need to remember is that in *photosynthesis*, a plant takes carbon dioxide from the air and combines it with water and sunlight to form the energy-rich molecules known as sugars, plus some oxygen.)

(a) (b)

FIGURE 20-8 Some protista (single-celled organisms with a nucleus) develop beautiful microscopic shells. *(a)* This shell of foraminifera houses amoeba-like cells. *(b)* Pond waters, here magnified approximately 100 times, contain a rich variety of protists.

5. **Animals**. Multicellular organisms that get their energy and nutrients by eating other organisms.

Different Divisions of Life

In the late 1970s, University of Illinois biologist Carl Woese employed the techniques of molecular genetics (see Chapter 24) to discover a large group of extremely simple one-celled organisms that have dramatically altered our view of life's diversity. These microbes, collectively known as *Archaea,* often thrive in extreme environments, including acidic springs, arctic ice, deep-ocean hydrothermal vents, and in solid rock kilometers below the surface. Genetic studies reveal that these cells have remarkably distinctive and varied chemical processes that set them apart from all other cellular life. The profound differences, which are reflected in the unique genetic makeup of *Archaea*, led Woese to propose a radically new division of life into three distinct **domains** of life.

According to this dramatically different and now widely accepted view, *Archaea* and *Bacteria* are separate domains of single-celled life without nuclei (i.e., these domains split the old kingdom of monera in two). Even though these organisms can look quite similar to each other, they differ in many of their internal chemical mechanisms. The third domain in Woese's scheme, *Eucaryea,* encompasses *all* life based on cells with nuclei, including the multicellular kingdoms of plants, animals, fungi, and the single-celled protista. The three-domain classification scheme reflects the fact that fungi, plants, and animals are chemically and genetically extremely similar to each other, at least compared to *Archaea* and *Bacteria.*

Yet another way of classifying living things comes from paleontology, the study of fossils, which deals with the history of organisms (see Chapter 25). In this scheme, called *cladistics,* organisms are grouped together if they appear to be descended from a common ancestor. Thus, human beings and the great apes form what is called a "clade" because they all descended from a common ancestor.

This variety of classification schemes points to an important fact: there is no one correct way to classify living things. Classification schemes are not right or wrong, they are simply convenient or inconvenient. Thus, if you are interested in living organisms, you will probably use the Linnaean scheme, whereas if you are interested in fossils and evolution you might prefer cladistics.

STOP & THINK Does it matter how many kingdoms or domains biologists recognize? How might the proposed change to three domains, two of which are microbes, affect our view of life on Earth?

SCIENCE BY THE NUMBERS
How Many Species Are There?

Biologists are now engaged in a lively debate on one of the most fundamental questions you can ask about the world: How many species inhabit our planet? Estimates range from 3 million to 30 million species.

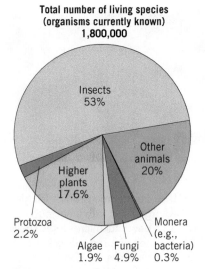

Total number of living species (organisms currently known) 1,800,000

Insects 53%

Other animals 20%

Higher plants 17.6%

Protozoa 2.2%

Monera (e.g., bacteria) 0.3%

Algae 1.9% Fungi 4.9%

FIGURE 20-9 A pie graph of species distribution among different kinds of living things reveals that insects account for more than half of all known species.

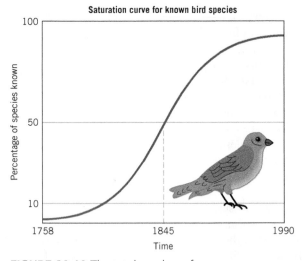

Saturation curve for known bird species

Percentage of species known

100

50

10

1758   1845   1990

Time

FIGURE 20-10 The total number of species of a given kind of living thing can be estimated by a graph that plots the number of known species versus time. As fewer and fewer species remain to be discovered, the plot should eventually flatten out to indicate the approximate number of species.

For large animals, such as the birds and mammals that command human attention, the situation isn't too bad. All experts agree, for example, that Earth is populated by about 9,000 species of birds and 4,000 of mammals, and only a few new ones are discovered each decade. For other kinds of organisms, however, we are still in a state of relative ignorance. For one thing, there is no central database where information on new species is summarized, so we can't even make a firm statement about the total number of species that have been discovered, much less about ones that haven't been. At the moment, an estimated 1.8 million species have been examined and recorded by scientists somewhere. The distribution of these species is shown in Figure 20-9.

Scientists have developed a number of methods for using current data to make estimates about the total number of species on Earth. If we make a graph of the total number of known species as a function of time, for example, we should get a curve like the one in Figure 20-10. As time goes by and more species become known, the curve should flatten. If we assume that the discovery curve for insects, for example, will follow this same pattern, then by making a guess as to where we are on the curve, we can estimate what the final level will be. Using this notion, estimates of the total number of insect species of from 5 million to 7 million are obtained.

Another estimation technique is to do an exhaustive survey of organisms in a small geographic area, determine the ratio of known to unknown species in that area, and assume that this ratio applies worldwide. A study in the Indonesian rain forest, for example, focused on a particular type of insect of which 1,065 species were known. A new exhaustive survey came up with 625 additional species, for a total of 1,690 species. Thus, the ratio of previously unknown to previously known species is:

$$\frac{\text{previously known species}}{\text{previously unknown species}} = \frac{1,605}{625} = 1.7$$

If we assume that this number applies to all insects worldwide (and that's a very big if) and accept that there are about 900,000 known species of insects, the total number of insect species in the world would then be about

$$\text{total species} = 1.7 \times \text{known species}$$
$$= 1.7 \times 900,000 \text{ species}$$
$$= 1,530,000 \text{ species}$$

Other studies of this type, making longer strings of assumptions about how to apply local numbers to the global system, have produced estimates for the number of insect species as high as 30 million. We will have to know a lot more about the kinds of species that actually exist before we can be comfortable with these sorts of estimates.

ONGOING PROCESS OF SCIENCE
Classifying Fungi

It may seem that providing the Linnaean classification for a new species would be a relatively simple matter, but for organisms such as fungi, it can get complicated. The problem is that, as we shall see below, fungi have two very different methods of reproduction. There is an asexual mode, in which a fungus reproduces by sending out runners or producing spores, and there is a sexual mode, when another member of the same species fertilizes a fungus. In most cases, the appearance of the fungus in these two modes is quite different. What appears to be a white mildew on a blueberry plant, for example, turns out to be the asexual representation of the brown, mushroom-like growths on blueberries that have fallen to the ground.

This sort of change is not unknown in other kingdoms—zoologists, for example, long ago decided to give a caterpillar and the butterfly it becomes the same binomial designation. The difficulty in following fungi through their complex life cycle, however, led to a situation in which the sexual and asexual organisms were given different names—often because it wasn't realized that they were the same species. The advent of DNA sequencing techniques (see Chapter 24), however, has opened the door to a resolution of this dilemma because both the sexual and asexual forms have the same DNA. Starting in 2006, mycologists (that's the word for scientists who study fungi) have been involved in a serious effort to reconcile the new information and species of fungi with their traditional nomenclature. It will be a long job.

Classifying Human Beings

Human beings are one member of the kingdom of animals. What is the rest of our address in the classification scheme? Among animals, we belong to the phylum called *chordates*, whose members have a thickened set of nerves down their back. Most chordates (and most of the organisms that come to mind when we hear the word "animal") have the nerve encased in bone. These animals form the subphylum **vertebrates**—animals with backbones. Because human beings have backbones, we belong to this subphylum, as do amphibians, fish, reptiles, and birds.

Among vertebrates, one class is made up of individuals that maintain the same body temperature regardless of the temperature of the environment, that have hair, and whose females nurse their young. Humans belong to this class, which is called **mammals**, as do wolves, rabbits, whales, and antelopes.

Among mammals, we belong to the order **primates**, which have grasping fingers and toes, eyes at the front of the head, a relatively large brain, and fingernails instead of claws (Figure 20-11). Monkeys and apes are also members of this order. Human beings are members of the *hominid* family (primates who walk erect) and the genus *Homo* (hominids who satisfy still more detailed anatomical criteria having to do with factors such as face shape, tooth shape and size, and brain size).

At this point in the process of zeroing in on our own species, we encounter an anomaly. Most animals have several close cousins, which are members of the same genus but different species, but this situation is not true of humans. The grizzly bear (*Ursus horribilis*) and the polar bear *(Ursus maritimus),* for example, are two species within the genus *Ursus* (bear). In the genus *Homo,* though, there is only one living species: *Homo sapiens* (us). In the past, there were other members of the family hominid and the genus *Homo* on Earth (we discuss some of them in Chapter 25), but at present we have no near relatives. All of those who might have been our near relatives are now extinct, perhaps by our own doing.

In any case, all humans can interbreed, so we are all part of a single species, ***Homo sapiens***, and we all inhabit the same smallest circle in the classification scheme.

FIGURE 20-11 Primates, such as this bonnet macaque from India, are characterized by grasping fingers and toes, eyes at the front of the head, a large brain, and fingernails instead of claws.

Implications of Linnaean Classification

As we have presented it here, and as Linnaeus originally conceived it in the eighteenth century, biological classification concerns itself solely with segregating living things according to their degree of physical similarity to each other. No attempt is made to explain why living things can be grouped in this way.

Today, however, most scientists would argue that there are compelling reasons why a classification scheme like the one we have outlined should exist. For one thing, scientists no longer have to be content with describing organisms purely in terms of their physical structure. In Chapter 23, for example, we will see that the information carried in the DNA molecules found in all organisms provides an alternative way of describing the organisms. One way of talking about how closely two organisms are related to each other, therefore, is to discuss how closely their DNA molecules resemble each other. The closeness of the relationship between two living things—the property that tells us where to draw the circles in Figure 20-5—can thus be determined in a quantitative way by comparing DNA and other specific molecules.

More importantly, the fact that living things can be grouped in successive layers strongly suggests that Linnaeus and his followers had discovered a kind of family tree. If, as we shall argue in Chapter 25, all living things descended from the same primordial ancestor, then the Linnaean groupings follow naturally. The amount of similarity or difference between two organisms depends on the amount of time and rate of change because the two shared a common ancestor. In addition, each classification group results from real events in the past when species split off from each other.

STOP & THINK **How does the classification of living things reflect the scientific method?**

◉ 20.4 Survival: A New Look at the Life Around You

A single-celled organism is one of the most remarkably complex structures known to science. Even the smallest cell features hundreds of interacting chemical processes that must be exquisitely balanced and regulated. Nevertheless, the survival strategies of single-celled organisms are relatively simple.

The first order of business for a cell is to absorb all the material it needs to maintain itself from its environment. In some simple cells, called *heterotrophs,* the cell must consume a variety of biomolecules including amino acids, lipids, and carbohydrates to survive (see Chapter 22). Other more chemically complex cells, called *autotrophs,* are able to manufacture these essential building blocks from simple molecules like H_2O, CO_2, and NH_3. Inside the cell, these materials are used in the chemical reactions needed to keep the cell alive and for it to reproduce. Waste products generated by these reactions leave the cell the same way that materials came in: they pass through the cell boundary and out into the surrounding environment. For most of Earth's history, all life consisted of such single cells.

With the advent of multicellular life, however, strategies became more complicated. Molecules that provided the cell's chemical energy could no longer simply move into individual cells from the environment (most cells in a multicellular organism, after all, are shielded from the environment by other cells). Instead, those molecules must be carried from distant parts of the organism to the cells where they are to be used. Similarly, waste products must be carried away from individual cells to the environment.

Some very primitive multicellular organisms (sponges, for example) are merely collections of cells that could just as well survive on their own. In higher organisms, however, specialized cells group together into organs and organ systems to take care of jobs such as moving energy-rich materials to cells and removing wastes. In humans, for example, the organ we call the heart and what we call blood vessels form an organ system known as the circulatory system, whose task it is to circulate the blood (see Appendix A).

One way to think about living things, then, is to identify tasks that all organisms must perform and then ask what processes have evolved that allow a particular organism to perform those tasks. Every multicellular organism, for example, must obtain and distribute molecules that supply energy and build the fabric of the organism, and every organism must reproduce itself.

Let's look at the marvelous diversity of living things with an eye toward seeing what strategies they have evolved to deal with these two basic tasks of life.

Strategies of Fungi

Fungi, a group that includes such diverse organisms as molds, mushrooms, and yeast, were once classified as plants, but they are so different from true plants that they are now given their own kingdom (Figure 20-12). Some types of fungi (yeast, for example) are single celled, but most of the ones with which we are familiar, such as mushrooms, are multicellular. Fungi grow by sending out filaments, which are slender, thread-like stalks sometimes no more than one or two cells across, and absorbing food directly through these stalks. In this way, the fungi play an important role in nature by breaking down dead organic material. For example, fungi often grow like shelves out of the sides of fallen trees in a forest, as well as on living trees.

The structure of fungi is fairly simple, consisting of little more than a mass of filaments. Because of this structure, complex systems that move materials around aren't necessary. No cell is far from the material on which the fungus lives; hence that material can be absorbed directly.

FIGURE 20-12 Fungi are a group of organisms that include *(a)* mold (here magnified approximately 100 times with a spore cap), *(b)* mushrooms (here shown magnified with filaments), and *(c)* yeast (here shown in a mass of single cells).

Fungi have developed a variety of reproductive strategies. First, they can reproduce by having their filaments break off and grow. More often, they produce spores, which are usually asexual reproductive organs through which a fungus can produce offspring without interacting with any other fungus. Spores can travel long distances through air and water, but once growth starts, fungi are as immobile as plants. Spores can also be produced by "mating," which is accomplished by the fusion of two cells in the filaments from different plants or the fertilization of one organism by another. Spores are often held in small containers that grow on top of stalks; in effect, they get a "running start" by being above the ground when the container breaks. The fuzzy appearance of mold on the old food in your refrigerator often comes from the spore containers on top of the stalks.

One of the most remarkable lifestyles displayed by fungi is observed in organisms called *lichens,* which are often seen as crusty coatings on rocks and which play an important role in the breakdown of rock into soil. Each lichen is actually a combination of two interdependent species, a fungus and a single-celled organism that can use the Sun's energy in photosynthesis. Lichens typically absorb most of the minerals they need from the air and rainfall, and hence can grow in inhospitable places such as mountaintops and deserts (Figure 20-13).

FIGURE 20-13 Lichens, *(a)* which grow on solid rock, sustain life through *(b)* a complex cooperative effort by fungi and algae.

SCIENCE IN THE MAKING
The Discovery of Penicillin

When you get an infection, or even just a bad cut, your doctor will very likely prescribe an *antibiotic,* a medicine capable of destroying foreign bacteria that otherwise would flourish in your body. It's hard for us, living in an age where antibiotics are common, to realize that less than a

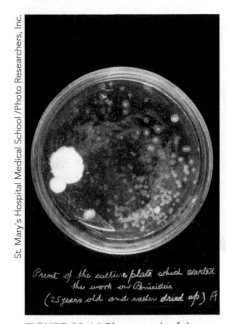

Print of the culture plate which started the work on Penicillin. (25 years old and rather dried up) A

FIGURE 20-14 Photograph of the original culture plate of the fungus *Penicillium notatum*, which led Scottish bacteriologist Sir Alexander Fleming to the discovery of the antibiotic penicillin in 1928.

century ago bacterial diseases such as pneumonia and minor cuts that became infected were major killers.

The discovery in 1928 of penicillin, the best known of the modern antibiotics, was the result of a botched experiment in the London laboratory of bacteriologist Alexander Fleming (later Sir Alexander). He was growing cultures of *Staphylococcus* (a common infectious bacterium) in dishes when he noticed that one of his experimental dishes had been contaminated by a common mold called *Penicillium* and that the bacteria didn't grow in that dish (Figure 20-14).

Other scientists had probably seen the same thing but had just thrown the contaminated plates away and continued with their experiments. Fleming, however, realized that the mold must have been secreting a substance that killed bacteria. When he finally isolated that substance, he named it *penicillin,* after the mold.

For a period after Fleming's discovery, penicillin could not be made in large quantities or in pure enough form to have much medical effect. In 1938, however, Howard Florey and Ernst Chain at Oxford University succeeded in producing relatively pure forms of the substance. Under the pressure of World War II, a major development program had the drug in mass production by 1943. It saved countless lives on the battlefields of that war and is now one of an array of substances used to maintain human health around the world. Fleming, Florey, and Chain shared the Nobel Prize for medicine in 1945.

The action of penicillin is a good illustration of how molecules function in living systems. The outside cell covering or cell membrane of the bacteria responsible for many infectious diseases is built from molecules that have short tails. Each bacterium cell also contains specialized molecules that link the tails together to create the *cell membrane*. Penicillin locks onto these specialized molecules and prevents them from attaching to the tails of the covering molecules, thus preventing the cell membrane from growing. Human cells don't use the same specialized molecules to build cell membranes, so the drug doesn't have this effect on us (although it can trigger allergic reactions in some people).

Strategies of Plants

Plants and algae, through the process of photosynthesis (see Chapter 21), take energy from the Sun and lock it up in the form of chemical energy in their tissues and cells. At the same time, they remove carbon dioxide and water from the air and produce oxygen as a waste product, including the oxygen you are breathing right now.

Biologists have not been able to agree about how to assign plants to various phyla, classes, orders, and so forth, or even on how to draw the boundaries of the plant kingdom. Algae, for example, are single-celled organisms (or simple multicellular ones) that carry out 50 to 90% of Earth's photosynthesis. *Blue-green algae,* or *cyanobacteria,* are single-celled organisms and are normally classified as monera; but other kinds of algae, including primitive multicellular organisms such as seaweeds and kelp (including green, red, and brown algae), are called plants in some schemes and protista in others.

For our purposes, we will define plants to be multicellular organisms that perform photosynthesis. Plants are found primarily on land, and the main divisions among them have to do with the way they reproduce and how they acquire and circulate water.

The Simplest Plants

The most primitive terrestrial plants are in the phylum of bryophytes, whose most familiar members are mosses and liverworts (Figure 20-15). These plants don't have roots, as more advanced plants do, but absorb water directly through their aboveground structures. For this reason, mosses are found in moist environments. They are anchored to the ground by filaments, as are fungi. Unlike fungi, however, bryophytes use the Sun's energy to produce their own food by photosynthesis.

Like all other plants, mosses and liverworts reproduce both sexually (involving sperm and egg) and asexually (involving spores). A generation produced sexually from the union of sperm and egg produces its offspring by means of spores. Then that asexually produced generation reproduces sexually, the two pathways alternating down through the generations.

(a)   (b)

FIGURE 20-15 The most primitive terrestrial plants are (a) mosses and (b) liverworts.

As we shall see in Chapter 25, life on Earth began in the oceans and migrated to land only about 400 million years ago. This history is evident in today's bryophytes in that they are not equipped to get moisture directly out of the soil and they cannot reproduce in a dry environment.

Vascular Plants

Most plants that play a role in our everyday life are in the phylum of **vascular plants** (Figure 20-16). These plants have an internal "plumbing" system consisting of roots, stems, and leaves capable of carrying fluids from one part of the plant to another. They also have ways of controlling water loss and protecting the sperm and egg so that they can survive outside of water. The development of internal plumbing not only adapted plants to life in the dry terrestrial environment, but it also began the process of providing internal structures to overcome the downward pull of gravity—both abilities crucial for land plants.

The most primitive vascular plants, a group whose most familiar members are in the class called *ferns*, still reproduce by producing sperm that must swim through water to fertilize eggs and generate spores. You can see the small yellow spore containers on the underside of the

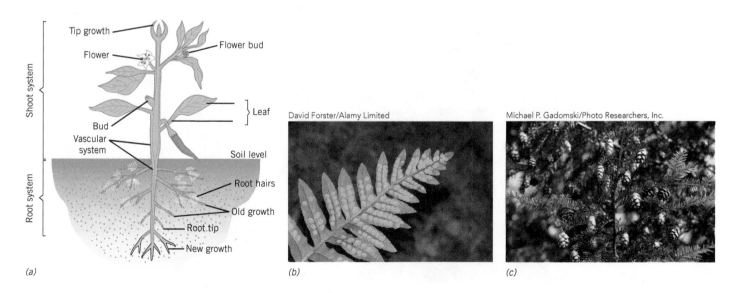

(a)   (b)   (c)

FIGURE 20-16 (a) The basic design of all vascular plants includes a root system below ground and a system of stems and leaves above ground. (b) A fern displays small yellow spore containers on the underside of the leaves. (c) Gymnosperms, including these conifers, produce seeds without flowers.

leaves of ferns. In this way they differ from the more advanced vascular plants, which, as we shall see, reproduce by means of seeds.

Although seedless vascular plants such as ferns play a relatively minor role on Earth today, they were the main form of plant life 300 million years ago. Huge forests of ferns and related trees blanketed the land, where they used photosynthesis to store the Sun's energy in plant tissues. When these plants died, they were buried and, over millions of years, turned into coal. Thus, you could say that the Industrial Revolution, which dramatically altered the structure of Western society in the nineteenth century depended on seedless vascular plants, as does much of modern technological civilization.

The most common classes of vascular plants today are the **gymnosperms** (plants that produce seeds without flowers; e.g., fir and pine trees) and the **angiosperms** (plants that produce seeds and flowers). The distinguishing feature of these plants, which have dominated the plant kingdom for the last 250 million years, is that they reproduce by means of seeds. All seeds contain a fertilized egg and some nutrient, both wrapped in a protective coating. Like spores, seeds are capable of lying dormant for long periods and hence can wait through times of cold or drought before they sprout. One way that seed-producing plants have become fully adapted to life on land is that the sperm part of these plants, familiar to us as pollen grains, typically moves through the air or is carried by insects. Thus, though seed plants may need water to grow, they do not need to be near standing water in order to reproduce.

The name "gymnosperm" means "naked seed" and refers to the fact that the seeds grow unprotected from the elements. The most familiar gymnosperms are evergreen trees, or conifers, such as the pine. On these trees, some cones produce pollen, which is dispersed by the wind. When pollen grains land on cones that contain unfertilized eggs, fertilization takes place. The seed, which as mentioned consists of a fertilized egg plus some stored nutrients, develops on the cone that originally held the egg, and, when conditions are right, is released and carried by the wind to a new location. Typically, hundreds or even thousands of seeds have to be released to produce one new seedling.

Angiosperms, which have been around for at least 100 million years and have dominated Earth's plant life for the last 65 million years, comprise the great bulk of known species of modern plants. These plants reproduce through the complex structure of their flowers. In a flower, the pollen grains containing the sperm grow on stalks known as stamens (Figure 20-17). Wind

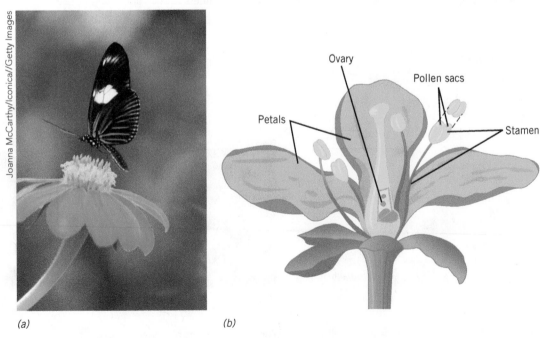

(a) *(b)*

FIGURE 20-17 Flowers produce sperm and eggs for sexual reproduction. *(a)* Pollinators such as bees and butterflies transport pollen from one flower to the next. *(b)* The structures of a flower are represented schematically.

or insects carry the pollen either to another part of the same flower or to other flowers. Once in its new location, each pollen grain grows a tube and enters the ovary, where the eggs are found. After fertilization, a seed forms within the ovary, and the ovary itself develops into fruit. When you cut into an apple or a peach, you can see the seeds and ovary quite clearly. When the fruit is ripe, it detaches itself from the plant. Many adaptations allow seeds to be carried long distances, from winged seeds (like those of some trees) to small seeds on berries that are eaten and passed through the digestive tracts of animals.

Although angiosperms can reproduce through fertilization, they also reproduce by sending out runners or shoots. Grass on a lawn, for example, reproduces this way if it is prevented from producing seeds by constant mowing. In the first case, reproduction is sexual (because a sperm and an egg come together); in the second case, it is asexual.

Strategies of Animals

Animals are multicellular organisms that must get their nourishment by capturing and consuming molecules produced by other life forms. The variety of organisms in this kingdom is truly staggering, ranging from sponges to tiny worms to eagles to students. Although the mass of all the plants on Earth far exceeds that of all the animals, the animal kingdom, with over 1.3 million known species, takes the prize for diversity. Depending on how lines are drawn, the kingdom can include more than 30 phyla. This diversity is summarized in Figure 20-18.

It's not easy to make generalizations about animals because of the great variety in this kingdom. However, the essential tasks of reproducing and acquiring energy and nutrients can help us get an overview. As you read the following, remember that respiration in animals is the reverse of photosynthesis in plants. In photosynthesis, a plant takes in carbon dioxide and gives

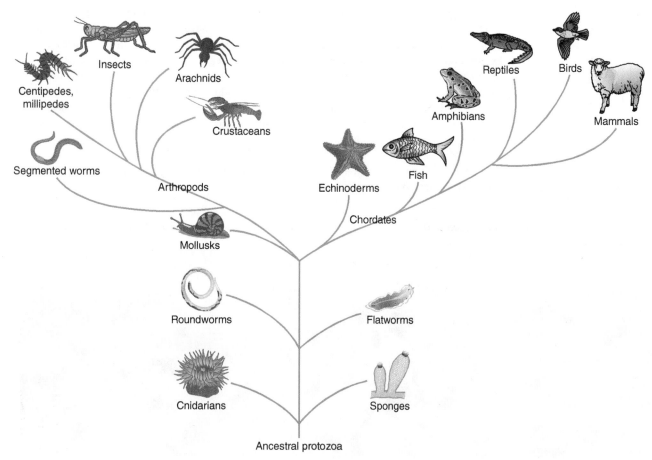

FIGURE 20-18 The family tree of animals, showing some of the major phyla.

off oxygen as a waste product. Animals, in contrast, use lungs or gills to breathe in the oxygen that is used in the body's chemical reactions, and then they exhale carbon dioxide as a waste product.

Invertebrates

When we think about animals, we usually visualize large organisms that fall under the sub-phylum of vertebrates, such as eagles, sharks, or elephants. Most animal species, however, are **invertebrates**—organisms without backbones that make up the 30 or so other animal phyla. The simplest invertebrates, such as sponges, exhibit characteristics somewhere between those of an aggregate of individual cells and those of true multicellular organisms. If a sponge is passed through a sieve, the individual cells not only survive, but also eventually reorganize themselves into a sponge. Corals, too, are colonies of countless separate minute organisms; break up the collection and each individual can function on its own.

Most of the phyla of the animal kingdom consist of worms, mollusks, and various micro-scopic organisms. Some of these animals have become incredibly specialized; one phylum of worms, for example, is represented by more than 70 species, each of which is found as a parasite in the noses, sinuses, and lungs of vertebrates. Sea cucumbers, jellyfish, earthworms, mollusks, snails, and tapeworms are all examples of the diverse invertebrate forms to be found in the animal kingdom.

Arthropods are by far the most successful phylum in the animal kingdom, in terms of both number of species and total mass. Arthropods include familiar forms such as spiders, insects (including beetles, ants, butterflies, and many other kinds of "bugs"), and crustacea (e.g., crabs, shrimp, and lobsters), all of which are animals with segmented bodies and jointed limbs (Figure 20-19). The more than 900,000 recognized species of insects account for at least 70% of all known animal species. There are more species of beetles than of any other type of animal and more individual ants than individuals of any other type. These facts prompted a famous com-ment by evolutionary theorist J. B .S. Haldane (1892–1964) who, when asked what his studies of biology had taught him about God, replied, "He has an inordinate fondness for beetles."

One of the problems that all land-dwelling organisms have to deal with is finding a way to support their structures against the pull of gravity. Arthropods solve this problem with a hard external covering known as an exoskeleton. This strategy is different from that of the verte-brates, whose weight is supported by an internal skeleton and whose outer coatings are usu-ally soft. You can see this same difference in strategy illustrated architecturally in the contrast between old buildings, whose weight is held up by massive stone walls and modern skyscrap-ers, whose weight is supported by a steel skeleton and whose outer skin may be nothing more substantial than thin sheets of glass.

STOP & THINK Can you think of any other strategies that living things could use to main-tain their structures?

The hard exoskeleton provides an evolutionary advantage to arthropods: it is a "coat of armor" that protects the animal from predators. Because the exoskeleton cannot grow, arthropods

FIGURE 20-19 Most known animal species are arthropods, with segmented bodies and jointed limbs. Arthropods include: (a) spiders, with eight legs and often several pairs of eyes, (b) insects, with six legs and three segments, and (c) crabs and other decapods with 10 legs.

Juan Carlos Muños/Age Fotostock America, Inc.

George Grail/National Geographic/Getty Images, Inc.

© Michael S. Nolan/Age Fotostock America, Inc.

(a)

(b)

(c)

usually shed their exoskeletons periodically, a process known as molting. A typical insect has a body divided into three segments. Three pairs of legs originate from the central segment, or thorax, while a pair of antennae for sensing the environment adorns the head (Figure 20-20). Many insects also have one or two pairs of wings. Insects have a heart but no lungs; they bring oxygen into their bodies through a set of tubes.

Vertebrates

Familiar vertebrate animals such as rabbits, birds, frogs, or fish have spinal cords encased in a backbone. The easiest way to understand the connection between the several branches of the vertebrate family tree is to think of each new branching up to reptiles as another step in the transition from water-dwelling animals to those fully adapted to life on land. As we shall see in Chapter 25, this line of thought follows the actual evolution of modern vertebrates, whose ancestors developed in the ocean and later made the move to a terrestrial environment.

The earliest fish, which became common about 400 million years ago, had no jaws; they fed by moving water through their mouths and filtering materials out. Lampreys (which look like eels without jaws) are modern descendants of these primitive fish. Over the following 100 million years, jaws evolved, and the advantage of speed over heavy protection led to a loss of bone. Modern fish such as sharks and stingrays, for example, have no bone at all, but skeletons made from cartilage, which is a structural material less rigid than bone. Modern fish absorb oxygen from water that flows through their gills.

Bony fish are a class of vertebrates that includes salmon, perch, trout, and most other organisms we think of when we hear the word "fish." Their skeletons are, as the name implies, made from bone. Oddly enough, the ancestors of these fish developed in fresh water and had both lungs and gills. In modern fish, these lungs have evolved into the swim bladder, an internal sac the fish can inflate to control its ability to float, while the gills function to supply oxygen (Figure 20-21). A few species of lungfish survive today. These fish live in stagnant water and gulp air occasionally to supplement what they can extract from the oxygen-poor water in which they live. Lungfish can also live out of water for short periods, allowing them to move from one pool to another during droughts.

The first vertebrates clearly adapted to live at least part of their lives on land were the class *amphibians*, whose modern descendants include frogs, toads, and salamanders. Most amphibians spend part of their life cycle in water, part on land. Frogs hatch in water as tadpoles, complete with gills and fins, and then develop into land-living adults with lungs and legs. They have a three-chambered heart and a circulatory system in which blood is pumped to the lungs to obtain oxygen, then returned and sent out into the body. Frogs also can absorb oxygen directly through their skin. Amphibians mark a halfway stage between water and land, in terms of both their anatomy and their place in evolution.

The class *reptiles*, including lizards, turtles, and snakes, include the first animals fully adapted to life on land. Reptiles are covered with hard scales, cutting down the loss of water through the skin. Eggs are fertilized within the body of the female, instead of relying on chance unions of egg and sperm in water, as with fish and amphibians. The young develop in eggs surrounded by a shell that can retain water and thus survive on land. Like amphibians, reptiles have a three-chambered heart, but with divisions in the chambers that allow oxygen to be used more efficiently. Amphibians and reptiles are so-called *cold-blooded* animals—that is, they must absorb heat from their environment to maintain body temperature.

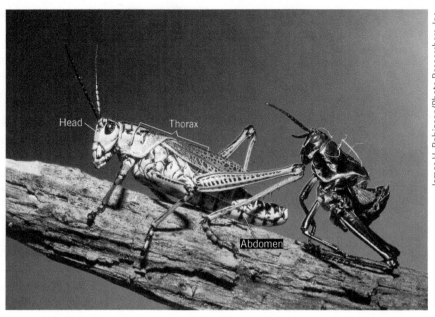

James H. Robinson/Photo Researchers, Inc.

FIGURE 20-20 Insects have three main body segments: the head, the thorax with three pairs of legs, and the abdomen. The body is shielded by a hard exoskeleton, which is shed periodically as the insect grows. Here a grasshopper has just completed molting.

FIGURE 20-21 In modern fish, what used to be lungs have developed into swim bladders, which helps the fish control its ability to float.

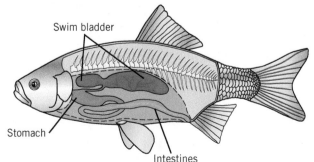

It should be noted, however, that a "cold-blooded" lizard lying in the sun may achieve a body temperature much higher than typical "warm-blooded" animals.

Birds are now widely thought to be modern descendants of reptiles, probably direct descendants of dinosaurs. Their anatomy differs from that of reptiles because of their adaptation to flight. In birds, the scales of the reptiles have evolved into feathers. Birds require high levels of energy to sustain flight, so their respiratory and circulatory systems are more complex than those in reptiles and amphibians. They have a four-chambered heart, as do humans. One side of the heart pumps blood to the lungs to take in oxygen, and the other side pumps this oxygen-rich blood around the body. This feature allows the bird to use the energy in its food with maximal efficiency, so that it is *warm-blooded,* maintaining a relatively constant body temperature in any environment.

Taxonomists recognize 18 living orders of the class *mammals* in the world today (Figure 20-22). Like birds, mammals maintain a constant body temperature by burning food. In almost all cases, the development of the fertilized egg takes place entirely inside the body of the mother, so that the young are born live. Once born, the young are nourished by milk from special glands in the female. Other adaptations to the terrestrial environment include hair to aid in temperature regulation, specialized teeth for breaking up food, legs located under the body, and, perhaps most important, an enlarged brain.

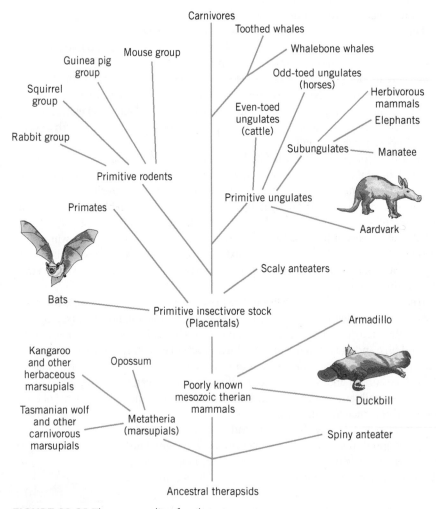

FIGURE 20-22 The mammalian family tree.

THE SCIENCE OF LIFE
The Microbiome

We are used to thinking of multicellular organisms like ourselves as a collection of specialized cells, all of which contain the same DNA. New research, however, may lead to a more complex picture of complex life. Your body, for example, contains about 10 microbial cells for each genetically human cell present, and perhaps 400 microbial genes for every human one. Although these microbes make up only a few pounds of our body weight, they inhabit our skin, our intestinal tract, our airways, and just about every other accessible part of our bodies. Our bacteria help to shelter us from disease and may have an important role in strengthening the immune system. These facts, along with research results on other animals, has led some scientists to suggest that we should think of ourselves and other animals as "superorganisms"—as an animal plus its microbiome.

Experiments in animals as diverse as mice and wasps have established that bacterial populations pass from mothers to offspring, and that a failure to inherit the right bacterial mix may result in serious problems for the offspring. Mice with autism-like symptoms, for example, apparently have microbial gut bacteria that produce chemicals that enter the bloodstream, whereas normal mice do not.

It is too early to tell where this new way of looking at complex life will take us, but it clearly creates a challenge to our understanding of our own bodies.

THINKING MORE ABOUT LIFE'S STRATEGIES

Eating Through the Phyla

Human beings consume an amazing variety of foods. One way to make the diversity of life more real to you is to think about the variety of kingdoms and phyla your meals come from. Consider, for example, a slice of mushroom pizza (Figure 20-23). The crust derives from wheat, a vascular plant. The mushrooms are fungi. The cheese comes from milk produced by a cow, a vertebrate animal, and the milk is converted into cheese through the action of a single-celled member of the kingdom monera. The remains of these organisms are still in the cheese when you eat it, so with one bite of pizza you are consuming representatives of four kingdoms. If you could imagine adding a dash of seaweed or kelp, which are protista (at least in some classification schemes), you could get all five kingdoms in one bite.

Biologist Harold Morowitz, in his book *Entropy and the Magic Flute* (Oxford University Press, 1993), points out that traditional Japanese cuisine incorporates more phyla than any other. It includes such delicacies as seaweeds (protista) and sea cucumbers (animals in the same phylum as starfish), as well as the usual crustaceans (arthropods), shellfish, and various bony fish. But even a Western meal such as seafood pasta accompanied by a salad with oil and vinegar dressing contains a wide variety of phyla. It has vascular plants (lettuce, tomato, and olive oil), a phylum of monera (which ferments the vinegar), clams and squid (phylum mollusca), and bony fish (vertebrates), not to mention flour (from angiosperms) and perhaps eggs (from vertebrates) in the pasta.

How many phyla combine to make your favorite meal?

FIGURE 20-23 A slice of mushroom pizza incorporates foods from many phyla.

Joel Glenn/Cole Group/Photo Disc, Inc./Getty Images

⬅ RETURN TO THE INTEGRATED QUESTION

What is life?

- A universal scientific definition of life has yet to be developed. The myriad and diverse life forms on Earth defy scientists' attempts to define life in unequivocal terms.
  - Any definition must possess a scope and breadth that encompasses all the organisms with which we are familiar, as well as those that have yet to be discovered.
  - Furthermore, any scientific definition must be subject to falsification, so all facets of the definition of life must be defined in terms that are both observable and measurable (Chapter 1).
- Despite the difficulties associated with constructing a universally acceptable definition of life, scientists have settled on a number of criteria that serve to classify the states of organization of matter that exist in our universe:

- Organization: To be considered "alive," an entity must exhibit a coherent structure and pattern of physiological development and morphology.
- Regulatory mechanisms: All organisms possess the ability to regulate their organism's internal environment via responses to a variety of both internal and external stimuli.
- Metabolism and growth: Life requires the consumption and transformation of energy to meet energy requirements. The synthesis, growth, and maintenance of cellular components are defining characteristics of living systems.
- Reproduction: All living species have the ability to reproduce, either through cell division or sexual reproduction.

SUMMARY

Biology, the study of living systems, began with efforts to describe the great variety of organisms on Earth. *Taxonomy,* the grouping of living things by their distinctive characteristics, has been aided by the *Linnaean classification* scheme, which groups organisms according to similarities in structure. Scientists now recognize five *kingdoms,* including *fungi,* which eat dead organic matter; *plants,* which make their own food by photosynthesis; and *animals,* which eat other organisms. Alternatively, all living organisms have been divided into three *domains* based on their genetic characteristics. A given *species* is placed in groups making up a series of increasingly specialized labels. The categories are, from most general to most specific, phylum, class, order, family, genus, and species.

The species, defined as an interbreeding population of individuals that produces fertile offspring, is the basic unit of classification.

Homo sapiens (the human species) is in the phylum chordata, the subphylum *vertebrates,* the class *mammals,* the order *primates,* the family hominids, and genus and species *Homo sapiens.* The fact that living things can be grouped in this way provides evidence that they all descended from a common ancestor.

Every multicellular organism must develop ways to obtain and distribute molecules for energy and structure, and to reproduce itself. Different life forms have evolved different ways to deal with these problems. Fungi absorb materials through slender filaments and reproduce through the production of spores. *Vascular plants,* the most abundant plants, use thin tubes to distribute water to their leaves. The two largest groups of vascular plants are *gymnosperms,* which have exposed seeds, and *angiosperms,* which have flowers. The most abundant animals are *invertebrates,* which are dominated by *arthropods* such as insects and spiders.

KEY TERMS

biology
taxonomy
Linnaean classification
species
kingdom
fungi

plants
animals
domains
vertebrates
mammals
primates

Homo sapiens
vascular plants
gymnosperms
angiosperms
invertebrates
arthropods

DISCOVERY LAB

Living things have quite a few characteristics that set them apart from nonliving things. One of the differences between living and nonliving things is that living things can metabolize sugar and produce carbon dioxide as a waste product. You can do an experiment to determine if the substance is living or nonliving. For the experiment you will need yeast, sugar, water, a thermometer, corn syrup, cornstarch, four bottles, and four 12-inch balloons.

Label four bottles with a number 1 through 4. In bottle 1, add yeast and fill it halfway with warm water. Mix it well and divide the mixture equally between all four bottles. In the first bottle add 2 heaping tablespoons of sugar. To the second bottle add 2 teaspoons of corn syrup. To the third bottle add 2 teaspoons of cornstarch, and do not add anything to the fourth bottle. Place all four bottles in a large dish containing warm water. The water bath will keep the contents of the bottle warmer for a longer time. Place one balloon over the neck of each bottle and make your observations. What does the size of the balloon indicate? Which balloon expands first? Why? Which bottle is the slowest? Why? Did all the bottles show evidence of metabolism? Why or why not? What would happen if you double the amount of sugar? How does this experiment indicate that yeast is a living thing? Would you have guessed the correct outcome without doing the experiment?

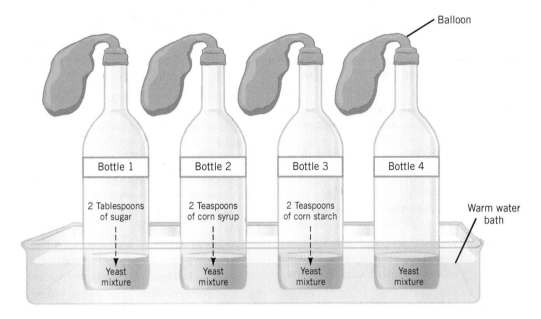

REVIEW QUESTIONS

1. What characteristics are shared by all living systems?

2. What is complexity? What is the most complex type of system that scientists study?

3. Scientific study often begins with description. To what part of the scientific method is taxonomy most important?

4. List the levels in the modern system of biological classification. At each level, identify the name of the group that includes humans.

5. How do organisms in the five kingdoms acquire energy?

6. Describe ways of classifying living things other than the Linnaean system. Why are they being developed?

7. Fungi were once classified as plants. How do fungi differ from plants and animals? (*Hint*: Think about energy-gathering strategies.)

8. Name two tasks that all living things carry out.

9. How can fungi reproduce without interacting with other fungi?

10. What characteristics distinguish vascular plants from others? Give examples of different kinds of vascular plants.

11. What are the differences between gymnosperms and angiosperms?

12. How does the structure of bryophytes differ from that of other plants?

13. What characteristics of angiosperms make them more abundant than other plants?

14. What are the four main structures of flowering plants? What is the function of each structure?

15. What are arthropods? How do they support their weight?

16. List the major groups of vertebrates and their distinguishing characteristics. Give an example of an animal from each group.

17. How are reptiles better adapted for life on land than amphibians?

18. What classes of animals are warm-blooded? What are the advantages of being warm-blooded?

19. Which subphylum contains more species: Vertebrates or invertebrates? Why?

20. What is the most successful phylum in the animal kingdom?

DISCUSSION QUESTIONS

1. What questions are important to ask when trying to classify an organism that you think belongs to a newly discovered species?

2. Why are there many different classification systems in common use?

3. With respect to survival and reproduction, what are the "problems" faced by all living organisms? How does evolution play a role in the success or failure to solve those problems over time?

4. Name three technological advances that have facilitated the scientific study of living organisms.

5. What are the benefits of using cladistics in the biological classification scheme? Are there disadvantages that you can think of?

6. What are some of the challenges biologists encounter when trying to estimate the number of species found on Earth? Do you think some or all of these challenges will be overcome some day? If so, what advances will be needed?

7. Given the definition of species, how many species of dog are there in the world? Do you think the definition of species can be applied in a practical way in all possibilities (e.g., a Chihuahua and a Great Dane)? How many species of human are there? Do you think that has always been true? Why or why not?

8. Why are biologists more confident of the total number of bird species than of insect species? What kinds of organisms are most likely to be accurately counted by scientists?

9. Imagine the natural Holiday/Christmas Tree you saw most recently. Would you classify it as a gymnosperm or an angiosperm? What evolutionary advantages do gymnosperms and angiosperms possess compared to seedless vascular plants such as ferns? If ferns are so disadvantaged, why are they still around?

10. Explain the difference between a vascular plant and a bryophyte and explain why vascular plants are more widely distributed.

11. Evolutionary biologist, J.D.S. Haldane, when asked what his studies of nature had taught him about God, famously answered, "He has an inordinate fondness for beetles." What do you suppose he meant?

12. If two different-looking animals breed and produce fertile offspring, are they the same species? Why is appearance not a productive way to classify organisms? (*Hint:* Does a Great Dane look like a Chihuahua?)

13. What is a "liger"? What is a tigon? If a liger and a tigon mate, will they produce offspring? Why or why not?

14. In what ways might changes in the nature of land plants have affected the evolution of land animals? Is it possible that changes in land animals have affected the evolution of land plants? If so, what ways do you think are possible?

15. Where are Earth's main coal deposits? What does this tell you about the location of forests hundreds of millions of years ago?

16. What are the properties of water that make it amenable to the development of life? Are there other substances with similar characteristics as water that might also allow life to develop? Why or why not?

17. What different structures have living things developed to support themselves against gravity? How do you think these structures would have developed if the strength of Earth's gravitational field were greater or if it were lesser?

18. Are insects or worms considered animals? Why or why not? Are they in the same phylum with humans?

19. Humans are the only species present in the genus *Homo,* and they are a part of the family of *Hominidae,* which includes two species of chimpanzee, two species of gorilla, and two species of orangutan. Do you think this amount of biodiversity within a family is typical for other life forms, or do you think it's unusual? Why?

PROBLEMS

1. Consider two islands of different sizes. If they exist in similar circumstances, the larger island is likely to have more different species than the smaller. Suppose this relationship is: (Number of Species) = (0.15 species/m)*sqrt(area). If the islands are approximately circular and the radius of the larger one is three times the radius of the smaller one, about how many species can you expect on the larger island if the smaller one has 400 species on it?

2. New species are discovered every day. Although determining the rate at which species are discovered is very complicated in practice, a very simplified model suggests that the current rate is about 18,000 new species per year. If there are 30 million total species and we have discovered 9 million of them, how long will it take to discover the remainder at the current rate?

3. The number of species in a given location has been shown to increase at a linear rate as the location gets closer to Earth's equator. For instance, the number of mammalian species at

15° latitude is approximately twice the number of mammalian species at 60° latitude. If 15 mammalian species are found in a small forest at 15° latitude, at what latitude would a similar forest have 10 mammalian species?

a. 20°

b. 30°

c. 40°

d. 45°

4. There are estimated to be about 1.5 million ants for each person on Earth. If the average human has a mass of 60 kg and the average ant has a mass of 4 mg, by what factor does the mass of all human beings compare with the mass of all ants in the world?

a. (Mass of All Ants) = (Mass of All Humans)

b. (Mass of All Ants) = 10 × (Mass of All Humans)

c. (Mass of All Ants) = 0.10 × (Mass of All Humans)

d. (Mass of All Ants) = 100 × (Mass of All Humans)

INVESTIGATIONS

1. In Chapter 18, we introduced a classification scheme for rocks. Which of the schemes that we have discussed in this chapter most closely resemble that for rocks? Justify your answer.

2. Find an example of the discovery of a new species, in the scientific journals or elsewhere. Describe how the new species was classified.

3. In the eighteenth and nineteenth centuries, many well-educated amateur naturalists made significant contributions to the study of plants, animals, and fossils. Statesman Thomas Jefferson, artist John James Audubon, and explorers Lewis and Clark are among the famous Americans who described unusual plants and animals. Read a biography of an amateur naturalist and discuss how his or her work contributed to the science of biology.

4. Investigate the research of Carl Woese of the University of Illinois. How did his discoveries alter thinking about the classification of living things?

5. Take a walk around your campus and see how many of the four major plant groupings—bryophytes, seedless vascular plants, gymnosperms, and flowering plants—you can identify. On most campuses you should be able to find all four, and even in the middle of a city you should be able to find two or three.

6. Go to your favorite supermarket and try to count how many different phyla of plants and animals are for sale. What is the average number of phyla per aisle? Does this number vary much from one store to another?

7. Many medicines were derived originally from plants. List some of them. Are any of the plants that produced those medicines now endangered?

8. Many single-celled organisms appear as tiny round objects about a millionth of a meter in diameter. Investigate the procedures a biologist might use to classify such an organism.

9. How many different kingdoms were in the dinner that you ate last night?

10. Why can some types of plants live without soil? Where do they get their nutrients? What are these plants called?

11. Investigate the role of cyanobacteria in the evolution and development of plants. What structures in modern plants are evolved forms of cyanobacteria?

The Living Cell

What is the smallest living thing?

PHYSICS

Nerve cells transmit electrical impulses over a distance. (Ch. 5)

BIOLOGY

Cells, the basic building blocks of life, come in a variety of shapes and carry out many different functions.

CHEMISTRY

Molecules such as ATP transfer energy in cells to power the chemical reactions necessary for life.

GREAT IDEA

Life is based on chemistry, and chemistry takes place in cells.

ENVIRONMENT

The amount of carbon dioxide in the atmosphere rises and falls in an annual cycle, as plants take in carbon dioxide in the spring and release it in the fall. (Ch. 19)

TECHNOLOGY

Electron and optical microscopes play a critical role in the study of cells.

ASTRONOMY

Plants convert radiant energy from the Sun into carbohydrates.

GEOLOGY

When living things go through the rock cycle, a fossil is created, providing a record of life at a given point in time. (Ch. 25)

HEALTH & SAFETY

Some viruses mimic the shape of food molecules to gain entrance into cells. (Ch. 23)

 = applications of the great idea discussed in this chapter

 = other applications, some of which are discussed in other chapters

Sunburn!

It's late afternoon at the beach when you notice that the tops of your feet are bright red. You've got sunburn. Hours earlier you used sunblock, but you missed those areas. Now they hurt!

Past experience tells you what will happen. For the next couple of days the tops of your feet will be tender and painful, especially when you get into a hot shower. Then the outer layers of skin will peel off. But within a week or so new skin will grow and your feet will be back to normal.

The human body is amazing. When injured, parts of the body like sunburned skin may die, but the skin is quickly regenerated. How is that possible? The answer lies in the behavior of cells—the fundamental building blocks of life.

Philippe Lissac/GODONG/NewsCom

◎ 21.1 The Nature and Variety of Cells

For centuries, scientists have tried to answer questions about nature's fundamental building blocks. In this context, dealing with living things is particularly complex. Although all living things are made out of atoms and molecules, as we saw in the previous chapter, living things are more than just collections of atoms. An entity must do many things such as reproduce and take in matter and energy for us to say that it is alive. These functions cannot be performed by a random collection of atoms; rather, they result from the collective behavior of large numbers of atoms organized into some kind of system. For our purposes, the **cell** can be considered to be the smallest identifiable unit capable of carrying on the basic tasks that we associate with living things.

An enormous number of different kinds of cells can be found in nature. Cells come in a wide range of sizes and shapes, and perform all sorts of functions. Although typical animal cells are about one-hundredth of a millimeter (a thousandth of an inch) in diameter, they can range in size from bacteria only a few hundred-thousandths of a centimeter across (much too small to see in most light microscopes and smaller than some large molecules) to the yolk portion of an ostrich egg that is much larger than most species of animals. Most cells are too small to be seen with the unaided eye but are easily studied with a microscope.

Cells also come in a wide variety of shapes. Plant cells are often rectangular or polygonal, whereas egg cells are usually spherical. Bacteria may be rod-shaped or spiral in form, muscle cells are extremely elongated, nerve cells sport a complex array of branching fibers, and a sperm

Andrew Syred/Photo Researchers, Inc.

FIGURE 21-1 The structure of cells, the basic unit of all living things, can be seen in this micrograph of cork (magnified approximately 50 times), which is taken from the bark of the cork oak tree.

cell has a tail-like flagellum that helps it swim. The recognition of common characteristics in this extraordinary collection represents one of the great advances in biology.

These differences in shape reflect the differences in the functions that the cells perform. Elongated muscle cells exert forces when they contract. Branching nerve cells (see Chapter 5) transmit impulses to many other cells. To fulfill their functions, cells constantly require raw materials and energy to live and reproduce. Living things use two very different strategies to satisfy these needs. On the one hand, some cells (such as bacteria and protista) operate as separate entities, ensuring their survival by reproducing in vast numbers. Multicellular organisms such as plants and animals, on the other hand, employ cells collectively. In these more complex life forms different groups of cells serve very different functions, with each group depending on others in a complex web of interdependence.

SCIENCE IN THE MAKING
The Discovery of Cells

An essential and distinctive feature of all cells is a membrane that isolates and protects the interior from the outer environment. In 1663, Robert Hooke (1635–1703), a brilliant and contentious contemporary of Isaac Newton, used one of the first microscopes to observe honeycomb structures in a thin slice of cork (Figure 21-1). It was Hooke who first called the tiny, box-like units "cells."

Within the next few years, Dutch merchant and self-taught scientist Anton van Leeuwenhoek (1632–1723) employed superb microscopes of his own design and construction to discover a rich variety of cells, including those in blood, saliva, semen, and the intestines. On October 9, 1676, van Leeuwenhoek sent a letter to the president of the Royal Society in London. He wrote, "In the year 1675 I discovered living creatures in Rain water, which had stood for a few days in a new earthen pot . . . ," and he went on to describe a series of "animacules" that were visible through his microscope.

◉ 21.2 The Cell Theory

In spite of van Leeuwenhoek's colorful descriptions, it was not until the nineteenth century that scientists finally accepted the idea that animals and plants are essentially aggregates of cells. In 1838, the German botanist Matthais Schleiden proposed that all plants are made of cells. In the following year his countryman, zoologist Theodor Schwann, extended this idea to animals and proposed what is now known as the *cell theory*. Three tenets of Schwann's cell theory are:

1. All living things are composed of cells.
2. The cell is the fundamental unit of life.
3. All cells arise from previous cells.

Thus, biologists recognized that only cells can produce other cells and that these tiny objects represent the indivisible units of life—a discovery as fundamental as the discovery of atoms in chemistry and quanta in physics. The cell theory initiated the field of cell biology, which remains one of the central efforts in biology.

> **STOP & THINK** The fact that cells require energy implies that they do work. What kind of work do cells do?

Observing Cells: The Light Microscope

Advances in understanding how cells work have relied in large part on the development of microscopes. Early microscopes were rather primitive affairs; consequently, scientists were unable to see many details of cell structure. Until the middle part of the twentieth century, science textbooks often spoke of something called "protoplasm." This substance was supposed to be a kind of uniform, molasses-like fluid that filled cells. Today, with much better microscopes we know that cells are very complex indeed. Advanced cells are full of specialized structures, as complicated in their own way as larger life forms such as human beings. In the next chapter we'll see that the molecules of life play a crucial role in the complex workings of the cell, with each performing a separate vital function. Today, we refer to the fluid that takes up the spaces between all this complexity as *cytoplasm*.

Early microscopes and their modern high-tech descendants all operate on the same basic principle shown in Figure 21-2a. Ordinary visible light passes through a specimen, which is often placed between two transparent layers of glass or plastic. The light transmits through a series of lenses so that a magnified image is presented in the eyepiece. This kind of apparatus is called an *optical microscope*, and today these instruments can magnify more than 1000 times and resolve details less than a ten-thousandth of a centimeter across—enough to make an ordinary cell look as big as a quarter. In many modern optical microscopes, a miniature video camera in the eyepiece allows the image to be displayed on a television screen.

Special dyes that are taken up by only one part of a specimen are often used to increase contrast in the image and hence to make internal structures clearer. For example, we shall see that parts of cells called *chromosomes* play an important role in reproduction. These features were first seen as colored structures in cells that had been stained, a fact that is reflected in their name.

The ability of a microscope to differentiate objects that are close to each other is called its resolving power. The resolving power of all microscopes is limited by the wavelength of the light used: objects about the size of one wavelength appear blurred. Light microscopes, for example, typically employ light waves with wavelengths on the order of a ten-thousandth of a centimeter; thus, objects about that size or smaller will appear as undifferentiated blurs in even the most perfectly designed instrument. This limitation means that many of the smaller structures in the cell cannot be seen with this sort of microscope.

Light microscope

— Ocular lens

— Objective lens
— Specimen

— Condenser lens

— Light source

(a)

Electron microscope

Electron gun

50–100 kV

Condenser lens

Specimen

Objective lens

Projector lens

Screen

(b)

FIGURE 21-2 Light microscope *(a)* and electron microscope *(b)*. In the light microscope, waves of ordinary visible light travel through a series of lenses to form an image. The electron microscope uses the wave-like nature of electrons (see Chapter 9) to accomplish the same purpose.

(a)   *(b)*

FIGURE 21-3 *(a)* Electron microscope photograph of a fruit fly with a wing mutation. *(b)* A scientist operates an electron microscope.

The Electron Microscope

In the 1930s, German scientist Ernst Ruska, working at a university in Berlin, introduced the *electron microscope,* a major new advance in microscopes that uses electrons instead of light to illuminate objects. In Chapter 9, we discussed the notion that quantum objects such as the electron can be thought of as tiny particles but also as energetic waves. The electron's wavelength depends on its energy—the greater the energy, the shorter the wavelength—and typical electron wavelengths in modern instruments are comparable to the size of a single atom. In a situation such as that shown in Figure 21-2b, where an electron beam is shot at a target, we are in effect examining the target with very short wavelengths and thus achieving resolving powers up to 100,000 times that of optical microscopes. Modern electron microscopes are often used to resolve atomic-scale features.

The electron microscope works this way: An electrical current heats a tungsten filament in a strong electric field—typically about 100,000 volts—to produce an electron beam. Electrons leave the negatively charged tungsten wire and accelerate toward the positive end of a tube. This beam of electron "waves" is focused by specially designed ring-shaped electromagnets, the analogs of glass lenses in a conventional microscope. The focused beam strikes the sample, and the electrons then hit a detector that converts the beam into an image, as shown in Figure 21-3. Modern electron microscopes are very expensive; it's not unusual for one to cost more than $500,000. Nevertheless, electron microscopes are an invaluable tool in all areas of science and industry that require examination of objects at extremely high magnification—particularly in the study of cells.

FIGURE 21-4 The cell is like an oil refinery. It takes in raw materials and energy and manufactures chemical products.

◉ 21.3 How Does a Cell Work?

As the fundamental unit of life, the cell must perform all of the varied tasks that we associate with living things (see Chapter 20). The cell must obtain atoms and energy from its environment, grow, respond to changes in environmental conditions, and reproduce. As we shall see, each of those tasks is accomplished by remarkable cellular mechanisms. But before examining those complex processes, it's useful to imagine the cell in a different way—as a factory that produces and distributes chemicals.

Have you ever driven by an oil refinery or other kind of chemical plant (Figure 21-4)? It's a place of bewildering complexity, laced with a maze of pipes and towers, bustling with diverse activity as energy and materials constantly flow in and out.

As complex and diverse as chemical plants might seem, they all share a few basic features. Every chemical plant must have walls, a control room, and facilities to provide and distribute energy. There must be loading docks to bring in supplies and remove trash, conveyor belts or pipes to move materials from one place to another, and storage rooms to keep a stock of critical items at the ready. And at the heart of every plant must be pieces of machinery that control chemical reactions and manufacture the desired chemical products.

A chemical plant is, in fact, a lot like a living cell.

Cell Membranes

Every cell must be isolated from its environment—just like a chemical factory, there must be an "inside" that is distinct from an "outside." In addition, complex cells also require different parts of the cell to be separated from each other by inner partitions. Both of these requirements are satisfied by **cell membranes**. The simplest cells have only one external membrane (Figure 21-5), whereas more complex cells have many internal membranes in addition to the outer envelope. The basic molecular structure of cell membranes is a flexible double layer of elongated molecules called lipids (see Chapter 22).

If a cell membrane were totally impermeable, life would not be possible. In order to be alive, a cell must take in raw materials from its surroundings and pass wastes and other chemicals into the environment, just like the loading docks and pipelines that run to and from a chemical plant. Materials are transported across cell membranes in many ways. The simplest is the movement of small individual molecules across the cell membrane. You may see this process at work in your local supermarket, where produce managers often spray fresh vegetables with water. They don't do this for decoration—they put water on the carrots, lettuce, and other vegetables so that it will move through the membranes into the cells, making up for water that has evaporated. In this way, vegetables maintain a fresher appearance for longer periods of time.

Cell membranes also incorporate various kinds of channels and molecular-sized openings, which allow specific materials to go back and forth. When nerve signals move through the human body, as we saw in Chapter 5, sodium and potassium ions move back and forth across nerve cell membranes to create the signal. The various kinds of channels that exist in different kinds of cells allow different kinds of atoms and molecules to pass through.

One important means of bringing material through a cell membrane, however, depends on the notion that the chemistry of life is controlled by the size and shape of molecules (see Chapter 22). Interspersed here and there in a cell membrane are large molecular structures, called **receptors**. Receptor molecules each have a specific geometrical shape, and each receptor will bind to a specific type of molecule in the environment. When that molecule is present, it is attracted to the receptor's binding site. Thus, receptors can be thought of as the cell's "door guard" looking over prospective molecular entrants and picking out only those nutrients whose shape is exactly right.

When a receptor "recognizes" a particular molecule, the molecule and receptor are attracted to each other, through hydrogen bonds, for example, and they fit together. A sequence of events such as that sketched in Figure 21-6 thus takes place. The receptor binds to the particle in question and holds it while the cell membrane deforms. Once the particle is inside, as shown, the membrane may nip off, enclosing the particle in its own special wrapping, and the cell membrane re-forms behind it. The tiny container, called a *vesicle*, then becomes the vehicle by which the particle moves around inside the cell. A similar process that works in reverse is used when molecules from inside the cell are moved out. Once in a while a receptor can be fooled. As we'll see in Chapter 23, some tiny disease-causing objects called viruses gain entrance into cells by mimicking the shape of particular molecules and thus triggering the receptor mechanism.

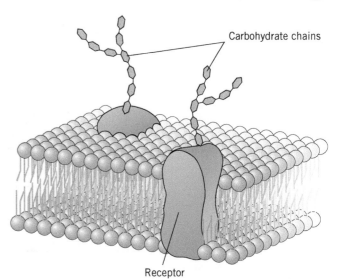

Carbohydrate chains

Receptor

FIGURE 21-5 All cells possess a lipid bilayer membrane, which is studded with protein receptors. The membrane separates the inside of the cell from the outside.

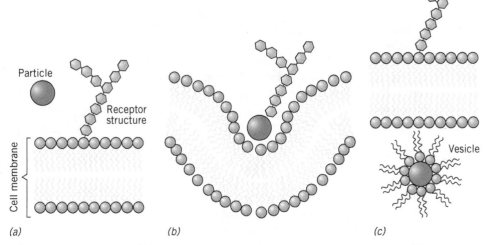

FIGURE 21-6 The action of receptors in a cell. *(a)* A food particle (in red) approaches a receptor. *(b)* The receptor bonds to the particle and draws it close to the cell membrane. *(c)* The particle is taken inside the cell and surrounded by lipids to form a vesicle.

FIGURE 21-7 A typical plant cell. *(a)* A generalized drawing with electron micrographs of some key organelles (see Table 21-2). *(b)* Micrograph of a cell of maize rust. The dark boundary is the cell wall, made from cellulose. The nucleus takes up almost half the area of the central part of the cell.

(a)

(b)

The outer covering of plant cells contains an additional structure in addition to the kind of flexible membranes we have described (Figure 21-7). Plant cells may also be connected to each other by a **cell wall**, which is a solid framework made of strong polymers, such as cellulose (see Chapter 22). Cell walls, which often account for about a third of a living plant's mass, give tree trunks, branches, and leaves the strength to grow upright against the force of gravity. In fact, it was cell walls (as opposed to cells per se) that Robert Hooke saw when he looked at his piece of cork in 1663 (see Figure 21-1).

STOP & THINK From a thermodynamic point of view, are cells open or closed systems? Explain.

The Nucleus

In many cells, the most prominent and important interior structure is the **nucleus**. The nucleus forms a relatively large enclosed structure that contains the cell's genetic material—its DNA (Figure 21-7b; see Chapter 23). This DNA contains the instructions for the day-to-day chemical operation of the cell, as well as the mechanism by which the cell reproduces itself. If we think of the cell as being analogous to a large chemical factory, then the nucleus can be thought of as the front office. There, the blueprints are stored and instructions for the operation of the entire system go out.

Not all cells have nuclei. In some cells, the DNA is present in a tight coil but is not separated from the rest of the material in the interior. Presumably, these sorts of primitive cells, called *prokaryotes* ("before the nucleus"), evolved first. The kingdom monera (see Chapter 20), including bacteria and their relatives, includes all cells that do not have a nucleus. The more advanced single-celled organisms, the *eukaryotes* ("true nucleus"), as well as all multicellular organisms (including human beings), are made from cells that do contain nuclei. The kingdom protista includes single-celled eukaryotic organisms. Virtually all of the organisms with which we are familiar are made up of eukaryotic cells. By now, you've probably noticed that quite a few words relate to different

TABLE 21-1 **Some Terms Related to Different Kinds of Cells and Single-Celled Organisms**

Archaea	One of Carl Woese's three domains of life; all Archaea are prokaryotes, and all are also members of the kingdom monera.
Bacteria	One of Carl Woese's three domains of life; all Bacteria are prokaryotes, and all are also members of the kingdom monera. Note that "bacteria" (not capitalized) is also sometimes used as a general term for microbes.
Eucarya	One of Carl Woese's three domains of life; Eucarya include all of the single-celled kingdom of protista, as well as the three multicelled kingdoms: fungi, plants, and animals.
Eukaryote	A cell with a nucleus; all organisms in Woese's domain Eucarya, are made of one or more eukaryotic cells.
Microbes	A general name for all microscopic single-celled organisms. Microbiology is the field of science devoted to the study of microbes.
Monera	The kingdom containing all cells without nuclei; monera is synonymous with prokaryotes, and it includes all single-celled organisms in the domains Bacteria and Archaea.
Protista	The kingdom containing single-celled organisms with nuclei; all protista are eukaryotes.
Prokaryote	A cell without a nucleus; all organisms in the kingdom monera, and in the domains Bacteria and Archaea, are prokaryotic cells.

kinds of cells and single-celled organisms. Table 21-1 summarizes this sometimes confusing vocabulary.

One interesting feature of the nucleus—a feature that may contain a good deal of information about the evolution of higher life forms—can be found in its confining membranes. The nucleus has not one but two membranes, as shown in Figure 21-8. The standard explanation of the double membrane in the nucleus is that it is a vestige of an earlier stage of development. The idea is that at some point in the past, a large cell engulfed a small one, much as modern cell membranes use receptors to engulf molecules. Over time, a symbiotic relationship developed between those first two cells. Each cell was able to do better in a partnership than it could do alone. The double-membrane nucleus is interpreted as having an inner membrane, descended from the original membrane of the swallowed cell, and an outer membrane, descended from the vesicle that formed when the first cell was enveloped.

Other structures in the cell also have a double membrane (see the following section), suggesting that, although cells are indeed the basic unit of life, individual cells in complex organisms may be more like colonies of smaller cells than a single cell.

The Energy Organelles: Chloroplasts and Mitochondria

Eukaryotic cells have many inner structures similar to the nucleus. Each of these structures carries out a special chemical function in the cell. Any specialized structure in the cell, including the nucleus, is called an **organelle**. Important organelles are shown in Figures 21-7 and 21-9, and a listing of some of their primary functions is given in Table 21-2.

FIGURE 21-8 The nucleus has a double membrane, perhaps because it evolved from an earlier stage in which a large cell engulfed a small one, as shown.

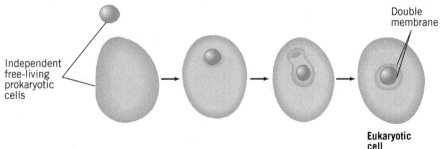

Independent free-living prokaryotic cells

Double membrane

Eukaryotic cell

Courtesy Tektoff-Rhone-Merieux, CNR/Photo Researchers

Biophoto Associates/ Photo Researchers

Rough endoplasmic reticulum

Don W. Fawcett/Photo Researchers, Inc.

Smooth endoplasmic reticulum

Nuclear membrane

Nucleus

Free ribosomes

Endoplasmic reticulum

Golgi apparatus

Secchi-Lecaque/Roussel-UCLA/CNRI/Photo Researchers

Vacuole

Mitochondrion

Cell membrane

Lysosomes

Gopal Murti/Phototake

Courtesy CNRI/Photo Researchers

FIGURE 21-9 A typical animal cell showing the nucleus, mitochondria, and various other organelles magnified several thousand times (see Table 21-1).

Every chemical factory requires energy, and living cells gather energy in two very different ways. Plants rely on the Sun for their energy, whereas animals ultimately depend on the chemical energy stored in plants.

Chloroplasts are the main energy transformation organelles in plant cells. As the name suggests, they are the places where molecules of *chlorophyll* are found. Chlorophyll absorbs

TABLE 21-2 **Some Organelles and Their Functions (See Figures 21-7 and 21-9)**

Nucleus	Stores DNA and controls the cell's chemistry
Endoplasmic reticulum	Contributes to protein and lipid synthesis
Mitochondria	Release energy from food by metabolism
Chloroplasts	Hosts photosynthesis (in plants only)
Ribosomes	Assemble amino acids into proteins
Nucleoli	Manufacture the subunits of ribosomes
Golgi apparatus	Processes proteins previously synthesized at the ribosomes
Lysosomes	Contain digestive enzymes for breakdown of wastes
Vesicles	Serve as small containers for chemical raw materials
Cytoskeleton	Provides cell structure and internal transport of vesicles
Vacuoles	Store waste and water
Amyloplasts	Store starch (in plants only)
Plasmodesmata	Act as water conduits between plant cells

the energy from sunlight and uses that energy to transform atmospheric carbon dioxide and water into energy-rich sugar molecules such as glucose. Chloroplasts have a double cell membrane, which suggests that they once may have been independent cells.

Mitochondria, sausage-shaped organelles, are places where molecules derived from the sugar glucose react with oxygen to produce the cell's energy. Mitochondria are, in effect, the furnaces where fuels are oxidized. A typical eukaryotic cell will have anywhere from a few hundred to a few thousand mitochondria.

Like the nucleus, chloroplasts and mitochondria have double cell membranes and even their own complement of DNA. Most scientists have concluded, therefore, that chloroplasts and mitochondria were originally independent cells in the early history of life on Earth.

Cytoskeleton

The *cytoskeleton* gives the cell its shape, keeps things anchored in place, and, in some cases, allows the cell to move. The cytoskeleton is a series of strong filaments that extend throughout the cell, more or less like a complex of spider webs (Figure 21-10). Inside the cell, the cytoskeleton serves as the transport system along which the vesicles that carry material from one place to another move. In some cases, cells can move by shortening and lengthening filaments inside the cell, or by causing structures related to the cytoskeleton that extend outside the cell to move like little oars.

FIGURE 21-10 In this fluorescent light micrograph of two cells, the cell nuclei appear purple and the cytoskeleton appears yellow. The cytoskeleton supports the cells' structures, allows the cells to move, and provides pathways for the movement of nutrients and waste.

◉ 21.4 Metabolism: Energy and Life

The cell's process of deriving energy from its surroundings is called **metabolism**. Cells need a means to transfer that energy from one place to another, powering the varied pieces of chemical machinery necessary for life.

The Cell's Energy Currency

Several molecules are used to store and distribute energy in all living cells. One way to understand this suite of molecules is to think about the money in your wallet. You may have some cash, but you also probably have credit cards, and perhaps even a check or two. Each of these items provides a way of moving money around, and each is appropriate for different situations. You pay cash for small purchases, make larger purchases with a credit card, and pay some of your bills by check. In the same way, a cell has different molecules that store different amounts of energy, each of which is appropriate to a particular use.

The most common of these energy carriers is *adenosine triphosphate (ATP)*—a molecule that provides energy for countless chemical processes in all living cells. A sketch of this molecule is given in Figure 21-11. The structure of ATP illustrates an important characteristic of life's molecular building blocks: they tend to be built from a few simple, small molecules. ATP contains three phosphate groups (collections of one phosphorus and oxygen atoms) at the end of the molecule (these three phosphates are what give ATP the "tri" part of its name). The other parts of the molecule consist of a sugar molecule called ribose, which is also a building block of the RNA structure (see Chapter 23), and the base adenine, which is part of both DNA and RNA.

A considerable amount of energy is required to put phosphate groups onto the ends of the tail of an ATP molecule. In the language of Chapter 10, putting the last phosphate group on the ATP tail is an endothermic

FIGURE 21-11 Sketch of ATP, the energy "money" of cells. Note that it is built from a sugar (ribose), a base (adenine), and three phosphate groups.

Base

Phosphate groups

Sugar

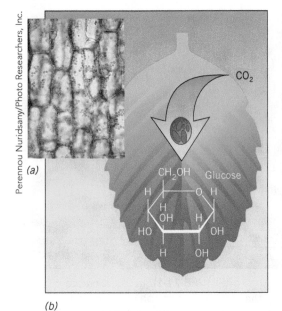

Perennou Nuridsany/Photo Researchers, Inc.

(a)

(b)

FIGURE 21-12 The process of photosynthesis. *(a)* Chloroplasts (shown here in a photomicrograph of a Canadian pondweed leaf) absorb energy from the Sun. *(b)* That energy is then used to convert carbon dioxide from the atmosphere and water into carbohydrates, such as glucose. Plants are green because of the presence of chlorophyll.

process. If the phosphate group is subsequently removed in another chemical reaction, that energy is available to drive other chemical reactions. Thus, the ATP molecule can carry energy in the form of phosphorus–oxygen bonds from one part of the cell to another.

In one place in a cell—in the mitochondria, for example—chemical reactions produce energy. This energy is used to produce molecules of ATP. These molecules then move out of the place where they are made to a place where energy is needed. At this point, ATP acts something like a tiny battery: an ATP molecule attaches to part of the cell's chemical machinery, a phosphate group is removed, and the stored chemical potential energy becomes available to drive the desired chemical reactions. The triphosphate (three phosphates) then becomes a diphosphate (two phosphates) ADP:

$$ATP \rightarrow ADP + PO_4 + energy$$

ATP is the molecule that serves as the cell's "cash" in the cell's energy system. A typical cell will have several million ATP molecules doing their job at any given time. Other, more complex molecules (represented by the letters FADH and NADH) correspond to the "credit cards" in the cell's energy system. They store up energy and can be cashed in on short notice when extra energy is required. One way of thinking about the role of ATP is to say that when a chemical reaction adds the last phosphate group to ATP, the molecule picks up the equivalent of a pocketful of money. That money can be spent later for almost any purpose.

Photosynthesis

Photosynthesis, the mechanism by which plants convert the energy of sunlight into energy stored in carbohydrates, provides the chemical energy for almost all species (Figure 21-12). In plants, this complex process operates as follows: A large molecule, usually chlorophyll, absorbs sunlight. After a series of chemical reactions, this energy is ultimately stored in a set of molecules that includes ATP. Once the energy has been captured in this way, it is used in another complex series of reactions to produce essential molecules called carbohydrates. The most important carbohydrate molecule is glucose, an energy-rich sugar that also provides the module from which all of a plant's cellulose and starch polymers are made (see Chapter 22). The end result is the conversion of the energy in the electromagnetic radiation from the Sun into chemical energy stored in the bonds holding the carbohydrate molecules together.

The shorthand way of thinking about photosynthesis is to say:

In words: Energy in the form of sunlight plus carbon dioxide plus water react to produce carbohydrate (such as glucose) plus oxygen.

In equation form:

$$energy + CO_2 + H_2O \rightarrow carbohydrate + O_2$$

The rate at which plants produce oxygen and carbohydrates is usually limited by the amount of carbon dioxide in the air.

The most familiar molecule involved in photosynthesis, chlorophyll, occurs in various forms that can absorb red and blue light. The energy that falls as sunlight on a leaf is white light, roughly equal mixtures of all colors of the visible spectrum (see Chapter 6). The leaf absorbs red and blue components of light from the Sun, while green light is scattered—a situation that explains why leaves appear green. In addition to chlorophyll, a number of secondary molecules are involved in photosynthesis. These molecules tend to absorb blue light, so they appear to be red and orange. A normal leaf contains much more chlorophyll than secondary molecules, so the color of the secondary molecules is masked. In the fall, however, when the leaf dies and chlorophyll is no longer produced, its underlying color can be seen. We say that the leaves "change color," although the brilliant fall colors were there all the time.

Glycolysis: The First Step in Energy Generation in the Cell

The primary source of energy for living things comes from the oxidation of carbohydrates such as glucose. These sorts of reactions, called **respiration**, are taking place in all of your cells at this very moment. Your lungs breathe in oxygen produced by plants, while blood in your circulatory system transports that oxygen to every cell in your body. At the same time carbon dioxide, which is the end product of the breakdown of carbohydrates that you ingest in your food, is removed by the circulatory system to the lungs and breathed out as waste.

Respiration retrieves the energy stored in glucose in a complex series of cellular chemical reactions. Chemical bonds of the glucose molecule store chemical potential energy. The more glucose bonds that are broken—that is, the smaller the pieces of the final molecules—the more energy the cell will have transferred. The first step in the extraction of energy from glucose is called **glycolysis** (the "lysis," or splitting, of glucose). This rather complex process takes place in nine separate steps (Figure 21-13), each of which is governed by a specific molecule called an enzyme (see Chapter 22).

In words: Glucose splits to form two molecules of pyruvic acid plus smaller energy-rich molecules.

In equation form:

$$\text{glucose} \rightarrow 2\ \text{pyruvic acid} + \text{energy}$$

Thus, at the end of the process, a single molecule of glucose, which contains six linked carbon atoms, is split into two smaller molecules called pyruvic acids, each containing three carbon atoms. In addition, the reaction makes two molecules of ATP and two molecules of another energy carrier called NADH. In most cells, the energy stored in NADH is converted into two or three more molecules of ATP before they leave the mitochondria. Thus, each glucose molecule can ultimately yield six to eight molecules of ATP through the process of glycolysis.

After glucose has been split by glycolysis, energy can be generated in two separate and distinct ways: respiration and fermentation. Respiration requires the presence of oxygen and is therefore said to be *aerobic*. The primary function of your lungs and circulatory system is to maintain this aerobic respiration. Fermentation, however, can occur in the absence of oxygen and is said to be *anaerobic*.

Fermentation: A Way to Keep Glycolysis Going

Pyruvic acid molecules still hold a great deal of chemical potential energy. In the absence of oxygen, however, that energy cannot be liberated to run cellular metabolism. In this situation, a process called **fermentation** can be used to provide energy to keep glycolysis going. As long as there is a supply of glucose, the cell can go on generating energy, albeit somewhat inefficiently. In some cases, as in single-celled yeast, the end product of fermentation is ethanol—ordinary beverage alcohol. This sort of fermentation provides the basis for the production of wine and other alcoholic drinks (Figure 21-14).

When cells have to use glucose in the absence of oxygen, only a fraction of the available energy is used, and a great deal of energy is left stored in other molecules. Yeast is a good example. You know that alcohol, which is produced by yeast during the process of fermentation, contains a great deal of energy—it can, after all, be burned as a fuel. The chemical energy in alcohol is left behind by the yeast cells that made it—energy that the cells could not use because they were not able to metabolize it.

A somewhat different kind of fermentation takes place in cells of animals. The energy in pyruvic acid is normally tapped by the process of respiration (see the following section). In the absence of oxygen, however, our muscles can use fermentation to keep glycolysis going (often taking glucose from materials stored in the muscles themselves). The end product of

FIGURE 21-13 In the process of glycolysis a single molecule of glucose, which contains six linked carbon atoms, is split into two smaller molecules called *pyruvic acid*, each of which contains three carbon atoms. In addition, the reaction produces two molecules of ATP and two molecules of another energy carrier called *NADH*. In most cells, the energy stored in NADH is converted into two or three more molecules of ATP before they leave the mitochondria. Thus, each glucose molecule can ultimately yield six to eight molecules of ATP through the process of glycolysis.

this sort of fermentation is lactic acid, a three-carbon molecule that then accumulates in the muscle. When we undergo strenuous exercise, if our bodies are not prepared to deliver all the oxygen that is needed, the cells will eventually fall back on this simpler process. The buildup of lactic acid is the cause of the burning sensation during after unaccustomed intense exercise.

The fact that some of our cells can operate both with and without oxygen—the fact that they have this reserve process to fall back on—is taken by some scientists to indicate that cells evolved fermentation reactions first and only later developed the ability to burn oxygen. You can think of the body's use of fermentation as analogous to writing a term paper with a pencil when a power outage makes a computer unavailable. It's not the most efficient way to work, but it gets the job done.

The Final Stages of Respiration

In human cells, the energy-rich products of glycolysis react in the mitochondria, and all the available energy that was stored in the glucose is retrieved. The end effect of these chemical reactions is that oxygen and the pyruvic acid molecules take part in a complex series of reactions to produce carbon dioxide, water, and a large amount of energy stored in ATP molecules.

In cells where oxygen is available, molecules of pyruvic acid (with three carbon atoms) are first broken down into two-carbon groups and then enter a complex series of chemical reactions called the *Krebs cycle*. In the course of this cycle, the original glucose is broken down and converted into carbon dioxide and water (Figure 21-15), some energy is released to ATP molecules, and the rest of the energy is stored in some of the other energy-carrying molecules. This process, then, is essentially the reverse of photosynthesis discussed above.

In words: Carbohydrate plus oxygen react to produce energy plus carbon dioxide plus water.

In equation form:

$$\text{carbohydrate} + O_2 \rightarrow \text{energy (in the form of ATP and other small molecules)} + CO_2 + H_2O$$

The exact number of ATP molecules produced from a single glucose molecule depends on details of the structure of the mitochondrial membranes and varies slightly from one cell to another. As a general rule, however, the metabolism of a single glucose molecule ultimately produces 36 to 38 molecules of ATP, which can then be used by the cell to run all the rest of its chemical machinery. Compare this production to the six to eight ATP molecules produced by glycolysis alone.

Thus, aerobic reactions yield significantly more energy per molecule of glucose than anaerobic processes. It can be argued that the large amounts of energy needed to maintain a multicellular organism would not have been available to organisms that had not developed respiration. The outcome of this line of thought is that before a significant amount of oxygen became available in the atmosphere, complex life forms could not have evolved. We will discuss the development of complex organisms in Chapter 25.

STOP & THINK Where did you get the energy that keeps you alive today?

⊙ 21.5 Cell Division

A key principle of the cell theory is that all cells arise from previous cells, but how does this process occur? Individual cells do not last forever. As you read this text, cells are dying and being replaced throughout your body. In order for this sort of replacement to occur, cells must be able to reproduce. Microscopic observations of living cells have revealed that cells divide and reproduce by two separate processes, called mitosis and meiosis.

FIGURE 21-14 Microscopic organisms undergo fermentation—a process that is critical to the production of cheese, bread, and wine.

FIGURE 21-15 The process of respiration expels water vapor, which appears as condensation on a cold day.

FIGURE 21-16 Mitosis, shown schematically for a cell with two pairs of chromosomes, one larger and one smaller. *(a)* In each pair, purple and green individual chromosomes are from different parents. *(b)* Chromosomes duplicate, resulting in two identical sets of two pairs. *(c)* Matched pairs of chromosomes are pulled along spindles to opposite ends of the cell. *(d)* A new membrane forms and separates the parent cell into two identical daughter cells. *(e)* Micrographs show a typical dividing cell.

Mitosis

(a)

(b)

(c)

(d)

(e)

Bajer, Mole-Bajer and Heneen (2010): The Beauty of Mitosis, University Version, https://www.createspace.com/292574

Mitosis

In the great majority of cell divisions in living organisms, a single cell splits, so that two cells appear where once there was only one. It is by means of this process of cell division, called **mitosis**, that organisms grow and maintain themselves. When you get a cut or sunburn, this process quickly replaces damaged cells. Mitosis involves the reproduction of individual cells but is not involved in sexual reproduction in higher plants and animals.

In Chapter 23, we will discover that DNA governs the chemical workings of any cell. DNA in eukaryotes is contained within the cell nucleus in structures called *chromosomes.* When chromosomes were first discovered in the nineteenth century, there was an intense debate about their function. Today, we understand that each chromosome is a long strand of the DNA double helix, with the strand wrapped around a series of protein cores like tape around a spool.

Chromosomes come in pairs, but there is no connection between the number of chromosomes and the complexity of an organism. Humans have 46 chromosomes (23 pairs), but the number of pairs varies from one species to another. Mosquitoes, for example, have 6 while dogs have 78.

The process of mitosis is shown schematically in Figure 21-16. Assume for simplicity that we begin with a cell that has just two pairs of chromosomes, one shown larger than the other in Figure 21-16a. Each individual chromosome of the pair, furthermore, differs slightly from the other because (as we shall see in the discussion of meiosis, below) one comes from the male parent and the other from the female parent. Individual chromosomes in a pair are thus illustrated in purple and green. These differences in size and color will help you follow the path of each chromosome through cell division.

The first step in mitosis is the copying of the chromosomes (a process we will describe in more detail in the next chapter). As shown in Figure 21-16b, a cell that is about to divide has twice the normal number of chromosomes, neatly paired off like socks that have been sorted after going through the laundry.

After duplication of the chromosomes, the nuclear membrane dissolves and a series of fibers called *spindle fibers* develop (Figure 21-16c). The matched chromosome pairs are pulled apart and migrate to opposite ends of the cell. After this separation, the nuclear membranes reform and the cell splits down the middle (Figure 21-16d). The result is two cells, each of which carries a set of chromosomes that are identical to the original. Powerful microscopes can capture photographs of these stages of mitosis in progress (Figure 21-16e).

Some cells in your body divide often; the cells in the lining of the small intestine, for example, are replaced every few days (Figure 21-17). Other cells, such as those of the nervous system, don't divide at all after maturity.

Meiosis

A remarkable, specialized kind of cell division called **meiosis** takes place in a few cells in organisms that reproduce sexually. In this process, a single cell with a full complement of chromosomes splits to form four daughter cells, or *gametes,* each of which has half the number of chromosomes found in most normal cells. The central function of meiosis is to generate the sperm and eggs (or ova) that will later combine in sexual reproduction to produce a new member of the species. Recall that in mitosis, two daughter cells are genetically identical to the original cell, but in meiosis each gamete has its own unique new combination of genetic material.

Key steps of meiosis are illustrated in Figure 21-18. As in Figure 21-16, we begin with a cell that has two pairs of chromosomes, one shown larger than the other and with distinctively colored individual chromosomes (Figure 21-18a). The first step of meiosis is the same as for mitosis—the chromosomes are copied so that the cell has twice the usual amount of DNA— two larger identical green chromosomes, two smaller identical purple chromosomes, and so on—in "X"-shaped pairs (compare Figures 21-16b and 21-18b). But from this point, meiosis differs from mitosis in several important and striking ways.

By an extraordinary mechanism, two X-shaped pairs of chromosomes (one all-purple and one all-green) cross over each other and can exchange short lengths of genetic material, thus generating chromosomes with a new mix of genetic material from both parents (this effect is illustrated as mixed purple and green in Figure 21-18c and one pair of chromosomes enlarged to show detail in 21-18k). Note that at this point the cell has eight chromosomes, some of which differ from any of the four original purple or green chromosomes.

The remaining steps of meiosis consist of a sequence of changes that sort out these eight chromosomes into smaller groups. First, the four X-shaped pairs of chromosomes segregate along spindle fibers so that each of two daughter cells has two X-shaped pairs of chromosomes—one longer and one shorter (Figure 21-18d–f). Then the X-shaped pairs of chromosomes in each daughter cell are pulled apart along more spindle fibers and these cells split again, producing a total of four gametes (Figure 21-18g–j). Each of these four sex cells has

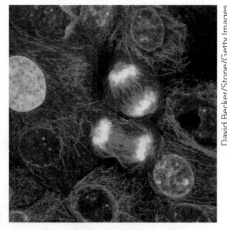

FIGURE 21-17 A human cell dividing. Genetic material shows as yellow, while the spindles appear dark pink in this false-color photomicrograph.

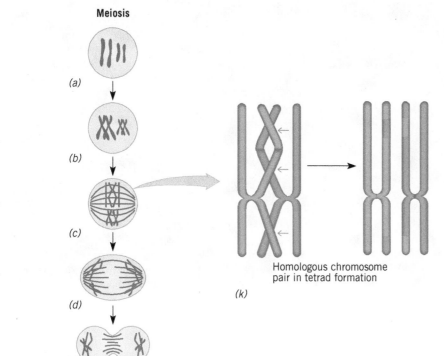

Homologous chromosome pair in tetrad formation

(k)

FIGURE 21-18 Meiosis, shown schematically (see text). As in mitosis, the chromosomes are duplicated and paired. The pairs separate and the cell divides for the first time. The chromosome pairs then separate and each daughter divides again, producing a total of four cells, each with half the normal complement of DNA. Crossing over between pairs of chromosomes results in the shuffling of genetic material to yield chromosomes with a new genetic makeup.

two individual chromosomes, or half the normal complement. These chromosomes eventually are incorporated into sperm or egg.

At first glance, this elaborate process of meiosis may seem to be an extravagant and unnecessary way to divide cells. However, as we shall see in Chapter 25, the ability of sexually reproducing organisms constantly to vary their genetic makeup can provide a tremendous advantage in the struggle to survive.

THINKING MORE ABOUT CELLS

Biochemical Evidence for Evolution

The most striking thing about the energy metabolism of cells is that every single living thing on Earth, from the lowest bit of pond scum to the cells in our own bodies, uses part or all of the same chemical reaction cycles to obtain energy. In other words, they share a common biochemical background.

Most cells get energy from glucose by the process of glycolysis. Cells in advanced organisms—those in your own body, for example—can get more energy by adding more oxidation steps to the process of glycolysis. Some cells cannot do this, and therefore obtain less energy from each glucose molecule. This difference turns out to be a universal feature of living things; that is, when you examine life's chemical reactions, you find that more specialized cells tend to use more chemical processes, but those specialized reactions are built up from chemical reactions present in more primitive cells.

You can think of the situation in cells as something like the way a complex chemical factory might develop. Long ago the factory may have made just one kind of chemical, perhaps white powdered lime for your lawn. As the factory grew and expanded, many new chemicals were produced—fertilizers and insecticides, for example. But the lime-making operation was still intact, ready to be used any time. We could, in fact, deduce the history of the factory by taking it apart and seeing how various chemical operations have been added on.

Scientists suspect that cells, the chemical factories of life, behave the same way. Biochemical evidence demonstrates that older, simpler chemical reactions lie at the heart of the more complex operations of today's cells. Some biologists argue that this fact implies that all life descended from a common ancestor. How could you make such an argument based on what you know of respiration and fermentation? What do you think the more primitive ancestors must have been like? Do you think the ancestors must have been in an environment that was rich in oxygen? Why or why not?

RETURN TO THE INTEGRATED QUESTION

What is the smallest living thing?

- All organisms consist of collections of atoms and molecules. Nevertheless, living things are more than just an assortment of atoms and subatomic particles. As we saw in Chapter 20, an entity must exhibit a number of characteristics for us to say that it is "alive."
  - The most basic attribute of life is the organization of matter into a system that is capable of ingesting matter and energy.
  - Reproduction is another essential feature of living systems.
- From this perspective, the smallest identifiable unit capable of these processes is the cell.
  - Many different kinds of cells can be found in nature; they come in a wide range of sizes and shapes and perform many varied functions.
- As a group, bacteria may be the smallest living things we know.
  - Bacteria are a group of single-cell microbes that are typically only a few dozen micrometers in length, though bacteria come in many different shapes and sizes.
  - Bacteria are ubiquitous, existing in nearly every known ecological niche from swamps to radioactive waste to the human body.

- Many times more bacteria live in your body than other types of cells. Most of these bacteria are in your digestive tract and on your skin.
  - Most bacteria are harmless and some are actually beneficial. For example, intestinal microbiota produce essential nutrients such as biotin and vitamin K.
  - Nevertheless, some bacteria are pathogenic and cause infectious diseases, including bubonic plague and one the most prevalent of the deadly bacterial diseases, tuberculosis.
- Other forms of matter such as viruses are considerably smaller than the smallest bacterium.
  - Viruses (from the Latin word for poison) are submicroscopic infectious agents that can be many hundreds of times smaller than most bacteria.
  - Viruses are unable to grow and reproduce without a host cell. Therefore, they are usually not considered to be "alive."
  - Viruses are responsible for diseases such as chicken pox and acquired immunodeficiency syndrome (AIDS).

SUMMARY

Cells, complex chemical systems with the ability to reproduce, are the fundamental units of life. All cells are bounded by a *cell membrane* consisting of a double layer of elongated molecules. Most plants also have a *cell wall* made of cellulose and other strong polymers. Nutrients move into and wastes pass out of the cell through the cell membrane at *receptors,* which bind to specific molecules because of their distinctive shapes.

Cells possess a complex internal structure with many different kinds of chemical machinery. All but the most primitive cells have a *nucleus,* a structure surrounded by a double cell membrane that contains DNA. Other discrete structures, or *organelles,* in the cell perform various specialized functions.

Every cell must have a chemical mechanism for obtaining and distributing energy—the process of *metabolism.* Plants absorb light from the Sun and convert this radiant energy into chemical energy in *chloroplasts* by the process of *photosynthesis.* Animals must eat food with chemical potential energy, primarily carbohydrates such as glucose originally derived from plants. The first step in getting energy from glucose is *glycolysis,* a series of chemical reactions that take place in *mitochondria,* by which the glucose molecule is split into pyruvic acid molecules. In the process of fermentation these molecules are broken down into molecules such as ethanol and lactic acid, and the energy is used to keep fermentation going. In the process of *respiration,* pyruvic acid molecules are broken down to carbon dioxide and water, liberating much more energy in the process.

Most cells divide by the process of *mitosis,* in which chromosomes are first duplicated, then separated. The cell then divides, producing two daughters, each of which has the same complement of DNA as the original cell. In *meiosis,* which produces sperm and eggs for sexual reproduction, chromosome duplication is followed by two divisions that result in a set of four cells, each of which has half the normal complement of DNA.

KEY TERMS

cell

cell membrane

receptor

cell wall

nucleus

organelle

chloroplasts

mitochondria

metabolism

photosynthesis

respiration

glycolysis

fermentation

mitosis

meiosis

DISCOVERY **LAB**

Fermentation is a method of changing sugars into alcohol in the absence of oxygen. Thus, energy and carbon dioxide are produced in the process. In fruits the sugar is converted to alcohol. Over time alcohol destroys the yeast cells and ultimately alcohol changes to vinegar by the action of microorganisms. To observe fermentation you will need baker's yeast, fruit, Ziploc bags of different sizes, pH paper (optional) and matches.

Place 1 heaping teaspoon of yeast in a large Ziploc bag. Cut up about 10 ounces of fruit and place it in a smaller Ziploc bag. Make numerous holes in the small bag. Squeeze the bag a little and put a few drops of fruit juice on the pH paper to determine the pH of fruit. Place the small bag inside the large bag. Close both bags and squeeze the small bag more tightly so that the fruit juice mixes with the yeast in the large bag. Set aside the bags for over an hour and observe. Light a match and carefully lower it inside the large bag. The gas inside the bag will extinguish the match. This indicates the presence of carbon dioxide. Test the pH of the products by using pH paper. Repeat the experiment at different temperatures. You can also test different fruits using the same procedure. Compare your

results and try to answer the following questions. What are some of the products of fermentation? What happened to the pH before, during and after the experiment? Why do you think pH changed? What happens to the sugar over time? Does temperature make a difference? Does the type of fruit make a difference?

REVIEW QUESTIONS

1. Why do scientists call the cell fundamental unit of life?
2. How big are the largest and smallest cells?

3. What is cell theory? State three tenets of the cell theory. How do they relate to plants and animals?

4. What is the difference between a light microscope and an electron microscope? What are the smallest things that can be seen with each? How does this compare to the wavelength of the radiation that each probe uses?

5. List all the ways that molecules can move across cell membranes.

6. How is the cell membrane analogous to the walls of a factory?

7. What is the function of receptors in the cell membrane?

8. How do cell walls differ from cell membranes?

9. What is the difference between a prokaryote and a eukaryote? Give examples of each.

10. What does the nucleus of the cell contain? What role does it play in the regulation of the cell?

11. What does the double membrane of the nucleus tell us about the evolution of eukaryotes?

12. What is metabolism?

13. What is ATP? What role does it play in the energy balance of a cell?

14. In what ways are chloroplasts and mitochondria similar? How do they differ?

15. Why aren't leaves always red and brown?

16. What are the products of photosynthesis? What molecules are involved in making photosynthesis happen in plants?

17. What is fermentation? Why is fermentation considered a way to "keep glycolysis going"? What are its end products?

18. What is respiration? How does it provide energy for living cells?

19. When does a human body use fermentation rather than respiration for energy?

20. In what ways are mitosis and meiosis similar? How do they differ?

DISCUSSION QUESTIONS

1. How is the theory that some organelles in a cell resulted from a symbiotic relationship in the distant past consistent with the observation of the double membrane of those organelles?

2. Is it accurate to say that nearly all life on Earth depends on photosynthesis? Why or why not?

3. Consider your last meal. Did each of your food items depend in some way—either directly or indirectly—on photosynthesis? If so, how?

4. What is the name of the process that forms alcohol? Can alcohol be used as a source of energy for people? What are the pros and cons, if any, of doing so?

5. Compare and contrast the cells of plants versus the cells of mammals. How are they similar? How are they different?

6. List all the ways you can think of in which cells are analogous to chemical factories.

7. How is having a semipermeable membrane important to the functioning of a cell? What role do receptors play in the transport of substances through a cellular membrane?

8. How does understanding the functions of a cell explain why your muscles are sore after a strenuous workout?

9. Does meiosis occur in all eukaryotic cells? If not, under what circumstances does it occur? How does this process create a new nucleus? What effect does this have on the genetic make-up of offspring?

10. What kind of cells do not have a nucleus? Are they capable of reproducing? How is this process different from those cells with a nucleus?

11. Discuss the ways a cell's energy metabolism is analogous to financial systems.

12. Much of our understanding of cellular behavior comes from the development of the electron microscope. What other technological advances have advanced our understanding of cellular and other biological processes?

13. Oxygen is important in respiration because the O_2 molecule is very chemically reactive. The ozone molecule, O_3, is even more chemically reactive, yet in sufficiently high concentrations—perhaps 100 parts per billion—ozone is toxic. Why do you think this is so?

14. Examining a specimen with an electron microscope is more complex than simply placing it on a slide and putting it in place as with an optical microscope. For one thing, most types of electron microscopes require that the specimen be examined in a vacuum. Why do you think this is? What other complications might there be in using an electron microscope compared to an optical microscope?

PROBLEMS

1. A eukaryotic cell can be anywhere from 10 to 100 μm (millionths of a meter) in diameter while the nucleus is around 5 μ in diameter. If we examine a cell with a diameter of 30 μm and assume the density of the overall cell is approximately the same as the density of the nucleus, then what percent of the cell's mass is the mass of the nucleus?

2. Over the course of a day, a 70-kg person will process an amount of ATP roughly equivalent to their body mass. On average, how many g of ATP are being converted into ADP + PO_4 + energy each second?

3. On average, an adult human will expend about 1,800 kilocalories per day. Processing a single ATP molecule produces about

1.2×10^{-23} kcal. How many ATP molecules must be processed each day to maintain energy levels?

4. The molecular formula for glucose is $C_6H_{12}O_6$. Consider the chemical equation for glycolysis given in the textbook: glucose → 2 pyruvic acid + energy. How many carbon atoms do you think are in a single molecule of pyruvic acid? (*Hint:* Although the actual chemical equation for glycolysis is more complicated than what is presented, you may assume that all of the carbon atoms on the right side of the equation are contained in pyruvic acid.)

a. 2

b. 3

c. 6

d. 12

5. Under favorable conditions, a prokaryotic cell like a bacterium can undergo the process of binary fission every 20 minutes. If you start with one bacterium, how many can you expect to have after 8 hours?

a. 24

b. 552

c. 576

d. 16.8 million

INVESTIGATIONS

1. Examine a drop of your own blood in a light microscope. What kinds of cells do you see?

2. How does the size of the smallest type of cell compare to the size of an atom?

3. How does an electron microscope work?

4. Many everyday products, including vinegar, Swiss cheese, and bread dough, rely on the process of fermentation. Investigate some of these varied products and the microorganisms that enable their manufacture.

5. We often hear of "aerobic" exercises. Is there any connection between these exercises and aerobic processes in cells?

6. Look at water from a local pond or lake under a microscope. If you were van Leeuwenhoek, seeing this for the first time, how would you describe it?

7. Which cells in the human body divide the fastest? Which do not divide at all? Investigate the medical implications of this.

8. Investigate what diseases are associated with cells that divide too rapidly or too slowly.

9. Visit a local vineyard and learn about the various forms of yeast and fermentation that are used to make wine. Why does sparkling wine and Champagne have carbonation? Where does the carbonation come from?

10. What forms of energy are used when someone lifts a barbell to momentary muscular failure? What are the by-products of this activity? Are they different from the by-products produced by a marathoner's muscles as the marathoner's race is completed?

11. Organelles perform various functions within each cell. Investigate the various functions that different types of cells perform within the human body.

12. Find out what happens in your muscle cells when you lift a weight.

Molecules of Life

What constitutes a healthy diet?

PHYSICS

Sugar molecules are the source of energy in the cells of living things.

BIOLOGY

Most of the structures of living things are made of proteins, carbohydrates, and lipids.

CHEMISTRY

The shape of organic molecules determines their chemical function in the cell.

GREAT IDEA

A cell's major parts are constructed from a few simple molecular building blocks.

TECHNOLOGY

Synthetic molecules are used as additives in food without affecting the body's digestive system.

GEOLOGY

Rocks, like cells, are modular; they are formed from many mineral grains. (Ch. 18)

ASTRONOMY

The action of the Sun's ultraviolet radiation on the skin can produce minute quantities of vitamin D in the body.

HEALTH & SAFETY

Your body needs a constant supply of minerals and organic molecules such as proteins to sustain itself and continue growing.

 = applications of the great idea discussed in this chapter

 = other applications, some of which are discussed in other chapters

An Afternoon Snack

A granola bar makes a tasty, energy-rich, mid-afternoon snack. You lie back on your beach towel, take a bite, and start to think about food. Why do we get hungry? What chemicals make up food? Why do some foods taste better than others?

Take a close look at the colorful granola bar wrapper and find the "Nutrition Facts" printed on the back. At the top of the list is "Calories"—a measure of food energy. Our bodies require energy to do work, just like every other physical system does. That's why we get hungry.

The nutrition facts also include information on specific kinds of molecules, notably fat, carbohydrates, and protein. These molecules are fundamental building blocks of every living thing, and so they are an essential part of our diets. We need a steady supply of these molecules because we are, quite literally, what we eat. Food tastes good because our taste buds are fine-tuned to these critical molecules.

Johnathan A. Meyers/Photo Researchers/Getty Images, Inc.

● 22.1 Organic Molecules

Next time you're outside, look closely at a tree. The trunk and limbs divide over and over again, a branching that is mirrored by the hidden root system. The tree has countless, almost identical leaves on every limb, as well as myriad seeds in their season. Repeating the same basic patterns over and over again results in the complex structure of the tree.

Structures in your city or town reveal the same kind of patterns. Buildings feature stacks of identical bricks, row after row of identical windows, and numerous identical shingles, slates, or other roofing materials. The sidewalk is made of slab after slab of concrete, while street lamps, signs, fence posts, and telephone poles also repeat over and over again.

Indeed, almost any complex structure found in nature or designed by humans is modular, composed of a few simple pieces that combine to form larger objects. Molecules of water form the ocean, mineral grains form rocks, and vast numbers of identical hydrogen atoms form stars. The chemicals of life are no different. A few basic molecules combine to create the wonderful complexity of life around us.

Four Basic Characteristics

Wood. Leather. Hair. Cotton. Skin. All of these materials originated in living systems on our planet. And, like all other materials found in living things, they share some basic chemical characteristics.

TABLE 22-1 **Atoms in the Human Body**

Element	Percent
Hydrogen	61.2
Oxygen	23.5
Carbon	11.7
Nitrogen	1.1
Calcium (mostly in bones)	2.0
Phosphorus	0.2
Sulfur	0.1
All others	0.2

1. Most Molecules in Living Systems Are Based on the Chemistry of Carbon

In Chapter 10, we saw that carbon atoms possess the unique ability to form molecules of almost any size and shape—long chains, branches, and rings. In fact, chemists usually refer to molecules containing carbon as **organic molecules**, whether or not they are part of a living system. The branch of science devoted to the study of such carbon-based molecules and their reactions is called *organic chemistry*.

2. Life's Molecules Form from Very Few Different Elements

In terms of the percentages of atoms, just four elements—hydrogen, oxygen, carbon, and nitrogen—comprise 97.5% of our bodies' weight. Calcium in bones accounts for 2%, whereas phosphorus, sulfur, and all the other elements make up the remaining 0.5% (see Table 22-1). These elements combine to form the molecules that control chemical reactions in all living things.

3. The Molecules of Life Are Modular, Composed of Simple Building Blocks

Large and complicated molecules could be put together in two contrasting ways. One way would be to build each one from scratch, so that no piece of one molecule would be part of another. Another very different way would be to make the molecules modular, that is, to build them from a succession of simpler, widely available parts so that each large molecule differs from another only in the arrangement of those parts. Nature, for the most part, displays modularity in the molecules of living systems.

Modern buildings illustrate the versatility of modular construction. All kinds of buildings, ranging from a humble cottage to a soaring skyscraper, can be built from a few basic parts—bricks, beams, windows, doors, stairs, and so on. The skyscraper and the cottage differ from each other both in the amount of material in them and in the arrangement of those materials, but they contain many of the same basic modules. This kind of modular construction is extremely efficient. It takes a great deal of work, time, and money to custom-design every door, window, and other component of your home. You might end up with a better-designed structure but at a very high price. By building your home with widely available parts, you save money and still end up with a very satisfactory dwelling.

Similarly, though life's molecules come in an extraordinary variety of shapes and functions, they are made from collections of just a few smaller molecules. This modularity does not mean that the final products are simple, just as there's nothing particularly simple about a skyscraper. It merely means that if we wish to understand how large molecules behave, we first have to talk about the simple pieces from which they are built.

4. Shape Helps to Determine the Behavior of Organic Molecules—In Other Words, Molecular Geometry Controls the Chemistry of Life

The connection between geometry and the behavior of organic molecules can be understood if you remember one important thing about chemical bonds. All chemical bonds result from the shifting of electrons among specific pairs or groups of atoms. This bonding property is particularly true of atoms that tend to form ionic, covalent, and hydrogen bonds (see Chapter 10).

A very large and complex molecule may have millions of atoms arranged in an intricate shape. If this large molecule is to take part in chemical reactions—if it is to bind to another molecule, for example—then that binding must take place through the actions of the valence electrons of atoms near the outsides of the two molecules. Specific atoms in each molecule must be able to get near enough to each other so that their electrons can form the bond. Consequently, the geometrical shape of a molecule plays a crucial role because it determines whether atoms that can form bonds in each molecule will be able to get close enough together for the bonds actually to form.

In principle, an infinite number of molecules could be constructed according to these four rules. In fact, when we examine natural systems, we find that only four general classes of molecules govern most of life's main chemical functions. We'll discuss three of these classes—proteins, carbohydrates, and lipids—in this chapter (the fourth important group of molecules, nucleic acids, are introduced in Chapter 23 on the genetic code). Throughout this discussion, you should keep in mind that all of these molecules conform to the four rules: they are carbon-based, they form from just a few elements, they are modular in structure, and their behavior depends on shape.

Chemical Shorthand

If we kept showing all of the atoms and bonds, as we do for an amino acid in Figure 22-1, diagrams of molecules would get very cluttered as the molecules become more complex. Consequently, chemists have adopted several standard shorthand ways of representing organic molecules. Many molecules can be represented by the following rules:

1. *No hydrogen atoms or bonds to hydrogen atoms are shown in the diagram.*
2. *Carbon atoms are not shown explicitly.*

As an example of how this notation works, look at the following diagram. Both of these drawings show molecules of benzene, which has the chemical formula C_6H_6 (a volatile liquid sometimes used as a motor fuel). On the left, all the atoms are shown, and you can see that each carbon atom forms four bonds to its neighboring atoms. On the right, the carbon atoms are not shown, but we know they are located at the points where the bonds come together. Similarly, the hydrogen atoms are not shown, but we see that each carbon atom has only three bonds shown. We infer the existence of the hydrogen atom by the "missing" bond. (Remember, each carbon atom forms four bonds.)

FIGURE 22-1 An amino acid, showing the amino (NH_2) and carboxylic acid (COOH) groups and the side group. The side group varies from one type of amino acid to another and gives that particular amino acid the chemical properties that distinguish it from any other.

All atoms and bonds are shown.

Only carbon–carbon bonds are shown. Carbon atoms, hydrogen atoms, and carbon–hydrogen bonds are implied.

 SCIENCE IN THE MAKING
The Synthesis of Urea

In the early 1800s, scientists were not convinced that molecules in living systems are formed according to the same chemical rules that govern those in nonliving systems. Such molecules, after all, had not been produced in the laboratory. In 1828, a German chemist by the name of Friedrich Wöhler (1800–1882) performed a series of experiments that were crucial in establishing the ordinariness of organic molecules.

Like many scientists at that time, Wöhler had a breadth of experience that is unusual today. Before he began his career as a chemistry teacher, for example, he became a medical doctor and qualified in the specialty of gynecology. He was also interested in the practical aspects of chemistry, and he collected minerals from the time he was a child. He described his crucial experiments this way: "I found that whenever one tried to combine cyanic acid (a common laboratory chemical) and ammonia, a white crystalline solid appeared that behaved like neither cyanic acid nor ammonia."

After extensive testing, Wöhler found that the white crystals were identical to urea, a substance routinely found in the kidneys and (as the name suggests) urine. In other words, the appearance of that "white crystalline solid" showed that it is possible to take ordinary chemicals off the shelf and produce a substance found in living systems. He had demonstrated that the same chemical processes typical of abiotic materials might form organic molecules.

With humor uncharacteristic of most academicians, Wöhler announced his findings in a letter as follows: "I can no longer, as it were, hold back my chemical urine: and I have to let out that I can make urea without needing a kidney, whether of man or dog."

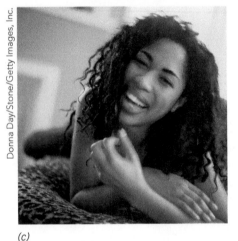

(a)

(b)

(c)

FIGURE 22-2 *(a)* A spider's silk, *(b)* fingernails, and *(c)* hair are everyday examples of structural proteins.

◉ 22.2 Proteins: The Workhorses of Life

The molecules we call proteins play many key roles in living systems. Some proteins form building materials from which large structures are formed. Your hair, your fingernails, the tendons that hold your muscles in place, and much of the connective tissue that holds your body together, for example, are made primarily of protein molecules (Figure 22-2). Proteins also serve as the *receptors* that regulate the movement of materials across cell walls, and thus control what goes into and out of each cell in your body (see Chapter 21). Proteins play many specialized roles in our bodies—for example, as hormones that regulate bodily functions and as antibodies that protect against infection and disease. In addition, proteins serve as enzymes, molecules that control the rate of complex chemical reactions in living things (see the following section). Indeed, proteins play a major role in almost every cellular function in your body.

Because of these many critical roles, proteins are vital components of your diet. You must regularly take in proteins to supply your body with building materials to effect repairs and growth.

Amino Acids: The Building Blocks of Proteins

Proteins are modular just like all complex biological molecules. They are made up of strings of basic building blocks called **amino acids**. A typical amino acid molecule is sketched in Figure 22-1. All biological amino acids incorporate a characteristic backbone of atoms. One end terminates in a *carboxylic acid group* (COOH), a combination of carbon, oxygen, and hydrogen atoms. On the other end is an *amino group* (NH_2), a nitrogen atom bonded to two hydrogen atoms. (These two groups give this category of molecules their name.) Between these two ends a carbon atom completes the backbone.

Branching off the central carbon atom is another atom or cluster of atoms, the "side group" that makes each kind of amino acids unique and interesting. Hundreds of different amino acids can be made in the laboratory, each with its different characteristic side group. A few common amino acids are sketched in Figure 22-3 to give you a sense of the kind of diversity that is possible within this basic structure.

Two amino acids can bond together in a very simple way. A hydrogen atom (H) from the amino end will connect to the hydroxyl (OH) group of the carboxylic acid end of another amino acid to form a molecule of water (H_2O). This water molecule separates from the two amino acids, leaving them bonded together in what is called a *peptide bond*. This process is identical to the *condensation polymerization* reaction that is often used to manufacture plastics and other polymers (see Chapter 10). Indeed, chemists often refer to a bonded chain of amino acids as a *polypeptide*.

Once two amino acids have joined together with a peptide bond, more amino acids can be hooked onto either end by the same process to form a long string of amino acids. A **protein** is

FIGURE 22-3 Several amino acids. Each has a distinctive side group (green box) that branches off the central carbon atom.

a large molecule formed by linking amino acids together in this way. There are many different amino acids to choose from, and different proteins correspond to a different ordering (as well as a different total number) of the amino acids in the string.

One of the great surprises that came out of the study of biochemistry in the early part of the twentieth century was that although chemists can synthesize hundreds of different amino acids, only 20 of these varied amino acids are produced in cells (although some of these can be modified slightly once the amino acid string is put together). The mystery of why only 20 amino acids are found in living things has a possible explanation in terms of the theory of evolution, which we explore in Chapter 25. Note, however, that even with only 20 basic building blocks, an almost infinite variety of different strings or proteins can be formed (see the following "Science by the Numbers" section).

The Structure of Proteins

Proteins are extremely complex molecules, sometimes consisting of many thousands of amino acids and millions of atoms. One of the great triumphs of modern science has been to determine the exact atomic structures of many of these large molecules. To accomplish this feat, biochemists first have to isolate quantities of pure protein, form delicate single crystals in which the large molecules line up in a regular array, and examine the crystals by X-ray techniques that reveal the distribution of atoms in space.

A protein's structure is usually described in four stages, each representing an increasing order of complexity (Figure 22-4).

1. Primary Structure

The exact sequence of amino acids that go into a given protein is called its *primary structure*. Every distinct protein has a different primary structure—that is, it has a different sequence of amino acids along its string.

2. Secondary Structure

Depending on the arrangements of amino acids in the primary structure, hydrogen bonds can form that give the final protein a specific shape. Some proteins, for example, take the form of a long helix or long spring. Others fold back on themselves repeatedly to form rough spheres. Shapes taken by the string of amino acids that makes up the primary structure of a protein are called its *secondary structure*.

When you cook an egg, you can see the effect of secondary structure. The proteins in egg white are wrapped up into tiny spheres scattered throughout the fluid. This is why normal egg white is transparent. When you cook the egg white, you break the hydrogen bonds that keep the protein wrapped up and allow the molecules to unfold. The tough mat they form when they interlock gives the cooked egg white its characteristic texture and appearance.

3. Tertiary Structure

As parts of the amino acid chain fold back on itself, atoms in the side groups can come into contact with each other. As a result, additional cross-linking chemical bonds form between side groups in amino acids in different parts of the chain. One common link occurs between sulfur atoms in different side groups. The distinctive shape of human insulin, for example, arises because of bonds that form between sulfur atoms in the amino acid cystine.

As a result of these links, a protein will twist around, bend, kink, and fold itself into a complex shape, much as a string will fold itself into a complex shape if it's dropped on a table. This complex folding is the *tertiary structure* of the protein. Note that the shape of the protein, as determined by its tertiary structure, is critical to its proper functioning. Many human diseases, including some forms of arthritis, sickle-cell anemia, and hemophilia occur when proteins fail to fold properly (see Chapter 24).

Amino acid sequence

(a) **Primary structure**

α-Helix

(or) Random coil

(or)

β-Pleated sheet

(b) **Secondary structure** (3 configurations)

Myoglobin

(c) **Tertiary structure**

Hemoglobin

(d) **Quaternary structure**

FIGURE 22-4 The structure of a protein can be described in four steps. *(a)* Primary structure is the sequence of amino acids. *(b)* Secondary structure is the way the sequence kinks or bends. *(c)* Tertiary structure is the shape of the completely folded protein. *(d)* Quaternary structure is the clustering of several proteins to form the active structure, in this case, hemoglobin, which carries oxygen in your bloodstream.

4. Quaternary Structure

Finally, two or more long chains, each with its own secondary and tertiary structure, may come together to form a single larger unit. This joining of separate protein chains determines the *quaternary structure* of the protein.

Predicting the exact shape that will be assumed by a given sequence of amino acids remains one of the great goals of modern biochemistry, a goal that we are still far from reaching. But whether or not we can predict the ultimate shape of a protein, the fact remains that each different sequence of amino acids will produce a large molecule with a different three-dimensional shape. This fact will become important when we consider the role of proteins in the cell's chemistry.

 ## SCIENCE BY THE NUMBERS
How Many Proteins Can You Make?

At first, it may seem that with only 20 different amino acids available to build proteins in living systems, the number of different kinds of proteins you could make would be rather limited. Let's do some calculations to see why this isn't the case.

Suppose we start by asking a simple question: How many different proteins, each 10 amino acids long, can we make from amino acids found in living systems? (Once you've seen the answer to this question, you'll be able to figure out for yourself how to calculate the answer for a protein with any number of amino acids.)

One way of thinking about this question is to imagine that each protein consists of 10 amino acids on a string and each amino acid can be selected from one of 20 different boxes. We could choose the first amino acid of the string from any one of 20 boxes. For each of these 20 choices for the amino acid in the first position, there are 20 choices we could make for the amino acid in the second position. Thus we could choose amino acids to fill the first two vacancies on the string in $20 \times 20 = 400$ different ways.

Following this logic, the number of ways to arrange 10 amino acids in a string is

$$20 \times 20 \times 20 \times 20 \times 20 \times 20 \times 20 \times 20 \times 20 \times 20 = 1.028 \times 10^{13}$$

Thus, we could make about 10 trillion different proteins that contain 10 amino acids. This number is huge—100 million times larger than the number of proteins used in the human body. And, of course, this is just the number of different proteins you could make containing exactly 10 amino acids. Typical proteins in living systems contain many more amino acids, usually hundreds to thousands of them. The bottom line of this calculation is that, although only 20 different amino acids appear in living systems, this number still allows for a tremendous diversity of proteins.

◉ 22.3 Proteins as Enzymes

One of the key roles that proteins play in living systems is to act as enzymes in chemical reactions in cells. An **enzyme** is a molecule with a specific shape and structure that facilitates chemical reactions between other molecules, but that is not permanently altered or used up in that overall reaction. Because of the presence of the enzyme, the chemical reaction takes place at a much faster rate than it otherwise would.

Enzymes play a role in every cell's chemical reactions similar to a broker or an agent in a business deal. The broker brings together a buyer and seller, but does no buying or selling. The buyer and seller eventually might find each other without the help of the broker, but the deal goes through much quicker if the broker is there. In the same way, a molecule that plays the role of an enzyme possesses a shape and structure that may bring together two other molecules in a cell and facilitate their forming a bond, or it may tear a molecule apart without itself being included in the chemical reaction. Because of the enzyme, the reaction takes place relatively quickly.

Enzymes illustrate the primary importance of geometrical shape in determining how chemical reactions take place among large molecules. You can easily visualize the workings of an enzyme (see Figure 22-5). Each large molecule has places on it, atoms or small groups of atoms, where chemical bonding can take place. Think of these locations as sticky spots somewhere on a large, convoluted molecular shape. In order for two or more molecules to interact, their respective sticky spots have to come into contact. More precisely, the atoms whose electrons will eventually form the bonds must be brought close enough together for the electrons to interact. This proximity is unlikely to happen at random.

Imagine each molecule as a large pile of string that is dumped in the corner of a room, and think of the spots that could form chemical bonds as patches of glue located at random places along the string. If, on one hand, you took two such pieces of string and tossed them together in the corner, the chances are very slight that any of the sticky spots would come near each other. If, on the other hand, you picked up the strings and arranged them so that the sticky spots were next to each other, you could make sure that they formed a bond. In this "chemical reaction," you are playing the role of the enzyme. You cause bonds to form that probably wouldn't form without you, but you do not become a part of the bond.

Enzymes perform an analogous function in organic reactions. Typically, an enzyme is a large molecule that has particular spots on its surface into which reacting molecules will just fit (Figure 22-6). The enzyme attracts first one of the molecules and then the other. In some enzymes, two specific molecules attach themselves in only one way, so it is guaranteed that their "sticky spots" will be near each other. The chemical bonds that hold them together will form. Once the bonds have formed, the overall shape of the resulting composite molecule suddenly becomes different from that of either of the two molecules that went into it. Consequently, the new large molecule no longer fits into the appropriate grooves and alleys of the enzyme, and it spontaneously breaks free and wanders off by itself. This separation leaves the enzyme free to mediate the same reaction again, each time with two new pieces. Another kind of enzyme, like those in your stomach, performs the opposite function, breaking apart large molecules into smaller units over and over again.

If you think about the way an enzyme works, you'll realize why molecular shape is so important (Figure 22-7). The ridges and grooves on the surface of an enzyme serve as resting places for the molecules that interact on the enzyme's surface. Tens of thousands of different protein molecules, each of which adopts a different shape and therefore provides a resting place for different interacting molecules, are ideally suited to function in this way. For precisely this reason, proteins participate in most of the chemical reactions in living organisms.

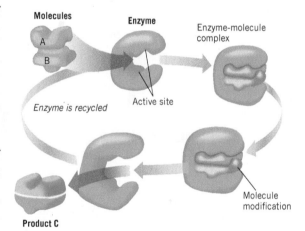

FIGURE 22-5 The atomic structure of human insulin arises because of bonds that form among amino acids.

FIGURE 22-6 An enzyme in action joins two molecules (designated A and B) and produces a product (C). The product is released, and the enzyme is free to repeat the process.

FIGURE 22-7 A computer-generated image of an enzyme in action. (a) A glucose molecule approaches the enzyme hexokinase. (b) When the two molecules combine, the shape and function of the enzyme change.

(a)

(b)

Courtesy T.A. Steitz, Department of Molecular Biophysics and Biochemistry, Yale University

Enzymes mediate the reactions of complex molecules in living systems. Thus, the molecules that act as enzymes in living systems play a crucial role in determining the properties of those systems.

STOP & THINK The relationship between an enzyme and the molecules that it reacts with is sometimes compared to a "lock and key" mechanism. What do you think is meant by this statement, and in what ways does it apply to enzymes?

THE SCIENCE OF LIFE
Proteins and Diet

Because proteins play such an important role in living systems, the cells in your body need a constant supply of all 20 amino acids. In adults, 12 of the 20 amino acids are synthesized in the body. The other eight, the so-called *essential amino acids,* have to be taken into the body in the proteins and other foods that we eat. Because amino acids, unlike fat, cannot be stored for long periods by the body, the essential amino acids have to be present in every meal in roughly the proportion in which they occur in the body's own proteins.

Foods vary widely in their total protein content, from about 1% in bananas and carrots to almost 30% in peanuts and some cheese. Foods that supply amino acids in roughly the same proportion as those in human proteins are called *high-quality proteins,* while those that supply too little of one or more amino acid are called *low-quality proteins.* In general, meat and dairy products supply high-quality proteins, whereas plant products supply low-quality proteins.

In Figure 22-8, we make this point by comparing the amount of each of the eight essential amino acids found in eggs (the food whose amino acids most closely match human protein proportions) and cornmeal. You should note, however, that it is not necessary for each food we eat, in and of itself, to supply all essential amino acids. It's possible to plan meals so that amino acids from one food make up for deficiencies of that amino acid in the other. Many traditional meals have this property. Milk, for example, provides the lysine that breakfast cereal lacks. The American staple, the peanut butter and jelly sandwich, provides the same kind of matching proteins. Many traditional foods from around the world do pretty well in supplying complementary sources of amino acids (Figure 22-9). Some examples: corn tortillas and beans (Mexico), rice and tofu (Japan), and rice and groundnuts (West Africa). Because plants provide low-quality protein, however, individuals on vegetarian diets must plan their food intake carefully to compensate for possible protein deficiencies.

By the way, have you ever wondered why we cook meats and other foods? High temperatures quickly depolymerize proteins (see Chapter 10), thus transforming long polymer chains into individual amino acid molecules. This chemical reaction breaks down tough protein fibers so that foods are more tender and easily digested. At the same time, any potentially harmful bacteria are killed when their proteins are destroyed.

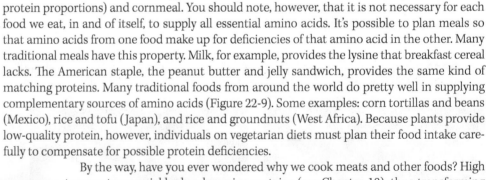

FIGURE 22-8 Proportions of essential amino acids in egg and cornmeal. The amino acid proportions for egg are close to those in the human body, whereas the cornmeal contains too little of the amino acids lysine, methionine, and tryptophan.

FIGURE 22-9 A mixture of tofu, spinach, and rice provides a balanced vegetarian diet with all eight of the essential amino acids.

How Drugs Work

Many of the drugs we take produce their effect because of the shape of their molecules. Some drugs, for example, alter our body chemistry by blocking the action of enzymes. You can understand how such a drug might work by looking at Figure 22-5, which illustrates the important enzyme insulin. The efficiency of the enzyme depends on the fact that the shape of its surface matches the shape of the molecules involved in the reaction. A drug molecule that attached itself to one of those crucial sites on the enzyme would block that site, preventing one of the molecules involved in the original reaction from occupying it. As a result, the enzyme would not be able to facilitate the reaction as it normally does, and the chemical balance of the cell would be changed. When you take an aspirin, for example, you are blocking the action of an enzyme that facilitates the production of molecules called prostaglandins. These molecules, among other things, affect the transmission of nerve signals.

Other drugs work in similar ways on other cellular processes. We saw in Chapter 21, for example, that part of the process of moving materials in and out of a cell across the cell membrane involves the fit between the molecules being moved and the specialized proteins, called receptors, in the membrane. A drug that attaches to the receptor or to the material that is being brought in or out of the cell will block this match and alter the traffic in and out of the cell. Similarly, in Chapter 5, we noted that nerve impulses are transmitted from one nerve cell to the next by special molecules called neurotransmitters. These molecules are shaped so that they fit into specific sites on the "downstream" nerve cell. Many drugs, including alcohol and Valium, gain their effect because they have the right shape to bind to the junctions between neurons and alter their operation.

As our understanding of the geometry of organic molecules has increased, scientists are increasingly able to produce molecules with the right shape from scratch. Products made in this way have been nicknamed "designer drugs." One such drug, called captopril, has been in use since 1975. This drug blocks the action of an enzyme that produces molecules that contribute to hypertension, and so is used to control that condition. Designer drugs for treating psoriasis, glaucoma, AIDS, and some forms of cancer and arthritis are in advanced stages of testing and may be on the market soon.

● 22.4 Carbohydrates

Carbohydrates, the second important class of modular molecules found in all living things, are made up of carbon, hydrogen, and oxygen atoms. Carbohydrates play a central role in the way that living things acquire and use energy, and they form many of the solid structures of living things. You use carbohydrates every day in many of the foods you eat, the fuels you burn, the clothes you wear, and even the paper of this book.

The simplest carbohydrates are **sugars**, molecules that usually contain five, six, or seven carbon atoms arranged in a ring-like structure. *Glucose,* an important sugar in the energy cycle of living things, is sketched in Figure 22-10. Glucose figures prominently in the energy metabolism of every living cell; it supplies the energy that we use to move and grow.

The general chemical formula for sugar is $C_nH_{2n}O_n$ or $C_n(H_2O)_n$. Glucose, for example, has the formula $C_6H_{12}O_6$. As often happens with organic molecules, other forms of the molecule have the same chemical composition but have the component arranged differently. In Figure 22-11, for example, we show fructose, a sugar commonly found in fruit. It has the same number of carbon, hydrogen, and oxygen atoms as glucose, but the atoms are arranged slightly differently and this different arrangement gives fructose a different chemical behavior.

Chemists call individual sugar molecules *monosaccharides,* meaning "one sugar." (The same root word is used when an overly sentimental story is described as "saccharine.") The carbohydrates that we eat, however, are usually formed from two or more sugar molecules. Ordinary table sugar, for example, is made from two sugars, glucose and fructose, linked together by covalent bonds.

When many sugars are strung together in a chain, the resulting molecule is called a *polysaccharide* ("many sugars"). The two most familiar polysaccharides are cellulose and starch. Both of these kinds of molecules are made from long chains of glucose molecules. They differ from each other only in the details of the way the glucose molecules bind to each other (Figure 22-12).

Glucose

FIGURE 22-10 The structure of glucose has six carbon atoms, six oxygen atoms, and twelve hydrogen atoms.

FIGURE 22-11 The structure of fructose, a common sugar in fruit. It has the same number and kinds of atoms as glucose but in a different arrangement.

Fructose

Glucose

(a)

(b) **Starch**

(c) **Cellulose**

(d)

(e)

FIGURE 22-12 *(a)* An individual glucose molecule has six carbon atoms as numbered. These molecules can be linked into different polymers such as *(b)* starch and *(c)* cellulose. Note the differences in the ways that the glucose molecules are linked to each other. *(d)* Potatoes, shown here with the potato plant roots, are formed from starch. *(e)* The cellulose fibers that hold these plants up are made from glucose.

Starches, a common component of the human diet, are a large family of molecules in which the glucose constituents link together at certain points along the ring. Starches are found in many plants, such as potatoes and corn (Figure 22-12d). Animals also form a glucose polymer, called *glycogen* or *animal starch,* which is stored in the liver and in muscle tissues. Humans break down starch molecules with an enzyme in the digestive system, thus releasing individual glucose molecules, which provide the fundamental energy fuel used by cells.

Cellulose, a long, stringy polymer that provides the main structural element in plants (Figure 22-12e), from stems and leaves to the trunks of trees, also forms from glucose molecules. Because the glucose molecules are linked in a different way, however, human beings cannot digest cellulose. We do not manufacture an enzyme that can separate individual glucose molecules from the cellulose polymer. Consequently, humans don't go out and graze on the lawn at lunchtime, though people on diets often eat celery and other "roughage" or "fiber." In contrast, species other than humans can digest cellulose , which is broken down by many bacteria. Cows, for example, have bacteria in their stomachs that perform this function for them, as do wood-eating termites.

> **STOP & THINK** Why do long-distance runners often load up on carbohydrates before a race?

The wood fibers in the paper on this page are made from glucose molecules bonded into cellulose, basically the same chemical found in the stalk of a celery stick. The same glucose molecules, bonded in a different way, form the flour in the spaghetti you ate the last time you had a pasta dinner. An amazing diversity can be built into organic molecules through modular construction.

◎ 22.5 Lipids

Lipids encompass a grab bag of vital organic molecules that go into making up every living thing. **Lipids** include a variety of molecules that will not dissolve in water, including fats in food, waxes in candles, greases for lubrication, and a wide variety of oils (Figure 22-13). If you think of drops of oil or bits of fat floating around on top of a pot of soup, you have a pretty good picture of what large clumps of lipid molecules are like.

At the molecular level, lipids play two important roles in living things. First, they form cell membranes that separate living material from its environment, as well as separate one part of a cell from other parts. They are also used to store energy. In fact, in the human body excess weight is usually carried in the form of fat, which is a different kind of lipid from those in cell membranes. Lipids are extremely efficient storehouses for energy. A typical gram of fat, for example, contains twice as many calories as a gram of either protein or carbohydrate.

Like proteins and carbohydrates, numerous lipid molecules can come together to form large modular structures in every cell. An important class of these molecules, called *phospholipids,* incorporate a long and thin carbon backbone, as shown in Figure 22-14. In phospholipids, a phosphate group (one phosphorus and four oxygen atoms) is incorporated into one end of the molecule. The oxygen atoms in this group tend to be negatively charged, so that this end of the molecule is attracted to water (we say it is hydrophilic). The other end of the molecule, however, is repelled by water (we say it is hydrophobic). These particular types of lipids play an extremely important role in living systems because, as we shall see, they are the materials from which cell membranes are made.

FIGURE 22-13 Lipids and water do not easily mix. Here a flask contains paraffin, which floats on top of the denser layer of cooking oil, which floats on top of the even denser layer of water.

Tony Robins/Getty Images, Inc.

FIGURE 22-14 A phospholipid molecule, showing the negatively charged phosphate group at one end, and ordinary hydrocarbon chains at the other. The end with the phosphate group is attracted to water, and the hydrocarbon end is repelled by it. Different collections of molecules in the group at the hydrophilic end correspond to different kinds of phospholipids.

(a)

(b)

(c)

Helene Rogers / Alamy

mediablitzimages (uk) Limited/Alamy

FIGURE 22-15 *(a)* Lipid molecules with saturated, monounsaturated (with just one carbon-carbon double bond), and polyunsaturated forms, showing the resulting kinks. *(b)* Lard, which is derived from hogs and other animals, is primarily saturated fat. *(c)* Vegetable oils contain a high percentage of unsaturated fats.

Saturated and Unsaturated Fats

Every carbon atom in a lipid chain forms exactly four bonds to neighboring atoms (see Chapter 10), as illustrated in Figure 22-15. In a straight chain, each carbon atom bonds to two adjacent carbon atoms along the chain and two hydrogen atoms on the sides. Carbon atoms of this type are *saturated*—fully bonded to four other atoms.

In some lipids, adjacent carbon atoms will have only three neighbors, including two carbon atoms and one hydrogen atom. An angled "double bond" will thus form between the two carbon atoms. A chain with one double bond is *monounsaturated,* whereas two or more double bonds yield a *polyunsaturated* lipid.

Saturated fats in the diet provide the raw materials from which the body can synthesize *cholesterol,* an essential component of all cell membranes. Unfortunately, high levels of cholesterol in the blood can also lead to fatty deposits that clog arteries. For these reasons, many food producers emphasize their use of cholesterol-free foods, rich in polyunsaturated fats. Advertising often suggests that unsaturated foods are "good for you."

Be warned, however. Many of these polyunsaturated products require a further processing step, called *hydrogenation,* to give them a pleasing texture and consistency. Popular chocolate candies, for example, must be made from fats and oils that soften near body temperature. Hydrogenation—the addition of hydrogen atoms back into the carbon chains—eliminates carbon–carbon double bonds. Each added hydrogen atom pulls one of the carbon bonds apart and thus partially saturates the lipid chains. Thus, if enough hydrogen atoms are added, the polyunsaturated lipid will become saturated again. Many popular cooking oils that begin with highly unsaturated lipids are "partially hydrogenated for freshness and consistency" at the manufacturing plant, a process that undoes the good of the unsaturated bonds.

TECHNOLOGY
Nonfattening Fats

Foods rich in fat were an expensive delicacy for much of human history. Today, however, the widespread availability of fatty foods has contributed to a serious problem with excess weight in the United States.

Until recently, there was little that people could do to keep their weight down except to eat a healthy balanced diet, reduce total food intake, and exercise regularly. Now, however, new abilities in molecular technology have added another option—we can eat foods that taste like fat, but that cannot be digested, and hence supply the body with no energy.

The first "no-fat fat" was approved for use in 1995 under the trade name Olestra (Figure 22-16). One ordinary fat found in foods consists of three long-chain molecules connected to a small alcohol molecule. The whole thing looks something like a capital Y, with the alcohol molecule at the center. In the intestines, specialized molecules from the digestive system attach to the alcohol and break off the "legs," which are then broken down further by other molecules. Olestra is shaped very similarly, except that it has eight chains attached to the alcohol instead of three. Because of the extra chains, enzymes in your digestive system can't get at the alcohol and the Olestra passes undigested through the human body. These and other low-calorie fat substitutes taste like fat but add no calories. Manufacturing specialized molecules like this to use in the human diet will be a growth industry in the future.

FIGURE 22-16 Potato chips made with "no-fat fat."

Cell Membranes

The most important single function of lipids in our bodies is the formation of *cell membranes*, the structure that separates the inside of every cell from its environment. Phospholipids, with their hydrophobic and hydrophilic ends, perform this function because, when placed in water, these molecules typically adopt a double-layered structure like the one shown in Figure 22-17. The hydrophobic ends of the molecule line up facing each other, whereas the hydrophilic ends face to the outside. In this way, water is kept away from the hydrophobic ends and nearer the hydrophilic ends. A double-layered structure of molecules like this functions very well as a membrane of a cell. It is flexible and can change its shape, but it also provides a tough barrier. Special protein receptors are required in order for anything to elbow its way through the bimolecular layer.

The structure of the lipid bilayers that make cell membranes is remarkably similar to liquid crystals (see Chapter 10). Like molecules in a liquid crystal, the lipid molecules are ordered in their orientation and spacing, but they are somewhat disordered in their exact positions side to side. This loose structure provides an important measure of flexibility to cell membranes.

One way to visualize the cell membrane is to think of a technique that's often used in moderate climates to protect swimming pools from freezing in the winter. Instead of draining water from the pool, an expensive and time-consuming operation, owners simply throw a large number of Styrofoam balls into the pool. These balls float next to each other. They cover the water, constantly touching, but also constantly jostling and moving around. They lift up and down when waves move across the water, but the covering retains its integrity. In the same way, cell membranes are made up of molecules stacked or arranged next to each other. These molecules can change shape and move around according to the dictates of their environment, but they retain their integrity and do not rupture. Thus, they perform the function of separating a cell from its environment.

FIGURE 22-17 The structure of a lipid bilayer. The hydrophobic ends of the molecules face each other, whereas the hydrophilic ends are in the surrounding water.

FIGURE 22-18 A multitude of different vitamin and mineral supplements are now available.

◉ 22.6 Minerals and Vitamins

Though most of our body is made of and operates with proteins, carbohydrates, lipids, and nucleic acids (see Chapter 23), other chemicals are also vital to life. These essential chemicals include the familiar minerals and vitamins that must form part of our diet (Figure 22-18).

Minerals

Minerals, in a nutritional context, include all chemical elements in our food other than carbon, hydrogen, nitrogen, and oxygen. The most abundant mineral in our bodies is calcium, which is concentrated in bones and teeth and comprises about 1.5% of our total weight. Even though bones appear to be solid, permanent structures, your calcium is constantly being replenished. In many women over 30, the rate of calcium uptake may lag behind calcium loss, which is a major cause of bone disease and injury.

Cellular fluids require small amounts of the elements potassium, chlorine, sodium, and magnesium to maintain proper body acidity and control electrical charges in nerve processes. A grab bag of minor or trace elements, from iodine in the thyroid gland to iron in the blood, are also involved in the body's chemistry.

Every few years the National Research Council publishes a list of Recommended Dietary Allowances (RDA, sometimes referred to as Recommended Daily Allowances) for minerals (see Table 22-2). These values are gradually being replaced by new Dietary Reference Intakes (DRI), which differ from earlier values. Calcium DRIs, for example, are significantly greater for most men and women than the earlier recommendations, while phosphorus DRIs are significantly less.

Vitamins

Biologists have discovered a host of complex organic molecules that, in small quantities, play an essential role in good health. These chemicals, though mostly unrelated to each other in

TABLE 22-2 Selected Recommended Dietary Allowances (RDAs and DRIs) for Minerals[a]

Gender	Age	Weight kg	Weight lb	Height cm	Height ft′ in″	Ca (mg)	P (mg)	Fe (mg)	Mg (mg)	Zn (mg)	I (μg[b])	Se (μg[b])
Both	0–0.5	6	13	60	2′	210	100	6	30	5	40	10
	0.5–1	9	20	71	2′4″	270	275	10	75	5	50	15
	1–3	13	29	90	2′11″	500	460	10	80	10	70	20
Men	15–18	66	145	176	5′9″	1300	1250	12	410	15	150	50
	19–24	72	160	177	5′10″	1000	700	10	420	15	150	70
	25–50	79	174	176	5′10″	1000	700	10	420	15	150	70
	51+	77	170	173	5′8″	1200	700	10	420	15	150	70
Women	15–18	55	120	163	5′4″	1300	1250	15	360	12	150	50
	19–24	58	128	164	5′5″	1000	700	15	310	12	150	55
	25–50	63	138	163	5′4″	1000	700	15	320	12	150	55
	51+	65	143	160	5′3″	1200	700	10	320	12	150	55
– Pregnant						1000	700	30	320	15	175	65
– Lactating (First 6 months)						1000	700	15	320	19	200	75
– Lactating (Second 6 months)						1000	700	15	320	16	200	75

[a]Condensed version of Recommendations by the Food and Nutrition Board of the National Research Council. For up-to-date information visit their web site: http://www4.nationalacademies.org/IOM/IOMHome.nsf/Pages/Food+and+Nutrition+Board.
[b]$1\,\mu g$ (one microgram) $= 10^{-6}\,g = 10^{-3}\,mg$.

any chemical or physiological sense, are known collectively as **vitamins**. They are generally designated by a letter, such as vitamin A. For historical reasons, a number of different vitamins were grouped together under vitamin B and have been given a series of numbers such as B1 (thiamine) and B2 (riboflavin).

With one exception, vitamins are not made in the body and must be taken in with our food. The exception, vitamin D, can be produced in the body through the action of ultraviolet radiation on the skin. However, in most parts of the world exposure to sunlight is normally too low to produce enough vitamin D. Thus, as a practical matter, all vitamins must be taken in as part of the diet.

FIGURE 22-19 Citrus fruits are an important source of vitamin C in our diets.

The vitamins in the B category, along with vitamin C, are *water-soluble vitamins*. As the name implies, these vitamins dissolve in water and hence are not retained by the body. The supply of water-soluble vitamins must be renewed daily. Vitamins A, D, E, and K, however, are *fat-soluble vitamins*. They can be stored in the body (in the liver, for example). In some cases, taking in too much of a fat-soluble vitamin can have unwanted or even harmful consequences. Too much vitamin D, for example, can lead to calcium deposits forming in the heart and kidneys, and too much vitamin A can be seriously toxic. (Too much beta-carotene, a precursor of vitamin A, can even turn your skin orange, but only temporarily.)

Vitamins serve a wide variety of functions in the body. Many of them assist enzymes in mediating the body's chemical reactions. In fact, most vitamins were discovered through the study of diseases that are caused by a chemical deficiency. The disease scurvy, for example, causes degeneration of tissues when the body fails to obtain enough vitamin C, a chemical abundant in citrus fruits (Figure 22-19). Scurvy was particularly common among sailors on long ocean voyages until the connection between diet and disease was made. Subsequently, sailors on British naval vessels were fed a regular diet of limes (hence the nickname "limeys"). Similarly, the bone disease rickets results from a deficiency of vitamin D. The modern diet with vitamin-enriched foods and vitamin supplements can virtually eliminate these deficiency diseases. As with minerals, the National Research Council publishes DRIs for vitamins. The DRIs for some vitamins are shown in Table 22-3.

TABLE 22-3 Selected Recommended Dietary Allowances (RDAs and DRIs) for Vitamins[a]

| | | Weight | | Height | | Fat-Soluble Vitamins | | | Water-Soluble Vitamins | | | | | | |
| | | | | | | A (RE[b]) | D (μg^c) | E (mg) (α-TE[d]) | Fola-cin (μg^c) | Niacin (mg) NE[e] | Ribo-flavin (mg) | Thia-mine (mg) | B_6 (mg) | B_{12} μg^c | C (mg[f]) |
Gender	Age	kg	lb	cm	ft'in"										
Both	0–0.5	6	13	60	2'	375	5	3	25	5	0.4	0.3	0.3	0.3	30
	0.5–1	9	20	71	2'4"	375	5	4	35	6	0.5	0.4	0.6	0.5	35
	1–3	13	29	90	2'11"	400	5	6	50	9	0.8	0.7	1.0	0.7	40
Men	15–18	66	145	176	5'9"	1000	5	10	200	20	1.8	1.5	2.0	2.0	60f
	19–24	72	160	177	5'10"	1000	5	10	200	19	1.7	1.5	2.0	2.0	60
	25–50	79	174	176	5'10"	1000	5	10	200	19	1.7	1.5	2.0	2.0	60
	51+	77	170	173	5'8"	1000	10	10	200	15	1.4	1.2	2.0	2.0	60
Women	15–18	55	120	163	5'4"	800	5	8	180	15	1.3	1.1	1.5	2.0	60
	19–24	58	128	164	5'5"	800	5	8	180	15	1.3	1.1	1.6	2.0	60
– Pregnant						800	5	10	400	17	1.6	1.5	2.2	2.2	70
– Lactating (First 6 months)						1300	5	12	280	20	1.8	1.6	2.1	2.6	95
– Lactating (Second 6 months)						1300	5	11	260	20	1.7	1.6	2.1	2.6	90

[a]Published in 1989; vitamin D values revised in 1997. For up-to-date information visit their website: http://www4.nationalacademies.org/IOM/IOM-Home.nsf/Pages/Food+and+Nutrition+Board.
[b]RE represents the number of retinol equivalents.
[c]1μg (one microgram) = 10^{-6} g = 10^{-3} mg.
[d]α-TE represents the number of α-tocopherol equivalents.
[e]NE represents the number of niacin equivalents.
[f]These represent recommended RDAs for nonsmokers. The RDAs of vitamin C for smokers are 67% greater than those for nonsmokers.

THINKING MORE ABOUT THE MOLECULES OF LIFE

Dietary Fads

The realization that the functioning of the body depends on the foods we eat is an old one and is bolstered by the understanding that the cell's basic structures are built from molecules brought in through the digestive system (see Appendix A). This understanding, coupled with the current preoccupation with health and fitness in the United States, leads occasionally to promotions and fads in which one food or another is touted as a new cure-all. It's hard to get enough information to analyze a fad while it's in full swing, but studies of fads after the fact can teach us a lot about them. The rise and fall of oat bran is a particularly enlightening case.

In the mid-1980s, people began to understand that high levels of cholesterol in the blood were correlated to the incidence of heart disease. Studies available at the time indicated that the inclusion of fiber in the diet, particularly oat bran, helped lower blood cholesterol levels. Oat bran became a fad food, and for a time it was virtually impossible for stores to keep it in stock.

Then, in 1990, newspaper headlines blared that a study in the prestigious *New England Journal of Medicine* showed that, although dietary fiber is an important part of a healthy diet, oat bran does not lower cholesterol levels. The oat bran industry, running at $54 million a year, collapsed. Processing plants closed and people lost their jobs.

Was this a reasonable response to the *New England Journal* paper? Let's look at the study that was reported and try to find out. The study took 20 people, all healthy hospital employees of ages 23 to 49 with low cholesterol levels, and tested them on diets with high-fiber oat bran and low-fiber foods for six-week periods. The result? The mean cholesterol levels of the subjects was 172 ± 28 milligrams per deciliter on the low-fiber diet, and 172 ± 25 on oat bran. (Physicians usually start to worry when your cholesterol level gets to the neighborhood of 220.) This inconclusive result, based on 20 healthy people, provided the basis for the headlines.

Does this study tell you anything about what would happen if someone with high cholesterol went on an oat bran diet? How representative of the entire population are 20 healthy hospital employees in Boston? Given the spread of cholesterol levels in the group, could the actual levels have gone down (or up) without the researchers being able to detect it?

 RETURN TO THE INTEGRATED QUESTION

What constitutes a healthy diet?

- A sound nutritional plan is one that provides all known essential nutrients, dietary fiber, water, and the appropriate amount of energy (i.e., calories) for the individual's needs.
  - The total amount of energy an individual needs is determined by three things. First, the energy needed to maintain the body at rest is typically 60 to 75% of the total energy expenditure.
  - The energy needed to process food that is taken in is typically about 10% of energy expenditure.
  - The energy associated with physical activity varies. In sedentary individuals, who accumulate less than 90 minutes of moderate exercise per week, activity accounts for ~15% of energy expenditures, whereas in active individuals it may account for as much as 25%.
- Essential nutrients are those compounds that the body cannot synthesize and therefore must be obtained through the diet. Essential nutrients can be divided into two main categories: macronutrients and micronutrients.
  - Macronutrients are needed in relatively large quantities in order to support metabolism. For humans, the essential macronutrients are proteins, lipids, and carbohydrates.
    - Proteins consist of chains of amino acids. Essential amino acids must be consumed if our body is to continue to grow and repair our tissues. Proteins are essential for all of the structural elements of our body such as muscles, tendons,

and bones as well as our internal organs. Proteins also mediate many of life's chemical reactions via their role as enzymes.
  - Lipids are an important macronutrient, and a number of essential fatty acids (EFA) must be included in the diet (e.g., omega-3 and omega-6 EFAs). Lipids form the membranes that separate the living cell from its environment, as well as separate one part of a cell from other parts. Lipids are also the body's long-term energy storehouse.
  - Carbohydrates are mainly used as an energy source. Our brain's primary source of energy is glucose, a monosaccharide (i.e., a simple sugar).
- Micronutrients are needed in smaller amounts and consist of trace elements (also known as microminerals) and vitamins.
  - Calcium, iron, copper, sodium, magnesium, and potassium are a few of the micronutrients necessary for survival.
  - Vitamins serve as coenzymes and cofactors and serve a number of important metabolic processes.
- The consumption of a healthy diet is a challenge in both developing and developed countries.
  - In developing countries, access to potable water and adequate caloric intake is often an issue.
  - In developed countries such as the United States, the combination of sedentary lifestyles and the overconsumption of calorie-dense foods has led to the current obesity epidemic.

SUMMARY

Organic molecules share the following characteristics: (1) they are based on carbon, (2) they usually form from only a few elements, (3) they are generally modular structures (that is, no matter how large or complex they are, they are formed from a few simple building blocks), and (4) their chemical function is largely determined by their geometrical shape. Three important types of biological molecules are proteins, carbohydrates, and lipids.

Proteins form from chains of *amino acids* to make many of the body's physical structures, such as hair and muscle. Proteins in cells also function as *enzymes,* which are molecules that increase reaction rates between other molecules but are themselves unaffected by the reaction. Proteins thus mediate many of life's chemical reactions.

Carbohydrates are modular molecules built from *sugars,* which are relatively simple molecules built from carbon, oxygen, and hy-drogen atoms. Carbohydrates provide an essential source of energy for all animals, and they provide much of the solid structure in the cellulose of plants.

Lipids, including fats and oils, are molecules that will not dis-solve in water. If the carbon atoms form single bonds, the lipid is saturated, whereas molecules on which adjacent carbon atoms form double bonds are unsaturated. All cell membranes are con-structed from bilayers of lipids, which are terminated by one end that attracts water and the other end that repels water.

In addition to the major nutrients proteins, carbohydrates, and lipids, humans also require small amounts of other chemicals—*minerals* and *vitamins*—that perform specialized chemical func-tions in the body. The National Research Council publishes Dietary Reference Intakes for both minerals and vitamins.

KEY TERMS

organic molecules	enzymes	sugars	minerals
amino acids	carbohydrates	lipids	vitamins
protein			

DISCOVERY LAB

We know from our chapter that lipids are found in many of the foods we eat. Fats, cholesterol, oils, and waxes are all li-pids. Lipids contain about twice as many calories as carbo-hydrates and proteins in a gram-for-gram comparison. They help make up cell membranes and are sometimes stored as fat for the body's potential energy use.

This experiment allows you to observe the greasy, oily effect of some lipids in everyday food items you may be consuming. Gather as many of the following items as you can, or similar food items: oil-based salad dressing, butter, cheddar cheese, cooked pork sau-sage, cooked chicken, corn chips, blueberry muffin, whole-grain bread, raisins, banana, apple, red pepper, and peanut butter. In ad-dition, obtain a paper grocery bag, scissors and a ballpoint pen.

Open the grocery bag, trim a rectangular shape at least 2 feet square, and lay it down flat on a table. Next, take about a table-spoon of each food item you gathered and smash it down into a spoon-sized area of the grocery bag, leaving about two inches between each sample. Identify the sample below each one. Mark the perimeter around each food sample with the ballpoint pen and wait 4 hours. Notice any greasy permeation around the food items and re-mark the distance traveled from the original mark-ing. Which foods demonstrated having more fat or lipid content? What effect can too many lipids have on your circulatory system? What are LDLs and HDLs, and which can be dangerous? Investi-gate what these abbreviations mean to your health.

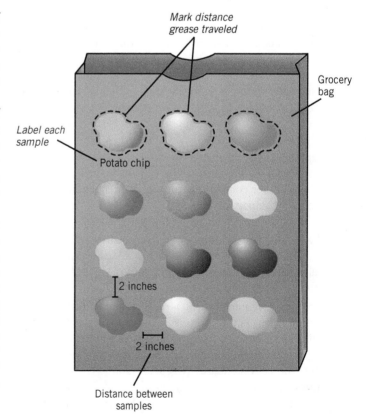

Mark distance grease traveled

Grocery bag

Label each sample

Potato chip

2 inches

2 inches

Distance between samples

REVIEW QUESTIONS

1. How is organic chemistry different from inorganic chemistry? What type of molecules do organic chemists study?

2. What is the difference between an organic and inorganic molecule? Give an example of each.

3. What are the most common elements from which the human body is made?

4. What is meant by the term *modularity*? Why is modularity an integral feature of organic chemistry?

5. What is the function of enzymes in living systems? Are enzymes destroyed when they are in chemical reactions?

6. What is a protein? Why are proteins sometimes referred to as polypeptides?

7. What are some of the biological functions of proteins?

8. What is an amino acid? What groups of atoms are common to all amino acids?

9. How is a protein constructed from amino acids? Why does this structure allow so many different proteins to be made?

10. Why does the shape of a drug molecule affect the functioning of living systems?

11. What are the basic building blocks of carbohydrates?

12. What is the difference between cellulose and starch at the molecular level? Give examples of each substance.

13. What is the relationship between cellulose and fiber?

14. What roles do lipids play in the human body?

15. How does the structure of cell membranes enable them to carry out their functions?

16. What is the difference between saturated and unsaturated fats? Give examples of each.

17. Why are minerals an important part of a balanced diet? Give some examples of minerals and describe their functions.

18. What are vitamins? Which are water soluble? Which are fat soluble?

19. Which vitamin can be synthesized by the body via exposure to ultraviolet radiation? Does the application of sunblock affect this process?

DISCUSSION QUESTIONS

1. Many varieties of diets exclude certain foods. So-called "semi-vegetarians" won't eat red meat but will eat poultry and fish. Pescetarians will eat fish but not other forms of meat. Ovo-lacto-vegetarians will eat eggs and consume dairy products but not eat meat of any sort. Vegans exclude all animal-based products, even excluding foods like honey. What foods should people in each of these groups eat to ensure they have a properly balanced diet?

2. Explain how complex organic molecules are made from simpler modular components. Provide some examples. Can you think of other complex systems that are made from simpler modular components?

3. Many restaurants will provide a detailed menu describing the nutritional properties of various food items. Examine one such menu and determine if their offerings would provide a balanced diet. If not, how would you consider changing the menu to allow for this balance?

4. Regulations require that drugs meet certain advertising standards. If a drug is claimed to stop hair loss or promote weight gain, for example, there has to be evidence that the drug actually works. Should vitamin and mineral supplements have to meet the same standard? Why or why not?

5. Although table salt is generally made of sodium chloride (NaCl) molecules, the salt that you buy in a store will have a small part of it composed of sodium iodide (NaI)? Do you think this is done intentionally or merely as a by-product of production? Why?

6. What does it mean to say that the chemistry of life is based on geometry?

7. What makes up an enzyme? Why is an enzyme considered a catalyst? Give an example of the role an enzyme plays in biochemical processes.

8. Should people be cautious before eating manufactured foods like Olestra? Why or why not?

9. What is a trans fat? Are there health risks associated with trans fatty acids? Give examples of foods that contain trans fats.

10. Is it preferable to get your essential vitamins from food versus from a pill or does it not matter? Why?

11. What role does the shape of an enzyme play in its ability to function?

12. Why can horses and cattle survive by eating grass or hay, and humans cannot?

13. How do termites digest wood? Why can't other animals do so?

14. Refer to Chapter 10's discussion on "Chemical Reactions and Energy: Rolling Down the Chemical Hill." Consider the process of glycolysis: $C_6H_{12}O_6 \rightarrow 2\ C_2H_5OH + 2CO_2$. This reaction is frequently catalyzed by an enzyme called "zymase." How do you think zymase affects the chemical "hill" up which a sugar molecule must be metaphorically pushed?

PROBLEMS

1. How many different polypeptides could be constructed out of 2 amino acids? How many could be constructed from 4 amino acids? How about 6?

2. Plot a graph with the number of polypeptides that could be made on the vertical axis versus the number of amino acids used on the horizontal axis (you can do this for just 1, 2, and 3 amino acids). How would you describe the resulting graph? Is it linear? Do you think something other than a linear scale would be appropriate for plotting higher values (e.g., a logarithmic scale)?

3. Determine the number of different polypeptides that could be made from using 20 amino acids. If a single sheet of paper is 0.1 mm thick, if you stacked the same number of sheets of paper as you have polypeptides, how high would the stack reach? Would it reach to the Andromeda galaxy (2.5 million light-years away)?

4. Lactose monohydrate is a disaccharide form of sugar with 12 carbon atoms per molecule. If it follows the usual pattern for the molecular formula of sugars, what is the molecular formula of lactose monohydrate?

5. When the amino acids alanine ($C_3H_7NO_2$) and glycine ($C_2H_5NO_2$) chemically react with each other, their products are water (H_2O) and a polypeptide known as glycylalanine. If there are no other products, what must be the molecular formula of glycylalanine?

6. You have a female friend, age 23, who smokes; she is otherwise in reasonable physical condition, childless, and not expecting. What is the minimum number of mg of vitamin C you would recommend that your friend take each day?
   a. 40 mg
   b. 60 mg
   c. 100 mg
   d. 160 mg

INVESTIGATIONS

1. Read the nutritional information on a box of standard cereal and on one that claims to be "natural." Which actually supplies more of the RDA of minerals and vitamins?

2. Make a detailed record of one week's intake of food, vitamins, and other supplements. Consult nutrition charts and determine the percentage by weight of protein, carbohydrate, fats, and other substances that you consumed. What percentage of the fat you consumed was saturated? What changes in your diet could reduce the total percentage of fat consumed and lower the ratio of saturated to unsaturated fat?

3. Investigate the effects of scurvy during the European exploration of the oceans in the seventeenth and eighteenth centuries.

4. Recommendations for vitamin intake are always changing. Find out which vitamins have had their RDA values increased or decreased recently. Why was this done?

5. In the text, we gave examples of the harmful consequences of too much intake of certain vitamins. Are there other examples like this?

6. How would you design a study to investigate whether a particular food additive lowered the probability of heart attacks?

7. Investigate the relationship between health and cholesterol levels. Is it possible for your cholesterol level to be too low?

8. Investigate how many amino acids must be supplied by the diet of various organisms for them to survive. How many amino acids do humans need to consume? How many are manufactured in our body?

9. Many animals manufacture vitamin C in their bodies. Which common animals do not?

10. Some athletes consume massive amounts of protein. Investigate exercise science journals and find the optimum amount of complete protein that a 150-pound endurance athlete should consume. Now compare that to how many grams per day a 200-pound strength athlete should consume.

11. Investigate why many endurance athletes "carb load" before a race. How does the term *hitting the wall* relate to stored energy? How long can an elite endurance athlete run before he or she runs out of stored energy?

23 Classical and Modern Genetics

Why do offspring resemble their parents?

PHYSICS
Nuclear radiation can damage DNA, causing mutations.

BIOLOGY
Genetic information is passed from parents to offspring when reproductive cells divide.

CHEMISTRY
Molecules of DNA and RNA carry the genetic code and produce proteins in the cell.

GREAT IDEA
All living things use the same genetic code to guide the chemical reactions in every cell.

TECHNOLOGY
New methods of altering the genetic code are used to develop new varieties of plants and animals. (Ch. 24)

ENVIRONMENT
Oxidizing chemicals in the environment may cause an increase in the rate of genetic mutations.

ASTRONOMY
The basic materials from which genetic molecules are made may have fallen to Earth in meteorites soon after the planet formed. (Ch. 25)

HEALTH & SAFETY
The principles of genetics have been used to trace cases of hereditary or genetic diseases. (Ch. 24)

GEOLOGY
Mineral-like combinations of iron and sulfur atoms in enzymes play a role in the transfer of energy to cells.

● = applications of the great idea discussed in this chapter

○ = other applications, some of which are discussed in other chapters

It's just about time to head back home after a great day in the sun. You'll have company during the drive because a friend has asked you to give her brother a ride back to campus. You've never met him before, but there's no mistaking the family relationship: the same wavy brown hair, the same wide-set eyes, the same distinctive shape to the nose.

One of life's most familiar characteristics is the similarity of offspring to their parents. Countless generations of animal breeders have relied on this fact, as have farmers who developed more productive strains of crops. And we see the same hereditary links in the faces of our families and friends.

From penguins to potatoes to people, like begets like.

Jose Luis Pelaez, Inc./Blend Images/Getty Images, Inc.

◉ 23.1 Classical Genetics

Genetics, the study of ways in which biological information is passed from one generation to the next, was pioneered by an Austrian monk named Gregor Mendel (1822–1884). Perhaps more than any other prominent scientist, Mendel closely matches the popular image of the lonely genius conducting exacting research in isolation. Working at the monastery in Brno, in what is now the Czech Republic, Mendel began to ask the kinds of questions we have been posing: Why do offspring resemble parents? And why do offspring differ from parents?

Mendel attempted to answer these questions, as any good scientist should—that is, by observing nature, doing experiments, and seeing what there was to see. In a series of studies with pea plants in his monastery garden, he delineated the basic laws that govern the inheritance of physical characteristics.

The technique that Mendel used is simple to describe, although it was difficult and tedious to carry out: He cross-pollinated different varieties of peas. For example, he would fertilize the flowers of **true breeding** tall pea plants—plants that always produced tall offspring—with the pollen from short ones, and then observe the characteristics of the "children" and "grandchildren," as shown in Figure 23-1. The offspring of two different strains, such as tall and short pea plants, are called **hybrids.**

When Mendel made these observations, he found that there were remarkable regularities in the characteristics of the offspring. All offspring from the first generation of a tall–short cross were tall. If these offspring were bred with each other, however, the results were quite different. On average, three-fourths of second-generation offspring were tall, whereas one-fourth reverted

① Parent
Tall and dwarf
varieties are
cross-fertilized.

Tall   x   Dwarf

② All the hybrid
progeny are tall.

Tall

③ First Generation
The hybrid
progeny are
self-fertilized.

Tall   x   Tall

④ Second Generation
Tall and dwarf
plants appear
among the
offspring of
the hybrids
approximately
in a ratio of
3 tall : 1 dwarf.

787 Tall   277 Dwarf

FIGURE 23-1 The parents, first, and second generations of tall versus short pea plants. On average, the second generation shows a 3:1 ratio of dominant traits. Three-fourths of the plants, for example, will be tall and one-fourth short.

to being short. Thus, in hybridization, shortness disappears for one generation, only to reappear in the next. Mendel observed the same kind of behavior in half-a-dozen other pea plant traits: seed pod shape, flower color, and so on (Figure 23-2).

Mendel invented the "unit of inheritance," what we now call the **gene**, to explain his findings. He had no idea what a gene might be, or even whether it had a real physical existence. Today, as we shall see shortly, the gene can be identified as part of a long molecule of DNA. For Mendel, however, the existence of DNA was unknown, and he deduced the presence of genes purely from mathematical analysis of how traits of his plants were inherited.

STOP & THINK In what ways were Mendel's experiments with peas similar to Galileo's experiments with falling bodies?

In the simplest version of Mendelian or **classical genetics**, we assume that every offspring receives two genes for every characteristic—one from the father and one from the mother. In the experiment with pea plants, for example, every offspring in every generation received a gene for height (either tall or short) from its mother (the plant that provided an egg) and another gene for height from its father (the plant that provided the pollen). Mendel concluded that pairs of genes determined every characteristic he observed and that the offspring may receive a different gene from the father than from the mother. So, if two genes are present, which characteristic is actually seen in the offspring? In the language of modern geneticists, we phrase the question by asking: Which gene is "expressed"?

Returning to our example of the pea plants, we recall that Mendel produced plants with both a gene for tallness and a gene for shortness in the first generation. The fact that all of these first-generation plants were tall means that, in all cases, the gene for tallness was expressed. Mendel stated this fact by saying that the gene for tallness is **dominant**. By this he meant that if an offspring receives a "tall gene" from one parent and a "short gene" from the other, that offspring will be tall. In this situation, the short gene is said to be **recessive**. The gene is present in the offspring, but it does not determine the offspring's physical characteristics; it is not expressed. That gene, however, can be passed along to subsequent generations. You should note that, in spite of the name, "dominant" is not the same as "good" or "strong" in the world of genes. Many fatal genetic diseases are passed from generation to generation by dominant genes.

Mendel's experiment can be understood in very simple terms. In the first generation, every hybrid receives a tall gene and a short gene. Because the tall gene is dominant, all of the first generation of hybrid plants will be tall. In the next generation, there are four possible gene combinations, as shown in Table 23-1. Each plant in the second generation can receive either a tall or a short gene from each of its parents. On average, the distribution of genes will be random so that we can argue as follows: In roughly one-fourth of the cases, the offspring will receive a tall gene from its mother and a tall gene from its father. In another one-fourth of the cases, the offspring will receive a short gene from its mother and a short gene from its father. In the remaining half of these cases, the offspring will receive a tall gene

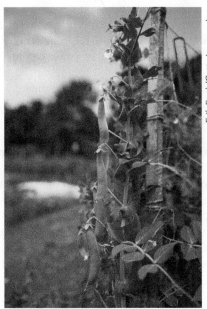

FIGURE 23-2 Pea plants, which possess varied traits such as height, flower color, and seed pod texture, were employed by Gregor Mendel in studies of genetic inheritance.

TABLE 23-1 **Tall (T) versus Short (t) Hybrids**

		Father's Genes	
		Tall	**Short**
Mother's genes:	**Tall**	TT	Tt
	Short	tT	tt

from its father and a short gene from its mother, or vice versa. (Note that in the table, a plant with Tt will have the same characteristics as a plant with tT—it makes no difference which parent donates a gene.)

Consequently, in the second generation approximately three out of every four offspring will have at least one gene for tallness, and only one in four will have two genes for shortness. Given the fact that tallness is a dominant characteristic, this distribution means that three of four off-spring in the second generation will be tall and only one will be short. This situation is precisely what Mendel observed.

EXAMPLE 23-1

BREEDING PEAS

You are given two true breeding pea plants. One plant has smooth pea pods and purple flowers (dominant traits). The other plant has wrinkled pea pods and white flowers (recessive traits). These characteristics are expressed independently of each other. What distribution of characteristics would you expect in the first generation of plants bred from these two parent plants? What distribution of traits would you see in the second generation?

Reasoning: Every plant in the first generation of offspring receives dominant genes for a smooth pea pod (S) and purple flower (P) from one parent, and recessive genes for a wrinkled pod (s) and white flower (p) from the other. Remember that it makes no difference which parent donates which gene. This means that the order of the letters in the table doesn't matter. All that matters is what letters are present. Every plant in the first generation, therefore, has exactly the same gene combination, abbreviated SsPp (which is the same as sSpP). All of these plants will appear with smooth pods and purple flowers because S and P are dominant.

The second generation, however, will display a mixture of traits. The easiest way to predict the distribution of these traits is to set up a matrix, similar to the one shown in Table 23-1. In this case, however, we must deal with four different genes in each parent (SsPp), so the matrix must be 4 × 4, as shown in Table 23-2.

This table shows that there are 16 different possible combinations of the four genes. On average, 9 out of every 16 plants will appear with smooth pods and purple flowers—both dominant genes will be expressed. In addition, 3 of 16 on average will display wrinkled pods but purple flowers, and 3 of 16 will have white flowers but smooth pods. Finally, only 1 in 16 of the second generation will display both recessive traits: white flowers and wrinkled pea pods.

Mendel's observation of this characteristic 9:3:3:1 distribution of second-generation traits for two different genes was instrumental in his development of the genetic theory.

TABLE 23-2 **SsPp Matrix with Resulting 9:3:3:1 Distribution**

	SP	Sp	sP	sp
SP	SSPP	SSPp	SsPP	SsPp
Sp	SSpP	SSpp	SspP	Sspp
sP	sSPP	sSPp	ssPP	sspP
sp	sSpP	sSpp	sspP	sspp

1 SSPP   2 SSPp   2 SsPP
4 SsPp   1 SSpp   2 Sspp
1 ssPP   2 ssPp   1 sspp

Smooth + Purple = 9
Smooth + white = 3
wrinkled + Purple = 3
wrinkled + white = 1

The Rules of Classical Genetics

Mendel's research can be summarized by three rules that frame classical genetics.

- *Rule 1.* Physical characteristics or traits are passed from parents to offspring by some unknown mechanism (we call it a gene).

- *Rule 2.* Each offspring has two genes for each trait, one gene from each parent.
- *Rule 3.* Some genes are dominant and some are recessive. When present together, the trait of a dominant gene will be expressed in preference to the trait of a recessive gene.

The rules of classical genetics were deduced during the early twentieth century. Careful records were kept on many kinds of organisms, from humans to cattle to agricultural plants, and large lists of dominant and recessive genes were compiled. In human beings, for example, dark hair and eye color are dominant over light, the ability to roll your tongue is dominant over inability, and hairy toe knuckles are dominant over hairless.

Qualitative versus Quantitative Genetics

In one sense, the qualitative aspects of Mendelian genetics have been understood for many centuries. Early human societies knew, for example, that if you saved the largest potatoes and planted them in the spring, the resulting crop would be better than if you just planted potatoes at random (Figure 23-3). They also knew that if you had a bull that gained weight rapidly and produced lots of meat, you should breed that bull to as many cows as possible so that some of the offspring would share the characteristics of the father.

But Mendel's careful statistical analysis of pea plant traits carried genetics beyond the qualitative level. By discovering the distinctive 3:1 and 9:3:3:1 ratios of traits in second-generation plants, Mendel was able to propose a predictive model of genetics—a model that recognized the equal importance of both parents, and the distinction between dominant and recessive traits. When Mendel's rather obscure publications were "discovered" at about the turn of the century, they provided a model that allowed breeders to approach their work in a far more controlled and directed manner.

The traits of prize bulls and racehorses, for example, are carefully documented, as are the pedigrees of their offspring. The success of plant and animal breeders in controlling the flow of genes from one generation to the next is attested to by the appearance of cattle such as Black Angus (which are little more than a rectangular block of beef on very short legs) and the many varieties of vegetables and fruits that stock supermarket shelves.

(a)

(b)

FIGURE 23-3 Farmers have long used selective breeding to improve characteristics of their crops, such as potatoes (a), and livestock, such as cattle (b).

Of equal importance, the laws of Mendelian genetics can now be used to trace cases of hereditary or genetic disease, such as the many cases of families with cystic fibrosis, a disease that affects approximately one in every 2,000 Caucasian children in North America. Individuals with cystic fibrosis suffer from thick mucus deposits that obstruct the lungs, as well as other abnormalities of the body's chemistry. When both parents carry the recessive gene for cystic fibrosis, their children have about a one-in-four chance of acquiring the disease.

Although we have chosen examples in which one physical characteristic is correlated to one gene, most cases of inheritance are not this simple. Human height and skin color, for example, are affected by the action of several genes, and nutrition as well as genetics can influence height. Thus, although the principles of classical genetics have widespread validity, the way that they work out in practice may be quite complex.

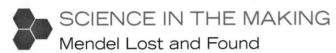

SCIENCE IN THE MAKING
Mendel Lost and Found

Gregor Mendel conducted his famous research over an intense eight-year span, during which he performed some 28,000 individual experiments. He published his results in 1866 in the proceedings of the local natural history society, and he sent copies of his paper to 133 other scientific societies and dozens of other scientists. He also planned to continue this line of research using other organisms, but his appointment as abbot of the monastery led to many new responsibilities and eventual abandonment of his scientific efforts. As so often happens in science, without Mendel's own follow-up experiments and active participation in the scientific community, his ideas were quickly forgotten.

A generation later, in the spring of 1900, Mendel's work was finally rediscovered when three European botanists, Karl Correns (1864–1933) of Germany, Erich von Tschermak (1871–1962) of Austria, and Hugo de Vries (1848–1935) of Holland, independently deduced Mendel's laws and subsequently found his earlier publication. Only then, a dozen years after his death, was Mendel recognized as a scientific pioneer.

STOP & THINK If Mendel's work was forgotten and his findings had to be rediscovered by other scientists a generation later, why do you think he is revered as the founder of genetics? Were the independent discoveries of Correns, von Tschermak, and de Vries of equal importance? Why or why not?

◉ 23.2 DNA and the Birth of Molecular Genetics

The key to understanding Mendel's genetic principles is **molecular genetics**, which is the study of the mechanism that passes genetic information from parents to offspring at the molecular level. In Chapter 22 we saw that cellular functions, the basic mechanisms of all life, depend on chemical interactions between molecules. Chromosomes, the distinctive elongated structures that appear to divide just prior to cell division, became an obvious focus for genetic study. Could these structures carry information and pass it from one generation to the next? Studies of cell division by meiosis pointed strongly in that direction. Recall that meiosis produces gametes—sex cells with half the usual number of chromosomes. Gametes from two parents are subsequently joined during sexual reproduction to yield a full complement of chromosomes.

By the mid-twentieth century, biochemists analyzed chromosomes and showed that they are made primarily of DNA, deoxyribonucleic acid. The discovery of the nature and function of nucleic acids has fundamentally transformed the study of biological systems in the past three decades. **Nucleic acids**, so called because they were originally found in the nucleus of cells, include **DNA** and **RNA**, the molecules that carry and interpret the genetic code. These chemicals govern both the inheritance of physical traits by offspring and the basic chemical

FIGURE 23-4 Ribose and deoxyribose are 5-carbon sugars that differ in the number of oxygen atoms.

FIGURE 23-5 A nucleotide is formed by a sugar, base, and phosphate group.

operation of the cell. These extraordinary molecules conform to the twin principles of modularity and geometry that are followed by all other organic materials (see Chapter 22).

Nucleotides: The Building Blocks of Nucleic Acids

On the one hand, proteins (chains of amino acids) and carbohydrates (clusters of sugar molecules) can form large structures from a single kind of building block. Nucleic acids, on the other hand, are assembled from subunits that are themselves made from three different kinds of smaller molecules. The assemblage of three molecules is called a *nucleotide,* and nucleic acids are made by putting nucleotides together in a long chain.

The first of the smaller molecules that go into an individual nucleotide is a sugar. The sugar in DNA is *deoxyribose* (thus giving DNA its complicated name, *deoxyribonucleic acid*), while in RNA (*ribonucleic acid*) the sugar is *ribose*. Ribose is a common sugar containing five carbon atoms. Deoxyribose, as the name implies, is like ribose but is missing one oxygen atom (Figure 23-4).

The second small molecule of the nucleotide is the phosphate ion, which includes one phosphorus atom surrounded by four atoms of oxygen (we met the phosphate group as a key component of ATP in Chapter 22).

Finally, each nucleotide incorporates one of four different kinds of molecules in DNA that are called *bases.* The four different base molecules are often abbreviated by a single letter: A for adenine, G for guanine, C for cytosine, and T for thymine.

Each nucleotide combines the three basic building blocks: a sugar, a phosphate, and a base (Figure 23-5). These three molecules bond together, with the sugar molecule in the middle. Think of a nucleotide as something like a prefabricated wall in a house. Both DNA and RNA are made by linking nucleotides together in a specific way.

DNA Structure

We can start putting DNA together by assembling a long strand of nucleotides. In this strand, the alternating phosphate and sugar molecules form a long chain, and the base molecules hang off the side. The whole thing looks like a half-ladder that has been sawn vertically through the rungs.

DNA consists of two such strands of nucleotides joined together to form a complete "ladder." The bases sticking out to the side provide the natural points for joining the two single strands. As you can see from Figure 23-6, however, the distinctive shapes of the four bases ensure that only certain pairs of bases can form hydrogen bonds. Adenine, for example, can form bonds with thymine but not with any of the other bases or with itself. Similarly, cytosine can form a bond with guanine but not with itself, thymine, or adenine. One way to look at it is to note that adenine and thymine have two places where they can form bonds, whereas guanine and cytosine have three.

As a consequence, only four possible rungs can exist in a DNA ladder. They are:

AT
TA
CG
GC

With the bonding of these base pairs, the complete DNA molecule is formed into a ladder-like double strand. Because of the details of the shape of the bases, each rung is twisted slightly with respect to the one before it. The net result is that this ladder comes to resemble a spiral staircase—a helical shape that gives DNA its common nickname, the **double helix**.

A quick review: as we shall see, genes are short segments of a DNA double helix. Separate segments of DNA wrapped around a protein core are called chromosomes, with each chromosome containing many genes. The sum of all DNA on all the chromosomes in an individual cell, called the genome, constitutes the entire set of genetic instructions for that organism. Every cell in an individual organism contains the same complement of DNA, with the exception of the sex cells.

Adenine pairs with thymine

Guanine pairs with cytosine

Thymine   Adenine   Cytosine   Guanine

RNA Structure

RNA is built in a manner similar to DNA with three important differences. First, RNA is only half the ladder; that is, it consists of only one string of nucleotides put together. Second, the sugar in the RNA nucleotide is ribose instead of deoxyribose. And third, the base thymine is replaced by a different base, uracil, abbreviated U. The shape of uracil is such that, like thymine, it will bond to the base adenine. As we shall see, the ability of uracil to bond to adenine plays an important role in regulating chemical reactions in the cell. Several different kinds of RNA operate in the cell at any given time. All of them, however, have the same basic structure.

Hydrogen bonding

The double helix of DNA
A = adenine
C = cytosine
G = guanine
T = thymine

P and S represent the phosphate and sugar (deoxyribose) units of the chain

The Replication of DNA

In Chapter 21, we described the processes by which cells divide. Prior to both mitosis and meiosis, DNA in the chromosomes is copied. Thus, DNA replication is one of the first steps in passing genetic information from one generation to the next.

DNA replication is possible because the geometry of the base pairs allows only certain kinds of bindings; that is, adenine (A) binds only to thymine (T), and cytosine (C) binds only to guanine (G). No other pairings are allowed. When a cell is about to divide, special enzymes move along the DNA double helix, breaking the hydrogen bonds that link the bases—in effect, breaking the "rungs of the ladder," as shown in Figure 23-7. As a result, the two split arms of the DNA ladder have exposed bases.

Consider an adenine (A) base that is no longer locked into its partner on the other side of the double helix. In the fluid around the DNA are many nucleotides, some of which contain an unattached thymine (T). With the aid of another enzyme, this thymine will bind to the exposed adenine in the original DNA strand. In the same way, an exposed cytosine (C) will bind to a nucleotide containing guanine (G) from the fluid in the nucleus. No other type of nucleotide can bind to that particular site.

The net result of these preferential bindings along a single strand of exposed DNA is that the missing strand is reconstructed, base by base. The same thing happens in mirror image to the other half of the exposed DNA strand. Thus, once the DNA is unraveled, each strand replicates its missing partner. The end product is two double-stranded DNA molecules, each of which is identical to the original molecule (Figure 23-8).

As we saw in Chapter 21, when a cell divides by means of mitosis, the genetic information contained in the DNA of one cell is passed on to its daughters. Thus, each daughter cell will have chromosomes identical to those of the parent. In meiosis, in contrast, each daughter cell has only one chromosome, which differs from either of the pair of chromosomes in the original cell through shuffling of genetic material. When a sperm and an egg come together during fertilization, the resulting cell once again has a full set of chromosomes, but now one chromosome in each pair comes from the father, the other from the mother.

The simple chemistry of the base pairs provides a mechanism for reproducing DNA. This feature of DNA molecular structure accounts for one of the striking facts about life—offspring do share many traits of their parents. Ultimately, chemical binding of base pairs results in the inheritance of parental traits.

FIGURE 23-6 The structure of DNA. AT and CG base-pair linkages are shown above the DNA strand. The dotted lines are hydrogen bonds (see Chapter 10).

P = phosphate
S = sugar

Key:

The double helix of DNA

A = adenine

C = cytosine

G = guanine

T = thymine

FIGURE 23-7 DNA replication. A DNA double helix may be split, thus exposing bases on both strands. Two new identical double helices may then be formed from the original.

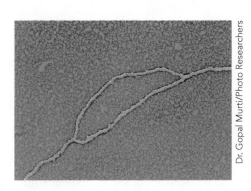

FIGURE 23-8 Electron microscope image of the DNA in a dividing human cancer cell.

Dr. Gopal Murti/Photo Researchers

◉ 23.3 The Genetic Code

DNA carries all our genetic information; this molecule is, in effect, the book of life. But how is the book read? How are the almost endless strings of DNA nucleotides translated into flesh and blood? That is the role of RNA.

Transcription of DNA

In addition to replicating itself so that cell division can take place, DNA also supplies the information that runs the chemistry within each individual cell. This process depends on the fact that all cells are governed by protein enzymes that run chemical reactions (see Chapter 22). Thus, the question of how cell chemistry is regulated boils down to how the information in DNA can be used to produce proteins. If we understand this step, then we will understand how DNA governs the chemical functioning of every cell in our body.

DNA is a very large molecule. In eukaryotic cells, it is found outside the nucleus only in mitochondria and chloroplasts. Thus, the first question we have to ask is how information in the DNA gets out into the cell at large. The answer to this question involves a process called *transcription,* which uses the other nucleic acid, RNA.

When it is time to fabricate a new protein to act as an enzyme in a cell, other enzymes "unzip" a section of DNA, as shown in Figure 23-9. Nucleotides of RNA that are always floating in the nuclear material are then hooked, with the aid of enzymes, onto the appropriate bases by a process exactly analogous to that which occurs in the replication of DNA. Each of the exposed bases on the "unzipped" strand of DNA binds to its appropriate nucleotide—A to U, C to G, and so forth. (Remember that in RNA, the base uracil, U, substitutes for the thymine in DNA.) In this way, a short strand of RNA is created that carries information from the original exposed strand of DNA. Think of the RNA as being the "negative" of the true picture, which is the DNA.

Because it is relatively short and not connected to anything else, the RNA strand can move out through tiny pores in the wall of the nucleus and into the cell at large. Thus, the function of this kind of RNA is to carry the information that was contained in the central DNA molecule out into the region of the cell where chemical reactions are going on. Because it carries a message, this kind of RNA (one of three important types in every cell) is called **messenger RNA, or mRNA** for short.

The Synthesis of Proteins

The exact sequence of base pairs on messenger RNA carries a coded message that contains chemical instructions. Once the mRNA arrives at the place in the cell where proteins are to be

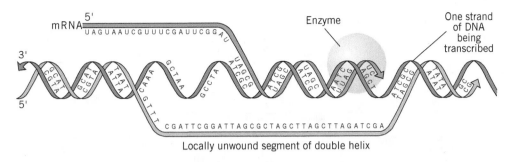

FIGURE 23-9 Transcription of DNA occurs when a segment of DNA is split and a single-stranded messenger RNA segment forms. The mRNA carries the same information that was on the original DNA segment.

synthesized, it encounters a second type of RNA—a molecule called **transfer RNA, or tRNA** for short. The job of tRNA is to read that coded message. Transfer RNA, whose shape is shown in Figures 23-10 and 23-11, has a shape at one end that attracts 1 of the 20 amino acids found in living things (see Chapter 22). At the other end is a small loop of molecules with three exposed bases on it. One of four different bases can be found in each of the places on the top loop. In other words, there are four possible choices for the first base in tRNA, and for each of these four possible choices for the second base. This means that there are 16 (4 × 4) possible combinations for the first two bases in tRNA, and for each of these 16 there are four possible choices for the third base. In the end, then, there are 64 (4 × 4 × 4) different possible kinds of tRNA molecules.

The sequence of bases along the mRNA is, as we have seen, a transcription of the information contained in the sequence of bases along the original DNA. Messenger RNA in effect carries a coded message, spelled out in four letters: A, U, C, and G. Each group of three exposed bases on the mRNA chain is like a word—a sequence of three letters that will bind to one, and only one, of the sets of bases on 1 of the 64 tRNA molecules. If a segment along the mRNA reads G-C-C, for example, then the tRNA molecule that has C-G-G as its unpaired bases will bond to that particular spot as shown in Figure 23-11.

The set of three bases on the mRNA, called a *codon*, determines which of the possible tRNA molecules will attach at that point. Each codon on the mRNA determines a single amino acid, and the string of codons determines the sequence of amino acids—what we have called the primary structure of the protein that is being assembled. This connection between the codons and the amino acid they select is called the **genetic code**, as detailed in Figure 23-12. All living things share this code.

As the tRNA molecules attach themselves along the mRNA, a string of amino acids in a specific order—a protein—is assembled as shown in Figure 23-13. Once its amino acid has been incorporated into the protein, a tRNA molecule moves away to be replenished with another amino acid and used again.

The protein synthesis takes place on ribosomes, which are large, irregularly shaped organelles made of proteins and yet another kind of RNA, called *ribosomal RNA*, or *rRNA*. As shown in Figure 23-13, the process of synthesis is somewhat more complex than the simple discussion we have given here. Ribosomes align the messenger RNA and transfer RNA during protein assembly. Thus three different kinds of RNA—transfer, messenger, and ribosomal—are involved in the synthesis of a single protein.

As a net effect of this rather complex molecular manufacturing process, the information encoded in the DNA molecule has been expressed as a particular sequence of amino acids that determines the identity of the appropriate protein enzyme. Thus, a specific stretch of DNA located on one chromosome produces the enzyme that runs a particular chemical reaction in the cell. This stretch of DNA is what we have called a gene. That chemical might have an influence on skin color, hair texture, or any of the other traits that we recognize.

One of the central rules of modern biology, often referred to as the "central dogma of molecular biology," is:

FIGURE 23-10 Computer-generated model of tRNA. The triplet of bases is shown in red, and the spot that binds to the amino acid (in this case, serine) is shown in yellow.

FIGURE 23-11 The interaction of mRNA and tRNA. One end of a tRNA molecule is attached to bases in the mRNA, and the other end to a specific amino acid. Enzymes hook the amino acids together to form a protein molecule.

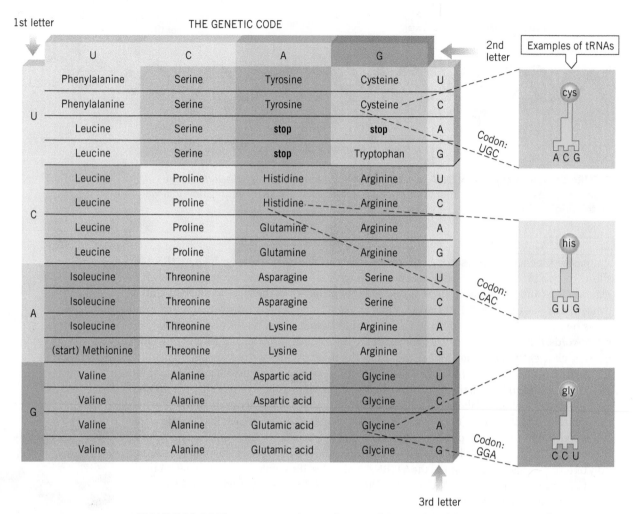

FIGURE 23-12 The genetic code matches 61 of the 64 possible combinations of three genetic letters (A, U, G, or C) to one of the 20 amino acids found in proteins. In addition, three codons—UAA, UAG, and UGA—indicate the end of the protein. Every known organism employs this code.

● One gene codes for one protein.

That is, one stretch of DNA will code for one mRNA molecule, which will code for the sequence of amino acids in one protein, which will drive one chemical reaction in the cell (Figure 23-14).

It was once believed that all genetic processes follow this rule. Today we understand that, although genes in prokaryotes are usually found on one continuous stretch of DNA, in eukaryotes like human beings the geometry of genes is often more complicated. A gene on human DNA does not always consist of a single continuous stretch of DNA; rather, the coding sections of the DNA of a single gene are often separated from each other by stretches of noncoding DNA. The parts of the DNA that code for the protein are called *exons*, whereas the noncoding sections that are interspersed between them are called *introns*. The cellular machinery that transcribes the gene is able to cut out the introns and assemble the protein only from exons. In the assembly process, however, the exons can be put together in different ways, so that a single gene can code for more than one protein. In humans, for example, a single stretch of DNA may contribute to three or more different proteins.

But the great truth of modern biology is this: more than a century ago, Mendel postulated the existence of a gene without knowing what it was. Today molecular biologists can tell you exactly where many specific genes lie along a stretch of DNA, as well as the sequence of base pairs along them.

FIGURE 23-13 The formation of a protein requires three kinds of RNA. (a) A strand of messenger RNA fits into a groove in a ribosome (an organelle formed from proteins and ribosomal RNA). (b) The ribosome attracts the appropriate transfer RNA, which carries with it an amino acid (shown in blue). (c) A second tRNA attaches to the ribosome, and the two adjacent amino acids are linked (d–f). The ribosome begins to shift along the mRNA, attracting new tRNA molecules and adding amino acids to the chain. Once the amino acids and tRNA are disconnected, the tRNA floats off to find another amino acid (g–h). The completed protein is assembled and released by the ribosome, and all the components are available to start the process over again.

FIGURE 23-14 A schematic diagram of protein production from DNA. (a) One stretch of DNA codes for one mRNA molecule. (b) One messenger RNA molecule attaches to a ribosome. (c) Transfer RNA molecules match an amino acid to each codon on the messenger RNA. (d) Amino acids link together to make one protein, which will drive one chemical reaction in the cell.

All living systems employ the genetic mechanism we have just described. The transfer of genetic information by DNA and the production of proteins by RNA is a process shared by every cell on Earth. Each species, and each individual within a species, has a slightly different message written on its DNA. The identity of every cell, as well as the organism of which the cell is a part, is determined by the chemical reactions that take place there. The enzymes determine the chemical reactions, and the enzymes are coded for in the DNA. Thus, DNA is truly the molecule that contains the code of life.

What is perhaps most remarkable about this process is that all living things use essentially the same code to translate between the messages carried in the genes of DNA, the messages carried in RNA, and the string of amino acids in proteins. This relationship explains why biologists speak of "the genetic code" when they refer specifically to the relationship between a triplet of base pairs on the mRNA and the corresponding amino acid in the protein. The basic "word" of the molecular world, then, is the triplet of bases along DNA—the codon. Each codon eventually codes to one amino acid in a string of proteins.

The fact that all living organisms, from single-celled yeast to human beings, use precisely the same biochemical apparatus and precisely the same technique for making proteins and running their chemistry is one of the great unifying ideas in the science of biology. Indeed, one of the great principles of science is:

● **All living things on Earth use the same genetic code.**

This finding in no way limits the tremendous variety and diversity one can find in living things. Just as many different books can be written using the 26 letters of the English alphabet, so too can many different life forms be constructed using the four "letters" in the genetic code.

Mutations and DNA Repair

If DNA were copied faithfully from one generation to the next, no living thing could be much different from its ancestors. But mistakes do happen, and many agents in nature can alter and even damage the DNA molecule. Numerous chemicals (particularly those that cause oxidation reactions in cells), nuclear radiation, X-rays, and ultraviolet light (which also produces oxidizing chemicals) are all examples of such agents. If the DNA of a parent's egg or sperm is altered, then the alteration will be faithfully copied by the process we have just described. The offspring will inherit the change, just as they inherit all other genetic information from the parents. Such a change in the DNA of the parent is called a **mutation**. As we shall see in Chapter 25, mutations have played a very important role in the development of life on Earth.

Recently, scientists have begun to realize that DNA is damaged at a far higher rate than had previously been thought. Careful chemical analyses indicate that damage to DNA in humans goes on at the rate of about 10,000 "hits" per cell per day. Fortunately, the body has developed repair mechanisms that take care of almost all of this damage as soon as it happens. The study of DNA repair, and the hope that it may help us deal with diseases such as cancer, represents a major frontier in science today and will be discussed more fully in Chapter 24.

Why Are Genes Expressed?

Every cell in your body except the reproductive cells contains an identical set of chromosomes —the exact same set of DNA molecules—yet your cells are not all alike. In fact, chemical reactions critical to one set of cells—those that produce insulin in your pancreas, for example—play no role whatsoever elsewhere. The genetic coding for making insulin is contained in every cell in your body but turned on only in a few. How do the cells in the pancreas "know" that they are supposed to activate the particular gene for insulin, whereas the cells in the brain know they are not supposed to?

The mystery of DNA's operation runs even deeper than this. It now appears that only about 5% of all DNA in human beings is actually taken up by the genes. The other 95% used to be called "junk DNA" because nobody understood why it was there. Scientists are increasingly coming to believe, however, that at least some of the rest of the DNA contains instructions for turning genes on and off. The study of gene control is a frontier field, and we understand very little about how it works. We do know, however, that genes are activated at certain times in the growth of plants or animals, and the triggers for this activation appear to be enzymes or other chemical agents.

Many scientists also think that the failure of these instructions leads to diseases such as cancer. If a cell is dividing and the mechanism that tells it when it's time to stop is faulty, the cell may continue to multiply and produce a tumor. Damage to the control mechanisms in a cell thus may be much more serious than damage to the genes themselves.

◎ 23.4 Viruses

If you have ever had influenza ("the flu") or a common cold, you've experienced the consequences of viruses. Viruses aren't alive in the sense that bacteria and other single-celled organisms are. Unlike the life forms we discussed in Chapter 20, viruses do not metabolize and are not capable of reproduction on their own. Rather, they rely on the genetic mechanisms of cells to reproduce.

A **virus** consists of nothing more than a short length of RNA or DNA wrapped in a protein coating (Figure 23-15). The protein is shaped so that it fits cell receptors and is taken into a cell. Once inside the cell, a variety of events may occur, depending on the exact nature of the virus. The viral DNA may replicate itself, producing its own mRNA, or viral RNA may serve directly as messenger RNA. Thus, the virus takes over the cell's machinery, using the cell's enzymes and tRNA to produce more viruses like itself, eventually killing the cell.

Note that a "computer virus" operates in the same way. This kind of virus is a set of instructions taken into a computer that highjacks the computer's machinery to its own ends.

Alternatively, as in the HIV (human immunodeficiency virus) that causes AIDS, the virus contains an RNA sequence that can be transcribed back into DNA along with some enzymes that insert the DNA into the cell's own DNA. Once that stretch of DNA is inserted, it acts just like any other gene and co-opts the cell into making more viruses. No matter what the mechanisms, however, the result is the same: the cell eventually dies.

HIV turns out to be an unusually complex virus (Figure 23-16). It has two coats of proteins: the outer coat contains molecules that fit receptors in cells in the human immune systems known as T cells, whereas the inner coat encloses the RNA that will be translated into DNA by attached enzymes. The net effect of the virus's action is to destroy cells that are essential to the operation of the immune system, making the infected person vulnerable to many deadly

Protein coat — Nucleic acid

CDC/Photo Researchers

(a)   (b)

FIGURE 23-15 (a) Viruses can have a wide variety of shapes and sizes. This diagram of a bacterial virus shows the protein coat containing DNA at the head. The tail fibers at the bottom attach the virus to the cell wall. DNA is then injected into the cell through the cylindrical core. (b) An electron microscope photograph of herpes viruses, enlarged more than 10,000 times, reveals the regular protein coating that surrounds a strand of DNA.

FIGURE 23-16 A diagram of the HIV virus. The reverse transcriptase is the enzyme in the virus that translates a strand of RNA into DNA.

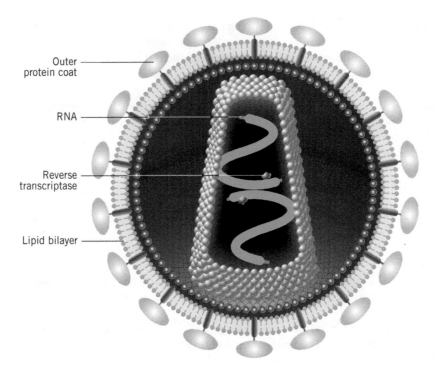

Outer protein coat

RNA

Reverse transcriptase

Lipid bilayer

diseases. We will discuss methods that have been developed for managing AIDS in the next chapter.

Viral Epidemics

There is an old joke about someone who goes to a doctor with a cold and is told to take a shower and stay outside in the cold with wet hair and without a coat.

"But if I do that, I'll get pneumonia," the patient protests.

"Of course," says the doctor, "but I can cure pneumonia."

The medical profession has enjoyed a great deal of success in dealing with diseases such as pneumonia that are caused by invading bacteria. Antibiotics often work by blocking particular enzymes in the bacteria. Because these enzymes don't operate in human cells, antibiotics can destroy the bacteria without harming the human whose body they are invading.

In contrast, viruses with their simple structure of a protein coat surrounding a piece of genetic material, are able to co-opt most of the host cell's machinery while antibiotics do not affect them. This difference is why viral diseases such as the common cold cannot be treated as effectively with commonly available drugs as bacterial infections. The most effective counter-measure for viral diseases has been vaccination, which stimulates the human immune system to produce antibodies that neutralize the virus (Figure 23-17). These antibodies are molecules that have a precise shape that binds to the virus and prevents them from attaching to cells. Poliomyelitis, smallpox, and yellow fever have all been dealt with in this way, and new vaccines against such threats as ebola and new strains of flu are constantly in development.

FIGURE 23-17 The human body produces immune system cells, called *phagocytes*, that destroy viruses, bacteria, and other foreign substances. This photo shows a phagocyte stalking a small bacterium.

Eye of Science/Photo Researchers, Inc.

Viruses not only hide inside cells; many of them also have the ability to change very rapidly, producing new forms as quickly as we find vaccines against them. The copying of DNA in cell division is subject to the cell's "proofreading" mechanisms so that daughter cells are the same as those of the parents. However, some viruses like HIV have no such proofreading, and consequently they mutate at a rate up to a million times faster than normal eukaryotic cells. The influenza virus adopts a different strategy. If two influenza viruses invade the same host, they have the ability to swap sections of their nucleic acids, producing a new strain in the process. This rapid rate of mutation in influenza viruses is the main reason that Americans are urged to get new flu shots each year. The new vaccine attempts to counteract whatever virus has developed since last year's shot.

As news about AIDS and possible epidemics of SARS, bird flu, ebola, and other diseases should remind us, viral diseases remain a very real threat to the human race. Several features of modern life make human beings particularly susceptible to viral attack. For one thing, we now tend to live together in cities, providing a large host population for new viruses. We also travel a great deal so that a virus that develops in one part of the world will quickly spread. Finally, humans are coming into more contact with isolated wilderness areas and therefore into contact with whatever viruses are already living on hosts in those areas. One example is the virus responsible for AIDS, which is believed to have arisen from a virus affecting monkeys in remote African forests. A hunter cutting his finger while skinning an infected monkey, for instance, could have introduced the virus to the human population.

STOP & THINK How much attention do you think governments and scientists should pay to the dangers of new viral diseases? Do you think an international medical center should be established to monitor the appearance of new diseases? What good would such an early warning system do?

◎ 23.5 The Human Genome

In the summer of 2000, the first phase of one of the most ambitious scientific projects in history was completed. Called the **Human Genome Project**, the project set a goal that was nothing less than a complete description of all the base pairs in human DNA—all three *billion* pairs on all 23 chromosomes.

In human beings, as in other eukaryotes, the DNA does not occur as one long, continuous molecule but instead is cut up into bundles called chromosomes. In a chromosome, a stretch of DNA is wrapped around a core of protein molecules. A human being receives 23 different chromosomes from each parent, and each gene has a specific location on a specific chromosome.

Different organisms have different numbers of chromosomes. Humans have a total of 23 pairs, for example, whereas goldfish have 47 pairs and cabbages have 9. There is no connection between the number of chromosomes and the complexity of the organism. It is best to think of chromosomes as the "packaging" into which the DNA is put.

Studying human DNA is particularly important in part because many diseases arise from mutations on specific genes. As we shall see in the next chapter, for example, a common form of cystic fibrosis results from a mutation on a specific gene on chromosome 7. In recent years, scientists have been able to pinpoint the causes of diseases such as sickle-cell anemia, some forms of arthritis, and familial tendencies to develop cancer on specific chromosomes.

DNA sequencing is the process of determining, base pair by base pair, the exact order of bases along a DNA molecule. The net result of a sequencing operation is a string of letters (ATTGCGCATT..., and so on), a sequence that tells us how the DNA is put together in that particular stretch (Figure 23-18). The entire sequence of base pairs in an organism's DNA is called the **genome** of that organism. For reference, the relationships among DNA, genes, chromosomes, and genomes are summarized in Table 23-3.

Many people are surprised to learn that a key ongoing goal of the Human Genome Project is to determine the complete genomes of hundreds of other species, including the mouse, the fruit fly, yeast, and numerous microbes. Our ability to read DNA has even advanced to the point, as we shall see in the next chapter, that the genome of extinct species such as Neanderthal Man have been sequenced. In addition, we shall see that reading the sequence of living species can help us unravel complex genealogies.

More importantly, it turns out that many life forms, even relatively primitive ones, have many of the same genes and thus reveal many of the same genetic

FIGURE 23-18 Two important goals of the Human Genome Project are DNA mapping and DNA sequencing. A genetic map shows the location and sequence of genes along a chromosome. It can be used to identify the genes for a specific trait. Scientists working on the Human Genome Project created physical maps that describe the chemical characteristics of the DNA molecule at any given point. The physical maps were used for DNA sequencing, which determined the exact sequence of base pairs along a DNA molecule.

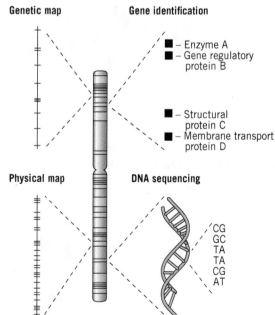

TABLE 23-3   **Relationships among DNA, Genes, Chromosomes, and Genomes**

DNA	The molecule that caries genetic information; it is in the shape of a double helix
Gene	A stretch of DNA that carries the code for making one or more proteins
Chromosome	A specific length of an organism's DNA wrapped around a protein core
Genome	The sum total of all the base pairs in an organism's DNA

mechanisms that occur in humans. One result of this sort of knowledge is that a gene sequence can be used to deduce the sequence of amino acids in a protein. This information, in turn, may give some insight into the function of that protein in the organism and prove useful in developing treatments for various diseases.

Keep watching the news for announcements of the latest progress in this mammoth undertaking.

SCIENCE IN THE MAKING
Connecting Genes and DNA

In 1911, an undergraduate student and a professor were talking at Columbia University. The professor was Thomas Hunt Morgan, who was studying the genetics of fruit flies in his laboratory. Like Mendel's pea plants, fruit flies are ideal organisms for this sort of work because they produce new generations in a matter of weeks. (Morgan, incidentally, was the great-grandson of Francis Scott Key, the man who wrote "The Star Spangled Banner"). The student was Alfred Sturtevant, a young man who went on to have a distinguished scientific career.

The two were discussing the fact that in their experiments, certain characteristics of the flies seemed to be inherited in groups—if one appeared in an offspring, the others were likely to appear as well. They were also finding, however, that occasionally this linkage was broken and that the frequency of the breaking of the link varied from one pair of genes to the next.

During the conversation, Sturtevant realized that if the genes were laid out in a linear array on the chromosomes, then the process of gene exchange that occurs during meiosis would be more likely to separate genes that lay far apart from each other than genes that are close together. In fact, the process of gene exchange would be like cutting up a highway map. Nearby towns would tend to be on the same piece of paper when the cutting was finished, whereas distant towns would be separated more often. Using this insight and the data on how often linkages were broken, Sturtevant came into the lab the next day with the first genetic map of a chromosome.

FIGURE 23-19 The genome of the extinct wooly mammoth (shown here in an artist's conception) is being sequenced on DNA extracted from 10,000 year-old animals frozen in ice.

Work in the Columbia "fly room" thus led to one of the most important basic tenets of modern genetics—that genes are laid out in a linear sequence on chromosomes. During the coming decades, with support from the Carnegie Institution, this lab remained at the center of genetic research. Morgan received the Nobel Prize in 1933 and, in a telling gesture, shared the prize money with Sturtevant and another former student in order to help the two men pay their childrens' college tuition bills.

SCIENCE BY THE NUMBERS
The Human Book of Life

In Chapter 10 we saw that information can be quantified in units of the "bit"—a simple statement about "yes or no" or "on or off." We can use this notion to calculate the amount of information in the human genome.

Each site along the DNA molecule can be occupied by one of four bases. This information can be represented by two bits. We could, for example, set up a code as follows:

A: on on
T: on off
C: off on
G: off off

Using this code, we could go down the molecule specifying two bits of information at each nucleotide, and this would tell us the sequence. For example, the sequence AGT would be rendered:

on on; off off; on off

The human genome contains about 3 billion bases, so the total information content is:

3,000,000,000 bases × 2 bits/base = 6,000,000,000 bits

Let's compare this information content to that of a familiar object—this textbook. A textbook transmits information by letters, numbers, and other symbols, each of which can be represented by eight bits (see Chapter 10). An average page of this book contains about 3,000 characters, for an information content of:

3,000 characters/page × 8 bits/character = 24,000 bits/page

The number of pages required to carry the entire human genome equals the number of bits per genome, divided by the number of bits per page:

$$\frac{(6,000,000,000 \text{ bits/genome})}{(24,000 \text{ bits/page})} = 250,000 \text{ pages}$$

It would take almost 400 volumes the size of this book to record the entire blueprint for a human being. It's amazing to think that all of that information is contained in every one of your cells.

TECHNOLOGY
New Ways to Sequence

When the Human Genome Project was starting, scientists estimated that it would take decades and cost billions of dollars. Even well into the project, the official estimate was that it wouldn't be completed until 2005 and would cost $3 billion (about $1 per base pair).

This situation was changed drastically when molecular biologist J. Craig Venter, who is now head of the Venter Institute, developed a new way of combining computers with automatic DNA sequencing machines (Figure 23-20;). As a result of his work, the Genome Project finished in 2000, 5 years ahead of schedule, with the cost of sequencing being only about 10 cents per base pair (and the price has now dropped to a few cents per base pair).

Venter's novel technique is called shotgun, and here's how it works: Long stretches of DNA are broken up into many small pieces. These pieces are fed into an army of sequencing machines, each of which "reads" only a short segment—a few hundred base pairs of the original. By

FIGURE 23-20 J. Craig Venter of the Venter Institute developed faster and cheaper methods to sequence DNA.

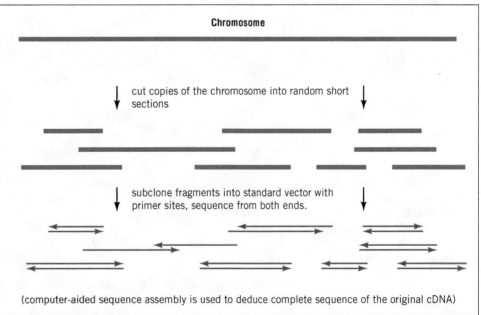

Chromosome

cut copies of the chromosome into random short sections

subclone fragments into standard vector with primer sites, sequence from both ends.

(computer-aided sequence assembly is used to deduce complete sequence of the original cDNA) identifying overlapping segments from among the thousands of short DNA strands, powerful computers are able to reconstruct the entire DNA sequence.

It is important to realize that in this technique, the contributions of computers are just as important as those of the sequencers. This is why scientists often speak of the Genome Project as an example of the *bioinformatics* revolution.

THE ONGOING PROCESS OF SCIENCE
Epigenetics

From the time of Mendel on, scientists studying the way traits are passed from one generation to another concentrated on genes. Today we understand that genes are stretches of base pairs along a DNA molecule, and our understanding of genetic change involves changes in the sequence of those pairs. Recent research, however, has shown that there is more to the story of genetic inheritance than this—that there are ways to influence inheritance that do not involve genes. These new modes of influence go under the name of epigenetics (literally "outside the genes").

It has long been known that a mother's behavior during pregnancy—smoking or drinking, for example—can influence the long-term health of her child. What is new, however, is the recognition that these sorts of effects can be passed on to that child's children. Experiments with laboratory mice have established that this process does not occur by changing the genes themselves, but by attaching markers to the DNA that influence whether or not a gene can be turned on. A common process that induces this kind of change is called methylation because it involves a simple methyl molecule (a carbon atom with three hydrogen atoms). This molecule attaches itself to a spot on the DNA chain and prevents the normal process of gene expression from starting. For some reason we do not yet understand, these tags survive the normal cleaning up of markers in the DNA of sperm and egg and are inherited. We know that these effects can be passed to several generations of mice and, in the case of a short-lived flatworm, to 30 generations.

Bottom line: your great grandmother's behavior may be influencing your DNA.

THINKING MORE ABOUT **GENETICS**

The Ethics of Genes

Advances in genetic research are dramatically altering our understanding of human health and behavior. Scientists now can detect many characteristics of an individual, including the presence of life-threatening diseases, before birth. Every year we learn more about genetic characteristics and thus are better able to foresee aspects of a child's future. But with this knowledge comes an ethical challenge that will face every American in the coming decades. What should we do with genetic information?

Eventually we may be able to test every fetus for a variety of incurable genetic diseases. Should those tests be mandated? Should parents be informed of their future child's fate? Should the prospect of an incurable disease provide grounds for abortion? It has also been suggested (though not proven in detail) that alcoholism and other behavioral disorders may be related, at least in part, to genetic factors. Suppose a person was found to carry a particular gene or combination of genes that were thought to predispose individuals toward alcoholism? To whom should that information be conveyed? To the individual? To his or her doctor? His or her employer? His or her insurance company?

Taking these issues a step further, we may soon be able to alter an individual's DNA in utero, perhaps even in the first weeks of pregnancy. Many people would probably agree to genetic manipulation if it could cure their child of a fatal disease, but where does society draw the line? Would you allow such a procedure to improve genetically defective eyesight, or perhaps prevent crippling arthritis in later years? Would you be willing to enhance your child's IQ or to make her more athletic? What about changing his height or hair color? As with many other aspects of science and technology, we must come to grips with the question of whether it is ethical to do something simply because we are able to do it.

◀ RETURN TO THE INTEGRATED QUESTION

Why do offspring resemble their parents?

- In the science of biology, the term *offspring* refers to new organisms that are produced by the process of reproduction.

- Offspring inherit traits from their parents. This fact is the basis of selective breeding, which has been used by humans for millennia to improve crops and domestic animal stocks.

- The modern science of genetics studies the phenomena of inheritance and began with the work of Gregor Mendel in 1865.

  - Mendel sought to understand the process of inheritance and the transmission of characteristics from parent to offspring.

  - In 1915, Thomas Hunt Morgan postulated the chromosome theory of inheritance. These early works became the foundation of classical or Mendelian genetics.

- Genetics and the laws of inheritance for sexual reproduction follow a few simple rules:

  - Physical characteristics or traits are passed from parents to offspring by some unknown mechanism (we call it a gene).

- Each offspring has two genes for each trait, one gene from each parent.

- Some genes are dominant and some are recessive. When present together, the trait of a dominant gene will be expressed in preference to the trait of a recessive gene.

- Genes play a large role in the appearance and behavior of all organisms.

  - Nevertheless, the environment in which an organism lives has a large influence on its ultimate development.

  - This idea is the basis of the "nature versus nurture" debate. In reality, both nature (i.e., genetic inheritance) and nurture (i.e., the totality of the environment of an organism) play complementary roles in the maturation and development of all characteristics.

  - A more correct formulation of the "nature versus nurture" debate: Genes interact with environment across time.

SUMMARY

Genetics, the study of the way in which biological information is carried from one generation to the next, is a field as old as the selective breeding of animals and the selection of seeds for crops. Gregor Mendel attempted to quantify aspects of this process by cross-pollinating *purebred* varieties of pea plants to produce *hybrids.* He discovered that all first-generation hybrids appeared the same, with the traits of just one parent plant, but the second generation displayed characteristics of both parents. Typically, three-fourths of the members of the second generation display one trait, one-fourth the other. Mendel explained his observations by developing laws of *classical genetics:* (1) traits are passed from parent to offspring by "units of inheritance" (we call them *genes*); (2) each parent contributes one gene for each trait; and (3) some genes are *dominant* and will be expressed, whereas others are *recessive* and will appear only if no dominant gene is present.

Modern *molecular genetics* seeks to understand the molecular basis for Mendel's observations. The key to understanding genetics lies in the unique structure of the *nucleic acids,* including *DNA,* with its *double helix,* ladder-like sequence of base pairs, and the closely related single-stranded *RNA.* The four different DNA bases, A, T, C, and G, which always come in the pairs AT or CG, act like letters of a coded message—the message of life. Because of its structure, DNA can replicate itself and store the information needed to make proteins.

Every cell has a set of chromosomes with the complete DNA blueprint in its nucleus. The process of copying DNA before cell division is called replication and involves splitting apart the two sides of the DNA double helix, thus exposing the complementary base pairs. Each exposed base binds to its complement, and so two complete DNA strands form where before there was only one.

The coded DNA message is read by RNA, a process called transcription. *Messenger RNA,* a single-stranded molecule, copies the sequence for one gene and carries it out of the nucleus to the part of the cell where proteins are made. *Transfer RNA* matches sequences of three base pairs to corresponding amino acids; thus an RNA sequence translates into a string of amino acids—a protein. The correspondence between base-pair sequences and amino acids is called the *genetic code,* which is shared by every living organism.

Although the DNA message is resilient to most damage, errors in the coded sequence can occur and cause *mutations.* Conversely, *viruses* cause sickness by usurping a cell's chemical factories with foreign genetic instructions.

Segments of DNA are wrapped around a protein core to form *chromosomes.* The complete description of an organism's genetic code is called its *genome.* Scientists determine a *genome* by first *mapping* the positions of every gene on every chromosome and then *sequencing* the exact order of base pairs on every gene. The *Human Genome Project* has produced the 3-billion-base-pair sequence of the human genome, as well as genomes for many other organisms.

KEY TERMS

genetics	classical genetics	nucleic acids
true breeding	dominant	DNA
hybrid	recessive	RNA
gene	molecular genetics	double helix

messenger RNA (mRNA)	mutation	DNA sequencing
transfer RNA (tRNA)	virus	genome
genetic code	Human Genome Project	

DISCOVERY LAB

DNA or deoxyribonucleic acid is the heredity material that contains vital information about your genetic traits and is found in every cell of your body. If you are curious to know how it looks like, then gather the following materials: 1/2 teaspoon of salt, 200 milliliters of water (mix the two to form a solution), dishwashing soap or a mild detergent (prepare a solution of 5 milliliters of the detergent mixed with 15 milliliters of water), 5 milliliters of ethanol (should be ice cold; rubbing alcohol can be substituted for ethanol), a glass rod, and a small jar with a lid.

Take the salt water solution and rinse your mouth with it. Make sure you swish the solution in your mouth for at least 30 seconds. Spit out the solution in the jar and pour 5 milliliters of the soap

solution in it. Shake the jar gently from side to side for a few minutes. Pour ethanol in the bottle by gliding it gently down the sides of the bottle. Let the solution stand for few minutes. The alcohol will float on the top. Take the glass rod and gently try to incorporate alcohol into the soap solution. At the boundary of soap solution and ethanol twist the glass rod and collect as much of the DNA as possible. Remove it from the bottle and put it in a container and seal it. Be gentle with the entire process from shaking of the jar to removing the DNA; if you are not careful, the DNA strands may break and clump up. If the DNA is microscopic, then why do you see it? What would you do with your DNA? Allow it to be seen and used by anyone? Or keep it away from falling into the hands of others?

REVIEW QUESTIONS

1. How did Mendel investigate the question of how biological information is passed from one generation to another?

2. How did Mendel define the gene? How do we define it today?

3. What is the difference between a true breeding plant and a hybrid?

4. Why was it important for Mendel to begin with true breeding plants for each trait he was studying?

5. What is the difference between a dominant and a recessive gene?

6. What is molecular genetics? How does this differ from Mendelian or classical genetics?

7. What is a nucleotide?

8. Name the four bases that occur in DNA. What pairs can they form?

9. Describe the construction of the double-helix structure of DNA.

10. How does RNA differ from DNA?

11. What are the main steps in the process of DNA replication?

12. How is the information of DNA copied onto mRNA?

13. What is the function of mRNA?

14. How does tRNA determine the primary structure of proteins?

15. What is a codon? What is the genetic code?

16. What can cause damage to DNA? How does the cell repair this damage?

17. What are chromosomes? How are they related to DNA?

18. What is a virus? Why do viral diseases not respond to antibiotics?

DISCUSSION QUESTIONS

1. The scientific method has been articulated only within the last few centuries. The selective breeding of plants and animals has been going on for millennia. Despite not knowing of the scientific method, do you feel these breeders were following the basic principles of the scientific method? Why or why not?

2. Is it possible for a recessive gene to skip more than one generation? Explain why or why not.

3. What is a genome? Do all humans have identical genomes? Why or why not? What advances do you think we might gain from the success of the Human Genome Project?

4. How did advances in technology aid the Human Genome Project? Would it have been worth doing the project without these advances?

5. How does cell chemistry, and therefore all life, depend on the production of proteins? What role do genes, RNA, and DNA play in the production of proteins?

6. State some of the arguments for and against genetic engineering. How do you feel about the prospect? Do you think there should be limitations? If so, who should determine those limitations and who should regulate them?

7. Inbreeding is the practice of mating closely related individuals. One of the most notoriously inbred people in history was Charles II of Spain, who had several instances of uncles marrying nieces in his ancestry. Inbreeding can perpetuate desired qualities but can also perpetuate harmful qualities. Explain why this is so.

8. All cells in your body have, more or less, exactly the same DNA. Yet there are many different types of cells. How do cells perform such different functions with the same set of instructions?

9. If you wished to make the case that viruses were alive, what evidence would you bring forth? What counter arguments might you face?

10. Is it possible for birth defects to be due to exposure of the parents to harmful agents long before the child is conceived? Given what you now know about the molecular basis of life, how could such an effect happen?

11. How many types of RNA are there in a cell? Why is more than one type necessary in the production of a DNA sequence?

12. Why do many cultures have a taboo and/or laws against marrying your close relatives? Why is incest a genetically unproductive practice?

13. Why do offspring resemble their parents? Attempt to include nucleotides, genes, chromosomes, RNA, DNA, mitosis, and meiosis in your answer.

14. The Human Genome Project cost about 3 billion dollars. Do you think it was worth the expense? Why or why not?

15. United States law says that no portion of the human genome can be patented. This means, for instance, if a company uncovers a portion of the genome that codes for a protein that is an effective fighter of cancer, that company can't claim it as their intellectual property. Do you think that a company should be allowed intellectual property rights and make money off such a discovery? Why or why not?

PROBLEMS

1. The *Encyclopedia Britannica* has about 1,500 words per page, 1,000 pages per volume, and 30 volumes. How many sets of the *Encyclopedia Britannica* would it take to transmit the same amount of information as is contained in human DNA? (*Hint:* Remember, the average word has five characters, and a single character has eight bits of information.)

2. Suppose one breed of rat has fur that is either all white or all brown and eyes that are either clear or pink. Suppose studies show that when purebred white rats are crossed with purebred brown rats their offspring are brown. Further, when purebred clear-eyed rats are bred with purebred pink-eyed rats, the resulting offspring have pink eyes. Which are the dominant and recessive traits for eyes and fur? What do you think would be the traits of the offspring if purebred brown, pink-eyed rats are bred with purebred white, clear-eyed rats?

3. Scientists studying genetics frequently use fruit flies (*Drosophilia melanogaster*) because they breed a new generation every 10 days. Assuming no other complications, how long would it likely have taken Mendel to perform his experiments with fruit flies to see the results he saw with pea plants? How long would it have taken if he were performing his experiment on apple trees, which have 5 years between generations?

4. Suppose it takes 1,000 base pairs in DNA to provide enough information to code a protein. DNA can make up to 100,000 different proteins. If there is no overlap between the sequences of base pairs in DNA that code for protein, how many base pairs are involved? If a typical molecule of human DNA has 3 billion base pairs, what percent of human DNA is involved in the coding of proteins?

5. The mutation rate in human DNA has been estimated to be 2.7×10^{-5} mutations/base pair every generation (approximated as 20 years). If there are 3 billion base pairs in human DNA, how many mutations can be expected after 20 years?

6. A tall pea plant is allowed to pollinate with a short pea plant; tallness is the dominant trait. If the tall plant is not purebred, what percent of offspring will be short?
    a. 25%
    b. 50%
    c. 75%
    d. 100%

7. Suppose you engage in sequencing the genome of a species of newt in which a DNA molecule has up to 15 billion base pairs. You purchase a sequencing device that can analyze 100 million base pairs per day. How long will it take you to sequence the genome of one newt?

    a. 5 months

    b. 3 hours, 36 minutes

    c. 100 days

    d. 15 days

INVESTIGATIONS

1. Prepare a report on a genetic disease. Has our ability to sequence DNA changed our understanding of this disease? What kinds of medical treatments are now available?

2. Read *The Double Helix* by James Watson, co-discoverer with Francis Crick of the DNA structure. What data did they use to unravel the structure? What were the key steps in solving the double-helix structure?

3. Investigate the role that Rosalind Franklin played in the history of DNA and the discovery of the double-helix structure. Was she properly recognized for her efforts? Why didn't she win the Nobel Prize for her discoveries?

4. Some psychological disorders are now believed to be caused by defects in the body's chemistry. Read about one such disease, and summarize the argument between those who believe that psychological problems all have a molecular basis and those who believe that they are all due to the environment in which the individual has lived.

5. Make a family tree for your own family, recording characteristics such as eye and hair color, height, causes of death, and so on. Can you apply Mendel's rules to this tree?

6. There have been many outbreaks of fatal viral diseases over the past several decades. Look up one such outbreak and describe how the medical community dealt with it.

7. Mendel used mathematical analyses to deduce the presence of genes despite the fact that he couldn't see them directly. What other great discoveries relied on the use of mathematics to prove the existence of something that was impossible to directly observe?

8. Investigate the "nature versus nurture" debate. Why do most scientists now state that it is usually nature and nurture, and not one or the other?

9. What is bioinformatics? Does your college or university have a bioinformatics department? What are you studying if you pursue a degree in bioinformatics or biotechnology?

10. Investigate the history of thoroughbred (i.e., racehorse) or canine (i.e., dog) pedigrees. Why are these valuable resources? What does it mean to own a "purebreed" dog? What does it mean to own a thoroughbred horse?

11. Find out how health authorities decide what flu vaccines have to be manufactured each year. Why does the vaccine have to be changed every year?

24 The New Science of Life

Can we cure cancer?

PHYSICS

DNA fingerprinting relies on the fact that short segments of DNA move faster than long segments in an electric field.

BIOLOGY

Genetic engineering is based on the fact that all life uses the same genetic code.

CHEMISTRY

Chemical reactions in the cell are used to repair damaged DNA.

GREAT IDEA

Our new understanding of genetic mechanisms is leading to enormous technological advances in medicine and other aspects of our lives.

TECHNOLOGY

Computers are being used to design drugs with a specific shape that will accomplish a particular function in the body.

ENVIRONMENT

Both natural and commercially produced pesticides can cause damage to DNA; it makes no difference where the pesticide molecules came from.

ASTRONOMY

Ultraviolet light from the Sun may damage DNA.

HEALTH & SAFETY

Regenerative medicine, based on the use of cloning and stem cell techniques, may soon be used to cure many diseases.

● = applications of the great idea discussed in this chapter

 = other applications, some of which are discussed in other chapters

A Break in the Case

You head down the highway, listening to your favorite music station, when the program is interrupted for a news flash. New DNA evidence has led police to the arrest of a suspect in a highly publicized murder. A few skin cells under the victim's fingernails, analyzed at an FBI crime lab, cracked the case. It seems as if DNA and genetic technologies are in the news every day. Paternity testing, cloning, tests for genetic diseases, DNA fingerprinting, stem cells, gene therapy, genetically modified foods—our world has been transformed by our understanding of the genetic code. What are these remarkable new technologies? How will they affect our lives and the lives of our children?

◎ 24.1 Genetic Engineering

FIGURE 24-1 Restriction enzymes act something like a pair of scissors that break a DNA chain at specific sequences. Biologists can use this procedure to insert or remove segments of DNA.

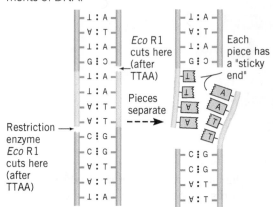

Fundamental new insights into the workings of nature often trigger dramatic changes in the human condition. The discovery of the nature of electricity and magnetism, for example, led to the electrification of entire continents. The discovery of the basic laws of quantum mechanics eventually led to the modern information revolution. Now, our new understanding of the genetic mechanisms of all living things is leading to changes every bit as profound and pervasive. This revolution has already begun, although its consequences are not always immediately visible to the general public. At research centers and hospitals around the world, the new molecular understanding of life is being put to work to cure disease and to better the human condition. In this chapter we present a few areas of current effort to give you a sense of what will soon become possible. Remember, though, that these advances are just the tip of the iceberg with respect to technologies of the new science of life.

Genetic engineering is a procedure by which foreign genes are inserted into an organism, or existing genes are altered, to modify the function of living things. The basic technique of genetic engineering is very simple. Certain proteins called *restriction enzymes* have the ability to cut a DNA molecule (as shown in Figure 24-1) at a spot where there is a specific sequence of bases. This process creates DNA that has several unattached bases at the cut end. Think of these exposed bases as something like pieces of Velcro at the ends of the DNA strands.

If another strand of DNA is cut in the same way, and if the exposed base pairs on that second strand are complementary to the base pairs on the original strand, then when the two strands are put together the bases will bind and the strands will stick together. This procedure allows researchers to take a stretch of DNA, cut it, and splice in another stretch of DNA that has the appropriate base pairs on its ends (Figure 24-2). The new DNA will contain an extra stretch of genetic information in it.

If the new stretch of DNA is a gene, then the same mechanism that drives the chemistry in every cell on Earth can start expressing that gene in its new environment. For example, more than 100 copies of the gene that makes human insulin have been spliced together into a loop of DNA called a *plasmid*. Biologists introduced that plasmid into the single-celled bacterium, *E. coli* (so called because it is common in the human colon), and the genetically modified *E. coli* copies the plasmid along with its own DNA when it divides. A vat full of genetically engineered *E. coli* thus produces large quantities of human insulin that is almost indistinguishable from insulin produced in your own pancreas. In fact, most of the insulin used to treat diabetes is now made this way. This genetically based process is a great improvement over the old method, which involved tedious extraction of pig insulin from the pancreases of slaughtered animals—insulin that resulted in an adverse immune response in some patients. The story of genetically engineered insulin is only a small part of the growing list of changes that are possible with genetic engineering.

In the United States, the biggest use of this technology is not in medicine but in agriculture. The first commercial genetically modified plants were introduced into American agriculture in 1996. In 2010 there were 365 million acres (148 million hectares) planted to these sorts of crops worldwide, which amounts to about 10% of the world's cultivated land area. More than 30 countries grow a dozen different types of genetically modified crops, and experts expect this number to grow steadily in the coming years (Figure 24-3a).

One reason for this rapid adoption of a new kind of crop can be seen by looking at the issue of pest control. Genes that contain the natural insecticide Bt, derived from a common bacterium, are inserted into the DNA of crop plants. Because of the presence of this gene, when insects such as the European corn borer start to feed, they are quickly killed. Besides the obvious advantage of allowing the plant to remain healthy, this process may also benefit the environment because genetically engineered plants require much less in the way of pesticide application.

Another use of genetic engineering involves dealing with the other great enemy of agriculture—weeds. In conventional agriculture, weeds are controlled by cultivation (turning soil over between rows of crop plants) and the spraying of herbicides. Both of these practices have the potential of damaging the environment, through either erosion or runoff. It is possible to engineer crop plants to be resistant to specific kinds of herbicides—a common technique involves so-called Roundup Ready plants (Roundup is a popular commercial herbicide). These crops can be planted in unplowed fields, which can then be sprayed to eliminate weeds. This so-called no-plow agriculture is gaining wide acceptance as a way of preventing soil erosion.

Other applications of genetic engineering in agriculture include strawberries that are highly resistant to frost or drought, plants that are unaffected by specific diseases, colored varieties of cotton, and crops that manufacture natural insect repellents. Genetic engineering of animals has led to varieties that grow faster or have other agricultural advantages, and researchers have recently patented varieties of mice especially "designed" for medical research (Figure 24-3b). There's even a patent for genetically engineered petroleum-eating bacteria to clean up oil slicks from tanker accidents.

FIGURE 24-2 The process of genetic engineering. Two strands of DNA are cut by restriction enzymes. Each cut is carefully made so that the exposed bases of each strand are complementary. The two strands are joined together to form one DNA molecule.

(a)

(b)

FIGURE 24-3 Genetic engineering has produced a variety of modified organisms, including *(a)* pest-resistant crops and *(b)* genetically identical mice for medical research.

Underlying all of this technology is the central fact that all life is based on the same genetic code—the translation of DNA sequences in a gene to amino acid sequences in a protein. The exact same geometrical shapes and chemical properties of the four base molecules occur in every living thing. That scientists can routinely switch genes from plants to animals and back again is simply another demonstration of the chemical unity of all life.

In the end, what's new about genetic engineering is that, unlike the selective breeders of the past, modern biologists can usually control exactly what gene is being added to or deleted from the organism being developed.

> **STOP & THINK** What harmful effects might result if a gene to prevent frost damage in strawberries were to get into other plants?

A number of groups around the world are attempting to ban or restrict the introduction of genetically modified foods. This opposition is largely motivated by the fear that introducing these kinds of foods may have unknown environmental and health consequences. In the United States, genetically modified organisms (GMOs) are controlled by three agencies. The Department of Agriculture is concerned with whether the crop is safe to grow, the Food and Drug Administration with whether it is safe to eat, and the Environmental Protection Agency with whether it is safe for the environment. The criterion used by the FDA is "reasonable expectation of no harm," with the primary test being whether the GMO is as safe as things that have been in the food supply for generations.

Historically, the concern has been that GMOs might contain unexpected allergens—that someone allergic to shellfish, for example, might encounter the protein responsible for that seafood allergy in an apple. The screening of GMOs, then, begins with excluding products that contain any one of a long list of allergens, as well as molecules that might have properties of known allergens. As more experience with GMOs accumulates, fears about unexpected health effects seem to be subsiding, and the main opposition has shifted to environmental issues, particularly the question of whether genes might be transferred to other plants such as weeds. No examples of this so-called lateral gene transfer have been documented, but it remains a point of controversy.

Today, different countries around the world have adopted different policies toward GMOs. In general, these crops are banned or rigidly controlled in Europe (fewer than a dozen types of genetically engineered crops are grown there), allowed in North America, and eagerly embraced in many Third World countries. As we have seen, however, the use of genetically engineered crops has grown substantially since they were first introduced. The reason for this growth is simple: genetically engineered crops typically increase yields by 5 to 25%, while at the same time cutting farmers' costs by as much as 50%.

We have not even begun to imagine the changes that can take place through the use of this technology. The social issues involved in genetic engineering are profound. In 1974, scientists working in the field of genetic engineering voluntarily undertook a moratorium on further research until more thought could be given to the question of how to keep potentially dangerous organisms from escaping into the environment. In most cases, such as the *E. coli* used in insulin production, the host bacteria are so specialized and so dependent on their laboratory culture that they could not survive in the wild. In this age of terrorism, however, officials must consider another threat—the deliberate release of genetically engineered pathogens into the environment, an activity known as *bioterrorism*.

TECHNOLOGY
Bioterrorism

In 2001, the United States got a dramatic introduction to a new kind of terrorism, one that uses biological agents to spread disease in a population. The term *bioterrorism* quickly became part of our vocabulary. In the 2001 attack, envelopes containing anthrax spores were mailed to several news outlets and government officials. As a result of this exposure, 5 people contracted anthrax and died, while 17 more became infected with the disease. The perpetrator of this attack was never brought to trial, but the events opened the eyes of officials to the possibility of bioterrorism in our country.

Anthrax is a common disease of livestock, and spores are commonly found in agricultural areas. Normally, however, spores clump together and do not float in the air, where they can be inhaled by humans. In a process known as weaponization, however, spores can be coated with various substances so that they become aerosol particles that can be inhaled. In this form, the spores can cause a fatal disease.

The anthrax attacks represent a rather low-tech form of bioterrorism. It has been estimated that someone with the proper scientific background could produce weaponized anthrax in a makeshift laboratory using a few thousand dollars worth of equipment. More high-tech types of bioterrorism might involve the spread of diseases such as smallpox (now eradicated in nature) or even the reengineering of the deadly virus that caused the great Spanish influenza epidemic in 1918—a virus that killed tens of millions of people worldwide. In 2012, for example, two major scientific journals voluntarily censored papers that were deemed to contain too much detailed information on how to engineer a deadly form of bird flu. The Department of Homeland Security has, over the past years, established many research programs to find ways to deal with bioterrorism. For obvious reasons, much of this research is done in secret.

FIGURE 24-4 The polymerase chain reaction (PCR) copies a sequence of DNA. (a) A strand of DNA is mixed in solution with DNA nucleotides (precursors), a primer that targets a specific piece of DNA, and an enzyme (polymerase) that helps to assemble DNA. The mix is heated to about 90°C to separate DNA strands. (b) When cooled to about 60°C, primers attach to the DNA strands. (c) At 70°C, nucleotides begin to attach to the DNA strands. (d) At the end you have two copies of the desired DNA.

TECHNOLOGY
The PCR Process

Development of a simple technique sometimes opens the door for all sorts of new applications. In biotechnology, the process called *polymerase chain reaction (PCR)* has played this role. In essence, PCR is a way of making copies of select strands of DNA so that, starting with a very small sample (a few cells, for example), investigators can produce as much of the desired DNA as they need. As we shall see below, the PCR technique is often used to amplify DNA prior to DNA fingerprinting.

The process is illustrated in Figure 24-4. A sample that contains the DNA to be copied is mixed in solution with three ingredients: DNA nucleotides (the building blocks or precursors of DNA), a short stretch of DNA known as the "primer" (which is designed to identify the desired section of DNA to be copied), and an enzyme called DNA polymerase that helps to assemble DNA strands. First, the mixture is heated to about 90°C to separate the DNA into two strands (Figure 24-4a). Once the strands are separated, the solution is cooled to 60°C, at which temperature primers attach to the desired portion of the DNA (Figure 24-4b). In the third step, the solution is heated to 70°C, which enables the polymerase to attach nucleotides onto the DNA strands (Figure 24-4c). Eventually, we have two identical DNA strands in place of the original (Figure 24-4d). This process, repeated many times, can create as many copies of the original DNA strand as needed.

SCIENCE BY THE NUMBERS
PCR Multiplication

How many times would you have to go through the heating and cooling cycle in the PCR process to multiply the original supply of DNA by a billion?

Each time you go through the cycle, you double the number of DNA molecules. This means that the number of molecules will grow as indicated in the following table.

Number of Repeats	Number of Molecules
1	2
2	4
3	8
.	.
.	.
10	1028

Roughly speaking, then, when you go through the cycle 10 times, you multiply the number of DNA molecules by 1000. This means that if you go through the cycle 20 times, you will multiply the number of molecules by approximately:

$$1,000 \times 1,000 = 1,000,000 = 1 \text{ million}$$

and if you do the cycle 30 times you will have:

$$1,000 \times 1,000 \times 1,000 = 1,000,000,000 = 1 \text{ billion}$$

It is this property of the PCR process that allows technicians to have enough DNA to identify individuals from a tiny drop of blood or tissue.

◉ 24.2 DNA Fingerprinting

The analysis of DNA in human tissue, a technique called **DNA fingerprinting**, is becoming increasingly important in the judicial system in the United States. Except for identical twins, no two human beings in the world have the same DNA. Thus analysis of blood, skin, or semen samples from the scene of a crime can be used to identify criminals in much the same way that fingerprints do (Figure 24-5; new photo?), and this process can also help to identify victims of airplane crashes and natural disasters.

In principle, one could sequence an individual's entire genome in order to make an unambiguous identification. In practice, this effort is both expensive and unnecessary. Instead, scientists pick specific segments of DNA that can be used to characterize a specific genome without knowing its entire sequence. Think of this process as being analogous to identifying a city by looking for familiar landmarks. If you saw the Eiffel Tower, for example, you would know that you were in Paris, and you wouldn't need a detailed street map.

The DNA fingerprinting techniques in common use depend on the fact that there are stretches of DNA where a certain sequence of nonsense bases repeats itself over and over. The number of repeats in these sections is essentially random, so by comparing the number of repeats in two samples of DNA at several different locations, it is possible to tell whether they come from the same individual.

The original DNA fingerprinting technique, accepted by U.S. courts in the 1990s, was accurate but cumbersome. It used relatively long repeating sections, known as variable number tandem repeat *(VNTR)* sequences, in which up to 80 nonsense phrases would appear in a row. Enzymes cut the DNA at places with a specific sequence of bases, so segments containing different VNTRs were of different lengths. These DNA segments were placed in a gelatin-like material, then subjected to an electrical field. The smaller segments moved through the gel faster, so that after a certain time, the different strands of DNA moved different distances. The DNA was then tagged with a radioactive tracer. The end result of this process was that the information in each person's DNA was reduced to something like a bar code. It was been found that five segments of DNA containing VNTR are enough to establish identification.

In the early years of the twenty-first century, DNA fingerprinting technology underwent a significant change. Instead of using the VNTR technique,

FIGURE 24-5 Evidence from modern biotechnology plays an important role in the television series *CSI*.

KIM KULISH/AFP/Getty Images, Inc.

which is accurate but slow, scientists found that they could use other segments of DNA to establish identification more easily and quickly. The new technique is based on stretches of DNA known as *short tandem repeats,* or STRs, which are stretches of DNA where a nonsense phrase is repeated a small number of times—typically from 2 to 25 times. The PCR technique is used to copy a given sample many times, and the primer molecules (see the "Technology" section above) are built to fluoresce (give off light) when a laser beam shines on them.

The products of the PCR process are then fed through a small, liquid-filled tube. An electric field causes segments of different lengths to separate from each other, a laser is shone on the molecules, and the light they give off is measured. The result is a curve like the one shown in Figure 24-6, in which each peak corresponds to a certain number of repeats of a specific type. These curves are then compared to standard curves obtained from known DNA sequences.

The Federal Bureau of Investigation's (FBI) databases have established the standard for STR analysis in America. Although there are hundreds of STR systems known in the human genome, it has been found that 13 different STR sites, spread across many chromosomes, are sufficient to produce an identification. The probability of two people having the same DNA sequence in all 13 sites is so low that it is unlikely that any two people in the United States would have identical STR profiles.

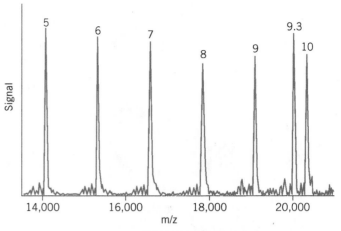

FIGURE 24-6 DNA fingerprinting using the STR method. Each spike in the curve corresponds to different lengths of DNA.

⊙ **24.3** Stem Cells, Cloning, and Regenerative Medicine

As we saw in Chapter 23, every cell in the human body (except for sperm and ova) contains exactly the same DNA. The DNA, which first comes together in the fertilized egg, is copied trillions of times during the period in which the human grows from an embryo to an adult, and every daughter cell receives a copy of that original genetic material.

Yet even though all cells have the same DNA, all cells do not carry out the same functions in the body. In an adult, blood cells cannot produce skin, nor can skin cells produce muscle tissue. This difference occurs because early on in the development process cells start to become specialized through a process by which genes in DNA are "switched off." Thus, although every cell contains the same 30,000 genes, in adult cells different combinations of those genes are turned off, so that in each adult cell only a small fraction of the genes actually produce protein enzymes to use in chemical reactions. Once a cell has become specialized in this way, the DNA copying process can only produce more cells of the same type. Yet early in the process of development there must be cells in which all of the genes are still capable of functioning. Such cells are said to be *pluripotent* because they have the potential of developing into any kind of cell in the body. Cells that have this potential are called **stem cells**.

When a single fertilized egg begins to divide, all of the genes in the resulting cells remain potentially active. A few days after fertilization, as shown in Figure 24-7, the embryo (at this point called a *blastocyst*) is a simple structure, consisting of a spherical outer cell wall and an inner cell mass. The outer cells will develop into the placenta when the embryo implants itself in the walls of the uterus during pregnancy, whereas the cells in the inner cell mass will develop into the fetus and, eventually, into an adult human being. The cells in this inner cell mass, then, will produce all of the cells in the human body and therefore qualify as stem cells. Because they are found in the embryo, they are called *embryonic stem cells.*

Two weeks later, the embryo has reached a stage (known as a *gastrula*) in which the cells are no longer pluripotent. By this time, the inner cell mass has evolved into three distinctive layers, as shown in the figure. Each of these layers

FIGURE 24-7 Early stages of embryonic development.

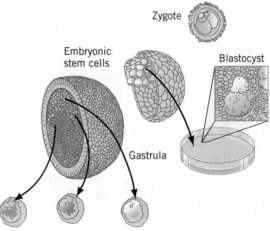

Zygote

Embryonic stem cells

Blastocyst

Gastrula

FIGURE 24-8 Dolly, the first cloned mammal, was the subject of great media attention.

will eventually produce different types of tissues in the adult. For example, cells from one layer will form organs such as the liver and lungs, those from another layer bone and blood vessels, and those from the third layer skin and neurons. This division of cells into specialized types is called *differentiation.*

The pattern of differentiation continues throughout the growth process. Even in adulthood, however, many cells in the body can produce a limited number of different kinds of tissue. Many different kinds of skin cells, for example, are derived from a single progenitor. Cells that have this limited ability are called *somatic stem cells,* or sometimes, *adult stem cells.* They form a kind of biological resupply system for the body, supplying new cells as old ones wear out.

Scientists have known about stem cells for a long time, but it wasn't until 1998 that a group under the direction of James Thomson at the University of Wisconsin managed to produce a line of cells that, while reproducing, never differentiated. Up to this time, when scientists tried to get stem cells to reproduce in the laboratory, some process (which we do not yet understand and is still under intense study) would cause them to turn into specialized tissue such as muscle. By finding just the right chemical environment for his stem cells, Thomson was able to keep the genes in his cells from being switched off. As the stem cells divided, they retained their pluripotency from one generation to the next. A collection of cells like this is called a *stem cell line.*

The medical potential of stem cells is enormous. Scientists immediately realized that if they could learn to coax stem cells into turning into different kinds of tissue, they could deal with diseases that are now untreatable. You could imagine, for example, generating new muscle to repair damaged hearts, new neurons to relieve the symptoms of Parkinson's disease, and new pancreatic cells to treat diabetes. Thus, worldwide attention was paid to this new development.

But the new development also raised serious moral and ethical issues in the minds of many. These issues center around two points. First, in order to obtain embryonic stem cells (the ones that seem to hold the greatest promise), it is necessary to destroy a blastocyst. In the United States, this means that the discussion of stem cells immediately became entangled in the abortion debate, one of the most difficult and insoluble public issues. (We should point out that in practice, human stem cells are almost never derived from an actual fetus, but from fertilized eggs not used in in vitro fertilization procedures—eggs that would otherwise be discarded.) A second concern has to do with the fear of many people that by manipulating stem cells we are, in essence, "playing God"—something that many people argue we ought to avoid. We will return to this difficult debate in the "Thinking More About" section at the end of this chapter.

FIGURE 24-9 Dr. Ian Wilmut, the scientist who carried out the first successful cloning of a mammal and whose work led to Dolly.

SCIENCE IN THE MAKING
Cloning Dolly the Sheep

In 1997, headlines around the world announced the birth of Dolly the sheep (Figure 24-8). She was the first cloned mammal in history and was treated accordingly in the popular media. The birth of Dolly was the product of research by Ian Wilmut at the Roslyn Institute in Scotland (Figure 24-9). The end result was a sheep whose DNA was identical to that of another adult sheep—in effect, Dolly was one of a pair of "twins" whose "sibling" had not been born from the same mother.

Here is how **cloning** is done: the nucleus, with its cargo of DNA, is removed from the egg of an adult female. This procedure can be carried out with a microscopic pipette (Figure 24-10). In Wilmut's work, the egg came from a Scottish Blackface ewe. A cell from another adult sheep (a Finn Dorset ewe in this case) with all its DNA was then fused with this egg by applying a small electrical shock. The egg, which now had a full complement of DNA, began to divide, and each daughter cell had a full complement of Finn Dorset DNA, as it would have in a normal development process. At the appropriate time, the developing embryo was implanted into the uterus of yet another adult sheep and allowed to come to maturity.

The key point in this process is that, although we do not know how to "turn on" the genes that were "switched off" in the development process that led to the adult Finn Dorset DNA, the egg seems to be able to do it. The DNA in the daughter cells of that first processed egg is exactly the same as the DNA that would have resulted from a normal fertilization, which means that all the genes are "switched on." How this process is done remains a subject of intense research.

Dolly lived in a media spotlight until her death in 2002. She gave birth to a lamb in 1998 (through the normal procedure). Since her birth, many other mammals have been cloned—mice, rats, pigs, cows, horses, and even monkeys. In 2004 a strange sect called the Raelians claimed that they had cloned a human being, but no evidence for this claim has been produced.

The birth of Dolly conjured up visions of armies of identical cloned human beings being produced. People imagined clones of Michael Jordan making up a "dream team" in basketball, or, on the darker side, clones being raised to produce organs for transplant.

FIGURE 24-10 A photograph showing foreign genetic material being introduced into an animal cell.

A moment's thought should convince you that neither of these nightmare scenarios is likely to happen. It may be that Michael's Jordan's physical attributes contributed to his skills, but it took years of dedicated work to mold those skills into a champion athlete. As one commentator put it, a Michael Jordan clone would be as likely to be a tall violinist as a basketball player.

As for the use of clones as sacrificial organ donors, it is necessary to remember that a cloned human, should one ever exist, would just be an adult whose DNA is identical to that of another adult. We have millennia of experience with people like that—we call them twins. And just as no one would imagine forcing one twin to donate an organ to another, we wouldn't allow that to happen to clones either.

Dolly is a result of what is called *reproductive cloning*—that is, the act of cloning was carried out with the intention of producing another adult. As we shall see in a moment, there is another way in which cloning can be used. Called *therapeutic cloning*, this process stops short of implanting an embryo and is carried out for medical purposes and to improve human health and wellbeing.

The real issues arise, however, when the ability to produce stem cell lines is combined with the process of cloning discussed here. If the DNA inserted into an egg is that of a given individual, then all of the cells in the blastocyst will have that individual's DNA, and any stem cell lines that are derived from that blastocyst will have that DNA as well. This situation means that any tissue derived from those stem cells and implanted in the donor will be genetically identical to that donor's cells and will not be rejected by his or her immune system. This compatibility is an important consideration because one of the great medical hurdles in transplant operations is that when a new organ such as a kidney or heart is implanted into a patient, that patient's immune system sees it as a foreign object and tries to destroy it. The possibility of organ rejection means that transplant patients must be given drugs that suppress their immune systems, a process that has to continue for the rest of the patient's life.

The expectation is that tissues grown from stem cells derived from that patient's own DNA will not be rejected by his or her immune system. This possibility means that sometime in the future it might be possible to grow tissues, and perhaps even entire organs, that can be transplanted surgically to replace parts that have become diseased or just worn out. The new field of research has been given the name *regenerative medicine.*

Many researchers are now trying to use cloning techniques to create human embryos that survive long enough in the laboratory to produce stem cell lines. Development of stem cell lines from embryonic stem cells in this way is called therapeutic cloning because the goal of the work is not to produce a new human being but to use the cells to treat humans that are already alive. Obviously, the same moral and ethical objections raised against stem cell research apply to this new technique.

Different countries have responded in different ways to this challenge, so that at present the world is a kind of patchwork of different regulations. In the United States, for example, former president George W. Bush ordered that research on stem cells lines developed before 2002 could be supported by the federal government, but not research on cell lines developed after that (there is at present no restriction on private funding for research on other lines). In 2004, the voters in the state of California passed a three billion dollar referendum that established an Institute for Regenerative Medicine to carry out this kind of research, while in 2006 the legislature of the state of Maryland passed a proposal to do the same in that state. In 2009, President Obama lifted the restrictions on funding stem cell research—an act that has more than quadrupled government funding for the field since 2002 levels.

On the international scene, the response has been just as varied. Some countries, such as Ireland, Norway, and Denmark, ban both reproductive and therapeutic cloning as well as research on human embryonic stem cells. Others, such as Germany, Austria, France, and the Netherlands, ban both reproductive and therapeutic cloning but not stem cell research. Still others, such as Great Britain, Belgium, Sweden, Spain, South Korea, Japan, and Singapore, allow and even encourage work on therapeutic (but not reproductive) cloning.

Although there is no relation in principle between cloning and stem cells, the fact remains that the only proven way to obtain stem cells with a single individual's DNA is through the cloning process. Buoyed by the possibility that we soon may be able to get around this difficulty by reprogramming adult cells, some scientists argue that this process, called *dedifferentiation*, may someday replace cloning as the source of stem cells. For these scientists, the results of work on human skin cells discussed above point the way to the future. This argument is bolstered by the fact that some animals have cells that are able to dedifferentiate. An amphibian such as the newt, for example, can regrow lost limbs by reprogramming its normal cells into stem cells at the site of the injury. Mammalian cells are not normally able to do this, but there is some indication that they might be manipulated into doing so. In experiments with mice in 2004, for example, a group at Scripps Research Institute was able to turn mouse muscle cells into bone and fat cells by producing a partial dedifferentiation. This kind of research remains a closely watched frontier in science.

STOP & THINK If scientists are successful in using therapeutic cloning techniques to grow new organs for implanting, how will people in the future have to answer the question "How old are you?"

FIGURE 24-11 Scanning electron micrographs showing the features of (a) normal and (b) cancerous rat kidney cells growing in culture. The normal cells adhere to the surface of the culture dish, forming monolayers of flat cells. The cancerous cells overgrow each other, forming clumps.

● 24.4 Cancer—A Different Kind of Genetic Disease

Cancer, a disease that strikes more than a million Americans every year, occurs when a group of cells in the body reproduce without restraint. Cancer is not a single disease, but rather a large collection of diseases that affect different organs in the human body in different ways.

The human body's trillions of cells have to maintain an exquisite balance. Complex chemical communication between cells ensures that the mechanism of cell division (see Chapter 21) operates only when new cells are needed and is turned off when that is not the case. Cancer occurs when these regulatory processes fail—when genetic defects cause a cell to divide again and again in a runaway fashion to form a tumor (Figure 24-11).

(a)

(b)

Normal cells recognize several different kinds of damage. Have there been mistakes in DNA duplication during cell division? If so, then fix the mistake or kill the cell. Has the DNA been duplicated fully and only once? If not, fix the mistake or kill the cell. Are the chromosomes correctly segregated? Is the cell correctly oriented to partition the chromosomes? At each transition, the cell stops to check whether everything is okay. Every step of mitosis—the cycle of DNA duplication and partitioning—has to be accomplished with the extraordinary fidelity that life demands. If not, kill the cell.

Cancer occurs when this fundamental guardianship fails. In cancer, the cell cycle continues unchecked, often despite profound damage to the DNA and to the chromosomes. And by ignoring chromosomal damage, additional harmful changes accumulate in the cell. The result is a terribly damaged cell that just keeps duplicating itself over and over again, making more copies of the defective cell.

Normally, no single DNA mutation is sufficient to turn a normal cell into a cancer cell. Rather, a handful of genetic abnormalities—perhaps five or six separate damaged genes in one single cell—are required. Many of these DNA changes are acquired or at least accelerated by exposure to mutagenic chemicals or radiation that damage DNA. In other cases, if some condition exists that causes cells to multiply more often than normal—a condition produced in the lungs by constant exposure to the chemicals in cigarette smoke, for example—the chances of a copying accident evading the cell's protection mechanisms increases. In these cases, it is usually possible to identify the cause of the cancer, as smoking has been identified as the major cause of lung cancer.

The situation is considerably worse for some individuals who are born with genetic defects. In the United States, about a tenth of cancer patients diagnosed each year have inherited an abnormality in one of their genes. Because these individuals already carry what is called the "first genetic hit" on the road to cancer in *all* of their cells, the probability that any single cell will accumulate the additional hits needed to make a tumor is much higher than normal. People with an inherited cancer gene can carry lifetime risks of developing cancer that may be more than twice the risk faced by the general population. The search for these cancer-related genes is one of the hottest areas of cancer research.

The growing recognition of a genetic basis for many cancers points to new approaches for its cure. Today the treatment of cancer, though often successful, usually involves heroic measures such as surgery, radiation therapy, and the use of deadly chemicals to remove or kill these rogue cells. But some day that therapy will be tailored to the specific genetic fingerprint of each person's cancer. Missing proteins will be synthesized and supplied; damaged genes will be repaired or bypassed. As we discover and identify a growing list of inherited and acquired cancer susceptibility genes, we'll be able to determine the best preventative treatments for individuals at risk.

One hope for the future involves a technique known as gene therapy, discussed later in this chapter. Try to imagine what it would be like to walk into a doctor's office, be diagnosed with cancer, and be given a virus-laden injection or a nose spray as your only treatment. Today this seems like a fairy tale, but if the work of molecular biologists in developing gene therapy is successful, having cancer in the future may be no worse than having an ear infection at the end of the twentieth century.

SCIENCE BY THE NUMBERS
Double-Blind Clinical Trials

One of the great problems medical researchers face in testing new medical procedures such as gene therapy is proving that the therapies actually work. It's often difficult for scientists to be certain that the treatment they prescribe is the cause of any improvement seen in the patient. To see why, imagine that you had a new medicine that you claimed cured the common cold. Suppose that you tried the medicine on some people with colds and found that after a few days all the people who tried the medicine got rid of their colds. Would this result prove that your medicine was effective? Of course not. We know that the human immune system also battles the common cold, so if you had just left those people alone and gave them no treatment at all they'd get better in a few days on their own. The medicine, as likely as not, was irrelevant.

To deal with these kinds of situations, researchers commonly use what is called the *double-blind clinical trial.* It works like this: A group of patients suffering from a particular disease is separated into two sections. Efforts are made to match the two sections in terms of age, gender, previous health history, and so on. One group is given the new treatment while the other group is given a placebo (that is, a sugar pill). For example, if the treatment being tested is a new drug, half the people will be given the new drug while the other half will be given either a placebo or the best conventional treatment. The patients are not told which treatment they are getting, nor do the physicians treating the patients know if a particular patient is getting the new drug. Thus, neither the patients themselves nor the physicians who will be judging the efficacy of the treatment know which patients are receiving the drug and which are not. This state of ignorance of both doctor and patient is why it is called a "double-blind" trial.

In order for a drug to be judged effective, it has to pass a clinical trial of this type. Unfortunately, new "wonder cures" are often tested without such experimental rigor. For example, a man recently stood up in a conference and claimed that he had found a cure for a particular kind of cancer based on a new-age therapy involving meditation and natural foods. He was asked what evidence he had; his reply was that he had a patient who had a tumor, and when he started the patient on this treatment, the tumor began to shrink in size. He was asked, "How do you know that it was your treatment that caused the tumor to shrink?" His reply: "What else could it have been?"

In fact, tumors left to themselves often grow and shrink in irregular and unpredictable ways. There is no way of knowing, based on this one example, whether the patient's tumor would have regressed on its own, as tumors sometimes do. This particular treatment, like any other, can be validated only by a double-blind trial, with two groups of people in the same medical condition, some of whom are not receiving the treatment.

◉ 24.5 Gene Therapy

Until quite recently, the only thing that physicians could do when faced with a genetic disease was to treat the symptoms. For example, in a disease such as diabetes, which is brought about by a failure of the body to produce the protein called insulin, treatment can run from modifying a patient's diet to injecting genetically engineered insulin on a daily basis. More recently, however, scientists have been exploring the possibility of using gene therapy, a new and potentially revolutionary kind of treatment.

Gene therapy is defined as a procedure for replacing a defective gene with a healthy one. Although still very much in the experimental stages, it holds enormous promise. Gene therapy can be done *in vitro* (that is, the gene can be injected into cells outside of the body, and the cells can then be introduced into the body) or *in vivo* (that is, the genes can be injected into cells in the body). As of this writing, only *in vitro* therapy has been accomplished in clinics, but many groups around the world are trying to develop *in vivo* techniques.

The first successful gene therapy took place in the early 1990s at the National Institutes of Health (Figure 24-12). Ashanti de Silva was born with a disease known as severe combined immunodeficiency (SCID). Because of faulty coding in one gene in her DNA, she was unable to produce a protein called adenosine deaminase, which is vital for the functioning of the immune system. Because her immune system didn't work, she had to be quarantined and was able to leave home only to visit her doctor. She was always sick and had a life that bore almost no resemblance to that of a normal child.

Children who are born with this defect are extraordinarily sensitive to any kind of contact with disease. Before the late twentieth century, most SCID babies died within their first year. In the late twentieth century, a few of these children lived into their teens by being kept in complete isolation from the external environment—they were called "bubble babies."

In September 1990, Ashanti de Silva became the first person to undergo a new kind of medical treatment. Doctors removed white blood cells from her veins and, using the new technology of genetic engineering, inserted normal copies of the defective gene. Over a period of months, the corrected cells were returned to her bloodstream, where they could produce the missing protein. The results seemed miraculous. From a sick, reclusive child, she was transformed into a normal, active preteen.

FIGURE 24-12 *(a)* Gene therapy was first used successfully in the treatment of SCID. (1) White blood cells were removed from the patient. (2) Normal copies of the defective gene were inserted into the blood cells. (3) The cells were placed in a culture (a medium of nutrients) to verify that the DNA would replicate and proteins would form in the cell. (4) The genetically modified cells were returned to the patient's bloodstream. Because white blood cells have a relatively short life span, patients must undergo treatment regularly to maintain a constant supply of normal genes. *(b)* Ashanti de Silva was the first patient to be treated with gene therapy.

(a)

(b)

Unfortunately, despite this promising beginning, gene therapy has not advanced rapidly in recent years. Many problems have been encountered, all traceable to our lack of knowledge of the detailed functioning of life at the molecular level. The *in vitro* technique that has the greatest promise is the use of a so-called therapeutic virus—a virus carrying copies of the healthy gene and engineered to match receptors in specific cells in then human body. The problem is that once the new DNA is inserted into a cell, there is no guarantee that it will wind up in the proper place in the cell's DNA. In some cases, genes have been found to insert themselves into the DNA sequence that governs tumor suppression, leading to the growth of tumors. In addition, many common diseases (diabetes, for example) involve multiple genes, and treating such diseases is currently beyond the scope of gene therapy techniques.

● 24.6 DNA Repair in the Cell

The transcription process we described in Chapter 23 shows how a specific sequence of bases along a DNA molecule is translated into the production of a specific protein in the cell. We also pointed out that if for some reason the DNA is damaged so that there is something wrong with the sequence of bases, the protein for which that gene codes will not be produced.

A common misconception about cellular DNA—one that is often encountered in popular writings on environmental problems—holds that the DNA in human cells is extremely fragile and is at the mercy of any kind of influence emanating from the environment. In fact, research that has been going on since the 1980s gives us a very different picture of DNA. It turns out that not all damage to DNA comes from outside the cell. Actually, most "hits" come from inside the cell itself. Cellular metabolism, for example, depends on respiration—a process with by-products, some of which may be quite harmful. The best-known harmful by-products of cellular respiration are a class of molecules called oxidants, such as the superoxide ion (O^{-2}). These ions are created copiously inside the cell and, if they make their way to the cell's nucleus, can cause damage to DNA. In addition, we ingest many kinds of molecules in our food, some processed, some natural, and these, too, can cause damage to the cells if they find their way to the cell's nucleus.

But the story doesn't end with the damage. Cells possess two different types of mechanisms for dealing with mistakes in DNA. Both of these mechanisms depend on sets of enzymes that wrap themselves around the DNA molecules and move up and down the spiral, looking for abnormalities. When abnormalities are found, these molecules call up one of two different kinds of repair mechanisms, depending on the kind of mistake that is found. Thus, our picture

FIGURE 24-13 DNA repair in the cell. Patrolling enzymes will identify defects in the DNA molecule, as indicated by a bulge in the double helix. Other enzymes will then remove the damaged section of DNA and allow the normal replication process to reconstruct the missing stretch.

of DNA in the cell's nucleus has to be a dynamic one, involving constant damage followed by constant repair.

One common kind of mistake in DNA, called a point defect, involves something like a simple misprint—the substitution of one base for another in the double helix. For example, the normal code for a particular spot on the DNA might require the base A, but for some reason we find the base T in that spot. In this case, the double helix will bulge slightly and the patrolling enzymes will detect the bulge. Other enzymes will come to that spot and snip out the offending bit of DNA, allowing the normal replication process to replace the blank spot with the correct base (Figure 24-13).

Other kinds of mistakes also occur. For example, two bases forming one side of the DNA double helix occasionally stick to one base on the other side. (This error may result when ultraviolet sunlight damages cells in the skin.) Alternatively, during the copying process, one strand of DNA can slide down, leaving a loop sticking out to the side. This kind of error is called a "mismatch." When these sorts of mistakes are encountered, a second kind of repair mechanism, called mismatch repair, is initiated and the entire side of the DNA molecule that contains the offending section is removed. As before, the normal processes of DNA replication then reconstruct the missing stretch of DNA.

STOP & THINK Given what you know about the effect of ultraviolet light on DNA, why should you wear sunscreen when you are outdoors?

What is perhaps most amazing about the way DNA operates in our cells is the sheer amount of damage that the molecules receive. As we said in the previous chapter, scientists measuring the chemical debris of the repair process estimate that every cell in your body sustains some 10,000 "hits" per day to its DNA and succeeds in repairing almost all of them.

The process of DNA repair seems to be very similar to the process of repairing a house that has been damaged by a hurricane. In the case of the house, you would be sure that the roof and walls were repaired and the electricity restored before you started worrying about replacing the carpets. In the same way, in the DNA there seems to be a hierarchy in the repair mechanisms. Highest in the hierarchy is the repair of those genes that are actually expressed in the cell in which damage has occurred. The point is that this repair has to be finished before the cell divides. If it is not, then the process of replication discussed in Chapter 23 will ensure that every descendant of the particular cell will contain the defect. Thus, the life of every cell can be thought of as a race between the repair mechanisms that we just described and the normal process of mitosis.

One important message to learn from the DNA repair story is that molecules cause damage to DNA. If a molecule possesses a particular shape, then it will produce a defect regardless of where that molecule came from. *It makes no difference whether the molecule is a product of our society or of nature.*

To underscore this point think about pesticides, which are among the most commonly cited causes of DNA damage. Some pesticides are produced commercially, of course, but many occur naturally in plants as a defense mechanism (Figure 24-14). In fact, it is estimated that only about one-tenth of 1% of the pesticides that human beings consume each day are commercially produced, with the rest being a normal part of the plants we eat. Once inside the body, however, it makes no difference where the pesticide molecule came from. About half of both the synthetic and natural pesticides are capable of causing cancer in laboratory animals.

◉ 24.7 Birth of Genomic Science

The first assembly of the human genome in 2000 was an expensive, time-consuming affair, taking billions of dollars and years of work. This heroic effort meant that the selection of what other organisms' genomes to study had to be done with some care. The first organism chosen was the chimpanzee, the closest relative to *Homo sapiens*, and the second was the laboratory rat, the workhorse of medical experimentation.

Since that time, however, the cost and time required to sequence a genome have fallen sharply. Today an organism's genome can be sequenced in a matter of days or weeks, and

(a)   (b)

FIGURE 24-14 *(a)* Pesticides are routinely sprayed on crops to cut down on insect pests, as in this field of snow peas in California. *(b)* Plants, like this common milkweed, have developed their own pesticides over the millennia.

medical scientists speak confidently of the day when the cost of sequencing an individual human genome will be less than $1,000. Today, literally thousands of genomes have been sequenced, including all of the major disease-causing microbes and viruses. All of the world's major food crops have also been sequenced, as have organisms of special interest such as the mosquito responsible for transmitting a large fraction of malaria. The list grows daily. This new information has led to important advances in many fields of science.

Medicine

The prospect of the $1,000 genome represents a major milestone in medicine because it would bring the cost of sequencing an individual genome into the range normally associated with routine medical tests. People speak confidently of a time when the genome of each newborn will be sequenced as a matter of course, becoming part of his or her medical file.

What effect this would have on health is a matter of debate. On the one hand, a complete genome would allow physicians to pick up evidence of serious genetic problems quickly. On the other hand, given our current limited understanding of the role of genetics in health, it's not clear how useful detailed genomic information might be. For example, if someone told you that your genome indicated that you had a 10% higher chance of developing type II diabetes after age 50 than the general population, what would you do with that information?

Developmental Biology

One of the most striking insights to come out of the massive genomic database that is being accumulated is the realization that the same genes appear over and over again as we work our way up through the phyla. It's almost as if nature, having found a genetic combination that works, keeps using it.

One example of this sort of genetic perseverance is a group of genes that go by the name *Hox*. In the fruit fly, these genes govern the order of the sections in the fly's thorax, from head to tail. In humans, the same genes from the same family govern the assembly of the backbone, making sure the vertebrae are in the right order. In addition to providing evidence to support the theory of evolution, which we will discuss in the next chapter, this kind of evidence has given rise to a whole new field of science called evolutionary development (evo-devo for short).

Tracing Ancestry

One way of tracing the "family tree" of living organisms is to look at their DNA. The basic idea is that the more differences there are in the DNA of any two given organisms, the longer it has been since they shared a common ancestor—since the two branched off from each other. In the next section we will see a specific example of this technique applied to mitochondrial DNA, but the method has a much wider applicability. Perhaps the most interesting to us is the human family tree. From the fact that human and chimpanzee DNA are so similar (they overlap more than 98% of the time) we can conclude that the splitting off of the lines that eventually led to modern humans and chimpanzees was the most recent branching on that tree. It must have occurred after the branching off of gorillas and orangutans (see Chapter 25).

Ancient DNA

When an organism dies, the DNA in its cells quickly breaks up into small snippets of the molecule. Reconstructing the DNA of long dead individuals, then, is a task analogous to putting a book together after its pages have been ripped up and scattered. Nevertheless, scientists have been able to carry out this procedure in a surprising number of cases. In the 1980s, for example, scientists were able to recover segments of DNA from the hide of a zebra-like animal known as the quagga, which had been hunted to extinction in South Africa in the 1880s. The information was used to clarify some outstanding issues about zebra family relationships. Later, bits of DNA from a mammoth frozen in Siberian permafrost were recovered and sequenced.

But by far the most ambitious DNA recovery project is the recently completed sequencing of the Neanderthal genome (see "Ongoing Process of Science"). As this field evolves, we can expect to see more such information being dug out of old fossils. Scientists are unanimous, however, in stating that there is no *Jurassic Park* scenario in our future, where these extinct organisms are brought back to life.

ONGOING PROCESS OF SCIENCE
Sequencing the Neanderthal Genome

In 2006, geneticist Svante Pääbo of the Max Planck Institute for Evolutionary Anthropology in Leipzig announced an ambitious project—the sequencing of the entire genome of the Neanderthal. As we shall see in the next chapter, Neanderthal Man is our closest relative on the human family tree. Neanderthals lived in Europe and Asia for hundreds of thousands of years, apparently well adapted to the successive Ice Ages. For reasons that are not entirely clear, Neanderthals went extinct about 35,000 years ago, at the same time that modern humans began moving northward out of Africa.

Pääbo's team obtained some fossils of Neanderthal bones and began the daunting task of extracting bits of DNA. Interestingly, the bones most useful to the geneticists were precisely those least useful to paleontologists. The reason is simple—those bones were usually shoved to the back of some forgotten drawer in museum archives and, because they were seldom handled, were the least contaminated with modern DNA. This sort of contamination is, in fact, one of the major problems scientists face in reconstructing ancient DNA—Pääbo estimates, for example, that 80% of the DNA in his samples comes from modern microbes.

In 2011, the group announced their surprising results. There was some limited interbreeding between modern humans and Neanderthals, so that people of European and Asian ancestry carry somewhere between 1% and 4% of Neanderthal genes in their DNA. Modern Africans do not have these genes, which indicates that the limited interbreeding took place after the ancestors of modern Europeans and Asians had left Africa.

◎ 24.8 Unraveling the Past: Mitochondrial DNA

One of the most engaging characteristics of science is that advances in one field often have profound and completely unpredictable effects in areas that seem, at first glance, to have no connection with the advance. The new genetic technologies provide a good example of this process because it turns out that they can shed light on the complex issues of human evolution that we will discuss in the next chapter.

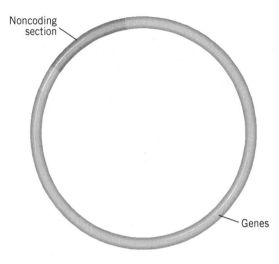

Noncoding section

Genes

FIGURE 24-15 The DNA in mitochondria is in the form of a loop. A noncoding section of about 1,000 base pairs is used in the studies described in the text.

In Chapter 21 we saw that there are many organelles inside the cells of eukaryotes like human beings. One of these, the mitochondria, is believed to represent the result of a symbiotic event in the distant past. These organelles, where carbohydrates are "burned" to provide the cell's energy, retain many characteristics as reminders of their independent past. One of these characteristics is the fact that mitochondria have their own small complement of DNA, completely independent of the DNA found in the nuclei of the cell.

The DNA of mitochondria, usually called mtDNA, consists of about 16,500 base pairs, a relatively small amount. As in bacteria, this DNA is arranged in a single loop (Figure 24-15). It contains 37 genes and has a small noncoding section at one point in the loop. This section, about 1,000 base pairs long, is not used to generate proteins, but acts as a kind of marker to tell you when you have gone all the way around the loop. Think of it as being analogous to the "12" at the top of a clock face. It is the sequence of bases on this stretch of DNA that scientists use to uncover the ancestry of modern humans.

The process of fertilization involves the sperm, which contain only enough mitochondria to allow movement, and the egg, which contains a full complement of the organelles. The sperm's mitochondria are destroyed soon after it enters the egg, so all of the mitochondria in the zygote come from the egg. This loss of the sperm's mitochondria means that mtDNA is transmitted exclusively from mother to child. Whether you are male or female, in other words, all of the mitochondria in your cells came from your mother.

In the language of genealogists, mtDNA descends in the maternal line. (As such, it is the mirror image of family names in European cultures, which descend in the male line, since the father's family name has traditionally been taken by all of his children.) You can get an estimate of how long it has been since two individuals shared a common female ancestor by comparing the sequence of their mtDNA—the more differences, the farther back in time that ancestor lived.

STOP & THINK How many differences in mtDNA would you expect to find between two brothers? Between a brother and his sister? Between two half brothers who had the same mother? The same father?

Sometimes work on mitochondrial DNA leads to surprising results. Scientists comparing mtDNA recovered from the fossils of cave bears with that of modern polar bears, for example, have been able to show that all modern polar bears are descended from a female Irish brown bear who mated with an ancient polar bear. The brown bear (the species is now extinct) contributed her mitochondria to those modern bears.

In the same way, researchers who study the process by which human beings populated the Americas routinely recover human mtDNA from archaeological sites between 6,000 and 14,000 years old. These samples tell a different story from that of the polar bears because they show that the "founding population" of Native Americans was quite diverse—a fact that probably indicates a long and complex history of migration.

Mitochondrial Eve

Like family names, mtDNA lines can disappear. In the language of genealogists, a family can "daughter out"—have only daughters in one generation, so that the family name doesn't get passed down. In the same way, women can "son out"—have only sons, so that their mtDNA does not get passed on. In both of these cases, the main DNA in the nucleus descends in an unbroken line.

SCIENCE BY THE NUMBERS
Daughtering Out

Suppose that you had a village with eight people in it—four men and four women—and that there were four family names. Assuming that each couple has two children and the birth of boys and girls is random, what is the shortest amount of time that would have to pass before everyone in the village had the same last name? In the first generation, you would expect one couple (call it couple A) to have two boys, one couple to have two girls (call it couple D), and the other two couples to have one each (call them couple B and C). After one generation, there would be only three family names—A (with two couples), B, and C (with one each). Couple D will have daughtered out.

If couple C daughters out in the next generation and one of the couples A has two sons, then by the third generation there will be only two names—A (three couples) and B. Thus, after three generations, we could easily have a village with only one family name.

More complex statistical arguments suggest that this is a likely outcome—that after several generations only one family name will survive. In the same way, lines of mtDNA will die out over time.

Using the technique of mtDNA analysis, scientists have argued that all living Europeans are descended from a set of seven women who lived from 40,000 to 10,000 years ago. Some have even claimed to have traced all living humans to a single woman who lived in Africa 200,000 years ago, although there is a good deal of controversy about this claim. The woman, should she exist, has been given the name "Mitochondrial Eve." More recently, similar analysis of the Y chromosome (the chromosome that is carried by males) has been undertaken to trace the descent of males.

One point to ponder: if there actually was a "Chromosomal Adam," he probably didn't live at the same time as "Mitochondrial Eve," and therefore couldn't have known her, much less fathered her children.

THINKING MORE ABOUT **EMBRYONIC STEM CELLS**

A worldwide debate rages on the ethical implications of embryonic stem cell research. In the United States, this debate is intimately related to the debate over the ethics of abortion. In essence, the question comes down to this: is the creation of a blastocyst for the purpose of producing stem cells morally allowable?

The answer to this question depends on what you think the blastocyst is. If, on one hand, you believe that human life begins at conception and that even a single-celled zygote is a human being entitled to the full protection of the law, then the destruction of the blastocyst and the harvesting of stem cells are equivalent to murder. If, on the other hand, you believe that an organism consisting of a few hundred cells is no more equivalent to a human

being than a blueprint is equivalent to a building, then there is a powerful moral compulsion to harvest the stem cells in order to relieve the real suffering of real people.

This is an example of a conflict that arises from advances in science but that cannot be answered by the scientific method. A biologist can tell you in great detail what the cellular structure and function of the blastocyst are, but she cannot tell you whether the blastocyst should have legal protection. In the end, that is a question to be decided on moral, religious, ethical, and legal grounds. It is the question of when the embryo becomes a "person" in the legal sense, entitled to full protection of the law. The answer to this question varies from one society to the next and has little to do with science. Many people have wrestled with this question without producing a consensus.

Here are some questions that might help you think about this difficult issue:

- If you believe that life begins at conception and that the blastocyst is a potential human life, how do you justify allowing real human beings to suffer to protect human beings that are only "potential"? If a treatment for Parkinson's disease based on stem cells were developed in a place like South Korea, would you ban Americans from seeking that treatment on moral grounds? Would you put them in jail if they did?

- If you believe that it is morally justifiable or even morally compulsory to harvest stem cells from blastocysts created specifically for that purpose, where do you draw the line? When is the destruction of the embryo not permissible? After it implants in the uterus? After the second trimester of pregnancy? One second before birth? How do you avoid the "slippery slope" and the ultimate devaluing of human life?

These are not simple questions, and, unless scientists find ways to reprogram somatic stem cells, they will remain with us for a long time.

RETURN TO THE INTEGRATED QUESTION

Can we cure cancer?

- Cancer strikes more than a million Americans every year. The American Cancer Society estimates that cancer care in the United States cost almost 100 billion dollars in 2013.

- Cancer is not a single disease but rather a collection of diseases that affect the human body in different ways. Its genesis lies in the mutation of DNA, and it occurs when groups of cells in the body reproduce without restraint.

  - Normally, the human body's trillions of cells maintain an exquisite balance between growth, repair, and cell death. During the progression of a cancer that growth regulation fails and cells divide repeatedly in a runaway fashion to form a tumor.

  - Normally, cells recognize the types of damage that lead to a tumor. If they are unable to fix the damage, the cell will be killed.

  - Unfortunately, the damage sometimes goes unrecognized or accelerates so that the damaged cell makes more copies of the cancerous cell.

- In most cases, a number of genetic abnormalities are necessary to cause a cell to become cancerous. Many of these unproductive alterations in DNA are acquired and/or accelerated by exposure to mutagenic chemicals (e.g., cigarette smoke) or radiation.

- Over the past few decades, the scientific community has begun to recognize the genetic basis of some cancers. Although many current forms of cancer treatment are successful, they usually involve extreme measures such as surgery, radiation therapy, and the use of deadly chemicals to remove or kill these rogue cells.

  - The hope is that in the near future, cancer therapy will be tailored to the specific genetic fingerprint of the individual.

  - At some point in the future, molecular biologists may develop therapeutic viruses that will render cancer as innocuous as the common cold.

SUMMARY

Our enhanced understanding of genetic mechanisms has led to new advances in *genetic engineering,* which involves the insertion of foreign genes into an organism, or the alteration of existing genes, to create modified life forms. A variety of genetically engineered plants for improved crops, animals for medical research, and single-celled organisms for drug production are now available. Our ability to manipulate genetic material has also been applied in *DNA fingerprinting,* which is used in many legal cases to establish the identity of individuals from their unique genetic makeup.

Stem cells are cells that can grow into any tissue in an adult organism. Embryonic stem cells can be harvested from the blastocyst, whereas somatic stem cells, though less versatile, can be obtained from adult tissue. *Cloning* is a procedure for producing a fertilized egg with the DNA of another adult. Therapeutic cloning

is the use of this technology for medical purposes, whereas reproductive cloning has as its aim the production of a new organism.

Cancer, a suite of diseases that afflicts millions of Americans, has its basis in the mutation of DNA. DNA repair mechanisms are known to operate inside the cell. A promising future technology is *gene therapy,* which involves replacing a defective gene with a healthy one.

The ability to sequence DNA easily has given rise to advances in many fields of science—in medicine, in understanding embryonic development, and in tracing the evolutionary tree of various organisms. A striking advance in this area is the recent sequencing of Neanderthal DNA, which indicates some slight interbreeding between Neanderthals and modern humans. Another result is the ability to trace ancestral lineages through the sequence of mitochondrial DNA.

KEY TERMS

genetic engineering **stem cells** **cancer**
DNA fingerprinting **cloning** **gene therapy**

DISCOVERY **LAB**

Hybridization and genetic engineering accomplish similar tasks. Genetic engineering uses technology to create organisms with modified genes, and hybridization is often used by plant breeders to produce crops with desired traits. Even though the two processes are different, we can use hybridization in the classroom setting to produce plants with desired traits.

For this lab you will need plants that grow fast. For example, wild-type dwarf rosette seeds or Wisconsin Fast Plants would work well.

Obtain the seeds and other supplies for growing plants. Follow the directions on the package to plant and grow the seeds. You will also need necessary planting materials for growing plants, disposable pipettes, and rulers.

After the seeds germinate, to avoid overcrowding let one or two plants grow in the pot and remove all others. Make a data table to record the length of the stem, color of the stem, size of the leaf, position of the leaf, leaf color, flower color, stem color, and so on. Record the length of the leaf, size of the leaf, and length of the stem on a daily basis. Examine one variable at a time.

Use the dried bees that come with the package to do the pollination. If you have your own plants, use a toothbrush or paintbrush for pollination. Brush the bees into the flowers of the plants (whose traits you desire); the bees will pick up and distribute pollen. Transfer pollen back and forth among several plants. Pollinate the flowers for 2 to 3 days. Look at the bees (or the brush) to see if they are picking up pollen. Cut off any new flowers after the final pollination. This is an important step that helps the plants have a good seed growth. Do not cut off flowers that were pollinated. Twenty days later, allow the plants to dry for one full week in

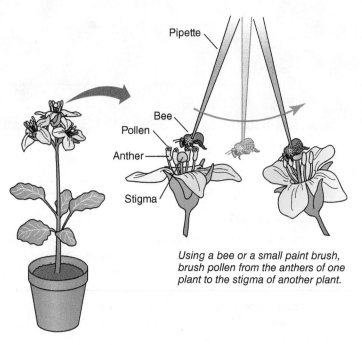

Using a bee or a small paint brush, brush pollen from the anthers of one plant to the stigma of another plant.

their pots until they are brown and crispy. Collect the seeds and germinate them.

Predict the ratio of phenotype you expect in the second generation. Record the ratio of phenotype you obtained in the second generation. Record the characteristics of the parent generation, first generation, and second generation. From the information collected, compare/contrast the traits in all the generations. Which traits changed? Which remained the same?

REVIEW QUESTIONS

1. What is genetic engineering?
2. What do restriction enzymes do? How are they used in genetic engineering?
3. Describe how the single-celled bacterium E. coli is used to produce the insulin to treat diabetes.
4. How might genetically engineered crops be used to reduce erosion on farmlands?
5. What parts of the world restrict the use of genetically engineered crops? What parts of the world welcome them?
6. What is PCR? What is its role in DNA fingerprinting?
7. What is a genetic disease? Give an example.
8. What is gene therapy?
9. What is unique about stem cells? Describe the differences between adult and embryonic stem cells.
10. What is a therapeutic virus?
11. What cell function appears to go awry in the case of cancer cells? How can this damage an individual?
12. What is a double-blind clinical trial? Why are such trials important in medical research?
13. What is DNA repair, and where does it take place?
14. Describe the process of cloning. How does therapeutic cloning differ from reproductive cloning? Which type produced the sheep named Dolly?
15. Why do antibiotics, which kill bacteria, gradually lose their effectiveness? Why do we need new antibiotics?
16. How can mitochondrial DNA be used to trace ancestry? Give an example.
17. How did scientists obtain the DNA from the Neanderthals to sequence?
18. Why might the "$1,000 Genome" be important in the future of medicine?

DISCUSSION QUESTIONS

1. What genetically engineered products do you currently use or consume? Do you think they are safe? Why or why not? What are the pros and cons of using these products compared to nongenetically engineered products?

2. How might genomic science influence the future of medicine?

3. How is DNA "fingerprinting" similar to traditional fingerprinting? How do the two methods differ? What are the advantages and disadvantages of DNA fingerprinting compared to traditional fingerprinting?

4. How does a stem cell differ from other cells? Why are people excited about the possibilities of stem cell research? What ethical and moral issues are there in stem cell research that utilizes embryonic stem cells? Do you think this avenue of research should be prevented? Why or why not?

5. In what ways does ultraviolet radiation affect a living cell? How is this damage repaired?

6. You typically don't have to look very hard or wait very long to find a headline trumpeting the latest pharmaceutical breakthrough that will cure cancer because it cures all sorts of cancer in mice. But why aren't these drugs placed on the market if they demonstrate such successes? Why is the process so slow?

7. Why are double-blind experiments double blind? Why is it important that the doctors not know which medicine is being administered? Why is it important that the patients not know which medicine they're receiving?

8. What is a therapeutic virus? What are some of the problems associated with the use of therapeutic viruses? Has a therapeutic virus ever been used successfully?

9. What is AIDS and why is it so hard to cure? How is HIV so insidious in its ability to attack cells in the body?

10. Some people claim that crystals, prayer, or vitamin supplements can cure cancer. How would you test their claims? If you tested a method on one person and that person recovered, could you be sure that your "treatment" was a success?

11. Why do you suppose your cells have such efficient mechanisms for repairing damage to DNA?

12. How does the research into mtDNA improve our understanding of human evolution?

13. What purpose does it serve to sequence the genome of Neanderthals? What benefits, if any, might this have for today's society?

14. In what way are the genetic processes between fruit flies and humans similar? What does this teach you about evolution?

15. Genomic studies have indicated that parents can pass several dozen mutations in their DNA to their children. What does this suggest to you about the effects of most mutations?

PROBLEMS

1. A pharmaceutical company claims that a new drug cuts in half the time an average patient suffers from a cold. Given a pool of 100 cold sufferers, describe a double-blind experiment that would test this claim.

2. A second company claims that two different drugs, working in combination, are even more effective than the single drug referred to in Problem 1. Given a pool of 200 cold sufferers, how would you test this claim in a double-blind clinical trial?

3. Some scientists argue that the data support a population growth model in which all living Europeans are descended from seven women who lived 10,000 years ago. Estimate how many generations of humans are possible in 10,000 years.

4. "Mitochondrial Eve" is supposed to have lived about 100,000 years ago. Assuming a generation time of 20 years with two offspring per person per generation, what is the maximum possible number of descendants there could be on Earth today? How does this compare to the present population?

5. A woman by the name of Henrietta Lacks died in 1951 from cervical cancer. Cells taken from her tumor have demonstrated the unusual cellular property of not dying; they have been named "HeLa" cells. Being easy to reproduce, approximately 20 tons' worth of HeLa cells have been made for use in research. If 1 HeLa cell has a mass of 3 nanograms (3×10^{-9} g) and 1 ton has a mass of 1,000 kg, approximately how many HeLa cells have been produced?

6. It's been reported that a 20-year-old father passes on an average of 25 random mutations to his children, whereas a 40-year-old father passes on 65 random mutations. If the increase in mutations passed to children is linear, how many mutations would a 30-year-old father pass on to his children? How about a 50-year-old father?

7. DNA molecules in a cell suffer traumas that result in around 10,000 molecular lesions per day. If a DNA molecule has 6 billion base molecules (resulting from having 3 billion base pairs), what percent of base pairs suffer damage each day?

   a. 6%

   b. 0.00006%

   c. 0.0000017%

   d. 0.00017%

8. Consider a double-blind study in which a medicine intended to shorten the duration of colds is tested. Fifty people are given the medicine, while another 50 people from the same population are given a placebo (the control group). The scientists decide that a successful trial would have the average duration of a cold in the people taking the medicine be no more than 75% of the average duration for the people taking the placebo. If the group taking the medicine report the duration of their cold to be an average of 26 hours, what must the minimum average duration of the cold be in the control group?

   a. 19.5 hours

   b. 34.7 hours

   c. 32.5 hours

   d. 45.5 hours

INVESTIGATIONS

1. Find out which DNA fingerprinting technique is used in your state or local courts.

2. Read Michael Crichton's novel *Jurassic Park* (or watch the movie), which describes genetic engineering experiments. Is the scenario realistic? How does this story illustrate the Law of Unintended Consequences?

3. Look over the newspapers for the last few months and find an announcement that scientists have discovered the gene behind a particular disease or condition. How does that discovery fit in with the material in this chapter?

4. From time to time, a new AIDS drug will receive publicity because of reportedly miraculous results. Should such a drug be made available immediately to AIDS sufferers? Why or why not?

5. Read the prize-winning novel *Arrowsmith* by Sinclair Lewis. How does the novel's hero, Martin Arrowsmith, test his new plague vaccine? Was this a double-blind procedure? What goes wrong with the experiment?

6. How long have genetically engineered foods been consumed? What problems have been encountered?

7. What does the acronym GMO stand for? What percentage of common vegetables is currently genetically modified?

8. Investigate the history of insulin production. What other drugs have been produced using the new science of genomics?

9. Many countries ban or regulate genetically modified organisms. What is the policy in the United States? Are our policies based on science? How would you test a genetically modified organism to ensure its safety?

10. What government organizations oversee the use of genetically engineered organisms?

11. The detailed sequencing of the Neanderthal genome was announced in 2011. How have our ideas of human evolution changed as a result?

25 Evolution

How did life emerge on the ancient Earth?

PHYSICS

Energy for synthesizing early life may have come from the Sun's radiation or Earth's internal heat.

CHEMISTRY

Miller and Urey synthesized amino acids by subjecting a mixture of water and simple gases to electric sparks.

BIOLOGY

Life evolves by the competitive process of natural selection.

TECHNOLOGY

The first humans to use stone tools lived more than 2 million years ago.

GREAT IDEA

All life on Earth evolved from single-celled organisms by the process of natural selection.

ENVIRONMENT

Asteroid impacts with Earth may cause drastic changes in the global environment and trigger mass extinctions.

ASTRONOMY

Recent exploration of Mars reveals compelling evidence for the existence of abundant water early in its history.

GEOLOGY

Fossils chronicle the history of life on Earth.

HEALTH & SAFETY

The appendix is a vestigial organ in humans; it can be removed without adverse effects.

 = applications of the great idea discussed in this chapter

 = other applications, some of which are discussed in other chapters

Awonderful day is almost over. You close your eyes and relive some of the sensations; the sights, the sounds, the smells. But one aspect of the day stands out—how amazingly rich with life our planet is. The green fields and forests that lined the road, the birds and insects (and people) along the shore, the tidal pools crowded with strange, colorful creatures; everywhere you look life abounds. How could such an incredible array of living things have developed on a once-lifeless planet? How could living things on our planet include such extraordinary variety, from seaweed to a whale? The answer to these questions requires us to think not only about what life is, but also how it got to be the way it is.

Georgette Douwma/Getty Images, Inc.

◉ 25.1 The Fact of Evolution

Earth started out as a hot, lifeless ball of molten rock (see Chapter 16). The first rocks were formed when the planet cooled, but even then Earth looked nothing like it does today. Water filled the ocean basins, but no fish swam in it and no algae floated on it. All of the countless millions of different life forms that would someday develop were absent in this early stage.

The transition from a lifeless planet to the modern living world came in two stages. The first stage involved the appearance of the first living cell from lifeless chemical compounds—rock, water, and gases. The laws of chemistry and physics that we have studied governed that process. The second stage was the multiplication, diversification, and transformation of that first living cell into the astonishing variety of life that we observe on Earth now. This ongoing process of change and diversification is called **evolution**.

Today, *virtually all scientists accept evolution as a historical fact.* Evolution—the concept that life has changed over vast spans of geological time—is an observational phenomenon that is as well established as the fact that Earth goes around the Sun or that a ball falls when you drop it.

As we shall see later in this chapter, this acceptance of evolution as a fact does not mean that there aren't debates about different *theories* of evolution. For example, scientists debate how fast evolution proceeds and by what mechanisms. But differences in opinion about these details should not be confused with the unambiguous observational *fact* that life has evolved on Earth for billions of years. A tremendous body of scientific literature is devoted to this subject, and we will discuss here only three of the most important pieces of evidence for the process of evolution: the fossil record, the evidence of biochemical similarity, and the occurrence of vestigial organs.

The Fossil Record

The most dramatic and compelling evidence for life's changes over geological time comes from **fossils**, the tangible evidence of past life. When a plant or animal dies, the remains are usually lost. A tree will rot, the carcass of an animal will be torn apart by scavengers and dispersed, a crab shell will be broken up by the action of the surf. Occasionally, however, an organism is removed quickly from the environment, typically by being buried in sediments and sealed off from the surface. The hard parts of such an organism may remain underground for a long period of time.

As time goes by, two things may happen. First, minerals in the water flowing through the surrounding area may gradually replace the calcium and other atoms in the buried hard parts, thus creating a fossil. Second, the material around the organism may go through the rock cycle, as described in Chapter 17, and be turned into sedimentary rock. The word "fossil" typically brings to mind a large dinosaur skeleton in a museum, but the term also refers to other records of past life, such as a leaf imprint on mud that changes into rock, or an insect preserved in amber (Figure 25-1).

The term *fossil record* refers to all of the fossils that have been found, catalogued, and analyzed since human beings first began to study them in a systematic way in the early part of the nineteenth century. The fossil record reveals how different organisms came to be what they are. The fossil record of horses, for example, includes a series of precursor animals beginning with one about the size of a cat some 50 million years ago and changing through many intermediate forms up to modern times (Figure 25-1a). Throughout this sequence of fossil mammals is a gradual transition from a small, quick animal to a large, grazing one.

The fossil record also contains some sequences of gradual changes in species. In order to do this, the fossil record has to be very complete, with many thousands of years of continuous sediments. Such continuity is rare, but in some instances the transitions from one species to another can be documented (Figure 25-2).

Even so, the major problem with the fossil record is that it is very incomplete. It is estimated that perhaps only one species (*not* one individual) out of every 10,000 early life forms is represented in the fossil record. Thus, in interpreting the past, we must always be aware that we are dealing with a very small and select sample of what was actually there. This sample is strongly biased toward organisms that were more likely to have been buried soon after death. Thus, we have a much better record of mollusks and clams, which had hard shells and lived in sediments on the continental shelf, than we do of insects that flew around primeval forests. Nevertheless, the fossil record provided the first substantial body of evidence that backed up the notion that life is constantly changing and evolving.

STOP & THINK From the preceding discussion, it is clear that animals with skeletons and shells will be fossilized more easily than those with soft bodies. What animals alive today are likely to be found as fossils a million years from now? Would future paleontologists get an accurate view of present-day life by examining those fossils?

FIGURE 25-1 A wide variety of fossils is found in rocks from every continent. *(a)* Fossil bones reveal that the ancestors of modern horses were small and agile. *(b)* A leaf fossil was preserved in the fine sediments of what was once a shallow lake. *(c)* A fossil insect was trapped in tree sap and thus preserved in the hardened residue, amber.

(a)   *(b)*   *(c)*

Jonathan Blair/©Corbis

Mark A. Schneider/Science Source Images

Alfred Pasieka/SPL/Photo Researchers

FIGURE 25-2 Fossil trilobites collected from a continuous sequence of 450-million-year old rocks near St. Petersburg, Russia, reveal a gradual increase in the length of eyestalks over a 3-million-year span. The longer eyestalks allowed these arthropods to bury themselves deeper in soft mud and thus escape primitive predatory fish.

Three key ideas quickly emerged from studies of fossils. First, the older the rocks, the more their communities of animal and plant fossils differ from modern forms. Mammals in 5-million-year-old rocks are not terribly different from today's fauna, but few species that existed 50 million years ago would be recognizable today, and dinosaurs rather than mammals were dominant 150 million years ago. Similar patterns occur in shells, plants, fish, and all other forms. Often, the earlier forms appear to combine characteristics of later organisms. Ancient insects preserved in amber, for example, show some forms that may be intermediate between ants and wasps. Similarly, early mammals have general mammalian characteristics, but not the specialized structures that evolved more recently in flying bats, swimming whales, or hopping rabbits.

Fossils also display general trends in overall complexity of form. All known fossils from before about 570 million years ago are either single-celled organisms or simple invertebrates such as jellyfish. Marine invertebrates with hard parts—mollusks, coral, and crustacea, for example—dominate the record for the next 200 million years or so. Simple land animals and plants appear next, followed by flowering plants and a much greater variety of large land animals. This long-term trend toward increasing complexity of organization is consistent with all theories of evolution.

Finally, the fossil record proves beyond a doubt that most species that have lived on Earth have died out and are now **extinct**. Scientists estimate that for every species on the planet today, perhaps a thousand species have become extinct at some time in the past. The average lifetime of a species in the fossil record seems to be a few million years. Species, like individuals, are born, live out their life, and die. This fact alone is ample evidence that some natural mechanism must exist to produce new species as the old disappear.

The Biochemical Evidence

As we saw in the previous chapter, we all carry within us evidence for the fact of evolution—a molecular record of our descent from the first primeval cell. The DNA of each living organism represents the sum of all the changes in the DNA that connect that organism back to the DNA in the first forms of life. If we can learn how to "read" the DNA in living organisms, then we should be able to deduce some things about the way those organisms developed.

According to the standard picture of evolution, for example, human beings and the great apes had a common ancestor about 7 or 8 million years ago. Much farther back in time, about 250 million years ago, human beings and reptiles shared a common ancestor. DNA evolves slowly under the influence of mutation and natural selection. The fact that we've had less than 10 million years for human DNA and ape DNA to differentiate, compared to 250 million years during which human DNA differentiated from the reptiles, suggests that there ought to be more similarities between human and primate DNA than there are between DNA of humans and reptiles.

DNA strands from two different organisms cannot always be compared directly, but from Chapter 23 we know that the proteins in cells are related to DNA in much the same way as a negative is to a photograph. You can get the same kind of information by comparing sequences of amino acids along proteins as you can by comparing base pairs along the DNA molecule. In a protein called cytochrome C that every living cell uses in its energy metabolism, for example, the difference between humans and chimpanzees (our closest relative) is nonexistent. The cytochrome C molecules from the chimpanzee and human are exactly the same. As you move farther and farther away from human beings in the main classification scheme (see Chapter 20), the differences become greater. In a rattlesnake, for example, there is an 86% overlap in the molecules, whereas in common brewer's yeast only 58% of the molecules are the same. The fact that our DNA is very similar to those organisms with which we shared the most recent ancestors is one of the most important pieces of evidence for evolution (Figure 25-3). If, for example, each plant and animal was created separately and specially, there would be no reason at all to see this kind of progression.

(a)

(b)

FIGURE 25-3 The closest living relative of the rhinoceros is the horse. Their most recent common ancestor was a grazing animal that lived 55 million years ago.

Evidence from Anatomy: Vestigial and Adapted Organs

Physical structures within our own bodies provide more compelling evidence for the fact of evolution. We have a number of internal features that appear to serve no useful function whatsoever—**vestigial organs** that are reminders of our mammalian ancestors. Organs that are well adapted to their environment, surprisingly, *do not* provide unambiguous evidence for evolution. The perfection of the human eye, for example, was often claimed in the nineteenth century as proof of God's special creation of human beings. The evidence for evolution comes instead from considering organs that have no obvious use or are even harmful to the organism in which they are found.

Consider the human appendix, a thin, closed tube connected to the upper part of the large intestine. This three-inch-long organ, which plays an important role in the digestion of some primates, has no proven function in modern humans, and it actually poses a threat to every one of us. Before the development of surgery, inflammations of the appendix were often fatal. The

FIGURE 25-4 The "wings" of a penguin are an adapted characteristic. Once used for flying, the wings have evolved to aid in swimming.

pressures of natural selection would never lead to the development of a harmful organ in a human being, yet the appendix sits there at the end of everyone's intestines. Unless the appendix has some as-yet-undiscovered function, it is hard to understand how this organ could come to be.

Vestigial organs such as the appendix can be explained by recognizing that they once had a function in our primate ancestors that they no longer have, and are in the process of disappearing. In a sense, modern humans are snapshots in a continuous process in which the appendix perhaps once served as an important part of the digestive system but is no longer needed.

Numerous examples of vestigial characteristics have been identified, and they provide important evidence against the argument that every organ in every creature is part of a grand design. Some whales have tiny internal vestigial hind legs, snakes have vestigial pelvises, and humans have vestigial tailbones and vestigial muscles to wag them. Another striking example of vestigial organs is found in species of cave-dwelling worms that evidently evolved from surface-dwelling worms with eyes. They now have no need of eyes, but they still have vestigial eye sockets *under their skin*.

In many other instances, an ancestral characteristic has evolved into a new function—a phenomenon known as *adapted characteristics*. For example, penguins cannot fly like their bird ancestors, but their wings are now used to swim (Figure 25-4).

◉ 25.2 Chemical Evolution

FIGURE 25-5 The Miller–Urey experiment. Several of the chemical compounds thought to have been present on the early Earth were mixed and subjected to electrical discharges. Within a few weeks, amino acids had formed.

Chemical evolution, the first step in life's long history, is the process by which rocks, water, and gases chemically combined to become the first living cell. The central question of chemical evolution is how one can start with the simple chemical compounds that were present on early Earth and wind up with an organized, reproducing cell. This area of research is relatively new and immensely challenging; few clear answers have yet emerged. The first important experiment relating to chemical evolution was performed in the early 1950s by Stanley Miller (1930–2007) and Harold Urey (1893–1981) at the University of Chicago. The novel apparatus of the **Miller–Urey experiment** is sketched in Figure 25-5.

Miller and Urey argued that Earth's early atmosphere contained simple compounds composed principally of hydrogen, carbon, oxygen, and nitrogen—compounds including water vapor (H_2O), methane (CH_4), hydrogen (H_2), and ammonia (NH_3). Miller and Urey mixed these materials together in a large flask that was half-filled with water. Then, realizing that powerful lightning would have laced the turbulent atmosphere of early Earth, they caused electrical sparks to jump between electrodes in the flask. After just a few days they noticed that the liquid in the flask became cloudy and started to turn a dark-brown color. Analysis revealed that this brownish liquid contained a large number of amino acids, carbohydrates, and other basic building blocks of life (see Chapter 22).

Thus, as early as the 1950s, experiments had shown scientists that natural processes in the oceans of early Earth might generate the modules of life's important molecules. Since that time, it has been found that energy sources such as ultraviolet radiation (from the Sun) and heat (for example, from volcanoes) will also produce key biomolecules. In subsequent experiments at the University of Chicago and dozens of other laboratories, scientists have used modified Miller–Urey experiments to more closely match what scientists now think were primitive Earth conditions, for example, by using nitrogen (N_2) and carbon dioxide (CO_2) instead of ammonia and methane, and adding common minerals to the mix. These experiments reveal how easy it is to make all sorts of organic molecules, including lipids and bases, as well as complex substances such as long protein chains and nucleic acids.

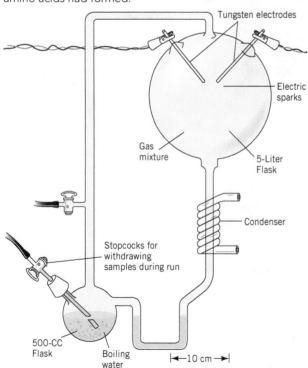

Tungsten electrodes

Electric sparks

Gas mixture

5-Liter Flask

Condenser

Stopcocks for withdrawing samples during run

500-CC Flask

Boiling water

|←—10 cm —→|

Origin-of-life researchers conclude that this scenario has important implications for early Earth. For perhaps several hundred million years, the hypothesis goes, the amino acids and other molecules created by the Miller–Urey process were concentrated in the ocean, producing a rich broth, sometimes called the *primordial soup*. Additional organic molecules were undoubtedly added to this chemical mixture in the early oceans by other sources, such as meteorites and comets, which are known to carry carbon-based molecules, and through reactions with hot, mineral-rich waters near volcanoes on the ocean floor (Figure 25-6). These enrichments of organic chemicals in Earth's early oceans required nothing beyond normal chemistry. By the 1990s, this small piece of the chemical evolution puzzle was well understood.

FIGURE 25-6 Some key biological molecules were delivered to the ancient Earth by meteorites, while others were synthesized through chemical reactions near volcanoes.

Our greatest gap in the evolutionary story comes next. Could the countless molecules floating in random patterns in the ocean have organized themselves into a functioning, reproducing cell? Although mechanisms such as condensation polymerization (see Chapter 10) can join simple organic molecules together, sunlight tends to break these bonds apart.

We do not know how the first cell formed, but a number of creative ideas are helping to close this significant gap in our knowledge. We know, for example, that lipid molecules (see Chapter 22) can form an oil slick on the ocean's surface that might have shielded life from the Sun's ultraviolet radiation, just like sunblock. In this environment, polymers and other complex molecules might have grown and diversified. If the concentration of organic molecules was high enough, then the sunlight breaking up these molecules would not have been able to overcome their formation rate and the concentrations might have increased even more.

Mineral surfaces, which can adsorb and concentrate organic molecules, may have also played a key role in selecting the molecules of life. For example, some scientists have proposed that the first cell may have evolved in a tidal pool lined with adsorbent clay minerals. If it turns out that something like a protected tidal pool is necessary for the development of life, then life may be relatively rare in the universe. Our present understanding is that the formation of a terrestrial planet together with a large moon (and, thus, the generation of significant tides) is an unlikely event.

STOP & THINK Many science fiction stories, from *Frankenstein* to *Jurassic Park*, revolve around the ability of humans to synthesize life. How close did Miller and Urey come to synthesizing life? Do you think scientists will ever be able to synthesize living cells beginning with organic molecules?

Black Smokers

In 1979, biologists diving to the deep-ocean floor in the submersible *Alvin* discovered an unexpected diverse ecosystem surrounding vents of mineral-rich hot water, called *black smokers*, near mid-ocean volcanoes (Figure 25-7). The remarkable bacteria that thrive in these extreme environments obtain their energy from Earth's internal heat rather than the Sun. These bacteria, among the most primitive life forms known, may be closer on the evolutionary tree to the first living cell than any organisms living at Earth's surface.

This discovery has led many scientists to wonder if deep, dark, hydrothermal zones on the ocean floor might have been the most likely sites of life's origins. These extreme environments are not only rich in the chemical energy needed to drive chemical evolution, but they also abound in mineral surfaces that are known to select, concentrate, and organize organic molecules into polymers and other large structures. Some researchers now speculate that warm, gas-rich water circulating through cracks and fissures near mid-ocean volcanic ridges provided an ideal protected environment for the origin of life. The surface of early Earth was repeatedly bombarded by large meteorites, was constantly bathed in harmful ultraviolet

UCSB, Univ. S. Carolina, NOAA, WHOI.

FIGURE 25-7 Diverse colonies of living things thrive three miles underwater at a mid-ocean volcanic vent near the mid-Atlantic Ridge. Some researchers think these energy-rich environments might have supported the first steps in life's origins.

radiation, and was continuously blasted by intense lightning. Deep-ocean environments were protected from these environmental insults.

Black smokers also provide an ideal chemical environment for organic synthesis because water at high temperature and pressure has physical properties very different from those that are familiar to us. For one thing, water at these extreme conditions is much less polar—less able to pull other molecules apart (see Chapter 10)—and thus may facilitate the synthesis of amino acids, lipids, and other key biological molecules, while promoting their assembly into larger structures by polymerization reactions. One of the authors (RMH) is now engaged in experiments to understand how organic chemical reactions proceed—and how life may have originated—in hot, pressurized water.

RNA Enzymes

On the one hand, today's cells run most of their chemistry by using protein enzymes, which, in turn, are coded for in DNA. On the other hand, in order to turn the DNA into a "working" protein, other enzymes are necessary. This cycle gets us into a kind of chicken-and-egg controversy. You need DNA to make the proteins, but you need the proteins to make the DNA. How could the first living cell have solved this dilemma?

Scientists have attempted to resolve this problem with a number of intriguing solutions, all of which share one assumption: that the very earliest life forms had a rather different (and much simpler) chemistry than the ones we see around us today. The problem facing scientists is something like trying to reconstruct the Wright Brothers' first airplane by examining a modern jetliner. Many of the original design features have been replaced by more efficient components. Similarly, the first cell's chemical mechanisms, being rather inefficient, may have been largely replaced when the DNA–RNA–protein system evolved later. Thus, we do not see these chemical mechanisms in living systems today, but perhaps we can deduce their properties from studies of biochemistry.

One particularly interesting observation is that some kinds of RNA molecules have been found to act as enzymes for chemical reactions, in addition to their usual role as nucleic acids. This behavior suggests one way that the present system of cell chemistry could have evolved. RNA molecules catalyzed reactions that created proteins, and, over time, the proteins necessary for the development of the more complex (and presumably more efficient) DNA coding system were developed. Alternatively, other scientists have suggested that some kind of clay or other inorganic mineral may have provided sites for chemical reactions, as well as catalytic properties to help those reactions along. And still other researchers have suggested that the first primitive chemical reactions took place without the action of any enzymes, and the modern chemical complexity of life developed later.

Speculative ideas about black smokers and RNA enzymes are not necessarily exclusive. It may well be that the best place for chemistry involving RNA as an enzyme to occur is a deep-ocean fissure. What is certain is that life's chemical evolution will remain an exciting challenge for scientists.

◉ 25.3 The Window of Opportunity

Whatever the chemical processes were that led to the first organism capable of reproducing itself, we know that those processes had to take place rapidly. We know that Earth, like all the other planets, went through the period of the great bombardment (see Chapter 16). During this period, large chunks of debris fell onto the planets from space, bringing enormous amounts of energy with them. An impact involving an asteroid several hundred miles across would heat Earth enough to boil off most of the oceans—most of the planet would literally be sterilized by such an impact, and the chances are that any life that might have developed would be wiped out. Therefore, the process that led to the ancestors of all present life on Earth probably could not have begun until after the last big impact. The best estimate for this date is about 4 billion years ago.

On the other hand, recent discoveries have convinced some paleontologists that as early as 3.85 billion years, life was not only present on Earth but flourishing. In 2010, Dominic Papineau and colleagues at the Carnegie Institution of Washington reported biochemical evidence for colonies of primitive bacteria in rocks that were laid down as sediment in a shallow bay in what is now western Greenland. Papineau identified carbon-rich remnants in thin slices of these old rocks and discovered traces of nitrogen, sulfur, and phosphorus as well—a suite of the essential elements of life (Figure 25-8). No process other than life is known to concentrate those distinctive elements in carbon. If these data hold up to scrutiny by other scientists, it means that the first cell must have appeared soon after the last big impact during the great bombardment.

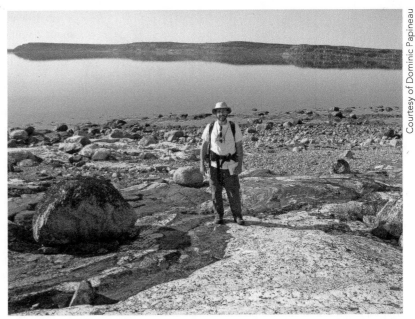

FIGURE 25-8 Ancient rocks that hold possible signs of life.

Courtesy of Dominic Papineau

The First Cell

Think about the unique status of the very first cell on Earth. It need not have been particularly efficient in using the chemicals found in its environment—after all, it had no competition. There were no predators and no other life forms to compete for the abundant stock of organic molecules that enriched the early ocean. Once the first cell formed, it may have multiplied rapidly.

Biologists have suggested that the special characteristics of the first cell may explain one of the great mysteries of modern biochemistry, the fact that living things today contain only 20 different kinds of amino acids (see Chapter 22). The notion is that, perhaps by chance or perhaps because this particular combination gave them a competitive edge, some early cells contained only these amino acids and it was the descendants of these cells that managed to dominate Earth. If we think that there is no reason why this particular suite of molecules would confer an advantage, then the combination of these particular 20 amino acids is something of a "frozen accident," one of perhaps many chance events in the formation of life on Earth. Like so many other questions about the origin of life, this one will remain unanswered until we know more about the subject than we do now.

SCIENCE BY THE NUMBERS
Cell Division

The first cell was a microscopic organism, but it may not have taken long for that first bit of life to spread great distances around the globe. To get a feel for this process, imagine how long it would take to fill up the Mediterranean Sea starting with a single microscopic cell that divides once a day, assuming all cells survive and continue to divide.

To get an answer, we must estimate the volume of an ordinary bacterium and compare it with the volume of the Mediterranean Sea. In Chapter 21 we learned that a typical bacterium is about a thousandth of a centimeter across, so its volume is approximately

$$(1/1000 \text{ cm})^3 = 10^{-9} \text{ cubic cm}$$

FIGURE 25-9 The number of bacteria grows rapidly, in what scientists call an exponential curve. In a matter of months, a single cell whose descendants divide once a day could easily populate a large ocean. (Note that the vertical scale is in factors of 10, or a logarithmic scale).

A recent world atlas gives the surface area of the Mediterranean Sea as about 2.5 million square kilometers, with an average depth of 1.4 kilometers, for a total volume of

$$2,500,000 \text{ km}^2 \times 1.4 \text{ km} = 3,500,000 \text{ km}^3 = 3.5 \times 10^6 \text{ km}^3$$

The question thus boils down to how many times you would have to double a 10^{-9} cm^3 bacterium to fill 3.5×10^6 km^3. To make things easier, we convert cubic kilometers to cubic centimeters:

$$1 \text{ km} = 10^5 \text{ cm}$$

so

$$1 \text{ km}^3 = 10^{15} \text{ cm}^3$$

The total volume of the Mediterranean in cubic centimeters is

$$3.5 \times 10^6 \text{ km}^3 \times 10^{15} \text{ cm}^3/\text{km}^3 = 3.5 \times 10^{21} \text{ cm}^3$$

How many bacteria would it take to fill this volume? We divide the immense volume of the Mediterranean Sea by the tiny volume of a single bacterium:

$$3.5 \times 10^{21} \text{ cm}^3/10^{-9} \text{ cm}^3 = 3.5 \times 10^{30} \text{ bacteria}$$

Starting with a single bacterium on the first day, there would be two on the second day, four on the third, eight on the fourth, and so on. After about 3 weeks, there would be more than a million bacteria, taking up only about a thousandth of a cubic centimeter.

Day by day, however, the number would increase geometrically. After 2 months there would be more than 10^{18} bacteria; after 3 months 10^{27} individuals, occupying more than 10,000 cubic kilometers. And in just 10 days more—only 100 days after the first cell began to divide—the Mediterranean Sea would be completely filled with bacteria (Figure 25-9).

Naturally, no body of water could be "completely filled" with bacteria. In addition, early life probably did not spread quite this fast, nor was the process so regular and predictable. But the implication is clear. Although it may have taken hundreds of millions of years for the first cell to evolve, a large number of descendants of that first cell could have spread throughout the world's oceans relatively quickly.

THE ONGOING PROCESS OF SCIENCE
Did Life Also Originate on Mars?

The development of life on Earth would not have been possible without the presence of liquid water on the planet's surface. As we saw in Chapter 16, there was probably liquid water on the surface of Mars during its early history. Some astronomers even argue that the entire Northern Hemisphere of the planet was covered by an ocean and that the wet period of Martian history may have lasted as much as a billion years. After this period, the planet lost most of its atmosphere and hydrosphere to space and became the barren world it is today.

This scenario raises an interesting possibility. Since life on Earth seems to have developed rapidly once the great bombardment came to a halt, could the same thing have happened on Mars? Could life have evolved in those Martian oceans, only to perish when the oceans disappeared? If so, there should be fossil evidence to mark its existence.

In 1996, a team of scientists suggested that they had found such evidence in a meteorite that was blasted off the surface of Mars millions of years ago. The meteorite, labeled ALH84001 (because it was the first meteorite collected in 1984 from the Allan Hills region of Antarctica), contains tiny gas bubbles whose chemical composition matches that of the Martian atmosphere (Figure 25-10a). The idea is that millions of years ago a large meteorite on our sister planet blew this rock fragment into space from which, after millions of years of wandering in the void, it fell to Earth. It is one of several dozen known meteorites thought to come from Mars.

In a lively press conference and subsequent *Science* article in August 1996, scientists from the National Aeronautics and Space Administration (NASA) and other laboratories presented

(a)   *(b)*

FIGURE 25-10 *(a)* This 4.5-billion-year-old rock, labeled meteorite ALH84001, is believed to have once been a part of Mars and has been claimed to contain fossil evidence that primitive life may have existed on Mars more than 3.6 billion years ago. The rock is a portion of a meteorite that was dislodged from Mars by a huge impact about 16 million years ago and that fell to Earth in Antarctica 13,000 years ago. *(b)* Micrographs of the Mars meteorite revealed tiny structures reminiscent of bacteria. Subsequent analyses showed that these objects are layered minerals viewed end on.

several lines of evidence that might point to past life. They observed complex organic molecules laced through the meteorite, magnetic mineral grains typical of those deposited by Earth bacteria, isotopic compositions characteristic of living things, and tiny structures reminiscent of bacteria (Figure 25-10b). They noted that any one of these features, by itself, would be little cause for excitement. Carbon-rich molecules, for example, are well known in meteorites and comets, as are magnetic grains of iron minerals. But some NASA scientists argue that these observations, taken together, "are evidence for primitive life on early Mars."

Over time, other scientists made additional observations that called these initial claims into question, and few scientists now accept the original interpretation. The "fossils," for example, turned out to be layered mineral deposits viewed end on. Nevertheless, the excitement generated by the possibility that Martian life had already been discovered led NASA to initiate a program in *astrobiology*—the search for the origin and distribution of life in the universe. Thanks to the support of NASA's Astrobiology Institute, hundreds of scientists are studying processes that may have led to life on Earth, Mars, and other worlds.

STOP & THINK **Think about the possibility that life exists on planets orbiting the billions of stars in each of the billions of galaxies. Would such an abundance of life affect your view of life on Earth? Should we spend more tax dollars to search for extraterrestrial life?**

◎ 25.4 Natural Selection and the Development of Complex Life

Once we get beyond the time when the first cell formed, our understanding of how life developed becomes much more detailed and precise. This understanding is due in large measure to the work of one man, Charles Darwin (1809–1882). His seminal work, *On the Origin of Species*, published in 1859, is arguably one of the most influential books ever written. In it he presents a view of the development of living things that, since his time, has been investigated, expanded, and developed to the point where it is fair to say that it is the single theory that unifies all of biology. A biochemist working on the transport of particular molecules across the cell membrane and a zoologist working on the ecology of a tropical lake will both share the central ideas of Darwin's theory, and hence will have a common vocabulary and a common way of attacking problems. Darwin's theory was influential and controversial because it identified a simple mechanism for evolving complex multicellular life forms from single-celled life. His entire theory is built around one central concept—natural selection.

Natural Selection

The easiest way to understand what Darwin meant by natural selection is to think first about the process that he called *artificial selection*. Farmers have known for millennia that the way to get bigger fruit, healthier plants, or animals with more meat on them is to carry out a conscious process of breeding. (Think back to Mendel's experiments discussed in Chapter 23.) If you want large potatoes, you should plant the eyes from only the largest potatoes in any given crop. Over long periods of time this practice will give you a new variety of potato that is significantly different from the one you started with. Because human choice, not nature, drives this process, it is given the name of artificial selection. It explains how you can get animals as different from each other as longhorn and Angus cattle, or Chihuahuas and Great Danes, from the same ancestral stock (Figure 25-11).

If human beings can introduce such wide-ranging changes in living things, Darwin reasoned, then nature should be able to do the same. The mechanism he proposed, which he called **natural selection**, depends on two basic facts for its operation:

1. *Every population contains genetic diversity.* The individual members of any population possess a range of characteristics. Some are able to run a little faster than others, some have quicker reactions than others, some are more resistant to new diseases, some have a slightly different color and so are better able to hide from predators than others, and so forth.

2. *Many more individuals are born than can possibly survive.* In nature, most individuals die in infancy, before they have a chance to reproduce. Therefore, those characteristics that make it more probable that a given member of the population will live long enough to reproduce will tend to be passed on to a greater percentage of the population's subsequent generations.

Think about a hypothetical example to see how natural selection works. Suppose an island supports a certain number of birds, and suppose that the environment of this island is such that having a color that blends in with the local green vegetation makes it easier for those birds to avoid their predators. Just by chance, some members of the bird population will have colors that match the colors of local leaves and trees better than others (Figure 25-12). As we saw in

FIGURE 25-11 Contrasting breeds of dogs, including *(a)* Collie, *(b)* Bulldog, and *(c)* Chihuahua, illustrate the changes possible with artificial selection.

(a)   *(b)*   *(c)*

Chapter 23, the birds' DNA would determine this property in those particular birds.

Better-camouflaged green birds will be less likely to be eaten by predators and, therefore, will be more likely to survive to adulthood and mate. You would expect, then, that the particular genes that give this advantage will be more likely to be passed to the next generation. In effect, natural forces influence the genes that are propagated in the next generation. In this case, the selection is based on the color of the feathers.

If this process goes on for a long period of time, most of the bird population will eventually begin to share those advantageous genes for green feather color, though genes for other colors could also persist. Natural selection works this way gradually to modify a gene pool, just as populations of farm animals now share genes for rapid growth and meat production. Nature "selects" those characteristics that will be propagated in any given species. A structure, process, or behavior that helps an organism survive and pass on its genes is called an **adaptation**.

FIGURE 25-12 Cobalt-winged parakeets are found in the Amazon Basin in the northern part of South America. Their green coloration provides excellent camouflage in the rain forest.

Natural selection also provides a mechanism for a species to change its traits in response to changes in the environment. If prolonged drought causes the local leaf color to change from primarily green to brown, for example, then darker-colored birds in the population may have more success in breeding, and the average color may change accordingly, in response to natural selection.

Natural selection, it should be remembered, is neither as controlled nor as rapid as artificial selection. It's always possible that birds that do not carry the selected gene will, in some generations, be more successful at mating than those who do. Over the long haul, however, the selective advantage granted by color will win. Thus, Darwin envisioned natural selection as a process that operates over long time periods to produce gradual changes in populations, not a process that can explain short-term variations in a few individual traits. It's important to understand that natural selection relates to changes in populations over time. Each individual in that population retains the DNA it was born with and does not change in response to environmental stresses.

 ## SCIENCE IN THE MAKING
The Reception of Darwin's Theory

Charles Darwin formulated the basic outline of his theory of natural selection in 1838, but he waited more than 20 years to publish his findings. This delay was not simple procrastination. He realized that the central precepts of his theory would cause a furor. Eventually, learning that another British naturalist, Alfred Russell Wallace, had developed similar ideas, Darwin hastened to get his *On the Origin of Species* into print (Figure 25-13).

Written in accessible prose and published in a widely available edition, his theory evoked intense reactions. Some theologians denounced the book for its denial of a miraculous creation and of a relatively short Earth history, which they claimed were demanded by a literal reading of the Bible.

Equally disturbing to Darwin was the reaction of many readers who embraced the "theory of evolution" as scientific evidence for God's hand in the progress of nature and thus proof of the human being's moral and spiritual superiority. They seized Darwin's discovery as an example of God's wisdom and beneficence. Some intellectuals of the late nineteenth century even went so far as to cite Darwin in their defense of an economically and socially stratified society—the most "fit" individuals rose to the top of society, they claimed.

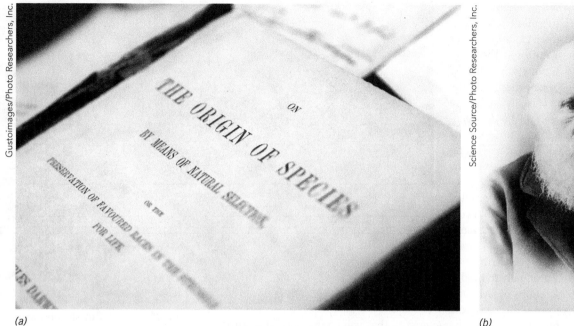

(a)

(b)

FIGURE 25-13 *On the Origin of Species by Means of Natural Selection (a)* first appeared in 1859 and quickly sold out. Charles Darwin *(b)* prepared several revised versions of the book over the next two decades.

Ironically, Darwin never intended his theory to suggest the idea of inevitable "progress" in nature—only inevitable change. Indeed, Darwin didn't use the word "evolution"—a word that connotes improvement—in the first edition of his book, nor did he address the question of human origins in *On the Origin of Species.* Far from being guided by a divine hand, he saw natural processes as violent and amoral—a constant struggle for survival in which the ability to reproduce fertile offspring was the only measure of success. He observed successful natural strategies that his contemporaries would have viewed as repulsive in any moral sense—species whose females devour their mates, species whose offspring eat each other until just a few survive, and parasites and predators that kill without thought in the frantic quest for energy to survive. To Darwin, human ascendancy seemed an evolutionary accident rather than a divine plan, and he saw no sign of God in the brutal process of natural selection. Nevertheless, in his own concluding words:

> *There is grandeur in this view of life, with its several powers, having been originally breathed by the Creator into a few forms or into one; and that, whilst this planet has gone cycling on according to the fixed law of gravity, from so simple a beginning endless forms most beautiful and most wonderful have been, and are being, evolved.*

◉ 25.5 The Story of Life

As soon as the first cell split into two competing individuals, natural selection began to operate. In that early environment, where the first cells were surrounded by energy-rich molecules and very few neighbors, competition would not have been very intense. Before long, however, genetic mutations would have started to occur and some cells would have been different from others. Some of those differences involved the efficiency with which cells were able to utilize the molecules that they found in their environment. Certain cells, for example, might have been able to get energy more quickly from those molecules (and therefore reproduce faster) than others. Over time, the beneficial mutations would come to be shared throughout the entire population by the process of natural selection.

At this early stage, just as in today's life forms, the vast majority of mutations and the resultant differences were not beneficial. Random changes in DNA, after all, are not likely to produce organisms that can interact with their environment more efficiently than their fellows. Nonbeneficial mutations died out quickly, and only beneficial mutations remained. This process is a little like our view of movies from the 1930s and 1940s. A great many poor films were made in those days, but we don't watch them anymore. What we remember and preserve are the most successful films, such as *Citizen Kane* and *Casablanca*. In the same way, only the "greatest hits" of all the mutations survived into the future.

Over time, you would expect the descendants of that first cell to spread around Earth's surface and to occupy most of the oceans. Some scholars have suggested that this spread may have taken as little as a few years, given the lack of competition for the environmental resources. (The results we calculated in the "Science by the Numbers" section of this chapter suggest that such a scenario might be reasonable.) In this process of spreading, some cells would wind up in different environments than others. Some, for example, would be in warm tropical waters, while others would be in the chilling Arctic. Some would be in deep oceans, while others would be in shallow water next to the shore. Each of these environments would exert slightly different pressures on the cells. An adaptation that might be very advantageous in the tropics, for example, might not be advantageous near the poles, and vice versa. The driving force of natural selection, coupled with the fact that many different environments existed on our planet, would quickly have produced a number of very different living things. Thus, we would expect the appearance of diversity—the process of speciation—to have begun quite early in the history of life.

Our knowledge of this early period of life is limited by the fact that we have very little in the way of hard physical evidence that pertains to it. As you might guess, it is difficult to find fossils of single-celled or microscopic organisms, though scientists have found them, and they have even unearthed a few cases of fossil bacteria caught in the act of dividing.

The best guess as to what went on until about a billion years ago is that the new varieties of single cells spread around the world and differentiated, driven all the while by natural selection and changes in Earth's climate. At some point in this evolutionary process, perhaps about 2.5 billion years ago, the oceans became dominated by cyanobacteria, which are single-celled life forms that produce oxygen as a by-product of photosynthesis. To an outside observer, Earth would have looked remarkably sterile. There was no life at all on land, but the margins of the oceans were covered with collections of green scum that were going about the business of taking in carbon dioxide and returning oxygen to the atmosphere (Figure 25-14).

About a billion years ago, symbiotic relationships were set up between cells that eventually led to the development of eukaryotes. At some point, smaller cells found that they did better living inside their larger neighbors than they could do on their own, and cells whose genetic materials were carried inside a nucleus were born. These cells, like their neighbors and ancestors the prokaryotes, remained as single-celled organisms.

Another important development that occurred early in the history of life was that cells began to clump together into mats or chains to form large colonies. At first, these objects were probably nothing more than clumps of single-celled organisms living next to each other. Later, however, they developed into larger bodies. Indeed, by about 600 million years ago the seas were probably full of large multicellular animals and plants. You can think of some of them as resembling modern jellyfish (Figure 25-15). The stage was set for one of the most important developments in the history of life, the hard shell.

About 540 million years ago a crucial development took place in living systems. By a process that we don't fully understand, but that may have involved a new enzyme that converted calcium in the ocean water into shell material, some animals began to grow hard shells (Figure 25-16). This new chemical trick was so advantageous that the seafloor was soon teeming with many different kinds of hard-shelled animals. As always happens when a new evolutionary path develops, there was a great deal of competition and experimentation among living things as they evolved outer shells, body designs, and metabolisms suited for each environment.

FIGURE 25-14 Columnar-shaped stromatolites, such as this example from 1.9 billion year-old rocks in the Hudson Bay of Canada, are remains of microbial colonies that thrived in shallow water.

FIGURE 25-15 This Australian fossil was once thought to be an elaborate clamshell but is now interpreted as burrows created by worm-like creatures searching for food in ocean silt.

FIGURE 25-16 This new species of fossil trilobite, which was discovered in limestone deposits near Utica, New York, in 2011, lived in a shallow reef environment approximately 450 million years ago.

From the scientist's point of view, one of the most important aspects of this development was that, for the first time, living things left large numbers of fossils. In fact, for most of the nineteenth and twentieth centuries, before discovery of the fossils that indicated the presence of primitive forms of life, it looked to scientists as if life suddenly exploded at the beginning of this period. This sudden change in life on Earth, therefore, is often referred to as the *Cambrian explosion*. (Geologists refer to the time during which skeletons developed as the Cambrian period, after Cambria, the old Roman name for Wales, where rocks from this period were first studied.)

Following the momentous development of shells, the last half-billion years or so have seen enormous growth in both the complexity and diversity of life. A summary of major developments is given in Table 25-1 (see Appendix B for more details).

TABLE 25-1 **Major Steps in the Evolution of Life**

Time (millions of years)	Event
≈3500	First cell
≈2500	Photosynthetic cells
2000	Eukaryotes
700	Multicellularity
542	Animals with shells
450	Vertebrates and land plants
400	Amphibians
350	Reptiles
251	Largest known mass extinction
140	Appearance of flowering plants
100	Placental mammals
65.5	Primates; extinction of dinosaurs
≈7–8	Hominids
2.5	The genus *Homo*
0.2	*Homo sapiens*

Geological Time

Before the development of radiometric dating in this century (see Chapter 12), scientists knew about the existence of fossils and could see that some fossils were older than others by the sequence of rock layers. Younger layers of fossil-bearing rocks are always deposited on top of older layers of rock. However, they had no way of attaching numbers to any of the changes they observed in the fossil record. Several landmarks that stand out in the process of evolution were used as boundaries in the delineation of past times.

In the nineteenth century, scientists were not aware of bacterial fossils, or even fossils of soft-bodied organisms. To them, fossils seemed to indicate that life suddenly appeared at the beginning of the Cambrian (when fossils of hard-bodied organisms first appeared). The era from the beginning of Earth's existence to 542 million years ago was therefore called the *Proterozoic* ("before life"). Next was the *Paleozoic* ("old life") era from about 542 to 251 million years ago. This era saw a marvelous diversification of life, including the development of many kinds of invertebrates, such as trilobites and mollusks, as well as fish, amphibians, land plants and animals, and rudimentary forms of reptiles. The third great era (251 to 65.5 million years ago) was the *Mesozoic* ("middle life"), also known as the age of dinosaurs, when the major vertebrate life forms on Earth were large reptiles. Finally, the *Cenozoic* ("new life") era began with the extinction of the dinosaurs some 65.5 million years ago and continues to the present day. This is the time when mammals proliferated and began to dominate Earth. The human species arose at the very end of the Cenozoic.

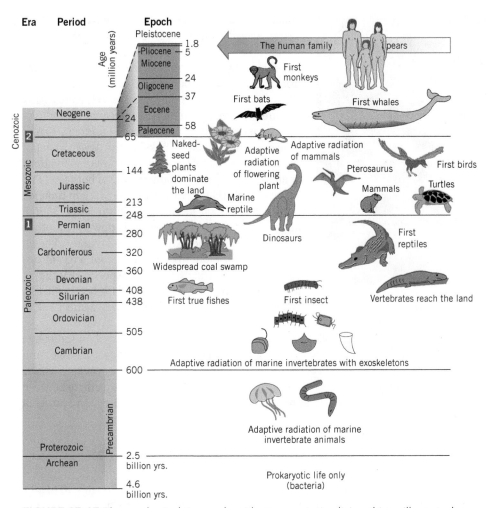

FIGURE 25-17 The geological timescale with representative living things illustrated.

Throughout this long and intricate process of change, the principle of natural selection was always at work, shaping and molding life forms (Figure 25-17).

THE ONGOING PROCESS OF SCIENCE
The Evolution of Whales

The power of Darwin's theory of evolution lies in its predictive power. For example, in the mid-1980s, critics of evolution pointed to the modern whale as an example of a form so specialized that it could not possibly have been produced by Darwinian evolution. An outspoken creationist, Alan Haywood, put it this way: "Darwinists rarely mention the whale because it presents them with one of their most insoluble problems. They believe that somehow a whale must have evolved from an ordinary land-dwelling animal, which took to the sea and lost its legs. . . . A land mammal that was in the process of becoming a whale would fall between two stools—it would not be fitted for life on land or sea, and would have no hope of survival."

Faced with such a challenge, one can test the theory. The theory of evolution predicts that a logical 50-million-year sequence of whales, the oldest with fully formed hind legs, then gradually shorter hind limbs through time, and ultimately recent whales with tiny vestigial hind leg bones, must have once swum in the seas. If Darwin is correct, then somewhere their fossils must lie buried. Furthermore, those strange creatures must have arisen during a relatively narrow interval of geological time, bounded by the era before the earliest known marine mammals (about 55 million years ago) and the appearance of streamlined whales of the present era (which

FIGURE 25-18 Dozens of different species of primitive fossil whales discovered in the past three decades reveal hind limbs and other features intermediate between land animals and whales.

appear in the fossil record during the past 30 million years). Armed with these predictions, several paleontologists have plotted expeditions into the field and targeted their search on shallow marine formations from the crucial gap between 35 and 55 million years ago for new evidence in the fossil record (Figure 25-18).

Sure enough, in the past two decades paleontologists have excavated more than one hundred different species of these "missing links" in the development of the whale—curious creatures that sport combinations of anatomical features characteristic of both land and sea mammals (Figure 25-19). Moving back in time, we find that one such intermediate form is the 35-million-year-old *Basilosaurus*—a sleek, powerful, toothed whale. This majestic extinct whale has been known from fossils for more than a century, but a recent discovery of an unusually complete specimen in Egypt for the first time included tiny hind leg bones. That's a feature without obvious function in the whale, but such atrophied legs provide a direct link to four-limbed ancestral land mammals.

And then a more primitive whale, *Rodhocetus*, discovered in 1994 in Pakistani sediments about 46 million years old, has more exaggerated hind legs, not unlike those of a seal. And in that same year paleontologists reported the new genus *Ambulocetus*, the "walking whale." This awkwardly beautiful 52-million-year-old creature represents a true intermediate between land and sea mammals. These and other recent discoveries underscore the predictive power of Darwin's theory.

Mass Extinctions and the Rate of Evolution

Under normal circumstances, the rate of extinction seems to be such that roughly 10 to 20% of the species represented in the fossil record at any given time will be extinct in a matter of 5 or 6 million years. The fossil record shows, however, that not all extinctions are "normal." **Mass extinctions**, rare catastrophic events in the past, have caused large numbers of species to become extinct suddenly (Figure 25-20).

By "large numbers of species," we mean anywhere from 30 to 90% of the species alive at the time. By "suddenly," we mean a time too short to be resolved by standard geological techniques. The extinction may have taken place over a period of a few tens of thousands of years, or over a couple of days.

The best known of these mass extinctions is the one in which the dinosaurs perished some 65.5 million years ago at the end of the Cretaceous period, which was also at the end of the

FIGURE 25-19 *Basilosaurus* was a sleek and powerful toothed whale that lived in the oceans 35 million years ago. It possessed tiny vestigial hind legs—a trait that hints at the whale's evolution from land animals."

Mesozoic era. In that extinction, about two-thirds of all living species disappeared. In some cases, as with ocean plankton, this number may have climbed as high as 98%. But the extinction at the end of the Mesozoic was neither the largest nor the most recent mass extinction. About 251 million years ago near the end of the Paleozoic era, about 80% of existing species disappeared in a single extinction event. A somewhat milder extinction, which wiped out 30% of existing species, appears to have taken place about 11 million years ago. In fact, geologists who study the past history of life in detail recognize five major mass extinction events and as many as another dozen smaller ones.

One of the most interesting explanations for how these mass extinctions could occur was put forward in 1980 by the father-and-son team of Luis Alvarez

(1911–1986; a Nobel laureate in physics) and Walter Alvarez (b. 1940; a geologist). Based on evidence they accumulated, they suggested that the impact of a large asteroid killed off the dinosaurs and other life forms. Such an impact would have raised a dust cloud that blocked out sunlight for several years. This catastrophe would have been such a shock to the world ecosystem that it is a wonder anything survived at all.

STOP & THINK What would happen if an asteroid like the one hypothesized by Luis and Walter Alvarez hit Earth today?

Most scientists today accept that an asteroid hit Earth at the end of the Cretaceous, and they agree that it was responsible for the mass extinction. This conclusion was bolstered in 1992, when a giant crater over 100 miles across dating from that time was discovered buried under the seafloor near the Yucatán Peninsula in Mexico (Figure 25-21). Less certain is the role that other factors played in these events. The world ecosystem was under a great deal of stress at that time because of rapid changes in climate and the recent creation of mountain chains, both of which were altering habitats.

Mass extinctions illustrate an important point about the history of life on our planet. Evolution is not a smooth, gradual progress through time. There are times when sudden changes (such as those in the mass extinctions) are followed by rapid evolution, as new species develop to take the place of those that disappeared. After the extinction of the dinosaurs, for example, the number of species of mammals increased dramatically. Scientists continue to debate about the rate of evolution. The two extremes in the debate have been the *gradualism* hypothesis, which holds that most change occurs as a result of the accumulation of small adaptations; and *punctuated equilibrium*, which holds that changes usually occur in short bursts, separated by long periods of stability. It now appears that both of these extremes, and probably any rate of evolution in between, occurred at some time in Earth's past.

1 Late Ordovician (−12%)
2 Late Devonian (−14%)
3 Late Permian (−52%)
4 Late Triassic (−12%)
5 Late Cretaceous (−11%)

FIGURE 25-20 The diversity of life on Earth has not increased steadily but has gone through a series of sharp changes. This graph of marine animals in the fossil record is indicative of the overall growth in families and of extinctions. The extinction of the dinosaurs is indicated by the event labeled 5.

FIGURE 25-21 (a) The location of the giant crater near the Yucatán Peninsula in Mexico. The effects of the asteroid's impact were recorded in rocks as far away as the red dashed circle. (b) A drill rig exploring another impact site on the Chesapeake Bay.

(a)

(b)

Pascal Goetgheluck/Photo Researchers, Inc.

FIGURE 25-22 A progression of skulls, showing (left to right) a lemur-like animal that lived around 50 million years ago; a primate called *Proconsul* (about 20 million years ago); *Australopithicus africanus* (about 3 million years ago); *Homo habilis* (about 2 million years ago); *Homo erectus* (about 1.8 million years ago); and skulls of two anatomically modern humans from different locations.

©The Natural History Museum, London/The Image Works

FIGURE 25-23 "Lucy," a 40%-complete skeleton of *Australopithecus afarensis*, lived 3.5 million years ago in what is now northern Africa. This skeleton proved that hominids of that period walked erect.

● 25.6 The Evolution of Human Beings

The evolution of our own species, *Homo sapiens*, provides a good illustration of the kind of process that must have occurred for every other species. The most widely accepted hypothesis of human evolution is that our branch of the family tree broke off from the branch that includes orangutans and other primates about 7 to 8 million years ago. A possible human family tree is shown in Figure 25-22.

Finding fossils of the oldest hominid has always been something of an obsession with paleontologists, but the problem is exceptionally difficult for three principal reasons. First, before modern times hominid populations were concentrated in Africa and were never very large, so fossils would be rare even if a significant fraction of individuals had been fossilized. Second, fossil-bearing sedimentary rocks from the period from 4 to 8 million years ago are rare in Africa, so relatively few individuals could have been fossilized. And third, many of the sedimentary formations that might contain hominid fossils are located in politically unstable regions where collecting is not possible. Nevertheless, slow progress is being made in this area.

Scientists have found fragments of a few fossils from the period of transition between our last common ancestor of humans and apes, but the actual picture of the line of evolution remains cloudy. For example, a few teeth that seem to be intermediate between apes and humans were found in 10-million-year-old sediments in Ethiopia, and in 2002 a single 6- to 7-million-year-old skull was found in Chad.

Another ancient hominid, *Ardipithecus ramidus* ("ground floor, root of humans"), is known from several partial skeletons about 4.5 million years old, as well as additional fossil fragments of a related species that date back as far as 5.8 million years. This 4-foot-tall ancestor appears to be midway in form between later hominids and modern great apes. The best-known early human fossils are bones of *Australopithecus afarensis* ("southern ape from the Afar triangle region of Ethiopia"), better known as *Lucy* after the name paleontologists gave to a nearly complete skeleton of the species (Figure 25-23). The name of this fossil, which was discovered in 1974, arose because the paleontologists celebrated their discovery around a campfire while playing tapes of the Beatles' song "Lucy in the Sky with Diamonds." Radiometric dating reveals that this species lived between about 3 and 4 million years ago. *A. afarensis* is a different species and different genus from our own **Homo sapiens** but it is closer to us than to any other known primate genus.

Lucy and her family walked erect but had brains about the size of a modern chimpanzee's. They were also rather small (the adults probably weighed no more than 60 to 80 pounds and were typically less than 5 feet tall) and may have been covered with hair. Scientists used to think that the development of large brains made human beings special and that the brain's development led to upright walking. Actually, the evolutionary story seems to be the other way around. We walked upright first, which freed the hands for use, and then the large brain developed. Some scientists have suggested that the evolutionary advantage bestowed by hand–eye coordination provided the competitive edge for *Australopithecus*, and that led to the large brain.

Following Lucy, the line of *Australopithecines* developed larger and larger brains, and at various times there were several different species within the genus. From our point of view, however, the most important event happened about 2.5 million years ago, when the first known member of the genus *Homo* appeared. Fossils of *Homo habilis* ("man the toolmaker") were discovered in East Africa in the mid-twentieth century. *Homo habilis* was larger than Lucy and had a larger brain. More importantly, *H. habilis* fossils are found with crude stone tools, so the association of human beings with tool making starts with this species. Shortly thereafter, another member of our genus, *Homo erectus* ("man the erect") appeared. *Homo erectus* fossils are found not only in East Africa but in Asia and the Middle East as well. Many of the famous fossil humans you may have heard of—Java Man and Peking Man, for example—were members of this species. *Homo erectus* lived at the same time as some of the later *Australopithecines* and survived until about 500,000 years ago. *Homo erectus* was the first in the line of human ancestors known to use fire.

Fossils that we recognize as anatomically modern humans begin to appear in rocks about 200,000 years old. About the same time, yet another type of human being appeared on the scene—the so-called **Neanderthal man** (Figure 25-24). We sometimes use "Neanderthal" to denote something stupid. This use of the word comes from the fact that early studies of Neanderthal fossils concluded that this species walked stooped over, knuckles swinging, and had the thick brow ridge we associate with gorillas. These early suggestions were based on the study of a single skeleton of an old man who had a severe case of arthritis. Modern studies on other fossils reveal that Neanderthals, though far from being identical to modern human beings, were not all that different. They tended to be short, with thick, powerful arms and legs, and a skull that is much more elongated and pulled forward than that of modern *Homo sapiens*. In contrast, Neanderthals had large brains, on the average 10% larger than those of modern humans. They had a complex social structure, cared for elderly and infirm members of their tribe, and performed burials with ritual—facts that suggest the presence of both a religion and a language. Thus, Neanderthal was not too different from its contemporaries among the anatomically modern humans.

Several mysteries and controversies surround Neanderthal. The first puzzle is how closely Neanderthals were related to modern human beings. The recent sequencing of Neanderthal DNA described in Chapter 24 has shown that modern humans and Neanderthals were closely enough related to interbreed, so that modern humans of European or Asian descent received anywhere from 1% to 4% of their genes from the Neanderthal. (It is not unusual for closely related species to be able to produce fertile offspring—it is well known that wolves and dogs, separate species, can do so).

The second great mystery about the Neanderthals—some would say *the* mystery about Neanderthals—is the question of what happened to them. In Europe, where the fossil record is most complete, it appears that Neanderthals flourished until 35,000 years ago and then disappeared rather suddenly. Their disappearance coincided with the entry into Europe of modern *Homo sapiens*. Several theories have been put forward to explain the Neanderthals's disappearance. Some suggest Neanderthals were wiped out by the invading members of our own species in what might be described as a prehistoric instance of genocide Others have suggested that Neanderthals couldn't compete with the more technologically advanced newcomers and simply died out. In this case, the Neanderthals were not wiped out by acts of war, but were simply

FIGURE 25-24 An artist's reconstruction of what a typical Neanderthal might have looked like.

moved away from the desirable settlement locations and eventually disappeared. Such a situation would be an example of the displacement of one species by another, a common phenomenon in the history of life.

The descent of modern human beings raises an important point. In the past, many different beings could be classed as "human"—many members of the hominid family have walked Earth's surface. For whatever reason, none of them survived to this day except ourselves. The processes of natural selection and extinction, in other words, have extensively pruned the branch of the family tree leading to human beings. This fact made it easy for people in the nineteenth century to discount or misinterpret Darwin and to believe that the human race was special and not related to the rest of the web of life that exists on our planet.

THINKING MORE ABOUT **EVOLUTION**

Young-Earth Creationism and Intelligent Design

Opposition to Darwin did not end in the nineteenth century. In the United States today, many vocal opponents to Darwin's theory believe in young-Earth creationism, which is based on a literal interpretation of the Bible. Three central tenets of young-Earth creationism are:

1. Earth and the universe were created relatively recently, no more than about 10,000 years in the past.
2. All life forms were created by God in a miraculous act in essentially their modern forms.
3. The present disrupted Earth's surface and the distribution of fossils are primarily the consequence of a great catastrophic flood.

These beliefs differ dramatically from many of the scientific ideas presented in this book. The big bang origin of the universe almost 14 billion years ago (Chapter 15), the origin of the solar system more than 4.5 billion years ago (Chapter 16), the immense subsequent span of geological history (Chapters 17 and 18), and the chemical origins of life and its evolution by the process of natural selection (this chapter) are all at odds with these religious beliefs. It's not surprising, therefore, that science and creationism have come into conflict. In particular, evidence in favor of evolution requires a very old Earth and a means for transforming one species into another. Darwin's idea of natural selection, particularly as applied to the origin of human beings, is uncomfortable to many people because *Homo sapiens* cannot lay claim to a history that is intrinsically different from that of other species.

In the early 1980s, the Arkansas State Legislature passed a law requiring that the biblical story of creation be taught alongside the theory of evolution in public schools. Federal courts eventually ruled that this law was an attempt to impose religious beliefs in the public schools, something expressly forbidden by the U.S. Constitution. It is now against the law to teach creationism as part of any public school science curriculum.

Young-Earth creationists then adopted a different strategy by trying to eliminate evolution from public school curricula. In a

FIGURE 25-25 In December 2005, in a case in the U.S. District Court involving the Dover Area High School, Judge John E. Jones ruled that intelligent design is based on a religious belief and therefore should not be introduced into public school science classrooms.

number of states, they have attempted to remove all mention of biological evolution (and sometimes the big bang as well) from state science requirements. This effort to eliminate science content remains an ongoing issue.

A more recent opposition to teaching evolution came in the guise of the "doctrine of intelligent design," or ID. Proponents of ID argue that life on Earth is so extraordinarily complex that it could not possibly have emerged through any natural process. An intelligent engineer must have done the job (though ID advocates usually avoid talking about who designed the designers). In 2005, U.S. District Judge John E. Jones heard a case centering on the science curriculum in the town of Dover, Pennsylvania, and ruled that ID is simply another form of creationism. Consequently, intelligent design cannot be taught as a scientific alternative to evolution in the public schools (Figure 25-25).

We maintain that it is reasonable, perhaps even desirable, to discuss different ways of knowing about the origin and evolution of life in classes on the history of ideas, or comparative religions, or even current events. However, we view efforts to eliminate the teaching of evolution or to promote the creationist agenda in a public school science classroom as misguided and a significant threat to the integrity of public science education. We argue that evolution is an essential unifying concept in biology and thus is a critical aspect of any scientific education. All students should be expected to *understand* the principle of evolution and to be familiar with the extensive observational evidence that scientists have discovered to support it, even if they don't *believe* that evolution actually happened.

To what extent do you think that parents or local school boards should have the right to decide what scientific theories and ideas are presented in schools? To what extent do you think parents ought to have the right to demand that opposing religious views be taught as well? Should the views of creationism, which are primarily based on one particular type of Christianity, be given special consideration?

RETURN TO THE INTEGRATED QUESTION

How did life emerge on the ancient Earth?

- The origin of life on Earth is a topic of intense research. Some facts are well documented, whereas others are open to speculation.
  - The first life on Earth was probably a single-celled prokaryote that thrived in the inhospitable environments that would have been prevalent on Earth a few billion years ago.
  - With the use of radiometric dating (Chapter 12), evidence for ancient microbes that were the product of millions of years of chemical reactions appear in the fossil record dating back to roughly 3.5 billion years ago.
- Early life developed in two stages.
  - The first stage was characterized as *chemical evolution*, during which chemical reactions among the oceans, atmosphere, and rock led to the first life form.
    - Ancient chemical evolution produced a gradual buildup of organic chemicals in the primitive oceans. In the early 1950s, the Miller–Urey experiment and subsequent research showed that simple compounds such as water, methane, ammonia, and hydrogen, subjected to electrical sparks, combine to make the building blocks of life—amino acids, lipids, and other molecules.
    - Subsequent experiments have demonstrated that energy sources such as solar ultraviolet radiation or heat from volcanoes can also produce organic molecules.
  - The second stage was the evolution of the first cell by natural selection. We do not know details of how the first cell formed;

nevertheless, we suspect it first appeared after the end of the great bombardment (Chapter 16). During this period, extraterrestrial debris crashed into Earth with enough energy to boil off most of the oceans, which would have effectively sterilized the planet. Therefore, the processes that led to the ancestors of all present life on Earth probably could not have begun until after the last big impact. The best estimate for this date is about 4 billion years ago.

- The biomolecules produced in the primordial oceans may have become concentrated on mineral surfaces, perhaps in deep volcanic zones. Through a sequence of events not yet well understood, a primitive but complex self-replicating chemical system developed. All the diversity of life that we see around us today evolved from the first cell that self-replicated.
- Once the first microscopic cell developed, it may have multiplied rapidly.
  - That first cell, free from competitors, could have quickly multiplied in the nutrient-filled oceans.
  - Over time, the oceans became populated with microscopic organisms, and a new phase of evolution began: natural selection.
  - The process of natural selection led to the multiplication, diversification, and transformation of that first living cell into the astonishing variety of life that we now observe on Earth. The process of change and diversification that we call evolution will continue as long as life exists on Earth.

SUMMARY

Many types of evidence support the fact of *evolution*. A rich record of *fossils* demonstrates that life began simply and increased in complexity over time. The older a rock, the more its fossils are likely to differ from modern forms because the vast majority of life forms have become *extinct*. Biochemical evidence also supports the fact of evolution. Not only do all life forms employ the same biochemical mechanism for translating DNA into proteins, but also many of those proteins are similar in very different species. Comparison of structural details reveals that closely related species, such as humans and chimpanzees, have nearly identical proteins, whereas those of more distantly related animals show more protein differences. *Vestigial organs*, such as the human appendix, provide yet another piece of evidence in the evolution story.

Life on Earth evolved in two stages. The first period of *chemical evolution* was characterized by the gradual buildup of organic chemicals in the primitive oceans. The *Miller–Urey experiment* and subsequent research showed that simple compounds, including water, methane, ammonia, and hydrogen, subjected to electrical sparks or some other energy source, combine to make the building blocks of life—amino acids, lipids, and other molecules. These chemicals may have become concentrated on mineral surfaces, perhaps in deep volcanic zones. Through a sequence of events not yet well understood, a primitive but complex self-replicating chemical system developed. All subsequent life evolved from that first cell.

The first cell, free from competitors, quickly multiplied in the nutrient-filled oceans. As oceans became crowded and competition for resources increased, a new phase of evolution, *natural selection*, began. The theory of natural selection, introduced by Charles Darwin in his 1859 monograph *Origin of Species,* is based on two facts: every species exhibits variations in traits, and some traits enhance an individual's ability to survive and produce offspring. Just as breeders develop new varieties of animals by selecting de-

sirable traits artificially, nature selects traits through the struggle for survival. These new traits are called *adaptations*. In this way, over immense spans of time, new species arise. Geological time is divided into Precambrian, Paleozoic, Mesozoic, and Cenozoic eras, depending on the kinds of fossils found from the period when the rocks formed. Although extinction is a continuous process, there have been a number of catastrophic episodes of *mass extinction*, when many species disappeared in a brief time interval. Asteroid impacts may account for some of these events.

Human evolution can be traced back approximately 6 million years to *Australopithecus*, a hominid that walked erect but had a brain about the size of a chimpanzee's. *Homo habilis*, the first member of our genus that appeared about 2 million years ago, was distinguished by a larger brain and the first appearance of stone tools. *Homo erectus*, who learned to use fire, evolved at about the same time but disappeared about half a million years ago. Modern humans of the species *Homo sapiens* are recognized in fossils as old as 200,000 years. DNA sequencing has established that there was some interbreeding between *Neanderthal Man* and early modern humans, so that people of European and Asian descent carry up to 4% Neanderthal genes.

KEY TERMS

evolution	**vestigial organ**	**natural selection**	***Australopithecus***
fossil	**chemical evolution**	**adaptation**	***Homo sapiens***
extinct	**Miller–Urey experiment**	**mass extinction**	**Neanderthal Man**

DISCOVERY LAB

Natural selection is a process in which organisms with favorable traits survive and pass on their traits to the next generation. Darwin presented the evidence of natural selection by his *survival of the fittest* theory. You can explore Darwin's theory of natural selection by collecting 50 red licorice candies, 50 pink licorice candies, and a brown paper bag. Let the red candy represent bears with fur with FF or Ff as their genotype, and the pink candy represent bears without fur with ff as their genotype.

Put 50 red candies with 50 pink candies in a brown paper bag and mix them well. Draw two candies at a time from the bag. If you pull two red candies, record it as FF (bear with homozygous dominant gene and fur present). If you pull out two pink candies, record this as ff (bear with homozygous recessive gene with no fur), and if you pull out one pink and one red candy,

record this as Ff (heterozygous, fur present). Set aside all the ff (pink candy) because bears without fur cannot survive harsh conditions. Write down the total of F and f candies that are left over. This time, restart the process representing the second generation. Mix all the remaining candies and start pulling two at a time and record the results as above. Discard all the ff candy pairs and count all the F and f candies that are left over. Calculate the gene frequency of F (red candies) by dividing the total number of F by the total number of candies. Similarly, find the gene frequency of f (pink candies) by dividing f by the total number of candies. Repeat the above procedure a number of times. Compare the frequency for the dominant allele with that of the recessive allele. How are the results of your experiment similar to evolution?

REVIEW QUESTIONS

1. What is the role of natural selection in the evolution of life?

2. What are fossils? What is the fossil record? What conditions are necessary for the formation of fossils?

3. How does the fossil record support the theory of evolution?

4. What are vestigial organs? How does their existence lend support to the fact of evolution?

5. What is the biochemical evidence that supports evolution?

6. What types of observational evidence point to the common ancestry of all living organisms?

7. Describe the major landmarks in the evolution of life on Earth. How many years passed between each of these milestones?

8. What is chemical evolution? When did it occur on Earth?

9. How does chemical evolution differ from natural selection?

10. Describe the Miller–Urey experiment. What historical role did it play in the study of the origin of life?

11. What are "black smokers"? What is unique about deep-ocean environments?

12. When was the "window of opportunity" for life to appear on Earth? What would have happened to life that developed before the window opened?

13. Where is the greatest gap in our knowledge of the evolution of life?

14. What recent evidence is consistent with the idea that life originated in a deep-ocean environment?

15. What are the two roles that RNA can play in living organisms? Why might this be significant?

16. Why does the modern relationship between DNA and proteins constitute a problem that must be explained in evolutionary theory?

17. What is natural selection? Give examples of natural selection at work.

18. How does natural selection differ from artificial selection?

19. State the two basic facts that govern the operation of natural selection.

20. Why did scientists believe that life began in the Cambrian explosion?

21. What is a mass extinction? What are some possible reasons for mass extinctions?

22. How does the overlap of human DNA with that of other living things support the theory of evolution?

23. When did the first members of the hominid family appear on Earth?

24. Which came first in human evolution, large brains or upright posture? How do scientists know this?

25. What does modern genetic evidence say about the relationship between modern humans and Neanderthal Man?

26. What are the basic tenets of young-Earth creationism? In what ways do these tenets counter scientific principles described in this book?

DISCUSSION QUESTIONS

1. Is Darwin's *On the Origin of Species* considered controversial in scientific circles? What about society in general? Explain your reasoning.

2. Chapter 17 discussed plate tectonics and the evidence for the existence of the continent Pangaea 300 million years ago. What effects do you think the breakup of Pangaea had on the evolution of the life forms that existed back then?

3. All scientific theories must each be capable of making predictions about phenomena that could subsequently be tested. What are some predictions that can be made from Darwin's theory of evolution by natural selection?

4. Describe the ongoing debate about the mechanisms of evolution. How does the Darwinian theory of evolution differ from other theories (e.g., the Lamarkian theory)?

5. What evidence leads many scientists to conclude that all life evolved from a single cell? What alternative hypotheses are there? Are these hypotheses scientifically testable? Why or why not?

6. What were the possible sources of energy for synthesizing the first forms of life on Earth?

7. If we were to find another planet with life as widespread as on Earth and if similar evolutionary forces were at work there, do you think we would find intelligent life? Why or why not?

8. Is the fossil record complete? Why are certain types of organisms "overrepresented"? Why are some species "underrepresented"? Give examples of both.

9. Fossils are usually found in sedimentary rocks. Why aren't they likely to be found in igneous rocks? What biases might this fact introduce into the fossil record?

10. How would you describe what it means to be evolutionarily fit? What advantages are there in being evolutionarily fit in terms of passing along your genes?

11. What is the estimate for the rate at which species are currently going extinct right now? What is the most likely reason for many of these extinctions? What kinds of species are currently most susceptible to becoming extinct?

12. Can intelligent design legitimately be described as a scientific theory? If yes, what are some testable predictions it makes? If it isn't, should we consider revising our understanding of what science is by saying that scientific theories can have logical explanations rather than strictly natural explanations?

13. Civilization has removed many of the evolutionary pressures that shaped our distant ancestors. Does this mean people are generally less subject to the principles of natural selection? Should this change be taken into account when shaping public policy? Why or why not?

14. Some young-Earth creationists will say that galaxies that are millions of light-years away were created at the same time as Earth but that we see them because light from those galaxies was created in transit, thus giving the universe the appearance of age. Is this hypothesis falsifiable? Can it be examined using the scientific method?

15. We know for sure that life exists in only one place in the solar system. Why does life appear to be such a rare phenomenon?

16. Evolution has been described as "survival of the fittest." Is this an accurate summary of the theory of evolution by natural selection? Why or why not?

17. If *Homo sapiens* doesn't go extinct, how do you think humankind will evolve over the next 1000 years? How about 100,000 years? 1 million years?

18. What are the most dramatic examples of artificial selection that you can think of?

PROBLEMS

1. If humans and chimpanzees share a recent common ancestor, then humans and chimps should have similar DNA. In fact, they are 98.7% similar. If there are 3 billion pairs in each DNA sequence and if each generation changes 30 of them through mutations and if each generation averages 15 years, how many years ago do you predict this common ancestor lived? The actual common ancestor is estimated to have lived around 8 or 9 million years ago. How well does your answer compare, and why might it be different from the actual value?

2. The Permian Extinction Event 250 million years ago caused the extinction of about 70% of all terrestrial vertebrate species. It is estimated that the extinctions took place over 25,000 years. If there were 20,000 terrestrial vertebrate species at the time, at what average rate were they going extinct? How does this compare with the estimated current extinction rate nowadays of 2.5 terrestrial vertebrate species per year?

3. Life first formed on Earth at least 3.5 billion years ago. *Homo sapiens* emerged no earlier than about 195,000 years ago. What percent of the entire history of life on Earth is shared by *Homo sapiens*?

   a. 1.8%
   b. 0.018 %
   c. 0.0056%
   d. 0.000056%

4. There have been 527 different genera of dinosaurs identified, though there are some disputed specimens. Mathematical models estimate this number is about one-fourth of all genera of dinosaurs that lived. Approximately how many dinosaur genera have yet to be discovered?

   a. 500
   b. 1600
   c. 2100
   d. 2600

INVESTIGATIONS

1. Read the National Academy of Science's pamphlet *Science and Creationism*. Who wrote this pamphlet and why? Does it make a convincing case?

2. Consult your geology department and find out the locations of the nearest fossil-bearing rocks. Find out what kinds of fossils are likely to be found in your neighborhood. How old are they?

3. Read accounts of any of the many recent debates to alter public school science curricula by eliminating evolution or by introducing intelligent design. How did members of the school board rationalize their votes? Have there been legal challenges to the ruling?

4. Investigate the concept of social Darwinism. When was it in fashion? Why is it not accepted as a scientific theory?

5. Read an account of Charles Darwin's visit to the Galapagos Islands while he was on the voyage of the *H.M.S. Beagle*. What did he see there that led him to his ideas about natural selection and evolution? Why did it take Darwin so long to publish his theory?

6. Read an account, such as *The Nemesis Affair* by David Raup, of the development of the hypothesis that an asteroid was responsible for the extinction of the dinosaurs. What role did the chemistry of the element iridium play in this hypothesis? Does the history of this idea support our argument in Chapter 1 that scientists must believe the data that result from their observations?

7. Read an account of the Scopes "Monkey Trial," or see a movie based on it—for example, *Inherit the Wind*. How was the conflict between science and religion portrayed in these writings and movies? What was the final verdict in the trial, and what was the penalty, if any? Is such a conflict between science and religion inevitable when it comes to the subject of life's origin and evolution?

8. Investigate mass extinctions. How many mass extinctions have there been? What evidence supports previous extinctions?

9. Is intelligent design just another name for creationism? Investigate the debate. Are there creation myths from other religions that should be taught in school?

10. Investigate the various theories that have been proposed over the course of time to explain the creation of life. Why were they rejected?

11. Investigate Jean-Baptiste Lamarck (1724–1829). What were his theories about evolution? What were his contributions?

12. Who is Sir Charles Lyell (1797–1875)? What were his contributions to the science of evolution? Why did Darwin have a copy of his book on the *HMS Beagle*?

Glossary

absolute zero The temperature, zero kelvins, at which no energy can be extracted from atoms; the coldest attainable temperature, which is equal to –273.16°C or –459.67°F. (Ch. 4)

absorption One of three possible responses of an electromagnetic wave encountering matter, in which light energy is converted into some other form, usually heat energy. See also *transmission*. (Ch. 6)

acceleration The amount of change in velocity divided by the time it takes the change to occur. Acceleration can involve changes of speed, changes in direction, or both.

acid rain A phenomenon that occurs when nitrogen and sulfur compounds in the air interact with water to form tiny droplets of nitric and sulfuric acid, which makes raindrops more acidic than normal. (Ch. 19)

adaptation A structure, process, or behavior that helps an organism survive and pass its genes on to the next generation. (Ch. 25)

air pollution A serious environmental problem, with immediate consequences for urban residents, from the emission of NOx compounds, sulfur dioxide, and hydrocarbons into the atmosphere. (Ch. 19)

alpha decay The loss by an atom's nucleus of a large and massive particle composed of two protons and two neutrons. (Ch. 12)

alternating current (AC) A type of electrical current, commonly used in household appliances and cars, in which charges alternate their direction of motion. (Ch. 5)

amino acids The building block of protein, incorporating a carboxyl group (COOH) at one end, an amino group (NH_2) at the other end, and a side group (which varies from one amino acid to the next). (Ch. 21)

angiosperms The class of vascular plants that flower. (Ch. 20)

animals Multicelled organisms that get their energy by eating other organisms; one of five kingdoms in the modern Linnaean classification. (Ch. 20)

antimatter Particles that have the same mass as their matter twins, but with an opposite charge, magnetic characteristics, and other properties. (Ch. 13)

applied research The type of research performed by scientists with specific and practical goals in mind. This research is often translated into practical systems by large-scale research and development projects. (Ch. 1)

arthropods All invertebrate animals with segmented bodies and jointed limbs. The most successful phylum in the animal kingdom in terms of numbers of species and total mass; includes insects, spiders, and crustacea. (Ch. 20)

asteroid belt A collection of small rocky planetesimals, located in a circular orbit between Mars and Jupiter, debris of material that never managed to collect into a single planet. (Ch. 16)

asteroids Small rocky objects, concentrated mostly in an asteroid belt between Mars and Jupiter, that circle the Sun like miniature planets. (Ch. 16)

astronomy The study of objects in the heavens. (Chs 1, 14)

atmospheric cycle The circulation of gases near Earth's surface, which includes the short-term variations of weather and the long-term variations of climate. (Ch. 18)

atom Fundamental building blocks for all matter; the smallest representative sample of an element. It consists of a positively charged nucleus surrounded by negatively charged electrons. (Ch. 8)

atomic number The number of protons in the nucleus, which determines the nuclear charge, and therefore the chemical identity of the atom. (Ch. 12)

Australopithecus The first hominid, a primate closer to humans than any other; lived approximately 4.5 to 1.5 million years ago, walked erect, and had a brain about the size of that of a modern chimpanzee. (Ch. 25)

basic research The type of research performed by scientists who are interested simply in finding out how the world works, in knowledge for its own sake. (Ch. 1)

battery A device that converts stored chemical energy into kinetic energy of charged particles (usually electrons) running through an outside wire. (Ch. 5)

beta decay A kind of radioactive decay in which a particle such as the neutron spontaneously transforms into a collection of particles that includes an electron. (Ch. 12)

big bang theory The idea that the universe began at a specific point in time and has been cooling and expanding ever since. (Ch. 15)

binding energy The energy needed to remove a proton or neutron from a nucleus. (Ch. 12)

biology The branch of science devoted to the study of living systems. (Ch. 20)

biotic Living. (Ch. 19)

bit Binary digit: a unit of measurement for information equal to "yes-no" or "on-off." (Ch. 11)

black hole Formed at the death of a very large star, an object so dense, with a mass so concentrated, that nothing—not even light—can escape from its surface. (Ch. 14)

Bohr atom A model of the atom, developed by Niels Bohr in 1913, in which electrons exist only in allowed energy levels. In these energy levels, the electrons maintain fixed energy for long periods of time, without giving off radiation. (Ch. 8)

byte In a computer, a group of eight switches storing eight bits of information; the basic information unit of most modern computers. (Ch. 11)

cancer A type of disease characterized by the uncontrolled growth of cells in the body. (Ch. 24)

carbohydrates A class of modular molecules made from carbon, hydrogen, and oxygen that form the solid structure of living things and play a central role in how living things acquire oxygen. (Ch. 22)

cell A complex chemical system with the ability to duplicate itself; the fundamental unit of life. (Ch. 21)

cell membrane A structure, formed from bilayers of lipids, that separates the inside of a cell from the outside, or separates one part of a cell from another. (Ch. 21)

cell wall A solid framework made from cellulose molecules and other strong polymers, by which plant cells are separated from one another. (Ch. 21)

change of state Transition between the solid, liquid, and gas states caused by changes in temperature and pressure. The processes involved are freezing and melting (for solids and liquids), boiling and condensation (for liquids and gases), and sublimation (for solids and gases). (Ch. 10)

chemical bond The attraction that results from the redistribution of electrons between two or more atoms, leading to a more stable configuration—particularly by filling the outer electron shells—and that holds the two atoms together. The principal kinds of chemical bonds are ionic, covalent, and metallic. (Ch. 10)

chemical evolution An area of research concerned with the process by which simple chemical compounds present in Earth's early atmosphere became an organized, reproducing cell. (Ch. 25)

chemical reaction The process by which atoms or smaller molecules come together to form large molecules, or by which larger molecules are broken down into smaller ones; involves the rearrangement of atoms in elements and compounds, as well as the rearrangement of electrons to form chemical bonds. (Ch. 10)

chemistry The branch of science devoted to the study of the combination of atoms and molecules. (Ch. 1)

chloroplasts The main energy transformation organelles in plant cells; places where the molecules of chlorophyll are found and photosynthesis occurs. (Ch. 21)

classical genetics The laws developed from the observations of Gregor Mendel: (1) traits are passed from parent to offspring by genes, (2) each parent contributes one gene for each trait, and (3) genes are either dominant or recessive. (Ch. 23)

climate The average weather conditions of a place or area over a period of years. (Ch. 18)

cloning The process of engineering a new individual entirely from the genetic material in a cell from another individual. A clone is genetically identical to the cell donor. (Ch. 24)

comet An object, usually found outside the orbit of Pluto, composed of chunks of materials such as water ice and methane ice embedded with dirt. A comet may fall toward the Sun, if its distant orbit is disturbed, and create a spectacular display in the night sky. (Ch. 16)

composite material A combination of two or more substances in which the strength of one of the constituents is used to offset the weakness of another, resulting in a new material whose strengths are greater than any of its components; for example, plywood and reinforced concrete. (Ch. 11)

computer A machine that stores and manipulates information. (Ch. 11)

conduction The movement of heat by collisions between vibrating atoms or molecules; one of three mechanisms by which heat moves. (Ch. 4)

conservation law Any statement that says that a quantity in nature does not change. (Ch. 3)

convection The transfer of heat by the physical motion of masses of fluid. Dense, cooler fluids (liquids and gases) descend in bulk and displace rising warmer fluids, which are less dense. One of three mechanisms by which heat moves. (Ch. 4)

convection cell A region in a fluid in which heat is continuously being transferred by a bulk motion of heated fluid from a heat source to the surface of the fluid, where heat is released. The cooled fluid then sinks and the cycle repeats. (Ch. 4)

convergent plate boundary A place where two tectonic *plates* are coming together. (Ch. 17)

core (*a*) In geology, the innermost and densest of Earth's layers, primarily iron and nickel metal, with a radius of about 3400 km (2000 mi). (*b*) In astronomy, a small region in the center of a star where hydrogen burning is generally confined. (Ch. 16, Ch. 17)

cosmic microwave background radiation Microwave radiation, characteristic of a body at about 3 K, falling to Earth from all directions. This radiation is evidence for the big bang. (Ch. 15)

cosmic rays Particles (mostly protons) that rain down continuously on Earth's atmosphere after being emitted by stars in our galaxy and in others. (Ch. 13)

cosmology The branch of science that is devoted to the study of the structure and history of the entire universe. (Ch. 15)

Coulomb's law An empirically derived rule that states that the magnitude of the electrostatic force between any two objects is proportional to the charges of the two objects, and inversely proportional to the square of the distance between them. (Ch. 5)

covalent bond A chemical bond in which neighboring molecules share electrons in a strongly bonded group of at least two atoms. (Ch. 10)

critical mass The minimum number of uranium-235 atoms needed to sustain a nuclear chain reaction to the point where large amounts of energy can be released. (Ch. 12)

crust In geology, Earth's outermost solid layer, formed from rocks less dense than in the mantle, ranging in thickness from 10 km (6 mi) in parts of the ocean to 70 km (45 mi) beneath parts of the continents. (Ch. 16)

crystal A group of atoms that occur in a regularly repeating sequence. Crystal structure is described by first determining the size and shape of the repeating boxlike group of atoms and then recording the exact type and position of every atom that appears in the box. (Ch. 10)

current A river of moving water, found in each of the ocean basins. (Ch. 18)

dark energy A mysterious substance that is causing the acceleration of the expansion of the universe. (Ch. 15)

dark matter Material that exists in forms that do not interact with electromagnetic radiation and that may constitute 90% of the matter of the universe. (Ch. 15)

differentiation The process by which heavy, dense materials (such as iron and nickel) sank under the force of gravity toward the molten center of the planet, while lighter, less dense materials floated to the top, resulting in the layered structure of the present-day Earth. (Ch. 16)

diffuse scattering A process by which light waves are absorbed and reemitted in all directions by a medium such as clouds or snow. (Ch. 6)

diode An electronic device that allows electrical current to flow in only one direction. (Ch. 11)

direct current (DC) A type of electrical current in which the electrons flow in one direction only; for example, in the chemical reaction of a battery. (Ch. 5)

divergent plate boundary A spreading zone of crustal formation; a place where neighboring plates move away from each other. (Ch. 17)

DNA See *deoxyribonucleic acid.*

DNA fingerprinting A procedure by which DNA in human tissue is used to match the tissue to an individual. This technique is becoming increasingly important in the judicial system in the United States. (Ch. 24)

DNA sequencing The process of determining, base pair by base pair, the exact order of bases along a specific stretch of a DNA molecule. (Ch. 23)

domains Region in magnetic material where neighboring atoms line up with each other to give a strong magnetic field. (Ch. 11)

dominant A genetic characteristic that always appears, or is expressed. (Ch. 23)

doping The addition of a minor impurity to a semiconductor. (Ch. 11)

Doppler effect The change in frequency or wavelength of a wave detected by an observer because the source of the wave is moving. (Ch. 6)

double helix The twisted double strand of nucleotides that forms the structure of the DNA molecule. (Ch. 23)

earth sciences Encompasses the study of the origin, evolution, present state, and future of planet Earth. (Ch. 1)

earthquake Disturbance caused when stressed rock on Earth suddenly snaps, converting potential energy into released kinetic energy. (Ch. 17)

ecological niche The habitat, functional role(s), requirements for environmental resources, and tolerance ranges within an ecosystem. (Ch. 19)

ecology The branch of science that studies interactions among organisms as well as the interactions of organisms and their environment. (Ch. 19)

ecosystem Interdependent collections of living things; includes the plants and animals that live in a given area together with their physical surroundings. (See *open ecosystem and closed ecosystem.*) (Ch. 19)

efficiency The amount of work you get from an engine, divided by the amount of energy you put in; a quantification of the loss of useful energy. (Ch. 4)

electric circuit An unbroken path of material that carries electricity and consists of three parts: a source of energy, a closed path, and a device to use the energy. (Ch. 5)

electric field The force that would be exerted on a positive charge at a position near a charged object. Every charged object is surrounded by an electric field. (Ch. 5)

electric generator A source of energy producing an alternating current in an electric circuit through the use of electromagnetic induction. (Ch. 5)

electric motor A device that operates by supplying current to an electromagnet to make the magnet move and generate mechanical power. Many motors employ permanent magnets and rotating loops of wire inside the poles of this magnet. (Ch. 5)

electrical charge An excess or deficit of electrons on an object. (Ch. 5)

electrical conductor Any material capable of carrying electrical current. (Ch. 11)

electrical current A flow of charged particles, measured in amperes. (Ch. 5)

electrical insulator Material that will not conduct electricity. (Ch. 11)

electrical resistance The quantity, measured in ohms, that represents how hard it is to push electrons through a material. High-resistance wires are used when electron energy is to be converted into heat energy. Low-resistance wires are used when energy is to be transmitted from one place to another with minimum loss. (Ch. 5)

electricity A force, more powerful than gravity, that moves objects both toward and away from each other, depending upon the charge. (Ch. 5)

electromagnet A device that produces a magnetic field from a moving electrical charge. (Ch. 5)

electromagnetic force A term used to refer to the unified nature of electricity and magnetism. (Ch. 5)

electromagnetic radiation See *electromagnetic wave.*

electromagnetic spectrum The entire array of waves, varying in frequency and wavelength, but all resulting from an accelerating electrical charge; includes radio waves, microwaves, infrared, visible light, ultraviolet, X-rays, gamma rays, and others. (Ch. 6)

electromagnetic wave A form of radiant energy that reacts with matter by being transmitted, absorbed, or scattered. A self-propagating wave made up of electric and magnetic fields fluctuating together. A wave created when electrical charges accelerate, but requiring no medium for transfer. Electromagnetic radiation. (Ch. 6)

electron Tiny, negatively charged particles that surround a positively charged nucleus of an atom. (Ch. 5)

element A material made from a single type of atom, which cannot be broken down chemically any further. (Ch. 8)

elementary particles Particles that make up the nucleus, together with particles such as the electron; the basic building blocks of the universe. (Ch. 13)

elementary-particle physics The study of particles that comprise the basic building blocks of the universe; for example, the particles that make up the nucleus, and particles such as electrons. Also known as high-energy physics. (Ch. 13)

energy (measured in joules) The ability to do work; the capacity to exert a force over a distance. A system's energy can be measured in joules or foot-pounds. (Ch. 3)

entropy The thermodynamic quantity that describes the degree of randomness of a system. The greater the disorder or randomness, the higher the statistical probability of the state, and the higher the entropy. (Ch. 4)

environment The nonliving chemical and physical parts of an ecosystem, including the water, soil, and atmosphere. (Ch. 19)

enzymes A molecule that facilitates reactions between two other molecules, but which is not itself altered or taken up in the overall reaction. (Ch. 22)

evolution An ongoing process of change. There are various theories of biological evolution that differ in regard to how fast it proceeds and by what mechanisms. (Ch. 25)

experiment The manipulation of some aspect of nature to observe the outcome. (Ch. 1)

extinct Species that have lived on Earth and have died out. Scientists estimate that for every species on the planet today, 999 species have become extinct. (Ch. 25)

extrusive rock See *volcanic rock.*

fact The result of an experiment or observation. (Ch. 1)

fermentation An anaerobic cellular process in which pyruvic acids are broken down and the energy is used by the cell to keep glycolysis going. (Ch. 21)

first law of thermodynamics The law of the conservation of energy. In an isolated system, the total amount of energy, including heat energy, is conserved. (Ch. 3)

fission A reaction that produces energy when heavy radioactive nuclei split apart into fragments that together have less mass than the original isotopes. (Ch. 12)

force A push or pull that, acting alone, causes a change in acceleration of the object on which it acts.

fossil Evidence of past life preserved in rocks; notably when atoms in the hard parts of the buried organism are replaced by minerals in the water flowing through the surrounding area. (Ch. 25)

frames of reference The physical surroundings from which a person observes and measures the world. (Ch. 7)

frequency The number of wave crests that go by a given point every second. A wave completing one cycle (sending one crest by a point every second) has a frequency of one hertz, 1 Hz. (Ch. 6)

fungi One of the five kingdoms in the Linnaean classification, organisms that obtain energy by absorbing materials through filaments and reproduce by production of spores. May be single-celled (e.g., yeasts) or multicellular (e.g. mushrooms). (Ch. 20)

fusion A process in which two atomic nuclei come together to form a third, larger nucleus. When this reaction combines light elements to make heavier ones, the mass of the final nucleus may be less than the mass of its constituent parts. The "missing" nuclear mass can be converted into energy. (Ch. 12)

galaxy A large assembly of stars (between millions and hundreds of billions), together with gas, dust, and other materials, that is held together by the forces of mutual gravitational attraction. (Ch. 15)

gamma radiation A kind of radioactivity involving the emission of energetic electromagnetic radiation from the nucleus of an atom, with no change to the number of protons or neutrons in the atom. (Ch. 12)

gamma ray The highest-energy wave of the electromagnetic spectrum with wavelengths less than the size of an atom, less than one-trillionth of a meter; normally emitted in very high-energy nuclear particle reactions. (Ch. 6)

gas Any collection of atoms or molecules that expands to take that shape and fill the volume available in its container. (Ch. 10)

gene A unit of biological inheritance, or a section of a long molecule of DNA. One gene carries the information needed to assemble one protein. (Ch. 23)

gene therapy A promising future technology that involves replacing a defective gene with a healthy one. (Ch. 24)

general relativity The second and more complex of two parts of Einstein's theory of relativity, which applies to any reference frames whether or not those frames are accelerating relative to each other. (Ch. 7)

genetic code The correspondence between base-pair sequences and amino acids. The connection, in all living things, between the codons and the amino acid for which they code. (Ch. 23)

genetic engineering A technology in which foreign genes are inserted into an organism, or existing genes altered, to modify the function of living things. (Ch. 24)

genetics The study of ways in which biological information is passed from one generation to the next. (Ch. 23)

genome The sum of all information contained in the DNA for any living thing; the sequence of all the bases in all the chromosomes. (Ch. 23)

glacier A large body of ice that slowly flows down a slope or valley under the infl uence of gravity; found primarily in Greenland and Antarctica. (Ch. 18)

glass A solid with predictable local environments for most atoms, but no long-range order to the atomic structure. Compared to crystal, glass lacks the repeating unit of atoms. (Ch. 10)

glycolysis The first step in the extraction of energy from glucose, which takes place in ten separate steps, each of which is governed by a specific enzyme, and which splits each glucose molecule into two smaller molecules called pyruvic acids. (Ch. 21)

gravity An attractive force that acts on every object in the universe.

great bombardment An event following the initial period of planetary formation in which meteorites showered down on planets, adding matter and heat energy. (Ch. 16)

greenhouse effect A global temperature increase caused by the fact that Earth's atmospheric gases trap some of the Sun's infrared (heat) energy before it radiates out into space. (Ch. 19)

groundwater Fresh water from the surface, which typically percolates into the ground and fills the tiny spaces between grains of sandstone and other porous rock layers. (Ch. 18)

gymnosperms The class of vascular plants that produce seeds without flowers, such as fir trees. (Ch. 20)

hadron Particles, including the proton and neutron, that are made from quarks and are subject to the strong force. (Ch. 13)

half-life The rate of radioactive decay measured by the time it takes for half of a collection of isotopes to decay into another element. (Ch. 12)

heat transfer The process by which heat moves from one place to another, through three different mechanisms: conduction, convection, or radiation. (Ch. 4)

hertz (Hz) The unit of measurement for the frequency of waves; one wave cycle per second. (Ch. 6)

high-energy physics See *elementary-particle physics.*

Homo sapiens The single species that includes all branches of the human race; recognized in fossils as old as 200,000 years. (Ch. 20)

hot spot A dramatic type of volcanism indirectly associated with plate tectonics. Large isolated chimney-like columns of hot rock, or mantle plumes, rising to Earth's surface; for example, Yellowstone National Park, Iceland, and Hawaii. (Ch. 17)

Hubble's law The law relating the distance to a galaxy, d, and the rate at which it recedes from Earth, V, as measured by the red-shift: *V=Hd,* where H is the Hubble constant. (Ch. 15)

Human Genome Project A large-scale scientific project that will result in a complete knowledge of the entire human genome, which includes 46 chromosomes and 3 billion base pairs. (Ch. 23)

hybrid An individual whose parents contribute different genetic traits. (Ch. 23)

hydrocarbon A chain-like molecule from a chemical compound of carbon and hydrogen, which provides the most efficient fuels for combustion, with only carbon dioxide and water as products. (Ch. 10)

hydrogen bond A bond that may form when polarized hydrogen atoms link to other atoms by a covalent or ionic bond. (Ch. 10)

hydrologic cycle The combination of processes by which water moves from repository to repository near Earth's surface. (Ch. 18)

hypothesis A tentative guess about how the world works, based on a summary of experimental or observational results and phrased so that it can be tested by experimentation. (Ch. 1)

Ice Age A period of several million years during which glaciers have repeatedly advanced and retreated, causing radical changes in climate and influencing human evolution. (Ch. 18)

ice cap Layers of ice that form at the north and south polar regions of Earth. (Ch. 18)

igneous rock The first rock to form on a cooling planet, solidified from hot, molten material; intrusive or extrusive (volcanic). (Ch. 18)

infrared radiation Wavelengths of electromagnetic radiation that extend from a millimeter to a micron; felt as heat radiation. (Ch. 6)

interference When waves from two different sources come together at a single point, they interfere with each other. The observed wave amplitude is the sum of the amplitudes of the interfering waves. (Ch. 6)

intrusive rock Igneous rock that cools and hardens underground. (Ch. 18)

invertebrates Organisms without backbones. (Ch. 20)

ionic bond A chemical bond in which the electrostatic force between two oppositely charged ions holds the atoms in place, often formed as one atom gives up an electron while another receives it, lowering chemical potential energy when atom shells are filled. (Ch. 10)

isotopes Atoms whose nuclei have the same number of protons but a different number of neutrons. (Ch. 12)

jet stream A high-altitude stream of fast-moving winds that marks the boundary between the northern polar cold air mass and the warmer air of the temperate zone. (Ch. 18)

Jovian planets Huge worlds also known as "gas giants" located in the outer solar system and made up primarily of frozen liquids and gases such as hydrogen, helium, ammonia, and water, with atmospheres of nitrogen, methane, and other compounds: Jupiter, Saturn, Uranus, Neptune. (Ch. 16)

kinetic energy The type of energy associated with moving objects; the energy of motion. Kinetic energy is equal to the mass of the moving object times the square of that object's velocity, multiplied by . (Ch. 3)

kingdom The broadest classification in the Linnaean classification system, corresponding to the coarsest division of living things. (Ch. 20)

Kuiper Belt A region close to our solar system that contains comets that orbit the Sun; a reservoir of new comets. (Ch. 16)

Large Hadron Collider The world's highest energy particle accelerator, located in Geneva, Switzerland. (Ch. 13)

law See *law of nature.*

law of unintended consequences A phenomenon demonstrating the interdependent nature of ecosystems: it is virtually impossible to change one aspect of an ecosystem without affecting something else, often inadvertently. (Ch. 19)

length contraction The phenomenon in relativity in which moving objects appear to be shorter than stationary ones in the direction of motion. (Ch. 7)

lepton A particle (such as the electron, muon, and neutrino) that participates in the weak and electromagnetic, but not the strong, interaction. (Ch. 13)

light A form of electromagnetic wave to which the human eye is sensitive. Light travels at a constant speed and needs no medium for transfer. (Ch. 6)

light-year The distance light travels in one year, 10 trillion kilometers (about 6.2 trillion miles). (Ch. 14)

Linnaean classification A systematic attempt by Swedish naturalist Carolus Linnaeus to catalogue the diversity of all living things according to their shared characteristics so that each organism is as close as possible to those things it resembles, and as far apart as possible from those it does not. (Ch. 20)

lipids An organic molecule that is insoluble in water. At the molecular level, lipids form the cell membranes that separate living material from its environment. Lipids are also an extremely efficient storage medium for energy; for example, fat in foods, wax in candles, and grease for lubrication. (Ch. 22)

liquid Any collection of atoms or molecules that has no fixed shape but maintains a fixed volume. (Ch. 10)

magnet Materials that exert a magnetic field on other objects. Magnetite or "lodestone" is a common natural magnet. (Ch. 5)

magnetic field A collection of lines that map out the direction that compass needles would point in the vicinity of a magnet. (Ch. 5)

magnetic force The force exerted by magnets on each other. (Ch. 5)

main-sequence star A star that derives energy from the fusion reactions of hydrogen burning; found on the Hertzsprung-Russell (H-R) diagram within a band-like pattern. (Ch. 14)

mammals One of a group of vertebrates made up of individuals that are warm-blooded, have hair, and whose females nurse their young. Human beings are mammals. (Ch. 20)

mantle The thick layer rich in oxygen, silicon, magnesium, and iron that contains most of Earth's mass; it overlies Earth's metal core. (Ch. 16)

mantle convection A force deep within Earth, driven by internal heat energy, that moves continents and the plates of which they are a part. (Ch. 17)

mass The amount of matter contained in an object, independent of where that object is found.

mass extinction Rare and catastrophic events in the past that have caused large numbers of species to become extinct suddenly. (Ch. 25)

mass number The number of neutrons plus the number of protons, which determines the mass of an isotope. (Ch. 12)

mathematics The branch of study devoted to the study of numbers, equations, and geometry. (Ch. 1)

measurement The act of determining the quantitative value of a variable of interest. (Ch. 1)

mechanics The branch of science that deals with the motions of material objects and the forces that act on them; for example, a rolling rock or a thrown ball.

meiosis The division process that produces cells with one-half the number of chromosomes in each somatic cell. Each resulting daughter cell has half the normal complement of DNA. See mitosis. (Ch. 21)

messenger RNA (mRNA) The single-stranded molecule that copies the sequence for one gene and carries that DNA information to the region of the cell where proteins are made. (Ch. 23)

metabolism The process by which a cell derives energy from its surroundings. (Ch. 21)

metal An element or combination of elements in which the sharing of a few electrons among all atoms results in more stable electron arrangement; characterized by a shiny luster and ability to conduct electricity. (Ch. 10)

metallic bond A chemical bond in which electrons are redistributed so that they are shared by all the atoms as a whole. (Ch. 10)

metamorphic rock Igneous or sedimentary rock that is buried and transformed by Earth's intense internal temperature and pressure. (Ch. 18)

meteor A piece of interplanetary debris that hits Earth's atmosphere and forms a bright streak of light from friction with atmospheric particles: a "shooting star." (Ch. 16)

meteorite The fragment of a meteor that hits Earth. (Ch. 16)

microchip A complex array of *p*- and *n*-type semiconductors, which may incorporate hundreds or thousands of transistors in one integrated circuit. (Ch. 11)

microwave Electromagnetic waves, with wavelengths ranging from approximately 1 meter to 1 millimeter, which are used extensively for line-of-sight communications and cooking. (Ch. 6)

Milky Way A collection of hundreds of billions stars that forms the galaxy of which the Sun is a part. (Ch. 15)

Miller–Urey experiment A demonstration of chemical evolution, performed in 1953 by Stanley Miller and Harold Urey, which showed that a combination of gases, believed to be present in the early atmosphere, and a series of electrical sparks, simulating the lightning on the early Earth, produce amino acids, a basic building block of life. (Ch. 25)

minerals In a nutritional context, all chemical elements in food other than carbon, hydrogen, nitrogen, and oxygen. (Ch. 22)

mitochondria Sausage-shaped organelles that are places where molecules derived from glucose react with oxygen to produce the cell's energy. (Ch. 21)

mitosis The process of cell division producing daughter cells with exactly the same number of chromosomes as in the mother cell. See meiosis. (Ch. 21)

molecular genetics The study of how the mechanism that passes genetic information from parents to offspring functions on the basis of molecular chemistry. (Ch. 23)

molecule A cluster of atoms that bond together; the basic constituent of many different kinds of material. (Ch. 8)

mutation A change in the genetic material of a parent that is inherited by the offspring. (Ch. 23)

natural selection The mechanism by which nature can introduce wide-ranging changes in living things over long periods of time by modifying the gene pool of a species. (Ch. 25)

Neanderthal Man A type of human with a large brain who lived until 35,000 years ago in groups with a complex social structure; either a separate species of the genus Homo or a subspecies of Homo sapiens. (Ch. 25)

nebulae Dust and gas clouds, common throughout the Milky Way galaxy, rich in hydrogen and helium. (Ch. 14, 15 & 16)

negative electrical charge An excess of electrons on an object. (Ch. 5)

neutron A type of subatomic particle, located in the nucleus of the atom that carries no electrical charge but has approximately the same mass as the proton; one of two primary building blocks of the nucleus. See proton. (Ch. 12)

neutron star A very dense, very small star, usually with a high rate of rotation and a strong magnetic field; the core remains of a supernova, held up by the degeneracy pressure of neutrons. (Ch. 14)

Newton's law of universal gravitation Between any two objects in the universe there is an attractive force (gravity) that is proportional to the masses of the objects and inversely proportional to the square of the distance between them. In other words, the more massive two objects are, the greater the force between them will be, and the farther apart they are, the less the force will be.

Newton's laws of motion Three basic principles, expressed as laws, that govern the motion of everything in the universe, from stars and planets to cannonballs and muscles. The first law states that a moving object will continue moving in a straight line at a constant speed, and a stationary object will remain at rest, unless acted on by an unbalanced force. The second law states that the acceleration produced on a body by a force is proportional to the magnitude of the force and inversely proportional to the mass of the object. The third law states that for every action there is an equal and opposite reaction.

nuclear reactor A device that controls fission reactions to produce energy when heavy radioactive nuclei split apart. (Ch. 12)

nucleic acids Molecule originally found in the nucleus of cells that carries and interprets the genetic code; includes DNA and RNA (Ch. 23)

nucleus (1) The very small, compact object at the center of an atom; made up primarily of protons and neutrons. (2) A prominent structure in the interior of a cell that contains the cell's genetic material—the DNA—and controls the cell's chemistry. (Ch. 8, Ch. 21)

observations The act of observing nature without manipulating it. (Ch. 1)

organelle Any specialized structure in the cell, including the nucleus. (Ch. 21)

organic molecules Carbon-based molecules that may or may not be part of a living system. (Ch. 22)

oxidation A chemical reaction in which an atom such as oxygen accepts electrons while combining with other elements; for example, rusting of iron metal into iron oxide, or animal respiration. (Ch. 10)

ozone A molecule made up of three oxygen atoms, instead of the usual two, which absorbs ultraviolet radiation. (Ch. 19)

ozone hole A volume of atmosphere above Antarctica during September through November in which the concentration of the trace gas ozone has declined significantly. (Ch. 19)

ozone layer A region of enhanced ozone (O_3) 20 to 30 miles above Earth's surface where most of the absorption of the Sun's ultraviolet radiation occurs. (Ch. 19)

particle accelerator A machine such as a synchrotron or linear accelerator that produces particles at near light speeds for use in the study of the fundamental structure of matter. (Ch. 13)

peer review A system by which the editor of a scientific journal submits manuscripts considered for publication to a panel of knowledgeable scientists who, in confidence, evaluate the manuscript for mistakes, misstatements, or shoddy procedures. Following the review, if the manuscript is to be published, it is returned to the author with a list of modifications and corrections to be completed. (Ch. 1)

periodic table of the elements An organizational system, first developed by Dmitri Mendeleev in 1869, now listing more than 110 elements by atomic weight (in rows) and chemical properties (in columns). The pattern of elements in the periodic table reflects the arrangement of electrons in their orbits. (Ch. 8)

photon A particle-like unit of light, emitted or absorbed by an atom when an electrically charged electron changes state. The form of a single packet of electromagnetic radiation. (Ch. 8)

photosynthesis The mechanism by which plants convert the energy of sunlight into energy stored in carbohydrates, the chemical energy of virtually all life on Earth: energy + CO_2 + H_2O → carbohydrate + oxygen. (Ch. 21)

physics The branch of science devoted to the study of matter and motion. (Ch. 1)

plants Multicelled organisms that get their energy directly from the Sun through photosynthesis. One of five kingdoms in the Linnaean classification. (Ch. 20)

plasma A state of matter existing under extremely high temperatures in which electrons are stripped from their atoms during high-energy collisions, forming an electron sea surrounding positive nuclei. (Ch. 10)

plastic Synthetic polymers that are formed primarily from petroleum. They consist of intertwined polymer strands, much like the strands of fiberglass insulation. When heated, these strands slide across each other to adopt new shapes. When cooled, the plastic fiber mass solidifies into whatever shape is available. (Ch. 10)

plate tectonics The model of the dynamic Earth that has emerged from studies of paleomagnetism, rock dating, and much other data. A theory that explains how a few thin, rigid tectonic plates of crustal and upper mantle materials are moved across Earth's surface by mantle convection. (Ch. 17)

Pluto Once described as the ninth planet of the solar system, Pluto is now considered to be the first plutoid to be discovered. (Ch. 16)

plutoid Planet-like bodies in the Kuiper Belt, including Pluto. (Ch. 16)

poles The two opposite ends of a magnet, named north and south, that repel a like magnetic pole and attract an unlike magnetic pole. (Ch. 5)

polymer Extremely long and large molecules that are formed from numerous smaller molecules, like links in a chain, with predictable repeating sequences of atoms along the chain. (Ch. 10)

polymerization A reaction that includes all chemical reactions that form long strands of polymer fibers by linking small molecules. (Ch. 10)

positive electrical charge A deficiency of electrons on an object. (Ch. 5)

potential energy The energy a system possesses if it is capable of doing work, but is not doing work now. Types of potential energy include magnetic, elastic, electrical, and chemical. Any type of energy waiting to be released; stored energy. (Ch. 3)

power (measured in watts or kilowatts) The rate at which work is done or energy is expended. The amount of work done, divided by the time it takes to do it. Power is measured in watts in the metric system, horsepower in the English. (Ch. 3)

prediction A guess about how a particular system will behave, followed by observations to see if the system did behave as expected within a specified range of situations. (Ch. 1)

primates An order of mammals that have grasping fingers and toes, eyes at the front of their heads, large brains, and fingernails instead of claws; includes monkeys, apes, and humans. (Ch. 20)

probability The likelihood that an event will occur or that an object will be in one state or another; how nature is described in the subatomic world. (Ch. 9)

protein An extremely complex molecule, which can consist of thousands of amino acids and millions of atoms formed in a chain structure. Proteins function as enzymes and direct the cell's chemistry. (Ch. 22)

proton One of two primary building blocks of the nucleus; with a positive electrical charge of +1 and a mass 1.672643×10^{-24}g approximately equal to that of the neutron. (Ch. 12)

pseudoscience A kind of inquiry falling in the realm of belief or dogma, which includes subjects that cannot be proved or disproved with a reproducible test. The subjects include creationism, extrasensory perception (ESP), unidentified flying objects, astrology, crystal power, and reincarnation. (Ch. 1)

pulsar A neutron star in which fast-moving particles speed out along the intense magnetic field lines of the rotating star, giving off electromagnetic radiation that we detect as a series of pulses of radio waves. (Ch. 14)

quantum jump See *quantum leap*.

quantum leap A process by which an electron changes its energy state without ever possessing an energy intermediate between the original and the final energy state; also known as a *quantum jump*. (Ch. 8)

quantum mechanics The branch of science that is devoted to the study of the motion of objects that come in small bundles, or quanta, which applies to the subatomic world. (Ch. 9)

quarks (pronounced "quorks") The truly fundamental building blocks of the hadrons. Particles that have fractional electrical charge and cannot exist alone in nature. (Ch. 13)

radiation The transfer of heat by electromagnetic radiation. The only one of the three mechanisms of heat transfer that does not require atoms or molecules to facilitate the transfer process. (Ch. 4) Also, the particles emitted during the spontaneous decay of nuclei. (Ch. 12)

radio wave Part of the electromagnetic spectrum that ranges from the longest waves—wavelengths longer than Earth's diameter—to waves a few meters long. (Ch. 6)

radioactive decay The process of spontaneous change of unstable isotopes. (Ch. 12)

radioactivity The spontaneous release of energy by certain atoms, such as uranium, as these atoms disintegrate. The emission of one or more kinds of radiation from an isotope with unstable nuclei. (Ch. 12)

radiometric dating A technique based on the radioactive half-lives of carbon-14 and other isotopes that is used to determine the age of materials. (Ch. 12)

receptor A large structure found in the cell membrane and made of proteins folded into a geometrical shape that will bond chemically only to a specific type of molecule. (Ch. 21)

recessive A characteristic that will appear only if no dominant gene is present. (Ch. 23)

red giant An extremely large star that emits a lot of energy but whose surface is very cool and therefore appears somewhat reddish in the sky; found in the upper right-hand corner of the H-R diagram. (Ch. 14)

redshift An increase in the wavelength of radiation received from a receding celestial body as a consequence of the Doppler effect. A shift toward the long-wavelength (red) end of the spectrum. (Ch. 14)

reduction A chemical reaction in which electrons are transferred from an atom to other elements, resulting in a gain in electrons for the material being reduced; for example, smelting of metal ores, and photosynthesis. (Ch. 10)

reflection A process by which light waves are scattered at the same angle as the original wave; for example, from the surface of a mirror. (Ch. 6)

refraction A response of an electromagnetic wave to matter, in which the wave slows down and alters direction. See also *absorption* and *transmission*. (Ch. 6)

reproducible A criterion for the results of an experiment. In the scientific method, observations and experiments must be reported in such a way that anyone with the proper equipment can verify the results. (Ch. 1)

research and development (R&D) A kind of research aimed at specific problems, usually performed in government and industry laboratories. (Ch. 1)

reservoirs Locations where a substance is to be found. Earth's water, for example, is found in oceans, rivers, ice caps, and several other reservoirs. (Ch. 18)

respiration The process by which animals retrieve energy stored in glucose, in a complex series of cellular chemical reactions, which include breathing in oxygen produced by plants, burning carbohydrates ingested for food, and breathing out carbon dioxide. (Ch. 21)

RNA See *ribonucleic acid*.

rock cycle An ongoing cycle of internal and external Earth processes by which rock is created, destroyed, and altered. (Ch. 18)

scientific method A continuous process used to collect observations, form and test hypotheses, make predictions, and identify patterns in the physical world. (Ch. 1)

second law of thermodynamics Any one of three equivalent statements: (1) heat will not flow spontaneously from a colder to a hotter body; (2) it is impossible to construct a machine that does nothing but convert heat into useful work; and (3) the entropy of an isolated system always increases. (Ch. 4)

sedimentary rock A type of rock that is formed from layers of sediment produced by the weathering of other rock or by chemical precipitation. (Ch. 18)

seismology The study and measurement of vibrations within Earth's interior, dedicated to deducing our planet's inner structure. (Ch. 17)

semiconductor Materials that conduct electricity but do not conduct it very well. Neither a good conductor nor a perfect insulator; for example, silicon. (Ch. 11)

solar system The Sun, the planets and their moons, and all other objects gravitationally bound to the Sun. (Ch. 16)

solar wind A stream of charged particles—mainly ions of hydrogen and electrons—emitted constantly by the Sun into the space around it. (Ch. 14)

solid Any material that possesses a fixed shape and volume, with chemical bonds that are both sufficiently strong and directional to preserve a large-scale external form. (Ch. 10)

special relativity The first of two parts of Einstein's theory of relativity that deals with reference frames that do not accelerate. (Ch. 7)

species The basic unit of the Linnaean classification; an interbreeding population of individual organisms. (Ch. 20)

specific heat capacity A measure of the ability of a material to absorb heat energy, defined as the quantity of heat required to raise the temperature of gram of that material by 1°C. Water displays the largest heat capacity of any common substance. (Ch. 4)

spectroscopy The study of emission and absorption spectra of materials in order to discover the chemical makeup of a material; a standard tool used in almost every branch of science. (Ch. 8)

spectrum The characteristic signal from the total collection of photons emitted by a given atom that can be used to identify the chemical elements in a material; the atomic fingerprint. (Ch. 8)

speed The distance an object travels divided by the time it takes to travel that distance.

speed of light(c) The velocity at which all electromagnetic waves travel, regardless of their wavelength or frequency; equal to 300,000 kilometers per second (about 186,000 miles per second). (Ch. 6)

star Objects such as our Sun that form from giant clouds of interstellar dust and generate energy by nuclear fusion reactions. (Ch. 14)

states of matter Different modes of organization of atoms or molecules, which result in properties of gases, plasmas, liquids, or solids. (Ch. 10)

static electricity A phenomenon caused by the transfer of electrical charge between objects. Often observed as lightning or as sparks produced when walking across a wool rug on a dry, cold day. (Ch. 5)

stem cells Cells that are undifferentiated (i.e., not yet specialized), and thus have the potential to become any kind of cell in the body. (Ch. 24)

strength The ability of a solid to resist changes in shape; directly related to chemical bonding. (Ch. 11)

string theories Theories that unify gravity with the other forces and visualize matter as made up of vibrating string. (Ch. 13)

strong force The force responsible for holding the nucleus together; one of the four fundamental forces in nature. This force operates over extremely short distances and between quarks to hold elementary particles together. (Ch. 12)

subduction zone The regions of Earth's deep interior where plates converge and old crust returns to the mantle. (Ch. 17)

sugars The simplest of the carbohydrates. Common sugars contain five, six, or seven carbon atoms arranged in a ringlike structure. (Ch. 22)

superconductivity The ability of some materials to exhibit the complete absence of any electrical resistance, usually when cooled to within a few degrees of absolute zero. (Ch. 11)

supernova A stupendous explosion of a star, which increases its brightness hundreds of millions of times in a few days; results from the implosion of the core of a massive star at the end of its life. (Ch. 14)

synchrotron A particle accelerator in which magnetic fields are increased as particles become more energetic, keeping them moving on the same track. (Ch. 13)

system A part of the universe under study and separated from its surroundings by a real or imaginary boundary. (Ch. 3)

taxonomy The science of cataloging living things, describing them, and giving them names. (Ch. 20)

technology The application of the results of science to specific commercial or industrial goals. (Ch. 1)

tectonic plate One of a dozen sheets of moving rock in various sizes forming Earth's surface. (Ch. 17)

telescope A device that focuses and concentrates radiation from distant objects; used by astronomers to collect and analyze radio waves, microwaves, light, and other radiation. (Ch. 14)

temperature A quantity that reflects how vigorously atoms are moving and colliding in a material. (Ch. 4)

terrestrial planets The relatively small, rocky, high-density planets located in the inner solar system nearest the Sun: Mercury, Venus, Earth, Earth's Moon, and Mars. (Ch. 16)

theory A description of the world that covers a relatively large number of phenomena and has met many observational and experimental tests. A conclusion based upon observations of nature. (Ch. 1)

theory of relativity The idea that the laws of nature are the same in all frames of reference. Einstein divided his theory into two parts—special relativity and general relativity. (Ch. 7)

thermal conductivity The ability of a material to transfer heat energy from one molecule to the next by conduction. When thermal conductivity is low, as in wood or fiberglass insulation, the transfer of heat is slowed down. (Ch. 4)

thermal energy (heat) The kinetic energy of atoms and molecules; what we normally call heat. (Ch. 3)

time dilation A phenomenon in special relativity in which moving clocks appear to tick more slowly than stationary ones. (Ch. 7)

transfer RNA (tRNA) The molecule with special configuration that attracts amino acids at one end, and, at the other end, attaches to a specific codon of mRNA. (Ch. 23)

transform plate boundary The type of boundary between plates that occurs when one plate scrapes past the other, with no new plate material being produced; for example, California's San Andreas Fault. (Ch. 17)

transistor A device that sandwiches p- and n-type semiconductors in an arrangement that can amplify or redirect an electrical current running through it; a device that played an essential role in the development of modern electronics. (Ch. 11)

transmission One of three responses of an electromagnetic wave encountering matter, in which light energy passes through the matter unaffected. See also *absorption* and *scattering*. (Ch. 6)

trophic level All organisms that get their energy from the same source. (Ch. 3)

true breeding Plants whose offspring are like the parents through many generations. (Ch. 23)

ultraviolet radiation High-frequency wavelengths, shorter than visible light, ranging from 400 nanometers to 100 nanometers. (Ch. 6)

uncertainty principle The idea quantified by Werner Heisenberg in 1927 that at a quantum scale, the location and velocity of an object can never be known at the same time, because quantum-scale measurement affects the object being measured. Specifically, "the error or uncertainty in the measurement of an object's position, times the error or uncertainty in that object's velocity, must be greater than a constant, h, divided by the object's mass." (Ch. 9)

unified field theory The general name for any theory in which fundamental forces are seen as different aspects of the same force. (Ch. 13)

uniform motion The motion of an object if it travels in a straight line at a constant speed. All other motions involve acceleration.

vascular plants The phylum of plants that have internal "plumbing" capable of carrying fluids from one part of the plant to another. (Ch. 20)

velocity The distance an object travels divided by the time it takes to travel that distance, including the direction of travel. The velocity of a falling object is proportional to the length of time that it has been falling.

vertebrates A subphylum of chordates in which the nerves along the back are encased in bone. (Ch. 20)

vestigial organ A bodily feature that serves no useful function at present and is compelling evidence for evolution. (Ch. 25)

virus A short length of RNA or DNA wrapped in a protein coating that fits cell receptors and replicates itself using the cell's machinery. (Ch. 23)

visible light Electromagnetic waves with a wavelength that can be interpreted by nerve receptors in the brain; wavelengths range from 700 nanometers for red light to 400 nanometers for violet light. (Ch. 6)

vitamins One of a host of complex organic molecules that, in small quantities, play an essential role in good health; for example, by mediating the body's chemical reactions. May be fat soluble and stored, or water soluble and not retained by the body. (Ch. 22)

volcanic rock Extrusive igneous rock that solidifies on Earth's surface. (Ch. 18)

volcano Places where subsurface molten rock breaks through to Earth's surface to form dramatic short-term changes in the landscape. (Ch. 17)

voltage The pressure produced by the energy source in an electric circuit, measured in volts. (Ch. 5)

wave A traveling disturbance that carries energy from one place to another without requiring matter to travel across the intervening distance. (Ch. 6)

wave energy The kinetic energy associated with different kinds of waves, such as kinetic energy possessed by large amounts of water in rapid motion, and electromagnetic radiation stored in changing electrical and magnetic fields. (Ch. 3)

wavelength The distance between adjacent wave crests, the highest points of adjacent waves. (Ch. 6)

weather Daily changes in rainfall, temperature, amount of sunshine, and other variables resulting partly from the general circulation in the atmosphere, and partly from local disturbances and variations. (Ch. 18)

weight The force of gravity on an object.

white dwarf A star that has a very low emission of energy but very high surface temperature; plots on the lower lefthand corner of the H-R diagram. (Ch. 14)

WIMP's *Weakly Interacting Massive Particles* Hypothetical particles that are candidates for dark matter. (Ch. 15)

work (measured in joules) The force that is exerted times the distance over which it is exerted; measured in joules in the metric system, in foot-pounds in the English. (Ch. 3)

X-rays High-frequency and high-energy electromagnetic waves that range in wavelength from 100 nanometers to 0.1 nanometer, used in medicine and industry. (Ch. 6)

Index